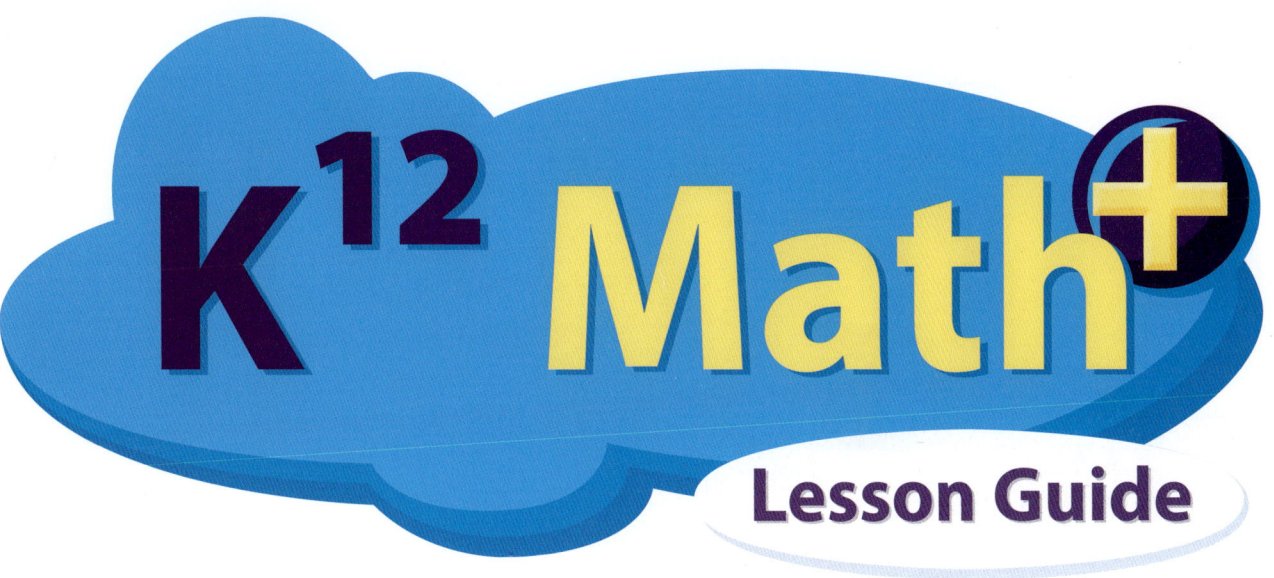

**Illustrations Credits**
All illustrations © K12 Inc. unless otherwise noted

Sidewalk. © Vita Vanaga/Fotolia
Cars. © bradwieland/iStockphoto.com

**About K12 Inc.**
K12 Inc., a technology-based education company, is the nation's leading provider of proprietary curriculum and online education programs to students in grades K–12. K[12] provides its curriculum and academic services to online schools, traditional classrooms, blended school programs, and directly to families. K12 Inc. also operates the K[12] International Academy, an accredited, diploma-granting online private school serving students worldwide. K[12]'s mission is to provide any child the curriculum and tools to maximize success in life, regardless of geographic, financial, or demographic circumstances. K12 Inc. is accredited by CITA. More information can be found at www.K12.com.

Copyright © 2011, 2010, 2009 K12 Inc. All rights reserved. K[12], the K[12] logo, and Unleash the xPotential are trademarks or registered trademarks of K12 Inc. or its affiliates in the U.S. and other countries. Other names may be trademarks of third parties.

No part of this document may be reproduced or used in any form or by any means, graphic, electronic, or mechanical, including photocopying, recording, taping, and information retrieval systems, without the prior written permission of K12 Inc.

ISBN: 978-1-60153-088-2
Printed by RR Donnelley, Shenzhen, China, March 2012, Lot 032012

# Contents

Program Overview .................................................. ix

## Whole Numbers and Powers

Round Whole Numbers in Story Problems ........................... 3
Estimate and Find Sums and Differences .......................... 6
Estimate Sums and Differences (A) .............................. 10
Estimate Sums and Differences (B) .............................. 12
Estimate and Find Products and Quotients ....................... 15
Estimate Products and Quotients (A) ............................ 18
Estimate Products and Quotients (B) ............................ 22
Bases and Exponents (A) ........................................ 29
Bases and Exponents (B) ........................................ 32
Solve Problems Involving Powers ................................ 35
Prime Factorization ............................................ 38
Unit Review .................................................... 45
Unit Checkpoint ................................................ 46

## Geometry

Angles (A) ..................................................... 49
Angles (B) ..................................................... 53
Perpendicular and Parallel Lines ............................... 57
Construct Triangles and Quadrilaterals ......................... 61
Angles and Triangles (A) ....................................... 69
Angles and Triangles (B) ....................................... 73
Angles in a Quadrilateral (A) .................................. 77
Angles in a Quadrilateral (B) .................................. 83
Transformations (A) ............................................ 86
Transformations (B) ............................................ 90
Draw 2-D Views of 3-D Objects .................................. 93

Unit Review .................................................................. 99
Unit Checkpoint ............................................................ 101

# Fractions: Multiplication and Division

Use Models to Multiply Fractions ........................................ 105
Understand Division of Fractions ........................................ 112
Multiply Fractions (A) ..................................................... 117
Multiply Fractions (B) ..................................................... 122
Multiply Fractions (C) ..................................................... 130
Divide Fractions (A) ....................................................... 137
Divide Fractions (B) ....................................................... 141
Divide Fractions (C) ....................................................... 144
Unit Review .................................................................. 147
Unit Checkpoint ............................................................ 148

# Problems Involving Fractions

Solve Fraction Story Problems (A) ...................................... 151
Solve Fraction Story Problems (B) ...................................... 157
Solve Fraction Story Problems (C) ...................................... 164
Add and Subtract Fractions (A) ......................................... 171
Add and Subtract Fractions (B) ......................................... 177
Add and Subtract Fractions (C) ......................................... 185
Add and Subtract Fractions (D) ......................................... 193
Unit Review .................................................................. 202
Unit Checkpoint ............................................................ 203

# Decimals: Addition and Subtraction

Round Decimals Through Hundredths ................................. 207
Estimate Decimal Sums, Differences (A) ............................. 213
Estimate Decimal Sums, Differences (B) ............................. 217
Reasonable Answers and Decimal Problems ........................ 221
Solve Story Problems with Decimals (A) .............................. 226
Solve Story Problems with Decimals (B) .............................. 231

Unit Review . . . . . . . . . . . . . . . . . . . . . . . . . . . . . . . . . . . . . . . . . . . . . . . . . . . . 235
Unit Checkpoint . . . . . . . . . . . . . . . . . . . . . . . . . . . . . . . . . . . . . . . . . . . . . . . 236

## Decimals: Multiplication and Division

Estimate Decimal Products, Quotients (A) . . . . . . . . . . . . . . . . . . . . . . . . . . 239
Estimate Decimal Products, Quotients (B) . . . . . . . . . . . . . . . . . . . . . . . . . . 244
Estimate Decimal Products, Quotients (C) . . . . . . . . . . . . . . . . . . . . . . . . . . 250
Multiply and Divide Decimals (A) . . . . . . . . . . . . . . . . . . . . . . . . . . . . . . . . . 254
Multiply and Divide Decimals (B) . . . . . . . . . . . . . . . . . . . . . . . . . . . . . . . . . 261
Multiply and Divide Decimals (C) . . . . . . . . . . . . . . . . . . . . . . . . . . . . . . . . . 269
Compute Decimal Story Problems (A) . . . . . . . . . . . . . . . . . . . . . . . . . . . . . 273
Compute Decimal Story Problems (B) . . . . . . . . . . . . . . . . . . . . . . . . . . . . . 276
Compute Decimal Story Problems (C) . . . . . . . . . . . . . . . . . . . . . . . . . . . . . 279
Unit Review . . . . . . . . . . . . . . . . . . . . . . . . . . . . . . . . . . . . . . . . . . . . . . . . . . 282
Unit Checkpoint . . . . . . . . . . . . . . . . . . . . . . . . . . . . . . . . . . . . . . . . . . . . . . . 283

## Integers

Explore Rational Numbers (A) . . . . . . . . . . . . . . . . . . . . . . . . . . . . . . . . . . . 287
Explore Rational Numbers (B) . . . . . . . . . . . . . . . . . . . . . . . . . . . . . . . . . . . 290
Explore Rational Numbers (C) . . . . . . . . . . . . . . . . . . . . . . . . . . . . . . . . . . . 293
Add and Subtract Integers (A) . . . . . . . . . . . . . . . . . . . . . . . . . . . . . . . . . . . 298
Add and Subtract Integers (B) . . . . . . . . . . . . . . . . . . . . . . . . . . . . . . . . . . . 304
Add and Subtract Integers (C) . . . . . . . . . . . . . . . . . . . . . . . . . . . . . . . . . . . 309
Integer Answers: Reasonable or Not? . . . . . . . . . . . . . . . . . . . . . . . . . . . . . 313
Unit Review . . . . . . . . . . . . . . . . . . . . . . . . . . . . . . . . . . . . . . . . . . . . . . . . . . 317
Unit Checkpoint . . . . . . . . . . . . . . . . . . . . . . . . . . . . . . . . . . . . . . . . . . . . . . . 319

## Semester Review and Checkpoint

Semester Review . . . . . . . . . . . . . . . . . . . . . . . . . . . . . . . . . . . . . . . . . . . . . 321
Semester Checkpoint. . . . . . . . . . . . . . . . . . . . . . . . . . . . . . . . . . . . . . . . . . 323

# Percents and Probability

Understand Percents (A) ... 327
Understand Percents (B) ... 331
Find Equivalents to Percents (A) ... 334
Find Equivalents to Percents (B) ... 340
Find Equivalents to Percents (C) ... 344
Percent of a Number (A) ... 349
Percent of a Number (B) ... 352
Percent of a Number (C) ... 355
Represent Probabilities ... 359
Identify Dependent and Independent Events ... 363
Probability and Predictions ... 368
Unit Review ... 376
Unit Checkpoint ... 377

# Algebra

Understand Variables in Algebra (A) ... 381
Understand Variables in Algebra (B) ... 385
Use the Distributive Property (A) ... 387
Use the Distributive Property (B) ... 391
One Variable in Algebraic Expressions ... 395
Expression and Equation Problems (A) ... 398
Expression and Equation Problems (B) ... 403
Expression and Equation Problems (C) ... 408
Unit Review ... 411
Unit Checkpoint ... 412

# Coordinate Planes

Quadrants in the Coordinate Plane ... 415
Ordered Pairs ... 420
Graph or Write an Equation (A) ... 425
Graph or Write an Equation (B) ... 430
Graph or Write an Equation (C) ... 435

Graph or Write an Equation (D) .................................................. 439
Unit Review ......................................................................... 444
Unit Checkpoint .................................................................... 445

# Perimeter, Area, and Volume

Find the Perimeter of Plane Figures .................................................. 449
Area of Parallelograms (A) .......................................................... 456
Area of Parallelograms (B) .......................................................... 460
Area of Triangles (A) ................................................................ 466
Area of Triangles (B) ................................................................ 471
Nets, Solids, and Surface Area ...................................................... 473
Area of Irregular Shapes ............................................................ 480
Volume of Solid Figures (A) ......................................................... 485
Volume of Solid Figures (B) ......................................................... 491
Units of Perimeter, Area, and Volume ............................................... 495
Unit Review ......................................................................... 500
Unit Checkpoint .................................................................... 501

# Math Reasoning: Methods and Strategies

Steps to Solve Story Problems (A) .................................................. 505
Steps to Solve Story Problems (B) .................................................. 507
Break Down Multistep Problems .................................................... 510
Mathematical Reasoning Methods (A) ............................................... 514
Mathematical Reasoning Methods (B) ............................................... 517
Mathematical Reasoning Methods (C) ............................................... 521
Choose and Use Strategies (A) ...................................................... 529
Choose and Use Strategies (B) ...................................................... 534
Choose and Use Strategies (C) ...................................................... 540
Solve Simple to Complex Problems (A) .............................................. 543
Solve Simple to Complex Problems (B) .............................................. 548
Unit Review ......................................................................... 554
Unit Checkpoint .................................................................... 555

## Math Reasoning: Solutions

| | |
|---|---|
| Solve Problems Logically (A) | 559 |
| Solve Problems Logically (B) | 563 |
| Estimation and Reasonable Answers | 567 |
| Decimal Solutions | 572 |
| Reasonable Solutions | 575 |
| Unit Review | 581 |
| Unit Checkpoint | 582 |

## Data Analysis and Representation

| | |
|---|---|
| Mean, Median, and Mode | 585 |
| Compare Mean, Median, and Mode | 590 |
| Organize Data to Draw Histograms (A) | 593 |
| Organize Data to Draw Histograms (B) | 599 |
| Create Circle Graphs | 606 |
| Intepret Graphs and Tables | 611 |
| Fractions, Percents, and Graphs | 613 |
| Choose an Appropriate Graph | 615 |
| Unit Review | 617 |
| Unit Checkpoint | 618 |

## Semester Review and Checkpoint

| | |
|---|---|
| Semester Review | 619 |
| Semester Checkpoint | 622 |

## Glossary ... A-1

# Program Overview

### Lesson Overview
The table at the beginning of each lesson tells you what activities are in the lesson and whether students are on the computer (**ONLINE**) or at a table or desk (**OFFLINE**). The expected time for each activity is given.

### Objectives and Prerequisite Skills
Each lesson teaches the Lesson Objectives. The lesson assumes that students know the Prerequisite Skills from their previous math experience. The Get Ready activity is designed to remind students of the prerequisite skills, and to prepare them for the lesson.

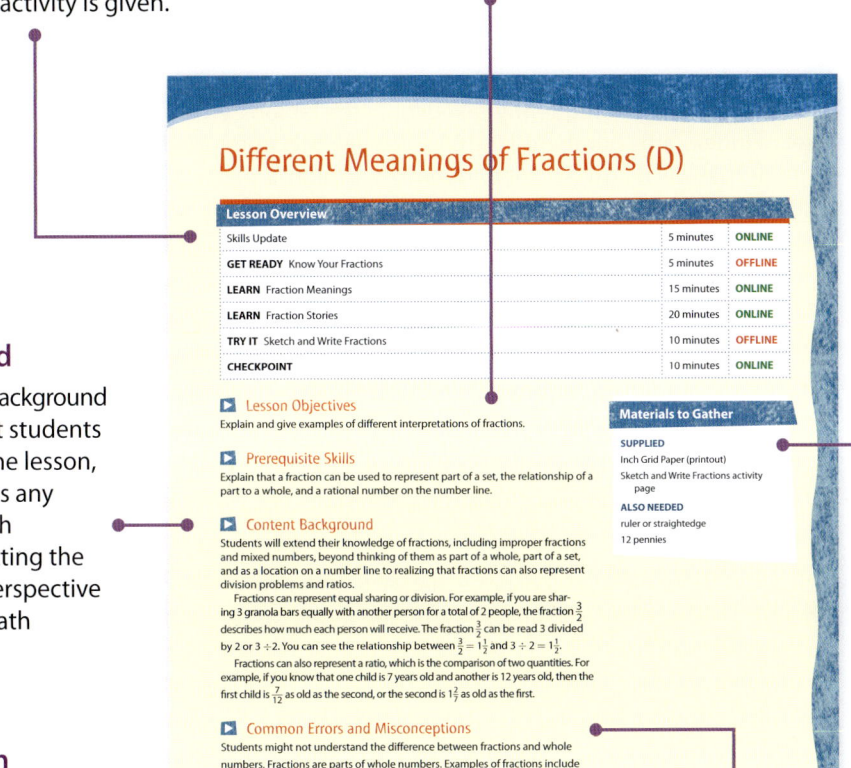

### Content Background
The Content Background tells you what students will learn in the lesson, and it explains any complex math concepts, putting the lesson into perspective with wider math knowledge.

### Advance Preparation
Some lessons require preparation that extends beyond gathering materials. In these cases, the lesson includes an Advance Preparation section.

### Materials
This box tells you what materials students will need in the lesson. More information about the materials is included on page x.

### Common Errors and Misconceptions
Research shows that students might misunderstand certain concepts, which then leads to misunderstanding of more advanced concepts. When certain research applies to a lesson, the lesson has a Common Errors and Misconceptions section.

## Materials

K[12] supplies this Lesson Guide and the Activity Book, the student book. K[12] also supplies a protractor, which students will use to measure angles.

## Printouts, Plastic Sheet Cover, and Dry-Erase Markers

A lesson may ask you to print a document showing a number line, a grid, or another math tool. These documents will be reused throughout the course. We recommend that you obtain a plastic sheet cover and dry-erase markers so students can place the sheet over the printout and write answers on the sheet. They can then erase the answers and reuse the printout multiple times.

**Important:** Some printouts, including graded Checkpoints, require students to measure shapes or angles. By default, many printers scale documents to fit to a printable area. Be sure to turn off page scaling so that documents print at 100% of their intended size.

## Number and Symbol Cards

Index cards labeled with numbers or symbols are frequently called for in the lessons. We recommend that you create a set of index cards numbered 0–100 and a few sets numbered 0–9. You can also create the symbols that will be used most frequently: − (minus), + (plus), × (multiplication), ÷ (division), = (equals), > (greater than), < (less than), ( (opening parenthesis), ) (closing parenthesis). You can then use these cards throughout the course.

## Math Notebook, Paper, and Pencil

Obtain a binder or spiral notebook to serve as the Math Notebook in which students will work problems, make sketches, and write answers to the problems in the Activity Book. Students should always have the Math Notebook, paper, and a pencil handy. These materials are not listed in each lesson.

## Also Needed

Other common items are called for in lessons, designated in the materials list as "Also Needed." Gather or purchase these materials, such as a ruler, scissors, and index cards.

# Working Through a Lesson

When you go online with students to do a math lesson, you will see a list of the activities that are included in the lesson. Some lessons begin with a Skills Update. Skills Updates are online activities that focus on previously learned math skills or addition, subtraction, multiplication, or division facts. *Required* Skills Updates are noted in the Lesson Guide. *Optional* Skills Updates appear online only. Students should complete Skills Updates independently.

The Lesson Guide gives an overview of the remaining lesson activities. Instructions for online activities are online. Students may complete these activities independently, or you may sit at the computer with them, reading text to them as necessary. The Lesson Guide may include a teaching tip or other information. In some cases, such as when an open-ended Learning Tool is used, there will be instructions to follow in the Lesson Guide. The online screen will guide you to follow these instructions.

Instructions for offline activities are in the Lesson Guide. These activities may use supplied or common materials, and some include pages from the Activity Book.

# Types of Activities

**Skills Update**  Short problem set covering topics taught in previous units or game to build fluency, or speed, with math facts. Skills Updates are online and may be required or optional. Required Skills Updates are listed in the Lesson Guide.

**Get Ready**  Review of previous math knowledge that will be needed for this lesson. The Get Ready activities can be online or offline.

**Learn**  Presentation of math concepts, or guided practice. The Learn activities can be online or offline.

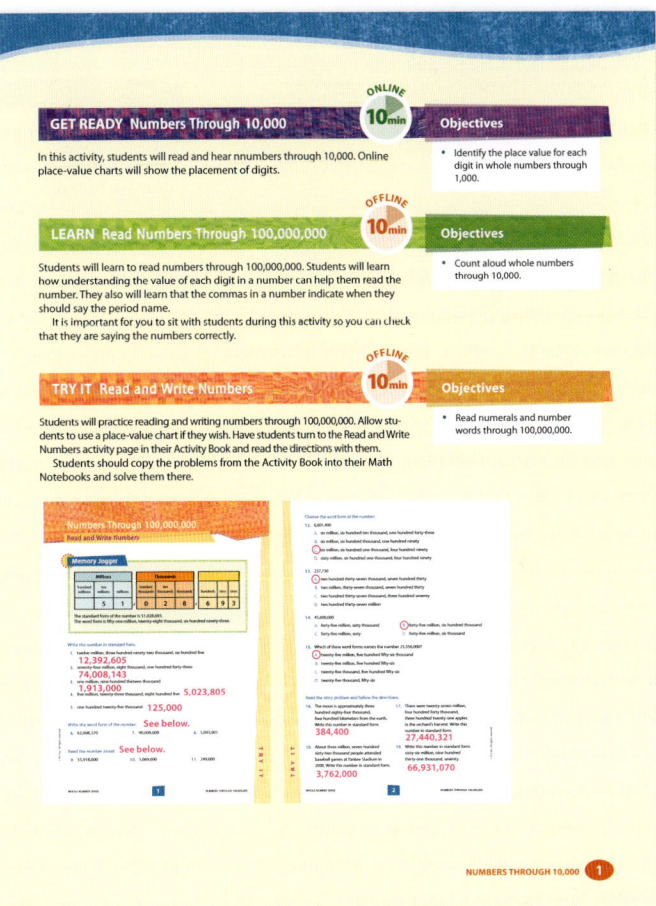

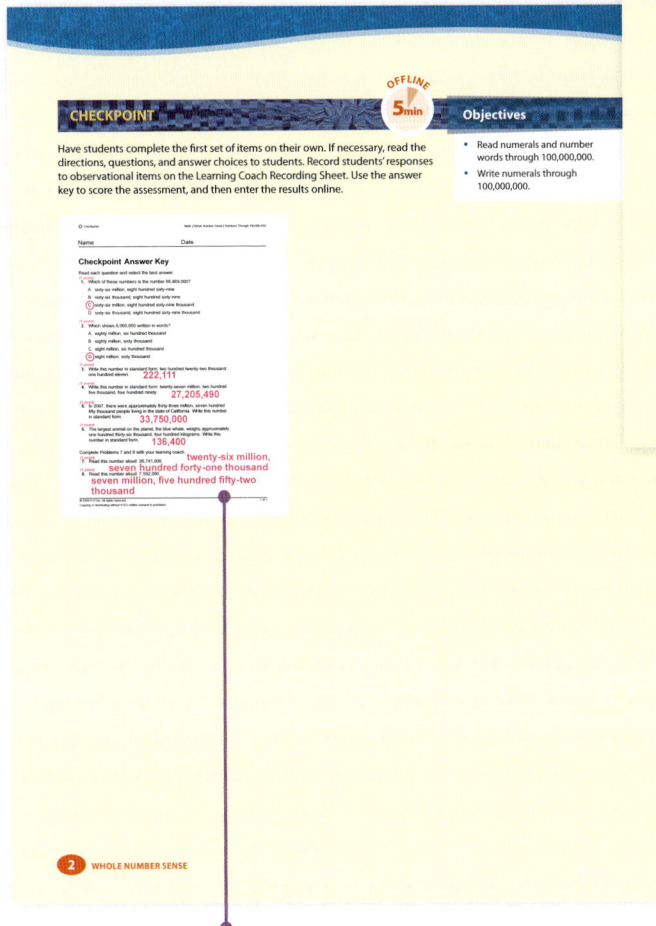

The Lesson Guide includes the answers, shown in magenta, to the Activity Book pages and offline Checkpoints.

**Try It**  Practice problems on the concepts taught in the lesson. Students should complete these problems independently. The Try It activities can be online or in the Activity Book.

**Checkpoint**  Assessments of whether students have learned the objectives taught in the lesson or lessons. Not every lesson has a Checkpoint. In some Checkpoints, students show or explain their answers, and you record their performance.

In addition to the regular Checkpoints, **Unit Reviews** and **Unit Checkpoints** are lessons at the end of each unit. Each semester ends with a **Semester Review** and **Semester Checkpoint**.

# Online Activities

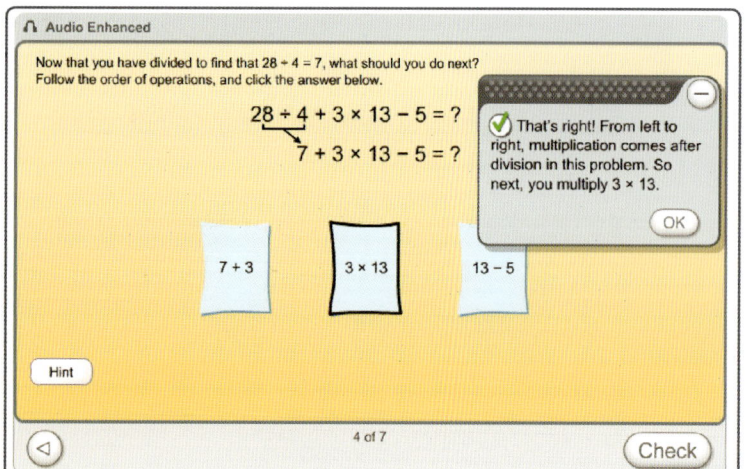

Online activities will show whether students answered correctly.

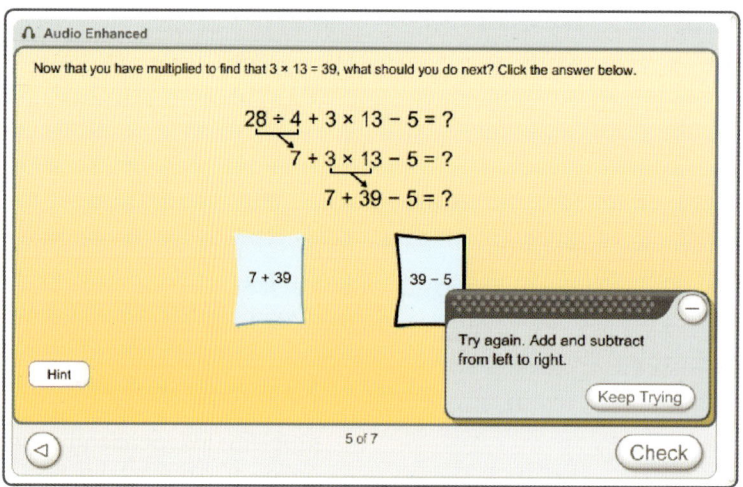

If students answer incorrectly, they will see feedback. They should click Keep Trying to try again. If they answer incorrectly a second time, they can click Show Me to see the correct answer.

Learning Tools are online activities that you set up to give students math exercises that will apply to what they are learning in a specific lesson.

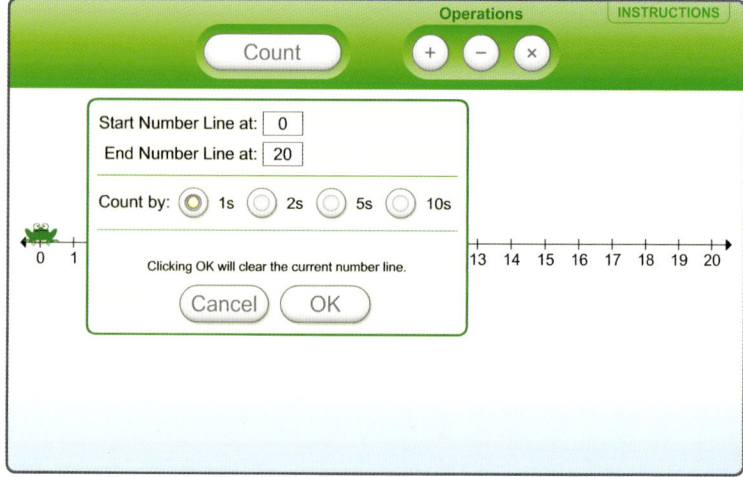

xii  PROGRAM OVERVIEW

# Whole Numbers and Powers

## ▶ Unit Objectives

- Round whole numbers in a story problem.
- Estimate or calculate a sum or a difference in a whole-number problem.
- Estimate or calculate a sum or a difference in a whole-number story problem.
- Estimate or calculate a product or a quotient in a whole-number problem.
- Estimate or calculate a product or a quotient in a whole-number story problem.
- Represent and compute a power by using repeated multiplication.
- Solve a problem that involves powers.
- Determine the prime factorization of a composite number.

## ▶ Big Ideas

Estimation can be a useful tool in problem solving.

## ▶ Unit Introduction

Students will explore whole numbers and powers in this unit. The unit begins with rounding whole numbers in story problems. Students will round whole numbers in the context of a problem but will not solve problems. The next sequence of lessons explores whole-number computation problems as well as story problems. Students will estimate and calculate in addition, subtraction, multiplication, and division number sentences. In the next part of this unit, students are introduced to powers with whole numbers, such as $5^3$, as well as how to represent a power using repeated multiplication. For example, $5^3$ can be shown as $5 \times 5 \times 5$ or $5 \cdot 5 \cdot 5$. Students will solve problems involving powers with whole numbers. They will complete the unit by finding the prime factorization of composite numbers. For example, the prime factorization of 30 is $2 \cdot 3 \cdot 5$.

## ▶ Keywords

addend
base
boundary number
clustering
composite number
cubed
difference
dividend

divisor
exponent
expression
factor
friendly numbers
minuend
power
prime factorization

prime number
product
quotient
round (v.)
squared
subtrahend
sum
whole numbers

# Round Whole Numbers in Story Problems

## Lesson Overview

| | | |
|---|---|---|
| **GET READY** Rounding Numbers | 10 minutes | ONLINE |
| **LEARN** Strategies for Rounding | 15 minutes | ONLINE |
| **LEARN** Rounding Distances | 15 minutes | ONLINE |
| **TRY IT** Round Numbers in Story Problems | 10 minutes | OFFLINE |
| **CHECKPOINT** | 10 minutes | ONLINE |

### ▶ Lesson Objectives

Round whole numbers in a story problem.

### ▶ Prerequisite Skills

- Round a whole number.
- Identify and explain when rounding is useful.

### ▶ Content Background

In this lesson, students will round whole numbers in a story problem. They will learn several methods of rounding, including front-end estimation, friendly numbers, and rounding to a specific place value. Students will learn to base their choice of an appropriate rounding strategy on the context of each problem. They will continue to use rounding strategies when they solve story problems in future lessons.

Rounding numbers makes it easier to estimate. Students have learned several rounding strategies. One rounding strategy is using friendly numbers. In that strategy, students round to the nearest 5, 10, 25, or 100. For example, they can round 28 to the friendly number 25. The number 25 is close to 28 and easy to work with.

In another strategy, front-end estimation, students round a number to its greatest place value. For example, with front-end estimation, 125 rounds to 100.

Finally, students may choose to round to a place value. Suppose students want to round 72,819 to the nearest thousand. They would choose between the boundary numbers 72,000 and 73,000. Because 72,819 is closer to 73,000, the answer is 73,000.

Students will learn to write numerals with commas between each period, or group of three digits. In this course, numbers with four or more digits include commas. For example, eleven thousand, two hundred twenty will be shown as 11,220.

You should encourage students to use commas when they enter numeric answers to questions online. The computer, however, will still score a question as correct if students omit the commas.

### Materials to Gather

**SUPPLIED**

Round Numbers in Story Problems activity page

## GET READY  Rounding Numbers

**ONLINE 10 min**

Students will use number lines to round whole numbers. The number lines will give students a way to round numbers to a place value. They will round to the nearest thousand, ten thousand, hundred thousand, million, and ten million.

### Objectives
- Round a whole number.

## LEARN  Strategies for Rounding

**ONLINE 15 min**

Students will review place value and learn three methods of rounding numbers:

- Round to a friendly number. Friendly numbers are usually multiples of 5, 10, 25, or 100.
- Use front-end estimation.
- Round to a certain place value.

Students should see that rounding makes working with numbers easier. Most importantly, students should understand that there is more than one way to round numbers.

### Objectives
- Round whole numbers in a story problem.

### Tips
Have students practice counting by 5s, 10s, 25s, and 100s to review the multiples of those numbers before they use friendly numbers to round a number.

## LEARN  Rounding Distances

**ONLINE 15 min**

Students will use a variety of ways to round whole numbers in story problems. Each problem presents the distance between two cities.

Students will round a number by using three different strategies. They will see how different rounding strategies produce different rounded numbers. For example, the number 1,969 rounds to 1,975 if the friendly-number strategy is used to round to a multiple of 25; to 2,000 if the front-end estimation strategy is used; and to 1,970 if the strategy is to round to the nearest 10.

### Objectives
- Round whole numbers in a story problem.

4  WHOLE NUMBERS AND POWERS

## TRY IT Round Numbers in Story Problems

OFFLINE 10 min

### Objectives

- Round whole numbers in a story problem.

Students will practice using different strategies for rounding numbers as they work with story problems. Have students turn to the Round Numbers in Story Problems activity page in their Activity Book and read the directions with them.

Students should copy the problems from the Activity Book into their Math Notebook as necessary and solve them there.

### Round Whole Numbers in Story Problems

#### Round Numbers in Story Problems

Reagan wants to buy a new van. The chart shows how much a new van costs at different car dealers. Use the two strategies in the table to round each price.

| | Car dealer | Friendly numbers | Nearest thousand |
|---|---|---|---|
| 1. | Car Dealer A $39,528 | $39,525 | $40,000 |
| 2. | Car Dealer B $36,102 | $36,100 | $36,000 |
| 3. | Car Dealer C $38,999 | $39,000 | $39,000 |

**Friendly-number answers will vary.**

4. Reagan wants to be sure he has enough money to buy the van from Car Dealer A. Which rounded number should Reagan use to estimate the amount of money he needs? Explain.
**See below.**

Round the numbers as directed.

5. In 1987, professional football player Walter Payton set a new record for career rushing yards. His record was 16,726 rushing yards. Round Payton's record to the nearest hundred yards. **16,700 yd**
6. The Empire State Building in New York City cost $24,718,000 to build in 1931. Round the total cost to the nearest million.
**$25,000,000**
7. In 2005 there were 3,844,829 people living in Los Angeles. Round the population to the nearest ten thousand.
**3,840,000**
8. The total cost of building the Washington Monument was $1,187,710. Round the total cost to the nearest ten thousand dollars.
**$1,190,000**
9. The total number of people attending professional football games for the 2007 regular season was 17,341,012. Round the total attendance to the nearest hundred thousand.
**17,300,000**



TRY IT



Choose the answer.

10. Last month the earth was about 91,348,000 miles from the sun. Which answer choice shows this distance rounded to the nearest ten million?
(A.) 90,000,000 mi B. 91,000,000 mi
C. 91,300,000 mi D. 91,400,000 mi

11. The distance between Sydney, Australia, and Paris, France, is 16,968 kilometers. Which answer choice shows this distance rounded to the nearest thousand?
A. 14,000 km B. 15,000 km
C. 16,000 km (D.) 17,000 km

12. The number of Americans who use text messaging is estimated to be more than 83,780,000. Which answer choice shows this number rounded to the nearest million?
A. 80,000,000 B. 83,000,000
(C.) 84,000,000 D. 90,000,000

13. The newspaper reported that the attendance at Yankee Stadium II in New York City in 2005 was 4,100,000 when rounded to the nearest hundred thousand people. Which could have been the exact attendance in 2005?
A. 4,017,598 B. 4,045,962
(C.) 4,090,696 D. 4,152,067

14. The height of Mount Chimborazo in Ecuador is 21,000 feet above sea level when rounded to the nearest thousand. But the height is 20,600 feet when rounded to the nearest hundred. Which could be the exact height of Mount Chimborazo?
A. 20,458 ft (B.) 20,561 ft
C. 20,672 ft D. 21,432 ft

TRY IT





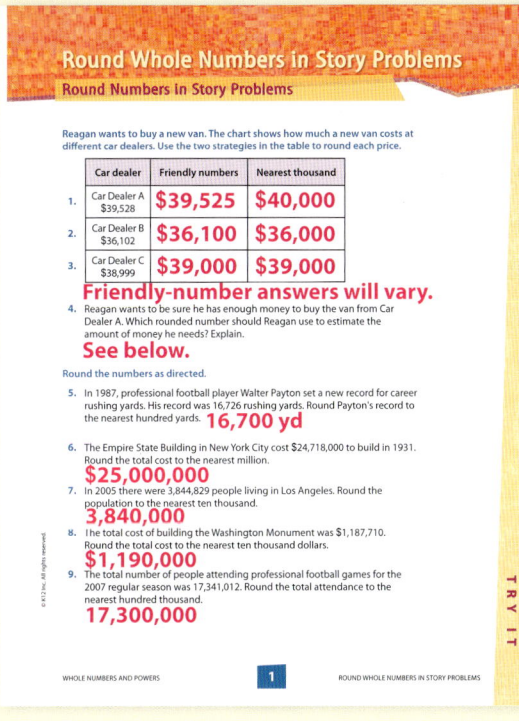

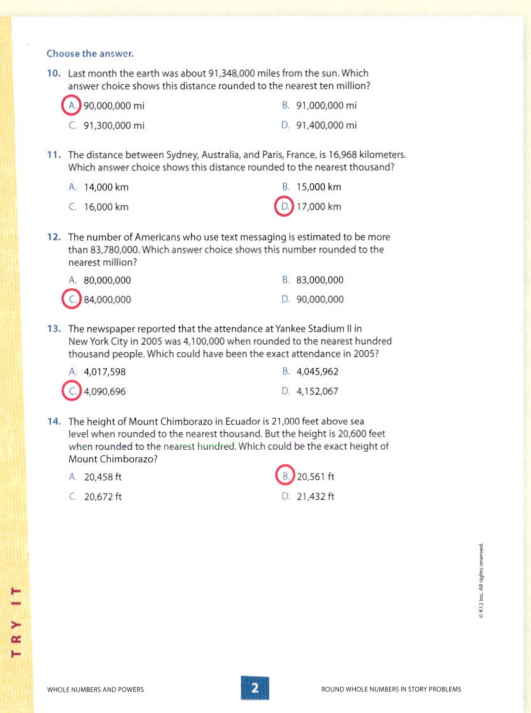

### Additional Answer

4. Reagan should use the number rounded to the nearest thousand. That number is greater than the exact price. The other rounded number is less than the exact price, so he wouldn't have enough money to buy the van.

## CHECKPOINT

ONLINE 10 min

### Objectives

- Round whole numbers in a story problem.

Students will complete an online Checkpoint. If necessary, read the directions, problems, and answer choices to students and help them with keyboard or mouse operations.

# Estimate and Find Sums and Differences

## Lesson Overview

| | | |
|---|---|---|
| **GET READY** Estimate & Work with a Number Line | 10 minutes | **OFFLINE** |
| **LEARN** Different Ways to Estimate | 25 minutes | **ONLINE** |
| **LEARN** Finding Estimates and Exact Answers | 15 minutes | **ONLINE** |
| **TRY IT** Estimate and Solve | 10 minutes | **OFFLINE** |

### ▶ Lesson Objectives

Estimate or calculate a sum or a difference in a whole-number problem.

### ▶ Prerequisite Skills

- Estimate sums and differences on a number line.
- Explain and apply standard step-by-step approaches for addition.
- Explain and apply standard step-by-step approaches for subtraction.

### ▶ Content Background

Students will learn different ways to estimate addition and subtraction problems. They will also calculate to find the exact answer to an addition or subtraction problem.

### ▶ Common Errors and Misconceptions

- Students might become so concerned about getting the correct answer when estimating that they first find the exact answer, and then round it. For example, when asked to estimate 348 + 176, students might find the sum (524), and then round it to the nearest hundred (500).
- Students might have difficulty accepting that there is more than one correct approach and answer to an estimation problem.

### ▶ Advance Preparation

The Number Line Creator Tool will print number lines that students will use in the Get Ready. The link to the Number Line Creator Tool is in the online Advance Preparation. Print one page of number lines at a time. Each page will have four identical number lines. You'll print three pages.

### Materials to Gather

**SUPPLIED**

Estimate and Solve activity page
number lines from Number Line Creator Tool

### DIRECTIONS FOR USING THE NUMBER LINE CREATOR TOOL

To create number lines from 0–60:

| 1. Set Range: | 2. Select Options: | 3. Print Number Line: |
|---|---|---|
| • Start Number Line at: 0<br>• End Number Line at: 60 | • Tick Marks: tens, ones<br>• Labels: tens | • Page Orientation: landscape<br>• Number Lines per Sheet: 4 |

WHOLE NUMBERS AND POWERS

**To create number lines from 0–220:**
Repeat Steps 1–3, but in Step 1, set the beginning of the number line as 0 and the end of the number line as 220. In Step 2, for tick marks, click hundreds and tens. For labels, click hundreds.

**To create number lines from 0–360.**
Repeat Steps 1–3, but in Step 1, set the beginning of the number line as 0 and the end of the number line as 360. In Step 2, for tick marks, click hundreds and tens. For labels, click hundreds.

## GET READY  Estimate & Work with a Number Line   OFFLINE 10 min

### Objectives
- Estimate sums and differences on a number line.
- Explain and apply standard step-by-step approaches for addition.
- Explain and apply standard step-by-step approaches for subtraction.

Students will use a number line to estimate sums in addition problems and then calculate the exact answers. They will then use a number line to estimate differences in subtraction problems and then calculate exact answers. Students will round to friendly numbers before estimating the sum or difference. If you haven't printed the number lines, go to Advance Preparation and use the Number Line Creator Tool.

Gather the number lines 0–60, 0–220, and 0–360 that you printed. Students may label additional tick marks on the printouts to help them.

### ESTIMATE SUMS

1. The first problem students will work with is 42 + 14 = ?
   Have students use a 0–60 number line to round the addends as follows:
   - Mark 0 to start.
   - Decide how to round 42 and 14 by using friendly numbers that are multiples of 5. Jump to 40, which is a multiple of 5.
   - Decide how to round 14 by using a friendly number that is a multiple of 5. Fifteen is a friendly number that is a multiple of 5 to use. Start at 40 and jump 15 spaces. Land on 55.

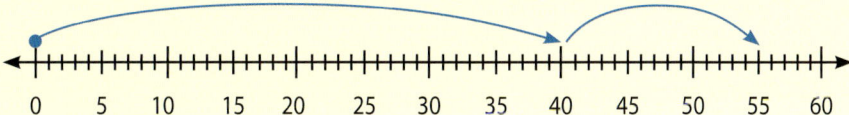

2. Now students will calculate the exact answer on another 0–60 number line. Guide them to use the number line as follows:
   - Mark 0 to start.
   - Jump and mark 42.
   - Jump and mark 14 more spaces. Land on 56.

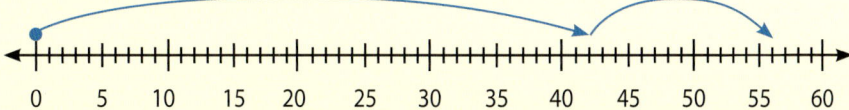

3. The estimated sum is 55. The exact sum is 56. Students should see that their estimated sum was reasonable because the exact sum is so close to the estimated sum.

4. Repeat Steps 1 and 2 with the 0–220 number line and this problem:
   51 + 138 = ? Round the numbers to friendly numbers that are multiples of 25.
   - The estimated sum should be 200.
   - The exact sum is 189. Ask students if their estimate is reasonable.

**ESTIMATE AND FIND SUMS AND DIFFERENCES**   7

5. Repeat Steps 1 and 2 with the 0–360 number lines and this problem:
   197 + 142 = ? Round the numbers to friendly numbers that are multiples of 10.
   - The estimated sum should be about 340.
   - The actual sum is 339. Ask students if their estimate was reasonable.

**ESTIMATE DIFFERENCES**

6. Tell students that they can also estimate to find the answer to a subtraction problem, the difference. The first problem they will work with is 347 − 23 = ? Round the numbers to friendly numbers that are multiples of 25.
   - Mark 0 to start at the beginning of a 0–360 number line.
   - Decide how to round 347. It can be rounded to 350. Jump and mark 350.
   - Decide how to round 23. It can be rounded to the friendly number of 25. Jump back 25 from 350, landing on 325. The estimated difference of 347 − 23, using rounded numbers, is 325.

7. Now students will calculate the exact answer on another 0–360 number line.
   - Mark 0 to start.
   - Jump and mark 347.
   - Jump back 23. Land on 324.
   - The exact difference is 324 and the estimated difference was 325. Ask students if their estimated difference was reasonable.

8. Repeat Steps 6 and 7 with the 0–220 number lines and this problem:
   221 − 108 = ? Round the numbers to friendly numbers that are multiples of 100.
   - The estimated difference should be about 100.
   - The exact difference is 113.

9. Tell students that, when they use the friendly numbers strategy to round numbers, they should look for a number on the number line that is close to the number given. The estimate will then be close to the exact answer. If they learn to make estimates that are close to exact answers, they will be able to rely on their estimating as they continue in math.

## LEARN  Different Ways to Estimate

ONLINE 25 min

**Objectives**
- Estimate or calculate a sum or a difference in a whole-number problem.

Students will work with different strategies for rounding numbers. They will see clustering and the use of friendly numbers for rounding. This activity also reviews rounding a whole number to a specific place. Students will use a number line to round whole numbers.

**Tips**  If students are having trouble deciding if their answers are reasonable, talk about what range of numbers is considered reasonably close to the answer.

## LEARN  Finding Estimates and Exact Answers

ONLINE 15 min

**Objectives**
- Estimate or calculate a sum or a difference in a whole-number problem.

Students will round numbers that are in the hundreds, thousands, and ten thousands. They will round numbers to a specified place value and then estimate answers to addition and subtraction problems. Then they will find the exact answer to decide if their estimate is reasonable.

  WHOLE NUMBERS AND POWERS

# TRY IT  Estimate and Solve

**OFFLINE 10 min**

Students will practice various ways to estimate sums and differences. They will also find the exact answer and determine if their estimate is reasonable compared to the exact answer. Have students turn to the Estimate and Solve activity page in their Activity book and read the directions with them.

Students should copy the problems from the Activity Book into their Math Notebook as necessary and solve them there.

## Objectives

- Estimate or calculate a sum or a difference in a whole-number problem.

### Estimate and Find Sums and Differences
**Estimate and Solve**

Use clustering to estimate the sum. Choose the answer.
1. 377 + 386 + 372 + 389 = ?
   A. 400
   B. 1,000
   **C. 1,600**
2. 43 + 32 + 44 + 35 = ?
   **A. 160**
   B. 120
   C. 200

Round to friendly numbers that are multiples of 100 to estimate. Choose the answer.
3. 9,629 + 8,573 = ?
   A. 17,000
   **B. 18,200**
   C. 19,200
4. 76,999 − 68,205 = ?
   A. 6,000
   B. 7,200
   **C. 8,800**

Estimate by rounding the numbers to the nearest ten thousand. Choose the answer.
5. 56,880 + 43,375 = ?
   A. 90,000
   **B. 100,000**
   C. 110,000
6. 325,686 − 124,478 = ?
   A. 200,000
   **B. 210,000**
   C. 250,000

Complete the table. Estimate each sum or difference by using one of the strategies above. Then find the exact answer. Decide if the estimate is reasonable.

| Problem | Estimate | Exact answer |
|---|---|---|
| 7. 2,134 + 7,322 = ? | ? | ? |
| 8. 34,672 − 13,440 = ? | ? | ? |

**See below.**

Estimate by first rounding the numbers to the nearest hundred thousand. Then find the exact answer. Are your estimate and exact answer close?

9. 8,925,181 + 2,820,084
   Estimated: 11,700,000
   Calculated: 11,745,265
10. 8,189,378 − 5,428,310
    Estimated: 2,800,000
    Calculated: 2,761,068

## Additional Answers

For Problems 7 and 8, estimates will vary. Sample estimates are given.

| | Problem | Estimate | Exact answer |
|---|---|---|---|
| 7. | 2,134 + 7,322 = ? | Friendly numbers that are multiples of 25: 2,125 + 7,325 = 9,450<br>Round to the nearest hundred: 2,100 + 7,300 = 9,400 | 9,456 |
| 8. | 34,672 − 13,440 = ? | Friendly numbers that are multiples of 25: 34,675 − 13,450 = 21,225<br>Round to the nearest thousand: 35,000 − 13,000 = 22,000 | 21,232 |

For Problems 7–10, if the estimate and the exact answer can be rounded to a place value and still be close, the estimate is reasonable. In Problem 10, for example, 11,745,265 rounded to the nearest hundred thousand is 11,700,00, which is the same number as the estimate. The estimate is reasonable.

**ESTIMATE AND FIND SUMS AND DIFFERENCES**

# Estimate Sums and Differences (A)

| Lesson Overview | | |
|---|---|---|
| **GET READY** Estimate in Different Ways | 20 minutes | **ONLINE** |
| **LEARN** Estimate Addition Story Problems | 15 minutes | **ONLINE** |
| **LEARN** Estimate and Calculate Addition | 15 minutes | **ONLINE** |
| **TRY IT** Estimate Story Problems | 10 minutes | **OFFLINE** |

## ▶ Lesson Objectives
Estimate or calculate a sum or a difference in a whole-number story problem.

## ▶ Prerequisite Skills
- Use estimation to predict a solution to a story problem and to verify the reasonableness of the calculated result.
- Estimate or calculate a sum or a difference in a whole-number problem.

## ▶ Content Background
Students will learn to estimate and calculate addition story problems. They should understand that comparing estimates to exact answers will help them decide if their estimate was reasonable.

## ▶ Common Errors and Misconceptions
- Students might become so concerned about getting the correct answer when estimating that they first find the exact answer, and then round it. For example, when asked to estimate 348 + 176, students might find the sum (524), and then round it to the nearest hundred (500).
- Students might have difficulty accepting that there is more than one correct approach and answer to an estimation problem.

### Materials to Gather

**SUPPLIED**
Estimate Story Problems activity page

---

**GET READY** Estimate in Different Ways  **ONLINE 20 min**

Students will review how to estimate sums by rounding the addends to a certain place value, using friendly numbers, and clustering. They will work problems that include data about U.S. national parks. The data will involve numbers up to the ten thousands place.

**Objectives**
- Use estimation to predict a solution to a story problem and to verify the reasonableness of the calculated result.
- Estimate or calculate a sum or a difference in a whole-number problem.

## LEARN Estimate Addition Story Problems

Students will use a variety of rounding strategies to round the addends in addition story problems that deal with national parks. Students will not solve the estimation problems in this activity. They will begin to learn how to determine which strategy would be best to use. The data will involve numbers up to the ten millions place.

### Objectives

- Estimate or calculate a sum or a difference in a whole-number story problem.

## LEARN Estimate and Calculate Addition

Students will estimate answers and find exact answers to addition story problems about national parks. They will check to see if their estimate was reasonable. They will determine which rounding strategy is best to use in the context of the story problem.

### Objectives

- Estimate or calculate a sum or a difference in a whole-number story problem.

## TRY IT Estimate Story Problems

Students will practice estimating and calculating addition story problems. They will use a rounding strategy to estimate sums and then compare their estimates to exact answers to find out if the estimate is reasonable. Have students turn to the Estimate Story Problems activity page in their Activity Book and read the directions with them.

Students should copy the problems from the Activity Book into their Math Notebook as necessary and solve them there.

### Objectives

- Estimate or calculate a sum or a difference in a whole-number story problem.

### Additional Answers

5. **Example:** Using front-end estimation: $52,000 ($24,000 + $28,000). The Kellys spent $52,368. The estimate should be close to the exact answer.

6. **Example:** Using front-end estimation: 50,000,000 (40,000,000 + 10,000,000). The website had 53,704,000 visitors. The estimate should be close to the exact answer.

7. **Example:** Rounding to the nearest hundred thousand: 5,100,000 (3,800,000 + 1,300,000). The two cities had a total population of 5,101,071. The estimate should be close to the exact answer.

8. **Example:** Rounding to the nearest thousand: 150,000 (76,000 + 74,000). There were 149,934 voters. The estimate should be close to the exact answer.

ESTIMATE SUMS AND DIFFERENCES (A) 11

# Estimate Sums and Differences (B)

## Lesson Overview

| | | |
|---|---|---|
| **GET READY** Estimate Differences in Story Problems | 10 minutes | **ONLINE** |
| **LEARN** Subtraction Estimates | 15 minutes | **ONLINE** |
| **LEARN** Subtraction Estimates and Exact Answers | 15 minutes | **ONLINE** |
| **TRY IT** Practice Estimating with Subtraction | 10 minutes | **OFFLINE** |
| **CHECKPOINT** | 10 minutes | **ONLINE** |

### ▶ Lesson Objectives
Estimate or calculate a sum or a difference in a whole-number story problem.

### ▶ Prerequisite Skills
- Use estimation to predict a solution to a story problem and to verify the reasonableness of the calculated result.
- Estimate or calculate a sum or a difference in a whole-number problem.

### ▶ Content Background
Students will learn to estimate and calculate subtraction story problems. They should understand that comparing estimates to exact answers will help them decide if their estimate was reasonable.

### ▶ Common Errors and Misconceptions
- Students might become so concerned about getting the correct answer when estimating that they first find the exact answer, and then round it. For example, when asked to estimate 348 + 176, students might find the sum (524), and then round it to the nearest hundred (500).
- Students might have difficulty accepting that there is more than one correct approach and answer to an estimation problem.

### Materials to Gather

**SUPPLIED**

Practice Estimating with Subtraction activity page

---

## GET READY  Estimate Differences in Story Problems   ONLINE 10 min

Students will review how to use different estimation strategies for subtraction: rounding to a place value and using friendly numbers. They will estimate differences in subtraction problems. They will also calculate the differences. Students will then compare their estimates to the differences and will decide if their estimate was reasonable.

### Objectives
- Use estimation to predict a solution to a story problem and to verify the reasonableness of the calculated result.
- Estimate or calculate a sum or a difference in a whole-number problem.

**12  WHOLE NUMBERS AND POWERS**

## LEARN  Subtraction Estimates     ONLINE 15 min

Students will use a variety of strategies to round numbers. Then they will estimate differences in subtraction story problems about space travel and the solar system.

**Objectives**
- Estimate or calculate a sum or a difference in a whole-number story problem.

## LEARN  Subtraction Estimates and Exact Answers     ONLINE 15 min

Students will estimate the differences in subtraction story problems about the planets and moon by using rounded numbers. Students will then calculate exact answers to determine if their estimate is reasonable.

Students may need paper and pencil to find the exact differences of the subtraction story problems. Allow them to solve the problems on paper and then type their answers online.

**Objectives**
- Estimate or calculate a sum or a difference in a whole-number story problem.

## TRY IT  Practice Estimating with Subtraction     OFFLINE 10 min

Students will practice estimating and calculating subtraction story problems. They will choose the rounding strategies to round the numbers. They will estimate differences and solve for exact answers. They will compare their estimates to exact answers to see if the estimate was reasonable. Have students turn to the Practice Estimating with Subtraction activity page in their Activity Book.

Students should copy the problems from the Activity Book into their Math Notebook as necessary and solve them there.

**Objectives**
- Estimate or calculate a sum or a difference in a whole-number story problem.

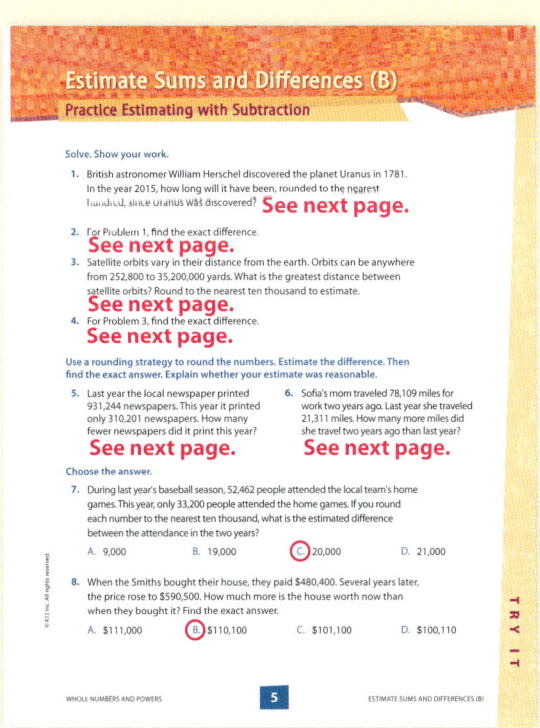

**ESTIMATE SUMS AND DIFFERENCES (B)**  13

**Additional Answers**

1. $2,000 - 1,800 = 200$    200 years
2. $2,015 - 1,781 = 234$    234 years
3. $35,200,000 - 250,000 = 34,950,000$    34,950,000 yards
4. $35,200,000 - 252,800 = 34,947,200$    34,947,200 yards
5. **Example:** Rounding to the nearest ten thousand to estimate the difference: 620,000 newspapers ($930,000 - 310,000$)

   Exact difference: 621,043 newspapers
   621,043 rounded to the greater ten thousand is 620,000. That is the same number as the estimate. The estimate is reasonable.

6. **Example:** Rounding to the nearest thousand to estimate the difference: 57,000 miles ($78,000 - 21,000$)

   Exact difference: 56,798 miles
   56,798 rounded to the nearest thousand is 57,000. That is the same number as the estimate. The estimate is reasonable.

## CHECKPOINT

ONLINE 10 min

Students will complete an online Checkpoint. If necessary, read the directions, problems, and answer choices to students and help them with keyboard or mouse operations.

### Objectives

- Estimate or calculate a sum or a difference in a whole-number problem.
- Estimate or calculate a sum or a difference in a whole-number story problem.

# Estimate and Find Products and Quotients

## Lesson Overview

| | | |
|---|---|---|
| **GET READY** Solve Flip-Card Problems | 15 minutes | ONLINE |
| **LEARN** Different Strategies to Estimate | 20 minutes | ONLINE |
| **LEARN** Find Estimates and Exact Answers | 15 minutes | ONLINE |
| **TRY IT** Estimate and Calculate Products and Quotients | 10 minutes | OFFLINE |

### ▶ Lesson Objectives
Estimate or calculate a product or a quotient in a whole-number problem.

### ▶ Prerequisite Skills
- Estimate or calculate a sum or a difference in a whole-number problem.
- Explain and apply standard step-by-step approaches for multiplication.
- Explain and apply standard step-by-step approaches for division.

### ▶ Content Background
Students will learn different strategies to round numbers for estimating products and quotients in multiplication and division problems. They will learn to decide if their estimates were reasonable by calculating the exact answers for the problems.

### ▶ Common Errors and Misconceptions
- Students might become so concerned about getting the correct answer when estimating that they first find the exact answer, and then round it. For example, when asked to estimate 348 + 176, students might find the sum (524), and then round it to the nearest hundred (500).
- Students might have difficulty accepting that there is more than one correct approach and answer to an estimation problem.

**Materials to Gather**

**SUPPLIED**
Estimate and Calculate Products and Quotients activity page

---

## GET READY  Solve Flip-Card Problems

ONLINE 15 min

Students will use online flip cards to review estimating and calculating addition and subtraction problems. Then they will calculate multiplication and division problems without estimating first.

**Tips**  If students are having difficulty multiplying or dividing problems with greater numbers, have them solve a few more problems with lesser numbers to review the steps for multiplication and division.

### Objectives
- Estimate or calculate a sum or a difference in a whole-number problem.
- Explain and apply standard step-by-step approaches for multiplication.
- Explain and apply standard step-by-step approaches for division.

ESTIMATE AND FIND PRODUCTS AND QUOTIENTS  **15**

## LEARN  Different Strategies to Estimate

ONLINE 20 min

**Objectives**

- Estimate or calculate a product or a quotient in a whole-number problem.

Students will learn different strategies to estimate the product or quotient: lower and upper bound, rounding one factor up and the other factor down, rounding the dividend and the divisor up, and estimating a quotient using multiplication. Then they will use the strategies to play a hidden-picture game.

## LEARN  Find Estimates and Exact Answers

ONLINE 15 min

**Objectives**

- Estimate or calculate a product or a quotient in a whole-number problem.

Students will round numbers in a multiplication or division problem to a specified place to estimate a product or quotient. Then they will find the exact answer to the problem to decide if their estimate is reasonable.

Students may need paper and pencil to find the exact products and quotients of the multiplication and division problems. Allow them to solve the problems on paper and then type the answers online.

## TRY IT  Estimate and Calculate Products and Quotients

OFFLINE 10 min

**Objectives**

- Estimate or calculate a product or a quotient in a whole-number problem.

Students will practice rounding factors, dividends, and divisors to estimate products and quotients. They will also find exact answers and determine if their estimates are reasonable. Have students turn to the Estimate and Calculate Products and Quotients activity page in their Activity Book and read the directions with them.

Students should copy the problems from the Activity Book into their Math Notebook as necessary and solve them there.

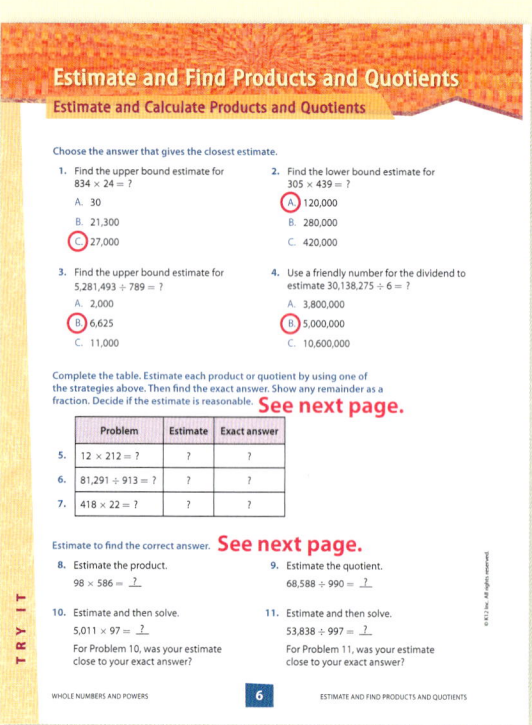

**WHOLE NUMBERS AND POWERS**

**Additional Answers**

For Problems 5–7, estimates will vary. Sample estimates are given. The estimate should be close to the exact answer. If the estimate and the exact answer can be rounded to a place value and still be close, the estimate is reasonable.

| | Problem | Estimate | Exact answer |
|---|---|---|---|
| 5. | 12 × 212 = ? | Friendly numbers that are multiples of 10: 10 × 210 = 2,100<br>Upper bound estimate: 20 × 300 = 6,000<br>Lower bound estimate: 10 × 200 = 2,000 | 2,544 |
| 6. | 81,291 ÷ 913 = ? | Friendly numbers that are multiples of 100: 81,300 ÷ 900 = 90 r 300<br>Upper bound estimate: 82,000 ÷ 1,000 = 82<br>Lower bound estimate: 81,000 ÷ 900 = 90 | 89 r 34 |
| 7. | 418 × 22 = ? | Friendly numbers that are multiples of 25: 425 × 25 = 10,625<br>Upper bound estimate: 500 × 30 = 15,000<br>Lower bound estimate: 400 × 20 = 8,000 | 9,196 |

8. **Example:** Use upper bound estimate: 60,000 (100 × 600). Other correct estimates are acceptable.

9. **Example:** Use upper bound estimate: 69 (69,000 ÷ 1,000). Other correct estimates are acceptable.

10. **Example:** Round one factor up and one factor down: 500,000 (5,000 × 100). Other correct estimates are acceptable.

    The exact answer is 486,067. The estimate should be close to the exact answer.

11. **Example:** Round the dividend and the divisor up: 54 (54,000 ÷ 1,000). Other correct estimates are acceptable.

    The exact answer is 54. The estimate should be close to the exact answer.

ESTIMATE AND FIND PRODUCTS AND QUOTIENTS

# Estimate Products and Quotients (A)

## Lesson Overview

| | | |
|---|---|---|
| Skills Update | 5 minutes | **ONLINE** |
| **GET READY** Estimate and Calculate in Different Ways | 10 minutes | **ONLINE** |
| **LEARN** Estimate and Calculate Distances | 10 minutes | **ONLINE** |
| **LEARN** Estimate Products and Solve Story Problems | 10 minutes | **ONLINE** |
| **LEARN** Compare Estimates and Exact Answer | 10 minutes | **OFFLINE** |
| **TRY IT** Estimate and Find Products | 15 minutes | **OFFLINE** |

### ▶ Lesson Objectives
Estimate or calculate a product or a quotient in a whole-number story problem.

### ▶ Prerequisite Skills
- Use estimation to predict a solution to a story problem and to verify the reasonableness of the calculated result.
- Estimate or calculate a product or a quotient in a whole-number problem.

### ▶ Content Background
Students will learn to estimate and calculate multiplication story problems. They should understand that comparing estimates to exact answers will help them decide if and why their estimate was reasonable.

### ▶ Common Errors and Misconceptions
- Students might become so concerned about getting the correct answer when estimating that they first find the exact answer, and then round it. For example, when asked to estimate 348 + 176, students might find the sum (524), and then round it to the nearest hundred (500).
- Students might have difficulty accepting that there is more than one correct approach and answer to an estimation problem.

**Materials to Gather**

**SUPPLIED**
Estimate and Find Products activity page

**WHOLE NUMBERS AND POWERS**

## GET READY  Estimate and Calculate in Different Ways  — ONLINE 10 min

**Objectives**
- Estimate or calculate a product or a quotient in a whole-number problem.

Students will review different strategies to estimate products. They will also review strategies for how to estimate and then calculate quotients.

## LEARN  Estimate and Calculate Distances  — ONLINE 10 min

**Objectives**
- Estimate or calculate a product or a quotient in a whole-number story problem.

Students will solve problems about the total number of miles delivery trucks drive in a year. They will use lower and upper bound estimates, and they will find the exact answers. They will compare their estimate to the exact answer.

## LEARN  Estimate Products and Solve Story Problems  — ONLINE 10 min

**Objectives**
- Estimate or calculate a product or a quotient in a whole-number story problem.

Students will estimate products by rounding one factor to a greater number and one factor to a lesser number. Then they will find the exact answer to the problem. They'll compare their estimate to the exact answer.

## LEARN  Compare Estimates and Exact Answer  — OFFLINE 10 min

**Objectives**
- Estimate or calculate a product or a quotient in a whole-number story problem.

Students will make two estimates for multiplication problems. They will find the first estimate by rounding one factor to a given place value and then multiplying. They will decide on another place value to round one factor to and will multiply again. Then students will find the exact answer to the problem. They will compare their estimates to the exact answer.

1. Read the following problem to students:
   - A packaging machine can put 2,387 nutrition bars into boxes in an hour. If the machine packs the same number of bars every hour, how many bars will it pack in 8 hours?
2. Tell students that they will first estimate the answer to the problem by rounding one factor to a given place value and then multiplying by the second factor.

   **Ask:** Why is it helpful to estimate the answer before finding the exact answer? An estimate helps you decide if you've correctly calculated the exact answer.
3. **Ask:** Round the number of nutrition bars packed every hour to the nearest thousand. What is 2,387 rounded to the nearest thousand? 2,000

   What is 2,000 × 8? 16,000

   About how many bars would be packed after 8 hours? about 16,000 bars

**ESTIMATE PRODUCTS AND QUOTIENTS (A)  19**

4. **Ask:** To what other place value could you round the number of nutrition bars packed every hour to try to get a closer estimate to the exact answer? Round the number of nutrition bars packed every hour to the nearest hundred.

5. Repeat Step 3. Have students round the number of nutrition bars to the nearest hundred. 2,400 × 8 = 19,200. About 19,200 bars would be packed after 8 hours.

6. Tell students that the next step to solve the problem is to calculate the exact answer. Students should find the product of 2,387 × 8. 19,096

7. Work with students to decide if the first estimate, 16,000, is reasonable compared to the exact answer, 19,096. One way to decide is to round an estimate and exact answer to the nearest ten thousand, and then compare.
   - 16,000 rounded to the nearest ten thousand is 20,000.
   - 19,096 rounded to the nearest ten thousand is 20,000.

   Since both the estimate and the exact answer can be rounded to the same number, this estimate is reasonable compared to the exact answer.

8. Repeat Step 7. Have students compare the second estimate of 19,200 bars to the exact answer of 19,096 bars by rounding the estimate and the exact answer to the nearest hundred. 19,200 rounded to the nearest hundred is 19,200. 19,096 rounded to the nearest hundred is 19,100. Since both the estimate and the exact answer can be rounded to numbers that are close to one another, this estimate is reasonable compared to the exact answer.

9. What is the answer to the problem? 19,096 bars can be packed in 8 hours.

10. **Ask:** To solve the problem, you used different estimation strategies and compared the results of each to the exact answer. Why should you use different strategies to estimate the answer to a problem? There are different strategies you can use to estimate the answer to a problem. Some strategies might give you an estimate that is closer to the exact answer than other strategies.

## TRY IT  Estimate and Find Products

**OFFLINE 15 min**

### Objectives
- Estimate or calculate a product or a quotient in a whole-number story problem.

Students will use different strategies to round numbers in multiplication story problems. Then they will estimate and calculate the answers by finding the products. Students will then determine if their estimate was reasonable. Have students turn to the Estimate and Find Products activity page in their Activity Book and read the directions with them.

Students should copy the problems from the Activity Book into their Math Notebook as necessary and solve them there.

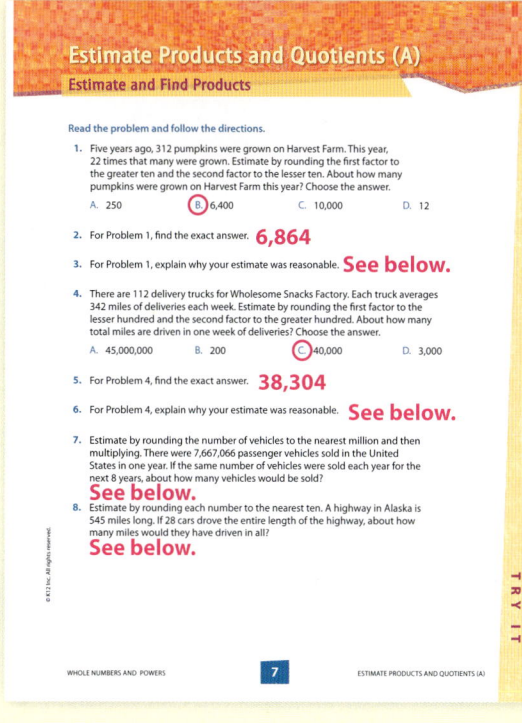
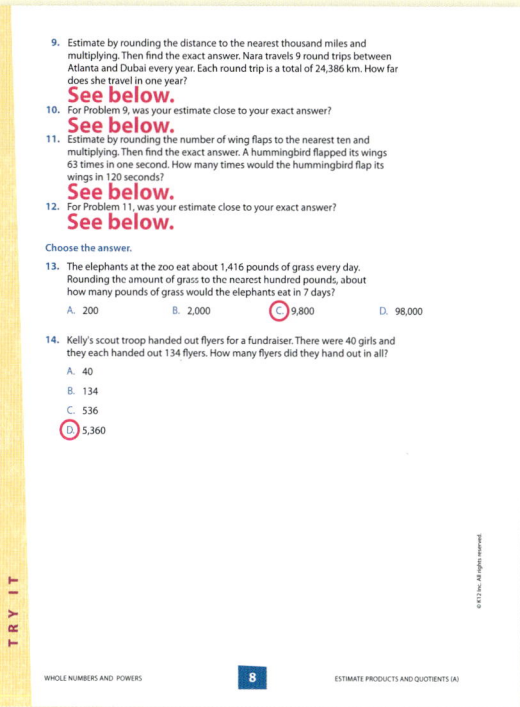

## Additional Answers

3. Answers will vary.
   **Sample answer:** My estimate was reasonable because 6,400 is close to 6,864.

6. Answers will vary.
   **Sample answer:** My estimate was reasonable because 40,000 is close to 38,304. In fact, 38,304 rounded to the nearest ten thousand is 40,000, which is the same as the estimate.

7. $8{,}000{,}000 \times 8 = 64{,}000{,}000$

8. $550 \times 30 = 16{,}500$

9. **Estimate:** $24{,}000 \times 9 = 216{,}000$
   **Exact answer:** $24{,}386 \times 9 = 219{,}474$

10. Answers will vary.
    **Sample answer:** My estimate was reasonable because 216,000 is close to 219,474. In fact, 216,000 rounded to the nearest ten thousand is 220,000, and 219,474 rounded to the nearest ten thousand is 220,000.

11. **Estimate:** $60 \times 120 = 7{,}200$
    **Exact answer:** $63 \times 120 = 7{,}560$

12. Answers will vary.
    **Sample answer:** My estimate was reasonable because 7,200 is close to 7,560.

**ESTIMATE PRODUCTS AND QUOTIENTS (A)** 21

# Estimate Products and Quotients (B)

## Lesson Overview

| | | |
|---|---|---|
| **GET READY** Estimate and Find Products | 5 minutes | **OFFLINE** |
| **LEARN** Round to a Place Value and Divide | 10 minutes | **ONLINE** |
| **LEARN** Estimate and Calculate Quotients | 10 minutes | **OFFLINE** |
| **LEARN** Understand Story Problem Remainders | 15 minutes | **OFFLINE** |
| **TRY IT** Story Problems About Division Estimates | 10 minutes | **OFFLINE** |
| **CHECKPOINT** | 10 minutes | **ONLINE** |

### ▶ Lesson Objectives
Estimate or calculate a product or a quotient in a whole-number story problem.

### ▶ Prerequisite Skills
- Use estimation to predict a solution to a story problem and to verify the reasonableness of the calculated result.
- Estimate or calculate a product or a quotient in a whole-number problem.

### ▶ Content Background
Students will learn to estimate and calculate answers to division story problems. They should understand that comparing estimates to exact answers will help them decide if their estimate was reasonable. Students will learn how to handle remainders to obtain appropriate answers for story problems.

### ▶ Common Errors and Misconceptions
- Students might become so concerned about getting the correct answer when estimating that they first find the exact answer, and then round it. For example, when asked to estimate 348 + 176, students might find the sum (524), and then round it to the nearest hundred (500).
- Students might have difficulty accepting that there is more than one correct approach and answer to an estimation problem.

### Materials to Gather

**SUPPLIED**

Estimate and Calculate Quotients activity page

Understand Story Problem Remainders activity page

Story Problems About Division Estimates activity page

## GET READY  Estimate and Find Products

**OFFLINE 5 min**

### Objectives

- Use estimation to predict a solution to a story problem and to verify the reasonableness of the calculated result.
- Estimate or calculate a product or a quotient in a whole-number problem.

To solve a multiplication story problem, students will estimate by rounding one factor to a greater number and the other factor to a lesser number. They will also find the exact answer. They will compare their estimate to the exact answer to verify the reasonableness of the estimate.

1. Tell students that they'll review estimating in multiplication problems and will estimate and calculate a product. Then they'll compare the estimate to the exact answer to decide if the estimate is reasonable.

2. Read the following problem to students:
   - An art museum opened a new exhibit. The museum limited the number of people who can visit each day to 779. If the exhibit will be open for 404 days, how many people can attend the new exhibit?

3. Tell students that they will first estimate the answer to the problem by rounding the first factor to a greater number and the second factor to a lesser number.

   **Ask:** Why is it helpful to estimate the answer before finding the exact answer?
   An estimate helps you decide if you've correctly calculated the exact answer.

4. **Ask:** Round the number of visitors every day to the greater hundred. What is 779 rounded to the greater hundred?  800

   Round the number of days the exhibit will be open to the lesser hundred. What is 404 rounded to the lesser hundred?  400
   What is 800 × 400?  320,000
   About how people can attend the new art exhibit?  about 320,000

5. Tell students that the next step to solve the problem is to calculate the exact answer. Students should find the product of 779 × 404.  314,716

6. Work with students to decide if the estimate, 320,000, is reasonable compared to the exact answer, 314,716.

   **Say:** One way to decide is to round the estimate and the exact answer to the nearest thousand, and then compare.
   - 320,000 rounded to the nearest thousand is 320,000.
   - 314,716 rounded to the nearest thousand is 315,000.

   **Ask:** What is the difference between the rounded estimate and the rounded exact answer?  5,000

7. **Say:** It may seem like the estimate and the exact answer aren't very close. But 5,000 is a small fraction of 320,000 or 315,000. So the estimate and the exact answer are close. The closeness of the two numbers means the estimate is reasonable compared to the exact answer.

## LEARN  Round to a Place Value and Divide

**ONLINE 10 min**

### Objectives
- Estimate or calculate a product or a quotient in a whole-number story problem.

Students will be given a story problem about dividing canned goods that were collected in a food drive. They will round the dividend and divisor to a place value and then divide. Then they will find the exact answer. Discuss with students whether the estimate is reasonable when compared to the exact answer.

Before you begin, review the parts of a division number sentence with students.

**Say:** Think about the problem $15 \div 3 = 5$.

**Ask:** Which number is the dividend? 15
Which number is the divisor? 3
Which number is the quotient? 5

## LEARN  Estimate and Calculate Quotients

**OFFLINE 10 min**

### Objectives
- Estimate or calculate a product or a quotient in a whole-number story problem.

Students will use multiple strategies to estimate quotients in division story problems. They will then calculate exact quotients. Students will compare the estimates to the exact answer to decide which estimate is reasonable.

1. Discuss with students how to decide on strategies for estimating quotients. It's often useful to decide how to round the divisor, and then decide how to round the dividend so you can use mental math to easily find the quotient.

2. Walk through this example: Think about $172 \div 17 = ?$ If the divisor is rounded to 20, the dividend should be rounded to 180 rather than 170, because 20 divides evenly into 180.

3. Have students turn to the Estimate and Calculate Quotients activity page. Discuss the worked example with them. Tell students that rounding to the nearest hundred and rounding to the nearest thousand are two different estimation strategies.

4. Compare the estimated and exact answers in the worked example.

    **Ask:** In the worked example, suppose the bus driver was estimating the number of miles to drive each day. Would an estimate greater than or less than the exact answer for the number of miles to drive every day be better if the driver wants to be sure not to run out of fuel? *If the estimated distance is greater than the actual distance, the bus driver might drive farther every day than the exact number of miles, which might result in problems with the amount of fuel used.*

5. Have students complete Problems 1–9 in their Math Notebook.

6. With students, compare the two estimates and the exact answer.

    **Say:** The second estimate, 70 miles per hour, is a more *accurate* estimate for the problem, because this estimate is closer to the exact answer than the first estimate.

    **Ask:** Think about the exact number of miles the bus would need to travel each hour and the two estimates. If the speed limit is 60 miles per hour, what do you know about the reasonableness of the two estimates for the miles per hour? *The estimates for the miles the bus would go each hour are 70 and 80 miles per hour. The estimates are correct for the problem but are not reasonable if the speed limit is 60 miles per hour. It would be illegal for the bus to go faster than the speed limit.*

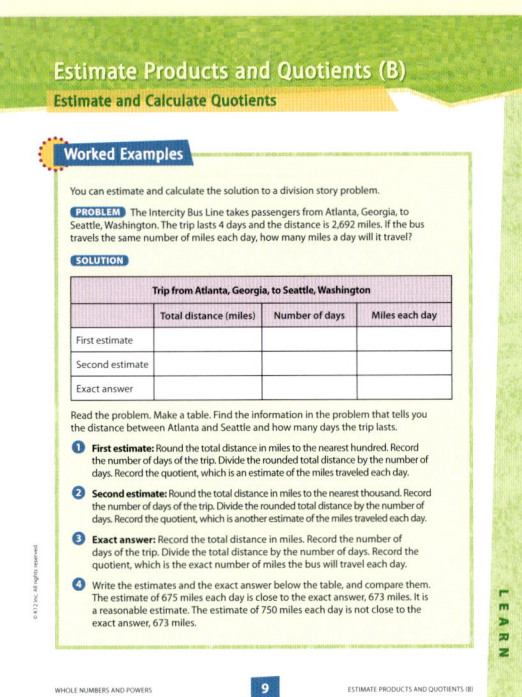

24  WHOLE NUMBERS AND POWERS

## Page 10 (left worked example)

**ANSWER**

| Trip from Atlanta, Georgia, to Seattle, Washington |||| 
|---|---|---|---|
|  | Total distance (miles) | Number of days | Miles each day |
| First estimate | 2,700 | 4 | 675 |
| Second estimate | 3,000 | 4 | 750 |
| Exact answer | 2,692 | 4 | 673 |

**First estimate:** 675 miles
**Second estimate:** 750 miles
**Exact answer:** 673 miles
The bus will travel 673 miles each day.

**LOOK BACK** To solve the problem, you estimated before you calculated the exact answer. You used two different estimation strategies to round the numbers in the problem. One estimate was closer to the exact answer. Some estimates are more reasonable in a problem than others.

Read the problem and follow the directions.
Every summer, the Intercity Bus Line carries eager vacationers 767 miles from Bloomington, Indiana, to Ocean City, Maryland. The passengers would like the trip to take 13 hours. How many miles does the bus need to travel each hour to make the trip in 13 hours?

1. Make a table. Fill it out as you answer the following questions. Use the table in the Worked Examples box as a model. **See below.**
2. For the first estimate, round the distance to the nearest hundred. What is the distance to the nearest hundred? **800 miles**
3. Round the number of hours to the nearest ten. What is the number of hours rounded to the nearest ten? **10 hours**

## Page 11 (right)

4. Divide. For the first estimate, how many miles each hour will the bus need to travel? **80 miles**
5. For the second estimate, round the distance to the lesser hundred. What is the distance rounded to the lesser hundred? **700 miles**
6. Round the number of hours to the lesser ten. What is the number of hours rounded to the lesser ten? **10 hours**
7. Divide. For the second estimate, how many miles each hour will the bus need to travel? **70 miles**
8. For the exact answer, write the total distance and number of hours from the problem. Divide the total distance by the number of hours. What is the exact number of miles the bus will need to travel each hour? **59 miles** Check to see that you have filled in all the cells in the table. **See below.**
9. Write *first estimate*, *second estimate*, and *exact answer* below the table. Write the estimates and exact answers, including the label "miles," next to the descriptions.

**First estimate: 80 miles**
**Second estimate: 70 miles**
**Exact answer: 59 miles**

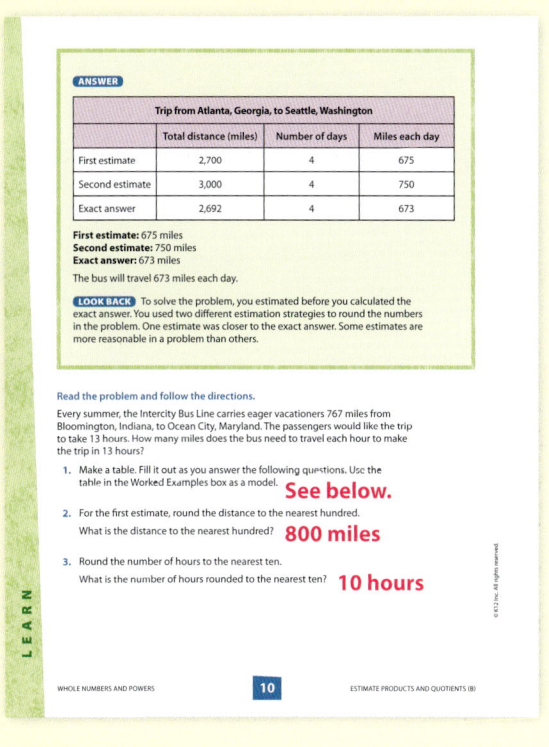

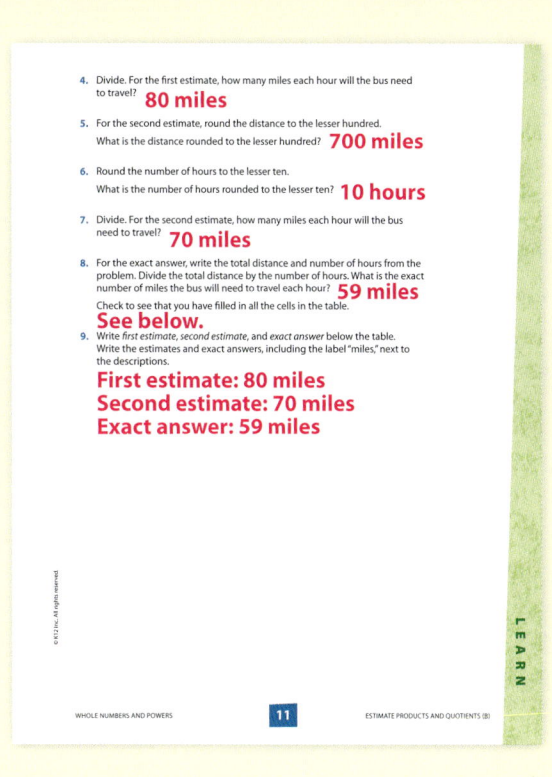

## Additional Answers

**1.**

| Trip from Bloomington, Indiana, to Ocean City, Maryland ||||
|---|---|---|---|
|  | Total distance (miles) | Number of hours | Miles each hour |
| First estimate |  |  |  |
| Second estimate |  |  |  |
| Exact answer |  |  |  |

**8.**

| Trip from Bloomington, Indiana, to Ocean City, Maryland ||||
|---|---|---|---|
|  | Total distance (miles) | Number of hours | Miles each hour |
| First estimate | 800 | 10 | 80 |
| Second estimate | 700 | 10 | 70 |
| Exact answer | 767 | 13 | 59 |

## LEARN  Understand Story Problem Remainders

OFFLINE 15 min

### Objectives
- Estimate or calculate a product or a quotient in a whole-number story problem.

Students will learn what to do with the remainder in a division story problem. They'll interpret the quotient and remainder in a problem and decide which of the following options to choose:

- Write the answer as a fraction or a mixed number.
- Increase the quotient by 1 and drop the remainder.
- Keep the quotient and ignore the remainder.

ESTIMATE PRODUCTS AND QUOTIENTS (B)  25

1. Remind students that when they solve a whole-number division problem and there is a remainder, the quotient can be written as a fraction, a mixed number, or a whole number with a remainder.

   The remainder in a division problem can be written as a fraction with the divisor as the denominator, or with "r" and a whole number. For example, in the problem $34 \div 5 = ?$, the quotient can be written as $6\frac{4}{5}$ or 6 r 4. In some problems, the remainder might be 0. In those cases, the remainder isn't written.

2. Have students turn to the Understand Story Problem Remainders activity page. Read and discuss the worked example with students.

   **Ask:** Why is Strategy 2 the correct one for this problem? The phone company charges for all minutes, including a part of a minute, so the remainder in this problem has to be counted as a whole number.

   **Ask:** Would you use the same strategy for any story problem about a phone company and its cost for phone calls per minute? No, the strategy would depend on the details of the phone company's plan and whether it charges for a part of a minute.

3. Have students complete Problems 1–6 in their Math Notebook.

   **Ask:** Why is this problem an example of using the strategy in which you keep the quotient the same and ignore the remainder? The problem says drivers are paid for whole miles and not additional parts of miles, so the remainder can be ignored.

4. Review with students the three strategies to decide what to do with the remainder in a division problem. Be sure that students understand that any of these three approaches might be an appropriate way to handle a remainder. Focus attention on phrases like "even if it's only a partial minute" and "keep track of exactly how long" that provide clues about what to do with the remainder in the problem.

5. Have students complete Problems 7–14 in their Math Notebook.

6. Review students' work to clarify any misconceptions about how to handle remainders in a division story problem.

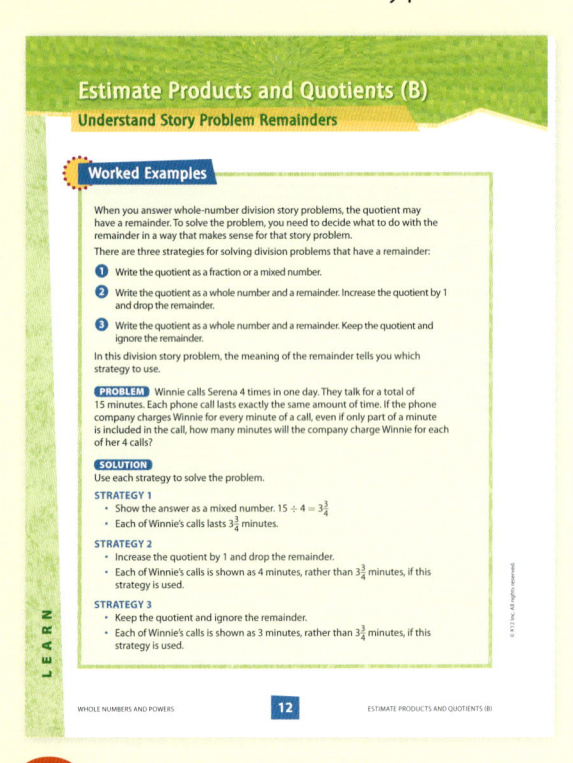

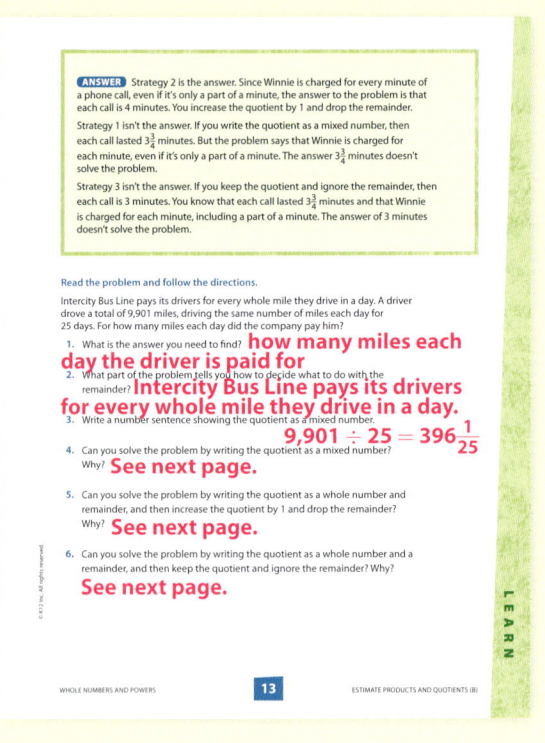

**26** WHOLE NUMBERS AND POWERS

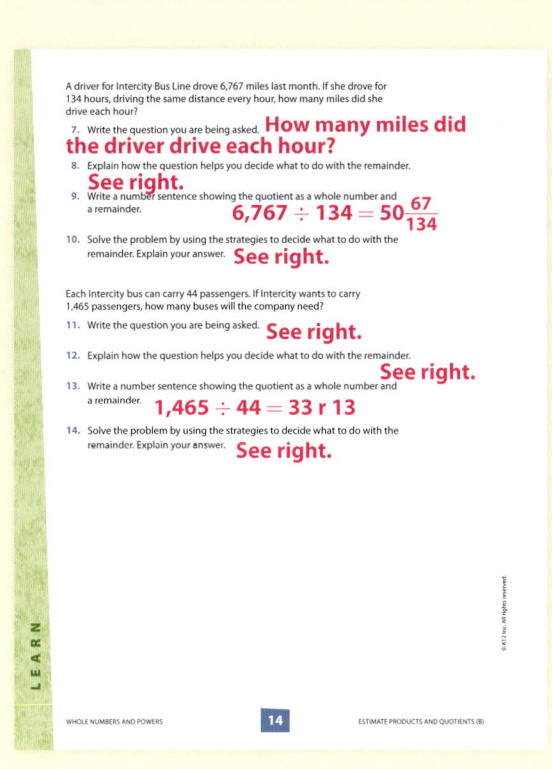

## Additional Answers

4. No, because the problem says that bus drivers are paid for every whole mile they drive in a day. They are not paid for parts of a mile. The answer $396\frac{1}{25}$ miles doesn't correctly solve the problem because it includes a fraction of a mile.

5. No, because the problem says that bus drivers are paid for every whole mile they drive in a day. Increasing the quotient and dropping the remainder so that the answer is 397 miles doesn't correctly solve the problem because this answer is greater than the actual number of miles driven.

6. Yes, because the problem says that bus drivers are paid for every whole mile they drive in a day. Writing the quotient as a whole number and ignoring the remainder so that the answer is 396 miles is the correct way to decide what to do with the remainder.

8. The problem doesn't say that only whole miles should be counted. The quotient can be written as a mixed number because it's possible to drive a distance that is between two whole numbers.

10. The answer to the problem is the driver drove $50\frac{67}{134}$ miles each hour. Writing the answer to this problem as the quotient and the remainder is correct. If the quotient was increased by 1 and the remainder was dropped, the number of miles driven would be greater than actual answer. If the quotient was kept and the remainder was ignored, the number of miles driven would be less than the actual answer. Using either of these strategies would not correctly solve the problem.

11. How many buses are needed to carry 1,465 passengers if each bus can carry 44 passengers?

12. You need enough buses to transport every passenger. You can put fewer than 44 passengers on a bus but not more than 44.

14. The answer to the problem is 34 buses. Writing the answer to this problem as a quotient and a remainder, and then increasing the quotient by 1 and dropping the remainder, is correct. Thirty-three buses plus one more bus to carry the remainder of the passengers are needed. Writing the answer to this problem as a mixed number means you would need a fraction of a bus for the remainder of the passengers. It isn't possible to have a fraction of a bus. If you write the answer as the quotient and the remainder and then keep the quotient and ignore the remainder, you won't have enough buses to carry all the passengers.

**ESTIMATE PRODUCTS AND QUOTIENTS (B)**

## TRY IT  Story Problems About Division Estimates

**OFFLINE 10 min**

### Objectives
- Estimate or calculate a product or a quotient in a whole-number story problem.

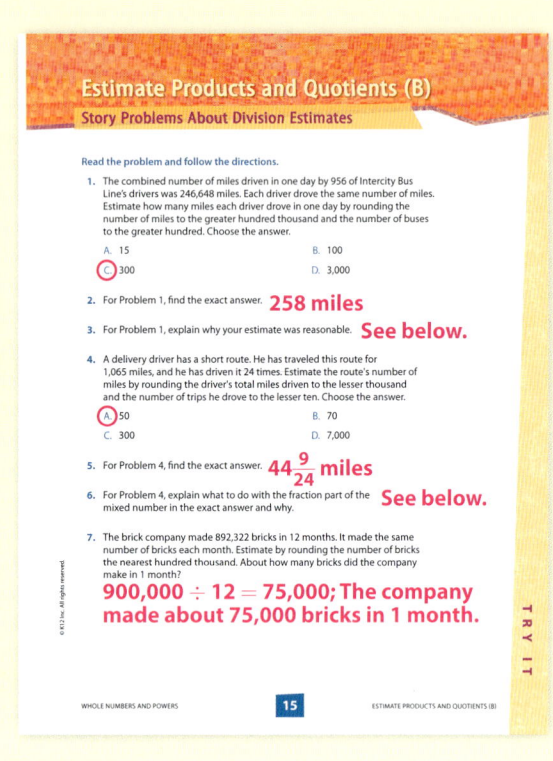

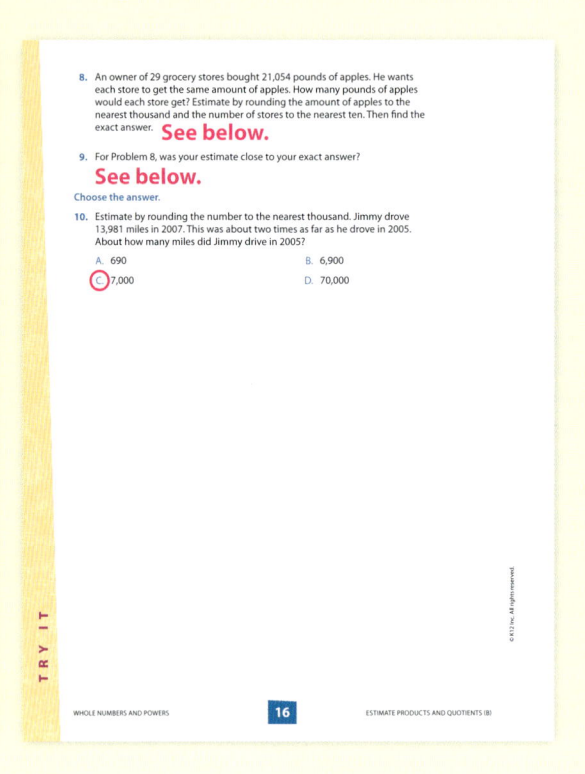

Students will practice estimating and calculating division story problems. They will also explain what to do with the remainder to accurately solve the problem. Have students turn to the Story Problems About Division Estimates activity page in their Activity Book and read the directions with them.

Students should copy the problems from the Activity Book into their Math Notebook as necessary and solve them there.

### Estimate Products and Quotients (B)
#### Story Problems About Division Estimates

**Read the problem and follow the directions.**

1. The combined number of miles driven in one day by 956 of Intercity Bus Line's drivers was 246,648 miles. Each driver drove the same number of miles. Estimate how many miles each driver drove in one day by rounding the number of miles to the greater hundred thousand and the number of buses to the greater hundred. Choose the answer.
   A. 15   B. 100
   **C. 300**   D. 3,000

2. For Problem 1, find the exact answer. **258 miles**

3. For Problem 1, explain why your estimate was reasonable. **See below.**

4. A delivery driver has a short route. He has traveled this route for 1,065 miles, and he has driven it 24 times. Estimate the route's number of miles by rounding the driver's total miles driven to the lesser thousand and the number of trips he drove to the lesser ten. Choose the answer.
   **A. 50**   B. 70
   C. 300   D. 7,000

5. For Problem 4, find the exact answer. $44\frac{9}{24}$ **miles**

6. For Problem 4, explain what to do with the fraction part of the mixed number in the exact answer and why. **See below.**

7. The brick company made 892,322 bricks in 12 months. It made the same number of bricks each month. Estimate by rounding the number of bricks the nearest hundred thousand. About how many bricks did the company make in 1 month?
   **900,000 ÷ 12 = 75,000; The company made about 75,000 bricks in 1 month.**

8. An owner of 29 grocery stores bought 21,054 pounds of apples. He wants each store to get the same amount of apples. How many pounds of apples would each store get? Estimate by rounding the amount of apples to the nearest thousand and the number of stores to the nearest ten. Then find the exact answer. **See below.**

9. For Problem 8, was your estimate close to your exact answer? **See below.**

**Choose the answer.**

10. Estimate by rounding the number to the nearest thousand. Jimmy drove 13,981 miles in 2007. This was about two times as far as he drove in 2005. About how many miles did Jimmy drive in 2005?
    A. 690   B. 6,900
    **C. 7,000**   D. 70,000

### Additional Answers

3. Answers will vary.
   **Sample answer:** My estimate was reasonable because 258 is close to 300. In fact, 258 rounded to the nearest hundred is 300, which is the same as the estimate.

8. 21,000 ÷ 30 = 700
   **Exact answer:** 726 pounds of apples for each store

6. **Sample answer:** The exact answer can be written as a mixed number because the driver can drive a fraction of a mile, so the route is $44\frac{9}{24}$ miles long.

9. Answers will vary.
   **Sample answer:** My estimate was reasonable because the exact answer, 726, rounded to the nearest hundred, is 700. That is the same as the estimate.

## CHECKPOINT

**ONLINE 10 min**

### Objectives
- Estimate or calculate a product or a quotient in a whole-number problem.
- Estimate or calculate a product or quotient in a whole-number story problem.

Students will complete an online Checkpoint. If necessary, read the directions, problems, and answer choices to students and help them with keyboard or mouse operations.

**28  WHOLE NUMBERS AND POWERS**

# Bases and Exponents (A)

## Lesson Overview

| | | |
|---|---|---|
| **LEARN** Expressions with Exponents | 10 minutes | ONLINE |
| **LEARN** Show Exponent Expressions | 20 minutes | ONLINE |
| **LEARN** Explain and Compute Exponents | 15 minutes | ONLINE |
| **TRY IT** Evaluate Expressions | 15 minutes | OFFLINE |

### ▶ Lesson Objectives
Represent and compute a power by using repeated multiplication.

### ▶ Prerequisite Skills
Explain and apply standard step-by-step approaches for multiplication.

### ▶ Content Background
In this lesson, students will learn about expressions like $7^3$ and identify which numeral is the base and which numeral is the exponent. Then they will learn how to use repeated multiplication to write and calculate expressions. Students will focus on exponents of 1, 2, and 3, or numbers to the first, second, and third powers. A number with an exponent of 2 is squared. A number with an exponent of 3 is cubed.

This lesson shows models as a way to represent square and cubic numbers. The lesson also helps students memorize the squaring of numbers through 10.

An expression is made up of numbers, symbols, or both and represents a mathematical relationship. In the expression $7^3$, 7 is the base and 3 is the exponent. There is a mathematical relationship between the base and the exponent. The base is the number that is multiplied, and the exponent tells how many times the base is a factor. Therefore, the expression $7^3$ is the same as $7 \times 7 \times 7$ or $7 \cdot 7 \cdot 7$.

### Materials to Gather
**SUPPLIED**
Evaluate Expressions activity page

**ALSO NEEDED**
index cards (optional)

## LEARN Expressions with Exponents
*ONLINE 10 min*

Students will learn why expressions with a base and an exponent make it easier to write greater numbers. They will also learn about the relationship between repeated multiplication and expressions with a base and an exponent.

### Objectives
- Represent and compute a power by using repeated multiplication.

## LEARN  Show Exponent Expressions

**ONLINE 20 min**

### Objectives

- Represent and compute a power by using repeated multiplication.

Students will learn about expressions that have various exponents. They will learn that bases with exponents can also be shown by using multiple equal factors. They will also learn to find the value, or standard form, of an expression with an exponent. For instance, the value, or standard form, of $3^2$ is 9. Students will learn ways to describe expressions with exponents—for example, "3 to the third power" or "3 cubed."

## LEARN  Explain and Compute Exponents

**ONLINE 15 min**

### Objectives

- Represent and compute a power by using repeated multiplication.

Students will describe and compare expressions that have bases and exponents. They will use the Grid Learning Tool to model expressions with an exponent of 2. They also will play a game to help them memorize the standard form for 1 squared through 10 squared.

Have students write the following in their Math Notebook. They will provide the answers when they use the Grid Learning Tool.

$1^2 = \underline{?}$   $2^2 = \underline{?}$   $3^2 = \underline{?}$   $4^2 = \underline{?}$
$5^2 = \underline{?}$   $6^2 = \underline{?}$   $7^2 = \underline{?}$   $8^2 = \underline{?}$
$9^2 = \underline{?}$   $10^2 = \underline{?}$

### Tips

To help students memorize the standard form of the expressions for 1 squared through 10 squared, have them create index cards with the exponent expression on one side and the standard form on the other side. Students can quiz themselves by looking at the exponent expression side and trying to name the standard form. Then they can turn the card over to see if they are correct.

**DIRECTIONS FOR USING THE GRID LEARNING TOOL**

1. Have students choose a color and then click one square. Tell them that the shaded square represents $1^2$ because it is 1 square long and 1 square wide.

2. Have students write 1 as the answer in the equation $1^2 = \underline{?}$ that they wrote in their Math Notebook. Tell them that 1 is the standard form for the expression $1^2$.

3. Have students choose another color and then click 4 squares in a 2 by 2 area model.

   **Ask:** How many squares long is the area you shaded? **2**

   **Ask:** How many squares wide is the area you shaded? **2**

   Tell students that the shaded area represents $2^2$ because it is 2 squares long and 2 squares wide.

4. **Ask:** What is $2^2$? **4**

   Have students write 4 as the answer in the equation $2^2 = \underline{?}$ in their Math Notebook. Tell them that 4 is the standard form for the expression $2^2$.

5. Have students clear the squares they have shaded.

6. Students should shade areas for the following expressions, clearing the squares as they need space. Have them write the standard form for each expression in their Math Notebook, completing the equations that they wrote at the beginning of the activity.

   $3^2 = 9$   $4^2 = 16$   $5^2 = 25$   $6^2 = 36$
   $7^2 = 49$   $8^2 = 64$   $9^2 = 81$   $10^2 = 100$

Students will then play an online game to help them memorize 1 squared through 10 squared in standard form.

## TRY IT  Evaluate Expressions

**OFFLINE 15 min**

### Objectives
- Represent and compute a power by using repeated multiplication.

Students will show the relationship between a base with an exponent and repeated multiplication. They will evaluate expressions with exponents of 2 and 3. Have students turn to the Evaluate Expressions activity page in their Activity Book and read the directions with them.

Students should copy the problems from the Activity Book into their Math Notebook as necessary and solve them there.

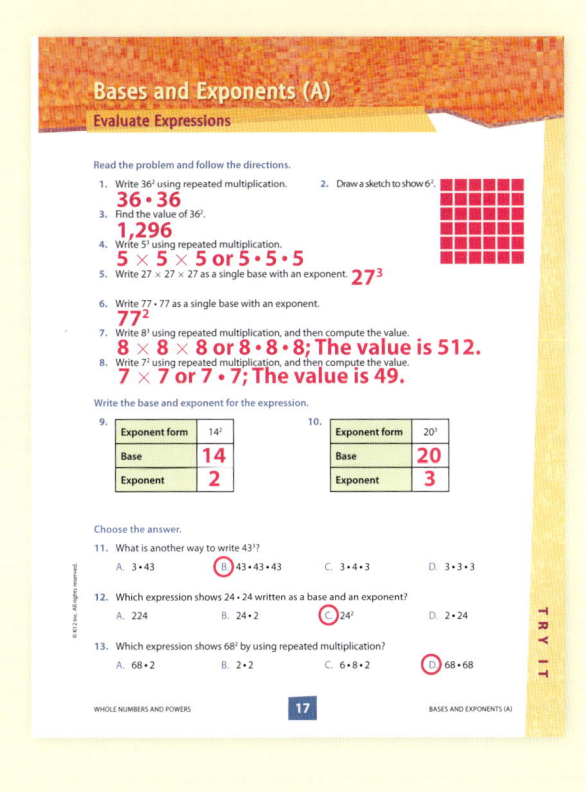

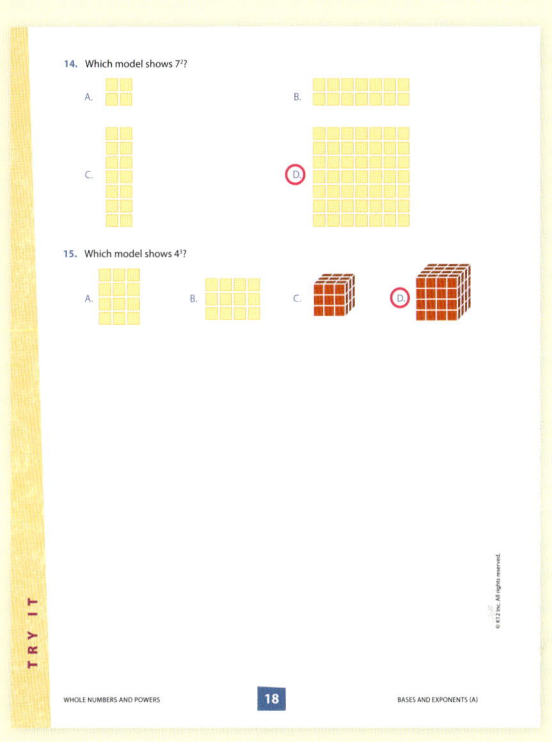

### Bases and Exponents (A)
**Evaluate Expressions**

Read the problem and follow the directions.

1. Write $36^2$ using repeated multiplication.
   **36 • 36**
2. Draw a sketch to show $6^2$.
3. Find the value of $36^2$.
   **1,296**
4. Write $5^3$ using repeated multiplication.
   **5 × 5 × 5 or 5 • 5 • 5**
5. Write $27 \times 27 \times 27$ as a single base with an exponent. **$27^3$**
6. Write $77 \cdot 77$ as a single base with an exponent.
   **$77^2$**
7. Write $8^3$ using repeated multiplication, and then compute the value.
   **8 × 8 × 8 or 8 • 8 • 8; The value is 512.**
8. Write $7^2$ using repeated multiplication, and then compute the value.
   **7 × 7 or 7 • 7; The value is 49.**

Write the base and exponent for the expression.

9. | Exponent form | $14^2$ |
   |---|---|
   | Base | **14** |
   | Exponent | **2** |

10. | Exponent form | $20^3$ |
    |---|---|
    | Base | **20** |
    | Exponent | **3** |

Choose the answer.

11. What is another way to write $43^3$?
    A. $3 \cdot 43$   **B. $43 \cdot 43 \cdot 43$**   C. $3 \cdot 4 \cdot 3$   D. $3 \cdot 3 \cdot 3$
12. Which expression shows $24 \cdot 24$ written as a base and an exponent?
    A. $224$   B. $24 \cdot 2$   **C. $24^2$**   D. $2 \cdot 24$
13. Which expression shows $68^2$ by using repeated multiplication?
    A. $68 \cdot 2$   B. $2 \cdot 2$   C. $6 \cdot 8 \cdot 2$   **D. $68 \cdot 68$**

14. Which model shows $7^2$?
    A.   B.   C.   **D.**

15. Which model shows $4^3$?
    A.   B.   C.   **D.**

**BASES AND EXPONENTS (A)**  31

# Bases and Exponents (B)

## Lesson Overview

| | | |
|---|---|---|
| **LEARN** Exponents: 1, 2, and 3 | 10 minutes | **ONLINE** |
| **LEARN** Exponents of 4 and 5 | 15 minutes | **ONLINE** |
| **LEARN** Compare Exponents of 4 and 5 | 15 minutes | **OFFLINE** |
| **TRY IT** Work with Exponents of 4 and 5 | 10 minutes | **OFFLINE** |
| **CHECKPOINT** | 10 minutes | **ONLINE** |

### ▶ Lesson Objectives
Represent and compute a power by using repeated multiplication.

### ▶ Prerequisite Skills
Explain and apply standard step-by-step approaches for multiplication.

### ▶ Content Background
Students will review modeling, explaining, and calculating expressions with exponents of 1, 2, and 3. Then they will extend their learning to model, explain, and calculate expressions with exponents of 4 and 5.

An expression is made up of numbers, symbols, or both, and represents a mathematical relationship. In the expression $7^3$, 7 is the base and 3 is the exponent. There is a mathematical relationship between the base and the exponent. The base is the number that is multiplied, and the exponent tells how many times the base is a factor. Therefore, the expression $7^3$ means that 7 is the same as $7 \times 7 \times 7$ or $7 \cdot 7 \cdot 7$.

**Materials to Gather**

**SUPPLIED**
Work with Exponents of 4 and 5 activity page

---

### LEARN  Exponents: 1, 2, and 3  (ONLINE 10 min)

Students will work with expressions with exponents of 1, 2, or 3. They will use their knowledge of expressions with bases and exponents to play a hidden pictures game. They will match expressions with models, written forms (for example, thirty-six), and standard forms (for example, 36).

**Objectives**
- Represent and compute a power by using repeated multiplication.

---

### LEARN  Exponents of 4 and 5  (ONLINE 15 min)

Students will learn how to evaluate expressions with exponents of 4 and 5. They are reminded that the exponent tells how many times the base appears as a factor in the multiplication expression.

**Objectives**
- Represent and compute a power by using repeated multiplication.

**Tips** Students may need paper and pencil. Allow them to work the problems on paper and then type their answers online.

## LEARN Compare Exponents of 4 and 5

**OFFLINE 15 min**

### Objectives
- Represent and compute a power by using repeated multiplication.

Students will model, explain, compare, and compute expressions with exponents of 4 and 5.

1. Students will review and compare exponents to the fourth and fifth powers. Have students write their answers to the questions in their Math Notebook.

2. Remind students that the base is the number to be multiplied. The exponent tells how many times the base will be a factor. Remind students that numbers with an exponent of 2 are said to be squared and numbers with an exponent of 3 are said to be cubed.

3. Remind students that they have seen models for expressions with exponents of 1, 2, and 3, but that they can't use geometric figures to show a model for expressions with exponents of 4 or greater. Tell them that they will use other ways, such as standard form or written form, to show expressions with exponents of 4 or greater.

4. Write $2^4$ and have students identify the base and the exponent. The base is 2 and the exponent is 4.

   Then have students write the multiple factors for $2^4$. $2 \cdot 2 \cdot 2 \cdot 2$

   Have students determine the standard form for $2^4$. 16

5. Repeat Step 4 with the expression $2^2$. base is 2; exponent is 2; multiple factors is $2 \cdot 2$; standard form is 4

6. Have students write "$2^2$ ? $2^4$" in their Math Notebook. Using Steps 4 and 5 as reference, help students compare the expressions by using the symbols < (less than), > (greater than), or = (equals). Discuss how the expressions $2^2$ and $2^4$ are alike and different. They are alike because they have the same base; they are different because they have different exponents; students should also compare the multiple factors and standard form for each expression.

   Students should conclude that the correct comparison is $2^2 < 2^4$.

7. Have students write $2^4$ ? $4^2$ in their Math Notebook.

   **Ask:** How are the two expressions different? They have different bases and exponents.

   **Say:** Compute the two expressions and compare them. Write the number sentence that compares them. $2^4 = 4^2$

8. Repeat Step 7 with students. Use the expressions $2^5$ and $5^2$. The correct comparison is $2^5 > 5^2$.

9. Have students work on their own to find the correct comparisons for these expressions:
   - $3^4$ and $4^3$  $3^4 > 4^3$
   - $3^5$ and $5^3$  $3^5 > 5^3$

10. **Ask:** After you have compared sets of expressions, is there a difference between the base and the exponent when you evaluate an expression? Why? There is a difference between the base and the exponent. The exponent tells you how many times the base is a factor in an expression.

BASES AND EXPONENTS (B)

## TRY IT  Work with Exponents of 4 and 5

**OFFLINE 10 min**

### Objectives
- Represent and compute a power by using repeated multiplication.

Students will practice identifying bases and exponents, using repeated multiplication to evaluate exponent expressions. They will also compare expressions that have exponents. Have students turn to the Work with Exponents of 4 and 5 activity page in their Activity Book.

Students should copy the problems from the Activity Book into their Math Notebook as necessary and solve them there.

## CHECKPOINT

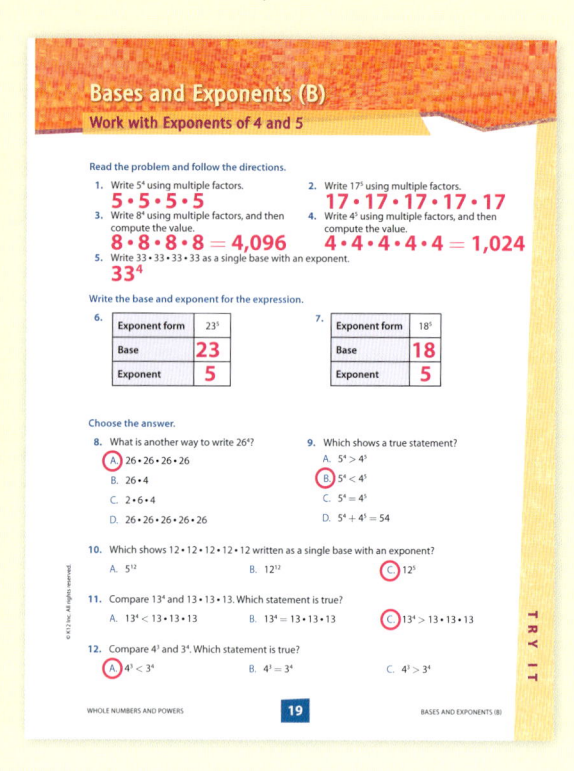

**ONLINE 10 min**

### Objectives
- Represent and compute a power by using repeated multiplication.

Students will complete an online Checkpoint. If necessary, read the directions, problems, and answer choices to students and help them with keyboard or mouse operations.

34  WHOLE NUMBERS AND POWERS

# Solve Problems Involving Powers

## Lesson Overview

| | | |
|---|---|---|
| **GET READY** Exponent Concentration | 10 minutes | ONLINE |
| **LEARN** Compare Exponent Expressions | 15 minutes | ONLINE |
| **LEARN** Problems with Exponents | 10 minutes | ONLINE |
| **TRY IT** Solve Problems with Exponents | 15 minutes | OFFLINE |
| **CHECKPOINT** | 10 minutes | ONLINE |

### ▶ Lesson Objectives
Solve a problem that involves powers.

### ▶ Prerequisite Skills
Represent and compute a power by using repeated multiplication.

### ▶ Content Background
In this lesson, students will use powers to solve problems. Students will understand the importance and usefulness of powers and exponents in everyday problems.

An exponent is a number used to show, or express, the number of times the base appears in the product. For example, instead of writing 3 • 3 • 3 • 3, you can write the expression $3^4$. So $3^4$ is a power with 3 as the base and 4 as the exponent. $3^4$ is read "3 to the fourth power."

An expression is a way to show a relationship between numbers. One way to represent an expression that is written as a base with an exponent is to show it with repeated multiplication. The expression $6^3$ can be written as 6 • 6 • 6. This product shows the base, 6, three times, because 3 is the exponent. As students continue to study mathematics, expressions become an important part of describing mathematical situations.

### Materials to Gather

**SUPPLIED**
Solve Problems with Exponents activity page

**ALSO NEEDED**
index cards (optional)

## GET READY  Exponent Concentration

**ONLINE 10 min**

Students will play an online game to match expressions that have exponents to expressions with repeated multiplication and the standard form of the expressions. Be sure students understand the directions before playing the game.

### Objectives
- Represent and compute a power by using repeated multiplication.

**Tips** To help students memorize the standard form of expressions in Exponent Concentration, have them make flash cards. They should write an exponent expression on one side and the standard form on the other side of each index card. Students can quiz themselves by looking at the exponent expression side and trying to name the standard form. Then they can turn the card over to see if they are correct.

## LEARN Compare Exponent Expressions

**ONLINE 15 min**

### Objectives
- Solve a problem that involves powers.

Students will explore expressions that have exponents. They will identify the base and the exponent in an expression.

They will be reminded to use repeated multiplication to compute expressions with exponents. Students will learn to find the value of expressions with exponents in order to compare two expressions.

Students will complete comparisons by identifying the correct base that makes a statement true. Finally, they will identify square and cubic numbers that divide evenly into specific numbers.

**Tips** Remind students that they can use repeated multiplication to compute expressions with exponents.

## LEARN Problems with Exponents

**ONLINE 10 min**

### Objectives
- Solve a problem that involves powers.

Students will learn to use expressions with exponents to solve problems. They will work through story problems to see how the problems can be solved by using repeated multiplication or expressions with exponents.

They must be able to relate repeated multiplication to expressions with exponents. Students will explain their thinking, so it is important that you sit with them while they work through the activity.

**Tips** Have students review how to compute powers by using repeated multiplication before this activity.

## TRY IT  Solve Problems with Exponents

**OFFLINE 15 min**

### Objectives
- Solve a problem that involves powers.

Students will practice solving problems with exponents. Have students turn to the Solve Problems with Exponents activity page in their Activity Book and read the directions with them.

Students should copy the problems from the Activity Book into their Math Notebook as necessary and solve them there.

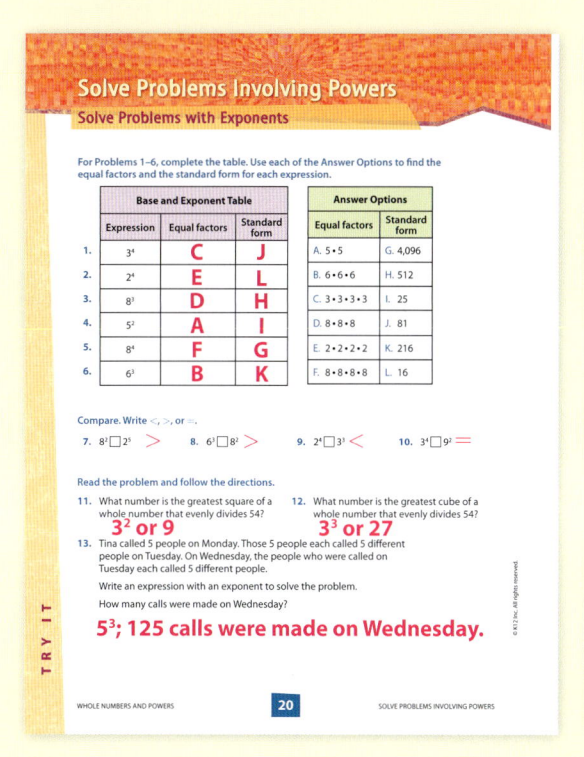

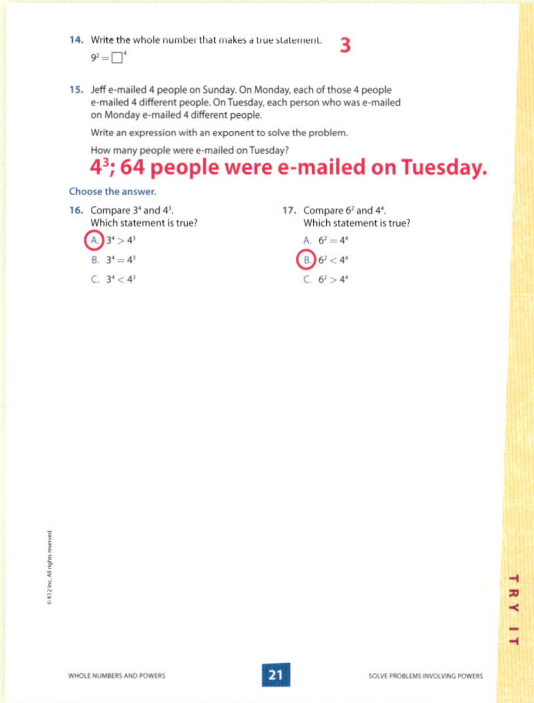

### Solve Problems Involving Powers
**Solve Problems with Exponents**

For Problems 1–6, complete the table. Use each of the Answer Options to find the equal factors and the standard form for each expression.

**Base and Exponent Table**

| | Expression | Equal factors | Standard form |
|---|---|---|---|
| 1. | $3^4$ | C | J |
| 2. | $2^4$ | E | L |
| 3. | $8^3$ | D | H |
| 4. | $5^2$ | A | I |
| 5. | $8^4$ | F | G |
| 6. | $6^3$ | B | K |

**Answer Options**

| Equal factors | Standard form |
|---|---|
| A. $5 \cdot 5$ | G. 4,096 |
| B. $6 \cdot 6 \cdot 6$ | H. 512 |
| C. $3 \cdot 3 \cdot 3 \cdot 3$ | I. 25 |
| D. $8 \cdot 8 \cdot 8$ | J. 81 |
| E. $2 \cdot 2 \cdot 2 \cdot 2$ | K. 216 |
| F. $8 \cdot 8 \cdot 8 \cdot 8$ | L. 16 |

Compare. Write <, >, or =.

7. $8^2 \;\boxed{>}\; 2^5$  8. $6^1 \;\boxed{>}\; 8^2$  9. $2^4 \;\boxed{<}\; 3^3$  10. $3^4 \;\boxed{=}\; 9^2$

Read the problem and follow the directions.

11. What number is the greatest square of a whole number that evenly divides 54?
    **$3^2$ or 9**

12. What number is the greatest cube of a whole number that evenly divides 54?
    **$3^3$ or 27**

13. Tina called 5 people on Monday. Those 5 people each called 5 different people on Tuesday. On Wednesday, the people who were called on Tuesday each called 5 different people.
    Write an expression with an exponent to solve the problem.
    How many calls were made on Wednesday?
    **$5^3$; 125 calls were made on Wednesday.**

14. Write the whole number that makes a true statement.
    $9^2 = \boxed{\phantom{3}}^{4}$   **3**

15. Jeff e-mailed 4 people on Sunday. On Monday, each of those 4 people e-mailed 4 different people. On Tuesday, each person who was e-mailed on Monday e-mailed 4 different people.
    Write an expression with an exponent to solve the problem.
    How many people were e-mailed on Tuesday?
    **$4^3$; 64 people were e-mailed on Tuesday.**

Choose the answer.

16. Compare $3^4$ and $4^3$. Which statement is true?
    **(A)** $3^4 > 4^3$
    B. $3^4 = 4^3$
    C. $3^4 < 4^3$

17. Compare $6^2$ and $4^4$. Which statement is true?
    A. $6^2 = 4^4$
    **(B)** $6^2 < 4^4$
    C. $6^2 > 4^4$

## CHECKPOINT

**ONLINE 10 min**

### Objectives
- Solve a problem that involves powers.

Students will complete an online Checkpoint. If necessary, read the directions, problems, and answer choices to students and help them with keyboard or mouse operations.

**SOLVE PROBLEMS INVOLVING POWERS**

# Prime Factorization

## Lesson Overview

| | | |
|---|---|---|
| **GET READY**  Classify Numbers | 10 minutes | **OFFLINE** |
| **LEARN**  Show Factors as Rectangles | 10 minutes | **ONLINE** |
| **LEARN**  Make Factor Trees | 10 minutes | **ONLINE** |
| **LEARN**  Prime Factors and Volume | 15 minutes | **ONLINE** |
| **TRY IT**  Find Prime Factorization | 10 minutes | **OFFLINE** |
| **CHECKPOINT** | 5 minutes | **ONLINE** |

### ▶ Lesson Objectives
Determine the prime factorization of a composite number.

### ▶ Prerequisite Skills
- Define and identify a prime number.
- Write equations to demonstrate that whole numbers can be factored in multiple ways.

### ▶ Content Background
Students will build upon the skills they acquired working with expressions with exponents and repeated multiplication to find the prime factorization of composite numbers.

Whole numbers are prime, composite, or neither, on the basis of their number of factors. A factor is one of the two or more numbers multiplied in a multiplication problem. A prime number has exactly two different factors: 1 and itself. For example, 17 is a prime number because its only factors are 1 and 17.

A composite number has more than two different factors. For example, 16 is a composite number because its factors are 1, 2, 4, 8, and 16. The number 1 is neither a prime number nor a composite number because the only way to write 1 as a product is 1 • 1 (with only one factor).

The prime factorization of a composite number shows the composite number as the product of prime numbers. For example, the prime factorization of 20 is 2 • 2 • 5. The prime factorization can also be written with powers of prime numbers as $2^2$ • 5. Factor trees are diagrams used to determine the prime factors of a number.

### ▶ Advance Preparation
Label 20 index cards with the numbers 1 through 20. Print the Table to Complete. Label the top with this title: **Types of Numbers and Their Factors**. Label the top of each column with a heading, starting from the left, as follows: **Prime numbers**, **Composite numbers**, **Numbers that are neither**, and **Factors**. This table will be used in two activities in this lesson.

### Materials to Gather

**SUPPLIED**
Find Prime Factorization activity page
Table to Complete (printout)

**ALSO NEEDED**
index cards – 20

## GET READY  Classify Numbers

**OFFLINE 10 min**

**Objectives**
- Define and identify a prime number.
- Write equations to demonstrate that whole numbers can be factored in multiple ways.

Students will write factors in equations to help them determine whether a number is prime, composite, or neither.

Gather the Types of Numbers and Their Factors table and the index cards you prepared. Students will work with the first three columns in this activity.

1. Review the definitions of *prime numbers* and *composite numbers*. Remind students that a prime number has exactly two different factors (1 and itself), while a composite number has more than two different factors. Give students the table and read the title and and column headings with them.

2. Place the number 1 card aside. Mix up the remaining number cards and place them face down in a stack.

3. Have students do the following:
   - Take the top card from the stack.
   - Write an equation in their Math Notebook that has two factors of the number, such as $2 \cdot 4 = 8$.
   - Think of an equation that uses two different factors for the same number. Don't forget that 1 and the number can be used for two factors.
   - Some numbers have several factors, but it isn't necessary to write equations with all factors of the number; two equations are enough.
   - Decide if the number on the card is prime, composite, or neither. Write the number in the correct column and row in the Types of Numbers and Their Factors table. For instance, the number 8 goes in the eighth row in the Composite numbers column.

4. Repeat Step 3 three times.

5. If students have not chosen a prime number card by this point, give them a prime number card and repeat Step 3.

6. Display the number card with 1. Have students write an equation in their Math Notebook for all the factors of 1. They should discover that the only equation is $1 \cdot 1 = 1$. Explain to students that since 1 is the only factor of 1, it is neither a prime number nor a composite number. Have students write 1 in the first row and under the column labeled Numbers that are neither.

7. Have students complete the chart for the remaining number cards. Check to make sure the numbers are in the correct rows and columns. Students do not need to write equations in their Math Notebook. The answers are shown in the following table:

PRIME FACTORIZATION  39

| Types of Numbers and Their Factors |||| 
|---|---|---|---|
| Prime numbers | Composite numbers | Numbers that are neither | Factors |
|  |  | 1 |  |
| 2 |  |  |  |
| 3 |  |  |  |
|  | 4 |  |  |
| 5 |  |  |  |
|  | 6 |  |  |
| 7 |  |  |  |
|  | 8 |  |  |
|  | 9 |  |  |
|  | 10 |  |  |
| 11 |  |  |  |
|  | 12 |  |  |
| 13 |  |  |  |
|  | 14 |  |  |
|  | 15 |  |  |
|  | 16 |  |  |
| 17 |  |  |  |
|  | 18 |  |  |
| 19 |  |  |  |
|  | 20 |  |  |

> **Tips**
>
> If students are having difficulty determining the factors for a composite number, suggest that they start with a factor of 1. They should write the equation of 1 times the number. Then they can try 2 as a factor in an equation, and then 3, and so on. Use questioning such as, "What number times 2 equals 8?"

8. Ask students to describe how all the numbers in the Composite numbers column are similar. Each composite number has more than two different factors.

9. Ask students to describe how all the numbers in the Prime numbers column are similar. Each prime number has exactly two different factors: 1 and itself.

10. Keep the filled-in table so students can use it in a later activity.

WHOLE NUMBERS AND POWERS

## LEARN  Show Factors as Rectangles

**ONLINE 10 min**

### Objectives

- Determine the prime factorization of a composite number.

Look at the example:

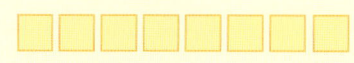

☐☐☐☐☐☐☐☐

This array represents 1 • 8 = 8.

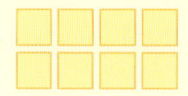

☐☐☐☐
☐☐☐☐

This array represents 2 • 4 = 8.

Students will use the Grid Learning Tool to make rectangles to determine if a number is prime or composite.

Gather the the Types of Numbers and Their Factors table on which students have filled out three columns. (Students used the Table to Complete printout.) Students will complete the fourth column, Factors.

Review the definitions of *prime numbers* and *composite numbers*. A prime number has exactly two different factors (1 and itself), while a composite number has more than two different factors. Review with students that the factors of 1 are 1 and 1. Since 1 has only one factor, it is neither a prime number nor a composite number. Review the fourth column heading, Factors.

Tell students that they will find factors of numbers. Finding factors of a number is a step toward finding the number's prime factorization. Students will find factors for the numbers 1–20.

### Tips

Point out to students that it is not necessary to make all the possible rectangles for a given number to decide if a number is prime or composite. If the number has more than 2 different factors, it is composite.

### DIRECTIONS FOR USING THE GRID LEARNING TOOL

1. Have students choose a color and shade 6 squares in a rectangle, such as a 2 by 3 rectangle.
2. Tell students that the number of rows and the number of columns in the rectangle show the factors of 6, such as 2 • 3.
3. Have students click Clear Chart and then shade 6 squares in a different rectangular shape, such as 1 row of 6. Remind students that rectangles can have 1 row or 1 column on the grid. Tell students that they are finding factors of 6 by creating rectangles made up of 6 squares.
4. Tell students that the factors of 6 are 1, 2, 3, and 6. Have them record the factors in the Factors column in their Types of Numbers and Their Factors table.
5. **Ask:** How can you know if 6 is a prime number or a composite number? *Students should state that 6 is a composite number because it has more than two different factors.*

    Talk about the different factors of 6 being 1, 2, 3, and 6. Have students click Clear Chart.
6. Repeat Steps 1–5 with students shading 5 squares. Students will discover that they can make only two rectangles with 5 squares—a 1 by 5 rectangle and a 5 by 1 rectangle. Help students conclude that 5 has only two factors—1 and 5. Therefore, 5 is a prime number. Have students record the factors in the fourth row of the table and then click Clear Chart.
7. Repeat as students shade 9 and then 11 squares. They should see that 9 is a composite number and 11 is a prime number.

PRIME FACTORIZATION

8. Have students use the Grid Learning Tool to make rectangles for the remaining numbers in the table and record the factors in the fourth column. The answers are shown in the following table:

| Types of Numbers and Their Factors |||| 
|---|---|---|---|
| Prime numbers | Composite numbers | Numbers that are neither | Factors |
|  |  | 1 | 1 |
| 2 |  |  | 1, 2 |
| 3 |  |  | 1, 3 |
|  | 4 |  | 1, 2, 4 |
| 5 |  |  | 1, 5 |
|  | 6 |  | 1, 2, 3, 6 |
| 7 |  |  | 1, 7 |
|  | 8 |  | 1, 2, 4, 8 |
|  | 9 |  | 1, 3, 9 |
|  | 10 |  | 1, 2, 5, 10 |
| 11 |  |  | 1, 11 |
|  | 12 |  | 1, 2, 3, 4, 6, 12 |
| 13 |  |  | 1, 13 |
|  | 14 |  | 1, 2, 7, 14 |
|  | 15 |  | 1, 3, 5, 15 |
|  | 16 |  | 1, 2, 4, 8, 16 |
| 17 |  |  | 1, 17 |
|  | 18 |  | 1, 2, 3, 6, 9, 18 |
| 19 |  |  | 1, 19 |
|  | 20 |  | 1, 2, 4, 5, 10, 20 |

## LEARN Make Factor Trees

ONLINE 10 min

### Objectives

- Determine the prime factorization of a composite number.

Students will complete factor trees to find the prime factors of composite numbers. A factor tree is a diagram that helps break down the factors of a product into prime numbers. Once students identify the prime factors of a number, they can write the prime factorization. They will also learn to use powers of prime numbers to write the prime factorization.

Remind students that although 1 is a factor of a number, it is not a prime number and it is not a composite number. Therefore, don't allow students to write 1 when they find prime factorization of a composite number.

### Tips

Encourage students to check each factor at the bottom branches of their factor trees to be sure that each number is a prime number.

## LEARN Prime Factors and Volume

**ONLINE 15 min**

### Objectives
- Determine the prime factorization of a composite number.

Students can use prime factorization in problems about measurements of boxes, or rectangular prisms. If they know the volume of the rectangular prism, students can find what the possible length, width, and height would be. Students will use the Volume Lab Learning Tool and prime factorization to build a three-dimensional rectangular prism where the volume is a composite number.

Students start the activity by reviewing how to find the prime factorization of a composite number. They will learn how to use the prime factorization to combine the prime factors into multiplication expressions with three factors. Those three factors become the length, width, and height that students will use in the Volume Lab Learning Tool to check whether each combination of dimensions match the given volume.

### Tips
Remind students that even though 1 is not a prime factor of a composite number, 1 can be a dimension of an object.

### DIRECTIONS FOR USING THE VOLUME LAB LEARNING TOOL

1. Click Build the Solid.
2. The learning tool will give the volume of a rectangular prism. Have students do the following:
   - Write the volume in their Math Notebook.
   - Create a factor tree to show the prime factorization of the volume.
   - Write the prime factorization of the volume without using powers of prime numbers.
3. Students should use the prime factorization to create a three-factor combination for the volume. For example, suppose the prime factorization of the volume is 2 • 2 • 2 • 2 • 7. Possible three-factor combinations for the volume include 8 • 2 • 7, 4 • 4 • 7, and 2 • 4 • 14.

   Students should move the sliders to set the values for the length, width, and height to match their chosen three-factor combination.
4. Click Next, and have students repeat Steps 2 and 3 with another problem.

## TRY IT Find Prime Factorization

**OFFLINE 10 min**

### Objectives
- Determine the prime factorization of a composite number.

Students will practice making factor trees to determine the prime factorization of composite numbers. Remind students to begin each factor tree with any pair of factors for the given composite number. Also remind students to write the prime numbers in order from least to greatest when recording the prime factorization. Have students turn to the Find Prime Factorization activity page in their Activity Book and read the directions with them.

Students should copy the problems from the Activity Book into their Math Notebook as necessary and solve them there.

PRIME FACTORIZATION  **43**

## Prime Factorization
### Find Prime Factorization

Make a factor tree for the composite number. Then show the composite number as the product of prime factors. Use powers of prime factors when possible.

1. 42

   42
   / \
   6 · 7
   / \
   2 · 3

   **2 · 3 · 7**

2. 20

   20
   / \
   4 · 5
   / \
   2 · 2

   **2 · 2 · 5 or $2^2$ · 5**

3. 27

   27
   / \
   9 · 3
   / \
   3 · 3

   **3 · 3 · 3 or $3^3$**

4. 48

   48
   / \
   8 · 6
   /|\ / \
   2·2·2 2·3

   **2 · 2 · 2 · 2 · 3 or $2^4$ · 3**

Read the problem and follow the directions.

5. Write the prime factorization of 24. **2 · 2 · 2 · 3 or $2^3$ · 3**

6. Write the prime factorization of 18 using powers of prime numbers. **2 · $3^2$**

7. Write 3 whole numbers less than 50 that have prime factors of only 2 or 3. **Answers may include 2, 3, 4, 6, 8, 9, 12, 16, 18, 24, 27, 32, 36, and 48.**

---

8. Allen said the prime factorization of 45 is 5 · 9. Is he correct? If he is wrong, explain why he is wrong, and write the correct answer.
**He isn't correct. 9 isn't prime. 5 · $3^2$ = 45**

9. Tom made this factor tree for 90. Make a different factor tree for 90. Write the prime factorization for both trees.

   90
   / \
   10 · 9
   / \ / \
   2·5 3·3

   90
   / \
   45 · 2
   / \
   9 · 5
   / \
   3 · 3

   **2 · 3 · 3 · 5 or 2 · $3^2$ · 5**

Choose the answer.

10. Which of the following shows the prime factorization of 30?
    - (A) 2 · 3 · 5
    - B. 5 · 6
    - C. 1 · 2 · 2 · 5
    - D. 3 · 10

11. Which of the following shows 28 factored into powers of prime numbers?
    - A. $3^2$ · 7
    - B. 2 · 2 · 7
    - (C) $2^2$ · 7
    - D. 4 · 7

---

## CHECKPOINT
**ONLINE 5 min**

Students will complete an online Checkpoint. If necessary, read the directions, problems, and answer choices to students and help them with keyboard or mouse operations.

### Objectives
- Determine the prime factorization of a composite number.

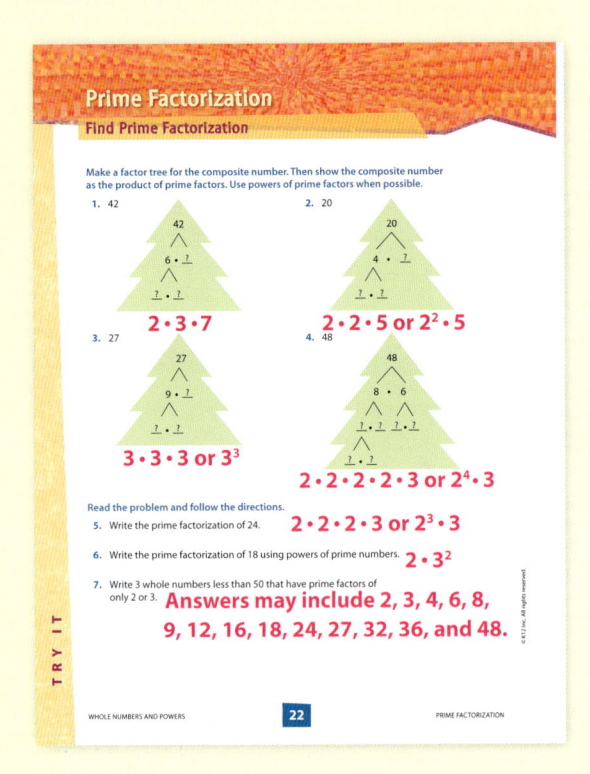

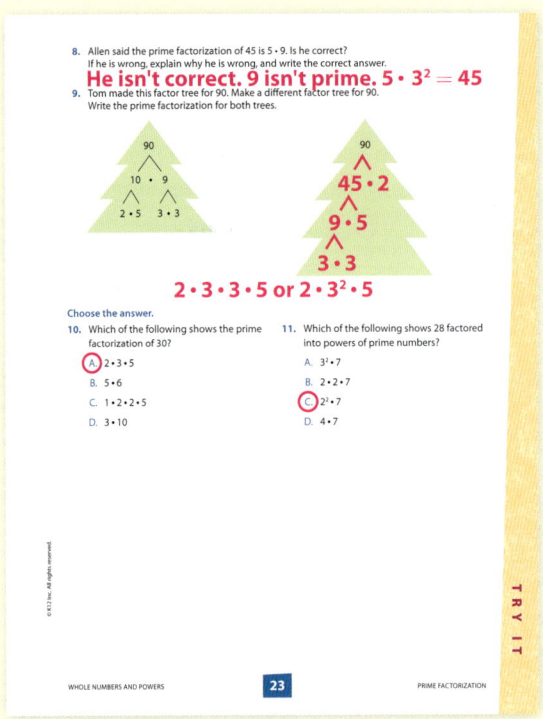

# Unit Review

## Lesson Overview

| | | |
|---|---|---|
| **UNIT REVIEW** Look Back | 10 minutes | **ONLINE** |
| **UNIT REVIEW** Checkpoint Practice | 50 minutes | **ONLINE** |
| ▶ **UNIT REVIEW** Prepare for the Checkpoint | | |

### ▶ Unit Objectives

This lesson reviews the following objectives:

- Round whole numbers in a story problem.
- Estimate or calculate a sum or a difference in a whole-number problem.
- Estimate or calculate a sum or a difference in a whole-number story problem.
- Estimate or calculate a product or a quotient in a whole-number problem.
- Estimate or calculate a product or a quotient in a whole-number story problem.
- Represent and compute a power by using repeated multiplication.
- Solve a problem that involves powers.
- Determine the prime factorization of a composite number.

### Materials to Gather

There are no materials to gather for this lesson.

### ▶ Advance Preparation

In this lesson, students will have an opportunity to review previous activities in the Whole Numbers and Powers unit. Look at the suggested activities in Unit Review: Prepare for the Checkpoint online and gather any needed materials.

## UNIT REVIEW Look Back

**ONLINE 10 min**

### Objectives
- Review unit objectives.

Students will review key concepts from the unit to prepare for the Unit Checkpoint.

## UNIT REVIEW Checkpoint Practice

**ONLINE 50 min**

### Objectives
- Review unit objectives.

Students will complete an online Checkpoint Practice to prepare for the Unit Checkpoint. If necessary, read the directions, problems, and answer choices to students. Have students answer the problems on their own. Review any missed problems with students.

### ▶ UNIT REVIEW Prepare for the Checkpoint

What you do next depends on how students performed in the previous activity, Unit Review: Checkpoint Practice. If students had difficulty with any of the problems, complete the appropriate review activity listed in the table online.

# Unit Checkpoint

## Lesson Overview

**UNIT CHECKPOINT** Online　　　　　　　　　　　　　60 minutes　**ONLINE**

### ▶ Unit Objectives

This lesson assesses the following objectives:
- Round whole numbers in a story problem.
- Estimate or calculate a sum or a difference in a whole-number problem.
- Estimate or calculate a sum or a difference in a whole-number story problem.
- Estimate or calculate a product or a quotient in a whole-number problem.
- Estimate or calculate a product or a quotient in a whole-number story problem.
- Represent and compute a power by using repeated multiplication.
- Solve a problem that involves powers.
- Determine the prime factorization of a composite number.

### Materials to Gather

There are no materials to gather for this lesson.

### UNIT CHECKPOINT  Online

ONLINE 60 min

Students will complete the online Unit Checkpoint. If necessary, read the directions, problems, and answer choices to students and help them with keyboard or mouse operations.

### Objectives

- Assess unit objectives.

# Geometry

## ▶ Unit Objectives

- Identify, measure, and draw angles with appropriate math tools.
- Identify and draw perpendicular or parallel lines with appropriate math tools.
- Construct rectangles or triangles with appropriate math tools.
- Identify that the sum of the interior angles of any triangle is 180° and solve related problems.
- Identify that the sum of the interior angles of any quadrilateral is 360° and solve related problems.
- Predict, describe, and perform transformations on two-dimensional shapes.
- Identify or draw a two-dimensional view of a three-dimensional object.

## ▶ Big Ideas

A right angle forms a square corner that measures 90°; an acute angle is less than a right angle and an obtuse angle is greater than a right angle.

## ▶ Unit Introduction

Students will investigate two- and three-dimensional figures in this geometry unit. They will use rulers, protractors, and compasses to draw angles, lines, quadrilaterals, and triangles. Students will explore the measures of the interior angles of triangles and quadrilaterals to understand the relationship between the sum of the angle measures and the number of angles in each shape. They will transform two-dimensional shapes by using translations (or slides), reflections (or flips), and rotations (or turns). Students will sketch and identify two-dimensional views of three-dimensional objects.

## ▶ Keywords

acute angle
acute triangle
angle
clockwise
compass
counterclockwise
degree
dilation
equiangular triangle
equilateral triangle
flip
interior angle
intersecting lines
isosceles triangle
obtuse angle

obtuse triangle
parallel lines
parallelogram
perpendicular lines
protractor
quadrilateral
ray
rectangle
reflection
rhombus (plural: rhombuses)
right angle
right triangle
rotation
ruler

scalene triangle
slide triangle
square
straight angle
sum of angle measures
tessellation
three-dimensional object
transformation
translation
trapezoid
triangle
turn
two-dimensional shape
vertex (plural: vertices)

# Angles (A)

## Lesson Overview

| | | |
|---|---|---|
| **GET READY** Sort Angles | 5 minutes | **ONLINE** |
| **LEARN** Angles and Shapes | 15 minutes | **ONLINE** |
| **LEARN** Tools for Measuring Angles | 25 minutes | **ONLINE** |
| **TRY IT** Measure Angles | 15 minutes | **OFFLINE** |

### ▶ Lesson Objectives
Identify, measure, and draw angles with appropriate math tools.

### ▶ Prerequisite Skills
- State and recognize the definitions of a right angle, an acute angle, an obtuse angle, and a straight angle.
- Demonstrate understanding of relative angle measures.

### ▶ Content Background
Students will measure angles with a protractor. On many protractors, there are two sets of numbers along the curved edge of the tool. These numbers are the scales for reading the measure of an angle in degrees. Each scale goes from 0 to 180. One scale goes from 0 on the left to 180 on the right. The other scale is arranged in the opposite direction to the first scale.

Having two scales on a protractor makes it easier to find the measure of an angle, no matter how the angle is oriented. Students should use one scale to measure an angle. They should check where the 0 and 180 degree marks are on the scale they are using, so they can accurately measure the angle.

### ▶ Common Errors and Misconceptions
Students might focus on the length of the line segments that form an angle's sides, the tilt of the top line segment, the area enclosed by the sides, or the proximity of the two sides rather than look at the actual size of the angle. For example, students might indicate that in the two triangles shown here, angle *A* is smaller than angle *X*.

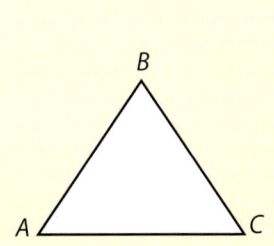

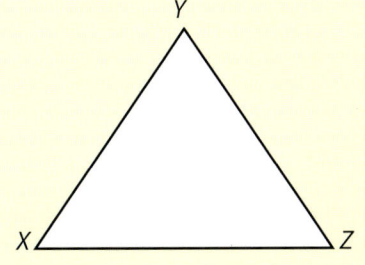

### Materials to Gather

**SUPPLIED**
protractor
Measure Angles activity page

**ALSO NEEDED**
ruler

ANGLES (A) 49

## GET READY  Sort Angles

**ONLINE 5 min**

Students will identify acute, right, obtuse, and straight angles. They will match the names of angles to correct angles.

### Objectives
- State and recognize the definitions of a right angle, an acute angle, an obtuse angle, and a straight angle.
- Demonstrate understanding of relative angle measures.

## LEARN  Angles and Shapes

**ONLINE 15 min**

Students will learn about the parts of an angle. Then they will use the Pattern Blocks Learning Tool to put shapes together to create other shapes. They will explore the angles in the shapes.

### Objectives
- Identify, measure, and draw angles with appropriate math tools.

**DIRECTIONS FOR USING THE PATTERN BLOCKS LEARNING TOOL**

1. Click Free Play. Then read the instructions, and click Start.

    **Ask:** What unit of measure do you use to describe an angle? a degree or degrees

2. Have students drag one triangle to the canvas.

    **Ask:** What type of angle is formed where two sides of this triangle meet in an angle less than 90°? acute

3. Have students drag five more triangles to the canvas near the first triangle. Show them how to rotate the triangles using the Rotate arrows.

4. Have students rotate the triangles and drag them next to each other to make a hexagon. Focus attention on the angles formed by the sides of the hexagon.

    **Ask:** What type of angle is formed where two sides of a hexagon meet? an obtuse angle measuring more than 90°

5. Have students drag three triangles to the canvas and make a trapezoid with them by using the Rotate arrows.

    **Ask:** Look at all the angles formed where two sides of the trapezoid meet. Are all the angles the same type? no

    **Ask:** What types of angles are formed by the sides of the trapezoid? obtuse and acute angles

6. Have students drag one square to the canvas.

    **Ask:** What is the measure of the angle formed where two sides of the square meet? 90°

    **Ask:** What is the name of a 90° angle? a right angle

    **Ask:** How many angles does a square have? 4

7. Have students drag two more squares to the canvas and join them with the first square to make a rectangle.

    **Ask:** What is the measure of the angle formed where two sides of a rectangle meet? 90°

    **Ask:** How many angles does a rectangle have? 4

8. Have students create other shapes from pattern blocks and describe the shapes' angles.

## LEARN  Tools for Measuring Angles

**ONLINE 25 min**

### Objectives
- Identify, measure, and draw angles with appropriate math tools.

Students will learn the parts of a protractor. Then they will learn step-by-step procedures for measuring angles with a protractor. They will measure given angles with an online protractor. Then they will create their own angles with the Advanced Protractor Learning Tool and will measure the angles.

**DIRECTIONS FOR USING THE ADVANCED PROTRACTOR LEARNING TOOL**

1. Click Draw an Angle.
2. Have students drag point *A* to make the following types of angles. Have them read aloud the measure of each angle they make.
   - acute
   - right
   - obtuse
3. Have students make a 0° angle.

   **Ask:** What is a 0° angle? an angle that measures no degrees and that lies on a ray
4. Have students make a straight angle.

   **Ask:** What is the measure of a straight angle? 180°

   **Ask:** What is the difference between a straight angle and a 0° angle? A straight angle lies on a line, and a 0° angle lies on a ray.
5. Click Menu. Then click Measure an Angle.
6. Have students drag point *A* to create an angle of any measure.
7. Have students drag the protractor over the angle, placing the origin on the vertex of the angle.
8. Have students read the angle's measure on the protractor and enter the measure in the box.
9. Have them click Check. The learning tool will either show the answer as correct or say how many degrees too small or too large the answer is.
10. Have students create acute, right, obtuse, and straight angles; measure them; and check answers.

## TRY IT  Measure Angles

**OFFLINE 15 min**

### Objectives
- Identify, measure, and draw angles with appropriate math tools.

Students will practice using a protractor to measure angles. They will classify the angle as acute, right, straight, or obtuse. Make sure they find the angle measure in degrees. Gather a protractor. Have students turn to the Measure Angles activity page in their Activity Book and read the directions with them.

Students should copy the problems from the Activity Book into their Math Notebook as necessary and solve them there.

ANGLES (A)  51

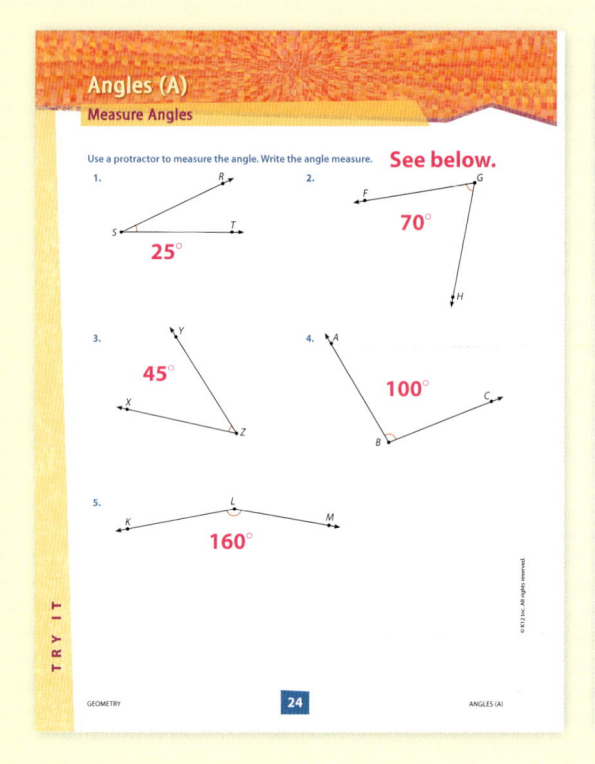

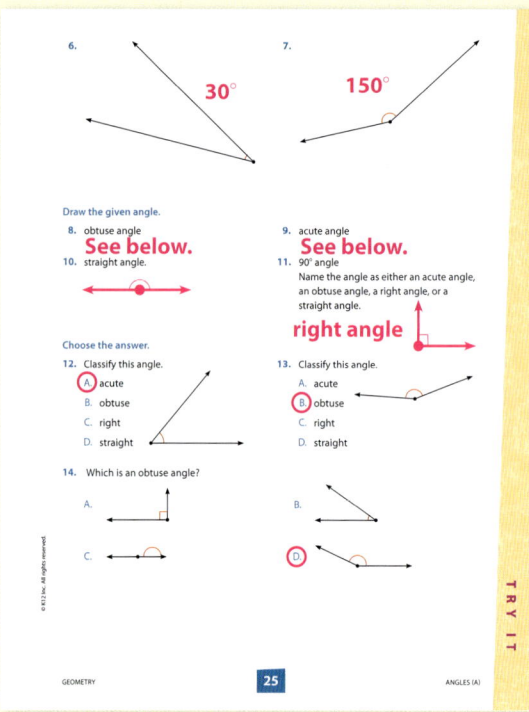

**Additional Answers**

**1–7.** Accept angle measurements that are within 2° of the given answer. For example, for Problem 1, which has an answer of 25°, students may answer 23°, 24°, 26°, or 27° and still be counted as correct.

**8.** Answers will vary. Other correct drawings are acceptable.

**9.** Answers will vary. Other correct drawings are acceptable.

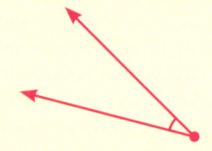

52 GEOMETRY

# Angles (B)

## Lesson Overview

| | | |
|---|---|---|
| **GET READY** Use Unit Angles | 10 minutes | **ONLINE** |
| **LEARN** How to Draw Angles | 10 minutes | **ONLINE** |
| **LEARN** Draw Angles with a Protractor | 15 minutes | **OFFLINE** |
| **TRY IT** Draw and Measure Angles | 15 minutes | **OFFLINE** |
| **CHECKPOINT** | 10 minutes | **OFFLINE** |

## ▶ Lesson Objectives
Identify, measure, and draw angles with appropriate math tools.

## ▶ Prerequisite Skills
- State and recognize the definitions of a right angle, an acute angle, an obtuse angle, and a straight angle.
- Demonstrate understanding of relative angle measures.

## ▶ Content Background
Student will continue to measure angles with a protractor. On many protractors, there are two sets of numbers along the curved edge of the tool. These numbers are the scales for reading the measure of an angle in degrees. Each scale goes from 0 to 180. One scale goes from 0 on the left to 180 on the right. The other scale is arranged in the opposite direction to the first scale.

Having two scales on a protractor makes it easier to find the measure of an angle, no matter how the angle is oriented. Students should use one scale to measure an angle. They should check where the 0 and 180 degree marks are on the scale they are using, so they can accurately measure the angle.

## ▶ Common Errors and Misconceptions
- Students might think that the size of an image of an angle relates to the angle's measurement. It is best to use terminology such as "the angle with the greater (or greatest) measure" instead of "the greater (or greatest) angle."
- Students might think they have to line up one ray of an angle with 0° on a protractor. Instead, they can line up one ray with a friendly number, and then subtract the readings where the two rays cross the protractor scale.

### Materials to Gather

**SUPPLIED**
protractor
Draw and Measure Angles activity page
Checkpoint (printout)

**ALSO NEEDED**
ruler

## GET READY  Use Unit Angles

**ONLINE 10 min**

### Objectives
- Demonstrate understanding of relative angle measures.

Students will learn how to compare angles to determine which angle has a greater measure than another angle and which has a lesser measure than another angle.

## LEARN  How to Draw Angles

**ONLINE 10 min**

### Objectives
- Identify, measure, and draw angles with appropriate math tools.

Students will learn to draw angles. They will learn how to draw an angle by using a ruler. They will also learn how to draw an angle by using a ruler and a protractor.

Point out that when students draw an angle with a ruler and do not use a protractor, they do not know the exact degree measure of the angle. But students can estimate the measure of the angle and classify the angle as acute, obtuse, right, or straight.

## LEARN  Draw Angles with a Protractor

**OFFLINE 15 min**

### Objectives
- Identify, measure, and draw angles with appropriate math tools.

### Tips
When students are using the protractor to *draw* angles, remind them to make sure the center of the protractor stays on the endpoint of the ray. When they use the protractor to *measure* angles, remind them to make sure the center of the protractor stays on the vertex of the angle.

Students will use tools to draw angles. Gather the ruler and the protractor.

1. Have students use only a ruler to sketch a 60° angle.

   **Ask:** How does a 60° angle compare in measure to a right angle? A right angle measures 90°, so a 60° angle has a lesser measure than a right angle.

   The sketch of the 60° angle should look like it has a lesser measure than a 90° angle.

2. Give students the protractor and guide them as they draw a 60° angle with the protractor and the ruler. Use the following directions:
   - Make a point on your paper. Label the point *B*. This will be the endpoint of the rays that form the angle. This endpoint is the vertex of the angle you will draw.
   - Use a ruler to draw a ray from the endpoint. Mark a point on the ray. Label the point *A*.
   - Place the center, or origin, of the protractor on the endpoint of the ray.
   - Line up the ray with any friendly degree measure on the protractor. A friendly degree measure is a number that is easy to compute mentally.
   - Locate the degree measure on the protractor that is 60° greater than the friendly degree measure you used. Mark a point at that location.
   - Draw a ray from the endpoint through the point. Label the point *C*. Make an arc inside the angle to mark the angle you drew. Label the arc 60°. The name of the angle is ∠*ABC*.

   You can also position the protractor to line up with the base line of 0° on the protractor. Use the following directions:
   - Make a point on your paper. Label the point *B*. This will be the endpoint of the rays that form the angle. This endpoint is the vertex of the angle you will draw.

**54  GEOMETRY**

- Use a ruler to draw a ray from the endpoint. Mark a point on the ray. Label the point A.
- Place the center of the protractor on the endpoint of the ray.
- Line up the protractor's base line with the ray so that the ray points to 0°.
- Locate 60° on the inside scale of the protractor. Mark a point at that location.
- Draw a ray from the endpoint through the point. Label the point C. Make an arc inside the angle to mark the angle you drew. Label the arc 60°. The name of the angle is ∠ABC.

3. Have students compare the angle they sketched with the angle they drew using a protractor. Point out that the angles should be about the same measure but will probably not be exactly the same measure.

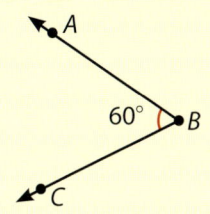

4. Repeat Steps 1–3 for a 75° angle, a 95° angle, a 150° angle, and a 180° angle. Students may choose different labels for the points on their sketches.

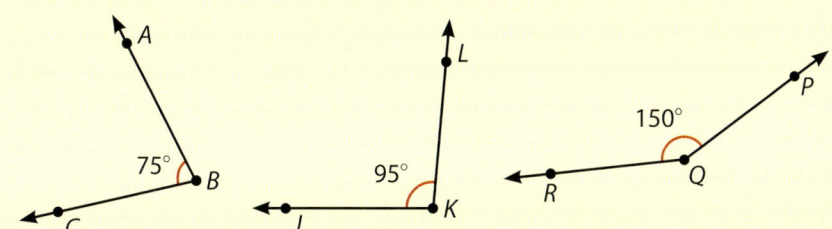

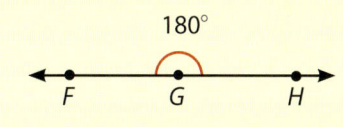

5. Repeat Steps 1–3, having students decide what angle measures they want to draw. Tell students that they should mark the vertex with a point and show an arc on the angle. They do not need to mark points on the rays or label the vertex. Use a protractor to check that the angles are correctly drawn.

## TRY IT  Draw and Measure Angles

OFFLINE 15 min

Students will practice measuring and drawing angles. Gather a protractor and a ruler. When students measure angles on the activity page with the protractor, accept answers that are 2° greater than or less than the answer given as correct. Have students turn to the Draw and Measure Angles activity page in their Activity Book and read the directions with them.

Students should copy the problems from the Activity Book into their Math Notebook as necessary and solve them there.

### Objectives

- Identify, measure, and draw angles with appropriate math tools.

### Tips

If needed, have students review the steps they learned for drawing and measuring angles before they begin the activity page.

ANGLES (B)  55

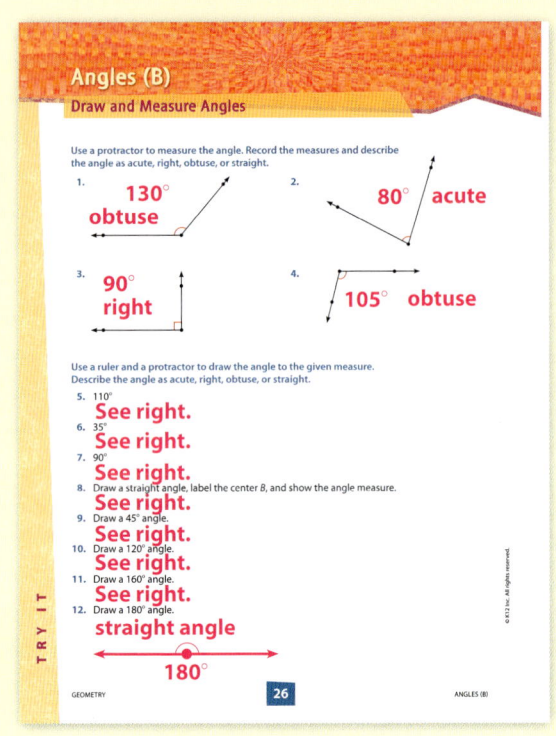

## Additional Answers

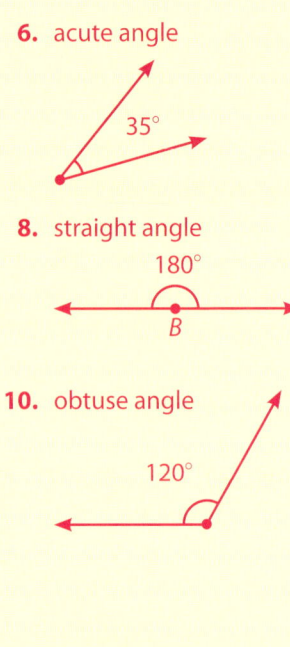

5. obtuse angle
110°

6. acute angle
35°

7. right angle
90°

8. straight angle
180°
B

9. acute angle
45°

10. obtuse angle
120°

11. obtuse angle
160°

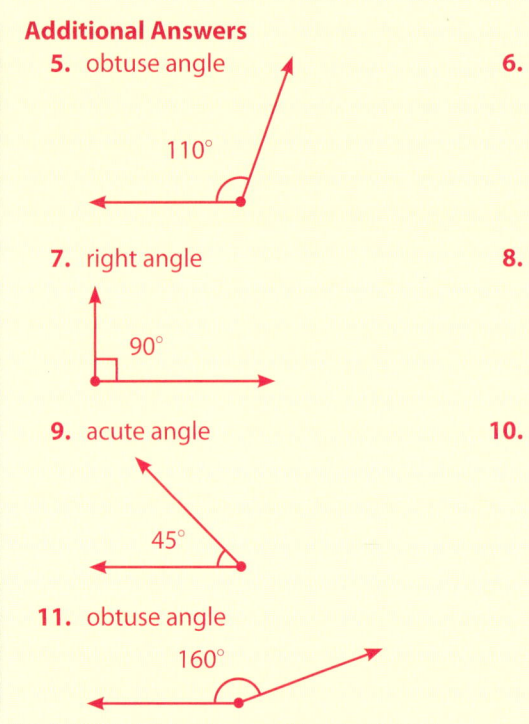

## CHECKPOINT

Have students complete the Checkpoint on their own. Give students a protractor. If necessary, read the directions, problems, and answer choices to students. Use the answer key to score the Checkpoint, and then enter the results online.

### Objectives

- Identify, measure, and draw angles with appropriate math tools.

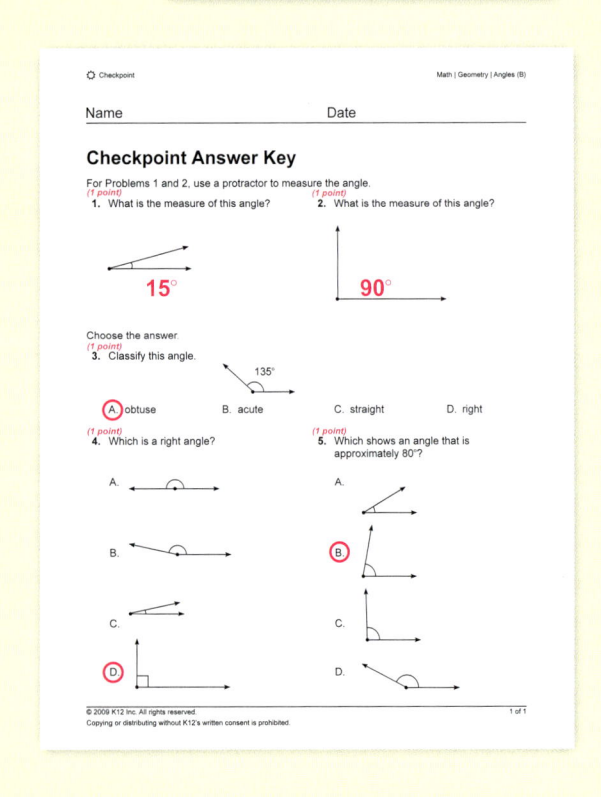

**56  GEOMETRY**

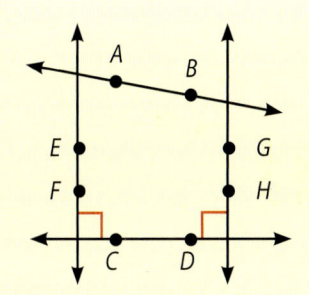

# Perpendicular and Parallel Lines

## Lesson Overview

| | | |
|---|---|---|
| **GET READY** Identify Lines | 10 minutes | ONLINE |
| **LEARN** Use a Compass to Construct Lines | 10 minutes | ONLINE |
| **LEARN** Construct Lines with a Compass | 20 minutes | OFFLINE |
| **TRY IT** Practice Types of Lines | 10 minutes | OFFLINE |
| **CHECKPOINT** | 10 minutes | ONLINE |

### ▶ Lesson Objectives
Identify and draw perpendicular or parallel lines with appropriate math tools.

### ▶ Prerequisite Skills
- Identify lines that are parallel or intersecting.
- Identify lines that are perpendicular.

### ▶ Content Background
Students will learn how mathematicians draw lines and angles and use math tools to draw and measure lines and angles.

Lines may be parallel, intersecting, or perpendicular. This drawing shows parallel, intersecting, and perpendicular lines.

1. Line *EF* is parallel to line *GH*.
2. Line *GH* intersects line *AB*.
3. Lines *EF* and *GH* are perpendicular to line *CD*.

### ▶ Safety
Make sure students handle the compass carefully and be sure to store it in a safe place.

### Materials to Gather

**SUPPLIED**
protractor
Practice Types of Lines activity page

**ALSO NEEDED**
compass
ruler

## GET READY  Identify Lines — ONLINE 10 min

### Objectives
- Identify lines that are parallel or intersecting.
- Identify lines that are perpendicular.

Students will review the meanings of the geometric terms *intersecting*, *parallel*, and *perpendicular*. Then they will identify intersecting, parallel, and perpendicular lines on a map.

**Tips** If students are having difficulty identifying intersecting, parallel, or perpendicular lines, have them look for the three types of lines in everyday places. Make a list of places each type of line is found. A set of railroad tracks is an example of parallel lines.

**PERPENDICULAR AND PARALLEL LINES** 57

## LEARN  Use a Compass to Construct Lines

Students will learn how to use a compass and a ruler to construct perpendicular and parallel lines.

### Objectives
- Identify and draw perpendicular or parallel lines with appropriate math tools.

## LEARN  Construct Lines with a Compass

Students will practice identifying and constructing parallel and perpendicular lines. Gather a compass, protractor, ruler, and sheet of paper.

### Objectives
- Identify and draw perpendicular or parallel lines with appropriate math tools.

### DRAWING AND CONSTRUCTING PERPENDICULAR LINES

1. Remind students that perpendicular lines intersect at one point. Perpendicular lines always make a right angle at the point where they intersect.
2. Have students sketch a line on a sheet of paper.
3. Have them sketch another line that looks perpendicular to the first line.
4. Remind students that to accurately construct perpendicular lines, they must use tools such as a compass and ruler.
5. Now have students draw a line segment about 3 inches long and label the endpoints A and B.
6. Have students set the point of the compass at point A and open the compass a width that is not all the way to point B, but beyond the middle of the segment. Ask students to draw an arc that extends from above the middle of the segment to below the middle of the segment. 
7. Have students leave the compass the same width and set the point of the compass at point B. Have them draw a second arc that crosses their first arc both above and below the segment. Students should label the point where the arcs cross above the segment as point C and the point where the arcs cross below the segment as point D.
8. Be sure students use a ruler to draw line CD, which will be perpendicular to line segment AB. Students should label the point where line CD and line segment AB intersect as point E. 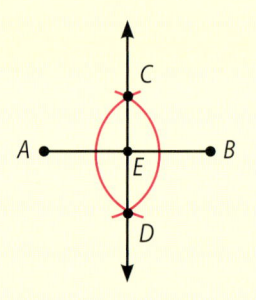
9. Have students use the protractor to measure angles CEA and CEB to check that each angle measures exactly 90°. Angles DEA and DEB will also measure exactly 90°.

### DRAWING AND CONSTRUCTING PARALLEL LINES

10. Remind students that parallel lines are always in the same plane, or two-dimensional space. Parallel lines are always the same distance apart. They never intersect, or cross each other.
11. Have students sketch a line on a sheet of paper.
12. Have students sketch another line that looks parallel to the first line.
13. Remind students that to accurately construct parallel lines, they must use tools such as a compass and ruler.

### Tips

If students are having trouble constructing parallel lines, practice constructing perpendicular lines several times before moving to parallel lines.

14. Using the line *CD* and line segment *AB* they have drawn, have students set the compass width the same as the length of segment *EB*. Then have them extend the line segment to the right beyond point *B* to a point they will label as point *F*. By using the compass, they should make the length of segment *BF* the same as the length of segment *EB*.

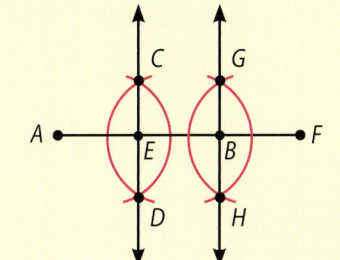

15. Have students repeat the construction of a perpendicular line to create a second perpendicular line to line segment *AF*, following Steps 7–9.

16. Have students set the point of the compass at point *E* and open the compass a width that is not all the way to point *F*, but beyond point *B*. Ask students to draw an arc that extends from above point *B* to below point *B*.

17. Have students leave the compass the same width and set the point of the compass at point *F*. Have them draw a second arc that crosses their first arc both above and below point *B*. Label the point where the arcs cross above the segment as point *G* and the point where the arcs cross below the segment as point *H*.

18. Be sure students use a ruler to draw line *GH*, which will be perpendicular to line segment *AF*.

19. **Ask:** Which lines are parallel? Lines *CD* and *GH* are parallel.

20. Point out that when two lines are each perpendicular to another line or segment, as *CD* and *GH* are to segment *AF*, they are parallel to each other.

## CONSTRUCTING PARALLEL AND PERPENDICULAR LINES TO MAKE A MAP

21. Have students create a simple map by making parallel and perpendicular lines. Students can label lines with names.

22. Remind students to use a ruler and compass as they construct the parallel and perpendicular lines.

23. Ask students to identify parallel and perpendicular lines on their map.

### TRY IT  Practice Types of Lines

OFFLINE 10 min

### Objectives

- Identify and draw perpendicular or parallel lines with appropriate math tools.

Following the steps they have learned for constructing lines, students will construct and draw intersecting, perpendicular, and parallel lines. They will give examples of where these types of lines can be found every day. Gather a ruler, compass, and protractor. Have students turn to the Practice Types of Lines activity page in their Activity Book and read the directions with them.

Students should copy the problems from the Activity Book into their Math Notebook as necessary and solve them there.

**Tips** To help students remember the differences between a perpendicular and a parallel line, write the word *parallel* for them. Point out the two l's in the middle of the word. These l's are parallel. Tell them to think of the parallel letter l's when they look for parallel lines.

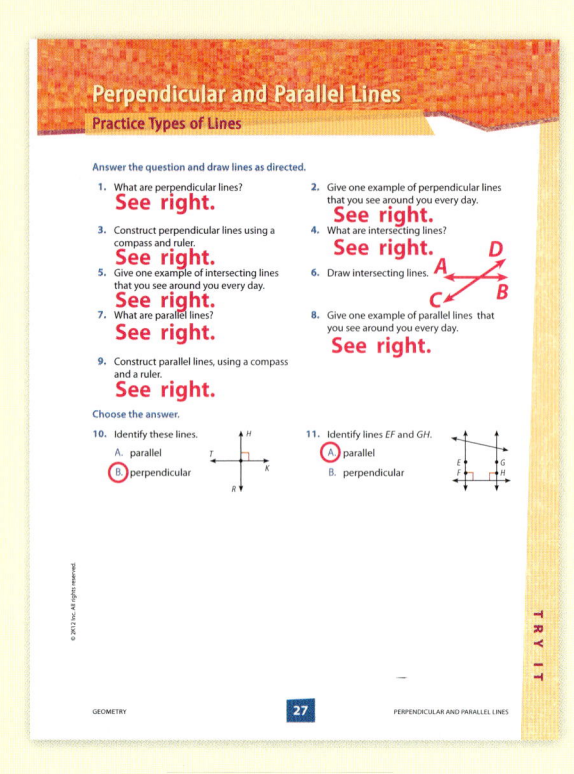

## Additional Answers

1. Perpendicular lines intersect at one point. Perpendicular lines always make a right angle at the point where they intersect.

2. Answers will vary. Other correct examples are acceptable.
   **Sample answer:** the place where edges of a dresser meet, the place where rungs on a ladder meet the sides of the ladder

3. Students should follow the steps they have learned for constructing lines with a compass and a ruler.

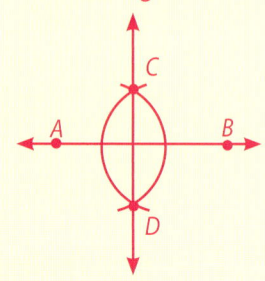

4. Intersecting lines cross each other. They can intersect, or cross each other, at one point or at all points.

5. Answers will vary. Other correct examples are acceptable.
   **Sample answer:** roads that cross each other, the cuts that make slices of pizza

7. Parallel lines are always in the same plane, or two-dimensional space. Parallel lines are always the same distance apart. They never intersect, or cross each other.

8. Answers will vary. Other correct examples are acceptable.
   **Sample answer:** railroad tracks, the rungs that make up a ladder

9. Students should follow the steps they have learned for constructing lines with a compass and a ruler.

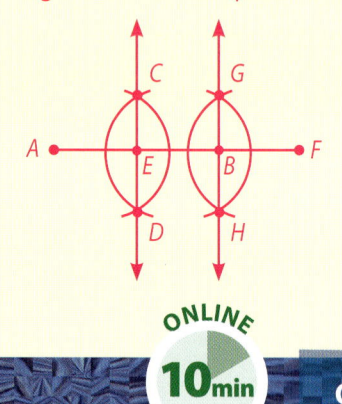

# CHECKPOINT

**ONLINE 10 min**

Students will complete an online Checkpoint. If necessary, read the directions, problems, and answer choices to students and help them with keyboard or mouse operations.

## Objectives

- Identify and draw perpendicular or parallel lines with appropriate math tools.

# Construct Triangles and Quadrilaterals

## Lesson Overview

| | | |
|---|---|---|
| **GET READY** Sketch Triangles and Quadrilaterals | 10 minutes | **OFFLINE** |
| **GET READY** Identify Triangles | 5 minutes | **ONLINE** |
| **LEARN** Construct Triangles and Quadrilaterals | 10 minutes | **ONLINE** |
| **LEARN** Construct Each Shape | 20 minutes | **OFFLINE** |
| **TRY IT** Practice Triangles and Quadrilaterals | 10 minutes | **OFFLINE** |
| **CHECKPOINT** | 5 minutes | **OFFLINE** |

### ▶ Lesson Objectives
Construct rectangles or triangles with appropriate math tools.

### ▶ Prerequisite Skills
- Define and sketch different types of triangles and identify their attributes.
- Know how to define and sketch different quadrilaterals.

### ▶ Content Background
Students will use tools such as a compass (a drawing tool with two legs that are hinged to each other at one end) and ruler to construct quadrilaterals and triangles.

### ▶ Safety
Make sure students handle the compass carefully and be sure to store it in a safe place.

### Materials to Gather

**SUPPLIED**
Construct Each Shape activity page
protractor
Practice Triangles and Quadrilaterals activity page

**ALSO NEEDED**
compass
ruler

---

## GET READY  Sketch Triangles and Quadrilaterals
**OFFLINE 10 min**

Students will sketch as well as describe the attributes of different types of triangles and quadrilaterals.
There are no materials to gather for this activity.

### Objectives
- Define and sketch different types of triangles and identify their attributes.
- Know how to define and sketch different quadrilaterals.

### SKETCHING TRIANGLES
1. **Ask:** How many sides and angles does a triangle have? **3 sides and 3 angles**
2. Have students sketch an equilateral triangle and describe its attributes. Use the Types of Triangles chart to check the sketch and the description.
3. If students do not accurately sketch or describe an equilateral triangle, use the chart to review the attributes with them.

**CONSTRUCT TRIANGLES AND QUADRILATERALS** 61

4. Repeat Steps 2 and 3 for these triangles:
   - isosceles triangle
   - scalene triangle
   - acute triangle
   - equiangular triangle
   - obtuse triangle
   - right triangle

| Types of Triangles | | |
|---|---|---|
| **Name** | **Description** | **Example** |
| equilateral triangle | All sides are the same length. | |
| isosceles triangle | Two sides are the same length. | |
| scalene triangle | All the sides are a different length. | |
| acute triangle | All angles measure less than 90°. | |
| equiangular triangle | All angles measure exactly 60°. | |
| obtuse triangle | One angle measures greater than 90°. | |
| right triangle | One angle measures exactly 90°. | |

## SKETCHING QUADRILATERALS

5. **Ask:** How many sides and angles does a quadrilateral have? 4 sides and 4 angles
6. Have students sketch an isosceles trapezoid and describe its attributes. Use the Types of Quadrilaterals chart to check the sketch and the description.
7. If students do not accurately sketch or describe an isosceles trapezoid, use the chart to review the attributes with them.
8. Repeat Steps 6 and 7 for these quadrilaterals:
   - scalene trapezoid
   - parallelogram
   - rectangle
   - rhombus
   - square

**62** GEOMETRY

| Types of Quadrilaterals |||
| --- | --- | --- |
| Name | Description | Example |
| isosceles trapezoid | Two sides are parallel and two sides are the same length. | |
| scalene trapezoid | Two sides are parallel; all four sides are different lengths. | |
| parallelogram | Opposite sides are parallel and equal in length. | |
| rectangle | Opposite sides are parallel and equal in length. All angles are 90°. | |
| rhombus | All four sides are equal in length. | |
| square | All four sides are equal in length and all angles are 90° | |

## GET READY  Identify Triangles

**ONLINE 5 min**

Students will match triangles to their descriptions. This matching activity includes acute, obtuse, equilateral, equiangular, right, scalene, and isosceles triangles.

**Tips** — If students are having difficulty remembering the different types of triangles or quadrilaterals, have them draw and label each type on a separate sheet of paper. Staple the drawings together to create a reference book.

### Objectives

- Define and sketch different types of triangles and identify their attributes.
- Know how to define and sketch different quadrilaterals.

## LEARN  Construct Triangles and Quadrilaterals

**ONLINE 10 min**

Students will watch a tutorial on how to use a compass and ruler to construct an equilateral triangle and square.

### Objectives

- Construct rectangles or triangles with appropriate math tools.

**CONSTRUCT TRIANGLES AND QUADRILATERALS  63**

# LEARN  Construct Each Shape

**OFFLINE 20 min**

Following the steps they have learned for constructing an equilateral triangle and square, students will construct and draw an equilateral triangle, square, right triangle, and rectangle. Gather a ruler, compass, and protractor. Have students turn to the Construct Each Shape activity page in their Activity Book and read the directions with them.

Students should copy the problems from the Activity Book into their Math Notebook as necessary and solve them there.

1. Review with students the Worked Examples, which show how to construct and draw perpendicular lines.
2. Have students follow the steps in Problem 1 to construct an equilateral triangle. If students struggle with a step, model the step for them.
3. Have students follow the steps in Problem 2 to construct a square. Again, if students have difficulty with a step, model that step for them.
4. Have students read the steps in Problem 3 to construct a right triangle. Answer any questions they may have before they begin constructing, and then have students construct a right triangle. Model any steps students have difficulty with.
5. Have students read the steps in Problem 4 to construct a rectangle. Answer students' questions, and then have them construct a rectangle. Model steps as needed.

You may share with students the steps shown in the answers, to help them construct the shapes.

## Objectives

- Construct rectangles or triangles with appropriate math tools.

## Tips

If students are having trouble remembering the steps for constructing triangles or rectangles, model most of the steps for them and have them finish. Then repeat, modeling fewer steps. Repeat until students can construct the shape(s) on their own.

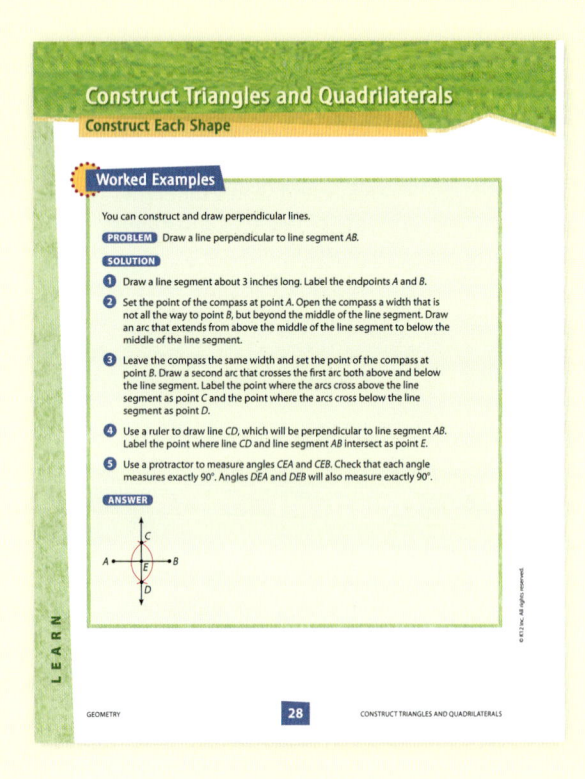

64  GEOMETRY

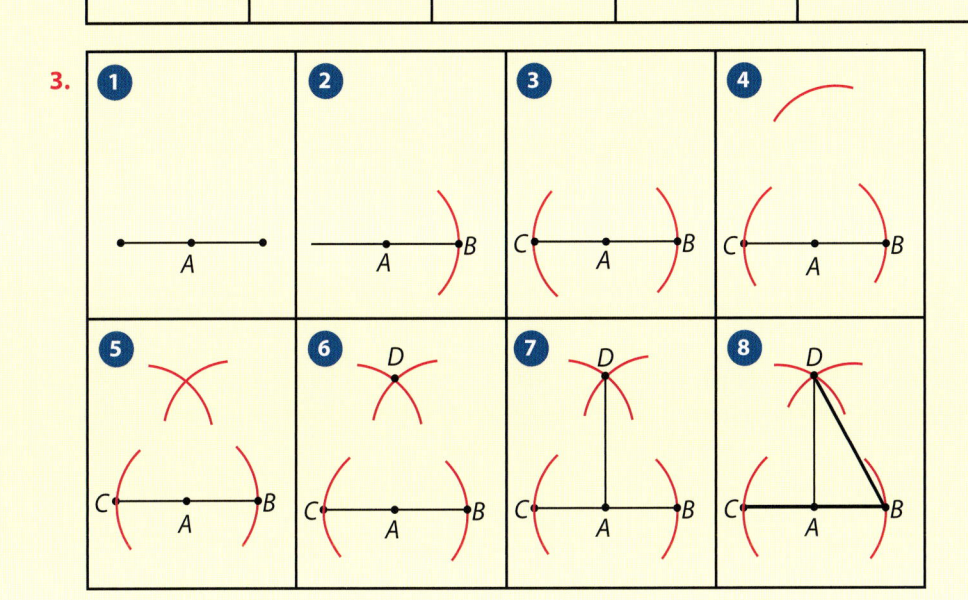

**Additional Answers**

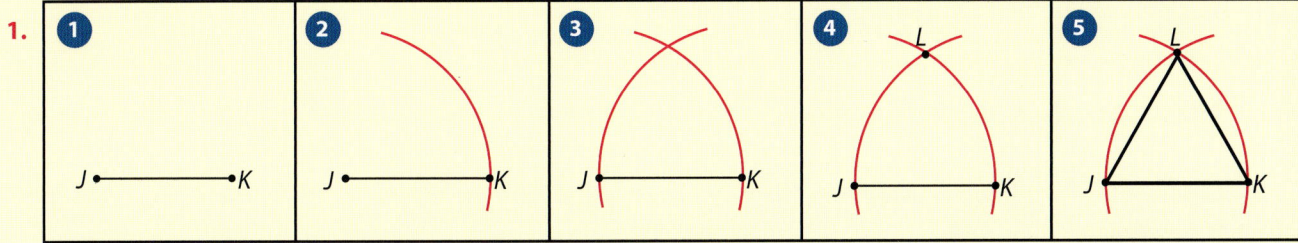

1.

2.

3.

CONSTRUCT TRIANGLES AND QUADRILATERALS

## Additional Answers

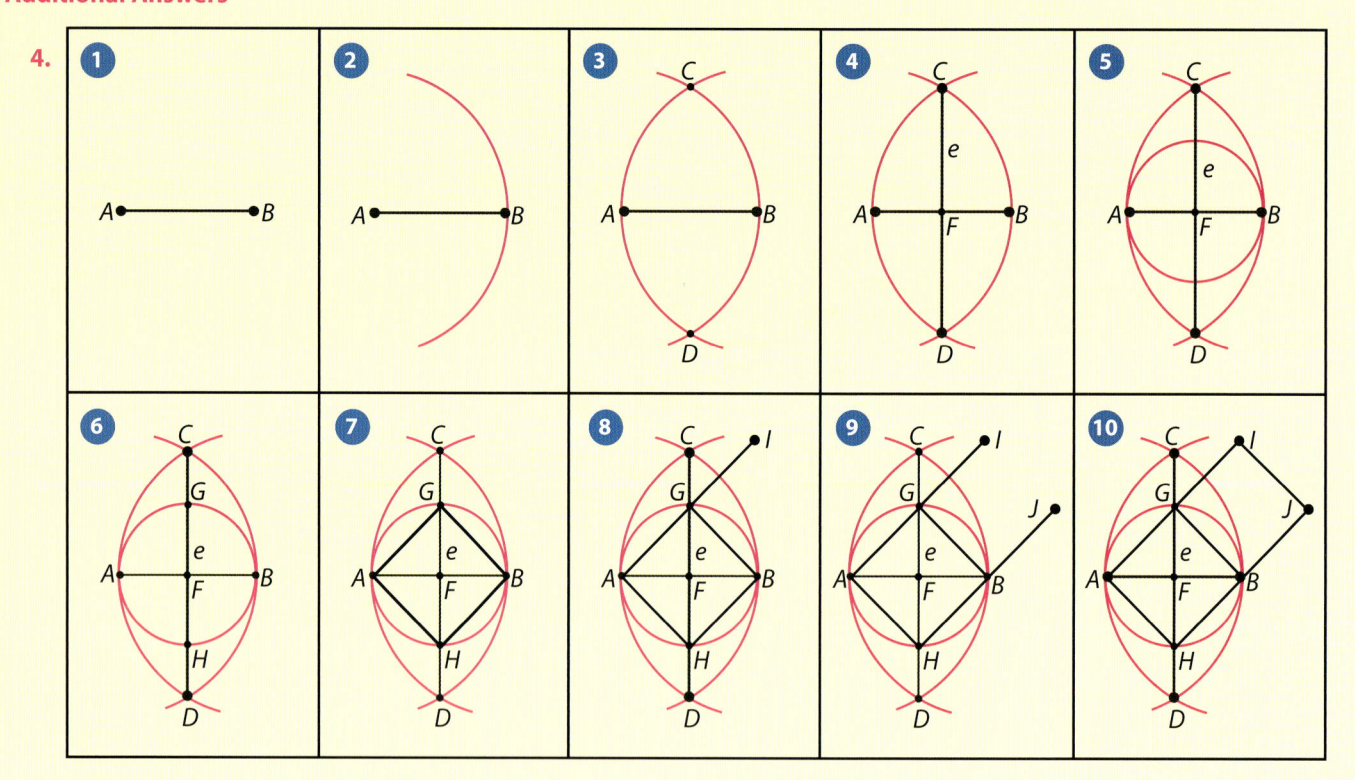

4.

**66 GEOMETRY**

# TRY IT  Practice Triangles and Quadrilaterals

OFFLINE 10 min

Students will practice using a compass and ruler to construct triangles and quadrilaterals. Gather a compass and ruler. Have students turn to the Practice Triangles and Quadrilaterals activity page in their Activity Book and read the directions with them.

Students should copy the problems from the Activity Book into their Math Notebook as necessary and solve them there.

## Objectives

- Construct rectangles or triangles with appropriate math tools

## Tips

Extend the lesson by challenging students to construct different types of quadrilaterals and triangles.

**Construct Triangles and Quadrilaterals**
Practice Triangles and Quadrilaterals

Draw the shape.
1. square
2. rectangle
3. equilateral triangle
4. right triangle

Use a compass and ruler to construct the shape.
5. right triangle   **See below.**
6. rectangle   **See next page.**

## Additional Answers

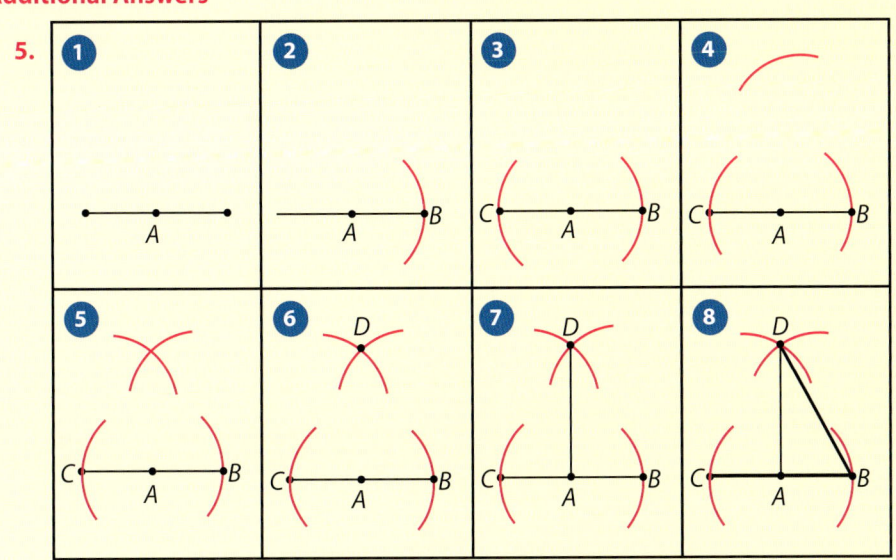

5.

| 1 | 2 | 3 | 4 |
|---|---|---|---|
| •——•——• A | •——•——•B A | C•——•——•B A | C•——•——•B A |

| 5 | 6 | 7 | 8 |
|---|---|---|---|
| C•——•——•B A | D C•——•——•B A | D C•——•——•B A | D C•——•——•B A (triangle) |

CONSTRUCT TRIANGLES AND QUADRILATERALS  **67**

6.

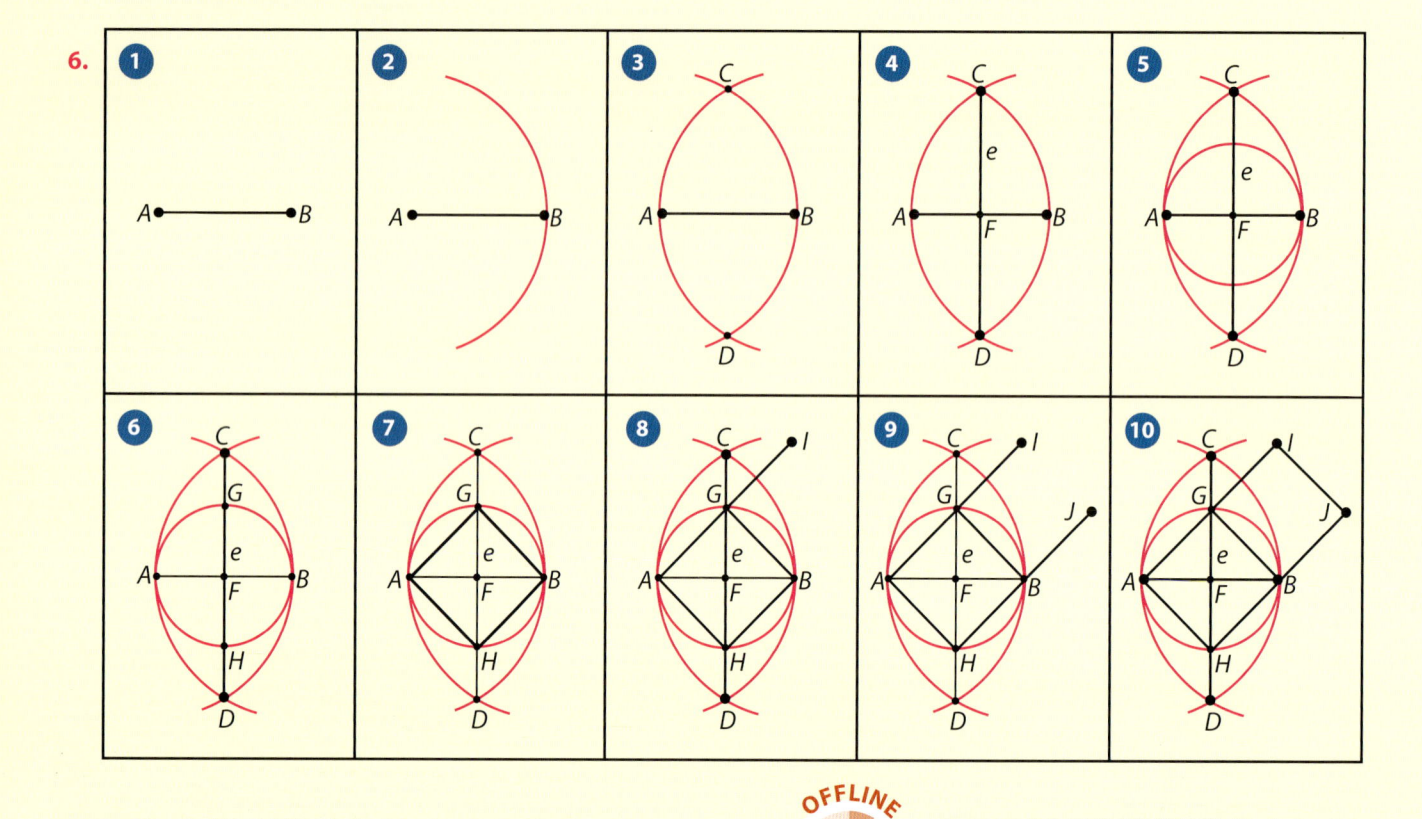

## CHECKPOINT

Give students a compass and a ruler. If necessary, read the directions, problems, and answer choices to students. Record students' responses to observational items on the Learning Coach Recording Sheet. Use the answer key to score the Checkpoint, and then enter the results online.

## Objectives

- Construct rectangles or triangles with appropriate math tools.

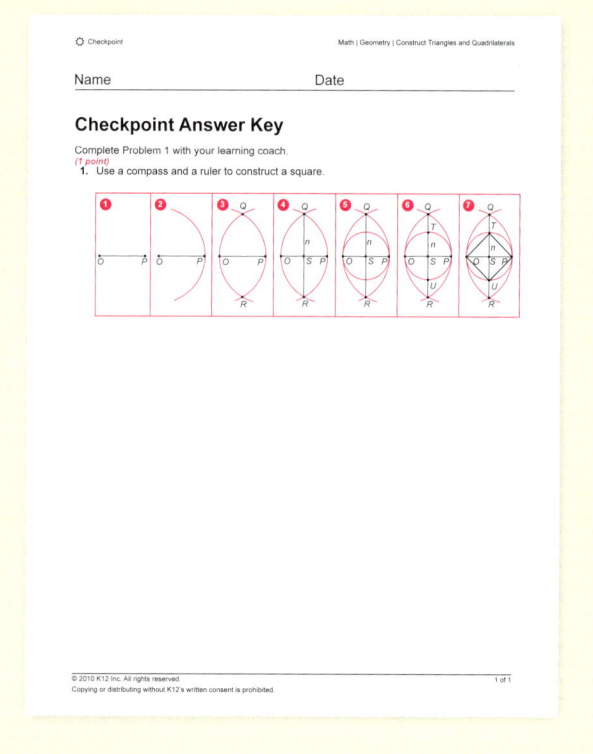

**68** GEOMETRY

# Angles and Triangles (A)

## Lesson Overview

| Skills Update | 5 minutes | ONLINE |
|---|---|---|
| **GET READY** Classify Triangles | 10 minutes | OFFLINE |
| **LEARN** Sum of Angles in Triangles | 15 minutes | ONLINE |
| **LEARN** Measure Angles in Triangles | 30 minutes | OFFLINE |

### ▶ Lesson Objectives

Identify that the sum of the interior angles of any triangle is 180° and solve related problems.

### ▶ Prerequisite Skills

- Define and sketch different types of triangles and identify their attributes.
- Identify attributes of isosceles, equilateral, and right triangles.

### ▶ Content Background

Triangles are two-dimensional shapes that have 3 sides made from line segments. Triangles can be classified by their characteristics. Equilateral triangles have 3 equal sides. Isosceles triangles have 2 equal sides. Scalene triangles have no equal sides.

One of the angles in a right triangle measures 90°. Acute triangles have 3 acute angles. Obtuse triangles have 1 obtuse angle and 2 acute angles. In equiangular triangles, all 3 angles have the same measure.

Students will learn that the sum of the angle measures of any triangle is 180°. They will also learn to find missing angle measures in triangles.

### ▶ Advance Preparation

Print the Triangles.

### ▶ Safety

Make sure students handle the scissors carefully and be sure to store them in a safe place.

---

**Materials to Gather**

**SUPPLIED**
protractor
Triangles (printout)
Measure Angles in Triangles activity page

**ALSO NEEDED**
scissors, pointed-end safety

## GET READY  Classify Triangles

**OFFLINE 10 min**

### Objectives
- Define and sketch different types of triangles and identify their attributes.
- Identify attributes of isosceles, equilateral, and right triangles.

Students will draw different types and sizes of triangles as preparation for learning that a triangle of any type has the same number of degrees. Tell them that they will sketch without measuring the triangles' sides. This activity is about recalling triangle attributes rather than exact measurements.

1. **Ask:** What type of triangle has all 3 sides the same length? *equilateral triangle*

2. Have students sketch and mark with tick marks the sides of an equilateral triangle. Then have them sketch a second equilateral triangle that is larger or smaller than the first one. Throughout this activity, the second triangle can be oriented in a different way from the first triangle.

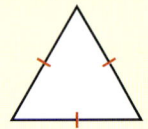

   **Ask:** What are the characteristics, or attributes of the two equilateral triangles? *The triangles have sides that are equal in length. Each side has a tick mark.*

3. **Ask:** What type of triangle has exactly 2 sides the same length? *isosceles triangle*

4. Have students sketch and mark an isosceles triangle. Then have them sketch a second isosceles triangle that is larger or smaller than the first one.

   **Ask:** What are the attributes of the two isosceles triangles? *The triangles have 2 sides that are of equal length and have a tick mark on them. The other side isn't of equal length and doesn't have a tick mark.*

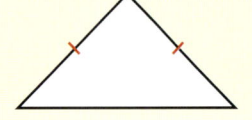

5. **Ask:** What type of triangle has no sides the same length? *scalene triangle*

6. Have students sketch a scalene triangle. Then have them sketch a second scalene triangle that is larger or smaller than the first one.

   **Ask:** What are the attributes of the scalene triangles? *The 3 sides are each of a different length. No tick marks are on the triangles because none of the sides are of equal length.*

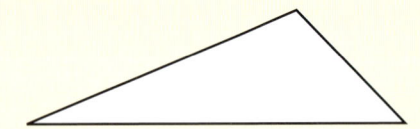

7. **Ask:** What type of triangle has one 90° angle? *right triangle*

### Tips

Scalene triangles may be a challenge for students to sketch. When you evaluate students' sketches of scalene triangles, have students describe the sketches to you. Their descriptions should indicate that no sides of a scalene triangle are the same length.

8. Have students sketch and put tick marks on a right triangle with 2 sides of the same length and mark the 90° angle to look like a small square. Then have them sketch and mark a second right triangle with 2 sides the same length that is larger or smaller than the first one.

   **Ask:** What are the attributes of the right triangles? Two of the sides are the same length and are marked with tick marks. The right angle is marked.

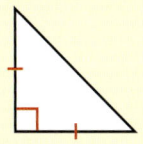

## LEARN Sum of Angles in Triangles

**ONLINE 15 min**

Students will watch a tutorial that shows them how to find the sum of a triangle's angle measures. They will see how cutting angles from a triangle and placing the angles together form a straight angle. They can then conclude that because the measure of a straight angle is 180°, the sum of angle measures of a triangle is 180°.

### Objectives
- Identify that the sum of the interior angles of any triangle is 180° and solve related problems.

## LEARN Measure Angles in Triangles

**OFFLINE 30 min**

Students will cut off angles and line them up on a straight angle to verify that angle measures of a triangle add up to 180°. To further demonstrate the idea, they will measure angles of triangles to test the idea that the angle measures of any triangle add to 180°. Using a protractor, students should find that angle measures add to 180°.

Gather scissors, a protractor, and the Triangles printout. Later in the activity, students will use the Measure Angles in Triangles activity page in their Activity Book. Read the directions with them. Students should copy the problems from the Activity Book into their Math Notebook as necessary and solve them there.

1. Give students scissors and the Triangles printout. Tell them that they will cut the three angles from each triangle and place the angles around a straight angle to show that the sum of the angle measures of a triangle is 180°.
2. Have students cut out one triangle. Guide them to carefully cut off each angle of the triangle.
3. Have students place angles together so they form a point on the straight angle at the top of the page.

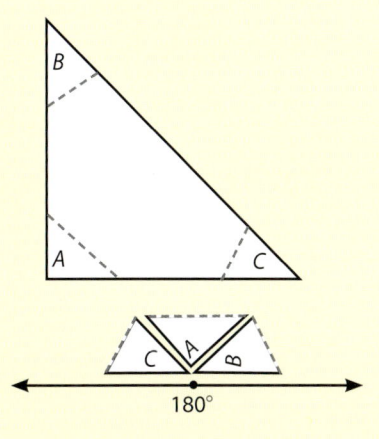

### Objectives
- Identify that the sum of the interior angles of any triangle is 180° and solve related problems.

### Tips
If students' measurements of the 3 angles in the triangle do not add up to 180°, review how to use a protractor to measure angles.

ANGLES AND TRIANGLES (A)

4. **Ask:** Do the three angle measures add to 180°? How do you know this is true? A straight angle measures 180°. When the three angles are cut from a triangle and placed together, the angles form a straight angle.

5. Repeat Steps 2–4 with the remaining four triangles from the printout. Have students describe the attributes of each triangle before using the angles to verify that the sum of the measures is 180°.

6. Have students number 1–5 in their Math Notebook. Tell students to use the protractor to measure the angles on the five triangles on the Measure Angles in Triangles activity page.

   Record the following for each triangle:
   - the three angle measures
   - the sum of the angle measures
   - the classification of each triangle: acute, right, obtuse, or equiangular.

   Tell them an acute triangle has 3 acute angles. A right triangle has 1 angle that measures exactly 90°. An obtuse triangle has 1 obtuse angle. An equiangular triangle has 3 angles of equal measure.

   In their Math Notebook, have students verify that the sum of the angle measures for each triangle on the activity page is 180°.

7. Point to the straight angle at the bottom of the page. Have students measure the straight angle and confirm that it measures 180°.

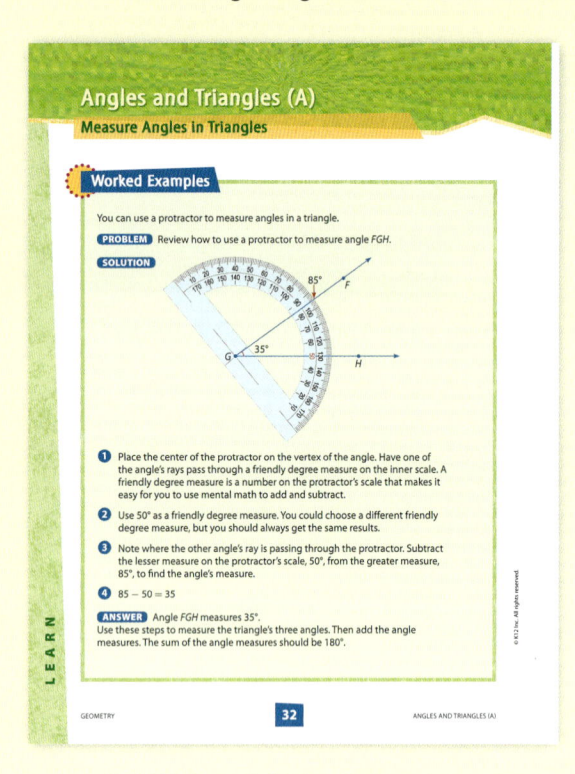

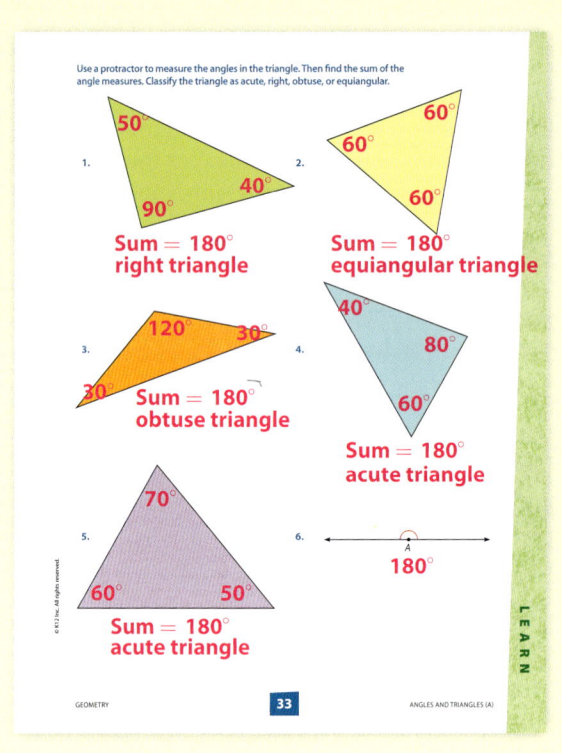

**GEOMETRY**

# Angles and Triangles (B)

## Lesson Overview

| | | |
|---|---|---|
| **GET READY** Types of Triangles | 10 minutes | **ONLINE** |
| **LEARN** Triangles and 180° | 15 minutes | **ONLINE** |
| **LEARN** Missing Angle Measures | 15 minutes | **ONLINE** |
| **TRY IT** Find Missing Angle Measures | 15 minutes | **OFFLINE** |
| **CHECKPOINT** | 5 minutes | **ONLINE** |

### ▶ Lesson Objectives
Identify that the sum of the interior angles of any triangle is 180° and solve related problems.

### ▶ Prerequisite Skills
- Define and sketch different types of triangles and identify their attributes.
- Identify attributes of isosceles, equilateral, and right triangles.

### ▶ Content Background
Triangles are two-dimensional shapes that have 3 sides made from line segments. Triangles can be classified by their characteristics. Equilateral triangles have 3 equal sides. Isosceles triangles have 2 equal sides. Scalene triangles have no equal sides.

One of the angles in a right triangle measures 90°. Acute triangles have 3 acute angles. Obtuse triangles have 1 obtuse angle and 2 acute angles. In equiangular triangles, all 3 angles have the same measure.

Students will continue to learn that the sum of the angle measures of any triangle is 180°. They will also learn to find missing angle measures in triangles.

### Materials to Gather

**SUPPLIED**
protractor
Find Missing Angle Measures activity page

**ALSO NEEDED**
ruler

---

## GET READY  Types of Triangles
**ONLINE 10 min**

### Objectives
- Define and sketch different types of triangles and identify their attributes.
- Identify attributes of isosceles, equilateral, and right triangles.

Students will create triangles using the Geoboard Learning Tool and describe each shape's attributes, or characteristics. See Triangles at the end of this activity for guidance about each triangle that students will create on the Geoboard.

**DIRECTIONS FOR USING THE GEOBOARD LEARNING TOOL**

1. Click Lesson Mode. If necessary, click Menu and Help to review the instructions for the learning tool.
2. Students will model different triangles on the Geoboard. Have students clear the Geoboard after they check their models.

   Note: Students can clear the Geoboard by clicking the scissors button.

3. **Say:** Make a triangle that has a right angle in the top left corner.

   **Ask:** What is the name of this type of triangle? right triangle

   **Ask:** What types of angles are the other angles in the triangle? acute angles

   Have students click the angle button to see the triangle's angle measures. Have them check that one angle is a right angle (measures 90°) and the other two angles are acute (each measures less than 90°).

4. **Say:** Click the isometric button at the bottom left of the Geoboard. Make a triangle with all sides the same length.

   **Ask:** What is the name of this type of triangle? equilateral triangle

   **Ask:** What do the three angles have in common? They are all acute angles that measure 60°.

   Have students click the angle button to see the triangle's angle measures. Have them check that each angle is an acute angle that measures 60°.

5. **Say:** Make a triangle that has an obtuse angle.

   **Ask:** What is the name of this type of triangle? obtuse triangle

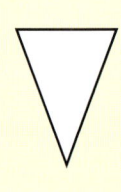

   **Ask:** What do you notice about the lengths of the sides of the triangle? Two sides are the same length, or no sides are the same length.

   Have students click the angle button to see the triangle's angle measures. Have them check that one angle is an obtuse angle (measures greater than 90° and less than 180°) and the other two angles are acute (each measures less than 90°).

6. **Say:** Make a triangle that has two sides the same length.

   **Ask:** What is the name of this type of triangle? isosceles triangle

   **Ask:** What do you know about the angles in an isosceles triangle? Two angles have the same measure and are at either end of the triangle side that doesn't have the same length as the other 2 sides.

   Have students click the angle button to see the triangle's angle measures. Have them check that two angles have the same measure.

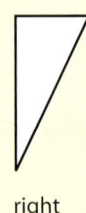

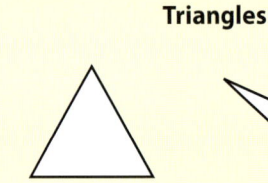

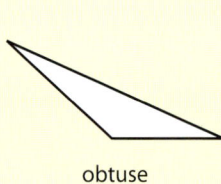

**Triangles**

right triangle | equilateral triangle | obtuse triangle | isosceles triangle

### Tips

Point out to students that the vertices of the triangles they draw should be on the dots of the Geoboard, but the sides of the triangles will not always cross over the dots.

Explain that on the Geoboard, the distance between two dots going up and down (vertically), or going sideways (horizontally), is one unit. This unit is not called an inch or a centimeter, because the distance may be different on different computers.

GEOMETRY

## LEARN  Triangles and 180°

ONLINE 15 min

Students will review how to find the sum of the angle measures of a triangle by seeing the relationship between the angle measures of a triangle and a straight angle. Then they will find the sum of the angle measures of right, isosceles, and equilateral triangles and reinforce the concept that the sum of the angle measures of any triangle is 180°. Students will also change the angle measures of a triangle to make acute, right, obtuse, and equiangular triangles.

### Objectives
- Identify that the sum of the interior angles of any triangle is 180° and solve related problems.

## LEARN  Missing Angle Measures

ONLINE 15 min

Students will find missing angle measures in triangles. They can use different strategies to solve the problems. Students may want to write an equation to find the missing angle measure, or they may choose to use mental math.

**Tips**  Some of the problems do not show a picture of a triangle. Students may find it helpful to sketch the triangle described in the problem and label the angles to help them find the missing angle measure in those problems.

### Objectives
- Identify that the sum of the interior angles of any triangle is 180° and solve related problems.

## TRY IT  Find Missing Angle Measures

OFFLINE 15 min

Students will practice finding the missing angle measures in different types of triangles. They will apply that skill to everyday situations. Gather a protractor. Have students turn to the Find Missing Angle Measures activity page in their Activity Book and read the directions with them.

Students should copy the problems from the Activity Book into their Math Notebook as necessary and solve them there.

### Objectives
- Identify that the sum of the interior angles of any triangle is 180° and solve related problems.

**Tips**

Suggest to students that they check their work by adding all three angle measures in each triangle. The sum should be 180°.

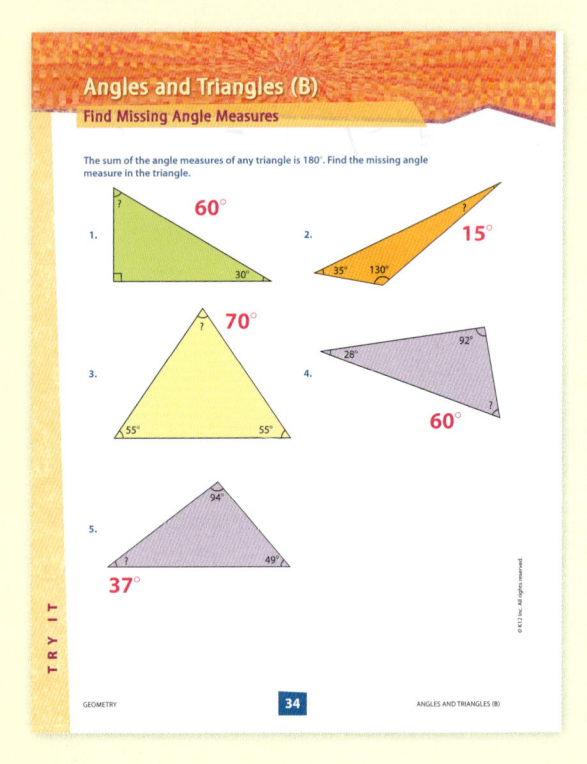

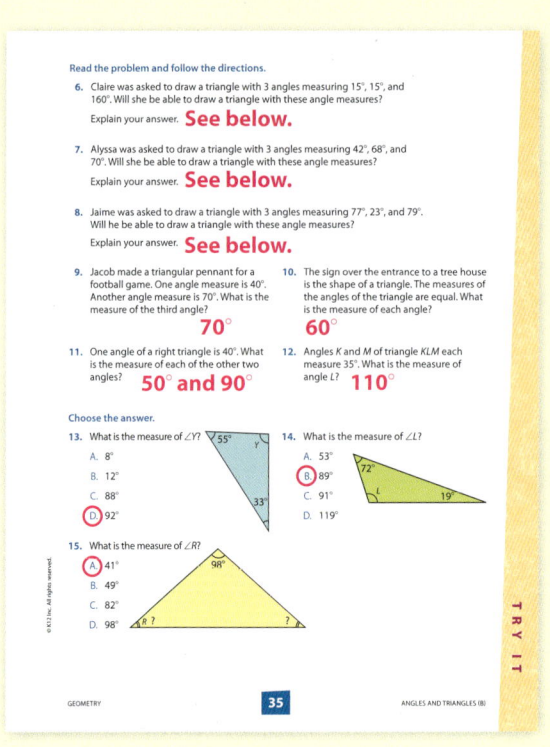

## Additional Answers

**6.** No. The sum of the measures of the angles of a triangle is always 180° and the sum of the measures of these angles is 190°.

**7.** Yes. The sum of the measures of the angles of a triangle is always 180° and the sum of the measures of these angles is 180°.

**8.** No. The sum of the measures of the angles of a triangle is always 180° and the sum of the measures of these angles is 179°.

## CHECKPOINT

ONLINE 5 min

Students will complete an online Checkpoint. If necessary, read the directions, problems, and answer choices to students and help them with keyboard or mouse operations.

### Objectives

- Identify that the sum of the interior angles of any triangle is 180° and solve related problems.

76 GEOMETRY

# Angles in a Quadrilateral (A)

## Lesson Overview

| | | |
|---|---|---|
| **GET READY** Sketch Quadrilaterals | 10 minutes | ONLINE |
| **LEARN** Total Angles to 360° | 15 minutes | ONLINE |
| **LEARN** 360° in a Quadrilateral | 15 minutes | OFFLINE |
| **LEARN** Measure Angles | 20 minutes | OFFLINE |

### ▶ Lesson Objectives
Identify that the sum of the interior angles of any quadrilateral is 360° and solve related problems.

### ▶ Prerequisite Skills
- Know how to define and sketch different quadrilaterals.
- Identify attributes of parallelograms, rectangles, and squares.

### ▶ Content Background
Quadrilaterals are two-dimensional shapes that have four sides made from line segments. Students will work with different types of quadrilaterals: trapezoids, parallelograms, rectangles, rhombuses, and squares.

### ▶ Common Errors and Misconceptions
Students might focus on the length of the line segments that form an angle's sides, the tilt of the top line segment, the area enclosed by the sides, or the proximity of the two sides rather than look at the actual size of the angle. For example, students might indicate that in the two triangles shown here, angle A is smaller than angle X.

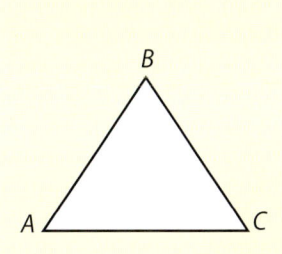

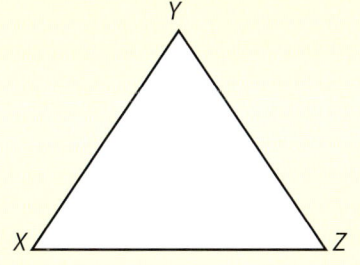

### Materials to Gather

**SUPPLIED**
Measure Angles activity page
360° in a Quadrilateral (printout)
protractor

**ALSO NEEDED**
ruler
scissors, pointed-end safety

### ▶ Advance Preparation
Print 360° in a Quadrilateral.

### ▶ Safety
Make sure students handle the scissors carefully and be sure to store them in a safe place.

# GET READY  Sketch Quadrilaterals

Students will model different quadrilaterals using the Geoboard Learning Tool and describe each shape's attributes.

**DIRECTIONS FOR USING THE GEOBOARD LEARNING TOOL**

Note: Students can check their models by clicking Show Info. After they check their models, they can clear the Geoboard by clicking the scissors button and not selecting any scissors options.

1. Click Lesson Mode. If necessary, click Menu and Help to review the instructions for the learning tool.

2. **Say:** Make a quadrilateral with one pair of opposite sides parallel and the other pair of opposite sides not parallel. (Refer to the Quadrilaterals chart.)

   **Ask:** What is the name of this type of quadrilateral? trapezoid

   Have students draw another trapezoid and orient it differently from their first one.

   Have students check their model by clicking Show Info and then clear the Geoboard.

3. **Say:** Make a quadrilateral that has each pair of opposite sides parallel and opposite sides equal in length. (Refer to the Quadrilaterals chart.)

   **Ask:** What is the name of this type of quadrilateral? parallelogram

   Have students click the yellow ruler button to check that opposite sides are equal in length. Then have them draw another parallelogram and orient it differently from their first one.

   Have students check their model and then clear the Geoboard.

4. **Say:** Make a quadrilateral with each of its four angles measuring 90° and opposite sides that are equal in length. (Refer to the Quadrilaterals chart.)

   **Ask:** What is the name of this type of quadrilateral? rectangle

   Have students click the yellow ruler button to check that opposite sides are equal in length and click the angle button to check that each angle measures 90°. Then have them draw another rectangle and orient it differently from their first one.

   Have students check their model and then clear the Geoboard.

5. **Say:** Make a quadrilateral with all four sides equal in length. (Refer to the Quadrilaterals chart.)

   **Ask:** What is the name of this type of quadrilateral? rhombus

   Note: Students can make a square with the grid Geoboard (chosen with the grid-isometric toggle button), but to make any rhombus other than a square, they must use the isometric Geoboard.

   Have students click the yellow ruler button to check that all four sides are equal in length. Then have them draw another rhombus and orient it differently from their first one.

   Have students check their model and then clear the Geoboard.

## Objectives

- Know how to define and sketch different quadrilaterals.
- Identify attributes of parallelograms, rectangles, and squares.

## Tips

Extend the activity by asking students to use paper and pencil to draw different examples of each type of quadrilateral. This will help them understand that quadrilaterals of the same kind can be different sizes and shapes.

6. **Say:** Make a quadrilateral that has all four sides equal in length and has four 90° angles. (Refer to the Quadrilaterals chart.)

   **Ask:** What is the name of this type of quadrilateral? square

   Have students click the yellow ruler button to check that opposite sides are equal in length and click the angle button to check that each angle measures 90°. Then have them draw another square and orient it differently from their first one.

### Tips

If students need more practice, have them draw quadrilaterals and then measure and total the angles.

## Quadrilaterals

| Name | Description | Example |
|---|---|---|
| trapezoid | Two sides are parallel and two sides are not. | |
| parallelogram | Opposite sides are parallel and equal in length. | |
| rectangle | All interior angles are 90° and opposite sides are equal in length. | |
| rhombus | All four sides are equal in length. | |
| square | All four sides are equal in length and all interior angles are 90°. | |

## LEARN  Total Angles to 360°

ONLINE 15 min

Students will learn that the measures of the interior angles of a quadrilateral total 360°. Then they will learn that a quadrilateral can be split into two triangles.

Students know that the sum of the measures of the angles of a triangle equals 180°. They will see that 6 torn angles from the two triangles formed by the split quadrilateral spiral around a straight angle. They will see that the sum of the angle measures equals 360°. They will also see that the sum of the angle measures of two triangles is 180 + 180 = 360. That means that the sum of the angle measures of a quadrilateral is 360°. Finally, students will apply these concepts by using Free Play on the Pattern Blocks Learning Tool.

Students will use the Pattern Blocks Learning Tool to apply the concept that in a quadrilateral, the sum of the interior angles is 360°.

**DIRECTIONS FOR USING THE PATTERN BLOCKS LEARNING TOOL**

1. Start the Pattern Blocks Learning Tool.
2. Click the Free Play option. Click Start.

### Objectives

- Identify that the sum of the interior angles of any quadrilateral is 360° and solve related problems.

### Tips

If students have trouble understanding that a quadrilateral can be split into two triangles, have them cut out different quadrilaterals, draw a line on each one to divide it into two triangles, and then cut along the line to divide each quadrilateral into two triangles.

ANGLES IN A QUADRILATERAL (A)   79

3. Have students put two squares next to each other.
4. Guide students to put two more squares below the first two squares so that their sides are touching.
5. Tell students that all four squares meet at a point.
6. Explain to students that the center point includes all four of a square's interior angles—the upper-right, lower-right, upper-left, and lower-left angles.
7. Tell students that the place where the four squares meet to form a large square has an angle measure of 360°.
8. Tell students that together, these four angles make a square. The sum of the angle measures of the four angles equals 360°.
9. Repeat Steps 3–8 for both types of rhombuses included in the tool. Students will need to use rotate tools while placing shapes.

## LEARN 360° in a Quadrilateral

**OFFLINE 15 min**

### Objectives

- Identify that the sum of the interior angles of any quadrilateral is 360° and solve related problems

Students will cut off the angles of quadrilaterals to demonstrate that the four angles can spiral around a straight angle to verify that the measures of the angles add up to 360°.

Gather scissors, a protractor, ruler, and the 360° in a Quadrilateral printout.

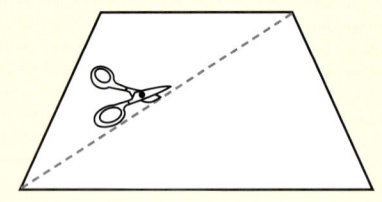

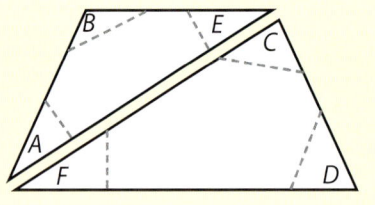

1. Point to the straight angle at top of the page. Have students use the protractor to measure the straight angle and confirm that it measures 180°.
2. Remind students that both sides of a straight angle measure 360°. Have them measure both sides of the straight angle to verify this fact.
3. Tell students that they will first use the ruler to draw a line to divide a trapezoid into two triangles. They will then cut the six angles from the two triangles formed from the trapezoid and place the angles around a straight angle to show that the sum of the angle measures of a quadrilateral is 360°.
4. Give students scissors, the ruler, and the 360° in a Quadrilateral printout. Have them use the ruler to draw the line to divide the trapezoid into two triangles. Cut the two triangles from the trapezoid. Guide them to carefully cut off each angle of each triangle.
5. Have students place the six angles together so they form a spiral around the straight angle at the top of the page.

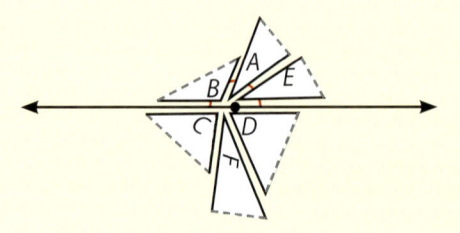

6. **Ask:** Do the six angle measures add up to 360°? How do you know this is true? *A straight angle measures 180°. The measure of the angles of both sides of a straight angle is 360°. When the six angles are cut from the two triangles and placed together, the angles form a spiral around the straight angle. The sum of the angle measures is 360°.*

7. Repeat Steps 3–6 with a parallelogram and a rectangle from the printout. Have students name each quadrilateral before dividing each shape into two triangles and using the angles to verify that the sum of the measures is 360°.

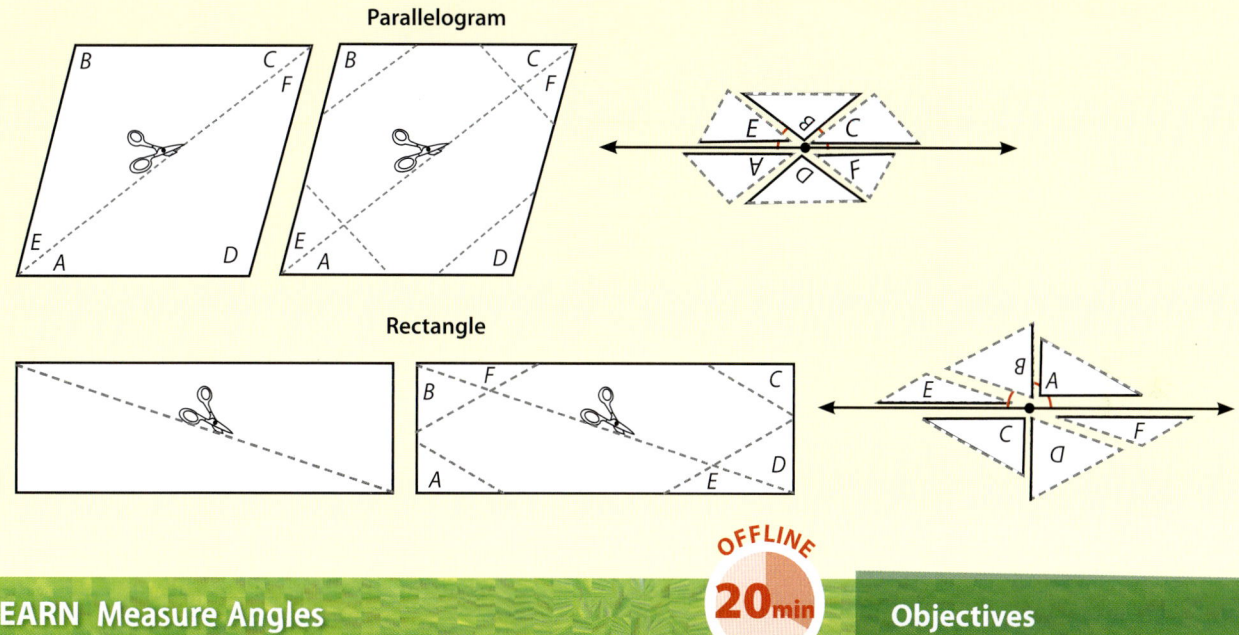

**Parallelogram**

**Rectangle**

## LEARN Measure Angles

OFFLINE
20 min

### Objectives

- Identify that the sum of the interior angles of any quadrilateral is 360° and solve related problems

Students will measure angles of quadrilaterals to test the idea that angle measures of any quadrilateral add to 360°. Using a protractor, they should find that angle measures do add up to 360°. Students will compare the sum of a quadrilateral's angle measures to the measure of both sides of a straight angle.

Gather a protractor. Have students turn to the Measure Angles activity page in their Activity Book and read the directions with them.

1. Point to the straight angle at bottom of the page. Have students measure the straight angle and confirm that it measures 180°.

2. Remind students that both sides of a straight angle measure 360°. Have them measure both sides of the straight angle to verify this fact.

3. Tell students that they will measure the four angles in quadrilaterals to find the sum of the angle measures. They will then compare the sum of the angle measures to the measure of both sides of a straight angle.

4. Have students number 1–5 in their Math Notebook. Tell students to use the protractor to measure the angles on the five quadrilaterals on the activity page. Record the following for each quadrilateral:
   - the four angle measures
   - the sum of the angle measures
   - the classification of each quadrilateral (trapezoid, parallelogram, rectangle, rhombus, or square)

**ANGLES IN A QUADRILATERAL (A)** 81

5. In their Math Notebook, have students verify that the sum of the angle measures for each quadrilateral is 360°.

6. **Ask:** What is the relationship between the sum of the angle measures of a quadrilateral and the measure of two sides of a straight angle? The sum of the angle measures of a quadrilateral are 360°. This is equal to the measure of both sides of a straight angle.

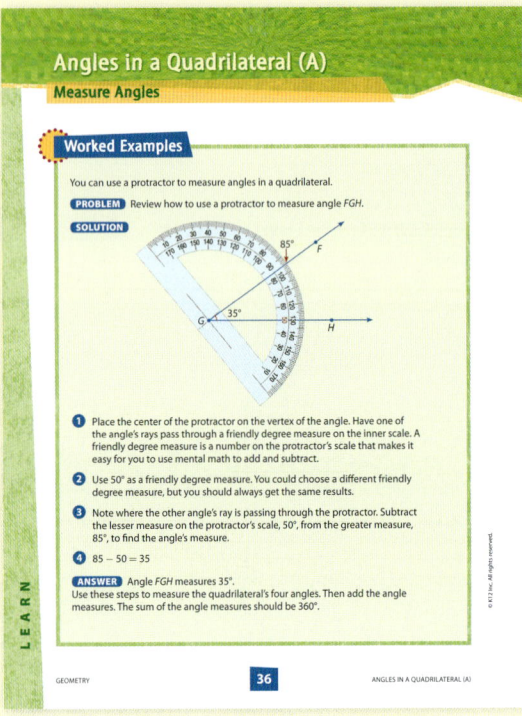

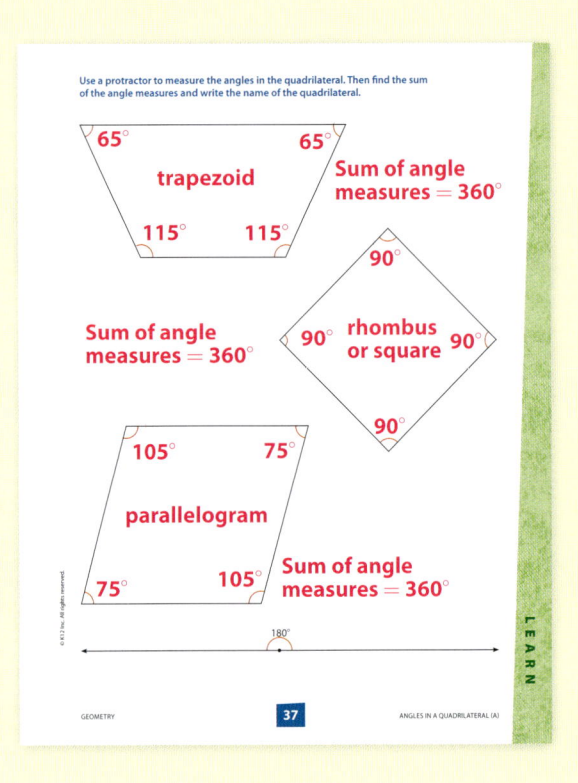

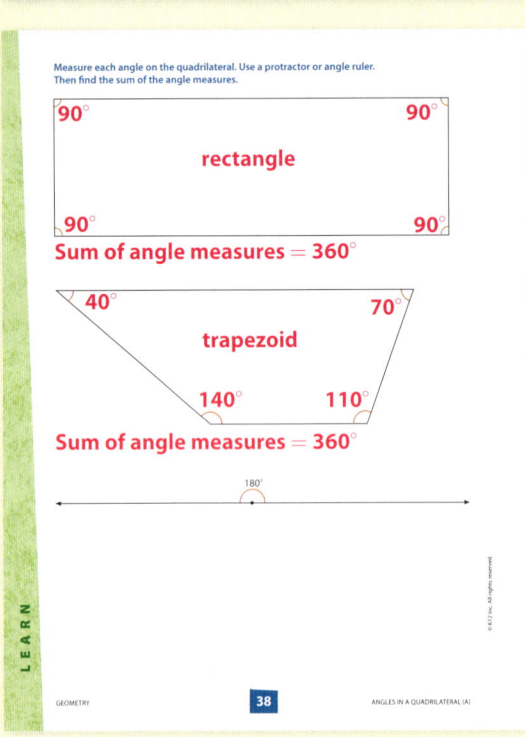

**82** GEOMETRY

# Angles in a Quadrilateral (B)

## Lesson Overview

| | | |
|---|---|---|
| **GET READY** Classify Quadrilaterals | 10 minutes | ONLINE |
| **LEARN** Quadrilateral Angles Total 360° | 15 minutes | ONLINE |
| **LEARN** Solve Problems with Angles | 20 minutes | ONLINE |
| **TRY IT** Practice Quadrilateral Angles | 10 minutes | OFFLINE |
| **CHECKPOINT** | 5 minutes | ONLINE |

### ▶ Lesson Objectives
Identify that the sum of the interior angles of any quadrilateral is 360° and solve related problems.

### ▶ Prerequisite Skills
- Know how to define and sketch different quadrilaterals.
- Identify attributes of parallelograms, rectangles, and squares.

### ▶ Content Background
Quadrilaterals are two-dimensional shapes that have four sides made from line segments. Students will continue to work with different types of quadrilaterals: trapezoids, parallelograms, rectangles, rhombuses, and squares.

There are different types of quadrilaterals, based on the measure of the angles that are formed by the sides of the shape, the relationships between the lengths of the sides of the shape, and the number of pairs of parallel sides of the shape. Students will learn to find missing angle measures of quadrilaterals.

### ▶ Common Errors and Misconceptions
Students might focus on the length of the line segments that form an angle's sides, the tilt of the top line segment, the area enclosed by the sides, or the proximity of the two sides rather than look at the actual size of the angle. For example, students might indicate that in the two triangles shown here, angle A is smaller than angle X.

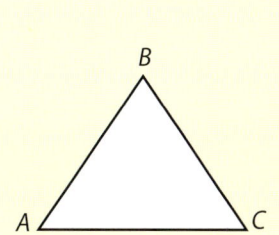

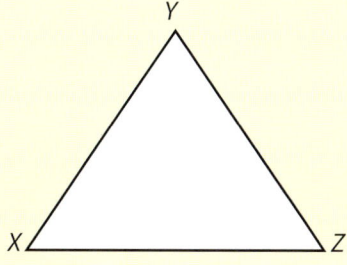

### ▶ Advance Preparation
Print the Features of Quadrilaterals.

### Materials to Gather

**SUPPLIED**

Practice Quadrilateral Angles activity page

Features of Quadrilaterals (printout)

**ANGLES IN A QUADRILATERAL (B)** 83

## GET READY  Classify Quadrilaterals

**ONLINE 10 min**

Students will determine which shapes can be classified as a specific type of quadrilateral. They will also match the names of quadrilaterals to shapes. Gather the Features of Quadrilaterals printout for students to use with the online activity.

### Objectives
- Know how to define and sketch quadrilaterals
- Identify attributes of parallelograms, rectangles, and squares.

## LEARN  Quadrilateral Angles Total 360°

**ONLINE 15 min**

Students will review that a quadrilateral can be split into two triangles and that the sum of the angle measures of the two triangles is 360°. Students will then investigate this concept by measuring and typing angle measures into a number sentence to show that the sum of the angle measures of a quadrilateral equals 360°.

### Objectives
- Identify that the sum of the interior angles of any quadrilateral is 360° and solve related problems

## LEARN  Solve Problems with Angles

**ONLINE 20 min**

Students will solve problems to find the interior angles of quadrilaterals. They will also find missing angle measures in quadrilaterals.

**Tips**  Students may find it helpful to sketch the quadrilateral described in the problem and label the angles to help them find the missing angle measure for problems that do not show a picture of the quadrilateral.

### Objectives
- Identify that the sum of the interior angles of any quadrilateral is 360° and solve related problems

## TRY IT  Practice Quadrilateral Angles

**OFFLINE 10 min**

Students will practice solving problems related to angle measures in quadrilaterals. Have students turn to the Practice Quadrilateral Angles activity page in their Activity Book and read the directions with them. Remind students that sometimes a 90° angle is indicated with a right angle corner, like the one shown here.

### Objectives
- Identify that the sum of the interior angles of any quadrilateral is 360° and solve related problems.

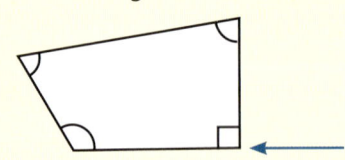

Students should copy the problems from the Activity Book into their Math Notebook as necessary and solve them there.

84  GEOMETRY

## Angles in a Quadrilateral (B)
### Practice Quadrilateral Angles

**Solve.**

1. A quadrilateral has angles that measure 77°, 108°, and 65°. What is the measure of the fourth angle? **110°**

2. A quadrilateral has angles that measure 91°, 96°, and 88°. What is the measure of the fourth angle? **85°**

3. A quadrilateral has angles that measure 87°, 69°, and 104°. What is the measure of the fourth angle? **100°**

4. What is the measure of angle K? **58°**

5. What is the measure of ∠B? **132°**

6. What is the measure of ∠S? **106°**

7. What is the measure of ∠E? **130°**

**Choose the answer.**

8. What is the measure of ∠C?
   A. 83°   B. 93°
   **C. 103°**   D. 123°

9. What is the measure of ∠C?
   A. 68°   B. 78°
   C. 88°   **D. 98°**

10. What is the measure of ∠F?
    A. 97°   B. 101°
    C. 111°   **D. 121°**

---

## CHECKPOINT

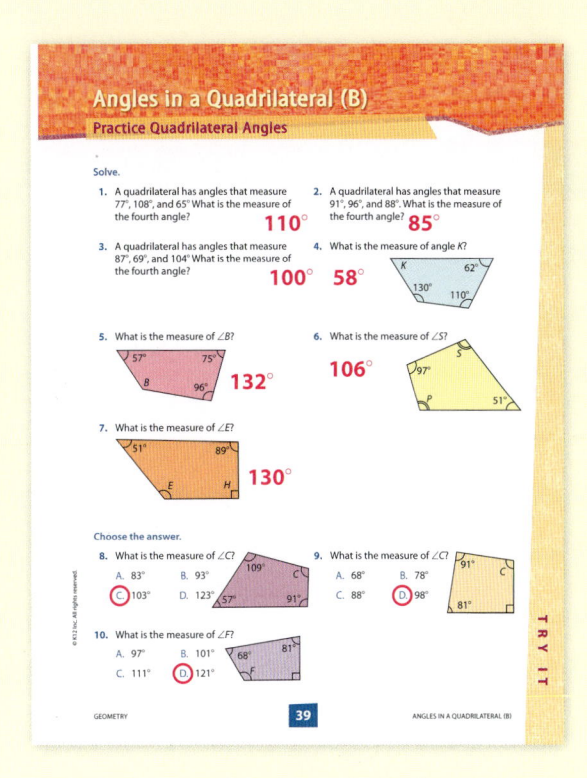

**ONLINE 5 min**

Students will complete an online Checkpoint. If necessary, read the directions, problems, and answer choices to students and help them with keyboard or mouse operations.

### Objectives

- Identify that the sum of the interior angles of any quadrilateral is 360° and solve related problems.

ANGLES IN A QUADRILATERAL (B) 85

# Transformations (A)

## Lesson Overview

| | | |
|---|---|---|
| **GET READY** Triangles and Quadrilaterals | 15 minutes | **OFFLINE** |
| **GET READY** Congruence | 15 minutes | **ONLINE** |
| **LEARN** Transform 2-D Shapes | 20 minutes | **ONLINE** |
| **LEARN** Perform Transformations | 10 minutes | **ONLINE** |

### ▶ Lesson Objectives
Predict, describe, and perform transformations on two-dimensional shapes.

### ▶ Prerequisite Skills
- Know how to define and sketch different quadrilaterals.
- Define and sketch different types of triangles and identify their attributes.
- Identify and explain why given figures are congruent.

### ▶ Content Background
A transformation is a movement of a shape. Three types of transformations are translations, rotations, and reflections.

- A *translation* (slide) is a slide along a straight line. The black outlined arrow is the original arrow and the red outlined arrow is its final image after the translation.
  
  **Example:**

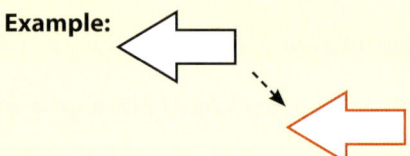

- A *rotation* (turn) is a turn around a fixed point. The black outlined arrow is the original arrow. The red outlined arrow is its final image after the rotation of the arrow 90° counterclockwise.
  
  **Example:**

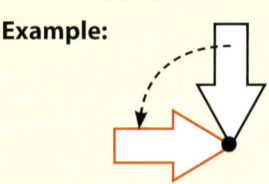

- A *reflection* (flip) is a flip over a line. The black outlined arrow is the original arrow and the red outlined arrow is its final image after the reflection over the vertical line. A reflection is like a mirror final image in which the reflection line is the mirror.
  
  **Example:**

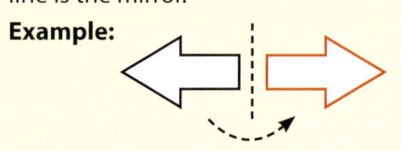

### Materials to Gather
There are no supplied materials to gather for this lesson.

**ALSO NEEDED**
ruler

**GEOMETRY**

## GET READY  Triangles and Quadrilaterals

**OFFLINE 15 min**

### Objectives
- Know how to define and sketch different quadrilaterals.
- Define and sketch different types of triangles and identify their attributes.

### Tips
Students' sketches do not need to be exact, but they should reflect students' understanding of the attributes of the shapes.

Students will use a pencil and ruler to sketch different types of quadrilaterals and triangles. As students work, ask questions to review the attributes of each shape. Encourage students to describe the shapes by numbers of pairs of parallel sides and angle measures.

1. Have students sketch a parallelogram.

   **Ask:** How many pairs of opposite sides of a parallelogram are parallel? two

   **Ask:** Do all the sides of a parallelogram need to be the same length for the shape to be a parallelogram? no

2. Have students sketch a different parallelogram, oriented differently from the first one.

   **Ask:** How are the two parallelograms alike? Both have 4 sides; both have two pairs of opposite sides that are parallel.

3. Have students sketch a trapezoid.

   **Ask:** How many pairs of opposite sides of a trapezoid are parallel? one

4. Have students sketch a different trapezoid, oriented differently from the first one.

   **Ask:** How are a parallelogram and a trapezoid alike? How are they different? A parallelogram and a trapezoid each have 4 sides, but a parallelogram has two pairs of opposite sides that are parallel, while a trapezoid has only one pair of opposite sides parallel.

5. Have students sketch a rectangle.

   **Ask:** How are a rectangle and a parallelogram alike? How are they different? A rectangle and a parallelogram are the same because they each have 4 sides and they each have two pairs of opposite sides that are parallel. They are different because in a rectangle, the sides meet at right angles.

6. Have students sketch an isosceles triangle, an obtuse triangle, and a right triangle.

   **Ask:** How many sides of an isosceles triangle have the same length? two

   **Ask:** How many angles of a right triangle are right angles? one

   **Ask:** How is an obtuse triangle different from a right triangle? An obtuse triangle has one angle that measures greater than 90°. A right triangle has one angle that measures exactly 90°.

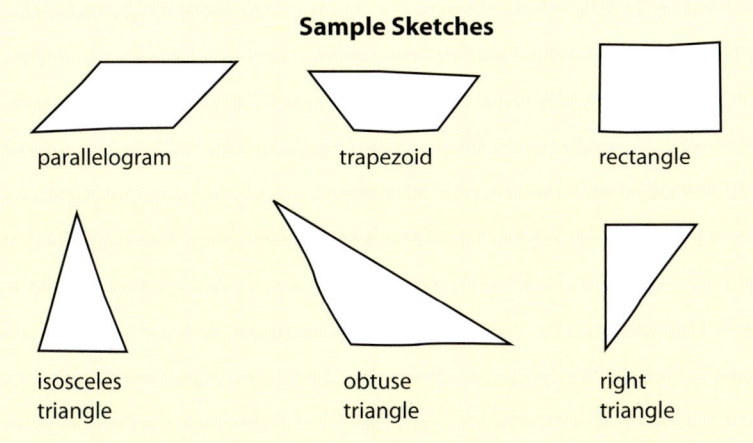

### Sample Sketches

parallelogram

trapezoid

rectangle

isosceles triangle

obtuse triangle

right triangle

TRANSFORMATIONS (A)

## GET READY  Congruence

**ONLINE 15 min**

### Objectives
- Identify and explain why given figures are congruent.

Students will identify figures that are congruent to given figures. They also will identify figures that are similar to given figures. Point out that a given figure might not be in the same orientation or position as a figure that is congruent to it or a figure that is similar to it. Two congruent figures are the same size and shape. Two similar figures are the same shape but different sizes.

## LEARN  Transform 2-D Shapes

**ONLINE 20 min**

### Objectives
- Predict, describe, and perform transformations on two-dimensional shapes.

Students will learn how translations, reflections, and rotations change the positions of shapes. They will watch animations of each type of transformation. Then students will identify the type of transformation that describes a pair of shapes.

## LEARN  Perform Transformations

**ONLINE 10 min**

### Objectives
- Predict, describe, and perform transformations on two-dimensional shapes.

Students will use the Geoboard Learning Tool to perform transformations on shapes.

### Tips
If students have trouble performing each transformation, have them draw geometric figures on paper, cut them out, and perform each transformation. This activity will help them see how the second figure would be transformed.

**DIRECTIONS FOR USING THE GEOBOARD LEARNING TOOL**

1. Click Lesson Mode. If necessary, click Menu and Help to review the instructions for the learning tool.
2. Have students start at the top of the work area and clear the Geoboard after creating each transformation and answering questions.
3. Have students click the yellow ruler button to show the lengths of the sides of the shapes they are creating.
4. Have students create a right triangle that has a vertical side that is 4 units long and a horizontal side that is 3 units long.
5. Have students select a new rubber band and create a final image of the right triangle, using the same side lengths as in the original triangle. They should translate, or slide, their final image of the triangle diagonally down. The original triangle and the final triangle will both be on the Geoboard. The final triangle will be the same size and shape as the original image but will be lower and to the right or left of the original triangle.
6. **Ask:** Are the two right triangles congruent? *yes*
7. Have students create a trapezoid that has a base 6 units long and a side parallel to the base that is 4 units long.
8. Tell students to select a new rubber band and create a final image of the trapezoid by reflecting, or flipping, the original trapezoid over a horizontal line. Have students create the horizontal line with a rubber band before they reflect the shape to make the final image.
9. **Ask:** How has the final trapezoid image changed from the position of the original trapezoid image? *Answers will vary.* **Example:** *The base of the original image that is 6 units long was at the top of the work area. When I reflected it over a horizontal line to create the final image, the base that is 6 units long is now at the bottom of the work area.*

10. Have students create an isosceles triangle that has a base that is 2 units long and two sides that are each 3.2 units long.

11. Tell students to rotate, or turn, the original triangle 90°. The turn should be made around a vertex on the triangle. Students will use a new rubber band for the final triangle.

12. **Ask:** How has the final triangle changed from the position of the original triangle? Answers will vary. **Example:** One vertex of the triangle was at the top of the work area. After rotating the triangle 90°, that vertex is now on the right side of the work area. That shows a 90° turn.

13. Repeat Steps 3–12 to translate, reflect, and rotate three different shapes.

# Transformations (B)

## Lesson Overview

| | | |
|---|---|---|
| **LEARN** Dilations and Tessellations | 15 minutes | **ONLINE** |
| **LEARN** Observe and Create Tessellations | 20 minutes | **OFFLINE** |
| **TRY IT** Tessellations Practice | 15 minutes | **OFFLINE** |
| **CHECKPOINT** | 10 minutes | **ONLINE** |

### ▶ Lesson Objectives
Predict, describe, and perform transformations on two-dimensional shapes.

### ▶ Prerequisite Skills
- Know how to define and sketch different quadrilaterals.
- Define and sketch different types of triangles and identify their attributes.
- Identify and explain why given figures are congruent.

### ▶ Content Background

A *tessellation* is a pattern created by figures that can cover a surface, leaving no spaces between the figures. The figures in a tessellation can be reflected, rotated, or translated to create the pattern. Some tessellations can be made by using more than one type of transformation, depending on the shape. Many tiled walls and floors, walkways, and brick walls are tessellations.

A transformation is a movement of a shape. Three types of transformations are translations, rotations, and reflections.

- A *translation* (slide) is a slide along a straight line. The black outlined arrow is the original arrow and the red outlined arrow is its final image after the translation.
  **Example:**

- A *rotation* (turn) is a turn around a fixed point. The black outlined arrow is the original arrow. The red outlined arrow is its final image after the rotation of the arrow 90° counterclockwise.
  **Example:**

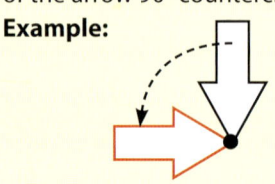

- A *reflection* (flip) is a flip over a line. The black outlined arrow is the original arrow and the red outlined arrow is its final image after the reflection over the vertical line. A reflection is like a mirror final image in which the reflection line is the mirror.
  **Example:**

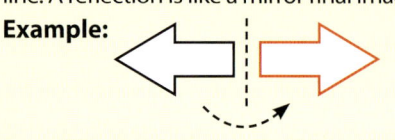

### Materials to Gather

**SUPPLIED**
Pattern Blocks (printout)
Tessellations Practice activity page

**ALSO NEEDED**
construction paper
scissors, pointed-end safety

- A figure can also get larger or smaller in a transformation called a *dilation*. The black outlined arrow is the original arrow and the red outlined arrow is its final image after the dilation from smaller to larger.

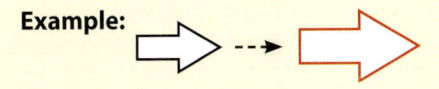

  **Example:**

## ▶ Advance Preparation
Print the Pattern Blocks.

## ▶ Safety
Make sure students handle the scissors carefully and be sure to store them in a safe place.

## LEARN Dilations and Tessellations
*ONLINE 15 min*

Students will learn how transformations are used to make tessellations. A tessellation is a pattern that repeatedly uses a figure and transforms it so there are no spaces. Students will be introduced to dilations, and review translations, rotations, and reflections.

### Objectives
- Predict, describe, and perform transformations on two-dimensional shapes.

## LEARN Observe and Create Tessellations
*OFFLINE 20 min*

Students will find examples of tessellations. They will then create their own tessellation by using reflections, rotations, or translations. Gather the Pattern Blocks printout, scissors, and construction paper.

### Objectives
- Predict, describe, and perform transformations on two-dimensional shapes.

### INVESTIGATING TESSELLATIONS
1. Remind students that a tessellation is a pattern that repeatedly uses the same figure and transforms it so there are no spaces.
2. Have students look for tessellations. They can look on the Internet or search their surroundings. Examples of tessellations in commonly found objects include kaleidoscopes, tile on a floor, stained glass windows, and some decorative pillows.
3. When students have found an example, have them look for the figure that makes up the tessellation.
4. Have students describe how the figure is transformed in the tessellation.
5. Have students predict how the transformations would continue if the tessellation continued.
6. Repeat Steps 2–5 for several tessellation examples.

### CREATING TESSELLATIONS
7. Give students the Pattern Blocks printout. You may print more than one copy. Have students choose a figure and cut it out.
8. Tell students that a tessellation can be made only from congruent figures. Figures that are *congruent* are the same size and shape.

### Tips
To extend students' understanding of tessellations, look up M.C. Escher. He is a noted graphic artist who created many tessellations.

9. Remind students that a reflection is a flip over a line. In a rotation, a figure turns around a point. A translation slides the figure. Have students perform these actions with their pattern block figure on paper. A dilation that changes the size of a figure is not used in tessellations.

10. Have students create a tessellation on construction paper. They will use their pattern block figure to trace the shapes for their tessellation. They should transform the figure in at least one way in their tessellation.

## TRY IT  Tessellations Practice

**OFFLINE 15 min**

### Objectives
- Predict, describe, and perform transformations on two-dimensional shapes.

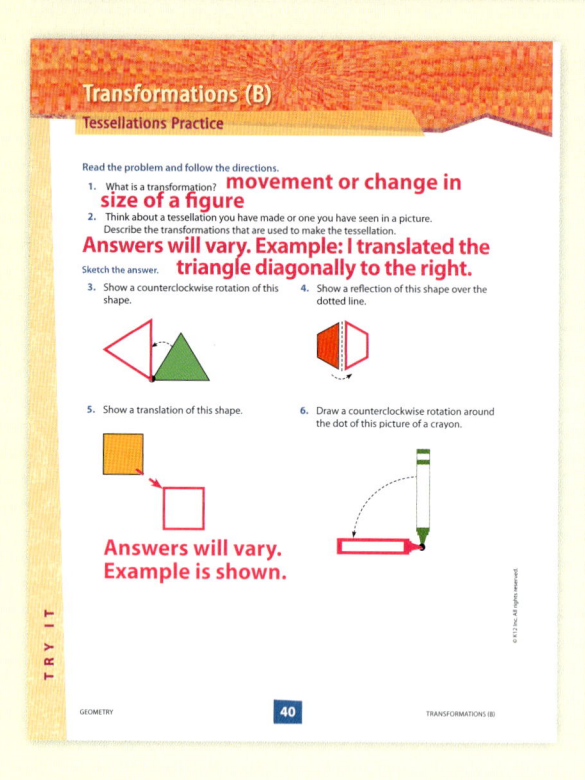

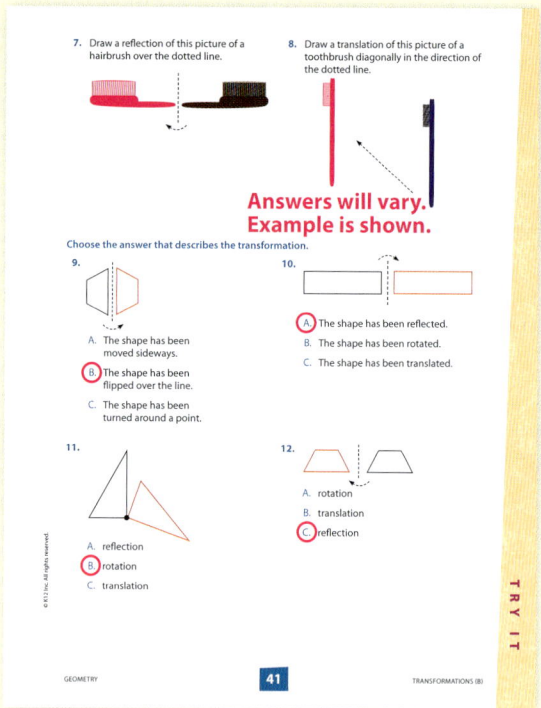

Students will describe a tessellation, preferably one they have created. Then they will draw sketches of transformations. Have students turn to the Tessellations Practice activity page in their Activity Book and read the directions with them.

Students should copy the problems from the Activity Book into their Math Notebook as necessary and solve them there.

**Tips**  If students need more practice identifying the different types of transformations within tessellations, find books or websites that show tessellations.

## CHECKPOINT

**ONLINE 10 min**

### Objectives
- Predict, describe, and perform transformations on two-dimensional shapes.

Students will complete an online Checkpoint. If necessary, read the directions, problems, and answer choices to students and help them with keyboard or mouse operations.

92  GEOMETRY

# Draw 2-D Views of 3-D Objects

## Lesson Overview

| | | |
|---|---|---|
| **GET READY** Sketch Views | 5 minutes | OFFLINE |
| **LEARN** Views of 3-D Objects | 15 minutes | ONLINE |
| **LEARN** Draw Different Views of 3-D Objects | 10 minutes | OFFLINE |
| **TRY IT** Draw and Sketch Views | 20 minutes | OFFLINE |
| **CHECKPOINT** | 10 minutes | OFFLINE |

### ▶ Lesson Objectives
Identify or draw a two-dimensional view of a three-dimensional object.

### ▶ Prerequisite Skills
Recognize and sketch a two-dimensional representation of a three-dimensional object.

### ▶ Content Background
A two-dimensional shape is one that has length and width. Some examples are squares, triangles, rectangles, and pentagons. A three-dimensional object is an object that has length, width, and height (or depth). Some examples are cubes, pyramids, and prisms. Three-dimensional objects are also called solid figures, or solids.

In this lesson, students will identify a two-dimensional view of a three-dimensional object. Many three-dimensional objects have faces, although some common objects do not. For example, a sphere does not have a face.

Three-dimensional objects with faces have a base, which is one of the faces and is used to name the figure, such as a pyramid or prism. When a three-dimensional object is seen from a certain perspective (or point of view), a two-dimensional shape, or a face, is seen. It is possible to see different two-dimensional shapes while viewing three-dimensional objects from different perspectives.

### ▶ Advance Preparation
Print the Centimeter Grid Paper and Views of 3-D Objects.

### Materials to Gather

**SUPPLIED**
Views of 3-D Objects (printout)
Centimeter Grid Paper (printout)
Draw and Sketch Views activity page
Checkpoint (printout)

**ALSO NEEDED**
household objects – several objects shaped like rectangular prisms, pyramids, cylinders, cones, spheres, or hexagonal or octagonal prisms

## GET READY  Sketch Views

**OFFLINE 5 min**

### Objectives
- Recognize and sketch a two-dimensional representation of a three-dimensional object.

Students will sketch the top, front, and side views of a three-dimensional rectangular prism. Gather the common household object shaped like a rectangular prism, such as a cereal box, stack of sticky notes, or CD case.

1. Tell students that three-dimensional objects such as rectangular prisms and square pyramids have three dimensions—length, width, and height. Two-dimensional shapes such squares and rectangles have two dimensions—length and width.

2. Give students the household object.

   **Ask:** What three-dimensional object is this shaped like? a rectangular prism or a cube, depending on what the object is

3. Tell students that the point of view in which they look at a three-dimensional object will reveal two-dimensional shapes. Tell students to look at their household object from different perspectives, or views.

4. Have students identify the front view, side view, and top view of their object. Ask students to sketch the two-dimensional shape they see from each view of a three-dimensional figure. For example, if students sketched a rectangular prism like the one shown below, the front, side, and top views would each look like a rectangle.

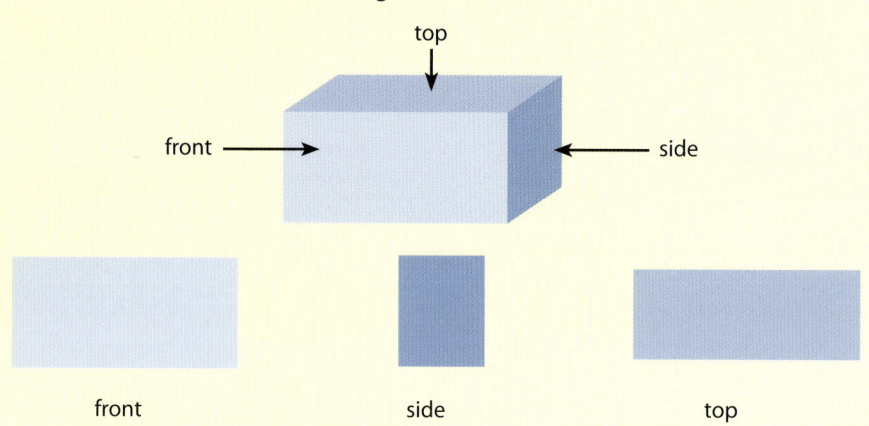

5. Have students describe what they sketched for each view. They should say a square or a rectangle.

94  GEOMETRY

## LEARN  Views of 3-D Objects

**ONLINE 15 min**

### Objectives
- Identify or draw a two-dimensional view of a three-dimensional object.

Students will look at a variety of three-dimensional objects from different views. The different perspectives, or views, will help them see the two-dimensional shapes that can be identified on each three-dimensional object. Students will then identify the two-dimensional shapes seen from different perspectives on three-dimensional objects. Give students the Views of 3-D Objects printout.

## LEARN  Draw Different Views of 3-D Objects

**OFFLINE 10 min**

### Objectives
- Identify or draw a two-dimensional view of a three-dimensional object.

Students will look at several household objects from different perspectives to draw the top, bottom, and side views. They will see that the different views of three-dimensional objects are various two-dimensional shapes.

The three-dimensional shape below is turned different ways to show that the sides, front, and top are two-dimensional shapes. The side view is a square and the front and top views are rectangles.

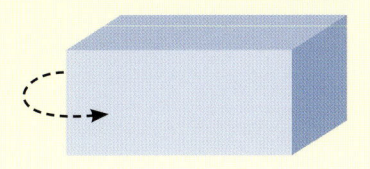

turning to show the side of the object

object turned to the side

side view

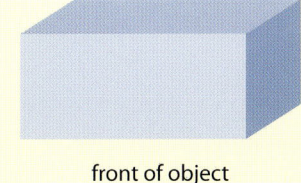

front of object

front view

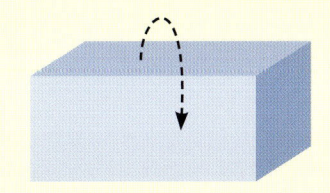

turning to show the top of the obejct

top view

Gather the centimeter grid paper and the household objects shaped like rectangular prisms, pyramids, cylinders, cones, spheres, or hexagonal or octagonal prisms. Some ideas for objects are a cereal box, oatmeal canister, can of vegetables, ball, tissue box, triangular piece of thick cheese, sandwich cut into triangles, party hat, book, and square pad of paper.

1. Give students the household objects and have them describe and name each object as a specific three-dimensional object, such as a rectangular prism.
2. Have students choose one of the objects. Ask them to name the different views of the object, such as top, bottom, side, front, and back.

### Tips
If students are having trouble correctly drawing the different views of the stacked objects, have them describe what two-dimensional shapes they see before they begin drawing.

3. Tell students to draw and label each view on grid paper. For example, if the object is a cereal box, which is a rectangular prism, they would draw rectangles of different proportions for the front/back, top/bottom, and the 2 sides.

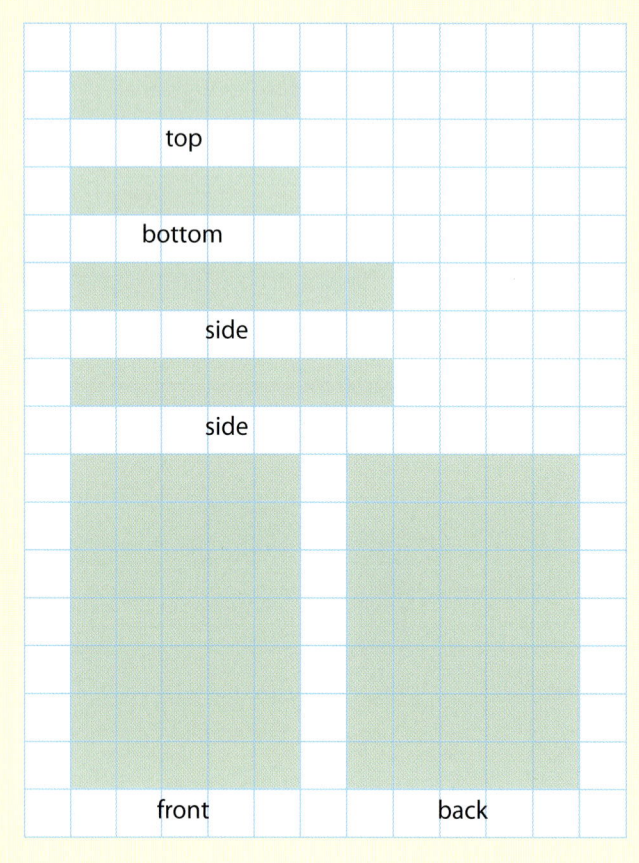

4. **Ask:** What did you draw for each view? Answers will vary. For a cereal box, students would say they drew rectangles for all views, and the rectangles had different lengths and widths.

5. Repeat Steps 2–4 with four or five more objects.

6. Extend the activity by stacking two household objects together. Tell students to look at the stacked objects and think of them as one object. Have students sketch the different views of the object.

7. Have students explain their drawings. Repeat Step 6 with two or three more sets of stacked objects, with two to five objects in each stack.

# TRY IT  Draw and Sketch Views

**OFFLINE 20 min**

Students will practice drawing different views of three-dimensional objects. Have students turn to the Draw and Sketch Views activity page in their Activity Book and read the directions with them.

Students should copy the problems from the Activity Book into their Math Notebook as necessary and solve them there.

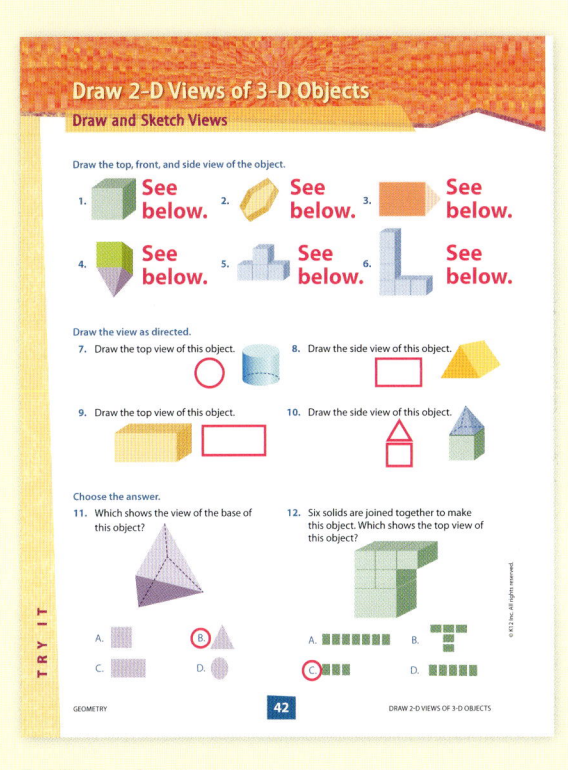

## Objectives

- Identify or draw a two-dimensional view of a three-dimensional object.

## Tips

If students are having difficulty transitioning from concrete objects to seeing the objects on paper, have them hold a household object shaped like the object in each problem.

## Additional Answers

1. ☐ (top, front, and side)

2. ⬡ (top)   ▱▱ (front, side)

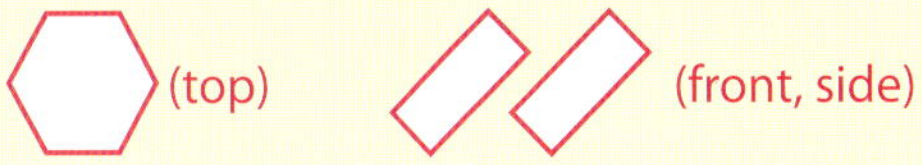

3. ▭ (top, front)   △ (side)

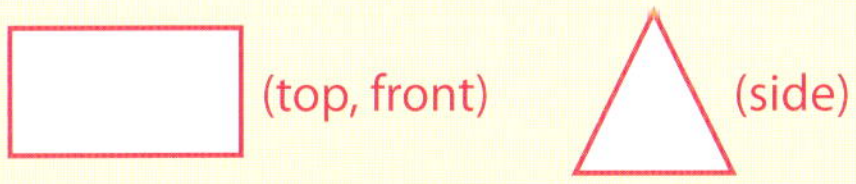

4. ▭ (top)   ▭▭ (front, side)   ▽▽

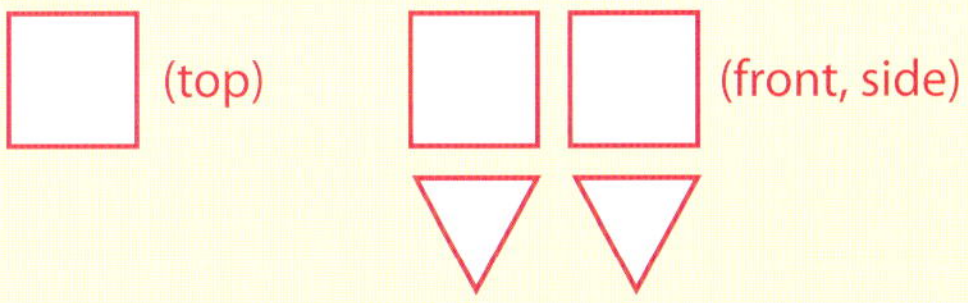

5. ▭▭▭ (top)   (front)   (side)

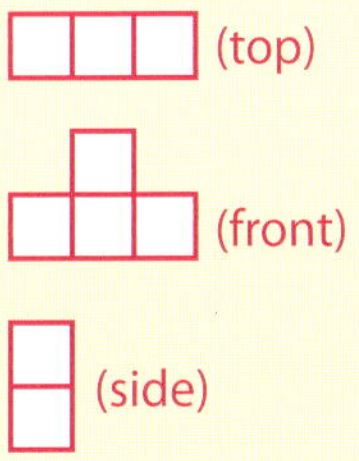

6. ▭▭▭ (top)   (front)   (side)

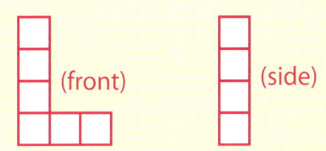

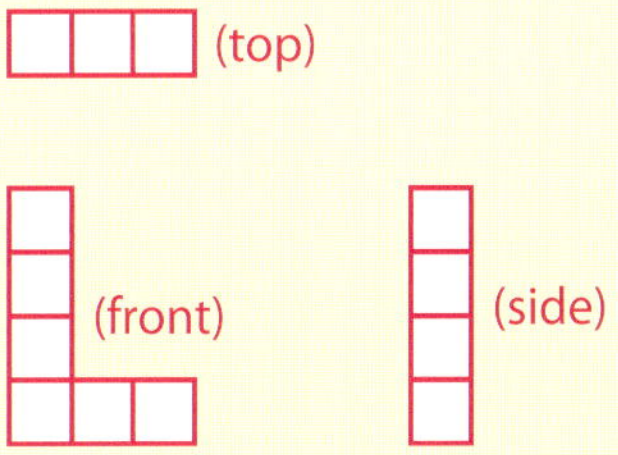

# CHECKPOINT

**OFFLINE 10 min**

## Objectives

- Identify or draw a two-dimensional view of a three-dimensional object.

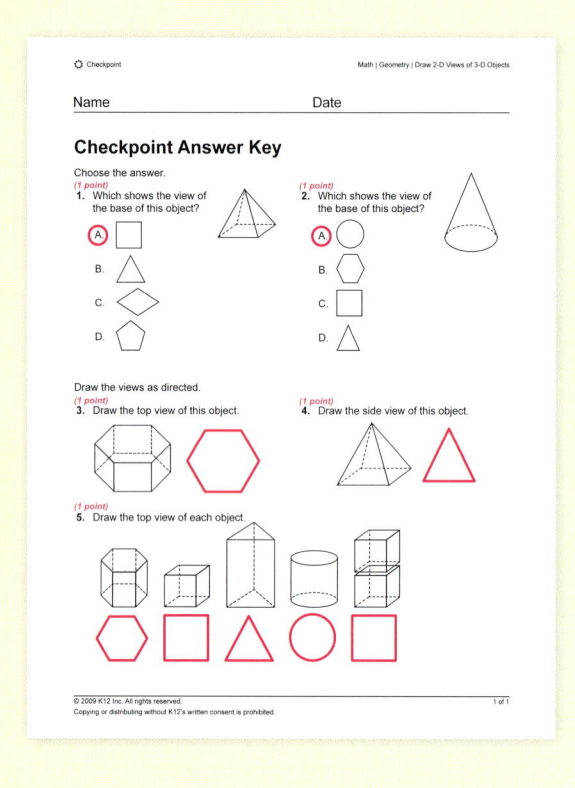

Have students complete the Checkpoint on their own. If necessary, read the directions, problems, and answer choices to students. Use the answer key to score the Checkpoint, and then answer the results online.

98 **GEOMETRY**

# Unit Review

## Lesson Overview

| | | |
|---|---|---|
| **UNIT REVIEW** Look Back | 10 minutes | **ONLINE** |
| **UNIT REVIEW** Checkpoint Practice | 50 minutes | **OFFLINE** |
| ▶ **UNIT REVIEW** Prepare for the Checkpoint | | |

### ▶ Unit Objectives

This lesson reviews the following objectives:

- Identify, measure, and draw angles with appropriate math tools.
- Identify and draw perpendicular or parallel lines with appropriate math tools.
- Construct rectangles or triangles with appropriate math tools.
- Identify that the sum of the interior angles of any triangle is 180° and solve related problems.
- Identify that the sum of the interior angles of any quadrilateral is 360° and solve related problems.
- Predict, describe, and perform transformations on two-dimensional shapes.
- Identify or draw a two-dimensional view of a three-dimensional object.

### Materials to Gather

**SUPPLIED**
Checkpoint Practice activity page
protractor

### ▶ Advance Preparation

In this lesson, students will have an opportunity to review previous activities in the Geometry unit. Look at the suggested activities in Unit Review: Prepare for the Checkpoint online and gather any needed materials.

## UNIT REVIEW Look Back

**ONLINE 10 min**

Students will review key concepts from the unit to prepare for the Unit Checkpoint.

### Objectives
- Review unit objectives.

## UNIT REVIEW Checkpoint Practice

**OFFLINE 50 min**

Students will complete a Checkpoint Practice activity page to prepare for the Unit Checkpoint. Gather the protractor. If necessary, read the directions, problems, and answer choices to students. Have students answer the problems on their own. Carefully review any missed problems with students.

### Objectives
- Review unit objectives.

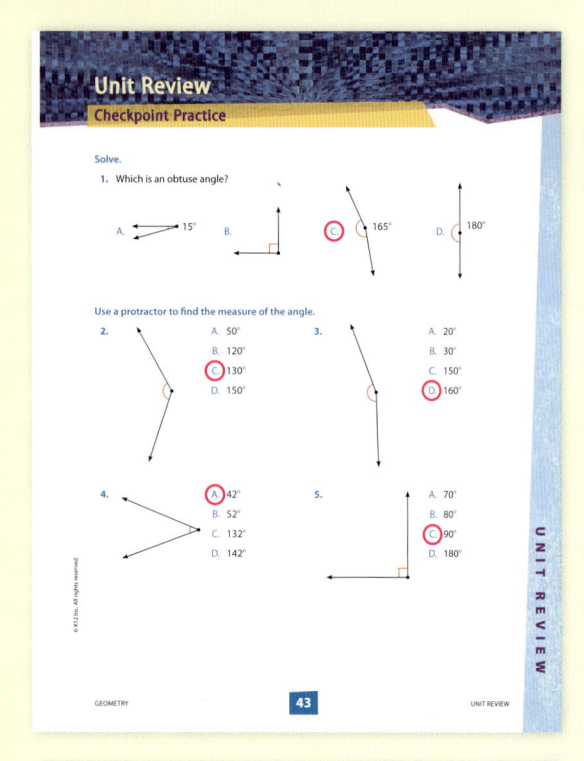

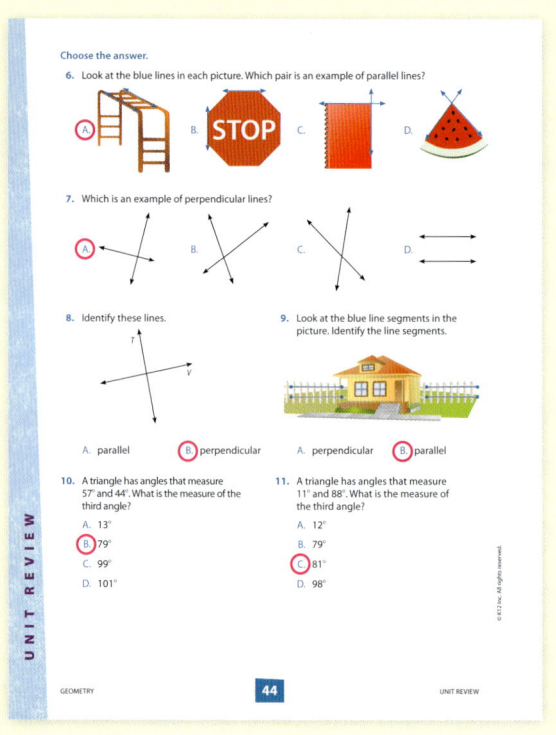

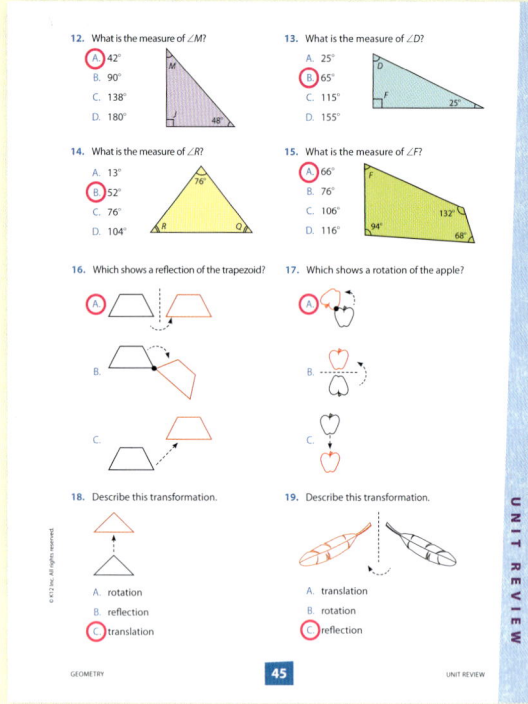

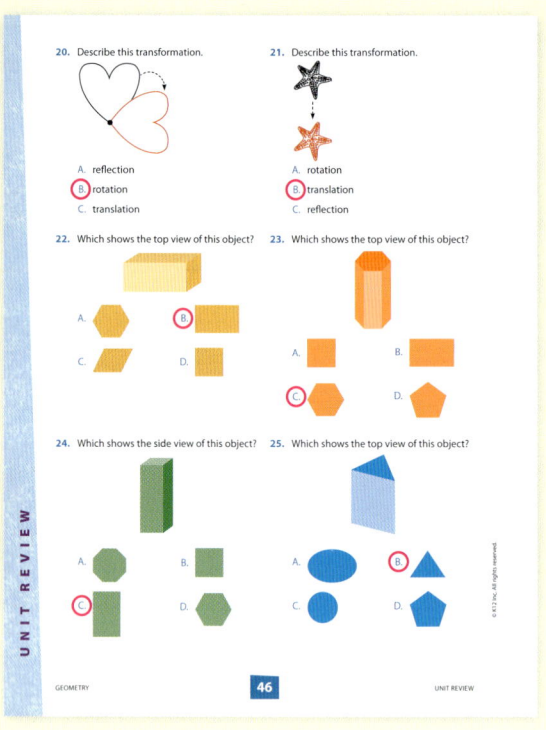

→ **UNIT REVIEW** Prepare for the Checkpoint

What you do next depends on how students performed in the previous activity, Unit Review: Checkpoint Practice. If students had difficulty with any of the problems, complete the appropriate review activity listed in the table online.

# Unit Checkpoint

## Lesson Overview

**UNIT CHECKPOINT** Offline — 60 minutes — **OFFLINE**

### ▶ Unit Objectives

This lesson assesses the following objectives:

- Identify, measure, and draw angles with appropriate math tools.
- Identify and draw perpendicular or parallel lines with appropriate math tools.
- Construct rectangles or triangles with appropriate math tools.
- Identify that the sum of the interior angles of any triangle is 180° and solve related problems.
- Identify that the sum of the interior angles of any quadrilateral is 360° and solve related problems.
- Predict, describe, and perform transformations on two-dimensional shapes.
- Identify or draw a two-dimensional view of a three-dimensional object.

**Materials to Gather**

SUPPLIED
Unit Checkpoint (printout)

## UNIT CHECKPOINT Offline — OFFLINE 60 min

### Objectives

- Assess unit objectives.

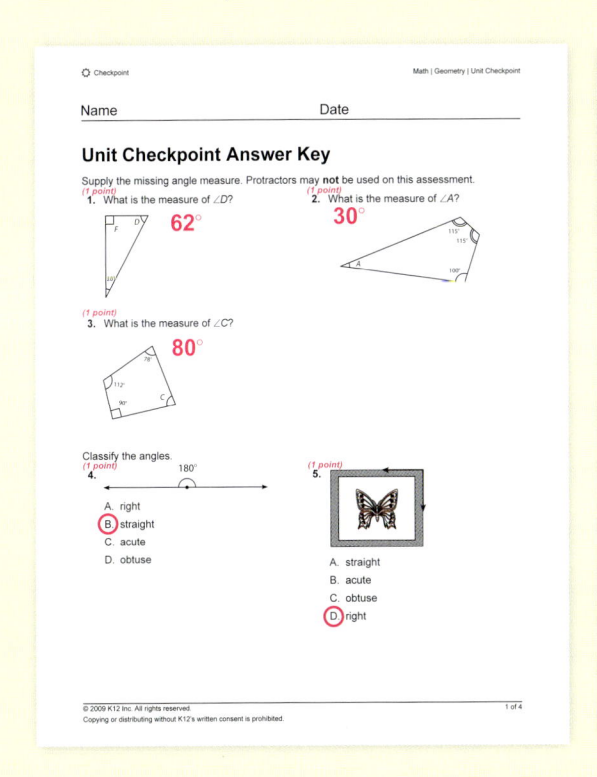

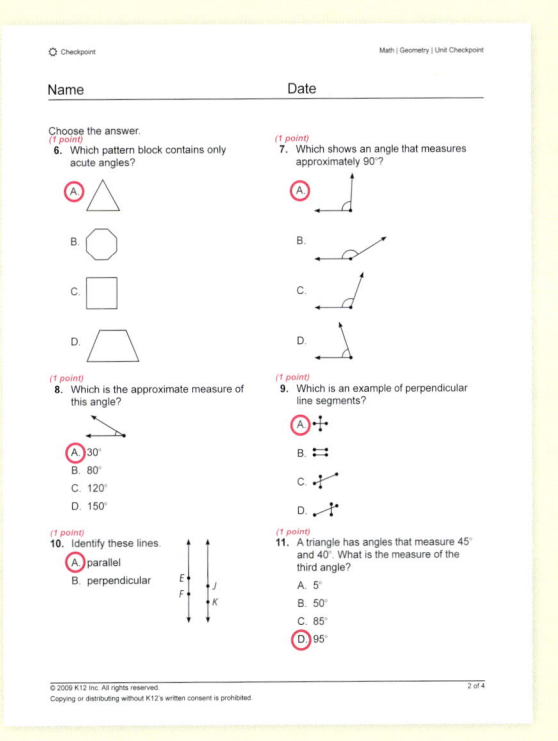

Students will complete the Unit Checkpoint on their own. Print the Unit Checkpoint. Read the directions, problems, and answer choices to students, if necessary. Use the answer key to score the Unit Checkpoint, and then enter the results online.

UNIT CHECKPOINT 101

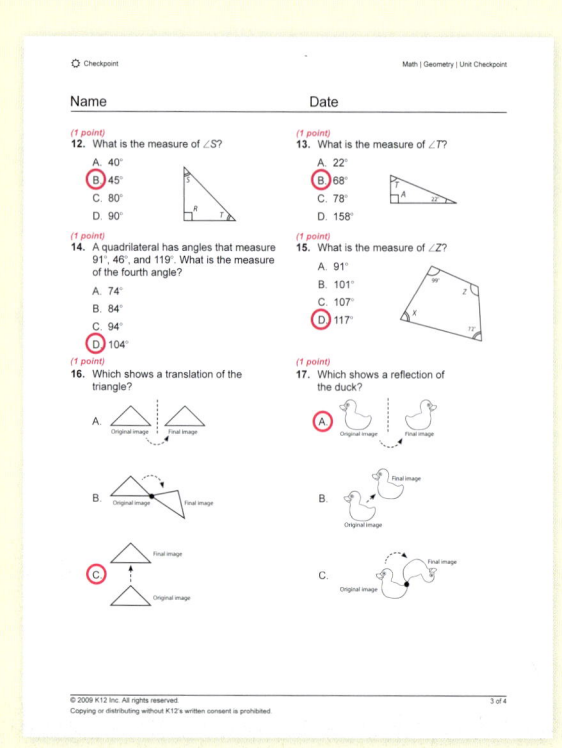

**Checkpoint** — Math | Geometry | Unit Checkpoint

Name _____ Date _____

*(1 point)*
12. What is the measure of ∠S?
    A. 40°
    **B. 45°**
    C. 80°
    D. 90°

*(1 point)*
13. What is the measure of ∠T?
    A. 22°
    **B. 68°**
    C. 78°
    D. 158°

*(1 point)*
14. A quadrilateral has angles that measure 91°, 46°, and 119°. What is the measure of the fourth angle?
    A. 74°
    B. 84°
    C. 94°
    **D. 104°**

*(1 point)*
15. What is the measure of ∠Z?
    A. 91°
    B. 101°
    C. 107°
    **D. 117°**

*(1 point)*
16. Which shows a translation of the triangle?
    A.
    B.
    **C.**

*(1 point)*
17. Which shows a reflection of the duck?
    **A.**
    B.
    C.

---

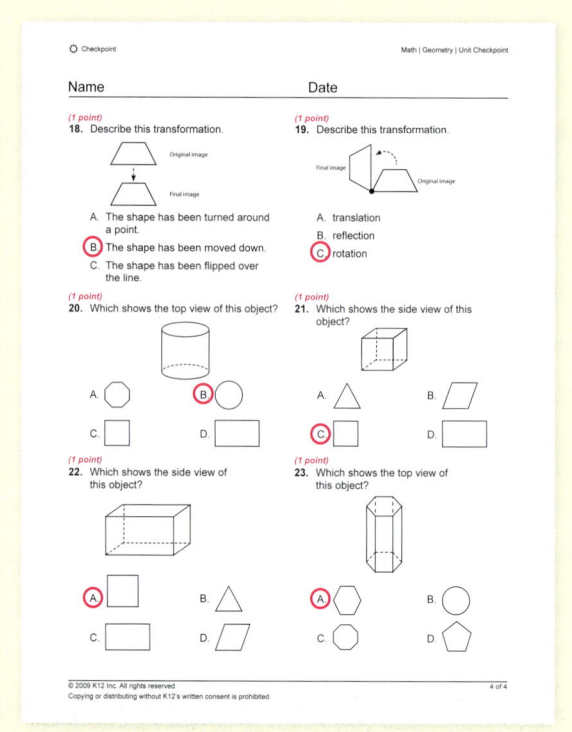

**Checkpoint** — Math | Geometry | Unit Checkpoint

Name _____ Date _____

*(1 point)*
18. Describe this transformation.
    A. The shape has been turned around a point.
    **B. The shape has been moved down.**
    C. The shape has been flipped over the line.

*(1 point)*
19. Describe this transformation.
    A. translation
    B. reflection
    **C. rotation**

*(1 point)*
20. Which shows the top view of this object?
    A.
    **B.**
    C.
    D.

*(1 point)*
21. Which shows the side view of this object?
    A.
    B.
    **C.**
    D.

*(1 point)*
22. Which shows the side view of this object?
    **A.**
    B.
    C.
    D.

*(1 point)*
23. Which shows the top view of this object?
    **A.**
    B.
    C.
    D.

**GEOMETRY**

# Fractions: Multiplication and Division

## ▶ Unit Objectives

- Multiply fractions and explain a step-by-step approach.
- Divide fractions and explain a step-by-step approach.

## ▶ Big Ideas

Fractions can be added, subtracted, multiplied, and divided.

## ▶ Unit Introduction

In this unit, students will learn about multiplication and division of fractions. First they will investigate different drawings and other models of multiplication and division of fractions. Then students will learn step-by-step approaches, also called algorithms, to multiply and divide with fractions.

Activities in this unit include multiplication of fractions by fractions, and multiplication of fractions by mixed numbers. Students will learn that they can divide out common factors before they multiply fractions to make computation easier.

Students will also divide fractions by fractions, mixed numbers by fractions, fractions by mixed numbers, and mixed numbers by mixed numbers.

## ▶ Keywords

algorithm
common factor
divide out a common factor
factor
fraction
improper fraction
least common multiple (LCM)
mixed number
reciprocal

**104** FRACTIONS: MULTIPLICATION AND DIVISION

# Use Models to Multiply Fractions

## Lesson Overview

| | | |
|---|---|---|
| **GET READY** Review Multiplying Fractions | 10 minutes | **ONLINE** |
| **LEARN** Multiply by 1 | 20 minutes | **OFFLINE** |
| **LEARN** Multiply Unit Fractions | 10 minutes | **OFFLINE** |
| **LEARN** Multiply Fractions Greater Than 1 | 10 minutes | **OFFLINE** |
| **TRY IT** Multiply Fractions | 10 minutes | **OFFLINE** |

### ▶ Lesson Objectives
Multiply fractions and explain a step-by-step approach.

### ▶ Prerequisite Skills
- Simplify factors in fraction multiplication problems in which numerators and denominators have common factors.
- Multiply a fraction by a whole number to solve a story problem.

### ▶ Content Background
In this lesson, students will use models to multiply fractions by fractions. They will sketch rectangles on centimeter grid paper to represent fractions. They will shade parts of the rectangles to represent multiplying by fractions.

First, students will multiply a fraction by a whole number represented as a fraction $\left(\text{as in } \frac{3}{3}\right)$. Then they will multiply a fraction by a unit fraction, which is a fraction with a 1 as the numerator. They also will multiply a fraction by an improper fraction, which is a fraction that has a numerator greater than the denominator.

Although students will most often see fractions written with a horizontal fraction bar in math, such as $\frac{2}{3}$ or $5\frac{5}{6}$, they will occasionally see a diagonal fraction bar, such as 2/3 or 5 5/6. Students will very likely see the diagonal fraction bar in everyday experiences, but be sure they understand that using the horizontal fraction bar in their work will make problems involving fractions easier to interpret and solve.

When students draw a rectangle on grid paper, the directions will give them the dimensions for the rectangle, such as 2 by 3. To draw the model, the first factor is the number of columns and the second factor is the number of rows. For example, a 2 × 3 rectangle would have 2 columns and 3 rows.

### ▶ Advance Preparation
Print three copies of Centimeter Grid Paper.

### Materials to Gather

**SUPPLIED**
Centimeter Grid Paper (printout)
Multiply Fractions activity page

**ALSO NEEDED**
ruler

## GET READY  Review Multiplying Fractions

**ONLINE 10 min**

### Objectives
- Simplify factors in fraction multiplication problems in which numerators and denominators have common factors.
- Multiply a fraction by a whole number to solve a story problem.

Students will review simplifying fractions that are the factors in a multiplication problem. Then they will see a model that shows multiplication of the simplified factors.

## LEARN  Multiply by 1

**OFFLINE 20 min**

### Objectives
- Multiply fractions and explain a step-by-step approach.

Students will use models on grid paper to multiply one fraction that is less than 1 by another fraction equal to 1. They will draw rectangles. Then they will divide the rectangles into equal sections and mark the centimeter squares in the equal sections to show the factors in the fraction multiplication. At the end of the problems, students should be able to see that a certain number of centimeter squares out of the total number of centimeter squares is the answer to the multiplication problem.

The rectangles' dimensions are set by the denominators of each factor. For instance, if the denominators in the problem are 4 and 2, the rectangle will be 2 by 4, and thus contain 8 centimeter squares. This fact is pointed out to students during the activity.

Gather a copy of the Centimeter Grid Paper.

1. **Say:** You will find $\frac{1}{2}$ of one whole. Finding $\frac{1}{2}$ of $\frac{1}{1}$ is the same as multiplying $\frac{1}{2}$ by $\frac{1}{1}$.
   - Draw a 1 by 2 rectangle on the grid paper.
   - Draw a horizontal line to divide the rectangle into two equal parts.
   - Draw a diagonal mark across each equal part to show one whole, or $\frac{1}{1}$.
   - Draw an opposite diagonal mark on one-half of the rectangle to show the fraction $\frac{1}{2}$. That centimeter square is now marked with an X because the two diagonal marks are crossing. The model shows $\frac{1}{2}$ of 1, or $\frac{1}{2}$ of $\frac{1}{1}$.
   - Write $\frac{1}{2} \times \frac{1}{1}$ next to the model.

   **Ask:** What expression is represented by this model? $\frac{1}{2} \times \frac{1}{1}$

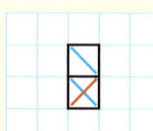

2. **Say:** The fraction $\frac{1}{1}$ is equal to 1. So you are really just multiplying $\frac{1}{2}$ by 1.
3. Discuss the model with students.
   **Ask:** How many equal parts is the whole rectangle divided into? 2
   **Ask:** How many of those equal parts have an X? 1
   **Ask:** What is 1 out of 2? $\frac{1}{2}$
   **Ask:** What is the product of $\frac{1}{2} \times \frac{1}{1}$? $\frac{1}{2}$

106  FRACTIONS: MULTIPLICATION AND DIVISION

4. **Say:** Now you're going to find the product of $\frac{1}{2} \times \frac{2}{2}$. Think about what you learned in the first problem as you work through this one. In this problem, you will need a 2 by 2 square to represent one whole.
   - Draw a 2 by 2 square on the grid paper.
   - Draw a horizontal line to divide the square into two equal parts.
   - Draw diagonal marks on each centimeter part to show one whole, or $\frac{2}{2}$.
   - Draw opposite diagonal marks on half the square to show the fraction $\frac{1}{2}$. Now 2 of the 4 centimeter squares have Xs on them. The model shows $\frac{1}{2}$ of 1, or $\frac{1}{2}$ of $\frac{2}{2}$.
   - Write $\frac{1}{2} \times \frac{2}{2}$ next to the model.
   
   **Ask:** What expression is represented by this model? $\frac{1}{2} \times \frac{2}{2}$

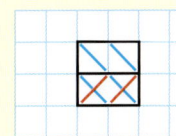

5. **Ask:** Can $\frac{2}{2}$ be simplified? Yes
   
   **Ask:** What is a common factor of 2 and 2? 2
   
   **Ask:** What is $\frac{2}{2}$ simplified? $\frac{1}{1}$

6. Discuss the model with students.
   
   **Ask:** How many centimeter squares are in the whole square and how many centimeter squares have an X on them? 4 in the whole square; 2 have an X
   
   **Ask:** What is the product of $\frac{1}{2} \times \frac{2}{2}$? $\frac{2}{4}$
   
   **Ask:** What is $\frac{2}{4}$ simplified? $\frac{1}{2}$

7. Tell students that they will now find the product of $\frac{1}{2} \times \frac{4}{4}$. Tell them to outline a 4 by 2 square. Tell them that by now they may have noticed that the dimensions of the rectangle are set by the denominators of the fractions in the problem.
   
   Repeat Steps 4–6 for the problem $\frac{1}{2} \times \frac{4}{4} = \frac{4}{8}$.

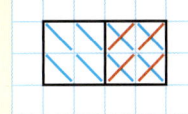

8. Summarize with the following questions about the multiplication problems and the models:
   
   **Ask:** What is the first factor in each problem? $\frac{1}{2}$
   
   **Ask:** What is the second factor in each problem equal to? 1
   
   **Ask:** What is the product of any factor and 1? the factor
   
   **Ask:** So what is the product of each of the three problems in simplest form? $\frac{1}{2}$

9. **Say:** Let's try another problem. Multiply $\frac{2}{3} \times \frac{2}{2}$. Outline a 2 by 3 rectangle. It has 2 columns and 3 rows because we are modeling one factor with a denominator of 2 and one factor with a denominator of 3.

10. **Say:** Divide the rectangle into three equal parts. Each equal part has 2 centimeter squares. Mark all squares with a diagonal to show one whole, or $\frac{2}{2}$. Then mark the centimeter squares in 2 of the 3 equal parts with an opposite diagonal mark.

USE MODELS TO MULTIPLY FRACTIONS

**Ask:** How many parts have Xs on them? What expression is represented by this model? 2 parts of the 3 total parts have Xs; $\frac{2}{3} \times \frac{2}{2}$

Write $\frac{2}{3} \times \frac{2}{2}$ next to the rectangle.

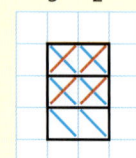

$\frac{2}{3} \times \frac{2}{2}$

11. Discuss the model with students.
    **Ask:** What can $\frac{2}{2}$ be simplified to? $\frac{1}{1}$
    **Ask:** What is the product of $\frac{2}{3} \times \frac{2}{2}$? $\frac{4}{6}$
    **Ask:** What is $\frac{4}{6}$ in simplest form? $\frac{2}{3}$

12. Repeat with $\frac{3}{5} \times \frac{2}{2}$. Guide students to understand that their rectangle will be 2 by 5 because the factors have denominators of 2 and 5. They will divide the rectangle into 5 equal parts. Then they will mark all the centimeter squares with a diagonal mark to show one whole, or $\frac{2}{2}$. They will mark centimeter squares in 3 of the 5 equal parts with opposite diagonal marks. They will end up with a model showing 6 centimeter squares with Xs out of the 10 total squares, so the model shows that the product is $\frac{6}{10}$, or $\frac{3}{5}$.

## LEARN Multiply Unit Fractions

OFFLINE 10 min

### Objectives

- Multiply fractions and explain a step-by-step approach.

Students will use a model to multiply a fraction by a unit fraction. Unit fractions are fractions with a numerator of 1.
Gather a copy of the Centimeter Grid Paper.

1. Have students outline a 5 by 4 rectangle on grid paper to model the problem. The rectangle has 5 columns and 4 rows.

2. Tell students they will use a model to find $\frac{3}{4}$ of $\frac{1}{5}$. Remind students that finding $\frac{3}{4}$ of $\frac{1}{5}$ is the same as multiplying $\frac{3}{4} \times \frac{1}{5}$.

3. **Say:** We will use a model to solve $\frac{3}{4} \times \frac{1}{5}$. First, divide the rectangle into 5 equal columns to represent the denominator of the factor $\frac{1}{5}$. Model $\frac{1}{5}$ by marking each centimeter square in the first column with diagonal lines. Label the model $\frac{1}{5}$.

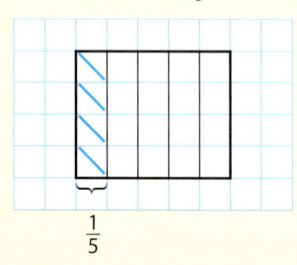

$\frac{1}{5}$

### Tips

Students learn to mark the second factor first when modeling fraction multiplication. They can actually mark either factor first and reach the correct answer.

4. **Say:** Add horizontal lines to divide the model into 4 equal parts to represent the denominator of the factor $\frac{3}{4}$. Model $\frac{3}{4}$ by marking each centimeter square in the top three rows with diagonal lines that cross the first diagonal lines you drew. The boxes marked with an X represent $\frac{3}{4} \times \frac{1}{5}$. Label the model $\frac{3}{4} \times \frac{1}{5}$.

108 FRACTIONS: MULTIPLICATION AND DIVISION

$\frac{3}{4} \times \frac{1}{5}$

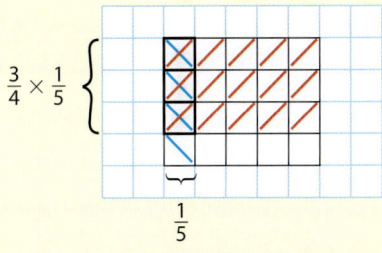

$\frac{1}{5}$

5. Discuss the model with students.

   **Ask:** How many equal parts is the whole rectangle divided into? 20

   **Ask:** How many equal parts are marked with an X? 3

   **Ask:** When you use the model you made, what can you tell is the product of $\frac{3}{4} \times \frac{1}{5}$? $\frac{3}{20}$

6. Repeat Steps 1–4 for $\frac{5}{6} \times \frac{1}{3}$.

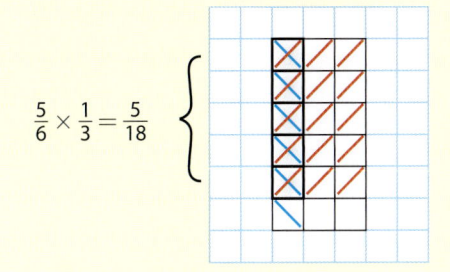

$\frac{5}{6} \times \frac{1}{3} = \frac{5}{18}$

7. Discuss the model with students.

   **Ask:** How many equal parts is the whole rectangle divided into? 18

   **Ask:** How many equal parts are marked with an X? 5

   **Ask:** When you use the model you made, what can you tell is the product of $\frac{5}{6} \times \frac{1}{3}$? $\frac{5}{18}$

8. Summarize the activity with the following questions about the multiplication problems and the models:

   **Ask:** Is the product of each multiplication problem in the activity less than or greater than the first factor in the problem? less than

   **Say:** When you multiply a fraction by a unit fraction, the product is always less than the first fraction factor.

OFFLINE 10 min

## LEARN Multiply Fractions Greater Than 1

### Objectives

- Multiply fractions and explain a step-by-step approach.

Students will use a model to multiply a fraction by an improper fraction with a value greater than 1. An improper fraction has a numerator equal to or greater than the denominator.

Gather a copy of the Centimeter Grid Paper. Tell students that each rectangle presents $\frac{6}{6}$ or one whole.

USE MODELS TO MULTIPLY FRACTIONS 109

1. Have students outline two 6 by 4 rectangles side by side on grid paper.

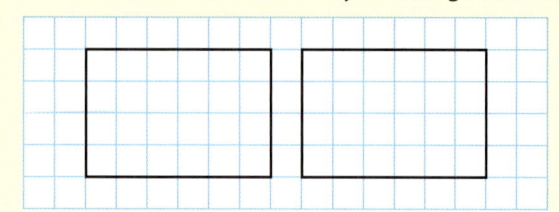

2. Tell students they will use a model to find $\frac{1}{4}$ of $\frac{7}{6}$. Explain to students that $\frac{7}{6}$ is called an improper fraction, meaning it is a fraction whose value is greater than 1 because the value of the numerator is greater than the value of the denominator. Remind students that finding $\frac{1}{4}$ of $\frac{7}{6}$ is the same as multiplying $\frac{1}{4} \times \frac{7}{6}$.

3. **Say:** You outlined two rectangles for your model because $\frac{7}{6}$ is greater than 1 and therefore it is an improper fraction. Use vertical lines to divide each rectangle into 6 equal parts. Model $\frac{7}{6}$ by marking each centimeter square in the first seven columns with diagonal lines. Label the model $\frac{7}{6}$.

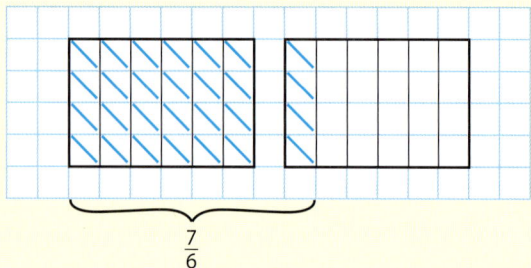

4. **Say:** Add horizontal lines to divide the model into 4 equal parts to represent the denominator of the factor $\frac{1}{4}$. Model $\frac{1}{4}$ by marking each centimeter square in the first row with diagonal lines that cross the first diagonal lines you drew. The boxes marked with an X represent $\frac{1}{4} \times \frac{7}{6}$. Label the model $\frac{1}{4} \times \frac{7}{6}$.

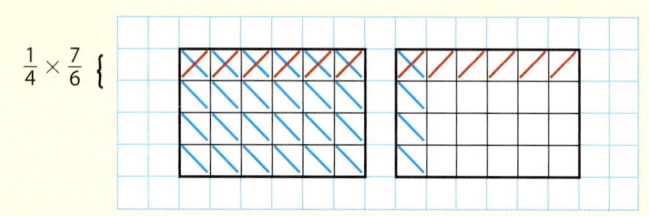

5. Discuss the model with students.
   **Ask:** How many equal parts is each rectangle divided into? 24
   **Ask:** How many equal parts in both rectangles combined are marked with an X? 7
   **Ask:** When you use the model you made, what can you tell is the product of $\frac{1}{4} \times \frac{7}{6}$? $\frac{7}{24}$

6. Repeat Steps 1–4 for $\frac{2}{5} \times \frac{4}{3}$.

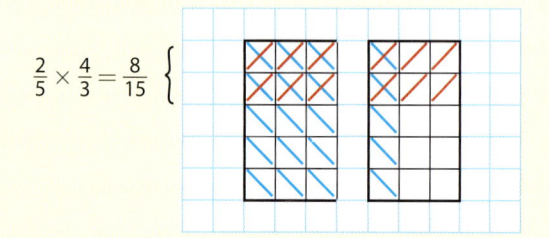

$\frac{2}{5} \times \frac{4}{3} = \frac{8}{15}$

### Tips

If students are confused about the denominator when using multiple models, remind students that each model stands for one whole and that the number of equal parts in one whole is the denominator.

110 FRACTIONS: MULTIPLICATION AND DIVISION

7. Discuss the model with students.

   **Ask:** How many equal parts is each whole rectangle divided into? **15**

   **Ask:** How many equal parts are marked with an X? **8**

   **Ask:** When you use the model you made, what can you tell is the product of $\frac{2}{5} \times \frac{4}{3}$? **$\frac{8}{15}$**

8. Summarize the activity with the following questions about the multiplication problems and the models:

   **Ask:** Is the second factor in each multiplication problem in the activity less than or greater than 1? **greater than**

   **Ask:** Is the product of each multiplication problem in the activity less than or greater than the first factor? **greater than**

   **Say:** When you multiply a fraction by an improper fraction, the product is always greater than the first fraction factor.

## TRY IT  Multiply Fractions

**OFFLINE 10 min**

### Objectives
- Multiply fractions and explain a step-by-step approach.

Students will practice multiplying fractions by drawing models on grid paper. Give students a copy of the Centimeter Grid Paper. Have students turn to the Multiply Fractions activity page in their Activity Book and read the directions with them.

Students should copy the problems from the Activity Book into their Math Notebook as necessary and solve them there.

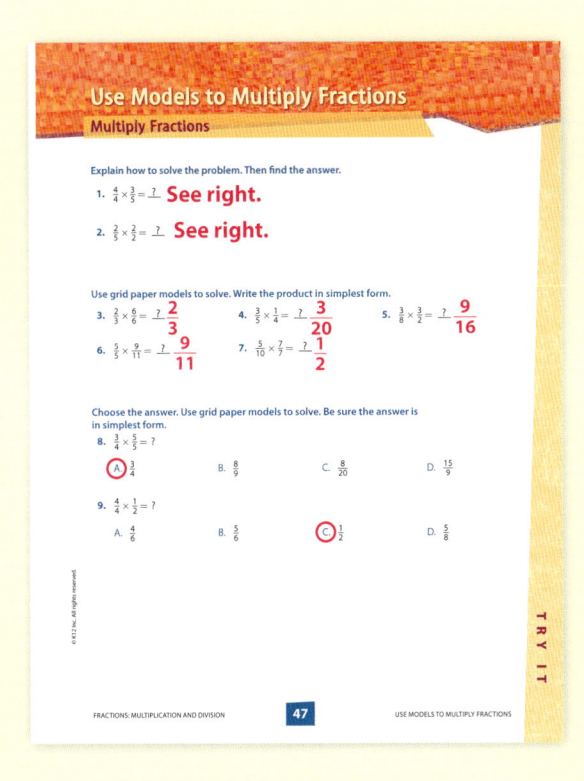

**Additional Answers**

1. Multiply $\frac{4}{4} \times \frac{3}{5}$. Since $\frac{4}{4}$ is the same as 1, multiply $\frac{3}{5}$ by 1 to get the answer. $\frac{3}{5} \times \frac{4}{4} = \frac{3}{5}$.

2. Multiply $\frac{2}{5} \times \frac{2}{2}$. Since $\frac{2}{2}$ is the same as 1, multiply $\frac{2}{5}$ by 1 to get the answer. $\frac{2}{5} \times \frac{2}{2} = \frac{2}{5}$.

USE MODELS TO MULTIPLY FRACTIONS **111**

# Understand Division of Fractions

## Lesson Overview

| | | |
|---|---|---|
| **GET READY** Solve Fraction Story Problems | 10 minutes | **ONLINE** |
| **LEARN** Divide by Values of 1 | 15 minutes | **OFFLINE** |
| **LEARN** Divide to Simplify Fractions | 15 minutes | **OFFLINE** |
| **LEARN** Divide by 1 with Reciprocals | 10 minutes | **ONLINE** |
| **TRY IT** Practice Dividing Fractions | 10 minutes | **OFFLINE** |

### ▶ Lesson Objectives
Divide fractions and explain a step-by-step approach.

### ▶ Prerequisite Skills
- Divide a whole number by a fraction to solve a story problem.
- Multiply fractions and explain a step-by-step approach.

### ▶ Content Background
In this lesson, students will learn to understand division of fractions by studying examples of fractions divided by 1 and reviewing the relationship between multiplication and division.

Once students have worked with models that show how to divide a fraction by a fraction, they will use a step-by-step approach to fraction division. The steps of the traditional approach to find the quotient of two fractions are to first convert to multiplication by the reciprocal of the divisor, and then to divide out common factors before multiplying. The last step is to express answers in the simplest form by dividing the answer by the largest fraction they can, in the form of $\frac{a}{a}$, and changing improper fractions to mixed numbers.

Although students will most often see fractions written with a horizontal fraction bar in math, such as $\frac{2}{3}$ or $5\frac{5}{6}$, they will occasionally see a diagonal fraction bar, such as 2/3 or 5 5/6. Students will very likely see the diagonal fraction bar in everyday experiences, but be sure they understand that using the horizontal fraction bar in their work will make problems involving fractions easier to interpret and solve.

When students draw a rectangle on grid paper, the directions will give them the dimensions for the rectangle, such as 2 by 3. To draw the model, the first factor is the number of columns and the second factor is the number of rows. For example, a 2 × 3 rectangle would have 2 columns and 3 rows.

### ▶ Materials to Gather

**SUPPLIED**
Practice Dividing Fractions activity page
Centimeter Grid Paper (printout)

### ▶ Common Errors and Misconceptions
Students might have difficulty understanding that numbers can look different, but still represent the same amount. For example, students might find it difficult to understand that though the numbers $\frac{1}{2}$, $\frac{3}{6}$, and $\frac{5}{10}$ look different, they are all equivalent, or represent the same part of a whole, part of a set, location on the number line, quotient, or ratio.

**112** FRACTIONS: MULTIPLICATION AND DIVISION

▶ **Advance Preparation**

Print one copy of Centimeter Grid Paper.

## GET READY  Solve Fraction Story Problems

**ONLINE 10 min**

**Objectives**
- Divide a whole number by a fraction to solve a story problem.
- Multiply fractions and explain a step-by-step approach.

Students will review how to solve a division problem in which a whole number is divided by a fraction. They also will review how to find equivalent fractions by finding a missing numerator in a problem.

## LEARN  Divide by Values of 1

**OFFLINE 15 min**

**Objectives**
- Divide fractions and explain a step-by-step approach.

Students will review division of whole numbers by 1 and then go on to learn about fractions divided by 1. They will follow the step-by-step process for division by a fraction when that fraction is equivalent to 1.

1. **Say:** You will solve $\frac{3}{10}$ divided by 1 in several different ways.

   But first you will look at dividing by 1.

   **Ask:** Suppose you were asked to divide 6 by 1. What is $6 \div 1 = ?$  6

   **Ask:** What about $126 \div 1 = ?$  126

   **Ask:** What do you think $\frac{3}{10} \div 1$ equals?  $\frac{3}{10}$

   **Ask:** What about $\frac{567}{943} \div 1?$  $\frac{567}{943}$

2. **Say:** Any fraction divided by 1 is just that same fraction.

   **Ask:** You also know that 1 can be written as $\frac{1}{1}$, so $6 \div \frac{1}{1} = 6$. What about $126 \div \frac{1}{1} = ?$  126

   **Ask:** What do you think $\frac{3}{10} \div \frac{1}{1}$ equals?  $\frac{3}{10}$

   **Ask:** What about $\frac{567}{943} \div \frac{1}{1}?$  $\frac{567}{943}$

3. **Ask:** You also know that $\frac{2}{2}$ is the same as 1. What are some other fractions that are the same as 1?  $\frac{3}{3}, \frac{5}{5}, \frac{8}{8}, \frac{102}{102}$; Answers will vary.

4. **Say:** When you divide $\frac{3}{10}$ by one of these values of 1, for example, $\frac{3}{10} \div \frac{2}{2}$, the quotient is $\frac{3}{10}$ or some fraction that is equivalent to $\frac{3}{10}$.

   In fact, $\frac{3}{10} \div \frac{2}{2} = \frac{3}{10} \times \frac{2}{2} = \frac{6}{20}$ and $\frac{6}{20}$ is equivalent to $\frac{3}{10}$.

   Also, $\frac{3}{10} \div \frac{5}{5} = \frac{3}{10} \times \frac{5}{5} = \frac{15}{50}$ and $\frac{15}{50}$ is equivalent to $\frac{3}{10}$.

   You could go on like this for many fraction values of 1.

   Now you can see that any fraction, when divided by a fraction that has a value of 1, such as $\frac{1}{1}, \frac{2}{2},$ or $\frac{5}{5}$ is just that same fraction or one that is equivalent.

5. Have students write four division number sentences in their Math Notebook. In each, the dividend should be a fraction, and the divisor should be a fraction equivalent to 1. They should explain how the quotient is equivalent to the dividend.

   For example, $\frac{4}{9} \div \frac{5}{5} = \frac{4}{9} \times \frac{5}{5} = \frac{20}{45}$, and $\frac{20}{45}$ is equivalent to $\frac{4}{9}$.

## LEARN  Divide to Simplify Fractions

**OFFLINE 15 min**

### Objectives
- Divide fractions and explain a step-by-step approach.

Students will simplify fractions by dividing the numerator and the denominator by their greatest common factor (GCF). This activity will help students because when they divide fractions by fractions, the answer might not be in simplest form, and they'll need to simplify it.

Gather the Centimeter Grid Paper.

1. Tell students that they will often be asked to simplify fractions, but how will they know if a fraction can be simplified?

    Fractions such as $\frac{3}{4}$, $\frac{2}{7}$, and $\frac{13}{15}$ cannot be simplified, but $\frac{2}{6}$, $\frac{9}{15}$, and $\frac{8}{12}$ can all be simplified. So, what's the difference?

    In each of the first set of fractions, there is no number greater than 1 that will evenly divide both the numerator and denominator of the fraction.

    - Only 1 can evenly divide the 3 and the 4 in $\frac{3}{4}$.
    - Only 1 can evenly divide the 2 and the 7 in $\frac{2}{7}$.
    - Only 1 can evenly divide the 13 and the 15 in $\frac{13}{15}$.

    But, in the second group of fractions, there is a number greater than 1 that can evenly divide both the numerator and denominator of the fraction.

    - 2 can evenly divide the 2 and the 6 in $\frac{2}{6}$.
    - 3 can evenly divide the 9 and the 15 in $\frac{9}{15}$.
    - Both 2 and 4 can evenly divide the 8 and the 12 in $\frac{8}{12}$.

    **Say:** Once you decide that a fraction can be simplified, you find the greatest number that will divide both the numerator and the denominator evenly. That number is called the *greatest common factor*, or the GCF.

    - The GCF for $\frac{2}{6}$ is 2.
    - The GCF for $\frac{9}{15}$ is 3.
    - The GCF for $\frac{8}{12}$ is 4, even though 2 also divides evenly.

    Once you know the GCF, you divide both the numerator and denominator by the GCF. For example, to simplify $\frac{2}{6}$,

    - $2 \div 2 = 1$
    - $6 \div 2 = 3$

    Once you've simplified $\frac{2}{6}$, you see that it is equivalent to $\frac{1}{3}$.

2. **Say:** Simplify $\frac{9}{15}$.

    **Ask:** What is the GCF?  3

    **Ask:** $9 \div 3 = ?$  3

    **Ask:** $15 \div 3 = ?$  5

    **Ask:** What is $\frac{9}{15}$ simplified?  $\frac{3}{5}$

    **Ask:** Is $\frac{3}{5}$ equivalent to $\frac{9}{15}$?  Yes

    **Say:** $\frac{3}{5}$ is the simplest form of $\frac{9}{15}$.

3. Let students practice with these fractions:

   **Ask:** What is $\frac{8}{12}$ simplified? $\frac{2}{3}$

   **Ask:** What is $\frac{5}{20}$ simplified? $\frac{1}{4}$

   **Ask:** What is $\frac{12}{18}$ simplified? $\frac{2}{3}$

   Students should be sure to choose the GCF and check that the two fractions are equivalent.

   **Say:** The simplified answers are also the simplest forms of the fractions.

4. Tell students that when they divide the numerator and denominator by the GCF, they get a fraction that is equivalent to the original fraction, which is the same result as if they divided by a value of 1.

   Give students the Centimeter Grid Paper.

   In Step 3, students simplified $\frac{8}{12}$ to $\frac{2}{3}$. Draw a 3 by 4 rectangle to show 12 squares inside. Mark a diagonal line in 2 columns, so you have marked $\frac{2}{3}$. Outline the interior squares, which means the sketch will then show 8 interior squares, or $\frac{8}{12}$.

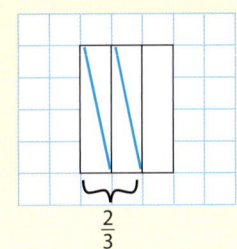

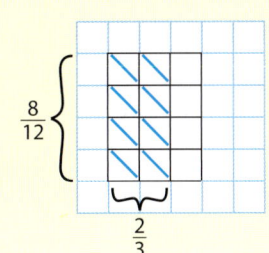

5. Give students the Centimeter Grid Paper. Ask them to simplify $\frac{3}{15}$ and draw two sketches to show the fractions are equivalent. (**Hint:** Start with a 5 by 3 rectangle.) $\frac{3}{15} = \frac{1}{5}$

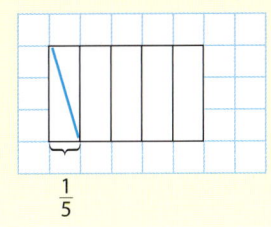

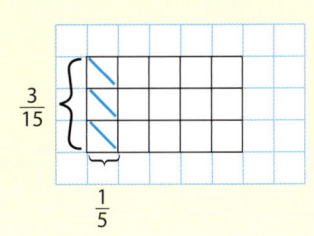

### Tips

To help students remember what the reciprocal means, play a game of Reciprocal Madness. Within 30 seconds, have students give you the reciprocals of five fractions that you say to them. After you say a fraction, students give the reciprocal, and you move on to the next fraction.

## LEARN Divide by 1 with Reciprocals

ONLINE 10 min

The division of any fraction by 1 always results in that fraction, or a fraction that is equivalent. Students will review using a reciprocal when they divide by a fraction. Then they will learn that multiplying by a fraction equal to 1 and dividing by a fraction equal to 1 result in the same answer.

### Objectives

- Divide fractions and explain a step-by-step approach.

UNDERSTAND DIVISION OF FRACTIONS 115

## TRY IT Practice Dividing Fractions

**OFFLINE 10 min**

### Objectives
- Divide fractions and explain a step-by-step approach.

Students will practice dividing fractions. Have students turn to the Practice Dividing Fractions activity page in their Activity Book and read the directions with them.

Students should copy the problems from the Activity Book into their Math Notebook as necessary and solve them there.

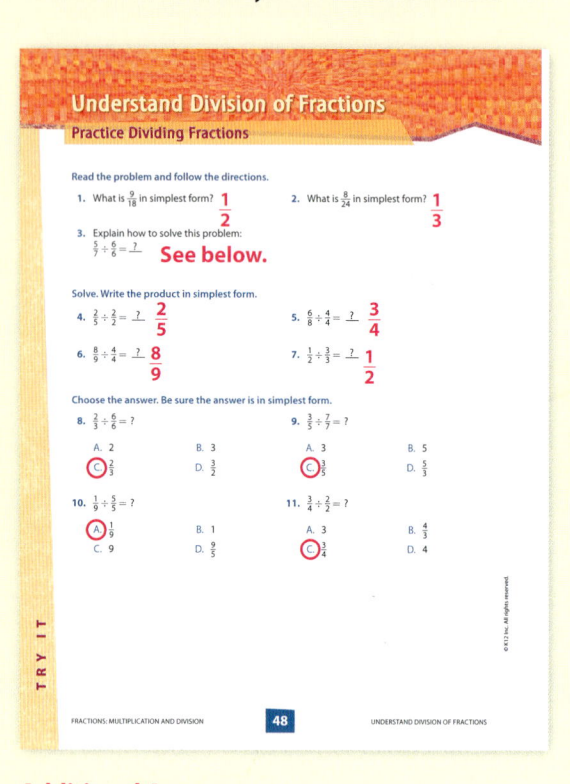

### Understand Division of Fractions
**Practice Dividing Fractions**

Read the problem and follow the directions.

1. What is $\frac{9}{18}$ in simplest form?  $\frac{1}{2}$
2. What is $\frac{8}{24}$ in simplest form?  $\frac{1}{3}$
3. Explain how to solve this problem:
   $\frac{5}{7} \div \frac{6}{6} = ?$   **See below.**

Solve. Write the product in simplest form.

4. $\frac{2}{5} \div \frac{2}{2} = ?$   $\frac{2}{5}$
5. $\frac{6}{8} \div \frac{4}{4} = ?$   $\frac{3}{4}$
6. $\frac{8}{9} \div \frac{4}{4} = ?$   $\frac{8}{9}$
7. $\frac{1}{2} \div \frac{3}{3} = ?$   $\frac{1}{2}$

Choose the answer. Be sure the answer is in simplest form.

8. $\frac{2}{3} \div \frac{6}{6} = ?$
   A. 2   B. 3
   **(C)** $\frac{2}{3}$   D. $\frac{3}{2}$

9. $\frac{3}{5} \div \frac{7}{7} = ?$
   A. 3   B. 5
   **(C)** $\frac{3}{5}$   D. $\frac{5}{3}$

10. $\frac{1}{9} \div \frac{5}{5} = ?$
    **(A)** $\frac{1}{9}$   B. 1
    C. 9   D. $\frac{9}{5}$

11. $\frac{3}{4} \div \frac{2}{2} = ?$
    A. 3   B. $\frac{4}{3}$
    **(C)** $\frac{3}{4}$   D. 4

*48*  *FRACTIONS: MULTIPLICATION AND DIVISION*  *UNDERSTAND DIVISION OF FRACTIONS*

### Additional Answers
3. **Example:** Because $\frac{6}{6}$ is the same as 1, and any number divided by 1 is itself, you know that $\frac{5}{7} \div \frac{6}{6}$ is equal to $\frac{5}{7}$.

**116  FRACTIONS: MULTIPLICATION AND DIVISION**

# Multiply Fractions (A)

## Lesson Overview

| | | |
|---|---|---|
| **GET READY** Review Multiplying | 10 minutes | ONLINE |
| **LEARN** Use Models | 10 minutes | OFFLINE |
| **LEARN** Connect to an Algorithm | 15 minutes | ONLINE |
| **LEARN** Use the Algorithm | 15 minutes | OFFLINE |
| **TRY IT** Practice Multiplying | 10 minutes | OFFLINE |

### ▶ Lesson Objectives
Multiply fractions and explain a step-by-step approach.

### ▶ Prerequisite Skills
- Simplify factors in fraction multiplication problems in which numerators and denominators have common factors.
- Multiply a fraction by a whole number to solve a story problem.

### ▶ Content Background
In this lesson, students will use paper models to represent how to multiply a fraction by a fraction. Then they will make the transition to using an algorithm to multiply fractions.

After students use models to multiply a fraction by a fraction, they will use a step-by-step approach to find the product. In the step-by-step approach, they should first divide out common factors, and then multiply. They should express answers in simplest form by dividing the answer by the greatest fraction equal to 1 that will divide evenly.

Although students will most often see fractions written with a horizontal fraction bar in math, such as $\frac{2}{3}$ or $5\frac{5}{6}$, they will occasionally see a diagonal fraction bar, such as 2/3 or 5 5/6. Students will very likely see the diagonal fraction bar in everyday experiences, but be sure they understand that using the horizontal fraction bar in their work will make problems involving fractions easier to interpret and solve.

### ▶ Common Errors and Misconceptions
Students might believe that multiplication always gives products that are greater than or equal to the factors. This is true for whole numbers; for example, $9 \times 8 = 72$, $50 \times 3 = 150$, and $1 \times 1 = 1$. However, students might not realize that the product of a whole number and fraction less than 1 is less than the whole-number factor; for example, $\frac{2}{3} \times 12 = 8$ and $63 \times \frac{5}{7} = 45$.

### ▶ Safety
Make sure students handle the scissors carefully and be sure to store them in a safe place.

### Materials to Gather

**SUPPLIED**
Practice Multiplying activity page

**ALSO NEEDED**
scissors, pointed-end safety

## GET READY  Review Multiplying

**ONLINE 10 min**

Students will work step by step to find the product of a fraction times a whole number to solve a story problem. They will also solve a problem by finding the product of two fractions after simplifying one of the fractions.

### Objectives

- Simplify factors in fraction multiplication problems in which numerators and denominators have common factors.
- Multiply a fraction by a whole number to solve a story problem.

## LEARN  Use Models

**OFFLINE 10 min**

### Objectives

- Multiply fractions and explain a step-by-step approach.

Students will use a paper model to represent how to multiply a fraction by a fraction. Gather paper and scissors for the activity. The paper is for folding and cutting. Students will write the problem in their Math Notebook.

1. **Say:** Write $\frac{3}{4} \times \frac{2}{3} = ?$
2. **Say:** You can use the multiplication symbol, ×, or the multiplication dot, •, to write the number sentence to solve the problem. Write the problem again using the multiplication dot.
3. Check to see that students wrote $\frac{3}{4} \cdot \frac{2}{3} = ?$
4. **Say:** Let's use paper to model the problem $\frac{3}{4} \cdot \frac{2}{3} = ?$
5. Have students fold a sheet of paper into 3 equal parts, or thirds, and then cut out each third. Dividing the paper into thirds uses a model to show the factor $\frac{2}{3}$.

   **Say:** The paper is cut into 3 equal-sized pieces. We will use 2 of those pieces to represent the factor $\frac{2}{3}$ in the problem, because the pieces show 2 out of 3 equal-sized parts.

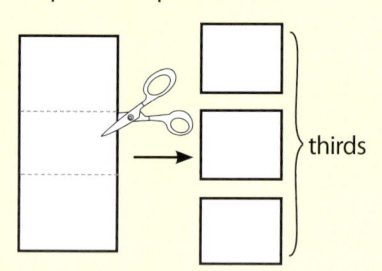

### Tips

Encourage students to come up with their own methods for using models to multiply fractions. Models can include folding and cutting paper or drawing diagrams.

6. Have students fold each of the cut-out thirds into fourths, and then cut out each fourth. Dividing each third into fourths uses a model to show the factor $\frac{3}{4}$.

   **Say:** Each third is cut into 4 equal-sized pieces.

**118** FRACTIONS: MULTIPLICATION AND DIVISION

7. **Ask:** If the sheet of paper represents one whole, how many equal parts is the whole divided into? 12

8. Take 3 of the cut-out fourths (representing $\frac{3}{4}$) from 2 sets of the cut-out thirds (representing $\frac{2}{3}$).

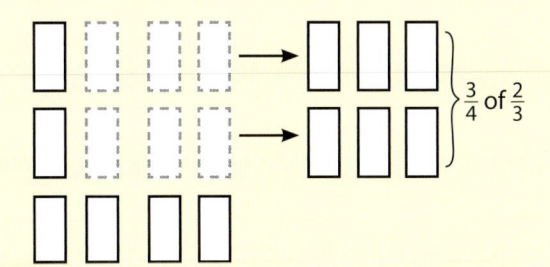

9. **Say:** We took $\frac{3}{4}$ from 2 sets of 3, or $\frac{2}{3}$. Each of the pieces represents $\frac{1}{12}$ of the whole. There are 6 pieces.

    **Ask:** How many twelfths are equal to $\frac{3}{4}$ of $\frac{2}{3}$? $\frac{6}{12}$

10. What is $\frac{3}{4} \cdot \frac{2}{3} = ?$ $\frac{6}{12}$

11. Tell students to write the answer to the number sentence.

## LEARN Connect to an Algorithm

ONLINE 15 min

Students will connect models to the algorithm for multiplying fractions. While models do not explicitly show the steps of the algorithm where students multiply the numerators and denominators of both fractions, the models do help students understand that the total number of parts is the same as multiplying the two denominators. Models also show that the number of parts removed from all the parts in the model is the same as multiplying the two numerators.

### Objectives
- Multiply fractions and explain a step-by-step approach.

## LEARN Use the Algorithm

OFFLINE 15 min

Students will use an algorithm to multiply a fraction by a fraction. They will write the problems and show their work in their Math Notebook.

### Objectives
- Multiply fractions and explain a step-by-step approach.

1. Have students write $\frac{1}{10} \times \frac{3}{7} = ?$

    A common factor is a number that will divide a numerator and a denominator evenly.

    **Ask:** Do the numerator 1 and the denominator 7 have any common factors other than 1? No

    **Ask:** Do the denominator 10 and the numerator 3 have any common factors other than 1? No

    **Say:** That means we are ready to multiply the fraction factors to find the product. Multiply the numerators.

    **Ask:** What is $1 \times 3$? 3

    **Say:** Multiply the denominators.

    **Ask:** What is $10 \times 7$? 70

    **Ask:** What is the product of $\frac{1}{10} \times \frac{3}{7}$? $\frac{3}{70}$

**Ask:** Can $\frac{3}{70}$ be simplified? Why? No, because there is no common factor other than 1 that divides 3 and 70 evenly.

**Ask:** What is the product of $\frac{1}{10} \times \frac{3}{7}$? $\frac{3}{70}$

Have students write the product of the number sentence.

2. Have students write $\frac{8}{9} \times \frac{3}{4} = ?$

   **Say:** You can divide out common factors greater than 1 before you multiply. Start with 8 and 4. A common factor of 8 and 4 is 4.

   **Ask:** What is $8 \div 4$? 2

   **Ask:** What is $4 \div 4$? 1

   **Say:** Cross out 8 and write 2 next to it. Cross out 4 and write 1 next to it. Now move to dividing out common factors for 9 and 3.

   **Say:** A common factor of 9 and 3 is 3.

   **Ask:** What is $9 \div 3$? 3

   **Ask:** What is $3 \div 3$? 1

   **Say:** Cross out 9 and write 3 next to it. Cross out 3 and write 1 next to it.

   **Say:** After dividing out common factors, $\frac{8}{9} \times \frac{3}{4}$ can be rewritten as $\frac{2}{3} \times \frac{1}{1}$. Multiply the numerators and then multiply the denominators.

   **Ask:** What is $2 \times 1$? 2

   **Ask:** What is $3 \times 1$? 3

   **Ask:** What is the product of $\frac{8}{9} \times \frac{3}{4}$? $\frac{2}{3}$

   Have students write the product of the number sentence.

3. Have students write $\frac{1}{10} \times \frac{5}{6} = ?$

   Guide students through this problem as you did in Step 2. Students should answer that there are no common factors of 1 and 6 greater than 1. They should say that 5 is a common factor of 10 and 5.

   When students divide out the common factor of 5, both fractions will have a numerator of 1. One fraction will have a denominator of 2. The other fraction will have a denominator of 6.

   **Ask:** What is the product of $\frac{1}{10} \times \frac{5}{6}$? $\frac{1}{12}$

4. Have students write $\frac{4}{9} \times \frac{3}{8} = ?$

   **Say:** Divide out common factors before you multiply.

   **Ask:** Are there any common factors in this problem? Yes, 4 and 3

   **Ask:** What is a common factor of 4 and 8? 4

   **Ask:** What is 8 divided by 4? 2

   **Ask:** What is 4 divided by 4? 1

   **Say:** Cross out 8 and write 2 next to it. Cross out 4 and write 1 next to it.

   **Ask:** What is a common factor of 9 and 3? 3

   **Ask:** What is 9 divided by 3? 3

   **Ask:** What is 3 divided by 3? 1

   **Say:** Cross out 9 and write 3 next to it. Cross out 3 and write 1 next to it.

   After dividing out common factors, $\frac{4}{9} \times \frac{3}{8}$ can be rewritten as $\frac{1}{3} \times \frac{1}{2}$.

   Multiply the numerators and then multiply the denominators.

   **Ask:** What is the product of $\frac{4}{9} \times \frac{3}{8} = ?$ $\frac{1}{6}$

# TRY IT  Practice Multiplying

**OFFLINE 10 min**

### Objectives
- Multiply fractions and explain a step-by-step approach.

Students will practice multiplying fractions by following a step-by-step approach. Have students turn to the Practice Multiplying activity page in their Activity Book and read the directions with them.

Students should copy the problems from the Activity Book into their Math Notebook as necessary and solve them there.

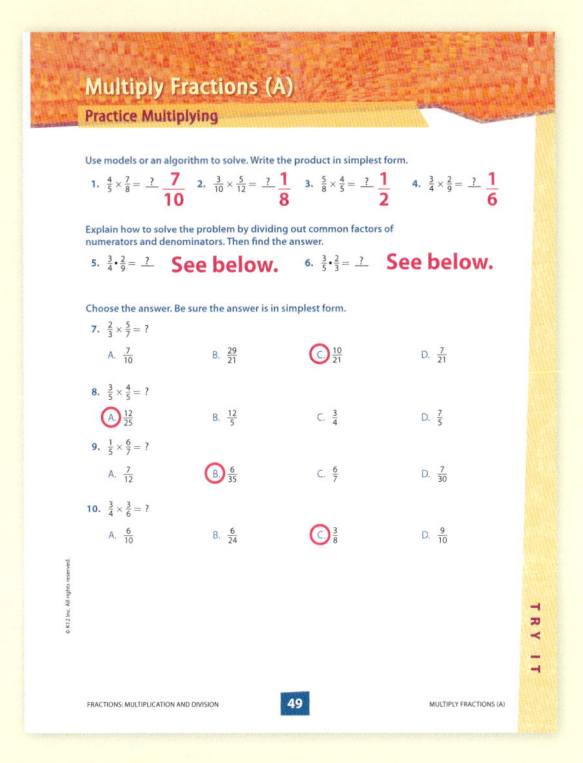

### Tips
Remind students to divide out common factors before they multiply. Tell students to check each product to make sure it is in its simplest form. If the product is not in simplest form, divide out common factors from the numerator and the denominator.

## Additional Answers

**5. Example:** Multiply $\frac{3}{4} \cdot \frac{2}{9} = ?$

Divide out the common factor 3 from 3 in the numerator and 9 in the denominator.

Divide out the common factor 2 from 4 in the denominator and 2 in the numerator.

Rewrite the problem as $\frac{1}{2} \cdot \frac{1}{3} = ?$

Multiply the numerators. Multiply the denominators. The answer is $\frac{1}{6}$.

**Check:** Can the answer be simplified? No. 1 and 6 only have a common factor of 1.

**6. Example:** Multiply $\frac{3}{5} \cdot \frac{2}{3} = ?$

Divide out the common factor 3 from 3 in the numerator and 3 in the denominator.

Rewrite the problem as $\frac{1}{5} \cdot \frac{2}{1} = ?$

Multiply the numerators. Multiply the denominators. The answer is $\frac{2}{5}$.

**Check:** Can the answer be simplified? No. 2 and 5 only have a common factor of 1.

# Multiply Fractions (B)

## Lesson Overview

| Skills Update | 5 minutes | **ONLINE** |
| **GET READY** Fraction Story Problems | 10 minutes | **OFFLINE** |
| **LEARN** Use Models to Multiply Mixed Numbers | 20 minutes | **OFFLINE** |
| **LEARN** Fraction Circles | 15 minutes | **OFFLINE** |
| **TRY IT** Multiply Mixed Numbers | 10 minutes | **OFFLINE** |

### ▶ Lesson Objectives
Multiply fractions and explain a step-by-step approach.

### ▶ Prerequisite Skills
- Simplify factors in fraction multiplication problems in which numerators and denominators have common factors.
- Multiply a fraction by a whole number to solve a story problem.

### ▶ Content Background
In this lesson, students will use models to multiply fractions.

After students use models to multiply a fraction by a fraction, they will use a step-by-step approach to find the product. In the step-by-step approach, they should first divide out common factors, and then multiply. They should express answers in simplest form by dividing the answer by the greatest fraction equal to 1 that will divide evenly.

Although students will most often see fractions written with a horizontal fraction bar in math, such as $\frac{2}{3}$ or $5\frac{5}{6}$, they will occasionally see a diagonal fraction bar, such as 2/3 or 5 5/6. Students will very likely see the diagonal fraction bar in everyday experiences, but be sure they understand that using the horizontal fraction bar in their work will make problems involving fractions easier to interpret and solve.

### ▶ Common Errors and Misconceptions
Students might believe that multiplication always gives products that are greater than or equal to the factors. This is true for whole numbers; for example, $9 \times 8 = 72$, $50 \times 3 = 150$, and $1 \times 1 = 1$. However, students might not realize that the product of a whole number and fraction less than 1 is less than the whole-number factor; for example, $\frac{2}{3} \times 12 = 8$ and $63 \times \frac{5}{7} = 45$.

### ▶ Advance Preparation
Print two copies each of the Fraction Circles and Centimeter Grid Paper.

### Materials to Gather

**SUPPLIED**
Fraction Circles (printout)
Centimeter Grid Paper (printout)
Multiply Mixed Numbers activity page

**122** FRACTIONS: MULTIPLICATION AND DIVISION

## GET READY  Fraction Story Problems

**OFFLINE 10 min**

### Objectives
- Simplify factors in fraction multiplication problems in which numerators and denominators have common factors.
- Multiply a fraction by a whole number to solve a story problem.

Students will write story problems that use fractions. They will need to multiply fractions by whole numbers and fractions by fractions to solve the problems.

There are no materials to gather for this activity. Have students write the problems in their Math Notebook. They should show their work as they answer the questions and solve the problems.

1. Discuss with students different everyday situations that involve fractions, such as gardening, sewing, cooking, wrapping gifts, and working with time and money. Encourage students to suggest their own ideas.

2. Tell students to think of a situation they are familiar and use it in a math story problem in which they will need to multiply 12 by $\frac{4}{6}$. Here is an example:
   - There are 12 eggs in a carton. When Claire opened a carton of eggs, she noticed that $\frac{4}{6}$ of the 12 eggs were cracked. How many eggs were cracked?

3. Have students read their story problem aloud. Check to make sure the solution to the problem requires multiplying $12 \times \frac{4}{6}$.

4. Have students write the number sentence $12 \times \frac{4}{6} = ?$

5. Guide students to use the algorithm to solve the problem.

   **Ask:** What is 12 written as a fraction with 1 as the denominator? $\frac{12}{1}$

   **Say:** Rewrite the number sentence using $\frac{12}{1}$ instead of 12.

   Students should rewrite the number sentence as $\frac{12}{1} \times \frac{4}{6} = ?$

   **Ask:** Can you divide out common factors? Yes, 6 is a common factor of 6 and 12.

   **Ask:** How do you divide out the common factor of 6, and how do you rewrite the number sentence? Cross out 12 and write 2 next to it. Cross out 6 and write 1 next to it. Rewrite the number sentence as $\frac{2}{1} \times \frac{4}{1} = ?$

   **Ask:** How do you find the product, and what is the product? Multiply the numerators. Multiply the denominators. The product of $12 \times \frac{4}{6} = 8$.

   **Ask:** Does 8 make sense as the answer to your story problem?

   Students should say that it does make sense. Check to make sure that the problem they wrote has the answer 8.

6. Repeat Steps 2–5 with the numbers $\frac{5}{8} \times 4$. The product is $\frac{5}{2}$.

7. Tell students to write a multiplication story problem that involves multiplying a fraction by a fraction. In the problem, have students use these fractions: $\frac{1}{3}$ and $\frac{3}{8}$. The product is $\frac{1}{8}$.

### Tips
Remind students that $12 \times \frac{4}{6}$ means $\frac{4}{6}$ of 12 and $\frac{1}{3} \times \frac{3}{8}$ means $\frac{1}{3}$ of $\frac{3}{8}$. This understanding will help students develop their story problems.

MULTIPLY FRACTIONS (B)

## LEARN Use Models to Multiply Mixed Numbers

**OFFLINE 20 min**

### Objectives

- Multiply fractions and explain a step-by-step approach.

Students will review multiplying a fraction by a fraction. Then they will draw a model on grid paper to show multiplication of a mixed number by a fraction. Then they will learn the algorithm, or step-by-step procedure, for multiplying a mixed number by a fraction.

Gather a copy of the Centimeter Grid Paper. Have students write the problems in their Math Notebook. They should show their work as they answer the questions and solve the problems.

1. Review the use of a model for multiplying a fraction by a fraction. Tell students they will multiply $\frac{6}{8} \times \frac{2}{3}$. Have them outline a 3 by 8 rectangle on grid paper.

2. In 6 of the 8 rows, have students mark each centimeter square with a diagonal mark to show $\frac{6}{8}$.

3. In 2 of the 3 columns, have students mark each centimeter square with an opposite diagonal mark to show $\frac{2}{3}$.

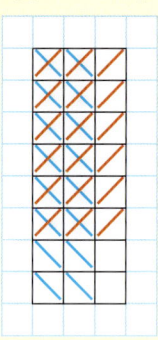

**Ask:** How many centimeter squares have an X, and how many squares are in the rectangle? *12 squares; 24 squares*

**Ask:** What fraction of the squares have Xs? $\frac{12}{24}$, or $\frac{1}{2}$

**Ask:** What is the product of $\frac{6}{8} \times \frac{2}{3} = ?$ $\frac{1}{2}$

4. Tell students they will multiply a fraction times a mixed number. Read the following problem to students:

   - Mike filled $1\frac{2}{6}$ pitchers with homemade lemonade. Each pitcher holds $\frac{3}{8}$ gallon. How many gallons of lemonade are in the pitchers?

   **Ask:** How do you write a number sentence that represents the problem? $1\frac{2}{6} \times \frac{3}{8} = ?$

5. Have students outline two 8 by 6 rectangles on grid paper. They will need two rectangles because the number sentence has a factor greater than 1 but less than 2. Each rectangle has 48 squares. That means that the answer will be the total number of Xs compared with 48.

   Students will start by marking the rectangles to show $\frac{3}{8}$. They will use diagonal marks on the columns. When students need to show a factor less than 1 (such as $\frac{3}{8}$) on a model with two rectangles, they need to mark the factor on both rectangles. The reason is that the factor is a factor for the entire model, not just one part of the model.

**124** FRACTIONS: MULTIPLICATION AND DIVISION

6. Have students mark 3 columns on the first rectangle and 3 columns on the second rectangle to show $\frac{3}{8}$ of the entire model.

7. Have students use opposite diagonal marks to show $1\frac{2}{6}$. They should do that by marking all 6 rows on the first rectangle and 2 of the 6 rows on the second rectangle.

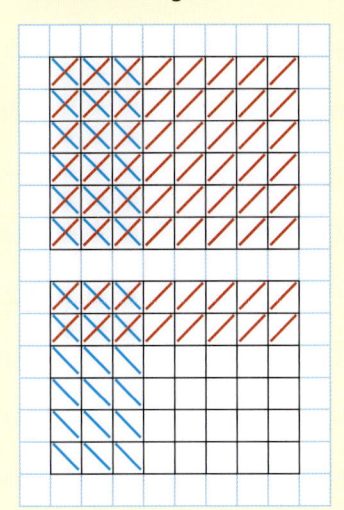

**Tips**

When students look to find common factors in two fractions before they multiply, remind them that they are looking for a common factor other than 1 to divide each number by.

**Ask:** When we have more than one rectangle in a multiplication model, we count the total squares in just one rectangle. How many squares is each rectangle divided into? 48

**Ask:** How many squares have Xs? 24

**Ask:** What fraction is represented by this model? $\frac{24}{48}$, or $\frac{1}{2}$

**Say:** Write the number sentence and the answer. $1\frac{2}{6} \times \frac{3}{8} = \frac{1}{2}$

8. Have students solve the same number sentence without using a model. Have them write $\frac{3}{8} \times 1\frac{2}{6} = ?$ in their Math Notebook. Use the following questions to lead them through multiplying the two fractions:

**Ask:** The first step in multiplying by a mixed number is to rewrite the mixed number as an improper fraction. In $1\frac{2}{6}$, the whole number part is 1. How many sixths are in 1? 6

**Ask:** Use the equivalent form of 1, $\frac{6}{6}$, and add the fraction part of the mixed number, $\frac{2}{6}$, to find the improper fraction for $1\frac{2}{6}$. What is $\frac{6}{6} + \frac{2}{6}$? $\frac{8}{6}$

Have students write $\frac{3}{8} \times \frac{8}{6} = ?$ in their Math Notebook.

**Ask:** How can you divide out common factors in $\frac{3}{8} \times \frac{8}{6}$? A common factor of 3 and 6 is 3. Divide 3 by 3 and 6 by 3. A common factor of 8 is 8, so divide each 8 by 8.

**Ask:** What is the number sentence after you divide out the common factors? $\frac{1}{1} \times \frac{1}{2} = ?$

**Ask:** How do you find the product, and what is the product? Multiply the numerators: $1 \times 1 = 1$. Multiply the denominators: $1 \times 2 = 2$. The product is $\frac{1}{2}$.

**Ask:** What is the original problem and the answer? $1\frac{2}{6} \times \frac{3}{8} = \frac{1}{2}$

**MULTIPLY FRACTIONS (B)** 125

9. Have students try another problem. They should write $\frac{5}{7} \times 1\frac{1}{3} = ?$ in their Math Notebook. Guide students to make a model as shown.

This model shows $1\frac{1}{3}$ marked:

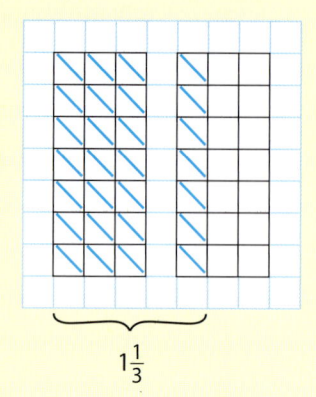

$\underbrace{\qquad\qquad}_{1\frac{1}{3}}$

This model shows $\frac{5}{7}$ of $1\frac{1}{3}$ marked:

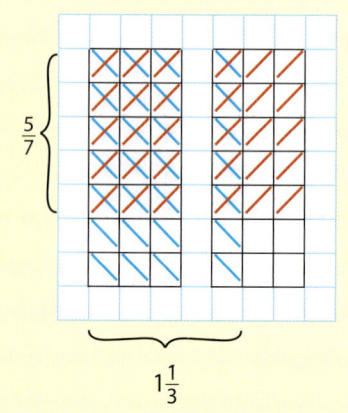

$\left.\vphantom{\rule{0pt}{2em}}\right\}\frac{5}{7}$

$\underbrace{\qquad\qquad}_{1\frac{1}{3}}$

**Ask:** How many squares are marked with an X, and how many squares does each rectangle contain? There are 20 squares marked with an X, and each rectangle contains 21 squares.

**Say:** So $\frac{5}{7} \times 1\frac{1}{3} = \frac{20}{21}$.

10. Tell students to solve the problem again by using a step-by-step procedure. Make sure students begin by rewriting $1\frac{1}{3}$ as the improper fraction of $\frac{4}{3}$ and then rewriting the problem as $\frac{5}{7} \times \frac{4}{3} = ?$

**Ask:** Are there any common factors that can be divided out before you multiply the numerators and the denominators? No

Have students explain how to solve the problem. **Example:** Multiply $5 \times 4 = 20$. That is the numerator of the product. Multiply $7 \times 3 = 21$. That is the denominator of the product. The product of $\frac{5}{7} \times 1\frac{1}{3} = \frac{20}{21}$.

**126** FRACTIONS: MULTIPLICATION AND DIVISION

## LEARN Fraction Circles

**OFFLINE 15 min**

### Objectives
- Multiply fractions and explain a step-by-step approach.

Students will use circles to model how to multiply a fraction and a mixed number. Gather a copy of the Fraction Circles printout.

1. Read the following problem to students:
   - Jesse likes to jump across the rectangles of cement in the sidewalk. He can jump $1\frac{1}{2}$ feet between the seams in the rectangles. How many feet can Jesse jump if he jumps 4 times in a row?

2. **Say:** The expression $1\frac{1}{2} \times 4 = ?$ represents the problem. We can use fraction circles to multiply $1\frac{1}{2} \times 4$. We can apply the commutative property to solve this problem. Using the property, change the problem to $4 \times 1\frac{1}{2} = ?$

3. Have students shade 4 groups of $1\frac{1}{2}$ circles.

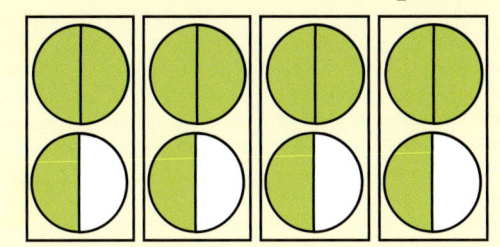

4. **Ask:** Count the number of shaded half-circles in the 4 groups of $1\frac{1}{2}$ shaded circles. How many shaded half-circles are there? **12**

   **Ask:** Look at all the circles. How many half-circles are in each circle? **2**

   **Say:** So $1\frac{1}{2} \times 4 = \frac{12}{2}$, which can be simplified to 6.

5. **Say:** Let's look at another problem where a mixed number and a fraction are multiplied.
   - Rhonda used $2\frac{3}{4}$ containers of strawberries to make fruit salad. Each container held $\frac{1}{3}$ quart of strawberries. How many quarts of strawberries did Rhonda use to make fruit salad?

   **Ask:** What number sentence represents the problem? $2\frac{3}{4} \times \frac{1}{3} = ?$

6. **Say:** We can use fraction circles to multiply $2\frac{3}{4} \times \frac{1}{3}$ and work in steps to find the product.

7. Have students shade $\frac{1}{3}$ of each of the first 2 circles in the second row on the Fraction Circles printout. They will work on the first part of the problem to find $2 \times \frac{1}{3}$.

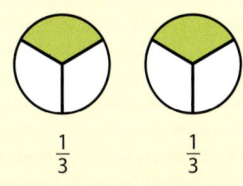

   $\frac{1}{3}$    $\frac{1}{3}$

8. **Ask:** How many thirds did you shade in all? **2**

   **Say:** The product of 2 times $\frac{1}{3}$ is $\frac{2}{3}$. This solves one step of the problem. Let's go to the next step to find the product by multiplying $\frac{3}{4} \times \frac{1}{3}$.

**MULTIPLY FRACTIONS (B)** 127

9. Tell students to shade $\frac{1}{3}$ of the third circle in the second row of the Fraction Circles printout and divide each third into fourths. This model represents $\frac{3}{4} \times \frac{1}{3}$.

10. **Ask:** How many equal parts is the circle divided into? 12

    Have students mark 3 of the shaded twelfths with an X.

    **Ask:** How many twelfths are now marked with an X? 3 twelfths

    **Ask:** The product of $\frac{3}{4} \times \frac{1}{3} = \frac{3}{12}$. In a previous step, you found the product of $2 \times \frac{1}{3}$. What was that? $\frac{2}{3}$

11. **Say:** We can add $\frac{2}{3} + \frac{3}{12}$ to find the product of $2\frac{3}{4} \times \frac{1}{3}$.

    **Ask:** $\frac{2}{3}$ is equivalent to $\frac{8}{12}$. Substitute $\frac{8}{12}$ for $\frac{2}{3}$, and the number sentence becomes $\frac{8}{12} + \frac{3}{12} = \frac{11}{12}$. So what is the product of $2\frac{3}{4} \times \frac{1}{3}$? $\frac{11}{12}$

12. Tell students they can also use a step-by-step process to multiply $2\frac{3}{4} \times \frac{1}{3}$.

    **Say:** The first step in multiplying a fraction by a mixed number is to rewrite the mixed number as an improper fraction. Rewrite $2\frac{3}{4}$ as an improper fraction.

    **Ask:** How many fourths are in 2? 8

    **Ask:** Add $\frac{8}{4}$, the number of fourths in 2 wholes, and $\frac{3}{4}$, the fraction part of the mixed number. What is $\frac{8}{4} + \frac{3}{4}$? $\frac{11}{4}$

    **Ask:** What is $2\frac{3}{4}$ written as an improper fraction? $\frac{11}{4}$

13. Have students write $\frac{11}{4} \times \frac{1}{3} = ?$ in their Math Notebook. Use the following questions to lead them through the multiplication process.

    **Ask:** Can you divide out any common factors in $\frac{11}{4} \times \frac{1}{3} = ?$ No

    **Ask:** How do you find the product of $\frac{11}{4} \times \frac{1}{3}$? Multiply the numerators: $11 \times 1 = 11$. Multiply the denominators: $4 \times 3 = 12$. Write the product of the numerators over the product of the denominators: $\frac{11}{12}$.

    **Ask:** What is the product of $\frac{11}{4} \times \frac{1}{3}$? $\frac{11}{12}$

    **Ask:** Going back to the original problem, what is $2\frac{3}{4} \times \frac{1}{3}$? $\frac{11}{12}$

14. **Ask:** Did you get the same product when you used the fraction circles and the step-by-step process? Yes

15. Have students use the third row of fraction circles on the Fraction Circles printout and the step-by-step algorithm to multiply $2\frac{1}{2} \times \frac{1}{4}$. $\frac{5}{8}$

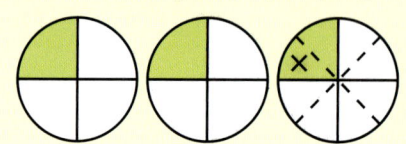

**128** FRACTIONS: MULTIPLICATION AND DIVISION

# TRY IT  Multiply Mixed Numbers

**OFFLINE 10 min**

Students will practice multiplying fractions and mixed numbers. Gather one copy each of the Centimeter Grid Paper and the Fraction Circles printout. Have students turn to the Multiply Mixed Numbers activity page in their Activity Book and read the directions with them.

Students should copy the problems from the Activity Book into their Math Notebook as necessary and solve them there.

### Objectives
- Multiply fractions and explain a step-by-step approach.

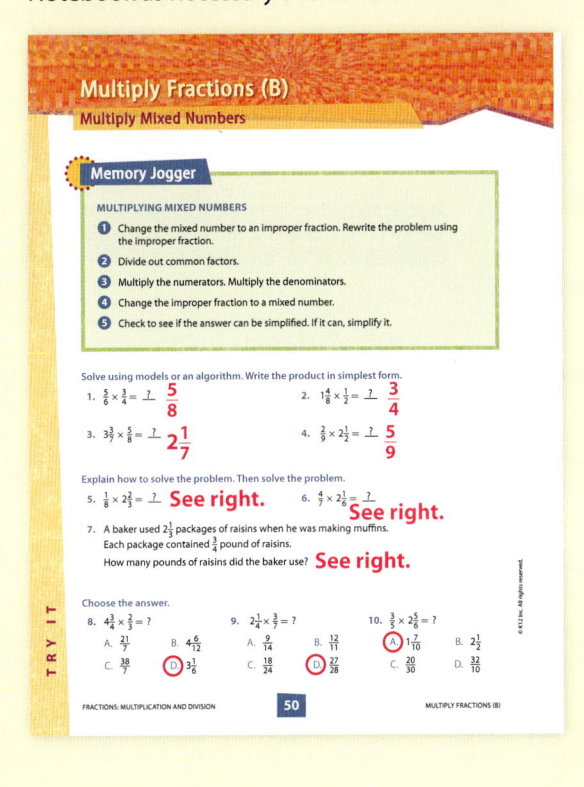

### Additional Answers

**5. Example:** I wrote the problem: $\frac{1}{8} \times 2\frac{2}{3} = ?$ I used the commutative property to change the problem to $2\frac{2}{3} \times \frac{1}{8} = ?$ I changed the mixed number $2\frac{2}{3}$ to the improper fraction $\frac{8}{3}$. I rewrote the problem to $\frac{8}{3} \times \frac{1}{8} = ?$ I looked for common factors. I divided out the common factor 8 from 8 in the numerator and 8 in the denominator. I rewrote the problem as $\frac{1}{3} \times \frac{1}{1} = ?$ I multiplied the numerators and denominators and found a product to the original problem: $\frac{1}{8} \times 2\frac{2}{3} = \frac{1}{3}$.

**6. Example:** Multiply $\frac{4}{7} \times 2\frac{1}{6} = ?$

Change $2\frac{1}{6}$ to the improper fraction $\frac{13}{6}$. Rewrite the problem to $\frac{4}{7} \times \frac{13}{6} = ?$

Divide out the common factor 2 from 4 in the numerator and 6 in the denominator.

Rewrite the problem as $\frac{2}{7} \times \frac{13}{3} = ?$

Multiply the numerators. Multiply the denominators. The product is $\frac{26}{21}$.

Change the improper fraction $\frac{26}{21}$ to the mixed number $1\frac{5}{21}$.

$\frac{4}{7} \times 2\frac{1}{6} = 1\frac{5}{21}$

**7. Example:** Multiply $2\frac{1}{3} \times \frac{3}{4} = ?$

Change $2\frac{1}{3}$ to the improper fraction $\frac{7}{3}$. Rewrite the problem to $\frac{7}{3} \times \frac{3}{4} = ?$

Divide out the common factor 3 from 3 in the denominator and 3 in the numerator.

Rewrite the problem as $\frac{7}{1} \times \frac{1}{4} = ?$

Multiply the numerators. Multiply the denominators. The product is $\frac{7}{4}$.

Change the improper fraction $\frac{7}{4}$ to the mixed number $1\frac{3}{4}$.

$2\frac{1}{3} \times \frac{3}{4} = 1\frac{3}{4}$

The baker used $1\frac{3}{4}$ pounds of raisins.

MULTIPLY FRACTIONS (B)

# Multiply Fractions (C)

## Lesson Overview

| | | |
|---|---|---|
| **GET READY** Story Problems with Fractions | 5 minutes | **ONLINE** |
| **LEARN** Multiply Mixed Numbers | 15 minutes | **OFFLINE** |
| **LEARN** Use a Step-by-Step Approach | 15 minutes | **OFFLINE** |
| **TRY IT** Practice Multiplying Fractions | 15 minutes | **OFFLINE** |
| **CHECKPOINT** | 10 minutes | **ONLINE** |

### ▶ Lesson Objectives
Multiply fractions and explain a step-by-step approach.

### ▶ Prerequisite Skills
- Simplify factors in fraction multiplication problems in which numerators and denominators have common factors.
- Multiply a fraction by a whole number to solve a story problem.

### ▶ Content Background
After students use models to multiply a fraction by a fraction, they will use a step-by-step approach to find the product. In the step-by-step approach, they should first divide out common factors, and then multiply. They should express answers in simplest form by dividing the answer by the greatest fraction equal to 1 that will divide evenly.

Although students will most often see fractions written with a horizontal fraction bar in math, such as $\frac{2}{3}$ or $5\frac{5}{6}$, they will occasionally see a diagonal fraction bar, such as 2/3 or 5 5/6. Students will very likely see the diagonal fraction bar in everyday experiences, but be sure they understand that using the horizontal fraction bar in their work will make problems involving fractions easier to interpret and solve.

### ▶ Common Errors and Misconceptions
Students might believe that multiplication always gives products that are greater than or equal to the factors. This is true for whole numbers; for example, $9 \times 8 = 72$, $50 \times 3 = 150$, and $1 \times 1 = 1$. However, students might not realize that the product of a whole number and fraction less than 1 is less than the whole-number factor; for example, $\frac{2}{3} \times 12 = 8$ and $63 \times \frac{5}{7} = 45$.

### Materials to Gather

**SUPPLIED**

Practice Multiplying Fractions activity page

## GET READY  Story Problems with Fractions

**ONLINE 5 min**

Students will solve a story problem by using the multiplication algorithm for a whole number times a fraction. They will go back to the original problem and make sure their calculated answer makes sense. They then will solve a story problem by using the multiplication algorithm for a fraction times a fraction.

### Objectives
- Simplify factors in fraction multiplication problems in which numerators and denominators have common factors.
- Multiply a fraction by a whole number to solve a story problem.

## LEARN  Multiply Mixed Numbers

**OFFLINE 15 min**

Students will use algorithms to multiply mixed numbers by mixed numbers. They will solve story problems in which they will multiply two mixed numbers. Students should write all algorithm steps in their Math Notebook.

### Objectives
- Multiply fractions and explain a step-by-step approach.

1. Review multiplying a fraction by a mixed number.

   Have students write $\frac{5}{8} \times 3\frac{1}{3} = ?$

   Ask students to use a step-by-step approach to solve the problem while explaining to you how they do each step. If necessary, guide them through the following steps. (See the answer text for responses that students should say or write.)

   - Rewrite $3\frac{1}{3}$ as an improper fraction. Add $\frac{9}{3}$, which equals 3, and $\frac{1}{3}$ to get $\frac{10}{3}$.
   - Use the improper fraction and rewrite the number sentence. $\frac{5}{8} \times \frac{10}{3} = ?$
   - Divide out the common factors. A common factor of 8 and 10 is 2, so divide 8 by 2 and 10 by 2. The number sentence is now $\frac{5}{4} \times \frac{5}{3} = ?$
   - Find the product. Multiply the numerators. Multiply the denominators. Change the answer from an improper fraction to a mixed number. $\frac{5}{4} \times \frac{5}{3} = \frac{25}{12}$ To change the improper fraction to a mixed number, you divide 25 by 12. Use the quotient, 2, as the whole number in the mixed number. Use the remainder, 1, as the numerator and 12 as the denominator of the fraction. The product as a mixed number is $2\frac{1}{12}$. $\frac{5}{8} \times 3\frac{1}{3} = 2\frac{1}{12}$.

2. Read the following problem to students:
   - Beth is picking strawberries. She fills $3\frac{1}{3}$ boxes with strawberries in 1 hour. How many boxes will Beth fill with strawberries in $2\frac{3}{4}$ hours?

3. **Ask:** What number sentence represents the problem? $3\frac{1}{3} \times 2\frac{3}{4} = ?$

4. **Ask:** Sometimes it is easier to multiply when the factors are in a different order. What property can you use to change the order of the factors in $3\frac{1}{3} \times 2\frac{3}{4} = ?$ commutative property

   **Ask:** What is $3\frac{1}{3} \times 2\frac{3}{4}$ when you apply the commutative property? $2\frac{3}{4} \times 3\frac{1}{3}$

5. Have students rewrite each mixed number as an improper fraction. $2\frac{3}{4} = \frac{11}{4}; 3\frac{1}{3} = \frac{10}{3}$

   Have students rewrite the problem using improper fractions. $\frac{11}{4} \times \frac{10}{3} = ?$

**MULTIPLY FRACTIONS (C)  131**

6. **Say:** Look for common factors in the number sentence $\frac{11}{4} \times \frac{10}{3} = ?$
   A common factor of 4 in the denominator and 10 in the numerator is 2. Divide out the common factor 2 and rewrite the number sentence.
   $\frac{11}{2} \times \frac{5}{3} = ?$

7. Tell students to multiply the numerators and then multiply the denominators to find the product.
   **Ask:** What is 11 × 5? 55
   **Ask:** What is 2 × 3? 6
   **Ask:** What is the product? $\frac{55}{6}$

8. Tell students to change the improper fraction $\frac{55}{6}$ to a mixed number by dividing 55 by 6. The quotient is the whole number in the mixed number. The remainder is the numerator and 6 is the denominator in the mixed number.
   **Ask:** What is $\frac{55}{6}$ as a mixed number? $9\frac{1}{6}$
   **Say:** Write the number sentence and solve the problem. $3\frac{1}{3} \times 2\frac{3}{4} = 9\frac{1}{6}$.
   Beth will fill $9\frac{1}{6}$ boxes in $2\frac{3}{4}$ hours.

9. Give students another example of multiplying a mixed number by a mixed number in an everyday situation. Read the following problem to students:
   - Jeff is making trail mix for summer camp. He uses $2\frac{1}{2}$ cups of raisins to make 1 batch of trail mix. He wants to make $2\frac{1}{6}$ batches. How many cups of raisins does Jeff need?

10. **Ask:** In this problem, use the multiplication dot instead of the multiplication symbol. What number sentence represents the problem? $2\frac{1}{2} \cdot 2\frac{1}{6} = ?$

11. **Ask:** What property can you use to change the order of the factors in the problem? commutative property
    **Ask:** What is $2\frac{1}{2} \cdot 2\frac{1}{6} = ?$ when you use the commutative property? $2\frac{1}{6} \cdot 2\frac{1}{2} = ?$

12. Have students change the mixed numbers to improper fractions and rewrite the problem with improper fractions. If needed, remind them that $2\frac{1}{6}$ is equal to $\frac{13}{6}$ and $2\frac{1}{2}$ is equal to $\frac{5}{2}$. $\frac{13}{6} \cdot \frac{5}{2} = ?$

13. **Say:** Look for common factors in the number sentence $\frac{13}{6} \cdot \frac{5}{2} = ?$ Are there any common factors to divide out? No

14. Tell students to multiply the numerators and then multiply the denominators to find the product.
    **Ask:** What is 13 • 5? 65
    **Ask:** What is 6 • 2? 12
    **Ask:** What is the product? $\frac{65}{12}$

15. Tell students to change the improper fraction $\frac{65}{12}$ to a mixed number by dividing 65 by 12. The quotient is the whole number in the mixed number. The remainder is the numerator and 12 is the denominator in the mixed number.
    **Ask:** What is $\frac{65}{12}$ as a mixed number? $5\frac{5}{12}$

16. Summarize the activity with the following questions:
    **Ask:** What is the product of $2\frac{1}{2} \cdot 2\frac{1}{6} = ?$ $5\frac{5}{12}$
    **Ask:** How many cups of raisins does Jeff need to make $2\frac{1}{6}$ batches of trail mix?
    $5\frac{5}{12}$ cups

FRACTIONS: MULTIPLICATION AND DIVISION

## LEARN  Use a Step-by-Step Approach

**OFFLINE 15 min**

### Objectives
- Multiply fractions and explain a step-by-step approach.

### Tips
Describing the steps needed to solve multiplication problems involving whole numbers, fractions, and mixed numbers helps students improve their computation skills.

Students will use algorithms to multiply fractions by various types of numbers. They will multiply a fraction by a fraction, a fraction by a whole number, a fraction by a mixed number, and mixed numbers by mixed numbers. Students should write the problems in their Math Notebook.

### MULTIPLY FRACTION BY FRACTION

1. Tell students they will multiply a fraction by a fraction to solve a problem. Read the following problem to students:
   - Inez has a stamp collection. Of the stamps she has, $\frac{3}{8}$ are from the United States. In her collection, $\frac{4}{5}$ of the stamps from the United States are from California. What part of Inez's stamp collection is from California?

2. Have students use the multiplication dot to write the number sentence that solves the problem: $\frac{4}{5} \cdot \frac{3}{8} = ?$

    Have students describe the steps they take as they find the product. Check that students say they need to divide out common factors and rewrite the number sentence if needed, multiply numerators, multiply denominators, write the product, and check to see that the answer is in simplest form and simplify if needed.

3. **Ask:** What is the product of $\frac{4}{5} \cdot \frac{3}{8} = ?$ in simplest form? $\frac{3}{10}$

    **Ask:** What part of Inez's stamp collection is from California? $\frac{3}{10}$

### MULTIPLY FRACTION BY WHOLE NUMBER

4. Tell students they will next multiply a fraction by a whole number to solve a problem. Read the following problem to students:
   - Jason's dog eats $\frac{2}{4}$ pound of dog food each day. How many pounds of dog food does Jason's dog eat in 3 days?

5. **Say:** Use an algorithm to multiply $3 \cdot \frac{2}{4} = ?$

6. **Ask:** What is 3 in fraction form? $\frac{3}{1}$

7. Have students use the multiplication dot to write the number sentence that solves the problem: $3 \cdot \frac{2}{4} = ?$

    Have students describe the steps they take as they find the product. Check that students say they need to rewrite the problem with the fraction form of 3, divide out common factors (which is not needed for this problem), multiply numerators, multiply denominators, write the product, and check to see that the answer is in simplest form and simplify if needed.

8. **Ask:** What is the product of $3 \cdot \frac{2}{4} = ?$ in simplest form? $1\frac{1}{2}$

    **Ask:** What is the answer to the problem? Jason's dog eats $1\frac{1}{2}$ pounds of dog food in 3 days.

    Have students use an algorithm to solve the next three problems. Tell students to use either the multiplication symbol or the multiplication dot in their number sentences.

**MULTIPLY FRACTIONS (C)  133**

## MULTIPLY FRACTION BY MIXED NUMBER

9. Tell students to write $\frac{5}{7} \times 2\frac{4}{5} = ?$

10. **Ask:** When you solve a problem where you multiply with a mixed number, what do you do first? Write the mixed number as an improper fraction.

11. **Ask:** What is $2\frac{4}{5}$ as an improper fraction? $\frac{14}{5}$

12. Have students rewrite the problem, replacing the mixed number with the fraction, as $\frac{5}{7} \times \frac{14}{5} = ?$

13. **Ask:** Can you divide out any common factors before you multiply $\frac{5}{7} \times \frac{14}{5} = ?$ Explain. Yes. You can divide 5 in the numerator and 5 in the denominator by a common factor of 5. You can also divide 7 in the denominator and 14 in the numerator by a common factor of 7.

14. **Ask:** What is the number sentence after you divide out the common factors? $\frac{1}{1} \times \frac{2}{1} = ?$

15. **Ask:** Take a look at the factors in the number sentence. Do you need to multiply the numerators and then multiply the denominators to multiply $\frac{1}{1} \times \frac{2}{1}$? Explain. No. Since $\frac{1}{1}$ is equal to 1, and the product of 1 and any factor is that factor, the product of $\frac{1}{1}$ and $\frac{2}{1}$ is 2.
**Ask:** What is the product of $\frac{5}{7} \times 2\frac{4}{5} = ?$ 2

## MULTIPLY MIXED NUMBER BY MIXED NUMBER

16. Tell students to write $1\frac{2}{9} \times 2\frac{4}{7} = ?$

17. Have them change $1\frac{2}{9}$ and $2\frac{4}{7}$ to improper fractions and write the new number sentence. $1\frac{2}{9} = \frac{11}{9}$; $2\frac{4}{7} = \frac{18}{7}$; The new number sentence is $\frac{11}{9} \times \frac{18}{7} = ?$

18. **Ask:** What is the next step before multiplying? Divide out common factors.

19. Have students divide out a common factor of 9 in 9 and 18. The number sentence is now $\frac{11}{1} \times \frac{2}{7} = ?$

20. **Say:** Find the product of $\frac{11}{1} \times \frac{2}{7} = ?$ and write the answer as a mixed number. Describe the steps you follow. Multiply the numerators. Then multiply the denominators. The product is $\frac{22}{7}$. Divide the product of the numerators by the product of the denominators. Write the quotient as a whole number and a fraction with the remainder as the numerator and 7 as the denominator. $1\frac{2}{9} \times 2\frac{4}{7} = 3\frac{1}{7}$

21. Tell students to write $3\frac{3}{5} \times 4\frac{1}{6} = ?$

22. Have students find the product. They will follow these steps:
    - Change each factor from a mixed number to an improper fraction.
    - Divide out common factors.
    - Multiply the numerators and multiply the denominators.
    - Check to see that the answer is in simplest form. Simplify if needed.

    Check that students found that the product of $3\frac{3}{5} \times 4\frac{1}{6} = 15$.

# TRY IT  Practice Multiplying Fractions

**OFFLINE 15 min**

## Objectives
- Multiply fractions and explain a step-by-step approach.

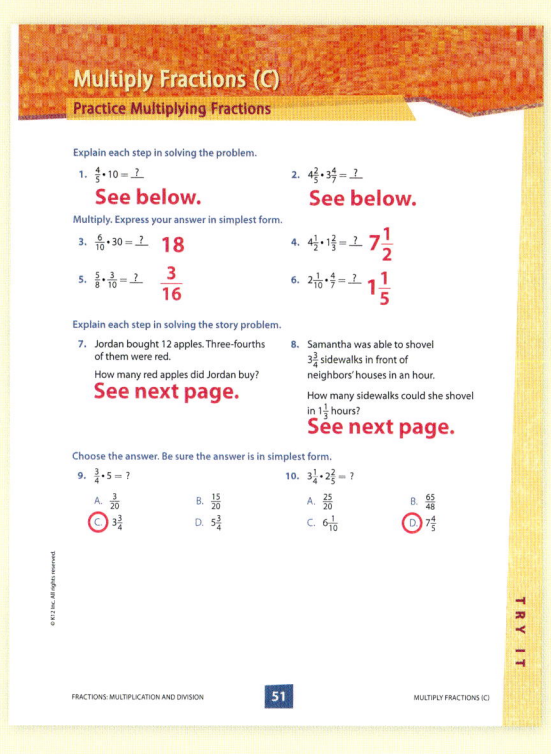

Students will practice multiplying various combinations of fractions and mixed numbers. Have students turn to the Practice Multiplying Fractions activity page in their Activity Book and read the directions with them.

Students should copy the problems from the Activity Book into their Math Notebook as necessary and solve them there.

### Multiply Fractions (C)
**Practice Multiplying Fractions**

Explain each step in solving the problem.
1. $\frac{4}{5} \cdot 10 = ?$  **See below.**
2. $4\frac{2}{5} \cdot 3\frac{4}{7} = ?$  **See below.**

Multiply. Express your answer in simplest form.
3. $\frac{6}{10} \cdot 30 = ?$  **18**
4. $4\frac{1}{2} \cdot 1\frac{2}{3} = ?$  **$7\frac{1}{2}$**
5. $\frac{5}{8} \cdot \frac{3}{10} = ?$  **$\frac{3}{16}$**
6. $2\frac{1}{10} \cdot \frac{4}{7} = ?$  **$1\frac{1}{5}$**

Explain each step in solving the story problem.
7. Jordan bought 12 apples. Three-fourths of them were red. How many red apples did Jordan buy? **See next page.**
8. Samantha was able to shovel $3\frac{3}{4}$ sidewalks in front of neighbors' houses in an hour. How many sidewalks could she shovel in $1\frac{1}{3}$ hours? **See next page.**

Choose the answer. Be sure the answer is in simplest form.
9. $\frac{3}{4} \cdot 5 = ?$
   A. $\frac{3}{20}$  B. $\frac{15}{20}$
   **(C)** $3\frac{3}{4}$  D. $5\frac{3}{4}$
10. $3\frac{1}{4} \cdot 2\frac{2}{5} = ?$
    A. $\frac{25}{20}$  B. $\frac{65}{48}$
    C. $6\frac{1}{10}$  **(D)** $7\frac{4}{5}$

## Additional Answers

1. **Example:** Multiply $\frac{4}{5} \cdot 10 = ?$
   - Change the whole number 10 to a fraction with a denominator of 1, $\frac{10}{1}$.
   - Rewrite the problem: $\frac{4}{5} \cdot \frac{10}{1} = ?$
   - Divide out the common factor 5.
   - Multiply the numerators.
   - Multiply the denominators.
   - Write the product: $\frac{4}{5} \cdot 10 = 8$.
   - Check: Can the answer be simplified? If so, simplify it. The answer is in simplest form.
   - The answer is 8.

2. **Example:** Multiply $4\frac{2}{5} \cdot 3\frac{4}{7} = ?$
   - Change the mixed numbers to improper fractions: $4\frac{2}{5} = \frac{22}{5}$ and $3\frac{4}{7} = \frac{25}{7}$.
   - Rewrite the problem: $\frac{22}{5} \cdot \frac{25}{7} = ?$
   - Divide out the common factor of 5.
   - Rewrite the problem: $\frac{22}{1} \cdot \frac{5}{7} = ?$
   - Multiply the numerators.
   - Multiply the denominators.
   - Write the product: $4\frac{2}{5} \cdot 3\frac{4}{7} = \frac{110}{7}$.
   - Check: Can the answer be simplified? If so, simplify it. $\frac{110}{7} = 15\frac{5}{7}$
   - The answer is $15\frac{5}{7}$.

7. **Example:** Multiply $\frac{3}{4} \cdot 12 = ?$ because $\frac{3}{4}$ of 12 apples were red.
   - Change the whole number 12 to a fraction with a denominator of 1, $\frac{12}{1}$.
   - Rewrite the problem: $\frac{3}{4} \cdot \frac{12}{1} = ?$
   - Divide out the common factor 4.
   - Multiply the numerators.
   - Multiply the denominators.
   - Write the product: $\frac{3}{4} \cdot 12 = 9$.
   - Check: Can the answer be simplified? If so, simplify it. The answer is in simplest form.
   - The answer is 9 apples.

8. **Example:** Multiply $3\frac{3}{4} \cdot 1\frac{1}{3} = ?$
   - Change the mixed numbers to improper fractions: $3\frac{3}{4} = \frac{15}{4}$ and $1\frac{1}{3} = \frac{4}{3}$.
   - Rewrite the problem: $\frac{15}{4} \cdot \frac{4}{3} = ?$
   - Divide out the common factor 4 and the common factor 3.
   - Rewrite the problem: $\frac{5}{1} \cdot \frac{1}{1} = ?$
   - Multiply the numerators.
   - Multiply the denominators.
   - Write the product: $3\frac{3}{4} \cdot 1\frac{1}{3} = 5$.
   - Check: Can the answer be simplified? If so, simplify it. The answer is in simplest form.
   - The answer is 5 sidewalks.

## CHECKPOINT

**ONLINE 10 min**

Students will complete an online Checkpoint. If necessary, read the directions, problems, and answer choices to students and help them with keyboard or mouse operations.

### Objectives
- Multiply fractions and explain a step-by-step approach.

# Divide Fractions (A)

## Lesson Overview

| | | |
|---|---|---|
| **GET READY** Division Story Problems | 5 minutes | ONLINE |
| **LEARN** Measure Out Division of Fractions | 15 minutes | OFFLINE |
| **LEARN** Use the Steps of Division | 15 minutes | ONLINE |
| **LEARN** Understand Inverse Operations | 15 minutes | ONLINE |
| **TRY IT** Practice Fraction Division | 10 minutes | OFFLINE |

### ▶ Lesson Objectives
Divide fractions and explain a step-by-step approach.

### ▶ Prerequisite Skills
- Divide a whole number by a fraction to solve a story problem.
- Multiply fractions and explain a step-by-step approach.

### ▶ Content Background
In this lesson, students will use different methods to divide fractions and explain the algorithm. They will also investigate the inverse relationship between multiplication and division.

After students use models to multiply a fraction by a fraction, they apply a step-by-step approach to multiplication, called an algorithm. Knowledge of the multiplication algorithm for fractions provides a giant step forward in the understanding of the division algorithm.

The division algorithm simply states that when students divide a fraction by a fraction, they first change the division problem into a multiplication problem using the reciprocal of the divisor. That is, the dividend divided by the divisor becomes the dividend multiplied by the reciprocal of the divisor. Students will actually grow to an understanding of this idea through the use of models.

In simple language, the reciprocal of a fraction is the fraction students get when they reverse the positions of the numerator and denominator. So the reciprocal of $\frac{3}{4}$ would be $\frac{4}{3}$. The product of a fraction and its reciprocal always equals 1, as can be seen in $\frac{3}{4} \times \frac{4}{3} = 1$.

The reciprocal of a whole number, such as 5 (or $\frac{5}{1}$), is $\frac{1}{5}$, because $5 \times \frac{1}{5} = 1$. The reciprocal of a mixed number, such as $2\frac{3}{4}$ (which is equal to the improper fraction $\frac{11}{4}$), would be $\frac{4}{11}$, because $\frac{11}{4} \times \frac{4}{11} = 1$.

Although students will most often see fractions written with a horizontal fraction bar in math, such as $\frac{2}{3}$ or $5\frac{5}{6}$, they will occasionally see a diagonal fraction bar, such as 2/3 or 5 5/6. Students will very likely see the diagonal fraction bar in everyday experiences, but be sure they understand that using the horizontal fraction bar in their work will make problems involving fractions easier to interpret and solve.

### Materials to Gather

**SUPPLIED**
Practice Fraction Division activity page

**ALSO NEEDED**
yarn
scissors, pointed-end safety

**DIVIDE FRACTIONS (A)** 137

## ▶ Common Errors and Misconceptions

- Students might believe that multiplication always gives products that are greater than or equal to the factors. This is true for whole numbers; for example, $9 \times 8 = 72$, $50 \times 3 = 150$, and $1 \times 1 = 1$. However, students might not realize that the product of a whole number and fraction less than 1 is less than the whole-number factor; for example, $\frac{2}{3} \times 12 = 8$ and $63 \times \frac{5}{7} = 45$.

- Students might believe that division always gives quotients that are less than or equal to the dividend, or number being divided. This is true for whole numbers; for example, $12 \div 6 = 2$ and $12 \div 1 = 12$. However, students might not realize that when a whole number is divided by a fraction less than 1, the quotient is greater than the dividend; for example, $12 \div \frac{1}{3} = 36$.

## ▶ Advance Preparation

Cut pieces of yarn as follows:

- 1 piece each – 4 inches and 12 inches
- 10 pieces – $\frac{1}{2}$ inch
- 18 pieces – $\frac{3}{4}$ inch

## ▶ Safety

Make sure students handle the scissors carefully and be sure to store them in a safe place.

## GET READY  Division Story Problems

**ONLINE 5 min**

### Objectives

- Divide a whole number by a fraction to solve a story problem.
- Multiply fractions and explain a step-by-step approach.

Students will solve story problems involving whole-number division and division of whole numbers by fractions.

1. Have students read each on-screen problem.
2. Have students write the number sentence to solve each story problem.
3. Have students solve to find the quotient. They should show all the steps they use, including writing the original problem.

## LEARN  Measure Out Division of Fractions

**OFFLINE 15 min**

### Objectives

- Divide fractions and explain a step-by-step approach.

Students will use pieces of yarn to model how to divide fractional measurements. Then they will verify their answers by using the algorithm for dividing fractions. The algorithm states that division by a fractional divisor is equivalent to multiplying by the reciprocal of the divisor.

Gather the pieces of yarn that you measured and cut.

1. **Say:** Let's use yarn to solve this problem: How many $\frac{1}{2}$-inch pieces of yarn can be cut from 4 inches of yarn? You can divide 4 by $\frac{1}{2}$ to find the answer.

    Give students the 4-inch piece of yarn and the ten $\frac{1}{2}$-inch pieces of yarn.

2. Have students lay the 4-inch piece of yarn in a straight line.

**138** FRACTIONS: MULTIPLICATION AND DIVISION

3. Model for students how to lay the $\frac{1}{2}$-inch pieces of yarn above the 4-inch piece of yarn. Start at one end and lay the $\frac{1}{2}$-inch pieces end to end until you reach the end of the 4-inch piece.

← $\frac{1}{2}$-inch pieces of yarn

← 4-inch piece of yarn

4. Count the number of $\frac{1}{2}$-inch pieces.

   **Say:** There are eight $\frac{1}{2}$-inch pieces in a 4-inch piece of yarn.

5. Tell students that dividing the 4-inch piece of yarn by the $\frac{1}{2}$-inch pieces of yarn models how to divide a whole number by the fraction. In this problem, the problem is $4 \div \frac{1}{2} = \underline{\ ?\ }$

   **Say:** 4 divided by $\frac{1}{2}$ equals 8.

6. Explain that the problem can also be solved with a step-by-step approach, which is called an algorithm.

7. Have students write down this division problem: $4 \div \frac{1}{2} = \underline{\ ?\ }$

8. **Say:** Use a step-by-step approach to find the quotient. After you write the problem, the next step is to write the division problem as a multiplication problem. When you do this, you keep the dividend and use the reciprocal of the divisor.

9. **Say:** $4 \times \frac{2}{1} = 4 \times 2 = 8$

10. **Say:** So you have shown by measuring with your lengths of yarn and by dividing fractions with a step-by-step approach that 4 divided by $\frac{1}{2}$ equals 8.

11. Repeat Steps 1–10 with the 12-inch piece of yarn and the $\frac{3}{4}$-inch pieces of yarn to model and then work out $12 \div \frac{3}{4}$. In this problem, students should divide out common factors in $12 \times \frac{4}{3}$ before they multiply. Also, have students explain each step, including changing the division problem to a multiplication problem. Students should explain that they write the reciprocal of the divisor when they write the multiplication problem.

## LEARN  Use the Steps of Division

ONLINE 15 min

Students will practice the steps needed to divide a fraction by a fraction and divide a whole number by a fraction.

### Objectives

- Divide fractions and explain a step-by-step approach.

### Tips

If students have difficulty remembering the order of steps for dividing fractions, practice by giving them a step and having them tell you what step is next.

DIVIDE FRACTIONS (A)

# LEARN  Understand Inverse Operations

**ONLINE 15 min**

Students will review the inverse relationship between multiplication and division and use multiplication to solve division fraction problems.

**Objectives**
- Divide fractions and explain a step-by-step approach.

# TRY IT  Practice Fraction Division

**OFFLINE 10 min**

Students will practice dividing fractions by using the reciprocal of the divisor. Have students turn to the Practice Fraction Division activity page in their Activity Book and read the directions with them.

Students should copy the problems from the Activity Book into their Math Notebook as necessary and solve them there.

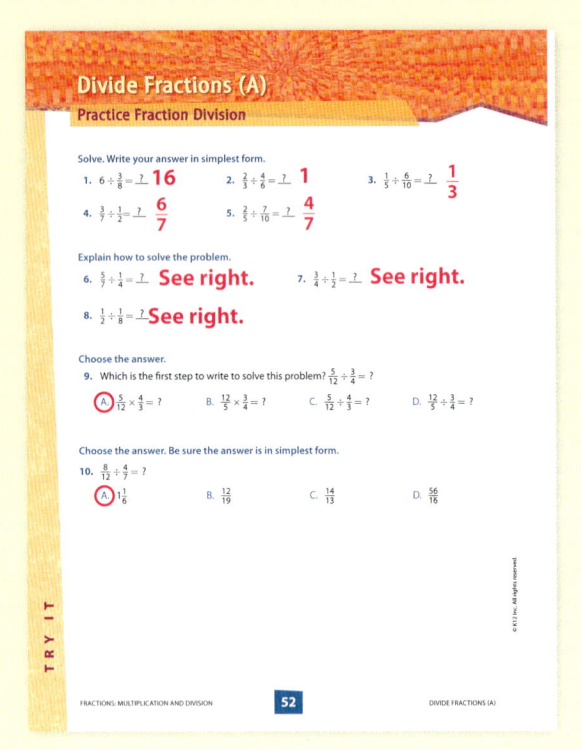

**Objectives**
- Divide fractions and explain a step-by-step approach.

### Additional Answers

6. **Example:** Divide $\frac{5}{7} \div \frac{1}{4}$. First write the division as $\frac{5}{7}$ multiplied by the reciprocal of $\frac{1}{4}$, which is $\frac{5}{7} \times \frac{4}{1}$. There are no common factors to divide out. Next multiply the numerators and the denominators $\left(\frac{20}{7}\right)$. Change the improper fraction to a mixed number $\left(2\frac{6}{7}\right)$. Finally check: Can the answer be simplified? No, the mixed number $2\frac{6}{7}$ is in simplest form.

7. **Example:** Divide $\frac{3}{4} \div \frac{1}{2}$. First write the division as $\frac{3}{4}$ multiplied by the reciprocal of $\frac{1}{2}$, which is $\frac{3}{4} \times \frac{2}{1}$. Then divide out the common factor 2. Next multiply the numerators and the denominators $\left(\frac{3}{2}\right)$. Change the improper fraction to a mixed number $\left(1\frac{1}{2}\right)$. Finally check: Can the answer be simplified? No, the mixed number $1\frac{1}{2}$ is in simplest form.

8. **Example:** Divide $\frac{1}{2} \div \frac{1}{8}$. First write the division as $\frac{1}{2}$ multiplied by the reciprocal of $\frac{1}{8}$, which is $\frac{1}{2} \times \frac{8}{1}$. Then divide out the common factor 2. Next multiply the numerators and the denominators $\left(\frac{4}{1}\right)$. Change the improper fraction to a whole number (4). Finally check: Can the answer be simplified? No, the whole number 4 is in simplest form.

140  FRACTIONS: MULTIPLICATION AND DIVISION

# Divide Fractions (B)

## Lesson Overview

| | | |
|---|---|---|
| **GET READY** Review Division and Multiplication | 15 minutes | **ONLINE** |
| **LEARN** Measure Out Quotients | 15 minutes | **OFFLINE** |
| **LEARN** Use Area to Understand Division | 20 minutes | **ONLINE** |
| **TRY IT** Practice Dividing Fractions | 10 minutes | **OFFLINE** |

### ▶ Lesson Objectives
Divide fractions and explain a step-by-step approach.

### ▶ Prerequisite Skills
- Divide a whole number by a fraction to solve a story problem.
- Multiply fractions and explain a step-by-step approach.

### ▶ Content Background
In this lesson, students will investigate different models to divide fractions and continue their work with the division of fractions algorithm.

Students will work with a combination of dividends and divisors, some simple fractions and some mixed numbers. Mixed numbers always need to be changed into their equivalent improper fractions before either multiplying or dividing fractions. Students are also instructed to simplify their quotients by changing improper fractions to mixed numbers and, if needed, divide the numerator and denominator of the fraction by the greatest common factor (GCF).

Although students will most often see fractions written with a horizontal fraction bar in math, such as $\frac{2}{3}$ or $5\frac{5}{6}$, they will occasionally see a diagonal fraction bar, such as 2/3 or 5 5/6. Students will very likely see the diagonal fraction bar in everyday experiences, but be sure they understand that using the horizontal fraction bar in their work will make problems involving fractions easier to interpret and solve.

### ▶ Common Errors and Misconceptions
- Students might believe that multiplication always gives products that are greater than or equal to the factors. This is true for whole numbers; for example, $9 \times 8 = 72$, $50 \times 3 = 150$, and $1 \times 1 = 1$. However, students might not realize that the product of a whole number and fraction less than 1 is less than the whole-number factor; for example, $\frac{2}{3} \times 12 = 8$ and $63 \times \frac{5}{7} = 45$.
- Students might believe that division always gives quotients that are less than or equal to the dividend, or number being divided. This is true for whole numbers; for example, $12 \div 6 = 2$ and $12 \div 1 = 12$. However, students might not realize that when a whole number is divided by a fraction less than 1, the quotient is greater than the dividend; for example, $12 \div \frac{1}{3} = 36$.

### Materials to Gather

**SUPPLIED**
Practice Dividing Fractions activity page

**ALSO NEEDED**
yarn
scissors, pointed-end safety
ruler

## ▶ Advance Preparation

Cut four pieces of yarn as follows:

- One piece $2\frac{1}{2}$ inches long. Use a pencil to mark the yarn every $\frac{1}{2}$ inch.
- One piece $7\frac{1}{2}$ inches long. Use a pencil to mark the yarn every $\frac{3}{4}$ inch.
- One piece $3\frac{1}{4}$ inches. Use a pencil to mark the yarn every $\frac{1}{4}$ inch.
- One piece $3\frac{3}{8}$ inches long. Use a pencil to mark the yarn every $\frac{3}{8}$ inch.

## ▶ Safety

Make sure students handle the scissors carefully and be sure to store them in a safe place.

## GET READY  Review Division and Multiplication   ONLINE 15 min

### Objectives

Students will practice dividing and multiplying fractions and whole numbers. They will measure out to practice division and use a step-by-step approach (an algorithm) for multiplication.

- Divide a whole number by a fraction to solve a story problem.
- Multiply fractions and explain a step-by-step approach.

## LEARN  Measure Out Quotients   OFFLINE 15 min

### Objectives

Students will practice dividing mixed numbers by fractions. They will measure out a mixed-number length of yarn and cut fractional lengths to divide the longer piece of yarn evenly to find the quotient.

- Divide fractions and explain a step-by-step approach.

Gather scissors, ruler, and the yarn you marked.

1. Write the number sentence $2\frac{1}{2} \div \frac{1}{2} = \underline{\phantom{?}}$ in your Math Notebook.
2. Show students the yarn. Tell them that they will use the yarn to model a division problem.
3. **Say:** You can use repeated subtraction to divide a whole number by a fraction.
4. Have students take the $2\frac{1}{2}$-inch piece of yarn and cut the yarn at each $\frac{1}{2}$-inch pencil mark.

   **Say:** Each cut is a repeated subtraction of $\frac{1}{2}$ inch.
5. **Ask:** How many pieces of $\frac{1}{2}$ fit into $2\frac{1}{2}$? 5
6. Remind students that the division problem $2\frac{1}{2} \div \frac{1}{2} = \underline{\phantom{?}}$ means "How many sets of $\frac{1}{2}$ are in $2\frac{1}{2}$?"
7. Have students use the algorithm to verify in their Math Notebook the answer they found using the yarn model. $2\frac{1}{2} \div \frac{1}{2} = \underline{\phantom{?}}$ 5
8. Have students repeat Steps 1–7 for the following problems:
   - $7\frac{1}{2} \div \frac{3}{4} = \underline{\phantom{?}}$ 10
   - $3\frac{1}{4} \div \frac{1}{4} = \underline{\phantom{?}}$ 13
   - $3\frac{3}{8} \div \frac{3}{8} = \underline{\phantom{?}}$ 9

Have students explain the steps they used when solving the problems using the algorithm.

### Tips

If students need more practice to understand how repeated subtraction works for dividing mixed numbers with fractions, measure everyday items and then see how many times a fraction goes into the measurement.

## LEARN Use Area to Understand Division

**ONLINE 20 min**

**Objectives**
- Divide fractions and explain a step-by-step approach.

Students will solve division problems with fractions and mixed numbers.

## TRY IT Practice Dividing Fractions

**OFFLINE 10 min**

**Objectives**
- Divide fractions and explain a step-by-step approach.

Students will practice dividing mixed numbers by fractions. Have students turn to the Practice Dividing Fractions activity page in their Activity Book and read the directions with them.

Students should copy the problems from the Activity Book into their Math Notebook as necessary and solve them there.

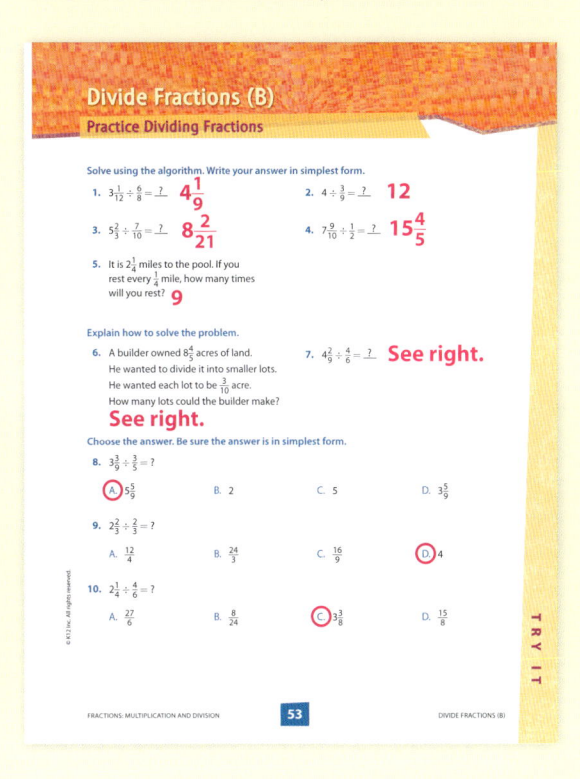

### Divide Fractions (B)
**Practice Dividing Fractions**

Solve using the algorithm. Write your answer in simplest form.

1. $3\frac{1}{12} \div \frac{6}{8} = \underline{?}$    **$4\frac{1}{9}$**
2. $4 \div \frac{3}{9} = \underline{?}$    **12**
3. $5\frac{2}{3} \div \frac{7}{10} = \underline{?}$    **$8\frac{2}{21}$**
4. $7\frac{9}{10} \div \frac{1}{2} = \underline{?}$    **$15\frac{4}{5}$**
5. It is $2\frac{1}{4}$ miles to the pool. If you rest every $\frac{1}{4}$ mile, how many times will you rest? **9**

Explain how to solve the problem.

6. A builder owned $8\frac{4}{5}$ acres of land. He wanted to divide it into smaller lots. He wanted each lot to be $\frac{3}{10}$ acre. How many lots could the builder make? **See right.**

7. $4\frac{2}{9} \div \frac{4}{6} = \underline{?}$ **See right.**

Choose the answer. Be sure the answer is in simplest form.

8. $\frac{3}{9} \div \frac{3}{5} = ?$
   - **A. $5\frac{5}{9}$**
   - B. 2
   - C. 5
   - D. $3\frac{5}{9}$

9. $2\frac{2}{3} \div \frac{2}{2} = ?$
   - A. $\frac{12}{4}$
   - B. $\frac{24}{3}$
   - C. $\frac{16}{9}$
   - **D. 4**

10. $2\frac{1}{4} \div \frac{4}{6} = ?$
    - A. $\frac{27}{6}$
    - B. $\frac{8}{24}$
    - **C. $3\frac{3}{8}$**
    - D. $\frac{15}{8}$

### Additional Answers

6. **Example:** Use the problem $8\frac{4}{5} \div \frac{3}{10} = \underline{?}$ to solve the problem. Change the mixed number $8\frac{4}{5}$ to the improper fraction $\frac{44}{5}$. Set up a multiplication problem with $\frac{44}{5}$ multiplied by the reciprocal of $\frac{3}{10}$, which is $\frac{44}{5} \times \frac{10}{3}$. Divide out the common factor 5 in 5 and 10. The rewritten problem is $\frac{44}{1} \times \frac{2}{3}$. Next multiply the numerators and the denominators $\left(\frac{88}{3}\right)$. Change the improper fraction to a mixed number $\left(29\frac{1}{3}\right)$. Next, check: Can the answer be simplified? No, the mixed number $29\frac{1}{3}$ is in simplest form. The owner could make $29\frac{1}{3}$ lots.

7. **Example:** Use the problem $4\frac{2}{9} \div \frac{4}{6} = \underline{?}$ to solve the problem. Change the mixed number $4\frac{2}{9}$ to the improper fraction $\frac{38}{9}$. Set up a multiplication problem with $\frac{38}{9}$ multiplied by the reciprocal of $\frac{4}{6}$, which is $\frac{38}{9} \times \frac{6}{4}$. Divide out the common factor 2 in 38 and 4 and the common factor 3 in 9 and 6. The rewritten problem is $\frac{19}{3} \times \frac{2}{2}$. Next multiply the numerators and the denominators $\left(\frac{38}{6}\right)$. Change the improper fraction to a mixed number $\left(6\frac{2}{6}\right)$. Next, check: Can the answer be simplified? Yes, the mixed number $6\frac{2}{6}$ can be simplified to $6\frac{1}{3}$.

# Divide Fractions (C)

## Lesson Overview

| | | |
|---|---|---|
| **GET READY** Steps for Division Problems | 10 minutes | ONLINE |
| **LEARN** Solve Division of Fractions Problems | 20 minutes | ONLINE |
| **TRY IT** Divide Mixed Numbers and Fractions | 20 minutes | OFFLINE |
| **CHECKPOINT** | 10 minutes | ONLINE |

### ▶ Lesson Objectives
Divide fractions and explain a step-by-step approach.

### ▶ Prerequisite Skills
- Divide a whole number by a fraction to solve a story problem.
- Multiply fractions and explain a step-by-step approach.

### ▶ Content Background
Students will continue to make sense of the division of fractions algorithm through models. They will practice the steps of the algorithm with a variety of combinations of fraction types.

Although students will most often see fractions written with a horizontal fraction bar in math, such as $\frac{2}{3}$ or $5\frac{5}{6}$, they will occasionally see a diagonal fraction bar, such as 2/3 or 5 5/6. Students will very likely see the diagonal fraction bar in everyday experiences, but be sure they understand that using the horizontal fraction bar in their work will make problems involving fractions easier to interpret and solve.

#### DIVIDE A MIXED NUMBER BY A MIXED NUMBER
The algorithm for dividing two mixed numbers involves the greatest number of steps to find the quotient: change each mixed number to its equivalent improper fraction; change the division problem to multiplication by the reciprocal of the divisor; divide out common factors between any combination of a numerator and denominator, if possible; multiply numerators and multiply denominators to create the fraction of the quotient; express the quotient in the simplest form by changing an improper fraction to a mixed number.

#### DIVIDE A MIXED NUMBER BY A FRACTION OR A FRACTION BY A MIXED NUMBER
The algorithm for dividing fractions when either the dividend or the divisor is a mixed number is very similar to the algorithm for dividing two mixed numbers, except there is one less step. There is only one mixed number to change into its equivalent improper fraction before changing the division problem to multiplication by the reciprocal of the divisor, and proceeding with the steps outlined above.

### Materials to Gather

**SUPPLIED**

Divide Mixed Numbers and Fractions activity page

**DIVIDE A FRACTION BY A FRACTION**

The algorithm for dividing two fractions begins by changing the division problem to multiplication by the reciprocal of the divisor, and proceeding with the steps outlined above.

▶ Common Errors and Misconceptions

- Students might believe that multiplication always gives products that are greater than or equal to the factors. This is true for whole numbers; for example, $9 \times 8 = 72$, $50 \times 3 = 150$, and $1 \times 1 = 1$. However, students might not realize that the product of a whole number and fraction less than 1 is less than the whole-number factor; for example, $\frac{2}{3} \times 12 = 8$ and $63 \times \frac{5}{7} = 45$.

- Students might believe that division always gives quotients that are less than or equal to the dividend, or number being divided. This is true for whole numbers; for example, $12 \div 6 = 2$ and $12 \div 1 = 12$. However, students might not realize that when a whole number is divided by a fraction less than 1, the quotient is greater than the dividend; for example, $12 \div \frac{1}{3} = 36$.

**GET READY** Steps for Division Problems — ONLINE 10 min

**Objectives**
- Multiply fractions and explain a step-by-step approach.

Students will review the steps to divide whole numbers, fractions, and mixed numbers.

**LEARN** Solve Division of Fractions Problems — ONLINE 20 min

**Objectives**
- Divide fractions and explain a step-by-step approach.

Students will order the steps to solve division of fractions and mixed numbers problems. They will also solve division of fractions problems using the measure-out model.

DIVIDE FRACTIONS (C) 145

## TRY IT  Divide Mixed Numbers and Fractions

**OFFLINE 20 min**

### Objectives
- Divide fractions and explain a step-by-step approach.

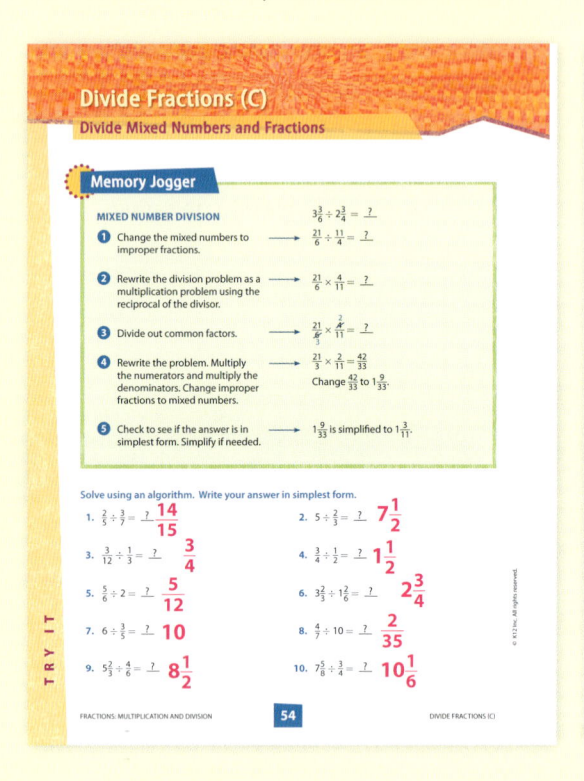

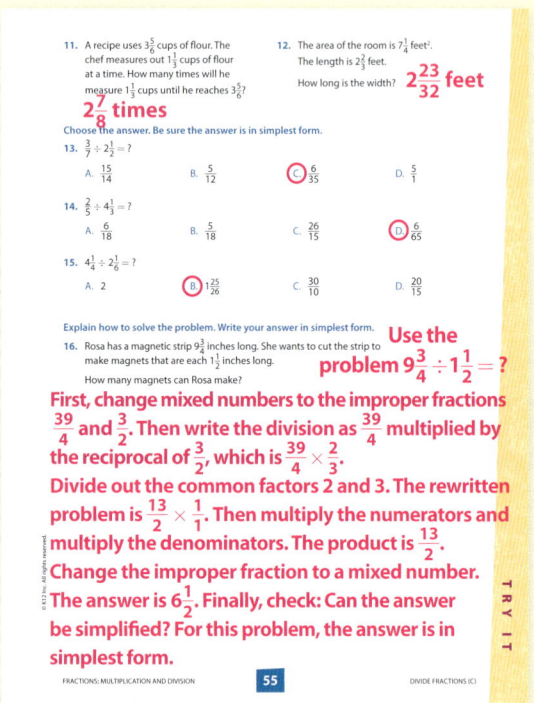

Students will practice dividing fractions, whole numbers, and mixed numbers. Have students turn to the Divide Mixed Numbers and Fractions activity page in their Activity Book and read the directions with them.

Students should copy the problems from the Activity Book into their Math Notebook as necessary and solve them there.

### Divide Fractions (C)
**Divide Mixed Numbers and Fractions**

**Memory Jogger**

**MIXED NUMBER DIVISION**   $3\frac{3}{6} \div 2\frac{3}{4} = ?$

1. Change the mixed numbers to improper fractions.  →  $\frac{21}{6} \div \frac{11}{4} = ?$
2. Rewrite the division problem as a multiplication problem using the reciprocal of the divisor.  →  $\frac{21}{6} \times \frac{4}{11} = ?$
3. Divide out common factors.  →  $\frac{21}{6} \times \frac{4}{11} = ?$
4. Rewrite the problem. Multiply the numerators and multiply the denominators. Change improper fractions to mixed numbers.  →  $\frac{21}{3} \times \frac{2}{11} = \frac{42}{33}$  Change $\frac{42}{33}$ to $1\frac{9}{33}$.
5. Check to see if the answer is in simplest form. Simplify if needed.  →  $1\frac{9}{33}$ is simplified to $1\frac{3}{11}$.

**Solve using an algorithm. Write your answer in simplest form.**

1. $\frac{2}{5} \div \frac{3}{7} = ?$   **$\frac{14}{15}$**
2. $5 \div \frac{2}{3} = ?$   **$7\frac{1}{2}$**
3. $\frac{3}{12} \div \frac{1}{3} = ?$   **$\frac{3}{4}$**
4. $\frac{3}{4} \div \frac{1}{2} = ?$   **$1\frac{1}{2}$**
5. $\frac{5}{6} \div 2 = ?$   **$\frac{5}{12}$**
6. $3\frac{2}{3} \div 1\frac{2}{6} = ?$   **$2\frac{3}{4}$**
7. $6 \div \frac{3}{5} = ?$   **10**
8. $\frac{4}{7} \div 10 = ?$   **$\frac{2}{35}$**
9. $5\frac{2}{3} \div \frac{4}{6} = ?$   **$8\frac{1}{2}$**
10. $7\frac{3}{8} \div \frac{3}{4} = ?$   **$10\frac{1}{6}$**

---

11. A recipe uses $3\frac{5}{6}$ cups of flour. The chef measures out $1\frac{1}{3}$ cups of flour at a time. How many times will he measure $1\frac{1}{3}$ cups until he reaches $3\frac{5}{6}$?   **$2\frac{7}{8}$ times**

12. The area of the room is $7\frac{1}{4}$ feet². The length is $2\frac{5}{8}$ feet. How long is the width?   **$2\frac{23}{32}$ feet**

**Choose the answer. Be sure the answer is in simplest form.**

13. $\frac{3}{7} \div 2\frac{1}{2} = ?$
    A. $\frac{15}{14}$   B. $\frac{5}{12}$   **C. $\frac{6}{35}$**   D. $\frac{5}{1}$

14. $\frac{2}{5} \div 4\frac{1}{3} = ?$
    A. $\frac{6}{18}$   B. $\frac{5}{18}$   C. $\frac{26}{15}$   **D. $\frac{6}{65}$**

15. $4\frac{1}{4} \div 2\frac{1}{6} = ?$
    A. 2   **B. $1\frac{25}{26}$**   C. $\frac{30}{10}$   D. $\frac{20}{15}$

**Explain how to solve the problem. Write your answer in simplest form.**

16. Rosa has a magnetic strip $9\frac{3}{4}$ inches long. She wants to cut the strip to make magnets that are each $1\frac{1}{2}$ inches long. How many magnets can Rosa make?

**Use the problem $9\frac{3}{4} \div 1\frac{1}{2} = ?$**
First, change mixed numbers to the improper fractions $\frac{39}{4}$ and $\frac{3}{2}$. Then write the division as $\frac{39}{4}$ multiplied by the reciprocal of $\frac{3}{2}$, which is $\frac{39}{4} \times \frac{2}{3}$. Divide out the common factors 2 and 3. The rewritten problem is $\frac{13}{2} \times \frac{1}{1}$. Then multiply the numerators and multiply the denominators. The product is $\frac{13}{2}$. Change the improper fraction to a mixed number. The answer is $6\frac{1}{2}$. Finally, check: Can the answer be simplified? For this problem, the answer is in simplest form.

## CHECKPOINT

**ONLINE 10 min**

### Objectives
- Divide fractions and explain a step-by-step approach.

Students will complete an online Checkpoint. If necessary, read the directions, problems, and answer choices to students and help them with keyboard or mouse operations.

**FRACTIONS: MULTIPLICATION AND DIVISION**

# Unit Review

## Lesson Overview

| | | |
|---|---|---|
| **UNIT REVIEW** Look Back | 10 minutes | **ONLINE** |
| **UNIT REVIEW** Checkpoint Practice | 50 minutes | **ONLINE** |
| ➔ **UNIT REVIEW** Prepare for the Checkpoint | | |

### ▶ Unit Objectives

This lesson reviews the following objectives:
- Multiply fractions and explain a step-by-step approach.
- Divide fractions and explain a step-by-step approach.

### ▶ Advance Preparation

In this lesson, students will have an opportunity to review previous activities in the Fractions: Multiplication and Division unit. Look at the suggested activities in Unit Review: Prepare for the Checkpoint online and gather any needed materials.

**Materials to Gather**

There are no materials to gather for this lesson.

## UNIT REVIEW  Look Back

**ONLINE 10 min**

Students will review key concepts from the unit to prepare for the Unit Checkpoint.

**Objectives**
- Review unit objectives.

## UNIT REVIEW  Checkpoint Practice

**ONLINE 50 min**

Students will complete an online Checkpoint Practice to prepare for the Unit Checkpoint. If necessary, read the directions, problems, and answer choices to students and help them with keyboard or mouse operations. Have students answer the problems on their own. Review any missed problems with students.

**Objectives**
- Review unit objectives.

## ➔ UNIT REVIEW  Prepare for the Checkpoint

What you do next depends on how students performed in the previous activity, Unit Review: Checkpoint Practice. If students had difficulty with any of the problems, complete the appropriate review activity listed in the table online.

# Unit Checkpoint

## Lesson Overview

**UNIT CHECKPOINT** Online  | 60 minutes | **ONLINE**

### ▶ Unit Objectives

This lesson assesses the following objectives:
- Multiply fractions and explain a step-by-step approach.
- Divide fractions and explain a step-by-step approach.

### Materials to Gather

There are no materials to gather for this lesson.

### UNIT CHECKPOINT  Online

**ONLINE 60 min**

Students will complete the online Unit Checkpoint on their own. If necessary, read the directions, problems, and answer choices to students and help them with keyboard or mouse operations.

### Objectives

- Assess unit objectives.

# Problems Involving Fractions

## ▶ Unit Objectives

- Solve a story problem involving multiplication or division of fractions.
- Solve a simple problem involving addition or subtraction of fractions.

## ▶ Big Ideas

Fractions can be added, subtracted, multiplied, and divided.

## ▶ Unit Introduction

In this unit, students will use what they know about multiplication and division of fractions and mixed numbers to solve story problems. They will learn how to decide what operation would be used to solve a fraction or mixed number story problem. They also will learn how to write number sentences to set up the solution to a fraction or mixed number problem. Students will learn how to add and subtract mixed numbers and fractions with like and unlike denominators.

## ▶ Keywords

common factor
denominator
divide out a common factor
factor
fraction
greatest common factor (GCF)
least common denominator (LCD)
least common multiple (LCM)
like denominators
mixed number
numerator
reciprocal
remainder
unlike denominators

# Solve Fraction Story Problems (A)

## Lesson Overview

| | | |
|---|---|---|
| **GET READY** Review Multiplying Fractions | 10 minutes | **ONLINE** |
| **LEARN** Understand Multiplication Story Problems | 20 minutes | **OFFLINE** |
| **LEARN** Solve Story Problems | 20 minutes | **OFFLINE** |
| **TRY IT** Practice Solving Story Problems | 10 minutes | **OFFLINE** |

### ▶ Lesson Objectives
Solve a story problem involving multiplication or division of fractions.

### ▶ Prerequisite Skills
- Multiply fractions and explain a step-by-step approach.
- Divide fractions and explain a step-by-step approach.

### ▶ Content Background

**MULTIPLY A FRACTION BY A FRACTION**

After students use models to multiply a fraction by a fraction, they will use a step-by-step approach. The steps of the traditional approach are as follows: First divide out common factors before multiplying. Then express the answer in its simplest form.

**MULTIPLY A FRACTION BY A MIXED NUMBER**

After students use models to multiply a fraction by a mixed number, they will use a step-by-step approach. The steps of the traditional approach are as follows: First change mixed numbers into improper fractions. Then divide out common factors before multiplying. Next express the answer in its simplest form by dividing the numerator by the denominator. If the answer is an improper fraction, the quotient is the whole-number part of the mixed number. The remainder is the numerator of the fractional part, and the divisor is the denominator of the fractional part.

**MULTIPLY A MIXED NUMBER BY A MIXED NUMBER**

Once students have worked with models that show how to multiply a mixed number by a mixed number, they will use a step-by-step approach. To find the product of two mixed numbers, the steps of the traditional approach are as follows: First change mixed numbers to improper fractions. Then divide out common factors before multiplying. Next express the answer in its simplest form by dividing the numerator by the denominator. The quotient is the whole-number part of the mixed number. The remainder is the numerator of the fractional part, and the divisor is the denominator of the fractional part.

---

**Materials to Gather**

**SUPPLIED**

Understand Multiplication Story Problems activity page

Practice Solving Story Problems activity page

### ▶ Common Errors and Misconceptions

Students might view the numerator and denominator of a fraction as separate, isolated numbers that can be operated on independently. This may lead to students "memorizing" rather than understanding fraction algorithms, and then using them incorrectly.

## GET READY  Review Multiplying Fractions

**ONLINE 10 min**

### Objectives

- Multiply fractions and explain a step-by-step approach.

Students will review the steps to solve a multiplication problem with mixed numbers. Then they will practice solving multiplication problems with fractions, whole numbers, and mixed numbers.

## LEARN  Understand Multiplication Story Problems

**OFFLINE 20 min**

### Objectives

- Solve a story problem involving multiplication or division of fractions.

Students will explain how to answer story problems. They will write number sentences to set up the solutions to multiplication story problems with fractions, whole numbers, and mixed numbers. Students will write the number sentences but will not solve them in this activity. Keep their number sentences for later use. Students will write these number sentences in their Math Notebook.

Have students turn to the Understand Multiplication Story Problems activity page in their Activity Book.

### Tips

If students are having trouble understanding the problem, have them draw a model to represent the parts that they know in the story problem.

1. Tell students that in this activity, they will write number sentences that set up the solution to a multiplication story problem.
2. Read and discuss Problem 1, including the Solution and the Answer, in Worked Examples with students.
3. Read Problem 1 in the problem set with students. Discuss what the problem is asking (the length of the side of the toy box).
4. Tell students that the problem states that the paintbrush is $\frac{3}{10}$ feet wide, and it takes 9 brushstrokes to paint the side. Tell students they can use a model to set up the number sentence needed to solve the problem.
5. Draw a rectangle and divide it into 9 equal sections. Tell students that the 9 sections represent the 9 brushstrokes. Label each section $\frac{3}{10}$.

| $\frac{3}{10}$ | $\frac{3}{10}$ | $\frac{3}{10}$ | $\frac{3}{10}$ | $\frac{3}{10}$ | $\frac{3}{10}$ | $\frac{3}{10}$ | $\frac{3}{10}$ | $\frac{3}{10}$ |
|---|---|---|---|---|---|---|---|---|

6. Explain that multiplication can be used to solve this problem because $\frac{3}{10}$ is painted 9 times to cover the side of the toy box. The $\frac{3}{10}$ measurement remains the same and occurs over and over again. Point to each section and tell students that $\frac{3}{10} + \frac{3}{10} + \frac{3}{10} + \frac{3}{10} + \frac{3}{10} + \frac{3}{10} + \frac{3}{10} + \frac{3}{10} + \frac{3}{10}$ is the same as $\frac{3}{10} \times 9$. The product of $\frac{3}{10} \times 9$ gives the length of the side.
7. Have students write the number sentence $\frac{3}{10} \times 9 = ?$ near the model. Tell them they will use the number sentences they write in this activity to solve the problems later.
8. Read Problem 2 in the problem set with students.
   **Ask:** What are you asked to find? *the length of the glass inserts*

**152**  PROBLEMS INVOLVING FRACTIONS

**Ask:** What facts are given? the length of the table and the portion the inserts will be

9. Draw a rectangle that is longer horizontally than vertically. Label the length $2\frac{1}{4}$ yards. Divide the rectangle into 6 equal sections. Explain to students that each of these sections is $\frac{1}{6}$ of the table's length.

10. Refer to the problem. Explain that the inserts are $\frac{4}{6}$ of the length, so 4 sections of the rectangle need to be shaded.

| $\frac{1}{6}$ | $\frac{1}{6}$ | $\frac{1}{6}$ | $\frac{1}{6}$ | $\frac{1}{6}$ | $\frac{1}{6}$ |
|---|---|---|---|---|---|

**Length = $2\frac{1}{4}$ yards**

11. Discuss why multiplication is used to solve the problem. Explain that $2\frac{1}{4}$ is the entire length of the table, and $\frac{1}{6}$ of it is multiplied 4 times.

12. Have students write the number sentence $2\frac{1}{4} \times \frac{4}{6} = ?$ near the model.

13. Read Problem 3 with students.

14. Guide students to understand the problem and write the number sentence to solve it.

    **Ask:** What are you asked to find? the length of the design in the door
    **Ask:** What facts are given? The length of the door is $2\frac{6}{9}$ feet. The design on the door is $\frac{3}{4}$ of this length.

15. Have students review the models they used to set up the first two problems. Tell students that they could make a model like the ones used for the previous two problems to solve this problem.

    **Ask:** What number sentence will you use to solve this problem? $2\frac{6}{9} \times \frac{3}{4} = ?$

16. Have students write the number sentence $2\frac{6}{9} \times \frac{3}{4} = ?$ in their Math Notebook.

17. Repeat Steps 13–16 for the remaining problems on the page.

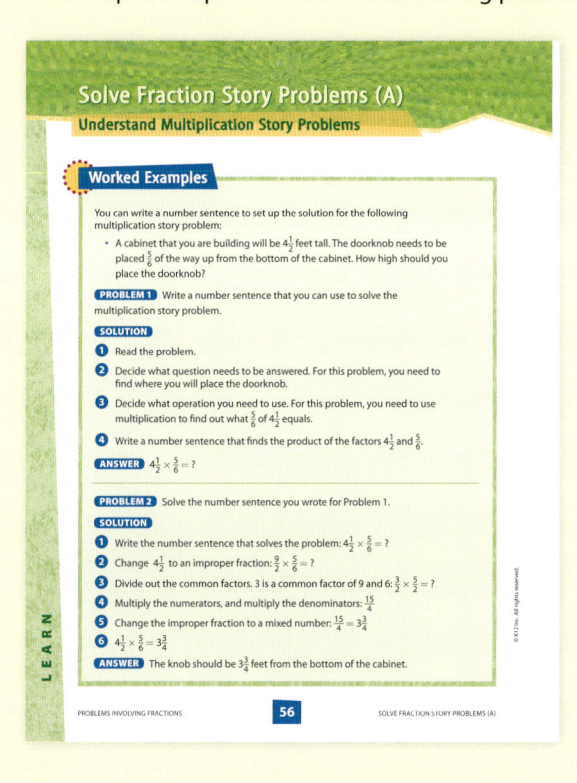

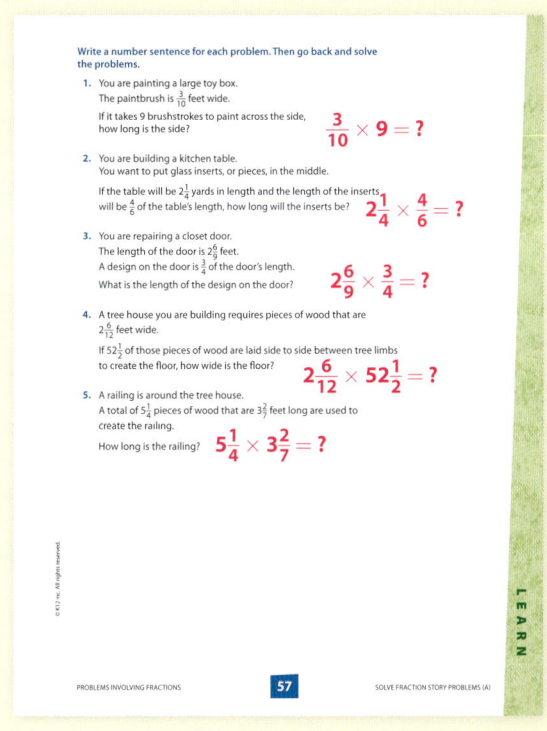

**SOLVE FRACTION STORY PROBLEMS (A)** 153

## LEARN Solve Story Problems

**OFFLINE 20 min**

### Objectives
- Solve a story problem involving multiplication or division of fractions.

Students will solve story problems that they explained and set up in the Understand Multiplication Story Problems activity. Students will write their answers in their Math Notebook.

Have students turn to the Understand Multiplication Story Problems activity page in their Activity Book. Gather the number sentences that students wrote for that activity.

1. Read and discuss Problem 2, including the Solution and Answer, in Worked Examples with students.

2. Have students review the number sentence they wrote for Problem 1 in the problem set. Remind students that the number sentence $\frac{3}{10} \times 9 = ?$ solves this story problem.

3. Remind students that when they multiply a fraction and a whole number, the first step is to change the whole number to fraction with a denominator of 1. Have students write $\frac{3}{10} \times \frac{9}{1} = ?$ below the original problem.

4. **Say:** There are no common factors to divide out in this problem, so multiply the numerators. $3 \times 9 = 27$. Write 27 as the numerator of the product.

5. **Say:** Multiply the denominators. $10 \times 1 = 10$. Write 10 as the denominator of the product.

6. Point to the product, $\frac{27}{10}$. Explain to students that since the product is an improper fraction, it should be changed to a mixed number. Tell students to divide 27 by 10. The quotient is 2, which is the whole-number part of the mixed number. The remainder is the numerator of the fractional part, and the divisor is the denominator of the fractional part. So the improper fraction $\frac{27}{10}$ becomes the mixed number $2\frac{7}{10}$.

7. Tell students that the product of $\frac{3}{10} \times 9$ is $2\frac{7}{10}$. Discuss with them that in this problem, multiplying a fraction by a whole number results in a product greater than one of the factors.

8. Remind students that the story problem asks how long the side of the toy box is. The product of $\frac{3}{10} \times 9$ shows that the side of the toy box is $2\frac{7}{10}$ feet long.

9. Have students review the number sentence they wrote for Problem 2 in the problem set.

10. Explain that the first step in multiplying with mixed numbers is to make each mixed number into an improper fraction. Have students change $2\frac{1}{4}$ to an equivalent improper fraction, $\frac{9}{4}$.

11. Have students rewrite the problem as $\frac{9}{4} \times \frac{4}{6} = ?$

12. **Say:** Divide out common factors. 3 is a common factor of 9 and 6. 4 is a common factor of 4 and 4. Rewrite the problem as $\frac{3}{1} \times \frac{1}{2} = ?$ underneath the original problem.

13. **Say:** Multiply the numerators. $3 \times 1 = 3$. Write 3 as the numerator of the product.

14. **Say:** Multiply the denominators. $1 \times 2 = 2$. Write 2 as the denominator of the product.

PROBLEMS INVOLVING FRACTIONS

15. Have students change the product, $\frac{3}{2}$, into a mixed number. Tell students to divide 3 by 2. The quotient is 1, which is the whole-number part of the mixed number. The remainder is the numerator of the fractional part, and the divisor is the denominator of the fractional part. The product is $1\frac{1}{2}$.

16. Have students read the problem and write the answer in the number sentence: $2\frac{1}{4} \times \frac{4}{6} = 1\frac{1}{2}$

17. **Say:** This problem multiplies a mixed number and fraction. The product, $1\frac{1}{2}$, is greater than one of the factors, $\frac{4}{6}$.

    **Ask:** What does this answer mean in terms of solving the problem? The glass inserts for the table are $1\frac{1}{2}$ yards long.

18. Repeat Steps 9–17 for the rest of the problems. It is important that students review the answer that they find by using multiplication and relate that answer to the story problem. Students should return to the problem in order to answer the question.

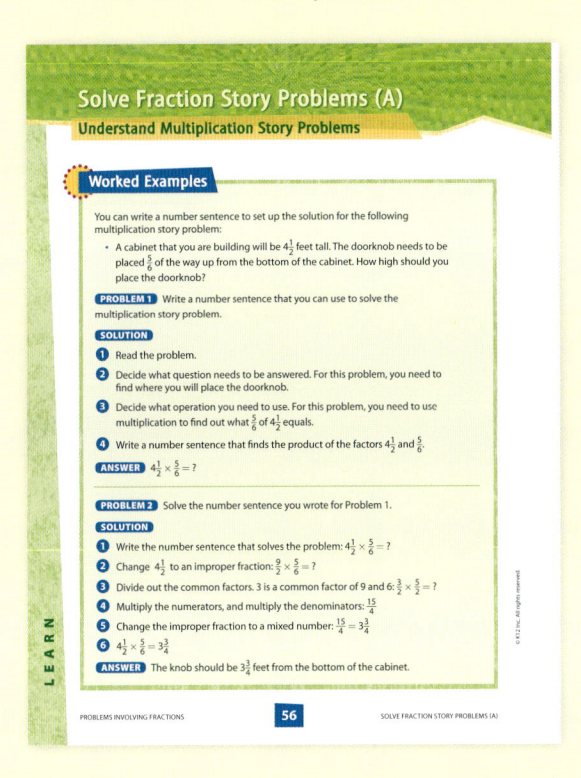

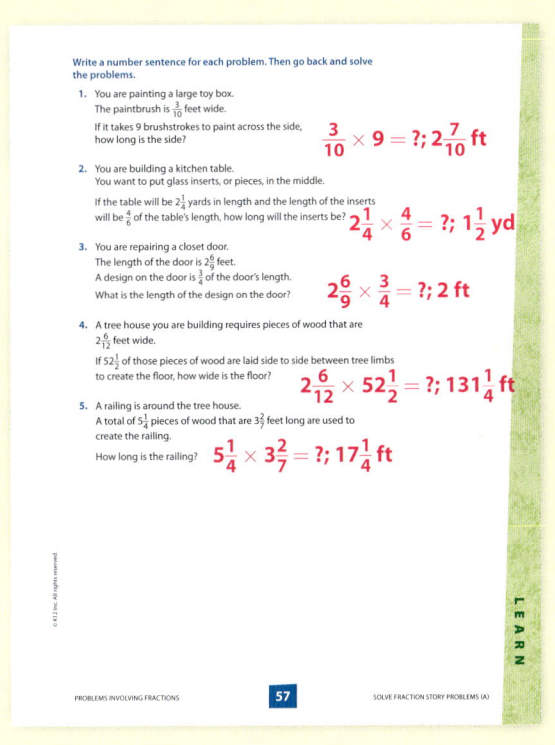

SOLVE FRACTION STORY PROBLEMS (A) 155

## TRY IT  Practice Solving Story Problems

**OFFLINE 10 min**

### Objectives
- Solve a story problem involving multiplication or division of fractions.

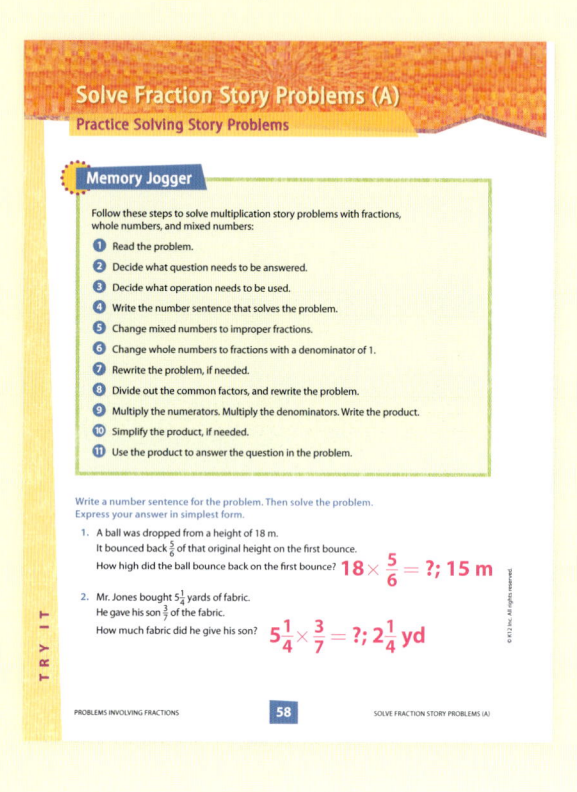

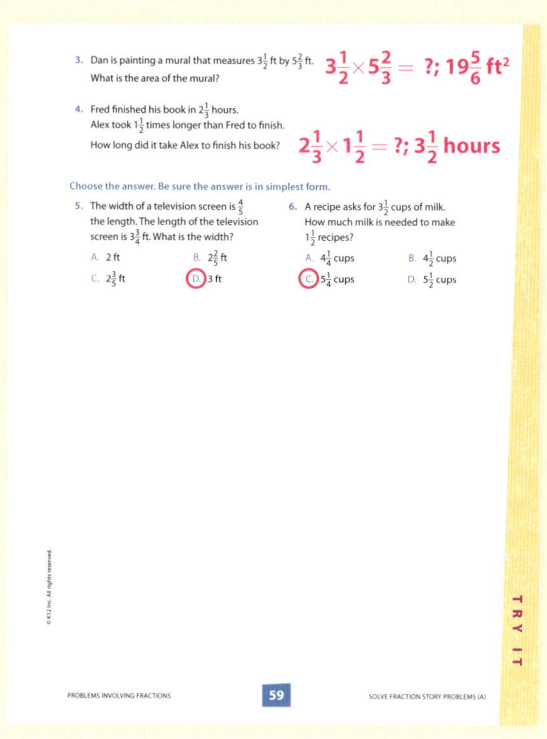

Students will practice solving multiplication story problems with fractions, whole numbers, and mixed numbers. Have students turn to the Practice Solving Story Problems activity page in their Activity Book and read the directions with them.

Students should copy the problems from the Activity Book into their Math Notebook as necessary and solve them there.

### Solve Fraction Story Problems (A)
**Practice Solving Story Problems**

**Memory Jogger**

Follow these steps to solve multiplication story problems with fractions, whole numbers, and mixed numbers:
1. Read the problem.
2. Decide what question needs to be answered.
3. Decide what operation needs to be used.
4. Write the number sentence that solves the problem.
5. Change mixed numbers to improper fractions.
6. Change whole numbers to fractions with a denominator of 1.
7. Rewrite the problem, if needed.
8. Divide out the common factors, and rewrite the problem.
9. Multiply the numerators. Multiply the denominators. Write the product.
10. Simplify the product, if needed.
11. Use the product to answer the question in the problem.

Write a number sentence for the problem. Then solve the problem. Express your answer in simplest form.

1. A ball was dropped from a height of 18 m. It bounced back $\frac{5}{6}$ of that original height on the first bounce. How high did the ball bounce back on the first bounce?  $18 \times \frac{5}{6} = ?$; 15 m

2. Mr. Jones bought $5\frac{1}{4}$ yards of fabric. He gave his son $\frac{3}{7}$ of the fabric. How much fabric did he give his son?  $5\frac{1}{4} \times \frac{3}{7} = ?$; $2\frac{1}{4}$ yd

3. Dan is painting a mural that measures $3\frac{1}{2}$ ft by $5\frac{2}{3}$ ft. What is the area of the mural?  $3\frac{1}{2} \times 5\frac{2}{3} = ?$; $19\frac{5}{6}$ ft²

4. Fred finished his book in $2\frac{1}{3}$ hours. Alex took $1\frac{1}{2}$ times longer than Fred to finish. How long did it take Alex to finish his book?  $2\frac{1}{3} \times 1\frac{1}{2} = ?$; $3\frac{1}{2}$ hours

Choose the answer. Be sure the answer is in simplest form.

5. The width of a television screen is $\frac{4}{5}$ the length. The length of the television screen is $3\frac{3}{4}$ ft. What is the width?
   A. 2 ft
   B. $2\frac{2}{5}$ ft
   C. $2\frac{3}{5}$ ft
   **D. 3 ft**

6. A recipe asks for $3\frac{1}{2}$ cups of milk. How much milk is needed to make $1\frac{1}{2}$ recipes?
   A. $4\frac{1}{4}$ cups
   B. $4\frac{1}{2}$ cups
   **C. $5\frac{1}{4}$ cups**
   D. $5\frac{1}{2}$ cups

**156  PROBLEMS INVOLVING FRACTIONS**

# Solve Fraction Story Problems (B)

## Lesson Overview

| | | |
|---|---|---|
| Skills Update | 5 minutes | ONLINE |
| **GET READY** Review Dividing Fractions | 5 minutes | ONLINE |
| **LEARN** Work with Fraction Story Problems | 20 minutes | OFFLINE |
| **LEARN** Solve Division Story Problems | 20 minutes | OFFLINE |
| **TRY IT** Practice Solving Division Problems | 10 minutes | OFFLINE |

## ▶ Lesson Objectives
Solve a story problem involving multiplication or division of fractions.

## ▶ Prerequisite Skills
- Mutiply fractions and explain a step-by-step approach.
- Divide fractions and explain a step-by-step approach.

## ▶ Content Background

### DIVIDE A FRACTION BY A FRACTION
Once students have worked with models that show how to divide a fraction by a fraction, they will use a step-by-step approach. To find the quotient of two fractions, the steps of the traditional approach are as follows: First change to multiplication by the reciprocal of the divisor. Next divide out common factors before multiplying. Then express the answer in its simplest form. Lastly change improper fractions to mixed numbers.

### FIND THE RECIPROCAL OF A WHOLE NUMBER, FRACTION, OR MIXED NUMBER
The reciprocal of a whole number is a fraction with a numerator of 1 and a denominator of the whole number. For example, the reciprocal of 6 is $\frac{1}{6}$. The product of a whole number and its reciprocal equals 1. The reciprocal of a fraction is a new fraction where the numerator and denominator switch places. For example, the reciprocal of $\frac{3}{4}$ is $\frac{4}{3}$. The product of a fraction and its reciprocal equals 1. The reciprocal of a mixed number is a fraction. To find the reciprocal, change the mixed number to an improper fraction. Then the numerator and denominator of the improper fraction switch places. For example, the reciprocal of $2\frac{1}{4}$, which equals $\frac{9}{4}$, is $\frac{4}{9}$. The product of a mixed number and its reciprocal equals 1.

### DIVIDE A MIXED NUMBER BY A FRACTION
Once students have worked with models that show how to divide a mixed number by a fraction, they will use a step-by-step approach. To find the quotient of a mixed number and a fraction, the steps of the traditional approach are as follows: First change the mixed number to an improper fraction. Next change to multiplication by the reciprocal of the divisor. Then divide out common factors before multiplying. Next express the answer in its simplest form by dividing the numerator by the denomina-

### Materials to Gather

**SUPPLIED**
Work with Fraction Story Problems activity page
Practice Solving Division Problems activity page

**ALSO NEEDED**
ruler

tor. If the answer is an improper fraction, the quotient is the whole-number part of the mixed number. The remainder is the numerator of the fractional part, and the divisor is the denominator of the fractional part.

**DIVIDE A FRACTION BY A MIXED NUMBER**

Once students have worked with models that show how to divide a fraction by a mixed number, they will use a step-by-step approach. To find the quotient of a fraction and a mixed number, the steps of the traditional approach are as follows: First change the mixed number to an improper fraction. Next change to multiplication by the reciprocal of the divisor. Then divide out common factors before multiplying. Next express the answer in its simplest form by dividing the numerator by the denominator. If the answer is an improper fraction, the quotient is the whole-number part of the mixed number. The remainder is the numerator of the fractional part, and the divisor is the denominator of the fractional part.

**DIVIDE A MIXED NUMBER BY A MIXED NUMBER**

Once students have worked with models that show how to divide a mixed number by a mixed number, they will use a step-by-step approach. To find the quotient of two mixed numbers, the steps of the traditional approach are as follows: First change each mixed number to an improper fraction. Next change to multiplication by the reciprocal of the divisor. Then divide out common factors before multiplying. Next express the answer in its simplest form by dividing the numerator by the denominator. The quotient is the whole-number part of the mixed number. The remainder is the numerator of the fractional part, and the divisor is the denominator of the fractional part.

▶ Common Errors and Misconceptions

Students might view the numerator and denominator of a fraction as separate, isolated numbers that can be operated on independently. This may lead to students "memorizing" rather than understanding fraction algorithms, and then using them incorrectly.

**GET READY** Review Dividing Fractions

ONLINE 5 min

**Objectives**

Students will review the steps to solve a division problem with mixed numbers. Then they will practice solving division problems with fractions, whole numbers, and mixed numbers.

- Divide fractions and explain a step-by-step approach.

**LEARN** Work with Fraction Story Problems

OFFLINE 20 min

**Objectives**

Students will explain how to answer story problems. They will write number sentences to set up the solutions to division story problems with fractions, whole numbers, and mixed numbers. Students will write the number sentence but will not solve them in this activity. Keep their number sentences for later use. Students will write these number sentences in their Math Notebook.

Gather the Work with Fraction Story Problems activity page and ruler.

- Solve a story problem involving multiplication or division of fractions.

**158** PROBLEMS INVOLVING FRACTIONS

1. Read Problem 1 in the problem set with students.
2. Guide students to understand the problem and write the number sentence to solve it.

   **Ask:** What are you asked to find? the number of volunteers needed to watch the finish line to record the times of the runners

   **Ask:** What facts are given? The length of the finish line is $5\frac{1}{2}$ meters. Volunteers are needed every $\frac{1}{2}$ meter.

3. In their Math Notebook, have students use a ruler to draw a line that is $5\frac{1}{2}$ centimeters long. Tell students that the line represents $5\frac{1}{2}$ meters.

4. Starting at the left side of the line, have students vertically mark every $\frac{1}{2}$ centimeter until they reach the right side of the line. Tell them that this line represents the finish line, and the vertical marks represent the places where volunteers will record the times of the runners.

5. Explain to students that division is used to solve this problem. $5\frac{1}{2}$ meters is the entire length of the finish line, and it is separated into $\frac{1}{2}$-meter segments.

   **Ask:** How are you going to solve this problem? $5\frac{1}{2} \div \frac{1}{2} = ?$

6. Have students write the number sentence $5\frac{1}{2} \div \frac{1}{2} = ?$ near the model.
7. Read Problem 2 with students.
8. Guide students to understand the problem and write the number sentence to solve it.

   **Ask:** What are you asked to find? how many boxes should be put at each table

   **Ask:** What facts are given? There are $6\frac{1}{2}$ boxes of water bottles and 4 tables.

9. Discuss with students why division would be used to solve this problem. Explain that $6\frac{1}{2}$ boxes of water bottles would be divided by 4 to find out how many boxes should go at each table.

10. Have students write the number sentence $6\frac{1}{2} \div 4 = ?$ in their Math Notebook.

11. Repeat Steps 7–10 for the remaining story problems.

> **Tips**
>
> If students are having trouble understanding the problem, have them draw a model to represent the parts that they know in the story problem.

**SOLVE FRACTION STORY PROBLEMS (B)**

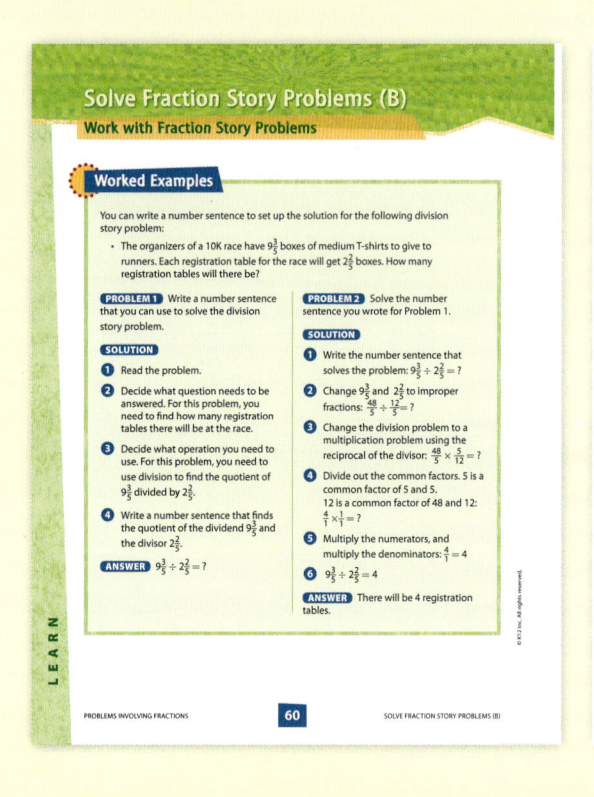

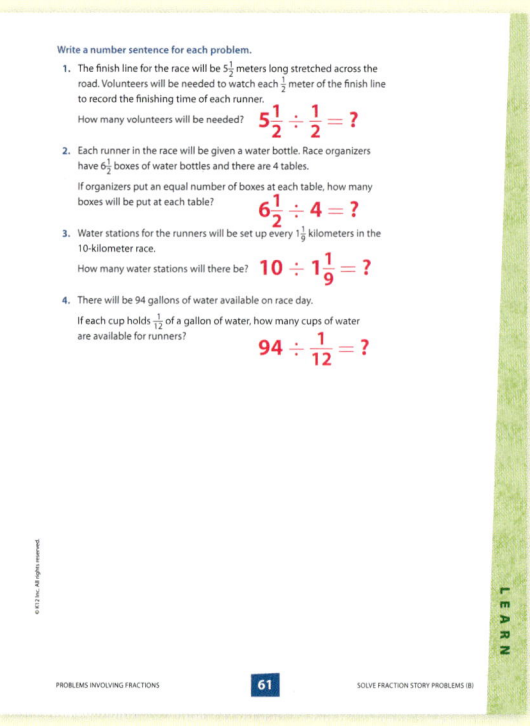

## LEARN  Solve Division Story Problems

**Objectives**
- Solve a story problem involving multiplication or division of fractions.

Students will solve story problems that they explained and set up in the Work with Fraction Story Problems activity. Students will write their answers in their Math Notebook.

Have students turn to the Work with Fraction Story Problems activity page in their Activity Book. Gather the number sentences that they wrote for the problems in that activity.

1. Tell students that in this activity, they will use number sentences to solve division story problem.
2. Discuss Problem 2, including the Solution and the Answer, in Worked Examples with students.
3. Have students review the number sentence they wrote for Problem 1 in the problem set. Remind students the number sentence $1\frac{1}{3} \div \frac{1}{6} = ?$ solves this story problem.
4. Remind students that the first step in solving a division problem with mixed numbers is to change the mixed numbers to improper fractions. Have students change the mixed number $1\frac{1}{3}$ to the improper fraction $\frac{4}{3}$. Have students write $\frac{4}{3} \div \frac{1}{6} = ?$ below the original problem.
5. **Say:** Next you change the problem from division to multiplication by multiplying by the reciprocal of the divisor.
6. Have students rewrite the problem as $\frac{4}{3} \times \frac{6}{1} = ?$
7. **Say:** Divide out common factors. 3 is a common factor of 3 and 6. Rewrite the problem as $\frac{4}{1} \times \frac{2}{1} = ?$

**160**  PROBLEMS INVOLVING FRACTIONS

8. **Say:** Multiply the numerators. 4 × 2 = 8. Write 8 as the numerator of the product.
9. **Say:** Multiply the denominators. 1 × 1 = 1. Write 1 as the denominator of the product.
10. Have students write the product, $\frac{8}{1}$, after the equals symbol. Remind students that any number divided by 1 equals itself, so $\frac{8}{1}$ = 8.
11. Tell students that $1\frac{1}{3} \div \frac{1}{6}$ = 8.
12. Remind students that the story problem asks how many food tables there were. The quotient of $1\frac{1}{3} \div \frac{1}{6}$ tells that there were 8 food tables.
13. Read Problem 2 in the problem set with students.
14. Guide students to solve the problem, having them show you the number sentence that solves. $5\frac{1}{2} \div \frac{1}{2}$ = ?
15. **Ask:** What is $5\frac{1}{2}$ as an improper fraction? $\frac{11}{2}$
16. Have students rewrite the problem: $\frac{11}{2} \div \frac{1}{2}$ = ?
17. **Say:** Change the problem to multiplication by multiplying by the reciprocal of the divisor.
    Have students rewrite the problem as $\frac{11}{2} \times \frac{2}{1}$ = ?
18. **Ask:** Are there any common factors to divide out? 2 goes into 2 once in the first denominator and in the second numerator.
    Have students rewrite the problem as $\frac{11}{1} \times \frac{1}{1}$ = ?
19. **Ask:** What is the product of the numerators? 11 × 1 = 11
    **Ask:** What is the product of the denominators? 1 × 1 = 1
20. Have students write the product, 11, in the number sentence.
21. Tell students that the quotient of $5\frac{1}{2} \div \frac{1}{2}$ = 11.
    **Ask:** What does this answer tell us about solving the problem? There will be 11 volunteers.
22. Read Problem 3 in the problem set with students.
23. Have students review the number sentence they wrote in their Math Notebook for this problem. Remind students that the number sentence $6\frac{1}{2} \div 4$ = ? solves this story problem.
24. Repeat Steps 13–21 with the third problem.
25. **Ask:** What is the quotient? $1\frac{5}{8}$
    **Ask:** What does the quotient mean in terms of the number of water-bottle stations? There will be $1\frac{5}{8}$ water-bottle boxes at each table.
26. Repeat Steps 22–25 with the remaining problems. It is important that students review the answer that they find by using division and relate the answer to the story problem. They should return to the problem to answer the question.

**SOLVE FRACTION STORY PROBLEMS (B)**

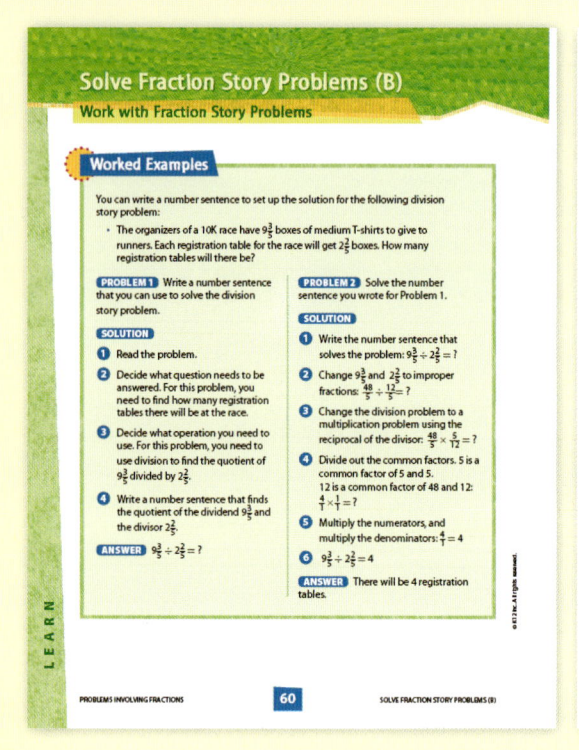

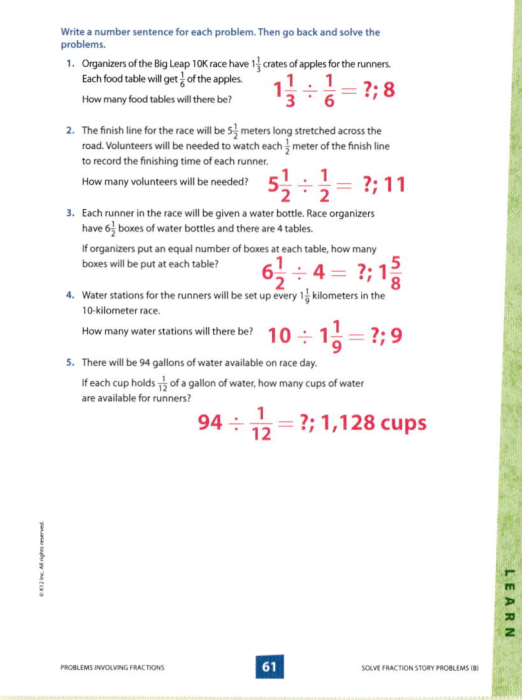

## TRY IT  Practice Solving Division Problems

**OFFLINE 10 min**

Students will practice solving division story problems with fractions, whole numbers, and mixed numbers. Have students turn to the Practice Solving Division Problems activity page in their Activity Book and read the directions with them.

Students should copy the problems from the Activity Book into their Math Notebook as necessary and solve them there.

### Objectives
- Solve a story problem involving multiplication or division of fractions.

**162** PROBLEMS INVOLVING FRACTIONS

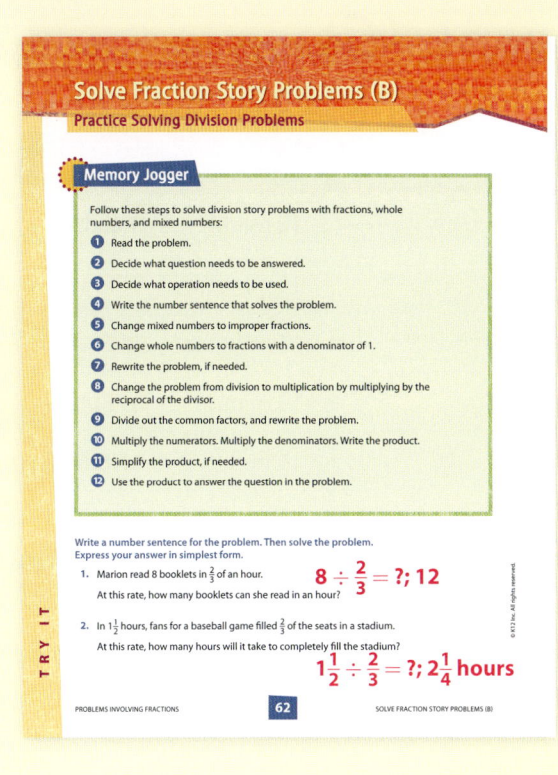

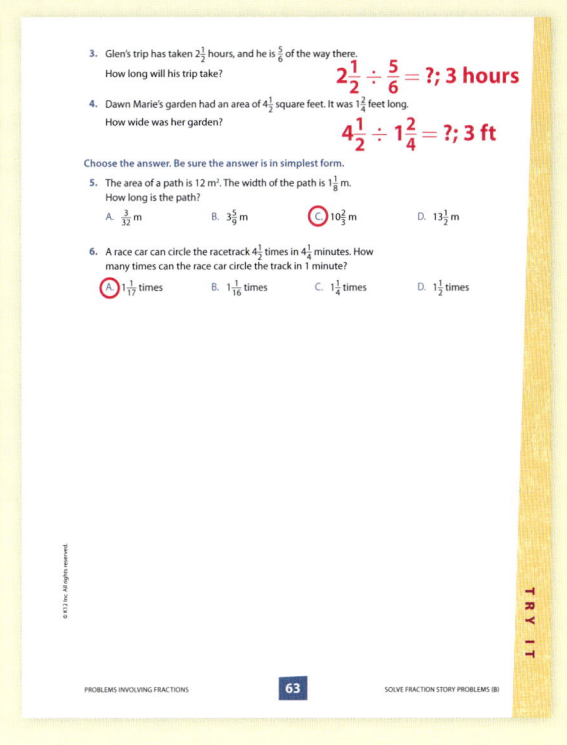

# Solve Fraction Story Problems (B)
## Practice Solving Division Problems

### Memory Jogger

Follow these steps to solve division story problems with fractions, whole numbers, and mixed numbers:

1. Read the problem.
2. Decide what question needs to be answered.
3. Decide what operation needs to be used.
4. Write the number sentence that solves the problem.
5. Change mixed numbers to improper fractions.
6. Change whole numbers to fractions with a denominator of 1.
7. Rewrite the problem, if needed.
8. Change the problem from division to multiplication by multiplying by the reciprocal of the divisor.
9. Divide out the common factors, and rewrite the problem.
10. Multiply the numerators. Multiply the denominators. Write the product.
11. Simplify the product, if needed.
12. Use the product to answer the question in the problem.

**Write a number sentence for the problem. Then solve the problem. Express your answer in simplest form.**

1. Marion read 8 booklets in $\frac{2}{3}$ of an hour. At this rate, how many booklets can she read in an hour?

    $8 \div \frac{2}{3} = ?; 12$

2. In $1\frac{1}{2}$ hours, fans for a baseball game filled $\frac{2}{3}$ of the seats in a stadium. At this rate, how many hours will it take to completely fill the stadium?

    $1\frac{1}{2} \div \frac{2}{3} = ?; 2\frac{1}{4}$ hours

3. Glen's trip has taken $2\frac{1}{2}$ hours, and he is $\frac{5}{6}$ of the way there. How long will his trip take?

    $2\frac{1}{2} \div \frac{5}{6} = ?; 3$ hours

4. Dawn Marie's garden had an area of $4\frac{1}{2}$ square feet. It was $1\frac{2}{4}$ feet long. How wide was her garden?

    $4\frac{1}{2} \div 1\frac{2}{4} = ?; 3$ ft

**Choose the answer. Be sure the answer is in simplest form.**

5. The area of a path is 12 m². The width of the path is $1\frac{1}{8}$ m. How long is the path?

    A. $\frac{3}{32}$ m  B. $3\frac{5}{9}$ m  **C. $10\frac{2}{3}$ m**  D. $13\frac{1}{2}$ m

6. A race car can circle the racetrack $4\frac{1}{2}$ times in $4\frac{1}{4}$ minutes. How many times can the race car circle the track in 1 minute?

    **A. $1\frac{1}{17}$ times**  B. $1\frac{1}{16}$ times  C. $1\frac{1}{4}$ times  D. $1\frac{1}{2}$ times

**SOLVE FRACTION STORY PROBLEMS (B)**

# Solve Fraction Story Problems (C)

## Lesson Overview

| | | |
|---|---|---|
| **GET READY** Review Fractions | 10 minutes | **ONLINE** |
| **LEARN** Understand Fraction Story Problems | 15 minutes | **OFFLINE** |
| **LEARN** Apply Fractions to Story Problems | 15 minutes | **OFFLINE** |
| **TRY IT** Multiply and Divide with Fractions | 10 minutes | **OFFLINE** |
| **CHECKPOINT** | 10 minutes | **ONLINE** |

### ▶ Lesson Objectives
Solve a story problem involving multiplication or division of fractions.

### ▶ Prerequisite Skills
- Multiply fractions and explain a step-by-step approach.
- Divide fractions and explain a step-by-step approach.

### ▶ Content Background

**MULTIPLY A FRACTION BY A FRACTION**

After students use models to multiply a fraction by a fraction, they will use a step-by-step approach. The steps of the traditional approach are as follows: First divide out common factors before multiplying. Then express the answer in its simplest form.

**MULTIPLY A FRACTION BY A MIXED NUMBER**

After students use models to multiply a fraction by a mixed number, they will use a step-by-step approach. The steps of the traditional approach are as follows: First change mixed numbers into improper fractions. Then divide out common factors before multiplying. Next express the answer in its simplest form by dividing the numerator by the denominator. If the answer is an improper fraction, the quotient is the whole-number part of the mixed number. The remainder is the numerator of the fractional part, and the divisor is the denominator of the fractional part.

**MULTIPLY A MIXED NUMBER BY A MIXED NUMBER**

Once students have worked with models that show how to multiply a mixed number by a mixed number, they will use a step-by-step approach. To find the product of two mixed numbers, the steps of the traditional approach are as follows: First change mixed numbers to improper fractions. Then divide out common factors before multiplying. Next express the answer in its simplest form by dividing the numerator by the denominator. The quotient is the whole-number part of the mixed number. The remainder is the numerator of the fractional part, and the divisor is the denominator of the fractional part.

**DIVIDE A FRACTION BY A FRACTION**

Once students have worked with models that show how to divide a fraction by a fraction, they will use a step-by-step approach. To find the quotient of two fractions, the steps of the traditional approach are as follows: First change to multi-

---

**Materials to Gather**

**SUPPLIED**

Understand Fraction Story Problems activity page

Multiply and Divide with Fractions activity page

plication by the reciprocal of the divisor. Next divide out common factors before multiplying. Then express the answer in its simplest form. Lastly change improper fractions to mixed numbers.

### FIND THE RECIPROCAL OF A WHOLE NUMBER, FRACTION, OR MIXED NUMBER

The reciprocal of a whole number is a fraction with a numerator of 1 and a denominator of the whole number. For example, the reciprocal of 6 is $\frac{1}{6}$. The product of a whole number and its reciprocal equals 1. The reciprocal of a fraction is a new fraction in which the numerator and denominator switch places. For example, the reciprocal of $\frac{3}{4}$ is $\frac{4}{3}$. The product of a fraction and its reciprocal equals 1. The reciprocal of a mixed number is a fraction. To find the reciprocal, change the mixed number to an improper fraction. Then switch the places of the numerator and denominator of the improper fraction. For example, the mixed number $2\frac{1}{4}$ is equal to the improper fraction $\frac{9}{4}$, so its reciprocal is $\frac{4}{9}$. The product of a mixed number and its reciprocal equals 1.

### DIVIDE A MIXED NUMBER BY A FRACTION

Once students have worked with models that show how to divide a mixed number by a fraction, they will use a step-by-step approach. To find the quotient of a mixed number and a fraction, the steps of the traditional approach are as follows: First change the mixed number to an improper fraction. Then change to multiplication by the reciprocal of the divisor. Next divide out common factors before multiplying. Next express the answer in its simplest form by dividing the numerator by the denominator. If the answer is an improper fraction, the quotient is the whole-number part of the mixed number. The remainder is the numerator of the fractional part, and the divisor is the denominator of the fractional part.

### DIVIDE A FRACTION BY A MIXED NUMBER

Once students have worked with models that show how to divide a fraction by a mixed number, they will use a step-by-step approach. To find the quotient of a fraction and a mixed number, the steps of the traditional approach are as follows: First change the mixed number to an improper fraction. Then change to multiplication by the reciprocal of the divisor. Next divide out common factors before multiplying. Next express the answer in its simplest form by dividing the numerator by the denominator. If the answer is an improper fraction, the quotient is the whole-number part of the mixed number. The remainder is the numerator of the fractional part, and the divisor is the denominator of the fractional part.

### DIVIDE A MIXED NUMBER BY A MIXED NUMBER

Once students have worked with models that show how to divide a mixed number by a mixed number, they will use a step-by-step approach. To find the quotient of two mixed numbers, the steps of the traditional approach are as follows: First change each mixed number to an improper fraction. Then change to multiplication by the reciprocal of the divisor. Next divide out common factors before multiplying. Next express the answer in its simplest form by dividing the numerator by the denominator. The quotient is the whole-number part of the mixed number. The remainder is the numerator of the fractional part, and the divisor is the denominator of the fractional part.

### ▶ Common Errors and Misconceptions

Students might view the numerator and denominator of a fraction as separate, isolated numbers that can be operated on independently. This may lead to students "memorizing" rather than understanding fraction algorithms, and then using them incorrectly.

## GET READY  Review Fractions   ONLINE 10 min

### Objectives
- Multiply fractions and explain a step-by-step approach.
- Divide fractions and explain a step-by-step approach.

Students will practice multiplying and dividing fractions and mixed numbers.

## LEARN  Understand Fraction Story Problems   OFFLINE 15 min

### Objectives
- Solve a story problem involving multiplication or division of fractions.

Students will explain how to answer story problems. They will write number sentences to set up the solutions to multiplication and division story problems with fractions, whole numbers, and mixed numbers. Students will write the number sentences but will not solve them in this activity. Keep their number sentences for later use. Students will write these number sentences in their Math Notebook.

Have students turn to the Understand Fraction Story Problems activity page in their Activity Book.

### Tips
If students are having difficulty determining whether a story problem is solved by using multiplication or division, suggest they solve it both ways and see which answer makes sense in relationship to the original problem.

1. Discuss Problems 1 and 3 in Worked Examples with students. Explain that in this activity, they will write number sentences that set up the solution to multiplication and division story problems.

2. Read Problem 1 in the problem set with students. Discuss what the problem is asking (how many servings are in $\frac{7}{8}$ of a tray).

3. Tell students that the problem states that $\frac{7}{8}$ of a tray is left and that each serving is $\frac{1}{10}$ of a tray. Tell students that they will set up the number sentence needed to solve the problem.

4. Explain to students that division is used to solve this problem because $\frac{7}{8}$ of the tray of lasagna is divided into servings that are $\frac{1}{10}$ of the tray. The quotient of $\frac{7}{8} \div \frac{1}{10}$ gives the number of servings, which is the solution to the problem.

5. Have students write the number sentence $\frac{7}{8} \div \frac{1}{10} = ?$ in their Math Notebook.

6. Read Problem 2 in the problem set with students.

7. Guide students to understand the problem and write the number sentence to solve it.

   **Ask:** What are you asked to find? the fraction of meals on the menu that have mayonnaise

   **Ask:** What facts are given? $\frac{4}{12}$ of the meals on the menu are sandwiches. Mayonnaise is on $\frac{7}{8}$ of the sandwiches.

8. Discuss why multiplication is used to solve the problem. Explain that $\frac{4}{12}$ of the meals on the menu are sandwiches and that $\frac{7}{8}$ of the sandwiches have mayonnaise on them.

   **Ask:** How are you going to solve this problem? $\frac{4}{12} \times \frac{7}{8} = ?$

**166**  PROBLEMS INVOLVING FRACTIONS

9. Have students explain why multiplication would be used instead of division. The sandwiches are not divided into equal groups, so we would not use division. Instead, we need to find $\frac{7}{8}$ of $\frac{4}{12}$ of the sandwiches.

10. Have students write the number sentence $\frac{4}{12} \times \frac{7}{8} = ?$ in their Math Notebook

11. Read Problem 3 in the problem set with students.

    **Ask:** What are you asked to find? the number of customers who ordered cheeseburgers and french fries

    **Ask:** What facts are given? During lunch, $\frac{3}{10}$ of the customers order cheeseburgers and french fries. There are 70 customers in the restaurant.

12. Discuss with students why multiplication would be used to solve this problem. Explain that $\frac{3}{10}$ of the orders would be multiplied by 70 customers to find how many customers order cheeseburgers and french fries.

13. Have students write the number sentence $\frac{3}{10} \times 70 = ?$ in their Math Notebook.

14. Repeat Steps 11–13 for the remaining story problems.

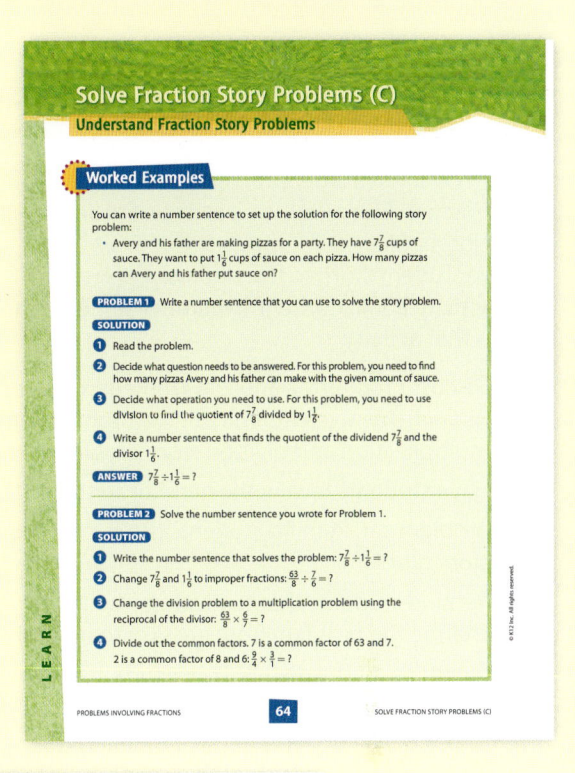

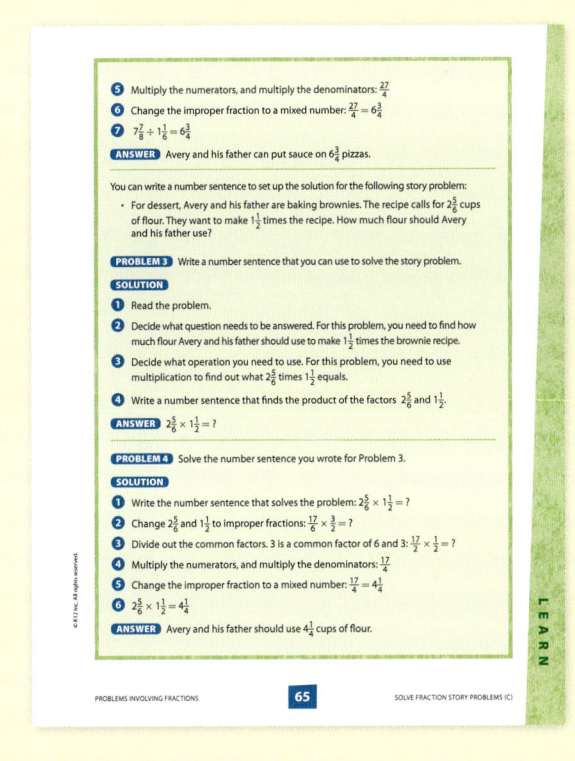

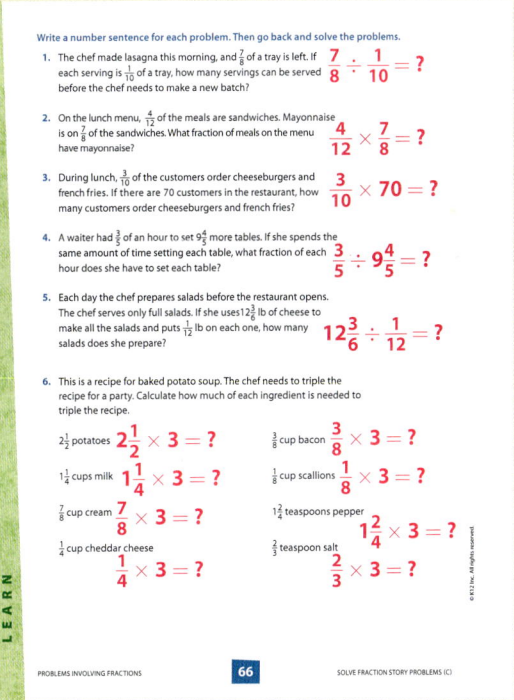

**SOLVE FRACTION STORY PROBLEMS (C)** 167

## LEARN  Apply Fractions to Story Problems

**OFFLINE 15 min**

### Objectives

- Solve a story problem involving multiplication or division of fractions.

Students will solve story problems that they explained and set up in the Understand Fraction Story Problems activity. Students will write their answers in their Math Notebook.

Have students turn to the Understand Fraction Story Problems activity page in their Activity Book. Gather the number sentences that they wrote for the problems in that activity.

1. Discuss Problems 2 and 4 in Worked Examples with students. Explain that in this activity, students will use the number sentences they wrote to solve the multiplication and division story problems.

2. Have students review the number sentence they wrote for Problem 1 in the problem set. Remind students the number sentence $\frac{7}{8} \div \frac{1}{10} = ?$ solves this story problem.

3. Remind students that to divide a fraction by a fraction, the first step is to change the problem from division to multiplication by multiplying by the reciprocal of the divisor. Have students rewrite the problem as $\frac{7}{8} \times \frac{10}{1} = ?$ below the original problem.

4. Guide students through the remaining steps of the problem (see Worked Examples for assistance). When students have finished the problem, emphasize that the quotient of $\frac{7}{8}$ divided by $\frac{1}{10}$ is $8\frac{3}{4}$.

5. Explain that the story problem asks how many servings of lasagna can be served before the chef needs to make a new batch. Discuss the number sentence and the answer in terms of the problem. The quotient of $\frac{7}{8} \div \frac{1}{10}$ tells us there are $8\frac{3}{4}$ servings. However, a restaurant doesn't usually serve $\frac{3}{4}$ of a serving. Eight servings are left before a new batch of lasagna needs to be made.

6. Have students review the number sentence they wrote for Problem 2 in the problem set.
   **Ask:** What number sentence solves this problem? $\frac{4}{12} \times \frac{7}{8} = ?$

7. Guide students through the remaining steps of the problem (see Worked Examples for assistance).
   **Ask:** What does the answer $\frac{7}{24}$ mean in terms of solving the problem? $\frac{7}{24}$ of the meals on the menu have mayonnaise.

8. Have students review the number sentence they wrote for Problem 3 in the problem set. Remind students the number sentence $\frac{3}{10} \times 70 = ?$ solves this story problem.

9. Explain to students that to multiply a fraction by a whole number, the first step is to change the whole number to a fraction with a denominator of 1.

10. Guide students through the steps to solve the problem. Then have students explain how they found the answer.
    **Ask:** What does the answer 21 mean in terms of solving the problem? 21 customers ordered cheeseburgers and french fries

168  PROBLEMS INVOLVING FRACTIONS

11. Repeat Steps 8–10 for the rest of the problems on the page. Remind students to refer to Worked Examples for the steps for multiplying and dividing mixed numbers by mixed numbers. These steps will help them calculate the answers. It's important that students review the answer that they find and relate it to the story problem. Students should return to the problem to answer the question.

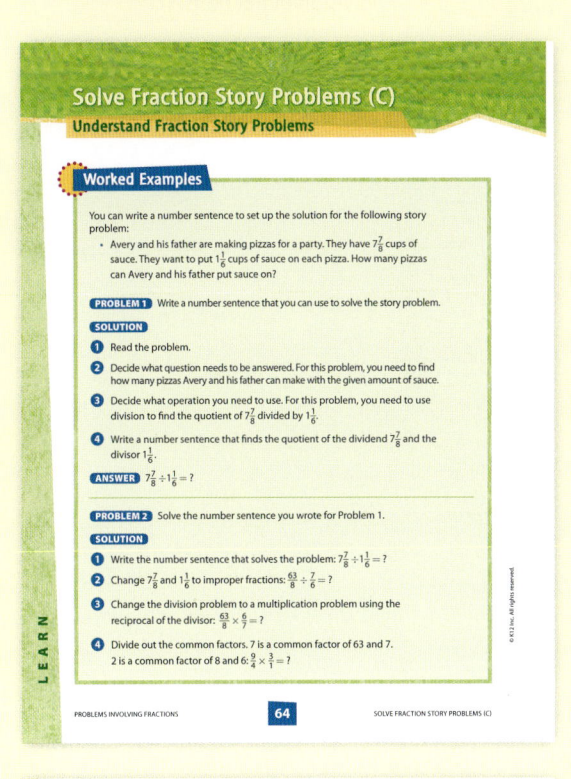

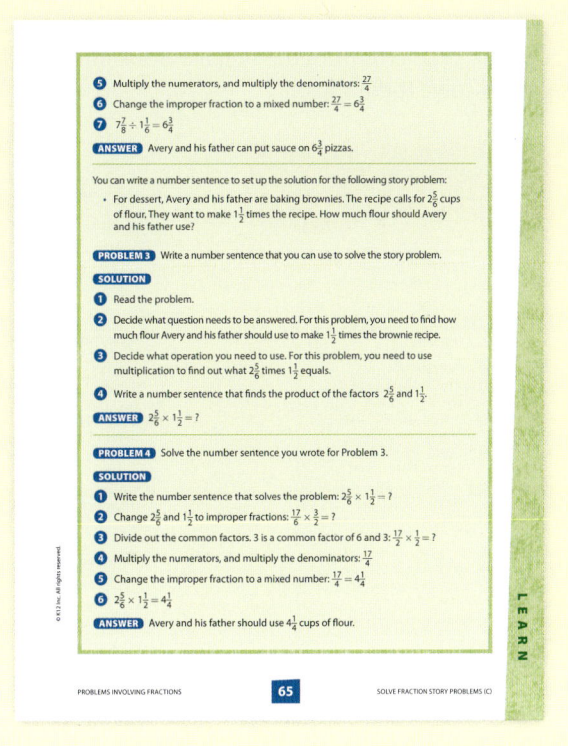

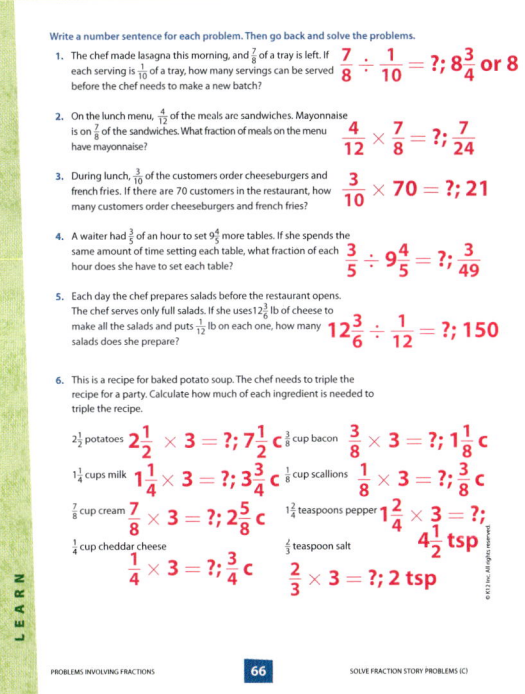

## TRY IT  Multiply and Divide with Fractions

**OFFLINE 10 min**

### Objectives
- Solve a story problem involving multiplication or division of fractions.

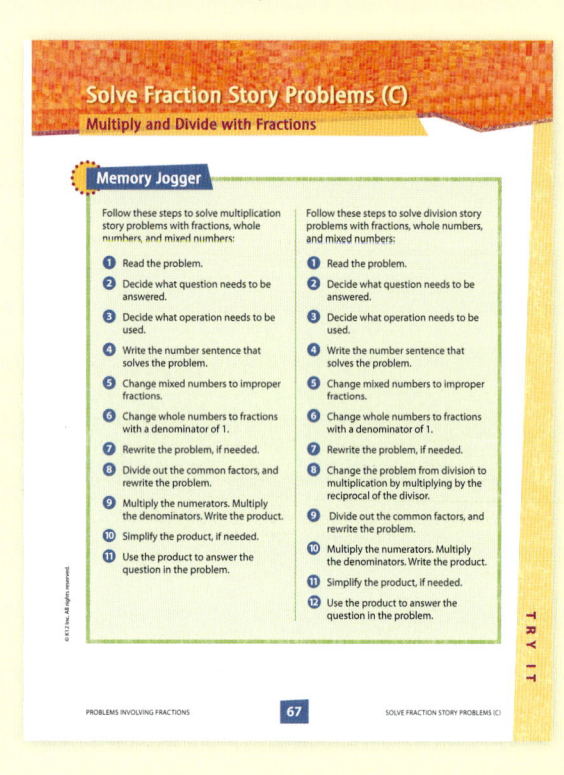

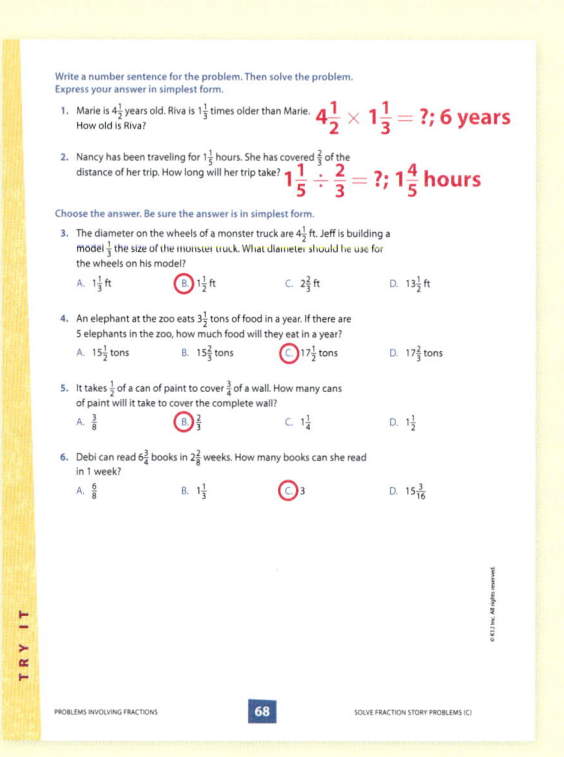

Students will practice solving multiplication and division story problems with fractions, whole numbers, and mixed numbers. Have students turn to the Multiply and Divide with Fractions activity page in their Activity Book and read the directions with them.

Students should copy the problems from the Activity Book into their Math Notebook as necessary and solve them there.

## CHECKPOINT

**ONLINE 10 min**

### Objectives
- Solve a story problem involving multiplication or division of fractions.

Students will complete an online Checkpoint. If necessary, read the directions, problems, and answer choices to students and help them with keyboard or mouse operations.

170  PROBLEMS INVOLVING FRACTIONS

# Add and Subtract Fractions (A)

## Lesson Overview

| | | |
|---|---|---|
| **GET READY** Use Models to Add Fractions | 5 minutes | **ONLINE** |
| **LEARN** Add Fractions with Like Denominators | 15 minutes | **OFFLINE** |
| **LEARN** Add Mixed Numbers – Like Denominators | 15 minutes | **OFFLINE** |
| **LEARN** Add Fractions and Mixed Numbers | 15 minutes | **ONLINE** |
| **TRY IT** Practice Adding Fractions | 10 minutes | **ONLINE** |

### ▶ Lesson Objectives
Solve a simple problem involving addition or subtraction of fractions.

### ▶ Prerequisite Skills
- Use objects or sketches to solve a story problem that involves addition or subtraction of fractions.
- Solve and simplify a problem that involves addition or subtraction of fractions with unlike denominators.

### ▶ Content Background
Students will add fractions with like denominators.

The traditional approach to finding the sum of fractions or mixed numbers, with or without like denominators, is to use regrouping to find the sum. The steps are:
- Leave mixed numbers as mixed numbers. Add the fractions and add the whole numbers in either order.
- If the fraction portion of the sum is an improper fraction, change the improper fraction to a mixed number, shown as a whole-number and fraction.
- Finally combine the whole-number portion of the sum and the whole number from the improper fraction with the fraction to express the answer in the simplest form, as a mixed number.

Although students will most often see fractions written with a horizontal fraction bar in math, such as $\frac{2}{3}$ or $5\frac{5}{6}$, they will occasionally see a diagonal fraction bar, such as 2/3 or 5 5/6. They will very likely see the diagonal fraction bar in everyday experiences, but be sure they understand that using the horizontal fraction bar in their work will make problems involving fractions easier to interpret and solve.

### ▶ Common Errors and Misconceptions
- Students might have difficulty understanding how different models represent fractions because they often see fractions represented as parts of circles—for example, pie and pizza illustrations. They might not recognize, for example, that the following models all represent the fraction $\frac{3}{5}$:

## Materials to Gather

**SUPPLIED**
Fraction Circles (printout)
number lines from the Number Line Creator Tool

**ALSO NEEDED**
pencils, coloring
ruler

$\frac{3}{5}$ is a point on the number line.

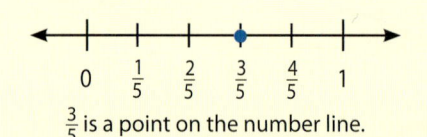

$\frac{3}{5}$ of the shapes are triangles.

$\frac{3}{5}$ of the rectangle is shaded.

- Students might not understand that for a model to accurately represent a fraction as a part of a whole, the model must show a whole divided into equally sized parts.
- Students might not see the relationship between the models (such as fraction strips and number lines) and the procedures for adding and subtracting fractions. Once they begin to use symbols without models, students might apply memorized rules without thinking about the reasons for the procedures.

▶ Advance Preparation

Print two copies of Fraction Circles.

Use the Number Line Creator Tool to print the number lines that students will use in the Add Mixed Numbers—Like Denominators activity. The link to the Number Line Creator Tool is in the online Advance Preparation. Print one page; there will be two identical number lines.

| DIRECTIONS FOR USING THE NUMBER LINE CREATOR TOOL |
|---|
| To Create Number Line from 0 to 4: |
| 1. Set Range:  •  Start Number Line at: 0  •  End Number Line at: 4 | 2. Select Options:  •  Tick Marks: ones, halves  •  Labels: ones, halves  •  Label Format: fractions | 3. Print Number Line:  •  Page Orientation: landscape  •  Number Lines per Sheet: 2 |

## GET READY  Use Models to Add Fractions  ONLINE 5 min

Students will use models to add fractions with like denominators in story problems.

**Objectives**
- Use objects or sketches to solve a story problem that involves addition or subtraction of fractions.

## LEARN  Add Fractions with Like Denominators  OFFLINE 15 min

Students will learn how to add fractions with like denominators. Have them write and draw their answers in their Math Notebook. Gather one copy of the Fraction Circles printout, ruler, and coloring pencils.

**Objectives**
- Solve a simple problem involving addition or subtraction of fractions.

1. Tell students to write $\frac{3}{10} + \frac{4}{10} = ?$

    **Ask:** What is the denominator of both fractions? 10

2. Have them use a ruler to draw a rectangle below the number sentence and divide it into 10 equal parts. This models a fraction strip divided into tenths. This model uses tenths because the common denominator of the fractions being added is 10.

172  PROBLEMS INVOLVING FRACTIONS

$$\frac{3}{10} + \frac{4}{10} = ?$$

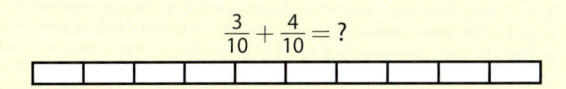

Tell students to model $\frac{3}{10} + \frac{4}{10}$ by shading the first 3 tenths in one color and the next 4 tenths in another color.

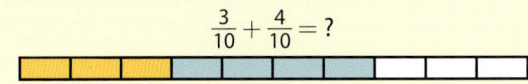

$$\frac{3}{10} + \frac{4}{10} = ?$$

**Ask:** How many tenths did you shade in all? 7 tenths

**Ask:** What is the sum of $\frac{3}{10} + \frac{4}{10}$? $\frac{7}{10}$

3. Have students write the number sentence $\frac{3}{10} + \frac{4}{10} = \frac{7}{10}$ below the fraction strip.

4. Use a number line to model the second problem. Tell students to write $\frac{3}{8} + \frac{2}{8} = ?$ in their Math Notebook.

   **Ask:** What is the denominator of both fractions? 8

5. Have students use a ruler to draw a number line and divide it into 8 equal parts with tick marks. Tell students to label the tick marks from left to right, 0 on the left end, $\frac{1}{8}$ through $\frac{7}{8}$ for the next set of tick marks, and 1 on the right end. Tell students that the number line is marked in eighths because the common denominator of the fractions being added is 8.

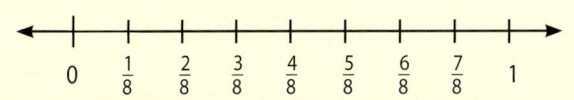

6. Have students mark a point at 0 and $\frac{3}{8}$ on the number line. Start at 0 and "hop" 3 eighths to the right of 0. Show an arc between 0 and $\frac{3}{8}$. Then have students "hop" 2 eighths to the right of $\frac{3}{8}$ to $\frac{5}{8}$. Show an arc between $\frac{3}{8}$ and $\frac{4}{8}$, and another arc between $\frac{4}{8}$ and $\frac{5}{8}$. Have students mark a point at $\frac{5}{8}$.

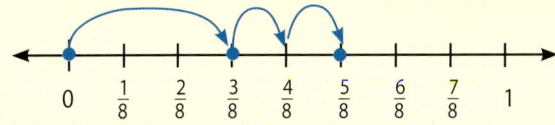

   **Ask:** What is the sum of $\frac{3}{8} + \frac{2}{8}$? $\frac{5}{8}$

7. Have students write the number sentence $\frac{3}{8} + \frac{2}{8} = \frac{5}{8}$ below the number line.

8. Use fraction circles to model the third problem. Give students the Fraction Circles printout. Tell them to write $\frac{1}{4} + \frac{3}{4} = ?$ in their Math Notebook.

   **Ask:** What is the denominator of both fractions? 4

9. Have students locate the row of fourths fraction circles on the Fraction Circles printout. They will use the fourths circle because the common denominator is 4. They will use only the first fraction circle in the row.

10. Have students model $\frac{1}{4} + \frac{3}{4} = ?$ by shading 1 fourth of the fraction circle in one color, and 3 fourths of the same fraction circle in another color.

**Tips**

If students have difficulty adding fractions without models, have them draw fraction strips, or use the Fraction Circles or number line printouts to model problems.

ADD AND SUBTRACT FRACTIONS (A)

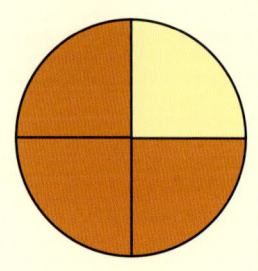

**Ask:** How many fourths did you shade in all? 4 fourths

**Ask:** How many whole fraction circles did you shade? 1

**Ask:** What is the sum of $\frac{1}{4} + \frac{3}{4}$? $\frac{4}{4}$ or 1

**Say:** Both $\frac{4}{4}$ and 1 are the correct sums. But 1 is the answer in simplest form.

11. Have students write the number sentence $\frac{1}{4} + \frac{3}{4} = 1$ in their Math Notebook.

12. Use a step-by-step approach to solve the last two problems. Explain to students that when fractions have like denominators, they can add the numerators. The denominator stays the same.

13. Have students write $\frac{2}{8} + \frac{4}{8} = ?$ in their Math Notebook.

    **Ask:** What is the sum of the numerators? 6

    **Ask:** What is the denominator in both fractions? 8

    **Ask:** What is the denominator for the sum? 8

    **Ask:** What is the sum of $\frac{2}{8} + \frac{4}{8}$? $\frac{6}{8}$

    **Ask:** How do you simplify $\frac{6}{8}$? Divide $\frac{6}{8}$ by a value of 1 in fraction form. In this case, use $\frac{2}{2}$.

    **Ask:** What is the sum of $\frac{2}{8} + \frac{4}{8}$ in simplest form? $\frac{3}{4}$

14. Have students write the number sentence $\frac{2}{8} + \frac{4}{8} = \frac{6}{8}$ in their Math Notebook.

15. Repeat Steps 13–14 with $\frac{5}{6} + \frac{2}{6} = ?$ Have students find the answer and explain how to simplify it from an improper fraction into a mixed number. $\frac{5}{6} + \frac{2}{6} = \frac{7}{6}$. To simplify the answer, divide the numerator by the denominator. The quotient is the whole number part of the mixed number. The remainder is the numerator of the fractional part and the divisor, 6, is the denominator of the fractional part $\left(1\frac{1}{6}\right)$.

## LEARN  Add Mixed Numbers – Like Denominators

**OFFLINE 15 min**

### Objectives

- Solve a simple problem involving addition or subtraction of fractions.

Students will use fraction strips, number lines, and fraction circles to model addition of mixed numbers with like denominators. These examples will lead them to use a step-by-step approach for adding mixed numbers.

Students should write and draw in their Math Notebook. Gather one copy of the Fraction Circles printout, coloring pencils, and number lines from the Number Line Creator Tool.

1. Tell students to write $1\frac{3}{5} + \frac{1}{5} = ?$ in their Math Notebook.

    **Ask:** What is the denominator of both fractions? 5

2. Have students use a ruler to draw two rectangles and divide each into 5 equal parts below the number sentence. This models a fraction strip

174  PROBLEMS INVOLVING FRACTIONS

divided into fifths. The model uses fifths because the common denominator of the fractions being added is 5. Tell them to shade all of the first fraction strip, and 3 fifths of the second fraction strip, in one color, to model $1\frac{3}{5}$. Have students shade the next fifth on the second fraction strip in a different color to model adding $\frac{1}{5}$ to $1\frac{3}{5}$.

$1\frac{3}{5} + \frac{1}{5} = ?$

**Ask:** How many whole fraction strips did you shade? 1

**Ask:** How many fifths did you shade in the second fraction strip? 4 fifths

**Ask:** What is the sum of $1\frac{3}{5} + \frac{1}{5}$? $1\frac{4}{5}$

3. Have students write the number sentence $1\frac{3}{5} + \frac{1}{5} = 1\frac{4}{5}$ below the fraction strips.

4. Use a number line to model the second problem. Give students the number line printout. Tell them to write $1\frac{1}{2} + 2\frac{1}{2} = ?$ on the page.

   **Ask:** What is the denominator of both fractions? 2

5. Tell students that the number line is marked in halves because the common denominator of the fractions being added is 2.

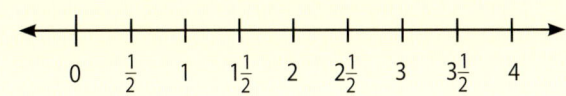

6. Have students mark a point at 0 and $1\frac{1}{2}$ on the number line. Start at 0 and "hop" one and one-half to the right of 0. Show an arc between 0 and $1\frac{1}{2}$.

   Then have students "hop" 2 wholes to the right of $1\frac{1}{2}$ to $2\frac{1}{2}$ then $3\frac{1}{2}$. Have students "hop" another $\frac{1}{2}$ to 4. Show arcs between $1\frac{1}{2}$ and $2\frac{1}{2}$, $2\frac{1}{2}$ and $3\frac{1}{2}$, and $3\frac{1}{2}$ and 4. Have students mark a point at 4.

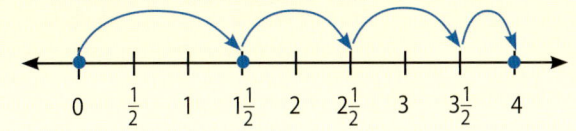

   **Ask:** What is the sum of $1\frac{1}{2} + 2\frac{1}{2}$? 4

7. Have students write the number sentence $1\frac{1}{2} + 2\frac{1}{2} = 4$ below the number line.

8. Use fraction circles to model the third problem. Give students the Fraction Circles printout. Have them write $1\frac{1}{3} + \frac{1}{3} = ?$ in their Math Notebook.

   **Ask:** What is the denominator of both fractions? 3

9. Have students locate the row of thirds fraction circles on the Fraction Circles printout. They will use the thirds fraction circles because the denominator is 3.

10. Have students model $1\frac{1}{3} + \frac{1}{3} = ?$ by shading 1 whole fraction circle, and 1 third of the next fraction circle, in one color, to model $1\frac{1}{3}$. Have students shade another third of the second fraction circle in a different color to model $\frac{1}{3}$.

ADD AND SUBTRACT FRACTIONS (A) 175

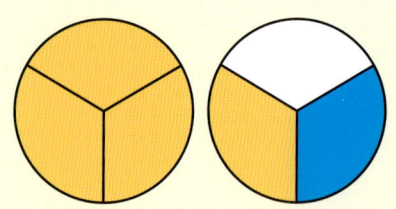

**Ask:** How many whole fraction circles did you shade? **1**

**Ask:** How many thirds of the second fraction circle did you shade? **2 thirds**

**Ask:** How many whole fraction circles and thirds of fraction circles did you shade in all? **$1\frac{2}{3}$**

**Ask:** What is the sum of $1\frac{1}{3} + \frac{1}{3}$? **$1\frac{2}{3}$**

11. Have students write the number sentence $1\frac{1}{3} + \frac{1}{3} = 1\frac{2}{3}$ in their Math Notebook.

12. Use a step-by-step approach to solve the last problem. Tell students that to add mixed numbers, they add the whole number and then add the fractions in any order.

13. Have students write $3\frac{7}{10} + 2\frac{8}{10} + 1\frac{3}{10} = ?$ in their Math Notebook.

    **Ask:** What is the sum of the whole numbers? **6**

    **Ask:** What is the sum of the fractions? **$\frac{18}{10}$**

    **Ask:** What is $\frac{18}{10}$ as a mixed number? **$1\frac{8}{10}$**

    **Ask:** What is $1\frac{8}{10}$ in simplest form? **$1\frac{4}{5}$**

    **Say:** Combine the sum of the whole numbers with the sum of the fractions.

    **Ask:** What is $6 + 1\frac{4}{5}$? **$7\frac{4}{5}$**

    **Ask:** What is the sum of $3\frac{7}{10} + 2\frac{8}{10} + 1\frac{3}{10}$ in simplest form? **$7\frac{4}{5}$**

14. Have students write the number sentence $3\frac{7}{10} + 2\frac{8}{10} + 1\frac{3}{10} = 7\frac{4}{5}$ in their Math Notebook.

## LEARN Add Fractions and Mixed Numbers

ONLINE 15 min

### Objectives
- Solve a simple problem involving addition or subtraction of fractions.

Students will practice adding fractions and mixed numbers with like denominators to solve story problems.

**Tips** Have students explain to you how they solved the last three problems in the activity. Encourage them to use the keywords for the lesson in their explanations.

## TRY IT Practice Adding Fractions

ONLINE 10 min

### Objectives
- Solve a simple problem involving addition or subtraction of fractions.

Students will complete an online Try It. If necessary, read the directions, problems, and answer choices to students and help them with keyboard or mouse operations.

PROBLEMS INVOLVING FRACTIONS

# Add and Subtract Fractions (B)

## Lesson Overview

| | | |
|---|---|---|
| **GET READY** Review Adding Fractions | 5 minutes | **ONLINE** |
| **LEARN** Use Models to Add Fractions | 15 minutes | **OFFLINE** |
| **LEARN** Add Fractions – Unlike Denominators | 15 minutes | **OFFLINE** |
| **LEARN** Add Mixed Numbers and Fractions | 15 minutes | **ONLINE** |
| **TRY IT** Practice Adding Mixed Numbers | 10 minutes | **ONLINE** |

## ▶ Lesson Objectives
Solve a simple problem involving addition or subtraction of fractions.

## ▶ Prerequisite Skills
- Use objects or sketches to solve a story problem that involves addition or subtraction of fractions.
- Solve and simplify a problem that involves addition or subtraction of fractions with unlike denominators.

## ▶ Content Background
Students will add fractions and mixed numbers with unlike denominators.
    Students will follow multiple steps to add fractions and mixed numbers with unlike denominators. The first step is to find the least common denominator of the fraction or fraction part of a mixed number and use the least common denominator to write equivalent fractions with like denominators. Then they add the like fraction parts and add the whole-number parts. Adding the fraction parts before the whole-number parts is important if the fraction parts of the sum add to an improper fraction. If the fraction part of the sum is an improper fraction, students change the improper fraction to a mixed number and combine the mixed number with the whole-number part of the sum. If the sum is not in simplest form, they simplify the sum.
    Although students will most often see fractions written with a horizontal fraction bar in math, such as $\frac{2}{3}$ or $5\frac{5}{6}$, they will occasionally see a diagonal fraction bar, such as 2/3 or 5 5/6. They will very likely see the diagonal fraction bar in everyday experiences, but be sure they understand that using the horizontal fraction bar in their work will make problems involving fractions easier to interpret and solve.

## ▶ Common Errors and Misconceptions
- Students might have difficulty understanding how different models represent fractions because they often see fractions represented as parts of circles—for example, pie and pizza illustrations. They might not recognize, for example, that the following models all represent the fraction $\frac{3}{5}$:

### Materials to Gather

**SUPPLIED**
Fraction Circles (printout)
Centimeter Grid Paper (printout)

**ALSO NEEDED**
ruler

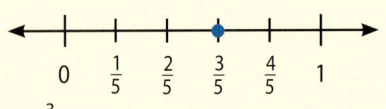

$\frac{3}{5}$ is a point on the number line.

$\frac{3}{5}$ of the shapes are triangles.

$\frac{3}{5}$ of the rectangle is shaded.

- Students might not understand that for a model to accurately represent a fraction as a part of a whole, the model must show a whole divided into equally sized parts.
- Students might not see the relationship between the models (such as fraction strips and number lines) and the procedures for adding and subtracting fractions. Once they begin to use symbols without models, students might apply memorized rules without thinking about the reasons for the procedures.

▶ Advance Preparation

Print one copy each of Fraction Circles and Centimeter Grid Paper.

**GET READY** Review Adding Fractions

ONLINE 5 min

Students will practice adding fractions with like and unlike denominators.

**Objectives**

- Solve and simplify a problem that involves addition or subtraction of fractions with unlike denominators.

**LEARN** Use Models to Add Fractions

OFFLINE 15 min

Students will use models to add fractions and mixed numbers with unlike denominators.
Gather the ruler and the Fraction Circles and Centimeter Grid Paper printouts.

**Objectives**

- Solve a simple problem involving addition or subtraction of fractions.

1. Give students the Fraction Circles printout. Tell them to write $\frac{1}{2} + \frac{1}{4} = ?$ on the printout, beneath the first two circles on the first row.

2. Have students shade $\frac{1}{2}$ of the first circle and label it $\frac{1}{2}$. Then have them use a ruler to draw a straight line through the next fraction circle to divide it into fourths. Have students shade $\frac{1}{4}$ and label it $\frac{1}{4}$. Tell students the half circle and one-fourth circle represent the two fractions.

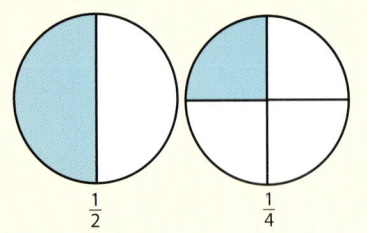

**Ask:** Look at the fractions. Do $\frac{1}{2}$ and $\frac{1}{4}$ have like denominators? No
**Say:** To add these fractions, the fractions need to have like denominators.

3. Tell students to use a ruler to draw a straight line through the first fraction circle to divide it into fourths. Then have students count the number of shaded fourths and add "$= \frac{2}{4}$" to the label $\frac{1}{2}$.

**178** PROBLEMS INVOLVING FRACTIONS

$\frac{1}{2} = \frac{2}{4}$  $\frac{1}{4}$

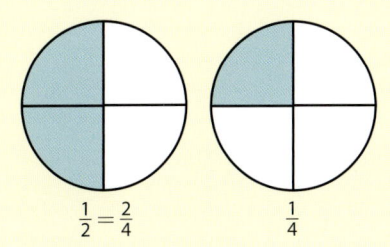

**Ask:** How many fourths is $\frac{1}{2}$ equal to? $\frac{2}{4}$

**Ask:** Look at the fractions. Do the $\frac{2}{4}$ and $\frac{1}{4}$ have like denominators now? Yes

**Ask:** What is the sum of $\frac{2}{4} + \frac{1}{4}$? $\frac{3}{4}$

**Ask:** What is the sum of $\frac{1}{2} + \frac{1}{4}$? $\frac{3}{4}$

4. Give students the grid paper and tell them to write $\frac{1}{6} + \frac{2}{3} = ?$ on it.

   Tell students they will draw rectangular models to solve this problem.

5. Have students outline two 3 by 2 rectangles side by side on the grid paper. Each rectangle will represent a fraction.

6. Tell students to draw 2 vertical lines and 1 horizontal line in the first rectangle to divide it into sixths. Have students shade $\frac{1}{6}$ and label it $\frac{1}{6}$.

7. Tell students to draw 2 vertical lines in the second rectangle to divide it into thirds. Have students shade $\frac{2}{3}$ and label it $\frac{2}{3}$.

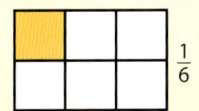

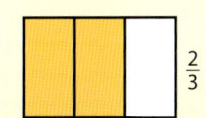

$\frac{1}{6}$   $\frac{2}{3}$

**Ask:** Look at the fractions. Do $\frac{1}{6}$ and $\frac{2}{3}$ have like denominators? No

8. Tell students to draw 1 horizontal line in the second rectangle to divide it into sixths. Then have students count the number of shaded sixths in the second rectangle. Have students add "$= \frac{4}{6}$" to the label $\frac{2}{3}$.

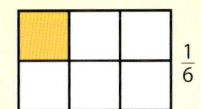

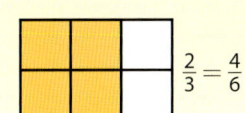

$\frac{1}{6}$   $\frac{2}{3} = \frac{4}{6}$

**Ask:** How many sixths is $\frac{2}{3}$ equal to? $\frac{4}{6}$

**Ask:** Look at the fractions. Do $\frac{1}{6}$ and $\frac{4}{6}$ have like denominators now? Yes

**Ask:** What is the sum of $\frac{1}{6} + \frac{4}{6}$? $\frac{5}{6}$

**Ask:** What is the sum of $\frac{1}{6} + \frac{2}{3}$? $\frac{5}{6}$

9. Have students find the circles divided into fourths on the Fraction Circles printout. Have them write this number sentence on the printout: $1\frac{2}{4} + \frac{3}{8} = ?$

ADD AND SUBTRACT FRACTIONS (B)

10. Have students shade all of the first circle and $\frac{2}{4}$ of the second circle to show $1\frac{2}{4}$ and label them $1\frac{2}{4}$. Then have students draw 2 diagonal lines through the third fraction circle to divide it into eighths. Have students shade $\frac{3}{8}$ and label it $\frac{3}{8}$.

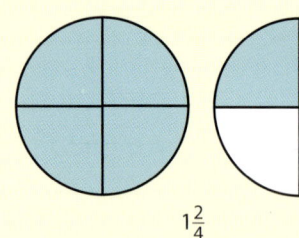

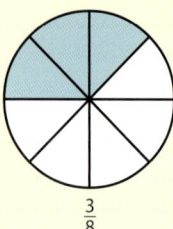

$1\frac{2}{4}$   $\frac{3}{8}$

**Ask:** Look at the fractions. Do $1\frac{2}{4}$ and $\frac{3}{8}$ have like denominators? No

**Say:** When you add mixed numbers, the fraction parts need to have like denominators.

11. Have students draw 2 diagonal lines through the fraction circle that shows $\frac{2}{4}$ to divide it into eighths. Then have them count the number of shaded eighths. Have them add "$= 1\frac{4}{8}$" to the label $1\frac{2}{4}$.

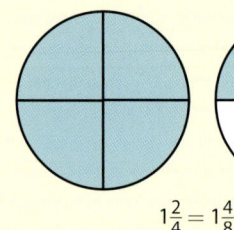

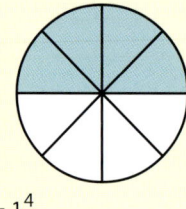

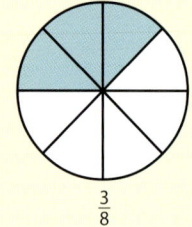

$1\frac{2}{4} = 1\frac{4}{8}$   $\frac{3}{8}$

**Ask:** How many eighths is $\frac{2}{4}$ equal to? $\frac{4}{8}$

**Ask:** Look at the fractions. Do the fraction part of $1\frac{4}{8}$ and the fraction $\frac{3}{8}$ have like denominators now? Yes

**Ask:** What is the sum of $\frac{4}{8} + \frac{3}{8}$? $\frac{7}{8}$

**Ask:** What is the sum of $\frac{2}{4} + \frac{3}{8}$? $\frac{7}{8}$

**Ask:** What is the sum of $1\frac{2}{4} + \frac{3}{8}$? $1\frac{7}{8}$

12. Tell students they will draw rectangular models on Centimeter Grid Paper to solve this problem: $1\frac{2}{5} + 1\frac{3}{10} = ?$

13. Have students outline two 5 by 2 rectangles side by side on the grid paper.

14. Tell students to draw 4 vertical lines in the second rectangle to divide it into fifths. Have students shade all of the first rectangle and $\frac{2}{5}$ of the second rectangle to show $1\frac{2}{5}$ and label them $1\frac{2}{5}$.

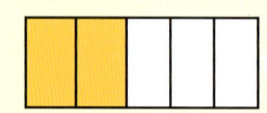

$1\frac{2}{5}$

15. Have students outline two more 5 by 2 rectangles side by side below the other rectangles.

**180** PROBLEMS INVOLVING FRACTIONS

16. Tell students to draw 4 vertical lines and 1 horizontal line in the second rectangle to divide it into tenths. Have students shade all of the first rectangle and $\frac{3}{10}$ of the second rectangle to show $1\frac{3}{10}$ and label them $1\frac{3}{10}$.

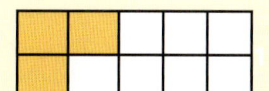

    $1\frac{3}{10}$

    **Ask:** Look at the fractions. Do $1\frac{2}{5}$ and $1\frac{3}{10}$ have like denominators? **No**

17. Have students explain how to change the model of $1\frac{2}{5}$ so that the two fraction parts of the mixed numbers have the same denominator. **Draw 1 horizontal line in the rectangle that shows $\frac{2}{5}$ to divide it into tenths.**

18. Have students count the number of shaded tenths.

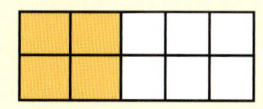

    $1\frac{2}{5} = ?$

    **Ask:** How many tenths is $\frac{2}{5}$ equal to? $\frac{4}{10}$

    **Ask:** Look at the fractions. Do the fraction parts $\frac{3}{10}$ and $\frac{4}{10}$ have like denominators now? **Yes**

    **Ask:** What is the sum of the fraction parts of $\frac{4}{10} + \frac{3}{10}$? $\frac{7}{10}$

    **Ask:** What is the sum of the fraction parts of $\frac{2}{5} + \frac{3}{10}$? $\frac{7}{10}$

    **Ask:** What is the sum of the whole-number parts in $1\frac{2}{5} + 1\frac{3}{10}$? **2**

    **Ask:** What is the sum of $1\frac{2}{5} + 1\frac{3}{10}$? Explain how you found the sum. $2\frac{7}{10}$
    **I changed the fraction parts of the mixed numbers to like denominators. I added the fraction parts and the whole-number parts.**

## LEARN Add Fractions – Unlike Denominators

**OFFLINE 15 min**

### Objectives

- Solve a simple problem involving addition or subtraction of fractions.

Students will use a step-by-step approach to add fractions and mixed numbers with unlike denominators.
There are no materials to gather for this activity. Have students write the steps in their Math Notebook.

1. Have students write $\frac{1}{3} + \frac{1}{2} = ?$

2. Tell students that to add $\frac{1}{3} + \frac{1}{2}$, they need to change the fractions to like denominators.

3. **Say:** To change $\frac{1}{3}$ and $\frac{1}{2}$ to fractions with like denominators, you need to find the least common multiple of the denominators. When a number is a multiple of two or more numbers, it is a common multiple of those numbers. If there is more than one common multiple, the number with the least value is the least common multiple. Let's find the least common multiple of 3 and 2.

    Have students write their answers to the following questions.
    - What are the first six multiples of 3? **3, 6, 9, 12, 15, 18**
    - What are the first six multiples of 2? **2, 4, 6, 8, 10, 12**

**ADD AND SUBTRACT FRACTIONS (B)**

- Which multiples are common to both 3 and 2? **6 and 12**
- Which of the common multiples is the least common multiple? **6**

**Say:** The least common multiple of 3 and 2 is 6, so the least common denominator of $\frac{1}{3}$ and $\frac{1}{2}$ is 6.

4. Tell students they will write fractions equivalent to $\frac{1}{3}$ and $\frac{1}{2}$ with a denominator of 6.

   **Ask:** Start with $\frac{1}{3}$. What number times 3 equals 6? **2**

   **Say:** Multiply $\frac{1}{3}$ by $\frac{2}{2}$ because $\frac{2}{2}$ is equal to 1.

   **Ask:** What fraction with a denominator of 6 is equivalent to $\frac{1}{3}$? **$\frac{2}{6}$**

   **Ask:** Now work with $\frac{1}{2}$. What number times 2 equals 6? **3**

   **Say:** Multiply $\frac{1}{2}$ by $\frac{3}{3}$ because $\frac{3}{3}$ is equal to 1.

   **Ask:** What fraction with a denominator of 6 is equivalent to $\frac{1}{2}$? **$\frac{3}{6}$**

5. Have students rewrite the problem as $\frac{2}{6} + \frac{3}{6} = ?$

   **Ask:** What is the sum of $\frac{2}{6} + \frac{3}{6}$? **$\frac{5}{6}$**

   **Ask:** Going back to the original problem, what is the sum of $\frac{1}{3} + \frac{1}{2}$? **$\frac{5}{6}$**

6. **Say:** Write $\frac{2}{3} + \frac{2}{4} = ?$ To change $\frac{2}{3} + \frac{2}{4}$ to fractions with like denominators, you need to find the least common multiple of the denominators.

7. Have students write the first four multiples of 3 and the first four multiples of 4. Students can refer to the multiples of 3 they wrote for the previous problem. **The first four multiples of 3 are 3, 6, 9, 12. The first four multiples of 4 are 4, 8, 12, 16.**

   **Ask:** What is the least common multiple of 3 and 4? **12**

   **Ask:** What is the least common denominator of $\frac{2}{3}$ and $\frac{2}{4}$? **12**

8. Have students write fractions equivalent to $\frac{2}{3}$ and $\frac{2}{4}$ with a denominator of 12.

   **Ask:** Start with $\frac{2}{3}$. What number times 3 equals 12? **4**

   **Say:** Multiply $\frac{2}{3}$ by $\frac{4}{4}$ because $\frac{4}{4}$ is equal to 1. **$\frac{8}{12}$**

   **Ask:** Now work with $\frac{2}{4}$. What number times 4 equals 12? **3**

   **Say:** Multiply $\frac{2}{4}$ by $\frac{3}{3}$ because $\frac{3}{3}$ is equal to 1. **$\frac{6}{12}$**

9. Have students write $\frac{8}{12} + \frac{6}{12} = ?$

   **Ask:** What is the sum of $\frac{8}{12} + \frac{6}{12}$? **$\frac{14}{12}$**

   **Say:** $\frac{14}{12}$ is an improper fraction. To change it to a mixed number, divide the numerator by the denominator. The quotient is the whole-number part of the mixed number. The remainder is the numerator of the fractional part, and the divisor is the denominator of the fractional part, which is 12.

   **Ask:** What is $\frac{14}{12}$ as a mixed number? **$1\frac{2}{12}$**

   **Ask:** How do you simplify $1\frac{2}{12}$? **Divide the fraction part, $\frac{2}{12}$, by $\frac{2}{2}$.**

   **Ask:** What is $1\frac{2}{12}$ in simplest form? **$1\frac{1}{6}$**

   **Ask:** What is the sum of $\frac{2}{3} + \frac{2}{4}$ in simplest from? **$1\frac{1}{6}$**

---

**Tips**

Have students choose one problem and model it with rectangles to make the connection between the models and the computation.

10. Have students solve the next problem on their own. Ask them to explain the steps they follow as they solve the problem. $\frac{2}{3} + \frac{4}{6} = ?$ Change the fractions to have a common denominator, which is 6. Rewrite the problem to $\frac{4}{6} + \frac{4}{6} = ?$ The sum is $\frac{8}{6}$. Change $\frac{8}{6}$ to the mixed number $1\frac{2}{6}$. Simplify $1\frac{2}{6}$ to $1\frac{1}{3}$.

11. Now add mixed numbers with unlike denominators.

    **Say:** Write $3\frac{1}{2} + 2\frac{7}{8} + 1\frac{1}{8} = ?$ You will add the fraction parts of the mixed numbers first. That's important if the fractions parts of the sum add to an improper fraction. The improper fraction can be changed to a mixed number and simplified. The fractions have unlike denominators, so you need to change the fraction parts $\frac{1}{2}$, $\frac{7}{8}$, and $\frac{1}{8}$ to fractions with like denominators.

12. Tell students that sometimes the denominator of one fraction is a multiple of the denominator of the other fractions.

    **Ask:** What are the first four multiples of 2? 2, 4, 6, 8

    **Say:** Eight is a multiple of 2 and it is the denominator of $\frac{7}{8}$, so the least common denominator of $\frac{1}{2}$, $\frac{7}{8}$, and $\frac{1}{8}$ is 8.

13. Have students write a fraction equivalent to $\frac{1}{2}$ that has a denominator of 8.

    **Ask:** What number times 2 equals 8? 4

    **Say:** Multiply $\frac{1}{2}$ by $\frac{4}{4}$ because $\frac{4}{4}$ is equal to 1. $\frac{4}{8}$

    **Say:** The fractions now have the same denominator, so you can add.

14. Have students write the sum of the fraction parts: $\frac{4}{8} + \frac{7}{8} + \frac{1}{8} = ?$

    **Ask:** What is the sum of $\frac{4}{8} + \frac{7}{8} + \frac{1}{8}$? $\frac{12}{8}$

    **Ask:** How do you change $\frac{12}{8}$ to a mixed number? Divide 12 by 8. The quotient is the whole-number part of the mixed number. The remainder is the numerator of the fractional part, and the divisor is the denominator of the fractional part, which is 8.

    **Ask:** What is $\frac{12}{8}$ as a mixed number? $1\frac{4}{8}$

    **Ask:** Is $1\frac{4}{8}$ in simplest form? No

    **Ask:** What is $1\frac{4}{8}$ in simplest form? $1\frac{1}{2}$

    **Ask:** What is the sum of the fraction parts of the mixed numbers? $1\frac{1}{2}$

15. Tell students the next step is to find the sum of the whole-number parts of $3\frac{1}{2} + 2\frac{7}{8} + 1\frac{1}{8} = ?$

    **Ask:** What is the sum of $3 + 2 + 1$? 6

    **Ask:** What is the sum of $6 + 1\frac{1}{2}$? $7\frac{1}{2}$

    **Ask:** What is the sum of $3\frac{1}{2} + 2\frac{7}{8} + 1\frac{1}{8} = ?$ $7\frac{1}{2}$

16. Repeat Steps 11–15 for $2\frac{3}{4} + 1\frac{3}{6} = ?$ Change the fractions to have a common denominator, which is 12. Rewrite the problem to $2\frac{9}{12} + 1\frac{6}{12} = ?$ The sum of the fraction parts is $\frac{15}{12}$. Change $\frac{15}{12}$ to the mixed number $1\frac{3}{12}$. Simplify $1\frac{3}{12}$ to $1\frac{1}{4}$. Add the whole-number parts: $2 + 1 = 3$. Add the whole-number parts and the fraction parts: $3 + 1\frac{1}{4} = 4\frac{1}{4}$.

ADD AND SUBTRACT FRACTIONS (B)

## LEARN  Add Mixed Numbers in Story Problems

ONLINE 15 min

**Objectives**
- Solve a simple problem involving addition or subtraction of fractions.

Students will add fractions and mixed numbers with unlike denominators to solve story problems.

## TRY IT  Practice Adding Mixed Numbers

ONLINE 10 min

**Objectives**
- Solve a simple problem involving addition or subtraction of fractions.

Students will complete an online Try It. If necessary, read the directions, problems, and answer choices to students and help them with keyboard or mouse operations.

# Add and Subtract Fractions (C)

## Lesson Overview

| | | |
|---|---|---|
| **GET READY** Subtract Fractions on a Walk | 5 minutes | **ONLINE** |
| **LEARN** Subtract Fractions | 15 minutes | **OFFLINE** |
| **LEARN** Subtract Mixed Numbers | 15 minutes | **OFFLINE** |
| **LEARN** Subtract Fractions and Mixed Numbers | 15 minutes | **ONLINE** |
| **TRY IT** Practice Subtracting Fractions | 10 minutes | **ONLINE** |

### ▶ Lesson Objectives
Solve a simple problem involving addition or subtraction of fractions.

### ▶ Prerequisite Skills
- Use objects or sketches to solve a story problem that involves addition or subtraction of fractions.
- Solve and simplify a problem that involves addition or subtraction of fractions with unlike denominators.

### ▶ Content Background
Students will subtract fractions and mixed numbers with like denominators.

The traditional approach to subtracting mixed numbers with like denominators is to leave the mixed numbers and not change them to improper fractions. The first step in subtracting mixed numbers is to subtract the fraction part of the mixed numbers. Students may need to regroup a whole number as a fraction with the like denominator to subtract the fraction parts. Then they subtract the whole-number parts of the mixed numbers. If the fraction part of the difference is an improper fraction, students change the improper fraction to a mixed number and combine it with the whole-number difference. This is the place where they might struggle. They add the fraction part and the whole-number part of the difference. Finally students write the difference in simplest form.

Although students will most often see fractions written with a horizontal fraction bar in math, such as $\frac{2}{3}$ or $5\frac{5}{6}$, they will occasionally see a diagonal fraction bar, such as 2/3 or 5 5/6. They will very likely see the diagonal fraction bar in everyday experiences, but be sure they understand that using the horizontal fraction bar in their work will make problems involving fractions easier to interpret and solve.

### ▶ Common Errors and Misconceptions
- Students might have difficulty understanding how different models represent fractions because they often see fractions represented as parts of circles—for example, pie and pizza illustrations. They might not recognize, for example, that the following models all represent the fraction $\frac{3}{5}$:

---

**Materials to Gather**

**SUPPLIED**
Fraction Circles (printout)
Centimeter Grid Paper (printout)
number lines from the Number Line Creator Tool

**ALSO NEEDED**
ruler

---

**ADD AND SUBTRACT FRACTIONS (C)** 185

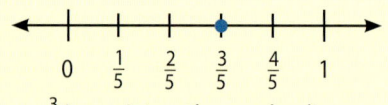

$\frac{3}{5}$ is a point on the number line.

$\frac{3}{5}$ of the shapes are triangles.

$\frac{3}{5}$ of the rectangle is shaded.

- Students might not understand that for a model to accurately represent a fraction as a part of a whole, the model must show a whole divided into equally sized parts.
- Students might not see the relationship between the models (such as fraction strips and number lines) and the procedures for adding and subtracting fractions. Once they begin to use symbols without models, students might apply memorized rules without thinking about the reasons for the procedures.

▶ Advance Preparation

Print two copies each of Fraction Circles and Centimeter Grid Paper.

Use the Number Line Creator Tool to print number lines that students will use in the Subtract Fractions and Subtract Mixed Numbers activities. The link to the Number Line Creator Tool is in the online Advance Preparation. Print one page of each type of number line at a time. Each page will have two identical number lines.

| DIRECTIONS FOR USING THE NUMBER LINE CREATOR TOOL |||
|---|---|---|
| To Create Number Line from 0 to 1: |||
| 1. Set Range:<br>• Start Number Line at: 0<br>• End Number Line at: 1 | 2. Select Options:<br>• Tick Marks: ones, tenths<br>• Labels: ones, tenths<br>• Label Format: fractions | 3. Print Number Line:<br>• Page Orientation: landscape<br>• Number Lines per Sheet: 2 |

| DIRECTIONS FOR USING THE NUMBER LINE CREATOR TOOL |||
|---|---|---|
| To Create Number Line from 0 to 4: |||
| 1. Set Range:<br>• Start Number Line at: 0<br>• End Number Line at: 4 | 2. Select Options:<br>• Tick Marks: ones, halves<br>• Labels: ones, halves<br>• Label Format: fractions | 3. Print Number Line:<br>• Page Orientation: landscape<br>• Number Lines per Sheet: 2 |

**GET READY** Subtract Fractions on a Walk

ONLINE 5 min

**Objectives**

Students will use models to subtract fractions with like denominators in story problems.

- Use objects or sketches to solve a story problem that involves addition or subtraction of fractions.

## LEARN Subtract Fractions

**OFFLINE 15 min**

### Objectives
- Solve a simple problem involving addition or subtraction of fractions.

Students will use rectangular models, number lines, and fraction circles to model subtraction of fractions with like denominators. These examples will lead students to use a step-by-step approach to subtract fractions.

Gather the ruler, Centimeter Grid Paper, number lines in tenths, and Fraction Circles printouts. Students will also write in their Math Notebook.

1. Give students the Centimeter Grid Paper. Tell them to write $\frac{7}{12} - \frac{2}{12} = ?$ on the paper.

   **Ask:** What is the denominator of both fractions? **12**

2. Have students use a ruler to draw a rectangle and divide it into 12 equal parts below the number sentence. The drawing is a fraction strip divided into twelfths. Use twelfths because the common denominator of the fractions being subtracted is 12. Tell students to model $\frac{7}{12}$ by shading the first 7 boxes on the left of the rectangle. Have students label $\frac{7}{12}$ above the shaded rectangles.

3. Tell students to mark an **X** on the 2 shaded boxes on the left and label them $\frac{2}{12}$ below the rectangle to show $\frac{7}{12} - \frac{2}{12} = ?$

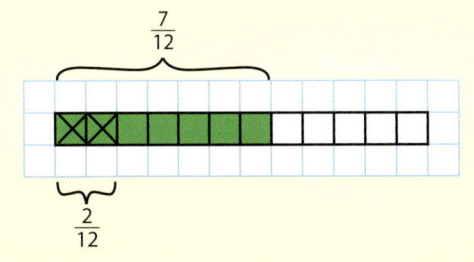

   **Ask:** How many shaded twelfths do not have an **X**? **5**

   **Ask:** Five of the shaded twelfths don't have an X, so what is $\frac{7}{12} - \frac{2}{12}$? $\frac{5}{12}$

   Have students write the number sentence $\frac{7}{12} - \frac{2}{12} = \frac{5}{12}$ below the fraction strip.

4. Use a number line to model the next problem. Give students the number line printout. Tell them to write $\frac{9}{10} - \frac{6}{10} = ?$ above the number line.

   **Ask:** What is the denominator of both fractions? **10**

5. Have students use the number line that has 10 equal parts with tick marks. Tell students that the number line is marked in tenths because the common denominator of the fractions being subtracted is 10. Remind them that $\frac{10}{10} = 1$.

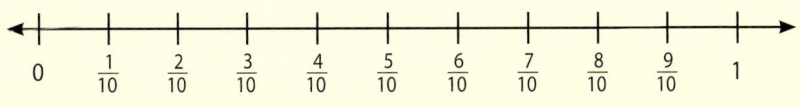

6. Have students mark points at 0 and $\frac{9}{10}$ on the number line. Start at 0 and "hop" 9 tenths to the right of 0. Show an arc between 0 and $\frac{9}{10}$.

ADD AND SUBTRACT FRACTIONS (C) 187

Then have students "hop" 6 tenths, with 1 hop for each tenth, to the left of $\frac{9}{10}$, to $\frac{3}{10}$. Show arcs between each tenth. Mark another point at $\frac{3}{10}$.

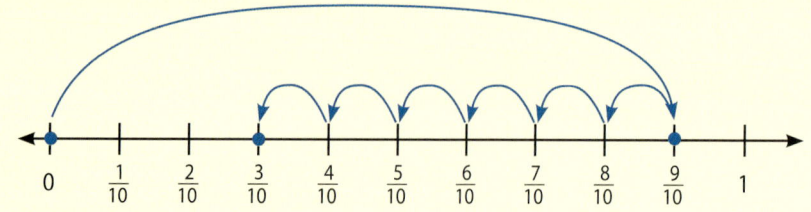

**Ask:** What is $\frac{9}{10} - \frac{6}{10}$? $\frac{3}{10}$

Have students write the number sentence $\frac{9}{10} - \frac{6}{10} = \frac{3}{10}$ below the number line.

7. Use fraction circles to model the following problem. Give students the Fraction Circles printout. Have students locate the row of thirds fraction circles and write $\frac{2}{3} - \frac{1}{3} = ?$ above the first circle. Use the thirds circle because the common denominator of the fractions being subtracted is 3.

    **Ask:** What is the denominator of both fractions? 3

8. Tell students to model $\frac{2}{3}$ by shading 2 of the 3 parts of the first circle.

9. Tell students to mark an **X** on 1 of the shaded parts to show $\frac{2}{3} - \frac{1}{3} = ?$

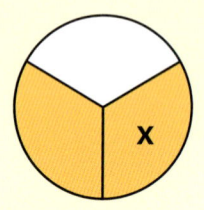

    **Ask:** How many shaded thirds do not have an **X**? 1

    **Ask:** One of the shaded thirds doesn't have an X, so what is $\frac{2}{3} - \frac{1}{3}$? $\frac{1}{3}$

    Have students write the number sentence $\frac{2}{3} - \frac{1}{3} = \frac{1}{3}$ below the fraction circle.

10. Explain that when fractions have like denominators, students need to subtract the numerators to find the difference. The denominator stays the same.

11. Use a step-by-step approach to solve the last problem. Have students write $\frac{7}{8} - \frac{5}{8} = ?$ in their Math Notebook. They should explain how to solve $\frac{7}{8} - \frac{5}{8} = ?$ Ask the following questions:

    - What is $7 - 5$? 2
    - What is the denominator in both fractions? 8
    - What is $\frac{7}{8} - \frac{5}{8}$? $\frac{2}{8}$
    - How do you simplify $\frac{2}{8}$ and what is the fraction in simplest form? Simplify $\frac{2}{8}$ by dividing a common factor of 2 from the numerator and the denominator. $\frac{2}{8}$ in simplest form is $\frac{1}{4}$.

    Have students write the number sentence $\frac{7}{8} - \frac{5}{8} = \frac{1}{4}$ in their Math Notebook.

**PROBLEMS INVOLVING FRACTIONS**

## LEARN Subtract Mixed Numbers

**OFFLINE 15 min**

### Objectives
- Solve a simple problem involving addition or subtraction of fractions.

### Tips
Have students explain to you how to regroup a mixed number so that the fraction parts of the two mixed numbers can be subtracted.

Students will use rectangular models, number lines, and fraction circles to model subtraction of mixed numbers with like denominators. These examples will lead students to use a step-by-step approach to subtract mixed numbers.

Gather the ruler, Centimeter Grid Paper, number lines marked in halves, and Fraction Circles printouts. Students will also write in the Math Notebook.

1. Have students use a ruler to draw two rectangles made up of 5 squares each and divide each into 5 equal parts. Tell them to write $1\frac{4}{5} - 1\frac{2}{5} = ?$ next to the rectangles. The drawings represent fraction strips divided into fifths. Use fifths because the common denominator of the mixed numbers is 5.

   **Ask:** What is the denominator of both fractions in the mixed numbers? 5

2. Tell students to model $1\frac{4}{5}$ by shading all of the first rectangle and the first 4 boxes on the left of the second rectangle. Have students label $1\frac{4}{5}$ above the shaded rectangles.

3. Tell them they will subtract the fraction part of the mixed numbers first. Have them mark an **X** on 2 of the 4 shaded boxes on the fraction strip that shows $\frac{4}{5}$.

4. Tell students they will subtract the whole-number part of the mixed numbers next. Have them mark an **X** on each box in the fraction strip that shows 1. Have students label $1\frac{2}{5}$ below the shaded rectangles.

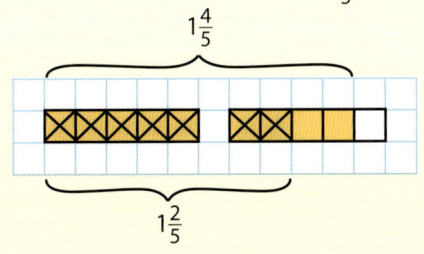

   **Ask:** How many squares of the whole shaded rectangle do not have an **X**? None

   **Ask:** How many shaded fifths of the second rectangle do not have an **X**? 2 shaded fifths don't have an **X**.

   **Ask:** What is $1\frac{4}{5} - 1\frac{2}{5}$? $\frac{2}{5}$

   Have students write the number sentence $1\frac{4}{5} - 1\frac{2}{5} = \frac{2}{5}$ next to the fraction strips.

5. Use a number line to model the next problem. Give students the number lines marked in halves. Tell them to write $3\frac{1}{2} - 2\frac{1}{2} = ?$ on the printout.

   **Ask:** What is the denominator of both fractions? 2

6. Tell students that the number line is marked in halves because the common denominator of the mixed numbers being subtracted is 2.

ADD AND SUBTRACT FRACTIONS (C) 189

7. Have students mark points at 0 and $3\frac{1}{2}$ on the number line. Start at 0 and "hop" 3 and one-half units to the right of 0. Show an arc between 0 and $3\frac{1}{2}$.

   Then have students "hop" to the left 2 whole units (from $3\frac{1}{2}$ to $2\frac{1}{2}$, and then from $2\frac{1}{2}$ to $1\frac{1}{2}$) and 1 half unit (from $1\frac{1}{2}$ to 1). Show arcs for each whole-unit hop and the half-unit hop. Mark another point at 1.

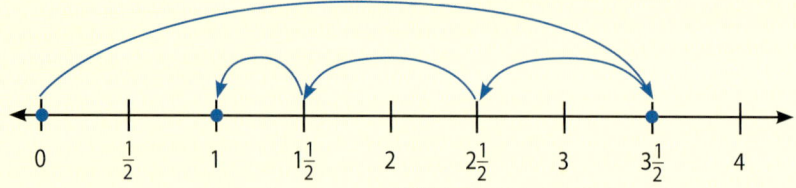

   **Ask:** What is $3\frac{1}{2} - 2\frac{1}{2}$? 1

   Have students write the number sentence $3\frac{1}{2} - 2\frac{1}{2} = 1$ below the number line.

8. Use fraction circles to model the next problem. Give students the Fraction Circles printout. Have them find the fourths fraction circles and write $1\frac{1}{4} - \frac{3}{4} = ?$ above two of those circles. Use the fourths circles because the common denominator of the fraction being subtracted from the mixed number is 4.

   **Ask:** What is the denominator of the fraction part of the mixed number and the fraction? 4

9. Tell students to shade 1 whole fraction circle and 1 of 4 parts of the next fraction circle to model $1\frac{1}{4}$.

10. What mixed number is shown with the shaded fraction circles? $1\frac{1}{4}$

11. Tell students they can regroup the whole number.

    **Ask:** How many fourths are in the whole shaded circle? 4

    **Say:** Mark an **X** on 2 of the shaded parts of the whole circle. Mark an **X** on the 1 shaded part of the circle that shows $\frac{1}{4}$. You marked an **X** on $\frac{3}{4}$ of the shaded parts. Remember that the shaded parts show $1\frac{1}{4}$. This model shows $1\frac{1}{4} - \frac{3}{4} = ?$

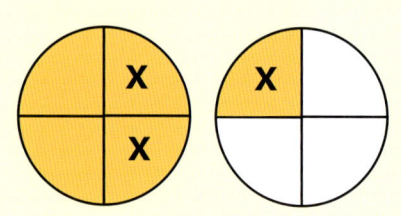

    **Ask:** If 3 shaded fourths have an **X** on them, how many shaded fourths do not have an **X**? 2 shaded fourths don't have an **X**.

    **Ask:** What is $1\frac{1}{4} - \frac{3}{4}$? $\frac{2}{4}$

    **Ask:** How do you simplify $\frac{2}{4}$ and what is the fraction in simplest form? Simplify $\frac{2}{4}$ by dividing a common factor of 2 from the numerator and the denominator. $\frac{2}{4}$ in simplest form is $\frac{1}{2}$.

    Have students write the number sentence $1\frac{1}{4} - \frac{3}{4} = \frac{1}{2}$ below the fraction circles.

**190** PROBLEMS INVOLVING FRACTIONS

12. Use a step-by-step approach to solve the last two problems. Tell students that when subtracting mixed numbers, they subtract the fraction parts first, then the whole-number parts.

13. Have students write $4\frac{5}{6} - 2\frac{1}{6} = ?$ in their Math Notebook. Use the following questions to guide students to find the answer:
    - Look at the fraction parts of the mixed numbers. Can you subtract the fraction parts of the mixed numbers, $\frac{5}{6}$ minus $\frac{1}{6}$, without regrouping? Yes
    - What is 5 − 1? 4
    - What is the denominator in both fractions? 6
    - What is $\frac{5}{6} - \frac{1}{6}$? $\frac{4}{6}$
    - What is $\frac{4}{6}$ in simplest form? $\frac{2}{3}$

    **Ask:** Now subtract the whole-number parts of the mixed numbers. What is 4 − 2? 2

    **Ask:** Combine the whole-number part difference and the fraction part difference. What is $4\frac{5}{6} - 2\frac{1}{6}$? $2\frac{2}{3}$

    Have students write the number sentence $4\frac{5}{6} - 2\frac{1}{6} = 2\frac{2}{3}$ in their Math Notebook.

14. Have students write $3\frac{7}{10} - 1\frac{8}{10} = ?$ in their Math Notebook.

    **Ask:** Can you subtract the fraction parts of the mixed numbers, $\frac{7}{10}$ minus $\frac{8}{10}$, without regrouping? No

    **Say:** Regroup 1 whole from $3\frac{7}{10}$ to rewrite the mixed number to $2\frac{17}{10}$.

    Have students write the problem as $2\frac{17}{10} - 1\frac{8}{10} = ?$

    **Ask:** Now that you have regrouped, can you subtract $\frac{8}{10}$ from $\frac{17}{10}$? Yes

    **Ask:** What is $\frac{17}{10} - \frac{8}{10}$? $\frac{9}{10}$

    **Say:** Look at the number sentence with regrouping. The next step is to subtract the whole-number parts of the two mixed numbers.

    **Ask:** What are the whole-number parts of the number sentence after the first mixed number was regrouped? 2 and 1

    **Ask:** What is 2 − 1? 1

    **Say:** Combine the whole-number part difference and the fraction part difference.

    **Ask:** What is $3\frac{7}{10} - 1\frac{8}{10}$? $1\frac{9}{10}$

    **Ask:** Is the answer in simplest form? Yes

    Have students write the number sentence $3\frac{7}{10} - 1\frac{8}{10} = 1\frac{9}{10}$ in their Math Notebook.

ADD AND SUBTRACT FRACTIONS (C)

## LEARN Subtract Fractions and Mixed Numbers

**ONLINE 15 min**

Students will practice subtracting fractions and mixed numbers with like denominators to solve story problems.

**Objectives**
- Solve a simple problem involving addition or subtraction of fractions.

## TRY IT Practice Subtracting Fractions

**ONLINE 10 min**

Students will complete an online Try It. If necessary, read the directions, problems, and answer choices to students and help them with keyboard or mouse operations.

**Objectives**
- Solve a simple problem involving addition or subtraction of fractions.

# Add and Subtract Fractions (D)

## Lesson Overview

| | | |
|---|---|---|
| **GET READY** Review Subtracting Fractions | 10 minutes | **OFFLINE** |
| **LEARN** Use Method to Subtract Mixed Numbers | 20 minutes | **OFFLINE** |
| **LEARN** Solve a Popcorn Story Problem | 10 minutes | **ONLINE** |
| **TRY IT** Subtraction Practice with Fractions | 10 minutes | **ONLINE** |
| **CHECKPOINT** | 10 minutes | **ONLINE** |

### ▶ Lesson Objectives
Solve a simple problem involving addition or subtraction of fractions.

### ▶ Prerequisite Skills
- Use objects or sketches to solve a story problem that involves addition or subtraction of fractions.
- Solve and simplify a problem that involves addition or subtraction of fractions with unlike denominators.

### ▶ Content Background
Students will subtract fractions and mixed numbers with unlike denominators.
   The step-by-step approach to subtracting mixed numbers with unlike denominators is to leave the mixed numbers as mixed numbers and not change them to improper fractions. The first step is to subtract the fraction part of the mixed numbers. Students rewrite the fraction parts as equivalent fractions with like denominators. They may need to regroup a whole number as a fraction with the like denominator to subtract the fraction parts. Then students subtract the whole-number parts of the mixed numbers. If the fraction part of the difference is an improper fraction, students change the improper fraction to a mixed number and combine it with the whole-number difference. This is the place where they might struggle. They add the fraction part and the whole-number part of the difference. Finally, students write the difference in simplest form.
   Although students will most often see fractions written with a horizontal fraction bar in math, such as $\frac{2}{3}$ or $5\frac{5}{6}$, they will occasionally see a diagonal fraction bar, such as 2/3 or 5 5/6. They will very likely see the diagonal fraction bar in everyday experiences, but be sure they understand that using the horizontal fraction bar in their work will make problems involving fractions easier to interpret and solve.

### ▶ Common Errors and Misconceptions
- Students might have difficulty understanding how different models represent fractions because they often see fractions represented as parts of circles—for example, pie and pizza illustrations. They might not recognize, for example, that the following models all represent the fraction $\frac{3}{5}$:

### Materials to Gather

**SUPPLIED**
Fraction Circles (printout)
Centimeter Grid Paper (printout)

**ALSO NEEDED**
ruler

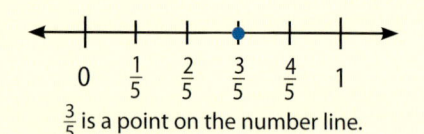

$\frac{3}{5}$ is a point on the number line.

$\frac{3}{5}$ of the shapes are triangles.

$\frac{3}{5}$ of the rectangle is shaded.

- Students might not understand that for a model to accurately represent a fraction as a part of a whole, the model must show a whole divided into equally sized parts.
- Students might not see the relationship between the models (such as fraction strips and number lines) and the procedures for adding and subtracting fractions. Once they begin to use symbols without models, students might apply memorized rules without thinking about the reasons for the procedures.

▶ Advanced Preparation

Print one copy each of Fraction Circles and Centimeter Grid Paper.

▶ Safety

If students make a recipe, have them follow kitchen safety rules. Be aware of any food allergies students might have.

## GET READY  Review Subtracting Fractions

**OFFLINE 10 min**

### Objectives

- Use objects or sketches to solve a story problem that involves addition or subtraction of fractions.
- Solve and simplify a problem that involves addition or subtraction of fractions with unlike denominators.

Students will use models to subtract fractions with unlike denominators in story problems. Gather the Centimeter Grid Paper and ruler.

1. Read the following problem to students:
   - There were $6\frac{1}{2}$ gallons of gas in Bill's car when he began driving to the beach. He used $3\frac{1}{4}$ gallons to drive to the beach. How many gallons of gas are left in Bill's car?

2. Tell students they will subtract $3\frac{1}{4}$ from $6\frac{1}{2}$ to solve the problem. Have them write $6\frac{1}{2} - 3\frac{1}{4} = ?$ at the top of the grid paper.

3. Tell students to sketch a model of $6\frac{1}{2}$ on the grid paper. Have them use a ruler to draw seven 2 by 2 squares. Have them shade 6 squares, to show 6 wholes. Have students draw a vertical line in the seventh square and shade half of it to show $\frac{1}{2}$.

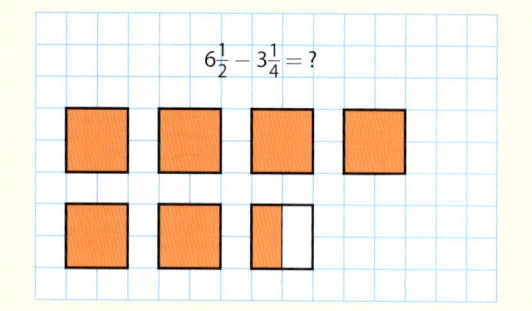

**194** PROBLEMS INVOLVING FRACTIONS

**Say:** You need like denominators to be able to find the answer to $6\frac{1}{2} - 3\frac{1}{4}$.

**Ask:** How can you change your model to show fractions with like denominators? Divide the half-shaded square into fourths.

4. Students should divide the half-shaded square into fourths and mark an **X** on a fourth to subtract $\frac{1}{4}$. They mark an **X** on 3 of the whole squares, to complete the subtraction of $6\frac{1}{2} - 3\frac{1}{4} = ?$.

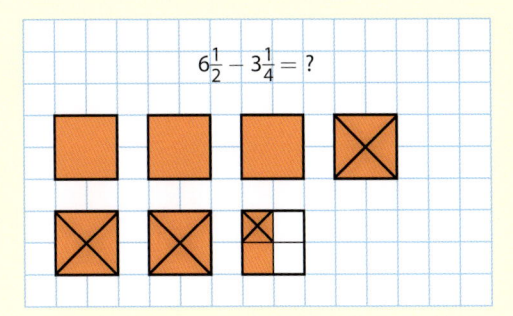

$6\frac{1}{2} - 3\frac{1}{4} = ?$

Guide students with the following questions:
- How many whole units remain unmarked with an X? 3
- How many shaded fourths remain unmarked with an X? 1
- What is $6\frac{1}{2} - 3\frac{1}{4}$? $3\frac{1}{4}$
- How many gallons of gas are left in Bill's car? $3\frac{1}{4}$ gallons

Have students write the number sentence $6\frac{1}{2} - 3\frac{1}{4} = 3\frac{1}{4}$ below the model.

5. Read the following problem to students:
   - Marisol filled a pitcher with $6\frac{1}{4}$ pints of lemonade. Her friends drank $3\frac{1}{2}$ pints of lemonade. How many pints of lemonade are left?

6. Tell students they will subtract $3\frac{1}{2}$ from $6\frac{1}{4}$ to solve the problem. Have them write $6\frac{1}{4} - 3\frac{1}{2} = ?$ on the grid paper.

7. Tell students to sketch a model of $6\frac{1}{4}$ on the grid paper. Have them use a ruler to draw seven 2 by 2 squares. Have them shade 6 squares, to show 6 wholes. Have students draw a vertical line and a horizontal line in the seventh square and shade a fourth of the square to show $\frac{1}{4}$.

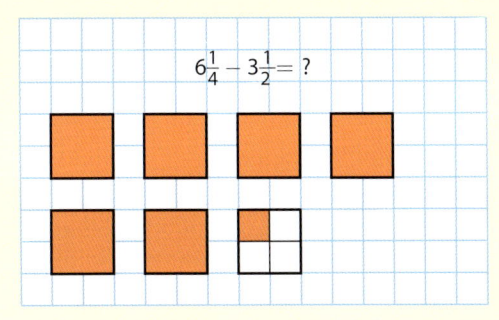

$6\frac{1}{4} - 3\frac{1}{2} = ?$

**Say:** You need like denominators to be able to find the answer to $6\frac{1}{4} - 3\frac{1}{2}$.

**Ask:** How many fourths is $\frac{1}{2}$ equal to? 2 fourths

**Say:** The square that shows $\frac{1}{4}$ doesn't have enough shaded squares to let us subtract $\frac{2}{4}$. We need to regroup.

ADD AND SUBTRACT FRACTIONS (D)  195

8. Tell students to draw a vertical line and a horizontal line in one whole square, so that 1 whole becomes $\frac{4}{4}$. To subtract the fractional part of $3\frac{1}{2}$, have students mark an **X** on the shaded fourth in the seventh square, and on 1 of the shaded fourths in the square that has been divided into fourths. Have them mark an **X** on 3 whole squares, to complete the subtraction $6\frac{1}{4} - 3\frac{1}{2} = ?$

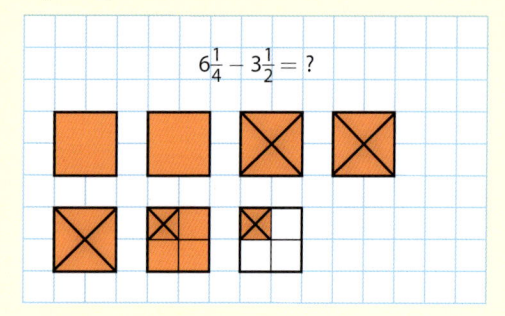

$6\frac{1}{4} - 3\frac{1}{2} = ?$

Guide students with these questions:
- How many whole units remain unmarked with an X? 2
- How many shaded fourths remain unmarked with an X? 3
- What is $6\frac{1}{4} - 3\frac{1}{2}$? $2\frac{3}{4}$
- How many pints of lemonade are left? $2\frac{3}{4}$ pints

9. Discuss both problems with students by asking these questions:
    - What fraction did you change to an equivalent form in both problems so you could subtract fraction parts of mixed numbers with like denominators? $\frac{1}{2}$
    - What fraction with a denominator of 4 is equivalent to $\frac{1}{2}$? $\frac{2}{4}$

    **Ask:** How is subtracting $6\frac{1}{2} - 3\frac{1}{4}$ different from subtracting $6\frac{1}{4} - 3\frac{1}{2}$?
    Is the answer to the first number sentence different from the answer to the second number sentence? Use the models you made to explain your answer. Students' explanations should show that when they subtracted $6\frac{1}{2} - 3\frac{1}{4}$, they changed $\frac{1}{2}$ to $\frac{2}{4}$ in the fraction they were subtracting from. That fraction is called the minuend. When they subtracted $6\frac{1}{4} - 3\frac{1}{2}$, they changed $\frac{1}{2}$ to $\frac{2}{4}$ in the fraction they were subtracting. That fraction is called the subtrahend. Students should say that the answer to the first number sentence is $3\frac{1}{4}$ and the answer to the second number sentence is $2\frac{3}{4}$, so there is a difference.

---

**LEARN Use Method to Subtract Mixed Numbers**  OFFLINE 20 min

**Objectives**

Students will first use a model to show subtracting of mixed numbers with unlike denominators. Then they will use a step-by-step approach to subtract mixed numbers with unlike denominators.
Gather the Fraction Circles printout. Students should write the steps for the step-by-step approach in their Math Notebook.

- Solve a simple problem involving addition or subtraction of fractions.

PROBLEMS INVOLVING FRACTIONS

## PROBLEM 1

1. Tell students they will solve the problem $5\frac{1}{2} - 3\frac{3}{4} = ?$ using fraction circles to model the problem.

2. Have students locate the row of halves fraction circles on the printout. Have them write $5\frac{1}{2} - 3\frac{3}{4} = ?$ above the fraction circles.

3. Tell students to model $5\frac{1}{2}$ by shading 5 circles, to show 5 wholes, and 1 of 2 halves of the sixth circle to show $\frac{1}{2}$.

    $5\frac{1}{2} - 3\frac{3}{4} = ?$

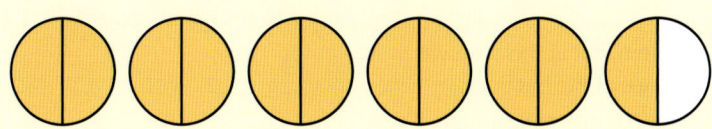

4. **Say:** You need like denominators to be able to find the answer to $5\frac{1}{2} - 3\frac{3}{4}$. You will subtract the fraction parts of the mixed numbers first.

    **Ask:** Do $\frac{1}{2}$ and $\frac{3}{4}$ have like denominators? No

    **Say:** When fractions are being subtracted, the fractions need to have like denominators. Draw one horizontal line in the half-shaded circle, and one horizontal line in one whole circle, so that 1 whole becomes $\frac{4}{4}$.

    $5\frac{1}{2} - 3\frac{3}{4} = ?$

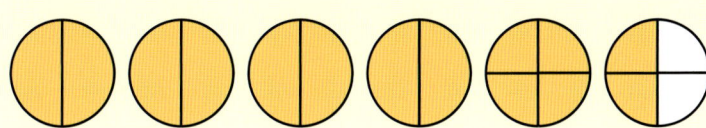

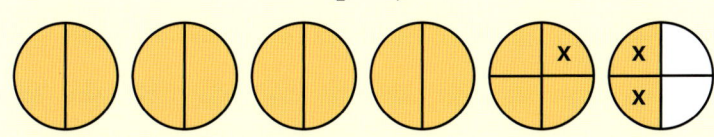

    Ask students these questions:
    - How many fourths is $\frac{1}{2}$ equal to? $\frac{2}{4}$
    - How many fourths are you subtracting from $\frac{2}{4}$? $\frac{3}{4}$
    - Before you subtract $\frac{3}{4}$ from $\frac{2}{4}$, what should you do? regroup

5. Tell students they can regroup a whole number.

    **Ask:** How many shaded fourths are in the whole circle next to the circle that shows $\frac{2}{4}$? $\frac{4}{4}$

    **Ask:** When you regroup the shaded fourths in the whole circle with the shaded fourths in the last circle, how many shaded fourths are there in all? $\frac{6}{4}$

6. **Say:** Now subtract $\frac{3}{4}$. Mark an **X** on 1 shaded fourth in the whole circle and 2 shaded fourths in the circle that shows $\frac{2}{4}$.

    $5\frac{1}{2} - 3\frac{3}{4} = ?$

    Ask students these questions:
    - How many shaded fourths in the last two circles do not have an **X**? 3
    - What is $\frac{6}{4} - \frac{3}{4}$? $\frac{3}{4}$

ADD AND SUBTRACT FRACTIONS (D) 197

7. Tell students to subtract the whole-number parts of the mixed numbers next. Have them mark an **X** on each of 3 of the circles that represent 3 wholes, to complete the subtraction $5\frac{1}{2} - 3\frac{3}{4} = ?$

$$5\frac{1}{2} - 3\frac{3}{4} = ?$$

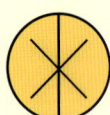

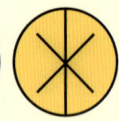

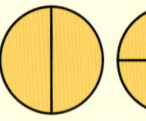

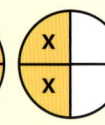

**Ask:** How many whole circles are left? Remember not to count the circle you used for regrouping. 1

**Say:** Remember that we are solving a subtraction problem. But at this step, we combine the whole-number difference with the difference of the fractions.

**Ask:** Combine the whole-number difference and the fraction difference. What is 1 and $\frac{3}{4}$? $1\frac{3}{4}$

**Ask:** What is $5\frac{1}{2} - 3\frac{3}{4}$? $1\frac{3}{4}$

Have students write the number sentence $5\frac{1}{2} - 3\frac{3}{4} = 1\frac{3}{4}$ below the fraction circles.

## PROBLEM 2

8. Tell students they will use a step-by-step approach to subtract mixed numbers.

9. Remind students that when subtracting mixed numbers, they subtract the fraction parts first, then the whole-number parts.

10. Have students write $4\frac{7}{12} - 2\frac{1}{4} = ?$ in their Math Notebook.

    **Say:** Look at the fraction parts of the mixed numbers. You need to find the least common denominator of $\frac{7}{12}$ and $\frac{1}{4}$ in order to subtract the fraction parts.

11. **Ask:** How do you find the least common denominator of two fractions? Find the least common multiple of the denominators. Think about the multiples of 12: 12, 24, 36, 48. Think about the multiples of 4: 4, 8, 12, 16.

    **Ask:** What is the least common multiple of 12 and 4? 12

    **Ask:** What is the least common denominator of $\frac{7}{12}$ and $\frac{1}{4}$? 12

12. **Ask:** What fraction with a denominator of 12 is equivalent to $\frac{1}{4}$? $\frac{3}{12}$

    Have students write $\frac{7}{12} - \frac{3}{12} = ?$ in their Math Notebook.

    **Ask:** What is $\frac{7}{12} - \frac{3}{12}$ in simplest form? $\frac{1}{3}$

13. **Say:** Now subtract the whole-number parts. What is $4 - 2$? 2

    **Ask:** Combine the whole-number difference and the fraction difference. What is 2 and $\frac{1}{3}$? $2\frac{1}{3}$

    **Ask:** What is $4\frac{7}{12} - 2\frac{1}{4}$? $2\frac{1}{3}$

    Have students write the number sentence $4\frac{7}{12} - 2\frac{1}{4} = 2\frac{1}{3}$ in their Math Notebook.

198 PROBLEMS INVOLVING FRACTIONS

## PROBLEM 3

14. Tell students they will use a step-by-step approach to subtract mixed numbers.
15. Remind students that when subtracting mixed numbers, they subtract the fraction parts first, then the whole-number parts.
16. Have students write $7\frac{1}{3} - 3\frac{3}{4} = ?$ in their Math Notebook.

    **Say:** Look at the fraction parts of the mixed numbers. You need to find the least common denominator of $\frac{1}{3}$ and $\frac{3}{4}$ in order to subtract the fraction parts.

17. **Ask:** How do you find the least common denominator of two fractions? Find the least common multiple of the denominators. Think about the multiples of 3: 3, 6, 9, 12, 15. Think about the multiples of 4: 4, 8, 12, 16.

    **Ask:** What is the least common multiple of 3 and 4? 12

    **Ask:** What is the least common denominator of $\frac{1}{3}$ and $\frac{3}{4}$? 12

18. **Ask:** What fraction with a denominator of 12 is equivalent to $\frac{1}{3}$? $\frac{4}{12}$

    **Ask:** What fraction with a denominator of 12 is equivalent to $\frac{3}{4}$? $\frac{9}{12}$

    **Ask:** Before you subtract $\frac{9}{12}$ from $\frac{4}{12}$, what should you do? regroup

19. Tell students they need to regroup a whole number in order to subtract the fraction parts of the mixed numbers.

    **Say:** Regroup 1 whole as $\frac{12}{12}$. $7\frac{1}{3}$ is equivalent to $7\frac{4}{12}$. The mixed number in the original problem changes to $6\frac{16}{12}$. Write $6\frac{16}{12} - 3\frac{9}{12} = ?$ in your Math Notebook.

    **Ask:** When we regrouped, we added $\frac{12}{12}$ to $\frac{4}{12}$. What is the improper fraction you are subtracting from now? $\frac{16}{12}$

    **Ask:** Now subtract to find the fraction part difference. What is $\frac{16}{12} - \frac{9}{12}$ in simplest form? $\frac{7}{12}$

20. **Say:** Now subtract the whole-number parts. We rewrote the problem when we regrouped to $6\frac{16}{12} - 3\frac{9}{12} = ?$ What is $6 - 3$? 3

    **Ask:** Combine the whole-number difference and the fraction difference. What is 3 and $\frac{7}{12}$? $3\frac{7}{12}$

    **Ask:** What is $7\frac{1}{3} - 3\frac{3}{4}$? $3\frac{7}{12}$

    Have students write the number sentence is $7\frac{1}{3} - 3\frac{3}{4} = 3\frac{7}{12}$ in their Math Notebook.

## PROBLEM 4

21. Have students write the problem in their Math Notebook and use a step-by-step approach to solve it on their own. Have them explain the steps they followed to solve the following problem:
    - $8\frac{1}{5} - 4\frac{1}{4} = ?$

22. Students should follow these steps to find the answer:
    - Subtract fraction parts of mixed numbers first, and then whole-number parts.
    - Look at the fraction parts of the mixed numbers. Find the least common denominator of the fractions $\frac{1}{5}$ and $\frac{1}{4}$. To do this, find the least common multiple of the denominators 5 and 4.

      Think about the multiples of 5: 5, 10, 15, 20, 25.

**ADD AND SUBTRACT FRACTIONS (D)** 199

Think about the multiples of 4: 4, 8, 12, 16, 20, 24.
The least common multiple of 5 and 4 is 20. The least common denominator of $\frac{1}{5}$ and $\frac{1}{4}$ is 20.
The fraction with a denominator of 20 that is equivalent to $\frac{1}{5}$ is $\frac{4}{20}$.
The fraction with a denominator of 20 that is equivalent to $\frac{1}{4}$ is $\frac{5}{20}$.

- Before you subtract the fraction parts of the mixed numbers, $\frac{4}{20} - \frac{5}{20}$, regroup a whole number from the mixed number $8\frac{1}{5}$.
- Regroup 1 whole as $\frac{20}{20}$. $8\frac{1}{5}$ is equivalent to $8\frac{4}{20}$.
- Add $\frac{20}{20}$ to $\frac{4}{20}$ to find the improper fraction $\frac{24}{20}$ to subtract $\frac{5}{20}$ from.
  The mixed number in the original problem changes to $7\frac{24}{20}$. Write the problem as $7\frac{24}{20} - 4\frac{5}{20} = ?$
- Subtract to find the fraction part difference. $\frac{24}{20} - \frac{5}{20} = \frac{19}{20}$
- Subtract to find the whole-number difference. The problem was rewritten when regrouped to $7\frac{24}{20} - 4\frac{5}{20} = ?$ So $7 - 4 = 3$.
- Combine the whole-number difference and the fraction difference. 3 and $\frac{19}{20}$ is $3\frac{19}{20}$.
- Write the number sentence with the answer: $8\frac{1}{5} - 4\frac{1}{4} = 3\frac{19}{20}$.

## LEARN Solve a Popcorn Story Problem

ONLINE 10 min

### Objectives

- Solve a simple problem involving addition or subtraction of fractions.

Students will subtract fractions and mixed numbers with unlike denominators to solve story problems about recipes.
  This activity can be extended if you and students make one or both of the recipes. Have students compare the ingredient amounts in the recipes to practice subtracting fractions and mixed numbers.

### Tips

Have students write their own popcorn snack recipe using fractions and mixed numbers.

**Winnie's Popcorn Snack**

$8\frac{1}{2}$ cups popped popcorn
$\frac{2}{3}$ cup dried apples
$2\frac{3}{4}$ cups pine nuts
$\frac{1}{4}$ teaspoon dry mustard

**Ron's Popcorn Snack**

$9\frac{2}{3}$ cups popped popcorn
$\frac{5}{8}$ cup raisins
$1\frac{5}{12}$ cups toasted walnuts
$\frac{1}{8}$ teaspoon dry mustard

PROBLEMS INVOLVING FRACTIONS

## TRY IT  Subtraction Practice with Fractions

**ONLINE 10 min**

Students will complete an online Try It. If necessary, read the directions, problems, and answer choices to students and help them with keyboard or mouse operations.

**Objectives**

- Solve a simple problem involving addition or subtraction of fractions.

## CHECKPOINT

**ONLINE 10 min**

Students will complete an online Checkpoint. If necessary, read the directions, problems, and answer choices to students and help them with keyboard or mouse operations.

**Objectives**

- Solve a simple problem involving addition or subtraction of fractions.

# Unit Review

## Lesson Overview

| | | |
|---|---|---|
| **UNIT REVIEW** Look Back | 10 minutes | **ONLINE** |
| **UNIT REVIEW** Checkpoint Practice | 50 minutes | **ONLINE** |
| ▶ **UNIT REVIEW** Prepare for the Checkpoint | | |

### ▶ Unit Objectives

This lesson reviews the following objectives:
- Solve a story problem involving multiplication or division of fractions.
- Solve a simple problem involving addition or subtraction of fractions.

**Materials to Gather**

There are no materials to gather for this lesson.

### ▶ Advance Preparation

In this lesson, students will have an opportunity to review previous activities in the Problems Involving Fractions unit. Look at the suggested activities in Unit Review: Prepare for the Checkpoint online and gather any needed materials.

## UNIT REVIEW  Look Back

ONLINE 10 min

**Objectives**
- Review unit objectives.

Students will review key concepts from the unit to prepare for the Unit Checkpoint.

## UNIT REVIEW  Checkpoint Practice

ONLINE 50 min

**Objectives**
- Review unit objectives.

Students will complete an online Checkpoint Practice to prepare for the Unit Checkpoint. If necessary, read the directions, problems, and answer choices to students. Have students answer the problems on their own. Review any missed problems with students.

### ▶ UNIT REVIEW  Prepare for the Checkpoint

What you do next depends on how students performed in the previous activity, Unit Review: Checkpoint Practice. If students had difficulty with any of the problems, complete the appropriate review activity listed in the table online.

# Unit Checkpoint

## Lesson Overview

**UNIT CHECKPOINT** Online | 60 minutes | **ONLINE**

### ▶ Unit Objectives

This lesson assesses the following objectives:
- Solve a story problem involving multiplication or division of fractions.
- Solve a simple problem involving addition or subtraction of fractions.

### Materials to Gather

There are no materials to gather for this lesson.

### UNIT CHECKPOINT Online

ONLINE 60 min

### Objectives

- Assess unit objectives.

Students will complete the Unit Checkpoint online. If necessary, read the directions, problems, and answer choices to students and help them with keyboard or mouse operations.

# Decimals: Addition and Subtraction

I wonder about how much one pound of each would cost?
$2.85 is about $3.00.
$1.74 is about $2.00.
My estimate is about $5.00.

$ 1.74 lb

$ 2.85 lb

## ▶ Unit Objectives

- Round a decimal number to any place through hundredths.
- Estimate the sum or difference in a problem involving decimal numbers.
- Solve an addition or subtraction problem involving decimal numbers.
- Verify that the calculated result of a problem involving addition or subtraction of decimal numbers is reasonable.
- Solve a story problem involving addition or subtraction of decimal numbers.

## ▶ Big Ideas

- Estimation is a useful tool in problem solving.
- Addition, subtraction, multiplication, and division can be represented by models and by using math symbols.

## ▶ Unit Introduction

This unit explores addition and subtraction of decimal numbers. Students will begin by rounding decimal numbers. Decimal numbers in this unit can be rounded through the hundredths place. Rounding strategies such as using a number line and rounding to a given place will be used. After students review rounding decimal numbers, they will round decimal addends, minuends, and subtrahends before estimating the sum or difference. Once they estimate sums and differences, they will find the actual sum or difference with decimal number sentences. Students will practice addition and subtraction with number sentences as well as in story problems. As they find solutions, they will verify that a calculated answer is reasonable by comparing an estimate of the sum or difference to the actual answer.

## ▶ Keywords

| decimal number | friendly numbers | round (v.) |
| estimate (n.) | hundredths | tenths |
| estimate (v.) | place value | thousandths |

# Round Decimals Through Hundredths

## Lesson Overview

| | | |
|---|---|---|
| **GET READY** Round Decimal Numbers | 5 minutes | ONLINE |
| **LEARN** Model Decimal Numbers | 10 minutes | ONLINE |
| **LEARN** Find Rounded Decimals | 15 minutes | ONLINE |
| **LEARN** Round Decimals in Stories | 15 minutes | ONLINE |
| **TRY IT** Practice Rounding Decimals | 10 minutes | OFFLINE |
| **CHECKPOINT** | 5 minutes | ONLINE |

### ▶ Lesson Objectives
Round a decimal number to any place through hundredths.

### ▶ Prerequisite Skills
Round a decimal number.

### ▶ Content Background
Students will round decimals to the hundredths place. Decimal numbers name wholes and parts of a whole. The names of the parts of a whole are tenths, hundredths, thousandths, and so on.

Rounding numbers in a problem can make finding an estimate easier. Decimals can be rounded to friendly numbers such as 0.05, 0.10, 0.25, 0.50, or 1. They can also be rounded to a specific place. For example, if people buy 4.381 gallons of gasoline, they could round the number of gallons to the nearest hundredth. Since 4.381 is between 4.38 and 4.39, but closer to 4.38, 4.381 rounds to 4.38.

When students round a number ending in a 5, they cannot round to the nearer number, since the 5 is halfway between two boundary numbers. For instance, 1.25 is halfway between 1.2 and 1.3. In this math course, numbers ending in 5 are rounded to the greater number. So 1.25 rounded to the nearest tenth is 1.3. There are other situations in which you might round numbers ending in 5 to the lesser number, but those situations are rare and will be discussed as specific cases.

When students write and compute with decimal numbers, they often use numbers that are between 0 and 1—for example, 0.1. While it is acceptable to write this number as .1, mathematicians usually write the leading zero, to show that the decimal number has zero for the part that is the whole number and to avoid confusion about the value of the number.

When students use a number line to help them round decimal numbers, all the numbers will show the same number of decimal places. For example, on a number line showing numbers in hundredths, numbers such as 42.80 will appear, rather than the equivalent value 42.8. When students find the rounded value of a number, they should give their answer to the decimal place being rounded. For example, when rounding 42.78 to the nearest tenth, they would answer 42.8, emphasizing the tenths place, even though the number line shows

### Materials to Gather

**SUPPLIED**
Round Decimals in Stories (printout)
Practice Rounding Decimals activity page

42.80. Be sure that students understand that numbers such as 42.8 and 42.80 show the same value and position on the number line but emphasize different place values.

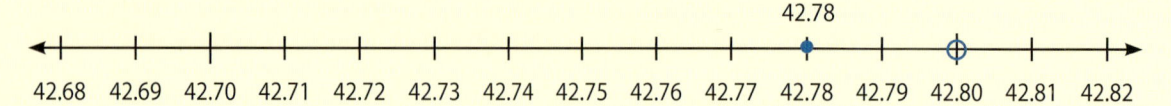

```
←┼────┼────┼────┼────┼────┼────┼────┼────┼────●────┼────○────┼────┼→
 42.68 42.69 42.70 42.71 42.72 42.73 42.74 42.75 42.76 42.77 42.78 42.79 42.80 42.81 42.82
                                                      42.78
```

### ▶ Common Errors and Misconceptions
- Students might become so concerned about getting the correct answer when estimating that they first find the exact answer, and then round it. For example, when asked to estimate 348 + 176, students might find the sum (524), and then round it to the nearest hundred (500).
- Students might have difficulty accepting that there is more than one correct approach and answer to an estimation problem.
- Students might have difficulty understanding rounding because traditional teaching focuses on how to round, not why to round. For example, students might have been taught to "round up" to the nearest ten if the digit in the ones place is 5 or greater. There are some situations, however, where "rounding down" would be more appropriate—having an understanding of why to round might help students identify these situations.

### ▶ Advance Preparation
Print the Round Decimals in Stories printout.

---

## GET READY  Round Decimal Numbers
**ONLINE 5 min**

Students will use data about the wingspans of birds to round decimal numbers to whole numbers and tenths.

**Objectives**
- Round a decimal number.

---

## LEARN  Model Decimal Numbers
**ONLINE 10 min**

Students will use the online Grid Learning Tool to model decimal numbers through the hundreths place.

**Objectives**
- Round a decimal number to any place through hundredths.

### DIRECTIONS FOR USING THE GRID LEARNING TOOL
1. Review the Grid Learning Tool with students. Tell students that when they use the grid to represent decimals, the whole grid represents 1 whole (1.0), each column represents 1 tenth (0.1), and each small square represents 1 hundredth (0.01). See the example grid that follows.

**Tips**

Make sure students understand that each place to the right is 10 times greater than the place to the immediate left. For example, a hundredth is 10 times greater than a thousandth.

**DECIMALS: ADDITION AND SUBTRACTION**

1 whole (1.0)

1 hundredth (0.01)

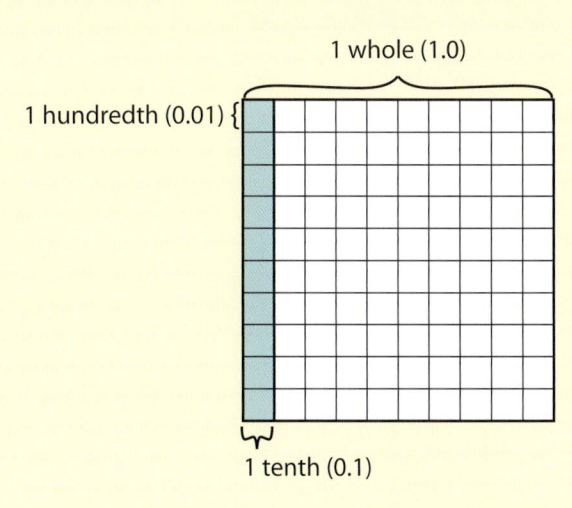

1 tenth (0.1)

2. Have students say 0.08 (eight hundredths). Then have students shade 0.08 with the learning tool. See the example answer.

3. Have students repeat Step 2 with the following decimal numbers. Use the arrows to scroll to screens that have more than one whole grid. Have students clear the grid between problems.
   - 0.6
   - 0.41
   - 1.53
   - 1.9

   After students model each decimal number, have them explain how the model shows each place value. For example, the model for 1.53 shows 1 whole, 5 tenths, and 3 hundredths. The model for 1.9 shows 1 whole and 9 tenths.

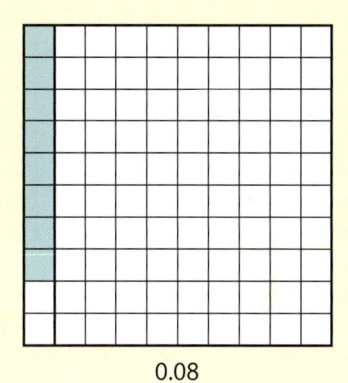

0.08

4. Use the arrows to scroll to the screen that has three whole grids. Now have students shade 2.90 with the learning tool.

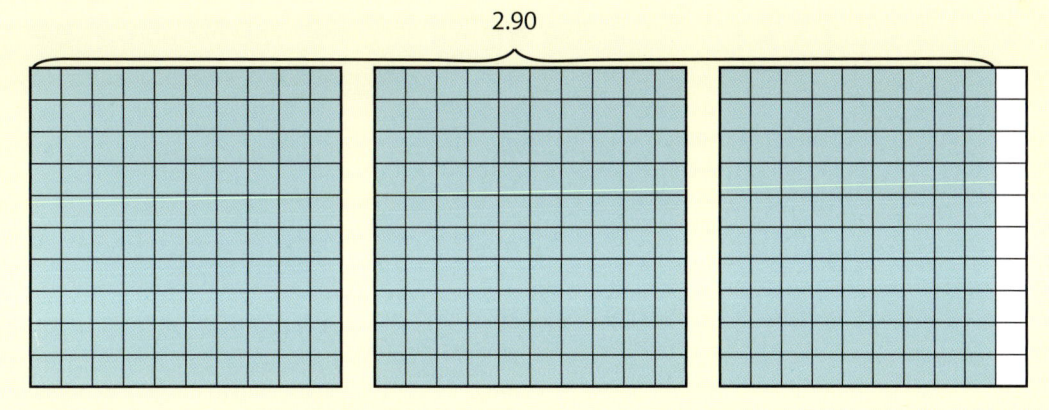

2.90

**Ask:** How many whole grids did you shade? 2

**Ask:** How many hundredths did you shade? 90

**Ask:** When you shaded 90 hundredths, how many tenths did you shade? 9

**Ask:** What decimal number is equivalent to 2.90? 2.9

5. Use the arrows to scroll to the screen that has one whole grid. Introduce students to thousandths. Explain to students that if they divided one whole grid by a thousand, each small square in the grid would have 10 equal parts, and the total grid would have 1,000 equal parts. Tell students that when they divide one hundredth into 10 equal parts, each part is one thousandth.

**ROUND DECIMALS THROUGH HUNDREDTHS** 209

6. Use the arrows to scroll to the screen that has two whole grids. Have students shade 1.62 by shading one whole grid, then the left six columns and two squares at the top of the seventh column on the second grid. Ask them to name the decimal number shaded. 1.62

   Tell students that 1.627 is greater than 1.62 because 1.627 has 7 in the thousandths place and 1.62 has 0 in the thousandths place. Show students the following example of how 1.627 would be shaded on the grid if it showed thousandths. Be sure to let students see the magnified part of one small square on one whole grid that shows 7 thousandths shaded.

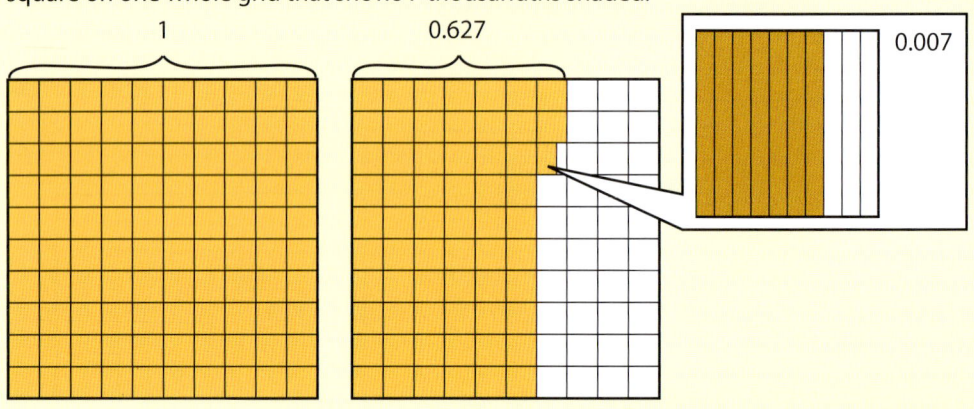

   1          0.627                    0.007

## LEARN  Find Rounded Decimals

**ONLINE 15 min**

### Objectives
- Round a decimal number to any place through hundredths.

Students will use number lines to round decimal numbers through hundredths. The activity will show students how one number can be rounded to different place values, which results in different rounded numbers for the original number.

## LEARN  Round Decimals in Stories

**ONLINE 15 min**

### Objectives
- Round a decimal number to any place through hundredths.

Students will round decimal numbers to solve story problems. Gather the Round Decimals in Stories printout. Students will write some answers in their Math Notebook.

1. Have students read the first on-screen problem.
2. Have students write 12.394 above the top two number lines on the printout. Have them count aloud from 12.390 to 12.400 using the top number line.

   **Say:** Let's use a number line to round numbers and solve the problem. What place does the question ask you to round 12.394 to? tenths

   **Ask:** Use the number line that is marked from 12.390 to 12.400. Mark 12.394 with a dot. Is 12.394 closer to 12.390 or 12.400? 12.390

   **Say:** We can write 12.390 and 12.400 as equivalent decimal numbers that have digits in the tenths and hundredths places. 12.390 is equivalent to 12.39 and 12.400 is equivalent to 12.40. So 12.394 rounded to the nearest hundredth is 12.39.

   Have students count aloud from 12.30 to 12.40 using the second number line.

### Tips

Tell students that when they need to round a number ending in 5, they should round to the greater number. For instance, 1.25 rounded to the nearest tenth is 1.3.

**Ask:** Use the number line that is marked from 12.30 to 12.40. Mark the approximate location of 12.394 with a dot. Is 12.394 closer to 12.30 or 12.40? 12.40

**Say:** We can write 12.30 and 12.40 as equivalent decimal numbers that have digits in the tenths places. 12.30 is equivalent to 12.3 and 12.40 is equivalent to 12.4. So 12.394 rounded to the nearest tenth is 12.4.

**Say:** What is the answer to the original problem? Nancy put about 12.4 gallons of gas in her car, rounded to the nearest tenth of a gallon.

3. Have students read the second on-screen problem.
4. Have students write 2.465 above the bottom three number lines on the printout. Have them count aloud from 2.460 to 2.470 using the top number line.

   **Say:** Let's use a number line to round numbers and solve the problem. What place does the question ask you to round 2.465 to? whole number

   **Ask:** Use the number line that is marked from 2.460 to 2.470. Mark the approximate location of 2.465 with a dot. Since 2.465 is halfway between 2.460 and 2.470, round 2.465 to the greater number. What is 2.465 rounded to the hundredths place? 2.470

   **Say:** We can write 2.460 and 2.470 as equivalent decimal numbers that have digits in the tenths and hundredths places. 2.460 is equivalent to 2.46 and 2.470 is equivalent to 2.47. So 2.465 rounded to the nearest hundredth is 2.470.

   Have students count aloud from 2.40 to 2.50 using the middle number line.

   **Ask:** Use the number line that is marked from 2.40 to 2.50. Mark the approximate location of 2.465 with a dot. Is 2.465 closer to 2.40 or 2.50? 2.50

   **Say:** We can write 2.40 and 2.50 as equivalent decimal numbers that have digits in the tenths place. 2.40 is equivalent to 2.4 and 2.50 is equivalent to 2.5. So 2.465 rounded to the nearest tenth is 2.5.

   Have students count aloud from 2.0 to 3.0 using the bottom number line.

   **Ask:** Use the number line that is marked from 2.0 to 3.0. Mark the approximate location of 2.465 with a dot. Is 2.465 closer to 2.0 or 3.0? 2.0

   **Say:** We can write 2.0 and 3.0 as equivalent decimal numbers that have digits in the ones place. 2.0 is equivalent to 2 and 3.0 is equivalent to 3. So 2.465 rounded to the nearest whole number is 2.

   **Say:** What is the answer to the original problem? Denny put about 2 gallons of gas in his riding lawn mower, rounded to the nearest gallon.

5. Have students read the third on-screen problem. They will not use a number line for this problem and the last problem.
6. Have students write 42.385 in their Math Notebook and round the number to the nearest hundredth of a gallon. They will write the answer in their Math Notebook.

   **Ask:** What is the closest hundredth that is less than 42.385? 42.38

   **Ask:** What is the closest hundredth that is greater than 42.385? 42.39

   **Say:** Since 42.385 is halfway between 42.38 and 42.39, round 42.385 to the greater number.

   **Ask:** What is the 42.385 rounded to the nearest hundredth? 42.39

   **Say:** What is the answer to the original problem? The trucker put about 42.39 gallons of diesel fuel in the truck, rounded to the nearest hundredth of a gallon.

7. Have students read the fourth on-screen problem.

8. Have students write 9.27 in their Math Notebook and round the number to the nearest tenth of a gallon. They will write the answer in their Math Notebook.

   **Ask:** What is the closest tenth that is less than 9.27? 9.2

   **Ask:** What is the closest tenth that is greater than 9.27? 9.3

   **Ask:** Look at the 7 in the hundredths place in 9.27. Which tenth is 9.27 closer to, 9.2 or 9.3? 9.3

   **Ask:** What is the 9.27 rounded to the nearest tenth? 9.3

   **Say:** What is the answer to the original problem? The farmer put about 9.3 gallons of fuel in the tractor, rounded to the nearest tenth of a gallon.

## TRY IT  Practice Rounding Decimals

OFFLINE 10 min

Students will practice rounding decimal numbers. Have students turn to the Practice Rounding Decimals activity page in their Activity Book and read the directions with them.

Students should copy the problems from the Activity Book into their Math Notebook as necessary and solve them there.

### Objectives
- Round a decimal number to any place through hundredths.

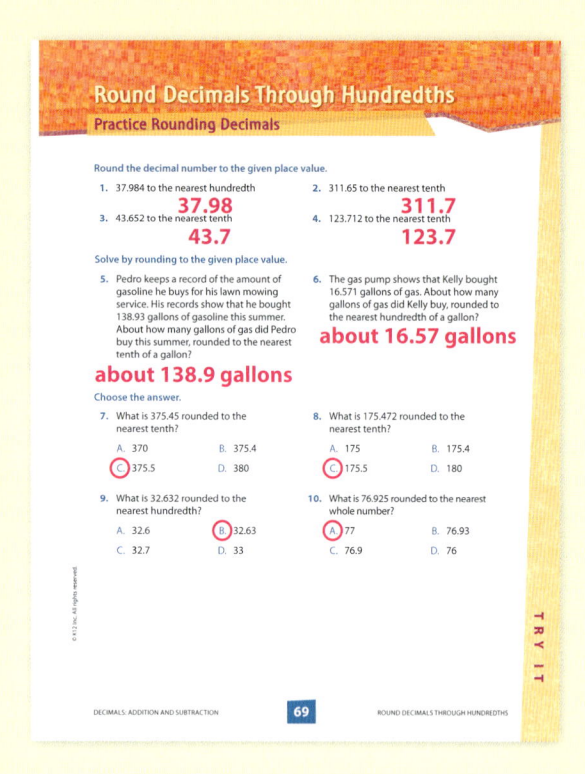

### Round Decimals Through Hundredths
**Practice Rounding Decimals**

Round the decimal number to the given place value.
1. 37.984 to the nearest hundredth   **37.98**
2. 311.65 to the nearest tenth   **311.7**
3. 43.652 to the nearest tenth   **43.7**
4. 123.712 to the nearest tenth   **123.7**

Solve by rounding to the given place value.
5. Pedro keeps a record of the amount of gasoline he buys for his lawn mowing service. His records show that he bought 138.93 gallons of gasoline this summer. About how many gallons of gas did Pedro buy this summer, rounded to the nearest tenth of a gallon?
   **about 138.9 gallons**
6. The gas pump shows that Kelly bought 16.571 gallons of gas. About how many gallons of gas did Kelly buy, rounded to the nearest hundredth of a gallon?
   **about 16.57 gallons**

Choose the answer.
7. What is 375.45 rounded to the nearest tenth?
   A. 370   B. 375.4
   **C. 375.5**   D. 380
8. What is 175.472 rounded to the nearest tenth?
   A. 175   B. 175.4
   **C. 175.5**   D. 180
9. What is 32.632 rounded to the nearest hundredth?
   A. 32.6   **B. 32.63**
   C. 32.7   D. 33
10. What is 76.925 rounded to the nearest whole number?
    **A. 77**   B. 76.93
    C. 76.9   D. 76

DECIMALS: ADDITION AND SUBTRACTION   69   ROUND DECIMALS THROUGH HUNDREDTHS

## CHECKPOINT

ONLINE 5 min

Students will complete an online Checkpoint. If necessary, read the directions, problems, and answer choices to students and help them with keyboard or mouse operations.

### Objectives
- Round a decimal number to any place through hundredths.

**212**   DECIMALS: ADDITION AND SUBTRACTION

# Estimate Decimal Sums, Differences (A)

## Lesson Overview

| | | |
|---|---|---|
| **GET READY** Estimate Decimal Sums | 10 minutes | **ONLINE** |
| **LEARN** Use a Number Line to Estimate | 20 minutes | **OFFLINE** |
| **LEARN** Estimate Sums in Story Problems | 15 minutes | **ONLINE** |
| **TRY IT** Practice Estimating Decimal Sums | 15 minutes | **OFFLINE** |

### ▶ Lesson Objectives
Estimate the sum or difference in a problem involving decimal numbers.

### ▶ Prerequisite Skills
- Round a decimal number.
- Estimate the sum or difference of positive decimal numbers.
- Round a decimal number to any place through hundredths.

### ▶ Content Background
One way to solve a problem is to use estimation. Students will estimate the sum in an addition number sentence using different strategies, or ways, to round the addends. To estimate sums, they will round each addend and then add the rounded numbers.

When students write and compute with decimal numbers, they often use numbers that are between 0 and 1—for example, 0.1. While it is acceptable to write this number as .1, mathematicians usually write the leading zero, to show that the decimal number has zero for the part that is the whole number and to avoid confusion about the value of the number.

When students use a number line to help them round decimal numbers, all the numbers will show the same number of decimal places. For example, on a number line showing numbers in hundredths, numbers such as 42.80 will appear, rather than the equivalent value 42.8. When students find the rounded value of a number, they should give their answer to the decimal place being rounded. For example, when rounding 42.78 to the nearest tenth, they would answer 42.8, emphasizing the tenths place, even though the number line shows 42.80. Be sure that students understand that numbers such as 42.8 and 42.80 show the same value and position on the number line but emphasize different place values.

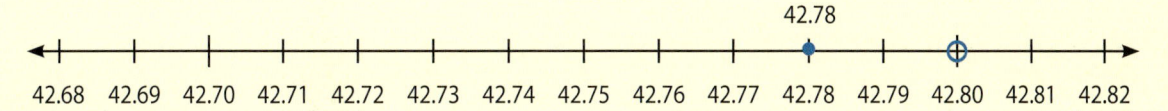

### Materials to Gather

**SUPPLIED**

Use a Number Line to Estimate (printout)

Practice Estimating Decimal Sums activity page

**ESTIMATE DECIMAL SUMS, DIFFERENCES (A)**

## ▶ Common Errors and Misconceptions

- Students might become so concerned about getting the correct answer when estimating that they first find the exact answer, and then round it. For example, when asked to estimate 348 + 176, students might find the sum (524), and then round it to the nearest hundred (500).
- Students might have difficulty accepting that there is more than one correct approach and answer to an estimation problem.

## ▶ Advance Preparation

Print the Use a Number Line to Estimate printout.

## GET READY  Estimate Decimal Sums

*ONLINE 10 min*

Students will estimate sums of decimal numbers to the nearest whole number or tenth to solve story problems about precipitation in cities.

### Objectives
- Round a decimal number.
- Estimate the sum or difference of positive decimal numbers.
- Round a decimal number to any place through hundredths.

## LEARN  Use a Number Line to Estimate

*OFFLINE 20 min*

Students will estimate sums of decimal numbers by first rounding the decimal numbers in the problem and then adding the rounded numbers. They will use number lines to round numbers in the first problems. Then they will round numbers without using number lines.

Gather the Use a Number Line to Estimate printout. Students will write some answers in their Math Notebook.

### Objectives
- Estimate the sum or difference in a problem involving decimal numbers.

### Tips
Allow students to use a number line to solve the last three problems.

### ROUND NUMBERS WITH A NUMBER LINE AND ADD

1. Tell students they will use number lines to estimate the sums of decimal numbers. Point out the first problem and the first two number lines on the printout. The first problem is 290.705 + 342.396.

2. **Say:** Use a number line to round each decimal number, 290.705 and 342.396, to the nearest hundredth. Then use the rounded numbers to estimate the sum.

3. Point to the number line showing 290.700 to 290.710 in thousandths.

   **Say:** Mark 290.705 with a dot.

   **Ask:** What hundredth should you round 290.705 to and why? **290.710. I round numbers ending in 5 to the greater number.**

   Have students circle 290.710 on the number line.

   **Ask:** What is 290.705 rounded to the nearest hundredth? **290.71**

**214**  DECIMALS: ADDITION AND SUBTRACTION

4. Point to the number line showing 342.390 to 342.400 in thousandths.

    **Say:** Mark 342.396 with a dot.

    **Ask:** Is 342.396 closer to 342.390 or 342.400? 342.400

    Have students circle 342.400 on the number line.

    **Ask:** What is 342.396 rounded to the nearest hundredth? 342.40

5. Have students use the rounded numbers and write the number sentence on the printout. Have them add the numbers. 290.71 + 342.40 = 633.11

    **Ask:** When you round the addends to the nearest hundredth, what is the estimated sum of 290.705 + 342.396? about 633.11

6. Repeat Steps 2–5 to guide students to estimate 18.514 + 27.304 to the nearest hundredth. They will use the number lines on the printout.

7. As they estimate, students should mark the number line to show that 18.514 rounded to the nearest hundredth is 18.51, and 27.304 rounded to the nearest hundredth is 27.30.

    **Ask:** When you round the addends to the nearest hundredth, what is the estimated sum of 18.514 + 27.304? about 45.81

## ROUND NUMBERS WITHOUT A NUMBER LINE AND ADD

8. Have students write 34.628 + 75.493 in their Math Notebook.

9. Tell students they will estimate the sum of 34.628 + 75.493. They will round the addends to the nearest hundredth without a number line.

10. **Ask:** Think about the number lines you used to round numbers to the hundredths place. What is 34.628 rounded to the nearest hundredth? 34.63

    **Ask:** What is 75.493 rounded to the nearest hundredth? 75.49

11. Have students find the estimated sum by adding 34.63 + 75.49.

    **Ask:** When you round the addends to the nearest hundredth, what is the estimated sum of 34.628 + 75.493? about 110.12

12. Have students write 7.651 + 6.862 in their Math Notebook.

13. Tell students they will estimate the sum of 7.651 + 6.862 to the nearest tenth. They will round the addends to the nearest tenth without a number line.

    **Ask:** Think about the number lines you used to round numbers to the hundredths place. What is 7.651 rounded to the nearest tenth? 7.7

    **Ask:** What is 6.862 rounded to the nearest tenth? 6.9

14. Have students find the estimated sum by adding 7.7 + 6.9.

    **Ask:** When you round the addends to the nearest tenth, what is the estimated sum of 7.651 + 6.682? about 14.6

15. Have students write 35.428 + 832.524 in their Math Notebook and repeat Steps 13 and 14, rounding each addend to the nearest hundredth and then finding the estimated sum. 35.43 + 832.52 = 867.95; When you round the addends to the nearest hundredth, the estimated sum of 35.428 + 832.524 is about 867.95.

ESTIMATE DECIMAL SUMS, DIFFERENCES (A) 215

## LEARN  Estimate Sums in Story Problems

**ONLINE 15 min**

### Objectives
- Estimate the sum or difference in a problem involving decimal numbers.

Students will practice estimating sums of decimal numbers in story problems. They will use a number line to round each addend in the problem and then add the rounded numbers to find the estimated sum. Some number lines in the activity show fractions as well as the decimal numbers. The fractions are shown to raise awareness of the relationship between fractions and decimals.

The story problems include an addend that is a decimal number ending in 5, which allows students to recall that numbers ending in 5 should be rounded to the greater number.

## TRY IT  Practice Estimating Decimal Sums

**OFFLINE 15 min**

### Objectives
- Estimate the sum or difference in a problem involving decimal numbers.

Students will practice estimating decimal sums. Have students turn to the Practice Estimating Decimal Sums activity page in their Activity Book and read the directions with them.

Students should copy the problems from the Activity Book into their Math Notebook as necessary and solve them there.

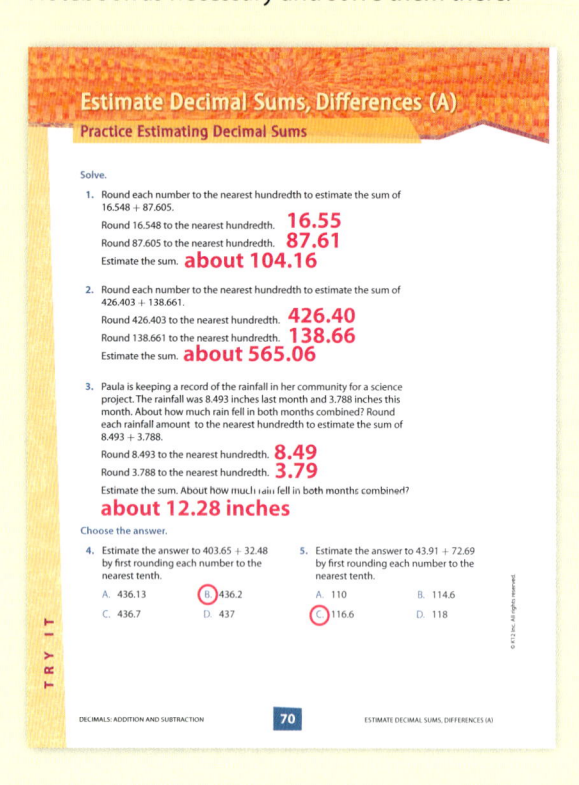

### Estimate Decimal Sums, Differences (A)
**Practice Estimating Decimal Sums**

Solve.

1. Round each number to the nearest hundredth to estimate the sum of 16.548 + 87.605.
   Round 16.548 to the nearest hundredth. **16.55**
   Round 87.605 to the nearest hundredth. **87.61**
   Estimate the sum. **about 104.16**

2. Round each number to the nearest hundredth to estimate the sum of 426.403 + 138.661.
   Round 426.403 to the nearest hundredth. **426.40**
   Round 138.661 to the nearest hundredth. **138.66**
   Estimate the sum. **about 565.06**

3. Paula is keeping a record of the rainfall in her community for a science project. The rainfall was 8.493 inches last month and 3.788 inches this month. About how much rain fell in both months combined? Round each rainfall amount to the nearest hundredth to estimate the sum of 8.493 + 3.788.
   Round 8.493 to the nearest hundredth. **8.49**
   Round 3.788 to the nearest hundredth. **3.79**
   Estimate the sum. About how much rain fell in both months combined?
   **about 12.28 inches**

Choose the answer.

4. Estimate the answer to 403.65 + 32.48 by first rounding each number to the nearest tenth.
   A. 436.13   **B. 436.2**
   C. 436.7    D. 437

5. Estimate the answer to 43.91 + 72.69 by first rounding each number to the nearest tenth.
   A. 110      B. 114.6
   **C. 116.6** D. 118

**216  DECIMALS: ADDITION AND SUBTRACTION**

# Estimate Decimal Sums, Differences (B)

## Lesson Overview

| | | |
|---|---|---|
| **GET READY** Estimate Decimal Differences | 10 minutes | **ONLINE** |
| **LEARN** Estimate with a Number Line | 15 minutes | **OFFLINE** |
| **LEARN** Estimate Differences in Story Problems | 15 minutes | **ONLINE** |
| **TRY IT** Practice Estimating Differences | 10 minutes | **OFFLINE** |
| **CHECKPOINT** | 10 minutes | **ONLINE** |

## ▶ Lesson Objectives

Estimate the sum or difference in a problem involving decimal numbers.

## ▶ Prerequisite Skills

- Round a decimal number.
- Estimate the sum or difference of positive decimal numbers.
- Round a decimal number to any place through hundredths.

## ▶ Content Background

One way to solve a problem is to use estimation. Students will continue to estimate the difference in a subtraction number sentence using different strategies, or ways, to round the minuend and subtrahend. To estimate differences, they will continue to round each number in the problem and then subtract the rounded numbers.

When students write and compute with decimal numbers, they often use numbers that are between 0 and 1—for example, 0.1. While it is acceptable to write this number as .1, mathematicians usually write the leading zero, to show that the decimal number has zero for the part that is the whole number and to avoid confusion about the value of the number.

When students use a number line to help them round decimal numbers, all the numbers will show the same number of decimal places. For example, on a number line showing numbers in hundredths, numbers such as 42.80 will appear, rather than the equivalent value 42.8. When students find the rounded value of a number, they should give their answer to the decimal place being rounded. For example, when rounding 42.78 to the nearest tenth, they would answer 42.8, emphasizing the tenths place, even though the number line shows 42.80. Be sure that students understand that numbers such as 42.8 and 42.80 show the same value and position on the number line, but emphasize different place values.

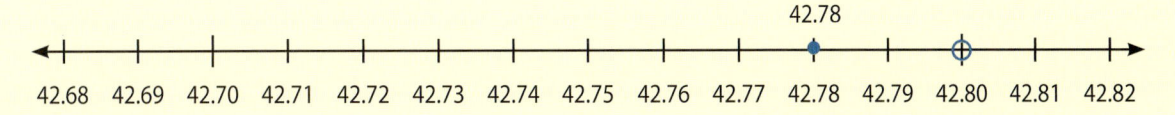

### Materials to Gather

**SUPPLIED**

Estimate with a Number Line (printout)

Practice Estimating Differences activity page

---

42.68  42.69  42.70  42.71  42.72  42.73  42.74  42.75  42.76  42.77  42.78  42.79  42.80  42.81  42.82

**ESTIMATE DECIMAL SUMS, DIFFERENCES (B)** 217

## ▶ Common Errors and Misconceptions
- Students might become so concerned about getting the correct answer when estimating that they first find the exact answer, and then round it. For example, when asked to estimate 348 + 176, students might find the sum (524), and then round it to the nearest hundred (500).
- Students might have difficulty accepting that there is more than one correct approach and answer to an estimation problem.

## ▶ Advance Preparation
Print the Estimate with a Number Line printout.

## GET READY  Estimate Decimal Differences
**ONLINE 10 min**

Students will estimate differences of decimal numbers to the nearest whole number or tenth to solve story problems about track and field events.

### Objectives
- Round a decimal number.
- Estimate the sum or difference of positive decimal numbers.
- Round a decimal number to any place through hundredths.

## LEARN  Estimate with a Number Line
**OFFLINE 15 min**

Students will estimate differences of decimal numbers by first rounding the decimal numbers in the problem and then subtracting. They will use number lines to round numbers in the first problems. Then they will round numbers without using number lines.

Gather the Estimate with a Number Line printout. Students will write some answers in their Math Notebook.

### Objectives
- Estimate the sum or difference in a problem involving decimal numbers.

### Tips
Alowl students to use a number line to solve the last two problems.

### ROUND NUMBERS WITH A NUMBER LINE AND SUBTRACT

1. Tell students they will use number lines to estimate the differences of decimal numbers. Point out the first problem and the first two number lines on the printout. The first problem is 561.293 − 280.684.

2. **Say:** Use a number line to round each decimal number, 561.293 and 280.684, to the nearest hundredth. Then use the rounded numbers to estimate the difference.

3. Point to the number line showing 561.290 to 561.300 in thousandths.
   **Say:** Mark 561.293 with a dot.
   **Ask:** Is 561.293 closer to 561.290 or 561.300? 561.290
   Have students circle 561.290 on the number line.
   **Ask:** What is 561.290 rounded to the nearest hundredth? 561.29

4. Point to the number line showing 280.680 to 280.690 in thousandths.
   **Say:** Mark 280.684 with a dot.
   **Ask:** Is 280.684 closer to 280.680 or 280.690? 280.680
   Have students circle 280.680 on the number line.
   **Ask:** What is 280.684 rounded to the nearest hundredth? 280.68

**DECIMALS: ADDITION AND SUBTRACTION**

5. Have students use the rounded numbers and write the number sentence on the printout. Have them subtract the numbers. 561.29 − 280.68 = 280.61

    **Ask:** When you round the minuend and subtrahend to the nearest hundredth, what is the estimated difference of 561.293 − 280.684? about 280.61

6. Repeat Steps 2–5 to guide students to estimate the difference of 42.347 − 16.621 by rounding each number to the nearest hundredth. Have them use the rounded numbers to estimate the difference. Have students use the number lines on the printout.

7. As they estimate, students should mark the number line to show that 42.347 rounded to the nearest hundredth is 42.35. They should mark the number line to show that 16.621 rounded to the nearest hundredth is 16.62.

    **Ask:** When you round the minuend and subtrahend to the nearest hundredth, what is the estimated difference of 42.347 − 16.621? about 25.73

## ROUND NUMBERS WITHOUT A NUMBER LINE AND SUBTRACT

8. Have students write 83.746 − 31.493 in their Math Notebook.

9. Tell students they will estimate the difference of 83.746 − 31.493, rounding the minuend and subtrahend to the nearest hundredth without a number line.

10. **Ask:** Think about the number lines you used to round numbers to the hundredths place. What is 83.746 rounded to the nearest hundredth? 83.75

    **Ask:** What is 31.493 rounded to the nearest hundredth? 31.49

11. Have students find the estimated difference by subtracting 83.75 − 31.49.

    **Ask:** When you round the minuend and subtrahend to the nearest hundredth, what is the estimated difference of 83.746 − 31.493? about 52.26

12. Have students write 978.561 − 633.247 in their Math Notebook and repeat Steps 10 and 11, rounding the minuend and subtrahend to the nearest hundredth and then finding the estimated difference. 978.56 − 633.25 = 345.31; The estimated difference of 978.561 − 633.247, when rounding the minuend and subtrahend to the nearest hundredth, is about 345.31.

**LEARN Estimate Differences in Story Problems**

ONLINE 15 min

**Objectives**

- Estimate the sum or difference in a problem involving decimal numbers.

Students will practice estimating differences of decimal numbers in story problems. They will use a number line to round each number in the problem and then subtract the rounded subtrahend from the minuend to find the estimated difference. Note that one of the problems will reinforce that students are to round a decimal number ending in 5 to the greater place.

## TRY IT  Practice Estimating Differences

**OFFLINE 10 min**

### Objectives
- Estimate the sum or difference in a problem involving decimal numbers.

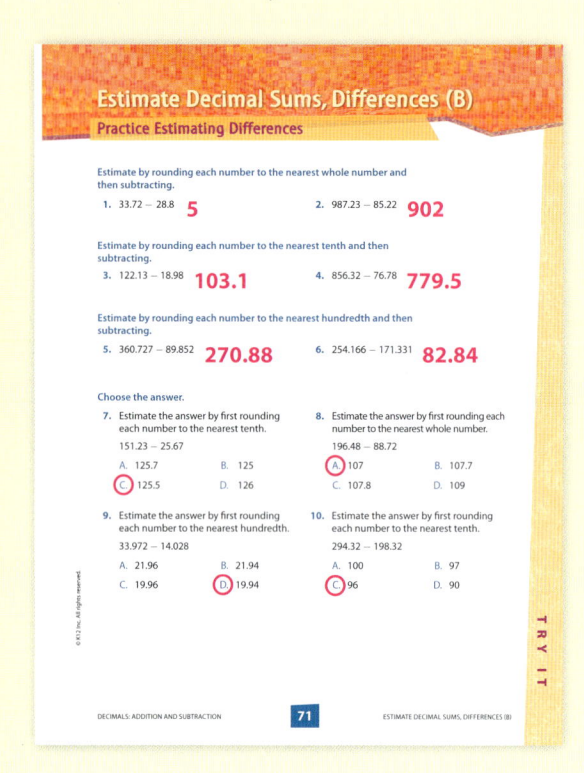

Students will practice estimating differences of decimal numbers. Have students turn to the Practice Estimating Differences activity page in their Activity Book and read the directions with them.

Students should copy the problems from the Activity Book into their Math Notebook as necessary and solve them there.

### Estimate Decimal Sums, Differences (B)
**Practice Estimating Differences**

Estimate by rounding each number to the nearest whole number and then subtracting.
1. 33.72 − 28.8   **5**
2. 987.23 − 85.22   **902**

Estimate by rounding each number to the nearest tenth and then subtracting.
3. 122.13 − 18.98   **103.1**
4. 856.32 − 76.78   **779.5**

Estimate by rounding each number to the nearest hundredth and then subtracting.
5. 360.727 − 89.852   **270.88**
6. 254.166 − 171.331   **82.84**

Choose the answer.

7. Estimate the answer by first rounding each number to the nearest tenth.
   151.23 − 25.67
   A. 125.7   B. 125
   **C. 125.5**   D. 126

8. Estimate the answer by first rounding each number to the nearest whole number.
   196.48 − 88.72
   **A. 107**   B. 107.7
   C. 107.8   D. 109

9. Estimate the answer by first rounding each number to the nearest hundredth.
   33.972 − 14.028
   A. 21.96   B. 21.94
   C. 19.96   **D. 19.94**

10. Estimate the answer by first rounding each number to the nearest tenth.
    294.32 − 198.32
    A. 100   B. 97
    **C. 96**   D. 90

## CHECKPOINT

**ONLINE 10 min**

### Objectives
- Estimate the sum or difference in a problem involving decimal numbers.

Students will complete an online Checkpoint. If necessary, read the directions, problems, and answer choices to students and help them with keyboard or mouse operations.

# Reasonable Answers and Decimal Problems

## Lesson Overview

| | | |
|---|---|---|
| **GET READY** Estimate with Story Problems | 10 minutes | **OFFLINE** |
| **LEARN** Add and Subtract Decimals | 15 minutes | **OFFLINE** |
| **LEARN** Verify Answers to Decimal Problems | 15 minutes | **ONLINE** |
| **TRY IT** Practice Verifying Decimal Answers | 15 minutes | **OFFLINE** |
| **CHECKPOINT** | 5 minutes | **ONLINE** |

### ▶ Lesson Objectives
- Solve an addition or subtraction problem involving decimal numbers.
- Verify that the calculated result of a problem involving addition or subtraction of decimal numbers is reasonable.

### ▶ Prerequisite Skills
- Estimate the sum or difference of positive decimal numbers.
- Compute the sum or difference of positive decimal numbers.
- Use estimation to predict a solution to a story problem and to verify the reasonableness of the calculated result.

### Materials to Gather

**SUPPLIED**
Centimeter Grid Paper (printout)
Practice Verifying Decimal Answers activity page

### ▶ Content Background
Students may already have a basic understanding of adding and subtracting decimals. In this lesson, they will calculate an addition or subtraction problem with decimal numbers and use an estimate to verify the reasonableness of their calculation.

Students build number sense when they have to decide whether the answer to a problem they have worked is reasonable. Estimating the answer before the problem is worked is one way to figure out if a calculated answer to a problem is reasonable. Students can compare the calculated answer to their estimate.

When students write and compute with decimal numbers, they often use numbers that are between 0 and 1—for example, 0.1. While it is acceptable to write this number as .1, mathematicians usually write the leading zero, to show that the decimal number has zero for the part that is the whole number and to avoid confusion about the value of the number.

### ▶ Advance Preparation
Print the Centimeter Grid Paper.

## GET READY  Estimate with Story Problems

**OFFLINE 10 min**

### Objectives
- Estimate the sum or difference of positive decimal numbers.
- Compute the sum or difference of positive decimal numbers.
- Use estimation to predict a solution to a story problem and to verify the reasonableness of the calculated result.

Students will estimate and solve addition and subtraction story problems with decimal numbers. Have students show their work and write their answers in their Math Notebook.

1. Read this story problem to students.
   - Yuki is buying two bags of apples at the store. The first bag weighs 3.12 pounds. The second bag weighs 2.65 pounds. How much do both bags weigh together?
2. **Ask:** Should addition or subtraction be used to solve this problem? addition
3. Have students estimate the sum by rounding each number to the nearest tenth and then adding the rounded numbers. Have students write the sum in their Math Notebook. $3.1 + 2.7 = 5.8$; about 5.8 pounds
4. Have students calculate the exact answer. Remind them to line up the decimal numbers by place values and start by adding the numbers in the hundredths place. $3.12 + 2.65 = 5.77$; 5.77 pounds
5. Have students look at the estimate. Ask them if the calculated answer is reasonable. Yes

    If students decide the calculated answer is not reasonable, they should check their addition and decide if the new answer is reasonable.
6. **Ask:** Why is the answer reasonable? The exact answer, 5.77, is close to the estimated answer, 5.8. In fact, 5.77 rounded to the nearest tenth is 5.8, which is the estimated answer.

    Have students write the answer to the problem. The two bags weigh 5.77 pounds together.
7. Read this story problem to students.
   - José was going to buy four bags of carrots that weighed 8.7 pounds, but decided to put one bag back. That bag weighed 2.3 pounds. How many pounds of carrots are in the three bags José is buying?
8. **Ask:** Should addition or subtraction be used to solve this problem? subtraction
9. Have students estimate the difference by rounding each number to the nearest whole number and then subtracting the rounded numbers. Have students write the difference in their Math Notebook. $9 - 2 = 7$; about 7 pounds
10. Have students calculate the exact answer. Remind them to line up the decimal numbers by place values and start by subtracting the number in the tenths place. $8.7 - 2.3 = 6.4$; 6.4 pounds
11. Have students look at the estimate. Ask them if the calculated answer is reasonable. Yes

    If students decide the calculated answer is not reasonable, have them check their subtraction and decide if the new answer is reasonable.
12. **Ask:** Why is the answer reasonable? The exact answer, 6.4, is close to the estimated answer, 7. In fact, rounding 6.4 to the greater whole number equals 7, which is the estimated answer.

    Have students write the answer to the problem. There are 6.4 pounds of carrots in the three bags.

DECIMALS: ADDITION AND SUBTRACTION

## LEARN Add and Subtract Decimals

**OFFLINE 15 min**

### Objectives
- Solve an addition or subtraction problem involving decimal numbers.
- Verify that the calculated result of a problem involving addition or subtraction of decimal numbers is reasonable.

Students will review the algorithm, or step-by-step method, for adding and subtracting decimals. For both addition and subtraction, they will see one worked-out example and then do a problem on their own. Gather the Centimeter Grid Paper.

1. Model for students how to write 125.379 + 62.85 on grid paper. Discuss with students that it is important to align each place value before adding, in order to be able to correctly calculate the sum.

```
      1   1
  1 2 5 . 3 7 9
+     6 2 . 8 5
  1 8 8 . 2 2 9
```

### Tips

If students are having trouble determining whether the place values are lined up, have them write an abbreviation for each place, such as H for hundreds, T for tens, O for ones, Te for tenths, Hu for hundredths, and Th for thousandths, in the squares in the grid above the problem.

2. Review the place value of each digit in both addends. Tell students that 125.379 has digits in the hundreds, tens, ones, tenths, hundredths, and thousandths places, while 62.85 has digits in the tens, ones, tenths, and hundredths places.

3. Guide students through the addition. Point to each place as you add the numbers. Remind students that 62.85 can be written as 62.850, by adding a zero to the thousandths place. Guide students to find the sum.
   - 9 thousandths plus 0 thousandths equals 9 thousandths.
   - 7 hundredths plus 5 hundredths equals 12 hundredths. Write 2 in the hundredths place and regroup 1 to the tenths place.
   - 3 tenths plus 8 tenths plus 1 tenth (regrouped from the hundredths) equals 12 tenths. Write 2 in the tenths place and regroup 1 to the ones place.
   - 5 ones plus 2 ones plus 1 one (regrouped from the tenths) equals 8 ones.
   - 2 tens plus 6 tens equals 8 tens.
   - 1 hundred plus 0 hundreds equals 1 hundred. 188.229

4. Have students vertically write 634.392 + 838.2 on grid paper and find the sum. Remind them to place a comma between the digits in the hundreds and thousands place. 1,472.592

5. Model for students how to write 985.345 − 3.12 on grid paper. Discuss with students that it is important to align each place value before subtracting, in order to be able to correctly calculate the difference.

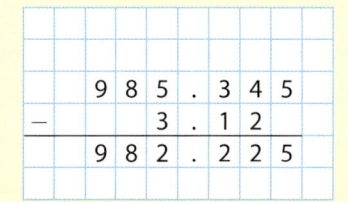

```
  9 8 5 . 3 4 5
−     3 . 1 2
  9 8 2 . 2 2 5
```

6. Review the place value of each digit in the minuend and subtrahend. Tell students that 985.345 has digits in the hundreds, tens, ones, tenths, hundredths, and thousandths places, while 3.12 has digits in the ones, tenths, and hundredths places.

**REASONABLE ANSWERS AND DECIMAL PROBLEMS**

7. Guide students through the subtraction. Point to each place as you subtract the numbers. Remind students that 3.12 can be written as 3.120, by adding a zero in the thousandths place. Guide students to find the difference.
   - 5 thousandths minus 0 thousandths equals 5 thousandths.
   - 4 hundredths minus 2 hundredths equals 2 hundredths.
   - 3 tenths minus 1 tenth equals 2 tenths.
   - 5 ones minus 3 ones equals 2 ones.
   - 8 tens minus 0 tens equals 8 tens.
   - 9 hundreds minus 0 hundreds equals 9 hundreds. 982.225

8. Have students vertically write 425.39 − 37.3 on grid paper and find the difference. Remind them that they will need to regroup as they subtract. 388.09

## LEARN  Verify Answers to Decimal Problems   ONLINE 15 min

Students will estimate and find exact answers to decimal addition and subtraction story problems. They will learn how to verify that the exact answer is reasonable by comparing the estimate to the exact answer. Students will also play a hidden picture game to practice adding and subtracting decimal numbers.

**Objectives**
- Solve an addition or subtraction problem involving decimal numbers.
- Verify that the calculated result of a problem involving addition or subtraction of decimal numbers is reasonable.

## TRY IT  Practice Verifying Decimal Answers   OFFLINE 15 min

Students will practice solving decimal addition and subtraction story problems. Using estimation, they will verify that the calculated answer is reasonable. Have students turn to the Practice Verifying Decimal Answers activity page in their Activity Book and read the directions with them.

Students should copy the problems from the Activity Book into their Math Notebook as necessary and solve them there.

**Objectives**
- Solve an addition or subtraction problem involving decimal numbers.
- Verify that the calculated result of a problem involving addition or subtraction of decimal numbers is reasonable.

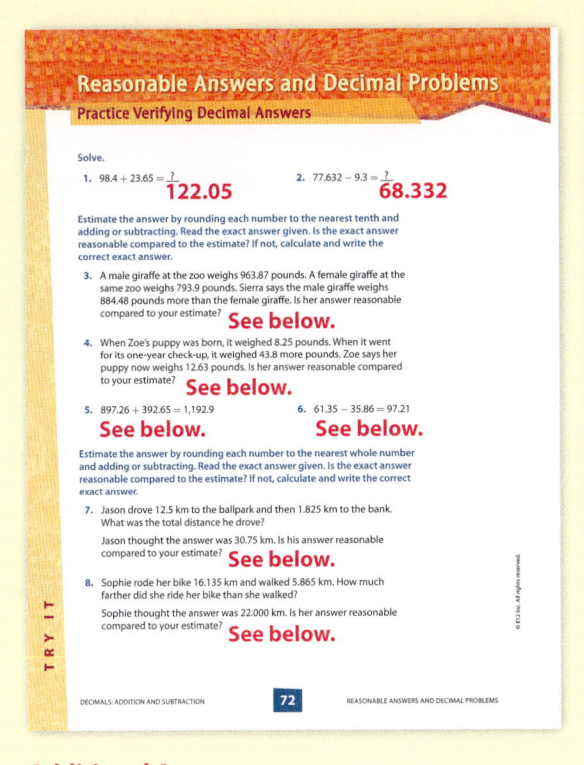

## Reasonable Answers and Decimal Problems
### Practice Verifying Decimal Answers

Solve.

1. $98.4 + 23.65 = ?$   **122.05**
2. $77.632 - 9.3 = ?$   **68.332**

Estimate the answer by rounding each number to the nearest tenth and adding or subtracting. Read the exact answer given. Is the exact answer reasonable compared to the estimate? If not, calculate and write the correct exact answer.

3. A male giraffe at the zoo weighs 963.87 pounds. A female giraffe at the same zoo weighs 793.9 pounds. Sierra says the male giraffe weighs 884.48 pounds more than the female giraffe. Is her answer reasonable compared to your estimate? **See below.**

4. When Zoe's puppy was born, it weighed 8.25 pounds. When it went for its one-year check-up, it weighed 43.8 more pounds. Zoe says her puppy now weighs 12.63 pounds. Is her answer reasonable compared to your estimate? **See below.**

5. $897.26 + 392.65 = 1,192.9$   **See below.**
6. $61.35 - 35.86 = 97.21$   **See below.**

Estimate the answer by rounding each number to the nearest whole number and adding or subtracting. Read the exact answer given. Is the exact answer reasonable compared to your estimate? If not, calculate and write the correct exact answer.

7. Jason drove 12.5 km to the ballpark and then 1.825 km to the bank. What was the total distance he drove?
   Jason thought the answer was 30.75 km. Is his answer reasonable compared to your estimate? **See below.**

8. Sophie rode her bike 16.135 km and walked 5.865 km. How much farther did she ride her bike than she walked?
   Sophie thought the answer was 22.000 km. Is her answer reasonable compared to your estimate? **See below.**

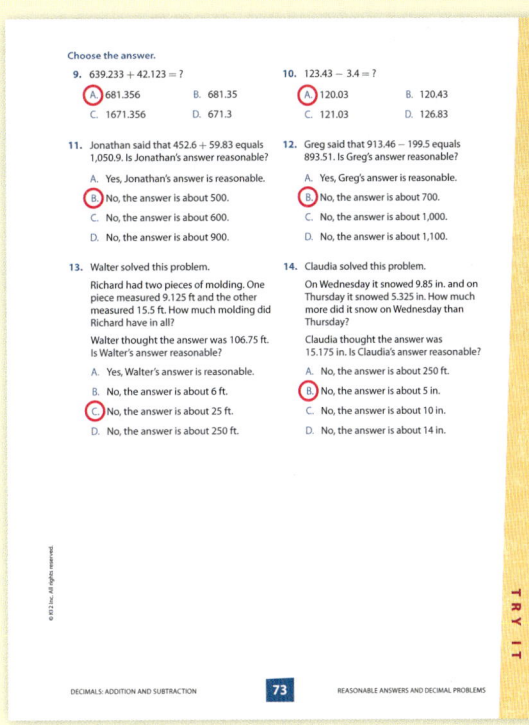

Choose the answer.

9. $639.233 + 42.123 = ?$
   A. 681.356  B. 681.35
   C. 1671.356  D. 671.3

10. $123.43 - 3.4 = ?$
    A. 120.03  B. 120.43
    C. 121.03  D. 126.83

11. Jonathan said that $452.6 + 59.83$ equals 1,050.9. Is Jonathan's answer reasonable?
    A. Yes, Jonathan's answer is reasonable.
    B. No, the answer is about 500.
    C. No, the answer is about 600.
    D. No, the answer is about 900.

12. Greg said that $913.46 - 199.5$ equals 893.51. Is Greg's answer reasonable?
    A. Yes, Greg's answer is reasonable.
    B. No, the answer is about 700.
    C. No, the answer is about 1,000.
    D. No, the answer is about 1,100.

13. Walter solved this problem.
    Richard had two pieces of molding. One piece measured 9.125 ft and the other measured 15.5 ft. How much molding did Richard have in all?
    Walter thought the answer was 106.75 ft. Is Walter's answer reasonable?
    A. Yes, Walter's answer is reasonable.
    B. No, the answer is about 6 ft.
    C. No, the answer is about 25 ft.
    D. No, the answer is about 250 ft.

14. Claudia solved this problem.
    On Wednesday it snowed 9.85 in. and on Thursday it snowed 5.325 in. How much more did it snow on Wednesday than Thursday?
    Claudia thought the answer was 15.175 in. Is Claudia's answer reasonable?
    A. No, the answer is about 250 in.
    B. No, the answer is about 5 in.
    C. No, the answer is about 10 in.
    D. No, the answer is about 14 in.

### Additional Answers

3. No, a reasonable answer would be about 170.0 pounds. The exact answer is 169.97 pounds.
4. No, a reasonable answer would be about 52.1 pounds. The exact answer is 52.05 pounds.
5. No, a reasonable answer would be about 1,290.0. The exact answer is 1,289.91.
6. No, a reasonable answer would be about 25.5. The exact answer is 25.49.
7. No, Jason's answer is not reasonable. A reasonable answer would be about 15 km. The exact answer is 14.325 km.
8. No, Sophie's answer is not reasonable. A reasonable answer would be about 10 km. The exact answer is 10.27 km.

### CHECKPOINT

**ONLINE 5 min**

Students will complete an online Checkpoint. If necessary, read the directions, problems, and answer choices to students and help them with keyboard or mouse operations.

### Objectives

- Solve an addition or subtraction problem involving decimal numbers.
- Verify that the calculated result of a problem involving addition or subtraction of decimal numbers is reasonable.

**REASONABLE ANSWERS AND DECIMAL PROBLEMS   225**

# Solve Story Problems with Decimals (A)

## Lesson Overview

| | | |
|---|---|---|
| **GET READY** Review Addition of Decimals | 5 minutes | ONLINE |
| **GET READY** Practice Addition and Subtraction | 10 minutes | ONLINE |
| **LEARN** Solve Addition Story Problems | 20 minutes | OFFLINE |
| **LEARN** Play with Decimal Addition | 15 minutes | ONLINE |
| **TRY IT** Add Decimals in Story Problems | 10 minutes | OFFLINE |

### ▶ Lesson Objectives
Solve a story problem involving addition or subtraction of decimal numbers.

### ▶ Prerequisite Skills
Solve an addition or subtraction problem involving decimal numbers.

### ▶ Content Background
Students may already have a basic understanding of adding decimal numbers. They will solve addition story problems with decimal numbers.

When students write and compute with decimal numbers, they often use numbers that are between 0 and 1—for example, 0.1. While it is acceptable to write this number as .1, mathematicians usually write the leading zero, to show that the decimal number has zero for the part that is the whole number and to avoid confusion about the value of the number.

### ▶ Advance Preparation
Print the Solve Addition Story Problems printout.

**Materials to Gather**

SUPPLIED
Solve Addition Story Problems (printout)
Add Decimals in Story Problems activity page

---

**GET READY** Review Addition of Decimals  ONLINE 5 min

**Objectives**
- Solve an addition or subtraction problem involving decimal numbers.

Students will solve decimal addition problems. The problems will require students to add decimal numbers of different places. For instance, they will add a number in the hundredths and a number in the thousandths.

226 DECIMALS: ADDITION AND SUBTRACTION

## GET READY  Practice Addition and Subtraction

**ONLINE 10 min**

### Objectives
- Solve an addition or subtraction problem involving decimal numbers.

Students will practice fluency with addition and subtraction by playing a facts practice game.

**DIRECTIONS FOR USING THE FAST FACTS LEARNING TOOL**

1. Have students enter their name and car number as well as choose the color of the car.
2. Choose the following options:
   - Choose the facts you want to practice: Addition, Subtraction
   - Choose: Work with sums from 0 to 100
         Work with minuends from 0 to 100
   - Mode: Race Mode
3. As each problem appears on the screen, have students type the answer and then press Enter. After students finish, review the results on the Fast Facts Results screen. Note how many problems students answered incorrectly. Also record their time for future reference. You can click under the Lap tables on this screen to see exactly which problems students answered correctly (shown in white) and which ones they missed (shown in red).
4. Repeat the activity. Have students try to beat their time and improve their accuracy.
5. If time remains, customize the Addition and Subtraction screen and specifically change the range of sums and minuends to give more practice with the facts with which students had difficulty. Then have them run another race.

### Tips
If you want to have students get used to the game first, go to Test Drive Mode and enter 5 for the number of problems. Then move to Race Mode.

## LEARN  Solve Addition Story Problems

**OFFLINE 20 min**

### Objectives
- Solve a story problem involving addition or subtraction of decimal numbers.

Students will use decimal number lines that also show related fractions to solve addition story problems. They will connect fractions and decimals as they do the activity. Students also will solve some problems using the algorithm, or step-by-step method, instead of using number lines.

Gather the Solve Addition Story Problems printout. Students will write in their Math Notebook.

### Tips
If students have difficulty adding decimal numbers without the number line, allow them to continue using the number line to gain conceptual understanding.

**ADD WITH A NUMBER LINE**

1. Have students read the first on-screen problem.
2. Tell students they will use a number line to solve the problem. Have them work with the first number line, labeled from 0 to 4. Have them label the equivalent fraction for each $\frac{1}{4}$, $\frac{1}{2}$, and $\frac{3}{4}$ on the number line below each decimal number, to build the connection between decimals and fractions. For example, students will write $\frac{1}{4}$ below 0.25, $\frac{1}{2}$ below 0.50, and $\frac{3}{4}$ below 0.75. Have students complete this for all decimal numbers between 0 and 4.
3. **Say:** 2.5 is the first addend needed to find the sum to solve the problem.
   **Ask:** What mixed number is equivalent to 2.5? $2\frac{1}{2}$
   Have students mark a point at 0 and 2.5 on the number line. Have them start at 0 and "hop" 2.5 to the right of 0. Show an arc between 0 and 2.5.

**SOLVE STORY PROBLEMS WITH DECIMALS (A)  227**

4. **Say:** The second addend used to solve the problem is 1.25.

   **Ask:** What mixed number is equivalent to 1.25? $1\frac{1}{4}$

   Have students "hop" one whole unit (from 2.5 to 3.5) and then one-fourth of a unit (from 3.5 to 3.75) to the right of 2.5. Have them show arcs for the whole-unit hop and the one-fourth-unit hop. Mark another point at 3.75.

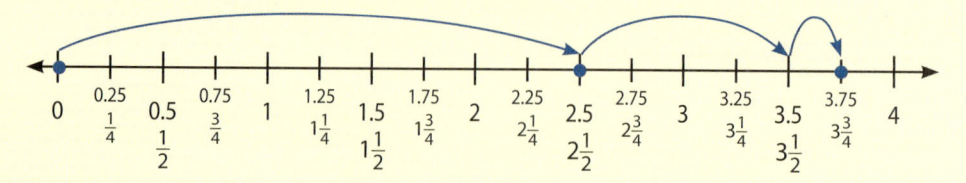

5. **Ask:** When you use the number line to compute the answer, what is 2.5 + 1.25? 3.75

   **Ask:** What mixed number is equivalent to 3.75? $3\frac{3}{4}$

   Have students also use an algorithm to find the sum. Have them write the number sentence 2.5 + 1.25 = ? and find the answer in their Math Notebook.

6. **Ask:** Returning to the original problem, what is the answer? Your family has 3.75 pounds of apples.

   Have students write the answer to the problem in their Math Notebook.

7. Have students read the second on-screen problem.

8. Tell students they will use a number line to solve the problem. Have students work with the number line labeled from 0 to 13. Have them label the equivalent fraction for each $\frac{1}{2}$ on the number line below each decimal number. For example, students will write $7\frac{1}{2}$ below 7.5. Have students complete this for all decimal numbers between 7 and 13.

9. **Say:** 7.5 is the first addend needed to find the sum to solve the problem.

   **Ask:** What mixed number is equivalent to 7.5? $7\frac{1}{2}$

   Have students mark a point at 0 and 7.5 on the number line. Have them start at 0 and "hop" 7.5 to the right of 0. Show an arc between 0 and 7.5.

10. **Say:** The second addend used to solve the problem is 5.25.

    **Ask:** What mixed number is equivalent to 5.25? $5\frac{1}{4}$

    Have students "hop" five whole units (from 7.5 to 8.5, 8.5 to 9.5, 9.5 to 10.5, 10.5 to 11.5, and 11.5 to 12.5) and then one-fourth of a unit (from 12.5 to 12.75) to the right of 7.5. Have them show arcs for the whole-unit hops and the one-fourth-unit hop. Mark another point at 12.75.

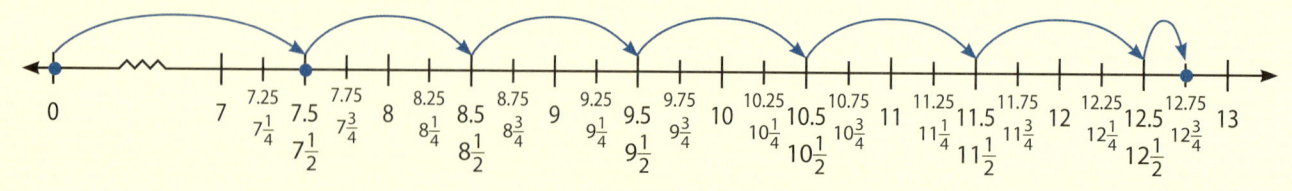

11. **Ask:** When you use the number line to compute the answer, what is 7.5 + 5.25? 12.75

    **Ask:** What mixed number is equivalent to 12.75? $12\frac{3}{4}$

    Have students also use an algorithm to find the sum. Have them write the number sentence 7.5 + 5.25 = ? and find the answer in their Math Notebook.

**228 DECIMALS: ADDITION AND SUBTRACTION**

12. **Ask:** Returning to the original problem, what is the answer? The athlete's combined score is 12.75 points.

    Have students write the answer to the problem in their Math Notebook.

**ADD WITHOUT A NUMBER LINE**

13. Have students read the third on-screen problem.

14. **Ask:** What do you need to do to solve the problem? Add the number of miles the family traveled each day to find how many miles they traveled in all.

    **Ask:** What number sentence is needed to solve the problem?
    $543.2 + 132.382 = ?$

    Have students write the number sentence needed to solve the problem and use an algorithm to find the answer in their Math Notebook.

    **Ask:** Returning to the original problem, what is the answer? The family traveled a total of 675.582 miles.

    Have student write the answer to the problem in their Math Notebook.

15. Have students read the fourth on-screen problem. Repeat Step 14 to solve the problem. Add the dollar amounts to find out how much money the family spent on food and tickets. $79.60 + 231.59 = 311.19$. The family spent $311.19 on food and tickets.

## LEARN  Play with Decimal Addition

ONLINE 15 min

### Objectives

- Solve a story problem involving addition or subtraction of decimal numbers.

Students will find a hidden picture by solving addition problems with decimal numbers.

## TRY IT  Add Decimals in Story Problems

OFFLINE 10 min

### Objectives

- Solve a story problem involving addition or subtraction of decimal numbers.

Students will practice solving addition story problems with decimal numbers. Have students turn to the Add Decimals in Story Problems activity page in their Activity Book and read the directions with them.

Students should copy the problems from the Activity Book into their Math Notebook as necessary and solve them there.

# Solve Story Problems with Decimals (A)
## Add Decimals in Story Problems

**Solve.**

1. Jeff bought 15.5 m of red felt and 8.75 m of green felt.
   How much felt did Jeff buy?
   **24.25 m**

2. Lola drove 16.125 km to the restaurant and then drove 4.9 km to the store.
   What is the total distance Lola drove?
   **21.025 km**

**Choose the answer.**

3. Angie filled her gas tank twice in one week. She spent $29.23 the first time and $27.12 the second time.
   How much did Angie spend on gas that week?
   A. $46.35
   **B. $56.35**
   C. $57.35
   D. $67.35

4. On Monday, 1.123 in. of rain fell. On Tuesday, another 2.599 in. of rain fell.
   What was the total rainfall in the two days?
   A. 3.622 in.
   B. 3.712 in.
   **C. 3.722 in.**
   D. 3.723 in.

5. Joel spent $15.23 on a gift for his sister and $18.90 on a gift for his mother.
   How much did Joel spend altogether?
   A. $33.13
   B. $34.03
   **C. $34.13**
   D. $34.23

6. Freddy rode his bike 18.125 km on Saturday and 13.5 km on Sunday.
   How far did Freddy ride his bike in the two days?
   A. 21.625 km
   B. 31.175 km
   C. 31.130 km
   **D. 31.625 km**

7. Mary drove 32.875 km to the restaurant and then 8.225 km to the store.
   What is the total distance Mary drove?
   A. 40.000 km
   B. 41.000 km
   C. 40.100 km
   **D. 41.100 km**

8. Holly saved $62.50 of her allowance and her grandfather gave her an additional $50.
   How much money did Holly have?
   A. $63.00
   B. $67.50
   **C. $112.50**
   D. $113.00

# Solve Story Problems with Decimals (B)

## Lesson Overview

| | | |
|---|---|---|
| **GET READY** Review Subtraction of Decimals | 10 minutes | **ONLINE** |
| **LEARN** Solve Subtraction Story Problems | 15 minutes | **OFFLINE** |
| **LEARN** Find Decimal Answers with Subtraction | 15 minutes | **ONLINE** |
| **TRY IT** Subtract Decimals in Story Problems | 10 minutes | **OFFLINE** |
| **CHECKPOINT** | 10 minutes | **ONLINE** |

### ▶ Lesson Objectives
Solve a story problem involving addition or subtraction of decimal numbers.

### ▶ Prerequisite Skills
Solve an addition or subtraction problem involving decimal numbers.

### ▶ Content Background
Students may already have a basic understanding of adding decimal numbers. They will solve subtraction story problems with decimal numbers.

When students write and compute with decimal numbers, they often use numbers that are between 0 and 1—for example, 0.1. While it is acceptable to write this number as .1, mathematicians usually write the leading zero, to show that the decimal number has zero for the part that is the whole number and to avoid confusion about the value of the number.

### ▶ Advance Preparation
Print the Solve Subtraction Story Problems printout.

### Materials to Gather

**SUPPLIED**
Solve Subtraction Story Problems (printout)
Subtract Decimals in Story Problems activity page

---

## GET READY  Review Subtraction of Decimals
**ONLINE 10 min**

Students will solve decimal subtraction problems to reveal a hidden picture. They should copy the problems shown on-screen into their Math Notebook as necessary and solve them there.

### Objectives
- Solve an addition or subtraction problem involving decimal numbers.

# LEARN  Solve Subtraction Story Problems

**OFFLINE 15 min**

## Objectives

- Solve a story problem involving addition or subtraction of decimal numbers.

## Tips

If students have difficulty subtracting decimal numbers without the number line, allow them to continue using the number line for the last two problems.

Students will use decimal number lines that also show fractions. They will solve subtraction story problems. They will connect fractions and decimals as they do the activity. Students will also solve some problems using the algorithm, or step-by-step method, instead of number lines.

Gather the Solve Subtraction Story Problems printout. Students will also write in their Math Notebook.

### SUBTRACT WITH A NUMBER LINE

1. Have students read the first on-screen problem.
2. Tell students they will use a number line to solve the problem. Have students work with the first number line, labeled from 0 to 11. Have them label the equivalent fraction or mixed number for each $\frac{1}{2}$ on the number line below each decimal number, to build the connection between decimals and fractions. For example, students will write $\frac{1}{2}$ below 0.5, and $1\frac{1}{2}$ below 1.5. Have students complete this for all decimal numbers between 0 and 11.
3. **Say:** 10 is the minuend needed to find the difference to solve the problem.

   Have students mark a point at 0 and 10 on the number line. Start at 0 and "hop" 10 to the right of 0. Show an arc between 0 and 10.
4. **Say:** The subtrahend, the number to subtract from the minuend, used to solve the problem is 1.250.

   **Ask:** What mixed number is equivalent to 1.250? $1\frac{1}{4}$

   Have students "hop" one whole unit (from 10 to 9) and then one-fourth of a unit (from 9 to 8.75) to the left of 10. Show arcs for the whole-unit hop and the one-fourth-unit hop. Mark another point at 8.75.

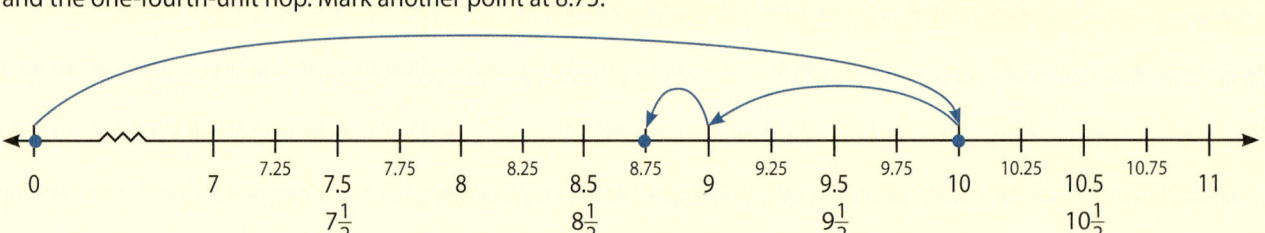

[Number line from 0 to 11 with tick marks at 7, 7.25, 7.5, 7.75, 8, 8.25, 8.5, 8.75, 9, 9.25, 9.5, 9.75, 10, 10.25, 10.5, 10.75, 11. Below: $7\frac{1}{2}$, $8\frac{1}{2}$, $9\frac{1}{2}$, $10\frac{1}{2}$.]

5. **Ask:** When you use the number line to compute the answer, what is 10 − 1.25? 8.75

   **Ask:** What mixed number is equivalent to 8.75? $8\frac{3}{4}$

   Students should also use an algorithm to find the difference. Have them write the number sentence 10 − 1.25 = ? and find the answer in their Math Notebook.
6. **Ask:** Returning to the original problem, what is the answer? It took the Magic 8.75 seconds to score their first basket.

   Have students write the answer to the problem in their Math Notebook.
7. Have students read the second on-screen problem.
8. Tell students they will use a number line to solve the problem. Have students work with the second number line, labeled from 0 to 9. Have them label the equivalent fraction or mixed number for each $\frac{1}{2}$ on the number line below each decimal number. For example, students will write $\frac{1}{2}$ below

**232  DECIMALS: ADDITION AND SUBTRACTION**

0.5, and $1\frac{1}{2}$ below 1.5. Have them complete this for all decimal numbers between 0 and 9.

9. **Say:** 7.875 is the minuend needed to find the difference to solve the problem. Since 7.875 doesn't have a tick mark on the number line, you'll mark a dot that's between 7.75 and 8. When you do that, you're finding the *approximate* location for the point for 7.875 on the number line.

   Have students mark a point at 0 and 7.875 on the number line. Start at 0 and "hop" 7.875 to the right of 0. Show an arc between 0 and 7.875.

10. **Say:** The subtrahend, the number to subtract from the minuend, used to solve the problem is 1.6.

    **Ask:** Think about decimal numbers and mixed numbers. What mixed number, in simplest form, is equivalent to 1.6? $1\frac{3}{5}$

    Have students "hop" one whole unit (from 7.875 to 6.875) and then six-tenths of a unit, with one hop for each tenth, to the left of 6.875, to 6.275. Show arcs for the whole-unit hop and each one-tenth-unit hop. Mark another point at 6.275. Remind students that they will be finding the *approximate* locations on the number line.

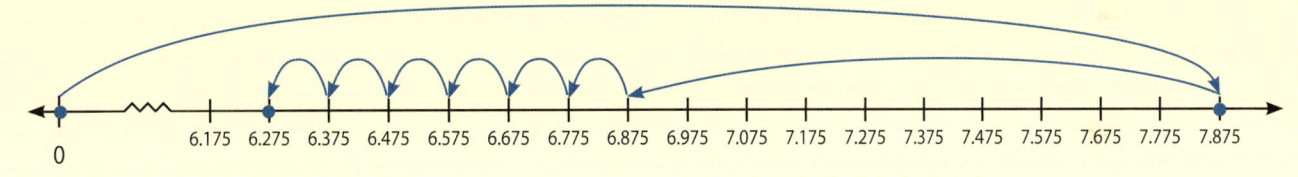

11. **Ask:** Using the number line to compute the answer, what is 7.875 − 1.6? 6.275

    Students should also use an algorithm to find the difference. Have them write the number sentence 7.875 − 1.6 = ? and find the answer in their Math Notebook.

12. **Ask:** Returning to the original problem, what is the answer? Andrew's grandfather's fish weighs 6.275 pounds.

    Have student write the answer to the problem in their Math Notebook.

## SUBTRACT WITHOUT A NUMBER LINE

13. Have students read the third on-screen problem.

14. **Ask:** What do you need to do to solve the problem? Subtract the distance Abby's family drove from the distance Sarah's family drove to find out how much farther Sarah's family drove than Abby's.

    What number sentence is needed to solve the problem? 783.23 − 438.694 = ?

    Have students write the number sentence needed to solve the problem and use an algorithm to find the answer in their Math Notebook.

    **Ask:** Returning to the original problem, what is the answer? Sarah's family drove 344.536 miles farther than Abby's.

    Have student write the answer to the problem in their Math Notebook.

15. Have students read the fourth on-screen problem. Repeat Step 14 to solve the problem. Subtract the cost of Tommy's book from the cost of Kevin's book. 37.32 − 35.27 = 2.05. Kevin's book cost $2.05 more than Tommy's book.

SOLVE STORY PROBLEMS WITH DECIMALS (B)

## LEARN Find Decimal Answers with Subtraction
**ONLINE 15 min**

Students will solve decimal subtraction story problems. Have students copy the problems into their Math Notebook as necessary and solve them there.

**Objectives**
- Solve a story problem involving addition or subtraction of decimal numbers.

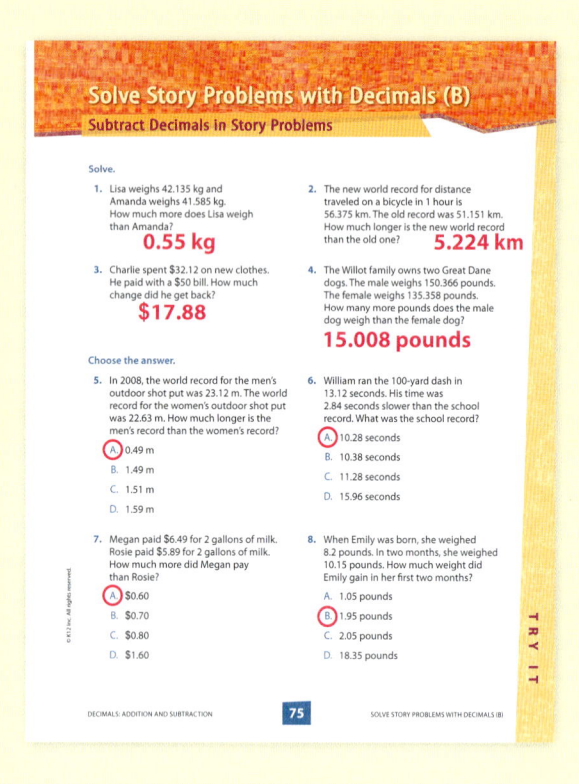

## TRY IT Subtract Decimals in Story Problems
**OFFLINE 10 min**

Students will practice solving subtraction story problems with decimal numbers. Have students turn to the Subtract Decimals in Story Problems activity page in their Activity Book and read the directions with them.

Students should copy the problems from the Activity Book into their Math Notebook as necessary and solve them there.

**Objectives**
- Solve a story problem involving addition or subtraction of decimal numbers.

### Solve Story Problems with Decimals (B)
**Subtract Decimals in Story Problems**

Solve.

1. Lisa weighs 42.135 kg and Amanda weighs 41.585 kg. How much more does Lisa weigh than Amanda?
   **0.55 kg**

2. The new world record for distance traveled on a bicycle in 1 hour is 56.375 km. The old record was 51.151 km. How much longer is the new world record than the old one?
   **5.224 km**

3. Charlie spent $32.12 on new clothes. He paid with a $50 bill. How much change did he get back?
   **$17.88**

4. The Willot family owns two Great Dane dogs. The male weighs 150.366 pounds. The female weighs 135.358 pounds. How many more pounds does the male dog weigh than the female dog?
   **15.008 pounds**

Choose the answer.

5. In 2008, the world record for the men's outdoor shot put was 23.12 m. The world record for the women's outdoor shot put was 22.63 m. How much longer is the men's record than the women's record?
   A. 0.49 m  *(circled)*
   B. 1.49 m
   C. 1.51 m
   D. 1.59 m

6. William ran the 100-yard dash in 13.12 seconds. His time was 2.84 seconds slower than the school record. What was the school record?
   A. 10.28 seconds  *(circled)*
   B. 10.38 seconds
   C. 11.28 seconds
   D. 15.96 seconds

7. Megan paid $6.49 for 2 gallons of milk. Rosie paid $5.89 for 2 gallons of milk. How much more did Megan pay than Rosie?
   A. $0.60  *(circled)*
   B. $0.70
   C. $0.80
   D. $1.60

8. When Emily was born, she weighed 8.2 pounds. In two months, she weighed 10.15 pounds. How much weight did Emily gain in her first two months?
   A. 1.05 pounds
   B. 1.95 pounds  *(circled)*
   C. 2.05 pounds
   D. 18.35 pounds

## CHECKPOINT
**ONLINE 10 min**

Students will complete an online Checkpoint. If necessary, read the directions, problems, and answer choices to students and help them with keyboard or mouse operations.

**Objectives**
- Solve a story problem involving addition or subtraction of decimal numbers.

# Unit Review

## Lesson Overview

| | | |
|---|---|---|
| **UNIT REVIEW** Look Back | 10 minutes | **ONLINE** |
| **UNIT REVIEW** Checkpoint Practice | 50 minutes | **ONLINE** |
| ▶ **UNIT REVIEW** Prepare for the Checkpoint | | |

## ▶ Unit Objectives

This lesson reviews the following objectives:

- Round a decimal number to any place through hundredths.
- Estimate the sum or difference in a problem involving decimal numbers.
- Solve an addition or subtraction problem involving decimal numbers.
- Verify that the calculated result of a problem involving addition or subtraction of decimal numbers is reasonable.
- Solve a story problem involving addition or subtraction of decimal numbers.

### Materials to Gather

There are no materials to gather for this lesson.

## ▶ Advance Preparation

In this lesson, students will have an opportunity to review previous activities in the Decimals: Addition and Subtraction unit. Look at the suggested activities in Unit Review: Prepare for the Checkpoint online and gather any needed materials.

### UNIT REVIEW Look Back — ONLINE 10 min

Students will review key concepts from the unit to prepare for the Unit Checkpoint.

**Objectives**
- Review unit objectives.

### UNIT REVIEW Checkpoint Practice — ONLINE 50 min

Students will complete an online Checkpoint Practice to prepare for the Unit Checkpoint. If necessary, read the directions, problems, and answer choices to students. Have students answer the problems on their own. Review any missed problems with students.

**Objectives**
- Review unit objectives.

### ▶ UNIT REVIEW Prepare for the Checkpoint

What you do next depends on how students performed in the previous activity, Unit Review: Checkpoint Practice. If students had difficulty with any of the problems, complete the appropriate review activity listed in the table online.

# Unit Checkpoint

## Lesson Overview

**UNIT CHECKPOINT** Online                    60 minutes    **ONLINE**

### ▶ Unit Objectives

This lesson assesses the following objectives:

- Round a decimal number to any place through hundredths.
- Estimate the sum or difference in a problem involving decimal numbers.
- Solve an addition or subtraction problem involving decimal numbers.
- Verify that the calculated result of a problem involving addition or subtraction of decimal numbers is reasonable.
- Solve a story problem involving addition or subtraction of decimal numbers.

### Materials to Gather

There are no materials to gather for this lesson.

### UNIT CHECKPOINT  Online

ONLINE 60 min

Students will complete the Unit Checkpoint online. If necessary, read the directions, problems, and answer choices to students and help them with keyboard or mouse operations.

### Objectives

- Assess unit objectives.

# Decimals: Multiplication and Division

## Unit Objectives

- Estimate the product or quotient of a computation problem involving decimal numbers.
- Solve a multiplication or division problem that involves decimal numbers.
- Verify that the calculated result of a problem involving multiplication or division of decimal numbers is reasonable.
- Solve a story problem that involves multiplication or division of decimal numbers.

## Big Ideas

- Estimation is a useful tool in problem solving.
- Multiplication and division can be represented by models and by using math symbols.

## Unit Introduction

Students will continue to develop number sense and computation skills with decimal numbers in this unit. They will estimate and find exact answers to computation and story problems involving products and quotients with decimal numbers. When solving computation problems, students will review their exact answers in terms of the estimated answers to be sure that the exact answers are reasonable.

## Keywords

decimal number
estimate (n.)
estimate (v.)
hundredths
tenths
thousandths

# Estimate Decimal Products, Quotients (A)

## Lesson Overview

| | | |
|---|---|---|
| **GET READY** Whole Number Multiplication | 5 minutes | ONLINE |
| **LEARN** Round to Estimate Products | 15 minutes | OFFLINE |
| **LEARN** Estimate Products with Friendly Numbers | 15 minutes | OFFLINE |
| **LEARN** Multiply Decimals by Multiples of 10 | 10 minutes | ONLINE |
| **TRY IT** Practice Estimating Products | 15 minutes | OFFLINE |

### ▶ Lesson Objectives
Estimate the product or quotient of a computation problem involving decimal numbers.

### ▶ Prerequisite Skills
Estimate or calculate a product or a quotient in a whole-number problem.

### ▶ Content Background
Students may already understand estimating products and quotients of whole numbers. In this lesson, they will estimate the products and quotients of decimal numbers by using rounding and friendly numbers.

When students write and compute with decimal numbers, they often use numbers that are between 0 and 1—for example, 0.1. While it is acceptable to write this number as .1, mathematicians usually write the leading zero, to show that the whole-number value for the decimal number is zero and to avoid confusion about the value of the number.

When students use a number line to help them round decimal numbers, all the numbers will show the same number of decimal places. For example, on a number line showing numbers in hundredths, numbers such as 42.80 will appear, rather than the equivalent value 42.8. When students find the rounded value of a number, they should give their answer to the decimal place being rounded. For example, when rounding 42.78 to the nearest tenth, they would answer 42.8, emphasizing the tenths place, even though the number line shows 42.80. Be sure that students understand that numbers such as 42.8 and 42.80 show the same value and position on the number line, but emphasize different place values.

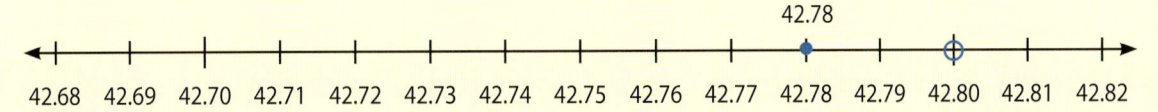

### Materials to Gather

**SUPPLIED**
Round to Estimate Products (printout)
Practice Estimating Products activity page

**ESTIMATE DECIMAL PRODUCTS, QUOTIENTS (A)** 239

## ▶ Common Errors and Misconceptions
- Students might become so concerned about getting the correct answer when estimating that they first find the exact answer, and then round it. For example, when asked to estimate 348 + 176, students might find the sum (524), and then round it to the nearest hundred (500).
- Students might have difficulty accepting that there is more than one correct approach and answer to an estimation problem.

## ▶ Advance Preparation
Print the Round to Estimate Products printout.

### GET READY  Whole Number Multiplication
*ONLINE 5 min*

Students will estimate the product of multiplication problems that involve whole numbers.

**Objectives**
- Estimate or calculate a product or a quotient in a whole-number problem.

### LEARN  Round to Estimate Products
*OFFLINE 15 min*

Students will estimate products of decimal numbers by first rounding the decimal numbers in the problem and then multiplying the rounded numbers as fractions. Using the fraction values will allow students to not only practice fraction multiplication, but also give them a better understanding of the rules they will learn for multiplying decimals. They will use number lines to round numbers in the first problems. Then they will round numbers without using number lines.

Gather the Round to Estimate Products printout. Students will write some answers in their Math Notebook.

**Objectives**
- Estimate the product or quotient of a computation problem involving decimal numbers.

**Tips**

If students have trouble writing equivalent fractions for decimals, make a number line from 1 to 2, marking tenths and quarters. Write the fraction equivalent below each decimal on the number line.

#### ROUND NUMBERS WITH A NUMBER LINE AND MULTIPLY
1. Tell students they will use number lines to estimate the product of decimal numbers. Point out the first problem—302 × 175 = ?—and the first two number lines on the printout.
2. **Say:** Use a number line to round each number, 302 and 175, to the nearest ten. Then use the rounded numbers to estimate the product.
3. Point to the number line showing 290 to 320 in whole numbers.
   **Say:** Mark 302 with a dot.
   **Ask:** Is 302 closer to 300 or 310? 300
   Have students circle 300 on the number line.
   **Ask:** What is 302 rounded to the nearest ten? 300
4. Point to the number line showing 160 to 190 in whole numbers.
   **Say:** Mark 175 with a dot.
   **Ask:** What is 175 rounded to the tens place? 180
   Have students circle 180 on the number line.
5. Have students use the rounded numbers and write the number sentence on the printout. Have them multiply the numbers. 300 × 180 = 54,000

**240**  DECIMALS: MULTIPLICATION AND DIVISION

**Ask:** When you round the addends to the nearest ten, what is the estimated product of 302 × 175? about 54,000

6. Repeat Steps 2–5 to guide students to estimate 200 × 37.29 to the nearest whole number. They will use the number lines on the printout.

7. As they estimate, have students mark the number line to show that 37.29 rounded to the nearest whole number is 37.

    **Say:** 37.29 is one factor needed to find the product. Since 37.29 doesn't have a tick mark on the number line, you'll mark a dot that's between 37.2 and 37.3. When you do that, you're finding the *approximate* location for the point for 37.29 on the number line.

    **Ask:** If we're rounding to the nearest whole number, what do you need to do to round 200? Since 200 is a whole number, it does not need to be rounded.

    **Ask:** When you round the factors to the nearest whole number, what is the estimated product of 200 × 37.29? about 7,400

## ROUND NUMBERS WITHOUT A NUMBER LINE AND MULTIPLY

8. Have students write 0.846 × 0.723 = ? in their Math Notebook.

9. Tell students they will estimate the product of 0.846 × 0.723. They will round the addends to the nearest tenth without a number line.

10. **Ask:** Think about the number lines you used to round numbers in the first two problems. What is 0.846 rounded to the nearest tenth? 0.8

    **Ask:** What is 0.8 in fraction form? $\frac{8}{10}$

    **Ask:** What is 0.723 rounded to the nearest tenth? 0.7

    **Ask:** What is 0.7 in fraction form? $\frac{7}{10}$

11. Have students find the estimated product by multiplying $\frac{8}{10} \times \frac{7}{10}$. $\frac{56}{100}$

    **Ask:** What is $\frac{56}{100}$ in decimal form? 0.56

    **Ask:** When you round the factors to the nearest tenth, what is the estimated product of 0.846 × 0.723? about 0.56

12. Have students write 1.47 × 0.381 = ? in their Math Notebook.

13. Tell students they will estimate the product of 1.47 × 0.381 to the nearest tenth.

    **Ask:** Think about the number lines you used to round numbers in the first two problems. What is 1.47 rounded to the nearest tenth? 1.5

    **Ask:** What is 1.5 in mixed number form and as an improper fraction? $1\frac{5}{10} = \frac{15}{10}$

    **Ask:** What is 0.381 rounded to the nearest tenth? 0.4

    **Ask:** What is 0.4 in fraction form? $\frac{4}{10}$

14. Have students find the estimated product by multiplying $\frac{15}{10} \times \frac{4}{10}$. $\frac{60}{100}$

    **Ask:** What is $\frac{60}{100}$ in decimal form? 0.6

    **Ask:** When you round the factors to the nearest tenth, what is the estimated product of 1.47 × 0.381? about 0.6

## LEARN  Estimate Products with Friendly Numbers  **OFFLINE 15 min**

### Objectives
- Estimate the product or quotient of a computation problem involving decimal numbers.

Students will use friendly numbers to estimate the product of decimal numbers. They will round factors to friendly numbers to the nearest tenth. Students will write their answers in their Math Notebook.

1. Guide students to estimate the product of 29 × 1.6. Have students write 29 × 1.6 = ? in their Math Notebook.

2. **Say:** To estimate the product, you first need to round each factor to a friendly number. To use friendly numbers, you round a number to the nearest 5, 10, 25, or 100.

3. Tell students that 30 is a friendly number for 29 because 30 is the nearest ten to 29.

4. **Say:** To round decimal numbers to friendly numbers, you can think about rounding a number to the nearest 0.1, 0.5, or 1.0. A friendly number for 1.6 is 1.5, because 1.5 is the nearest 0.5 to 1.6.

5. **Say:** Now you can change 1.5 to a mixed number and an improper fraction: $1\frac{5}{10} = \frac{15}{10}$

6. Have them write the number sentence $30 \times \frac{15}{10} = ?$ in their Math Notebook. Have students multiply to find the estimated product as an improper fraction and then simplify the answer to decimal form. $30 \times \frac{15}{10} = \frac{450}{10} = 45$

    **Ask:** When you round the factors using friendly numbers, what is the estimated product of 29 × 1.6? about 45

7. Guide students to estimate the product of 2.382 × 12.163. Have students write 2.382 × 12.163 = ? in their Math Notebook.

8. **Say:** To estimate the product, you first need to round each factor to a friendly number. To round decimal numbers to friendly numbers, you can think about rounding a number to the nearest 0.1, 0.5, or 1.0.

9. **Ask:** What is a friendly number for the factor 2.382? A friendly number for 2.382 is 2.5 because 2.5 is the closest 0.5 to 2.382.

    **Ask:** What is a friendly number for the factor 12.163? A friendly number for 12.163 is 12.0, because 12.0 is the closest 0.5 to 12.163.

10. **Say:** Now change 2.5 to a mixed number and then to an improper fraction. $2\frac{5}{10} = \frac{25}{10}$

11. Have students write the number sentence $\frac{25}{10} \times 12 = ?$ in their Math Notebook. Have them multiply to find the estimated product as an improper fraction and then simplify the answer to decimal form. $\frac{25}{10} \times 12 = \frac{300}{10} = 30$

12. **Ask:** When you round the factors using friendly numbers, what is the estimated product of 2.382 × 12.163? about 30

13. Have students write 0.123 × 0.767 = ? in their Math Notebook and repeat Steps 8–12, rounding the factors to friendly numbers and then finding the estimated product. $0.1 \times 0.8 = \frac{1}{10} \times \frac{8}{10} = \frac{8}{100} = 0.08$. When you round the factors to friendly numbers, the estimated product of 0.123 × 0.767 is about 0.08.

**242**  DECIMALS: MULTIPLICATION AND DIVISION

## LEARN  Multiply Decimals by Multiples of 10

**ONLINE 10 min**

### Objectives
- Estimate the product or quotient of a computation problem involving decimal numbers.

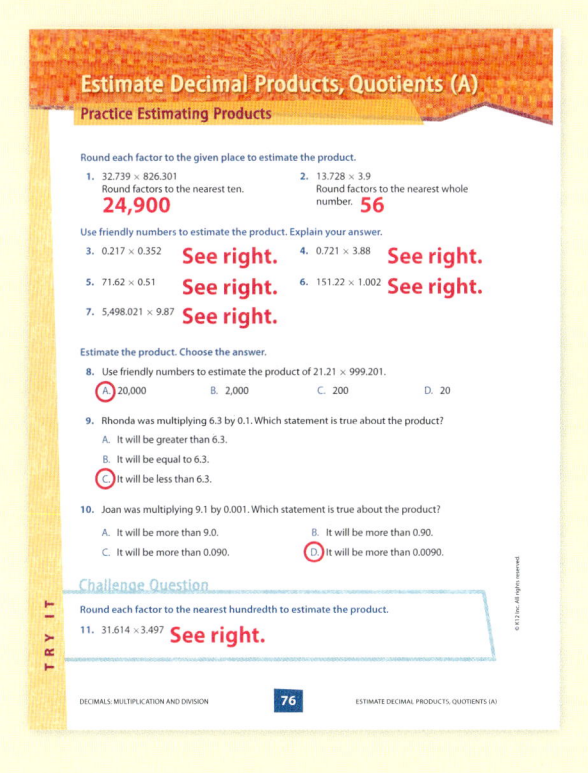

Students will multiply decimal numbers by multiples of 10. They will see that when a decimal number is multiplied by a number greater than or equal to 1, the product is greater than or equal to the decimal number. They will also see that when a decimal number is multiplied by a number less than 1, the product is less than the decimal number.

## TRY IT  Practice Estimating Products

**OFFLINE 15 min**

### Objectives
- Estimate the product or quotient of a computation problem involving decimal numbers.

Students will practice estimating products with decimal numbers. Have students turn to the Practice Estimating Products activity page in their Activity Book and read the directions with them.

Students should copy the problems from the Activity Book into their Math Notebook as necessary and solve them there.

### Additional Answers

3. **Example estimate:** 0.08; **Example explanation:** 0.217 can be rounded to the friendly number 0.2. 0.352 can be rounded to the friendly number 0.4.

   $0.2 \times 0.4 = \frac{2}{10} \times \frac{4}{10} = \frac{8}{100} = 0.08$. The estimated product of $0.217 \times 0.352$ is about 0.08.

4. **Example estimate:** 2.73; **Example explanation:** 0.721 can be rounded to the friendly number 0.7. 3.88 can be rounded to the friendly number 4.

   $0.7 \times 4 = \frac{7}{10} \times 4 = \frac{7}{10} \times \frac{4}{1} = \frac{28}{10} = 2.8$. The estimated product of $0.721 \times 3.88$ is about 2.8

5. **Example estimate:** 36; **Example explanation:** Round the factors to $72 \times 0.5$.

   $72 \times 0.5 = 72 \times \frac{1}{2} = 36$. The estimated product of $71.62 \times 0.51$ is about 36.

6. **Example estimate:** 150; **Example explanation:** Round the factors to $150 \times 1.0$.
   The estimated product of $151.22 \times 1.002$ is about 150.

7. **Example estimate:** 55,000; **Example explanation:** Round the factors to $5,500 \times 10$. The estimated product of $5,498.021 \times 9.87$ is about 55,000.

11. Round 31.614 to 31.61. Round 3.497 to 3.50.

    $31.61 \times 3.5 = 31\frac{61}{100} \times 3\frac{5}{10} = \frac{3,161}{100} \times \frac{35}{10} = \frac{110,635}{1,000} = 110.635$. The estimated product of $31.614 \times 3.497$ is about 110.635.

**ESTIMATE DECIMAL PRODUCTS, QUOTIENTS (A)**

# Estimate Decimal Products, Quotients (B)

## Lesson Overview

| | | |
|---|---|---|
| **GET READY** Whole Number Division | 5 minutes | **ONLINE** |
| **LEARN** Round to Estimate Quotients | 15 minutes | **OFFLINE** |
| **LEARN** Estimate Quotients with Friendly Numbers | 15 minutes | **OFFLINE** |
| **LEARN** Divide Decimals by Multiples of 10 | 10 minutes | **ONLINE** |
| **TRY IT** Practice Estimating Quotients | 15 minutes | **OFFLINE** |

### ▶ Lesson Objectives
Estimate the product or quotient of a computation problem involving decimal numbers.

### ▶ Prerequisite Skills
Estimate or calculate a product or a quotient in a whole-number problem.

**Materials to Gather**

**SUPPLIED**
Round to Estimate Quotients (printout)
Practice Estimating Quotients activity page

### ▶ Content Background
Students may already understand estimating products and quotients of whole numbers. In this lesson, they will continue to learn different ways to estimate the quotient in a division problem with decimal numbers.

When students write and compute with decimal numbers, they often use numbers that are between 0 and 1—for example, 0.1. While it is acceptable to write this number as .1, mathematicians usually write the leading zero, to show that the whole-number value for the decimal number is zero and to avoid confusion about the value of the number.

When students use a number line to help them round decimal numbers, all the numbers will show the same number of decimal places. For example, on a number line showing numbers in hundredths, numbers such as 42.80 will appear, rather than the equivalent value 42.8. When students find the rounded value of a number, they should give their answer to the decimal place being rounded. For example, when rounding 42.78 to the nearest tenth, they would answer 42.8, emphasizing the tenths place, even though the number line shows 42.80. Be sure that students understand that numbers such as 42.8 and 42.80 show the same value and position on the number line, but emphasize different place values.

```
         42.78
◄──┼────┼────┼────┼────┼────┼────┼────┼────┼────●────┼────○────┼────┼──►
  42.68 42.69 42.70 42.71 42.72 42.73 42.74 42.75 42.76 42.77 42.78 42.79 42.80 42.81 42.82
```

### ▶ Common Errors and Misconceptions
- Students might become so concerned about getting the correct answer when estimating that they first find the exact answer, and then round it. For example, when asked to estimate 348 + 176, students might find the sum (524), and then round it to the nearest hundred (500).

**DECIMALS: MULTIPLICATION AND DIVISION**

- Students might have difficulty accepting that there is more than one correct approach and answer to an estimation problem.

▶ **Advance Preparation**

Print the Round to Estimate Quotients printout.

## GET READY  Whole Number Division

*ONLINE 5 min*

Students will round to the nearest hundred and use friendly numbers to estimate the quotient of whole-number division problems.

**Objectives**

- Estimate or calculate a product or a quotient in a whole-number problem.

## LEARN  Round to Estimate Quotients

*OFFLINE 15 min*

Students will estimate quotients of decimal numbers by first rounding the decimal numbers for the dividend and the divisor in the problem and then dividing the rounded numbers as fractions. Using the fraction values will allow students to not only practice fraction division, but also give them a better understanding of the rules they will learn for multiplying decimals. They will use number lines to round numbers in the first problems. Then they will round numbers without using number lines.

Gather the Round to Estimate Quotients printout. Students will write some answers in their Math Notebook.

**Objectives**

- Estimate the product or quotient of a computation problem involving decimal numbers.

**Tips**

If students have trouble finding the reciprocal and multiplying after rounding the dividend and the divisor, review how to divide a fraction by a fraction, or a fraction by a mixed number, or a mixed number by a fraction.

### ROUND NUMBERS WITH A NUMBER LINE AND DIVIDE

1. Tell students they will use number lines to estimate the quotient of decimal numbers. Point out the first problem—802 ÷ 22 = ?—and the first two number lines on the printout.

2. **Say:** Use a number line to round the dividend (802) and the divisor (22) to the nearest ten. Then use the rounded numbers to estimate the quotient.

3. Point to the number line showing 790 to 820 in whole numbers.

   **Say:** Mark 802 with a dot.

   **Ask:** Is 802 closer to 800 or 810? 800

   Have students circle 800 on the number line.

   **Ask:** What is 802 rounded to the nearest ten? 800

4. Point to the number line showing 10 to 40 in whole numbers.

   **Say:** Mark 22 with a dot.

   **Ask:** Is 22 closer to 20 or 30? 20

   Have students circle 20 on the number line.

   **Ask:** What is 22 rounded to the nearest ten? 20

5. Have students use the rounded numbers and write the number sentence on the printout to estimate the quotient. Have them divide the numbers. 800 ÷ 20 = 40

   **Ask:** When you round the dividend and the divisor to the nearest ten, what is the estimated quotient of 802 ÷ 22? about 40

ESTIMATE DECIMAL PRODUCTS, QUOTIENTS (B)   245

6. Point out the second problem—6.0 ÷ 0.51 = ?—and the number line on the printout.

7. **Say:** Round the dividend (6.0) and the divisor (0.51) to the nearest tenth. Then use the rounded numbers to estimate the quotient.

8. **Ask:** If we're rounding to the nearest tenth, what do you need to do to round 6.0? Since 6.0 is a whole number, it does not need to be rounded.

9. Point to the number line showing 0.40 to 0.70 in tenths.

    **Say:** Mark 0.51 with a dot.

    **Ask:** Is 0.51 closer to 0.50 or 0.60? 0.50

    Have students circle 0.50 on the number line.

    **Ask:** What is 0.51 rounded to the nearest tenth? 0.5

    **Ask:** What is 0.5 in fraction form? $\frac{5}{10}$

10. Have students find the estimated quotient of $6.0 \div \frac{5}{10}$.

    $\frac{6}{1} \div \frac{5}{10} = \frac{6}{1} \times \frac{10}{5} = \frac{60}{5} = 12$

    **Ask:** When you round the dividend and the divisor to the nearest tenth, what is the estimated quotient of 6.0 ÷ 0.51? about 12

## ROUND NUMBERS WITHOUT A NUMBER LINE AND DIVIDE

11. Have students write 0.268 ÷ 0.603 = ? in their Math Notebook.

12. Tell students they will estimate the quotient of 0.268 ÷ 0.603. They will round the dividend and divisor to the nearest tenth without a number line.

13. **Ask:** Think about the number lines you used to round numbers in the last two problems. What is 0.268 rounded to the nearest tenth? 0.3

    **Ask:** What is 0.3 in fraction form? $\frac{3}{10}$

    **Ask:** What is 0.603 rounded to the nearest tenth? 0.6

    **Ask:** What is 0.6 in fraction form? $\frac{6}{10}$

14. Have students find the estimated quotient by dividing $\frac{3}{10} \div \frac{6}{10}$. Remind students to divide out common factors when multiplying by the reciprocal of the divisor.

    $\frac{3}{10} \div \frac{6}{10} = \frac{3}{10} \times \frac{10}{6} = \frac{3}{6} = \frac{1}{2}$

    **Ask:** What is $\frac{1}{2}$ in decimal form? 0.5

    **Ask:** When you round the dividend and the divisor to the nearest tenth, what is the estimated quotient of 0.268 ÷ 0.603? about 0.5

15. Have students write 0.246 ÷ 2.501 = ? in their Math Notebook.

16. Have students find the estimated quotient by dividing $\frac{25}{100} \div \frac{250}{100}$. Remind students to divide out common factors when multiplying by the reciprocal of the divisor.

    $\frac{25}{100} \div \frac{250}{100} = \frac{\cancel{25}^{1}}{\cancel{100}} \div \frac{\cancel{100}^{1}}{\cancel{250}_{10}} = \frac{1}{10}$

    **Ask:** What is $\frac{1}{10}$ in decimal form? 0.1

    **Ask:** When you round the dividend and the divisor to the nearest hundredth, what is the estimated quotient of 0.246 ÷ 2.501? about 0.1

DECIMALS: MULTIPLICATION AND DIVISION

## LEARN Estimate Quotients with Friendly Numbers

**OFFLINE 15 min**

### Objectives
- Estimate the product or quotient of a computation problem involving decimal numbers.

Students will use friendly numbers to estimate division of decimal numbers. They will round dividends and divisors to friendly numbers. Students will write their answers in their Math Notebook.

1. Guide students to estimate the quotient of 132 ÷ 6.53. Have students write 132 ÷ 6.53 = ? in their Math Notebook.

2. **Say:** To estimate the quotient, you first need to round the dividend and the divisor to a friendly number. To use friendly numbers, you round a number to the nearest 5, 10, 25, or 100.

3. Tell students that 130 is a friendly number for 132, because 130 is the nearest ten to 132.

4. **Say:** To round decimal numbers to friendly numbers, you can think about rounding a number to the nearest 0.1, 0.5, or 1.0. A friendly number for 6.53 is 6.5, because 6.5 is the nearest 0.5 to 6.53.

5. **Say:** Now you can change 6.5 to a mixed number: $6\frac{5}{10}$. Then you can change $6\frac{5}{10}$ to an improper fraction: $\frac{65}{10}$.

6. Have students write the number sentence $130 \div \frac{65}{10} = ?$ in their Math Notebook. Have them divide to find the estimated quotient as an improper fraction and then simplify the answer to decimal form. Remind students to divide out common factors when multiplying by the reciprocal of the divisor.

$$130 \div \frac{65}{10} = \frac{\overset{2}{\cancel{130}}}{1} \times \frac{10}{\underset{1}{\cancel{65}}} = \frac{20}{1} = 20$$

**Ask:** When you round the dividend and the divisor using friendly numbers, what is the estimated quotient of 132 ÷ 6.53? **about 20**

**Ask:** What is $\frac{1}{10}$ in decimal form? **0.1**

**Ask:** When you round the dividend and the divisor to the nearest hundredth, what is the estimated quotient of 0.246 ÷ 2.501? **about 0.1**

7. Guide students to estimate the quotient of 9.615 ÷ 3.223. Have students write 9.615 ÷ 3.223 = ? in their Math Notebook.

8. **Say:** To estimate the quotient, you first need to round the dividend and the divisor to a friendly number. To round decimal numbers to friendly numbers, you can think about rounding a number to the nearest 0.1, 0.5, or 1.0.

9. **Ask:** What is a friendly number for the dividend, 9.615? **A friendly number for 9.615 is 9.6 because 9.6 is the closest 1.0 to 9.615.**

   **Ask:** What is a friendly number for the dividend, 3.223? **A friendly number for 3.223 is 3, because 3 is the closest 1.0 to 3.223.**

10. **Say:** Now change the dividend and the divisor to mixed numbers and then to improper fractions.

    **Ask:** What is 9.6 as a mixed number and then an improper fraction? $9\frac{6}{10} = \frac{96}{10}$

    **Ask:** What is 3 as an improper fraction? $\frac{3}{1}$

**ESTIMATE DECIMAL PRODUCTS, QUOTIENTS (B)** 247

11. Have students write the number sentence $\frac{96}{10} \div \frac{3}{1} = ?$ in their Math Notebook. Have them divide to find the estimated quotient as an improper fraction and then simplify the answer to decimal form. Remind students to divide out common factors when multiplying by the reciprocal of the divisor.

$$\frac{96}{10} \div \frac{3}{1} = \frac{\overset{32}{\cancel{96}}}{10} \times \frac{1}{\underset{1}{\cancel{3}}} = \frac{32}{10} = 3.2$$

12. **Ask:** When you round the dividend and the divisor using friendly numbers, what is the estimated quotient of $9.615 \div 3.223$? about 3.2

13. Have students write $0.798 \div 0.018 = ?$ in their Math Notebook and repeat Steps 8–12, rounding the dividend and the divisor using friendly numbers and then finding the estimated quotient.

$$0.8 \div 0.02 = \frac{8}{10} \div \frac{2}{100} = \frac{\overset{4}{\cancel{8}}}{\underset{1}{\cancel{10}}} \times \frac{\overset{10}{\cancel{100}}}{\underset{1}{\cancel{2}}} = \frac{40}{1} = 40.$$

When you round the dividend and the divisor to friendly numbers, the estimated quotient of $0.798 \div 0.018$ is about 40.

14. Have students write $0.56 \div 1.22 = ?$ in their Math Notebook and repeat Steps 8–12, rounding the dividend and the divisor using friendly numbers and then finding the estimated quotient.

$$0.6 \div 1.2 = \frac{6}{10} \div \frac{12}{10} = \frac{\overset{1}{\cancel{6}}}{\underset{1}{\cancel{10}}} \times \frac{\overset{1}{\cancel{10}}}{\underset{2}{\cancel{12}}} = \frac{1}{2} = 0.5.$$

When you round the dividend and the divisor to friendly numbers, the estimated quotient of $0.56 \div 1.22$ is about 0.5.

## LEARN  Divide Decimals by Multiples of 10

**ONLINE 10 min**

### Objectives
- Estimate the product or quotient of a computation problem involving decimal numbers.

Students will divide decimal numbers by multiples of 10. They will see that when a decimal number is divided by a number greater than or equal to 1, the quotient is less than or equal to the decimal number. They will also see that when a decimal number is divided by a number less than 1, the quotient is greater than the decimal number.

## TRY IT  Practice Estimating Quotients

**OFFLINE 15 min**

### Objectives
- Estimate the product or quotient of a computation problem involving decimal numbers.

Students will practice estimating quotients with decimal numbers. Have students turn to the Practice Estimating Quotients activity page in their Activity Book and read the directions with them.

Students should copy the problems from the Activity Book into their Math Notebook as necessary and solve them there.

**248** DECIMALS: MULTIPLICATION AND DIVISION

## Estimate Decimal Products, Quotients (B)
### Practice Estimating Quotients

**Estimate the quotient. Explain your answer.**

1. 5.253 ÷ 0.749   **See below.**
2. 352.3 ÷ 0.53   **See below.**
3. 4,512.091 ÷ 0.11   **See below.**
4. 9,032.87 ÷ 44.912   **See below.**

**Use friendly numbers to round the dividend and divisor. Then divide to find the estimated quotient. Choose the answer.**

5. 9.59 ÷ 0.24
   - A. 0.2
   - B. 2.8
   - C. 6.1
   - **D. 40**

6. 76.12 ÷ 4.901
   - A. 1.5
   - **B. 15**
   - C. 150
   - D. 1,500

**Round the dividend and divisor to the nearest tenth. Then divide to find the estimated quotient. Choose the answer.**

7. 8.07 ÷ 0.87
   - A. 0.9
   - B. 8.1
   - **C. 9**
   - D. 81

8. 8.39 ÷ 1.22
   - A. 0.013
   - B. 0.07
   - **C. 7**
   - D. 10

**Round the dividend and divisor to the nearest whole number. Then divide to find the estimated quotient. Choose the answer.**

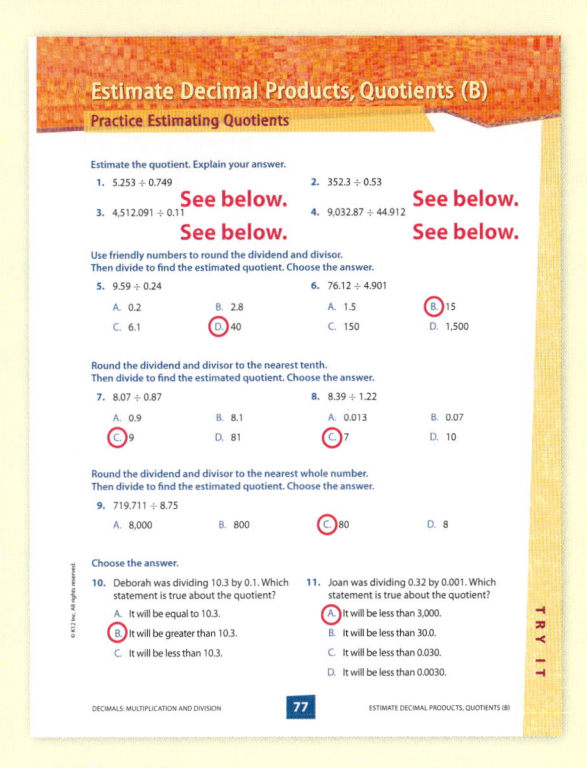

9. 719.711 ÷ 8.75
   - A. 8,000
   - B. 800
   - **C. 80**
   - D. 8

**Choose the answer.**

10. Deborah was dividing 10.3 by 0.1. Which statement is true about the quotient?
    - A. It will be equal to 10.3.
    - **B. It will be greater than 10.3.**
    - C. It will be less than 10.3.

11. Joan was dividing 0.32 by 0.001. Which statement is true about the quotient?
    - **A. It will be less than 3,000.**
    - B. It will be less than 30.0.
    - C. It will be less than 0.030.
    - D. It will be less than 0.0030.

## Additional Answers

1. **Example estimate:** 20
   **Example explanation:** Round 5.253 to the nearest hundredth as 5.0. Round 0.249 to the nearest hundredth as 0.25. Change the decimals to equivalent fractions $\left(5.0 = \frac{5}{1} \text{ and } 0.25 = \frac{25}{100}\right)$. Write the division problem as a multiplication problem by multiplying the dividend by the reciprocal of the divisor. $\left(\frac{5}{1} \times \frac{25}{100}\right)$. Divide out common factors and multiply $\left(\frac{\overset{1}{\cancel{5}}}{1} \times \frac{100}{\underset{5}{\cancel{25}}} = \frac{100}{5} = 20\right)$.

2. **Example estimate:** 700
   **Example explanation:** Round dividend to 350 and divisor to 0.5, and divide: $350 \div 0.5 = \frac{350}{1} \div \frac{5}{10} = \frac{350}{1} \times \frac{10}{5} = \frac{3,500}{5} = 700$.

3. **Example estimate:** 45,000
   **Example explanation:** Round dividend to 4,500 and divisor to 0.1, and divide: $4,500 \div 0.1 = \frac{4,500}{1} \div \frac{1}{10} = \frac{4,500}{1} \times \frac{10}{1} = \frac{45,000}{1} = 45,000$.

4. **Example estimate:** 200
   **Example explanation:** Round dividend to 9,000 and divisor to 45, and divide: $9,000 \div 45 = 200$.

# Estimate Decimal Products, Quotients (C)

## Lesson Overview

| | | |
|---|---|---|
| **LEARN** Move the Decimal Point | 15 minutes | **ONLINE** |
| **LEARN** Change the Decimal Place | 15 minutes | **OFFLINE** |
| **LEARN** Estimate Products and Quotients | 10 minutes | **ONLINE** |
| **TRY IT** Practice Estimating Decimal Answers | 15 minutes | **OFFLINE** |
| **CHECKPOINT** | 5 minutes | **ONLINE** |

### ▶ Lesson Objectives
Estimate the product or quotient of a computation problem involving decimal numbers.

### ▶ Prerequisite Skills
Estimate or calculate a product or a quotient in a whole-number problem.

### ▶ Content Background
Students will see what happens to the product or quotient when a decimal point is moved in a factor, dividend, or divisor. Exploring these relationships will help students better understand multiplication and division of decimal numbers.

When students write and compute with decimal numbers, they often use numbers that are between 0 and 1—for example, 0.1. While it is acceptable to write this number as .1, mathematicians usually write the leading zero, to show that the whole-number value for the decimal number is zero and to avoid confusion about the value of the number.

### ▶ Common Errors and Misconceptions
- Students might become so concerned about getting the correct answer when estimating that they first find the exact answer, and then round it. For example, when asked to estimate 348 + 176, students might find the sum (524), and then round it to the nearest hundred (500).
- Students might have difficulty accepting that there is more than one correct approach and answer to an estimation problem.

### Materials to Gather

**SUPPLIED**

Practice Estimating Decimal Answers activity page

## LEARN Move the Decimal Point

*ONLINE 15 min*

### Objectives
- Estimate the product or quotient of a computation problem involving decimal numbers.

To begin, students will move the decimal point to different places in the two factors of a multiplication problem to see how the value of the product changes as the value of the factors changes. They will learn that when the decimal point moves to the left, decreasing the value of either factor, the product decreases. They will also learn that when both factors are less than 1, the product is less than 1. As students move the decimal point in the factors, ask them how changing the value of either factor, either by increasing or decreasing, affects the value of the product.

Then students will move the decimal point to different places in the dividend and divisor of a division problem to see how the value of the quotient changes. They will learn that when the decimal point moves to the left in the dividend, decreasing its value, the quotient decreases. They will also learn that when the decimal point moves to the left in the divisor, decreasing its value, the quotient increases. As students move the decimal point in the dividend and the divisor, ask them how changing the value of the dividend or divisor, either by increasing or decreasing, affects the value of the quotient.

## LEARN Change the Decimal Place

**OFFLINE 15 min**

### Objectives

- Estimate the product or quotient of a computation problem involving decimal numbers.

Students will write multiplication and division sentences in which they will move the decimal point to different places to see how the value of the product or the quotient changes.

### MOVE THE DECIMAL POINT IN MULTIPLICATION NUMBER SENTENCES

1. Have students write the following multiplication problem in their Math Notebook: $268 \times 587 = 157{,}316$.

2. Have students rewrite the problem. This time, they should move the decimal point in the first factor so that its value is less than 1. They should not find the product. $0.268 \times 587 = ?$

3. **Say:** Moving the decimal point to change a whole number to a number that is less than 1 decreases the value of that factor. The product of $0.268 \times 587$ is 157.316. Write that product to solve the number sentence.

4. **Ask:** Compare the two number sentences. What happens to the product when one of the factors decreases to less than 1? When the value of one of the factors decreases to less than 1, the product decreases.

5. Have students rewrite the problem. This time, they should keep the decimal point in the same place in the first factor, 0.268, and change the second factor so that its value is less than 1. They should not find the product. $0.268 \times 0.587 = ?$

6. **Say:** Moving the decimal point to change a whole number to a number that is less than 1 decreases the value of that factor. The product of $0.268 \times 0.587$ is 0.157316. Write that product to solve the number sentence.

7. **Ask:** Compare the three number sentences. What happens to the product when both of the factors decrease to be less than 1? When both factors are less than 1, the product is less than 1.

8. Have students write the problem $2.68 \times 5.87 = ?$ in their Math Notebook. **Say:** Look at the three number sentences you have written. Without multiplying, what do you think the product of $2.68 \times 5.87$ is? To find the correct place for the decimal point in the product, notice that you moved the decimal point two places to the left in the first factor and two places to the left in the second factor. You can check the placement of the decimal point in your answer by estimating the product by rounding the decimal numbers. 15.7316

**ESTIMATE DECIMAL PRODUCTS, QUOTIENTS (C)** 251

## MOVE THE DECIMAL POINT IN DIVISION NUMBER SENTENCES

9. Have students write the following division problem in their Math Notebook: 628 ÷ 16 = 39.25.

10. Have students rewrite the problem. This time, they should move the decimal point one place in the dividend to make its value less than its value in the first number sentence. They should not find the quotient. 62.8 ÷ 16 = ?

11. **Say:** Moving the decimal point to change the dividend's value so that the new dividend is less than the original dividend decreases the value of the dividend and decreases the value of the quotient. The quotient of 62.8 ÷ 16 is 3.925. Write that quotient to solve the number sentence.

12. Have students rewrite the problem. This time, they should place a decimal point in the divisor so that its value is less than its value in the first number sentence. They should not find the quotient. 628 ÷ 0.16 = ?

13. **Say:** Moving the decimal point to change the divisor's value so that the new divisor is less than the original divisor decreases the value of the divisor *but increases the value of the quotient*. The quotient of 628 ÷ 0.16 is 3,925. Write that quotient to solve the number sentence.

14. **Say:** To find the quotient when the decimal point moves in the dividend, the divisor, or both, follow these steps:
    - Move the decimal point in the quotient the number of places and the direction it moved in the dividend.
    - Move the decimal point in the quotient the number of places in the *opposite* direction it moved in the divisor.

15. Have students rewrite the problem 6.28 ÷ 160 = ? in their Math Notebook. They should not find the product.

    **Say:** To find the quotient of 6.28 ÷ 160 start with the original quotient, 39.25.

    **Say:** Because the dividend's decimal point was moved two places to the *left*, move the decimal point in the quotient two places to the *left*. That would make the quotient 0.3925.

    **Say:** Because the divisor's decimal point was moved one place to the *right*, move the decimal point in the quotient one place to the *left*. The quotient of 6.28 ÷ 160 is 0.03925.

    **Say:** Look at the two number sentences and the steps you took. Without dividing, what do you think the quotient of 6,280 ÷ 1.6 is? To find the correct place for the decimal point in the quotient, move the decimal point one place to the right (since the dividend's decimal point moved one place to the right) and then one more place to the right (since the divisor's decimal point moved one place to the left). 3,925

**252** DECIMALS: MULTIPLICATION AND DIVISION

## LEARN Estimate Products and Quotients

**ONLINE 10 min**

Students will estimate products and quotients with decimal numbers. They will uncover a hidden picture by matching the multiplication and division problems with the correct products and quotients.

**Objectives**
- Estimate the product or quotient of a computation problem involving decimal numbers.

## TRY IT Practice Estimating Decimal Answers

**OFFLINE 15 min**

Students will practice estimating products and quotients with decimal numbers. Have students turn to the Practice Estimating Decimal Answers activity page in their Activity Book and read the directions with them.

Students should copy the problems from the Activity Book into their Math Notebook as necessary and solve them there.

**Objectives**
- Estimate the product or quotient of a computation problem involving decimal numbers.

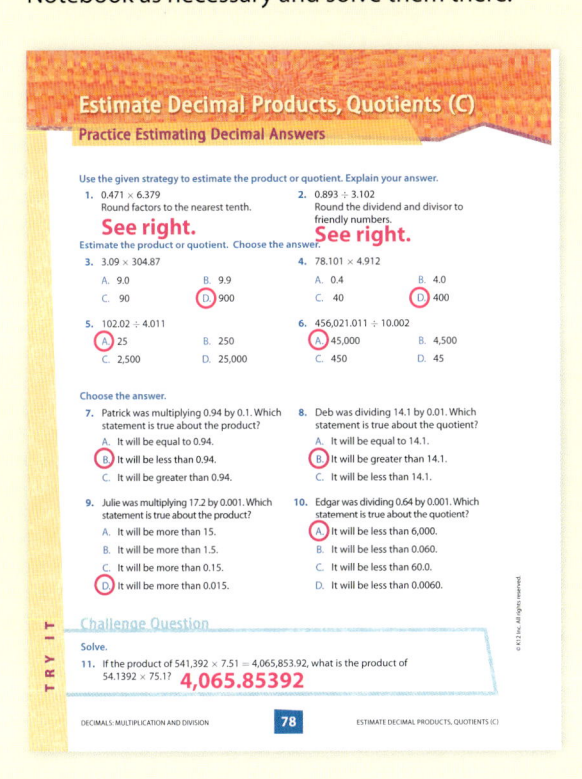

### Additional Answers

1. **Answers will vary. Example explanation:** 0.471 rounded to the nearest tenth is 0.5. 6.379 rounded to the nearest tenth is 6.4.

$$0.5 \times 6.4 = \frac{5}{10} \times 6\frac{4}{10} = \frac{1}{2} \times \frac{64}{10} = \frac{32}{10} = 3\frac{2}{10} = 3.2$$

The estimated product of $0.471 \times 6.379$ is about 3.2.

2. **Answers will vary. Example explanation:** 0.893 can be rounded to the friendly number 0.9. 3.102 can be rounded to the friendly number 3.0.

$$0.9 \div 3.0 = \frac{9}{10} \div \frac{3}{1} = \frac{9}{10} \times \frac{1}{3} = \frac{3}{10} = 0.3$$

The estimated quotient of $0.893 \div 3.102$ is about 0.3.

## CHECKPOINT

**ONLINE 5 min**

Students will complete an online Checkpoint. If necessary, read the directions, problems, and answer choices to students and help them with keyboard or mouse operations.

**Objectives**
- Estimate the product or quotient of a computation problem involving decimal numbers.

**ESTIMATE DECIMAL PRODUCTS, QUOTIENTS (C)** 253

# Multiply and Divide Decimals (A)

## Lesson Overview

| Skills Update | 5 minutes | ONLINE |
| **GET READY** Multiply Whole Numbers | 5 minutes | ONLINE |
| **LEARN** Multiply a Whole Number by a Decimal | 15 minutes | OFFLINE |
| **LEARN** Multiply a Decimal by a Decimal | 20 minutes | OFFLINE |
| **TRY IT** Practice Multiplying Decimals | 15 minutes | OFFLINE |

### ▶ Lesson Objectives
Solve a multiplication or division problem that involves decimal numbers.

### ▶ Prerequisite Skills
Estimate or calculate a product or a quotient in a whole-number problem.

### ▶ Content Background
Decimal numbers and whole numbers can be factors when finding products. Students will learn to use a step-by-step algorithm to multiply decimal numbers by whole numbers and decimal numbers by decimal numbers.

When students write and compute with decimal numbers, they often use numbers that are between 0 and 1—for example, 0.1. While it is acceptable to write this number as .1, mathematicians usually write the leading zero, to show that the whole-number value for the decimal number is zero and to avoid confusion about the value of the number.

### ▶ Advance Preparation
Print two copies of the Hundredths Decimal Squares printout.

### Materials to Gather

**SUPPLIED**
Hundredths Decimal Squares (printout)
Multiply a Whole Number by a Decimal activity page
Multiply a Decimal by a Decimal activity page
Practice Multiplying Decimals activity page

**ALSO NEEDED**
markers, coloring

---

## GET READY  Multiply Whole Numbers
*ONLINE 5 min*

Students will practice estimating and computing products of whole numbers in a game setting. They will use rounding to the nearest ten and friendly numbers.

### Objectives
- Estimate or calculate a product or a quotient in a whole-number problem.

## LEARN  Multiply a Whole Number by a Decimal

**OFFLINE 15 min**

### Objectives
- Solve a multiplication or division problem that involves decimal numbers.

Students will learn how to multiply a whole number by various decimal numbers. First they will estimate products. Then they will use models to multiply. They will check the reasonableness of their answers by comparing the exact answers to their estimates.

Gather the Hundredths Decimal Squares printout and markers. The small squares on the decimal grids represent hundredths. The columns represent tenths.

Have students turn to the Multiply a Whole Number by a Decimal activity page in their Activity Book and read directions with them. Students should copy the problems from the Activity Book into their Math Notebook as necessary and solve them there.

1. Tell students they will start by estimating the product of $0.9 \times 3$. Ask them how to estimate each factor to the nearest whole number. 0.9 rounds to 1, and 3 is a whole number and doesn't need to be rounded.

   **Say:** Write the number sentence to estimate the product in your Math Notebook. Estimate: $1 \times 3 = ?$

   **Ask:** What is the estimated product of $0.9 \times 3$? 3

   Have students write the answer to the number sentence for the estimate.

   **Say:** An estimate can help you later. After you solve the problem, you can compare the exact answer to the estimate to see if your exact answer is reasonable.

   In their Math Notebook, have students write the following:

   Exact answer: $3 \times 0.9 = ?$
   An estimate of $0.9 \times 3$ is about 3.

2. Tell students they will now model the expression $0.9 \times 3$ on the printout to see how a whole number is multiplied by a decimal number. Explain that it is easier to model an expression when the whole number is the first factor.

   **Ask:** If you change the order of the factors in $0.9 \times 3$, what is the new problem? $3 \times 0.9$

   **Ask:** What property did you use to change the order of the factors? commutative property

3. Give students a copy of the printout. Have them write the number sentence $3 \times 0.9 = ?$ above a 10 by 10 grid.

4. Tell students to shade 0.9 three times on adjoining 10 by 10 grids with a different color each time.

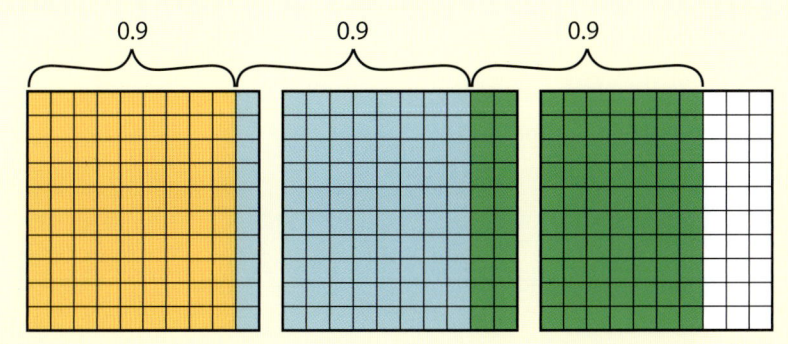

   0.9     0.9     0.9

   **Ask:** Count the shaded tenths in the decimal grids. The tenths are the columns in each grid. How many tenths did you shade in all? 27 tenths

MULTIPLY AND DIVIDE DECIMALS (A)  **255**

**Ask:** What is 27 tenths in improper fraction form? $\frac{27}{10}$

**Ask:** What is $\frac{27}{10}$ as a mixed number? $2\frac{7}{10}$

**Ask:** What is $2\frac{7}{10}$ in decimal form? 2.7

**Ask:** What is $3 \times 0.9$? 2.7

Have students write $3 \times 0.9 = 2.7$ as the exact answer in their Math Notebook.

5. Tell students they can also use a step-by-step approach, or algorithm, to find the product of $3 \times 0.9$. Have students read the first problem in the Worked Examples on the activity page. Guide them to follow the steps for multiplying a decimal number by a whole number.

6. Be sure students understand that they are not "bringing the decimal point straight down into the answer" even though that appears to be the case here. It will not be the case when they multiply a decimal number by another decimal number. They are using place value to determine the placement of the decimal point.

7. Have students review the exact answer ($3 \times 0.9 = 2.7$) in their Math Notebook under their estimate and compare the two answers.

    **Ask:** How do you know that 2.7 is a reasonable answer? The exact answer, 2.7, rounded to the nearest whole number, is 3, which is the same as the estimated answer. So the exact answer, 2.7, is reasonable.

8. Have students write $2 \times 0.87 = ?$ above another 10 by 10 grid on the printout.

    **Say:** Write another number sentence to estimate $2 \times 0.87$. Round 0.87 to the nearest whole number and find the estimated product. $2 \times 1 = 2$

9. Have students model the exact answer to the problem on adjoining 10 by 10 grids, telling them that the squares are the hundredths on the grids. Tell them to shade 0.87 two times with a different color each time.

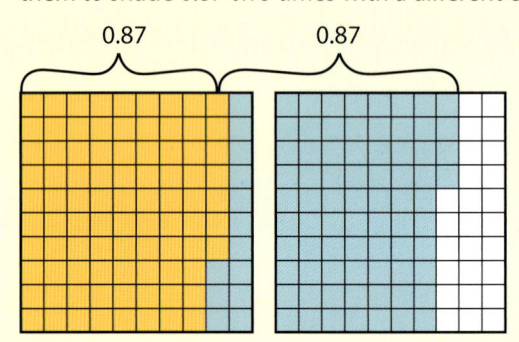

    **Ask:** Count the shaded hundredths on the grids. How many hundredths did you shade in all? 174 hundredths

    Have students write 174 hundredths as a fraction, mixed number, and decimal. $\frac{174}{100}$, $1\frac{74}{100}$, 1.74

10. **Ask:** What is the product of $2 \times 0.87$ written as a decimal number? 1.74

    Have students write 1.74 as the exact answer on their decimal grid.

11. Have students read the second problem in the Worked Examples on the activity page to see how to find the product using a an algorithm.

12. Have students compare their decimal grids to the product.

    **Ask:** How does your model show 1 one, 7 tenths, and 4 hundredths? One whole grid shows 1 one. Seven shaded columns show 7 tenths. Four shaded squares show 4 hundredths.

**256** DECIMALS: MULTIPLICATION AND DIVISION

Have students use their estimate to explain whether the exact answer of 1.74 is reasonable. The exact answer, 1.74, rounded to the nearest whole number, is 2, which is the same as the estimated answer. So the exact answer, 1.74, is reasonable.

13. Tell students they will solve the next problem without decimal grids.

    Have students write 5.231 × 3 = ? in their Math Notebook.

    **Say:** What is the estimated product of 5.231 × 3, with factors rounded to whole numbers? Write a number sentence in the Math Notebook to estimate 5.231 × 3. Round 5.231 to the nearest whole number and find the estimated product. 5 × 3 = 15

14. Have students read the third problem in the Worked Examples on the activity page. Guide them to follow the steps for multiplying a whole number by a decimal number. Then have them write 5.231 × 3 = 15.693 in their Math Notebook.

15. Have students use their estimate to explain whether the exact answer of 15.693 is reasonable. The estimate, 15, rounded to the nearest ten, is 20. The exact answer, 15.693, rounded to the nearest ten, is 20. Both answers can be rounded to the same number. So the exact answer, 15.693, is reasonable.

16. Have students complete the activity page problems in their Math Notebook.

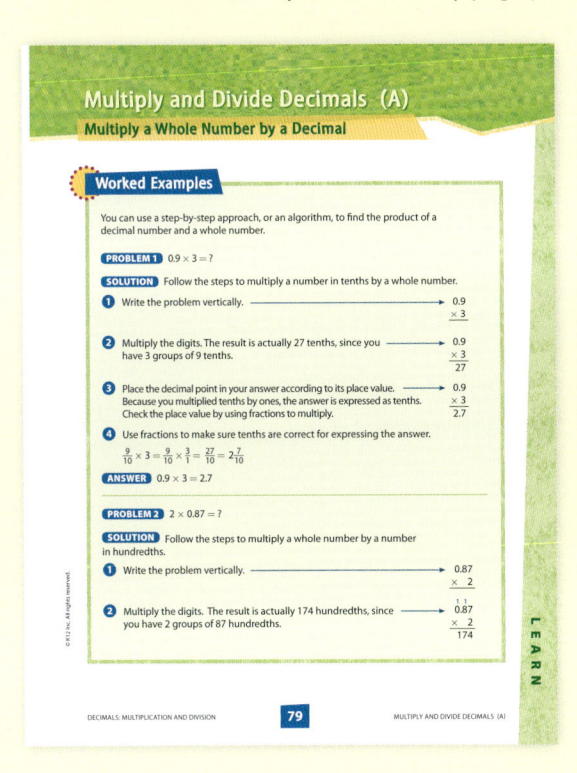

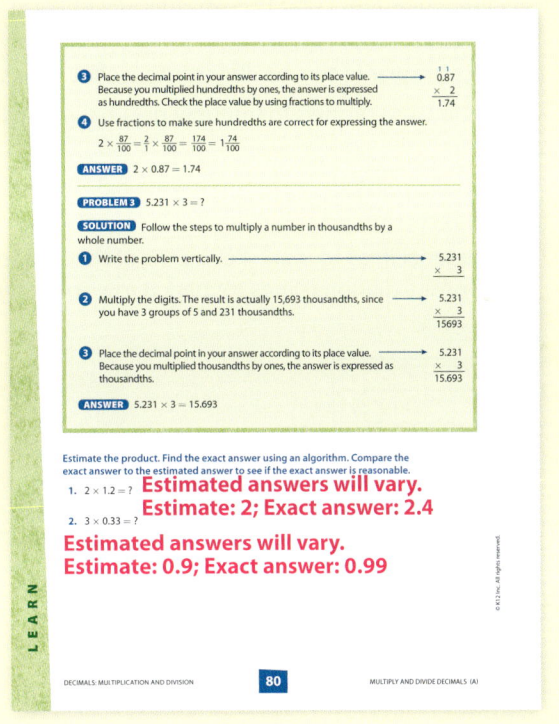

### Tips

Have students explain how their models relate to the steps of the algorithm.

**MULTIPLY AND DIVIDE DECIMALS (A)** 257

## LEARN Multiply a Decimal by a Decimal

**OFFLINE 20 min**

### Objectives
- Solve a multiplication or division problem that involves decimal numbers.

Students will learn to multiply decimal numbers by decimal numbers. First they will estimate products. Then they will use models to multiply. They will compare their estimates to their exact answers to check the reasonableness of their answers.

Gather the Hundredths Decimal Squares printout and markers.

Have students turn to the Multiply a Decimal by a Decimal activity page in their Activity Book and read directions with them. Students should copy the problems from the Activity Book into their Math Notebook as necessary and solve them there.

### Tips
Have students describe each step they take as they use an algorithm to multiply.

### MULTIPLY BY TENTHS AND HUNDREDTHS

1. Tell students they will use friendly numbers to estimate the product of $0.8 \times 0.4$ before they model the problem.

   **Ask:** What are the friendly numbers closest to 0.8 and 0.4? *A friendly number for 0.8 is 1, and a friendly number for 0.4 is 0.5.*

   **Say:** Write the number sentence to estimate the product in your Math Notebook. *Estimate: $1 \times 0.5 = ?$*

   **Ask:** What is the estimated product of those two friendly numbers? *$1 \times 0.5 = 0.5$*

   Have students write the answer to the number sentence for the estimate.

2. Tell students they will now use models to multiply decimal numbers by decimal numbers.

3. Give students a copy of the printout. Have them write $0.8 \times 0.4 = ?$ above a 10 by 10 grid.

4. Tell students to use diagonal lines to mark 4 columns of the grid to show 0.4. Have them use opposite diagonal lines to mark 8 rows of the grid to show 0.8.

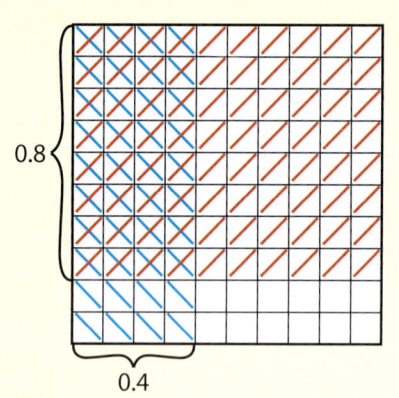

5. Tell students that the Xs formed by both diagonal lines show the product of $0.8 \times 0.4$. Have them count the squares with Xs. Each square is equal to 1 hundredth.

   **Ask:** How many hundredths have Xs? *32 hundredths*

   **Ask:** What is the product of $0.8 \times 0.4$? *0.32*

   Have students write 0.32 as the exact answer in the number sentence above the grid.

**258** DECIMALS: MULTIPLICATION AND DIVISION

6. Tell students they can also use a step-by-step approach, or an algorithm, to find the product of 0.8 × 0.4. Have students read the first problem in the Worked Examples on the activity page. Guide them as necessary.

7. Have students compare their estimate of 0.8 × 0.4 to the exact answer.

   **Ask:** What was your estimate of 0.8 × 0.4? 0.5

   **Ask:** How do you know that your exact answer, 0.32, is reasonable? The exact answer, 0.32, can be rounded to the friendly number 0.5, which is the same as the estimated answer. So the exact answer, 0.32, is reasonable.

8. Tell students they will multiply decimal numbers without a model in the next problem. Have them write 4.08 × 0.25 = ? in their Math Notebook. Tell them to use friendly numbers to estimate the product. For 4.08, they should write the friendly number 4, and 0.25 is already a friendly number. Remind students that $0.25 = \frac{1}{4}$. Have them write "Estimate: $4 \times \frac{1}{4} = ?$" in their Math Notebook.

   **Ask:** What is $4 \times \frac{1}{4}$? 1

   Have students write 1 as the answer in the estimate number sentence.

9. Tell students they can also use an algorithm to find the product of 4.08 × 0.25. Have students read the second problem in the Worked Examples on the activity page. Guide them as necessary.

10. Have students compare their estimate of 4 × 0.25 to the exact answer.

    **Ask:** What is the product of 4.08 × 0.25? 1.02

    Have students write 1.02 as the answer in the exact number sentence.

    **Ask:** How do you know if your answer is reasonable? The exact answer, 1.02, rounded to the nearest whole number, is 1, which is the same as the estimated answer. So the exact answer, 1.02, is reasonable.

## MULTIPLY BY THOUSANDTHS

11. Tell students they will multiply by thousandths in the next problem. Have them write 0.75 × 7.808 = ? in their Math Notebook.

    **Say:** The first factor in the problem, 0.75, which is equal to $\frac{3}{4}$, is already a friendly number.

    **Ask:** What is a friendly number that is close to the other factor, 7.808? 8

    Have them write "Estimate: $\frac{3}{4} \times 8 = ?$" in their Math Notebook.

    **Ask:** What is $\frac{3}{4} \times 8$? 6

    Have students write 6 as the answer in the estimate number sentence.

12. Tell students to read the third problem in the Worked Examples on the activity page. Guide them as necessary.

    **Ask:** What is the product? 5.856

    Have students write 5.856 as the answer in the exact number sentence.

    **Ask:** How do you know if your answer is reasonable? The exact answer, 5.856, rounded to the nearest whole number is 6, which is the same as the estimated answer. So the exact answer, 5.856, is reasonable.

13. Have students complete the activity page problems in their Math Notebook.

**MULTIPLY AND DIVIDE DECIMALS (A)**

## Multiply and Divide Decimals (A)
### Multiply a Decimal by a Decimal

**Worked Examples**

You can use a step-by-step approach, or an algorithm, to find the product of two decimal numbers.

**PROBLEM 1** $0.8 \times 0.4 = ?$

**SOLUTION** Follow the steps to multiply two numbers in tenths.

1. Write the problem vertically. → $\begin{array}{r} 0.8 \\ \times 0.4 \end{array}$
2. Multiply the digits. The result is actually 32 hundredths, since you have tenths multiplied by tenths. $\left(\frac{1}{10} \times \frac{1}{10} = \frac{1}{100}\right)$ → $\begin{array}{r} 0.8 \\ \times 0.4 \\ \hline 32 \end{array}$
3. Place the decimal point in your answer according to its place value. Because tenths multiplied by tenths is hundredths, the number of decimal places to the right of the decimal would be two places. Check the place value by using fractions to multiply. → $\begin{array}{r} 0.8 \\ \times 0.4 \\ \hline 0.32 \end{array}$
4. Use fractions to make sure hundredths are correct for expressing the answer. → $\frac{8}{10} \times \frac{4}{10} = \frac{32}{100}$

**ANSWER** $0.8 \times 0.4 = 0.32$

**PROBLEM 2** $4.08 \times 0.25 = ?$

**SOLUTION** Follow the steps to multiply two numbers in hundredths.

1. Write the problem vertically. → $\begin{array}{r} 4.08 \\ \times 0.25 \end{array}$
2. Multiply the digits. The result is actually 10,200 ten thousandths, since you have hundredths multiplied by hundredths. $\left(\frac{1}{100} \times \frac{1}{100} = \frac{1}{10,000}\right)$ → $\begin{array}{r} 4.08 \\ \times 0.25 \\ \hline 2040 \\ +8160 \\ \hline 10200 \end{array}$
3. Place the decimal point in your answer according to its place value. Because hundredths multiplied by hundredths is ten thousandths, the number of decimal places to the right of the decimal would be four places. Check the place value by using fractions to multiply. → $\begin{array}{r} 4.08 \\ \times 0.25 \\ \hline 2040 \\ +8160 \\ \hline 1.0200 \end{array}$ This answer is the same as 1.02.
4. Use fractions to make sure ten thousandths, simplified to hundredths, are correct for expressing the answer. $4\frac{8}{100} \times \frac{25}{100} = \frac{408}{100} \times \frac{25}{100} = \frac{10,200}{10,000} = 1\frac{200}{10,000} = 1\frac{2}{100}$

**ANSWER** $4.08 \times 0.25 = 1.02$

**PROBLEM 3** $0.75 \times 7.808 = ?$

**SOLUTION** Follow the steps to multiply a number in hundredths by a number in thousandths.

1. Write the problem vertically. → $\begin{array}{r} 7.808 \\ \times 0.75 \end{array}$
2. Multiply the digits. The result is actually 585,600 hundred thousandths, since you have hundredths multiplied by thousandths. $\left(\frac{1}{100} \times \frac{1}{1,000} = \frac{1}{100,000}\right)$ → $\begin{array}{r} 7.808 \\ \times 0.75 \\ \hline 39040 \\ +546560 \\ \hline 585600 \end{array}$
3. Place the decimal point in your answer according to its place value. Because hundredths multiplied by thousandths is hundred thousandths, the number of decimal places to the right of the decimal would be five places. → $\begin{array}{r} 7.808 \\ \times 0.75 \\ \hline 39040 \\ +546560 \\ \hline 5.85600 \end{array}$ This answer is the same as 5.856.

**ANSWER** $0.75 \times 7.808 = 5.686$

Estimate the product. Find the exact answer by using an algorithm. Compare the exact answer to the estimated answer to see if the exact answer is reasonable.

1. $0.9 \times 4.04 = ?$ **Estimated answers will vary. Estimate: 4; Exact answer: 3.636**
2. $5.05 \times 2.22 = ?$ **Estimated answers will vary. Estimate: 10; Exact answer: 11.211**
3. $0.025 \times 0.52 = ?$ **Estimated answers will vary. Estimate: 0.015; Exact answer: 0.013**

---

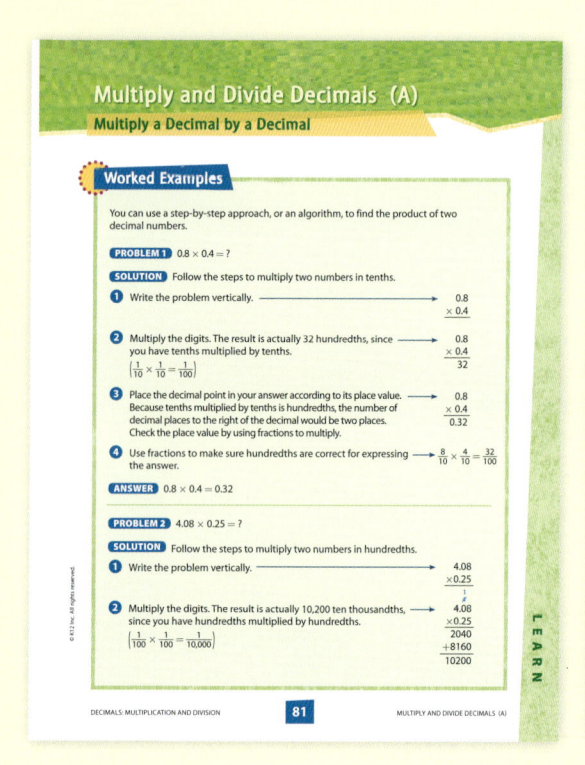

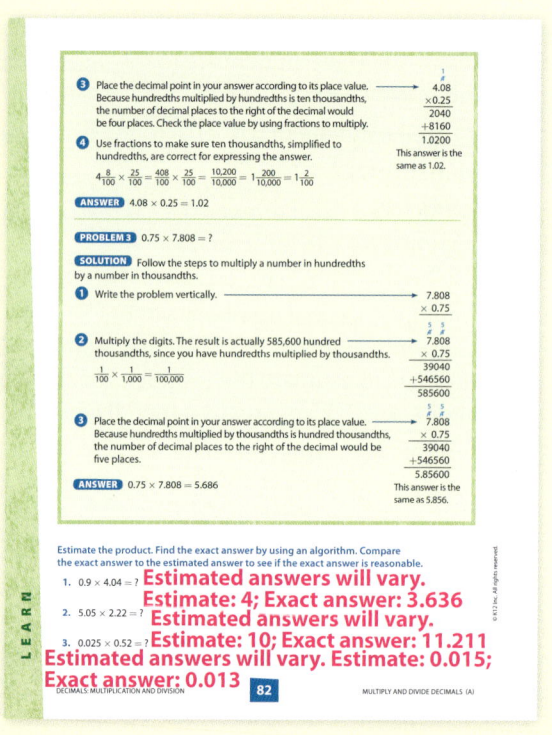

## TRY IT  Practice Multiplying Decimals

**OFFLINE 15 min**

### Objectives
- Solve a multiplication or division problem that involves decimal numbers.

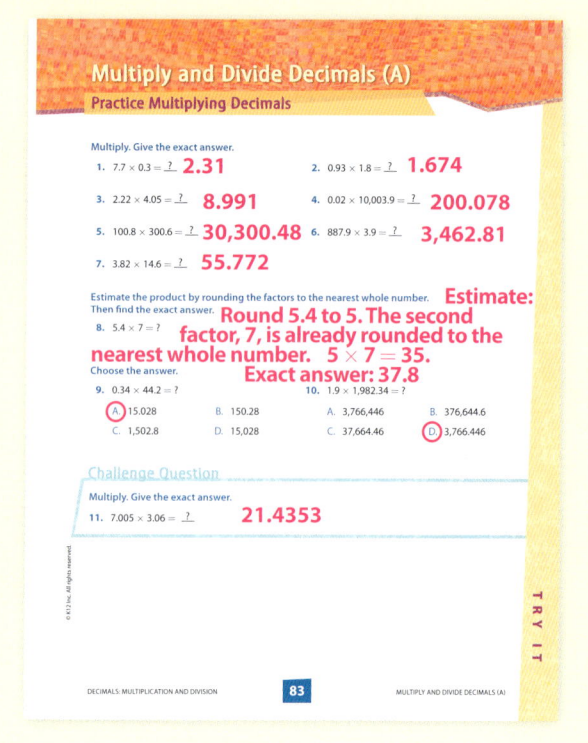

Students will practice estimating products with decimal numbers. Have students turn to the Practice Multiplying Decimals activity page in their Activity Book and read the directions with them.

Students should copy the problems from the Activity Book into their Math Notebook as necessary and solve them there.

### Multiply and Divide Decimals (A)
**Practice Multiplying Decimals**

Multiply. Give the exact answer.

1. $7.7 \times 0.3 = ?$ **2.31**
2. $0.93 \times 1.8 = ?$ **1.674**
3. $2.22 \times 4.05 = ?$ **8.991**
4. $0.02 \times 10,003.9 = ?$ **200.078**
5. $100.8 \times 300.6 = ?$ **30,300.48**
6. $887.9 \times 3.9 = ?$ **3,462.81**
7. $3.82 \times 14.6 = ?$ **55.772**

Estimate the product by rounding the factors to the nearest whole number. Then find the exact answer.

8. $5.4 \times 7 = ?$ **Estimate: Round 5.4 to 5. The second factor, 7, is already rounded to the nearest whole number. $5 \times 7 = 35$. Exact answer: 37.8**

Choose the answer.

9. $0.34 \times 44.2 = ?$
   A. **15.028** ✓
   B. 150.28
   C. 1,502.8
   D. 15,028

10. $1.9 \times 1,982.34 = ?$
    A. 3,766.446
    B. 376,644.6
    C. 37,664.46
    D. **3,766.446** ✓

**Challenge Question**

Multiply. Give the exact answer.

11. $7.005 \times 3.06 = ?$ **21.4353**

---

**260** DECIMALS: MULTIPLICATION AND DIVISION

# Multiply and Divide Decimals (B)

## Lesson Overview

| | | |
|---|---|---|
| **GET READY** Divide Whole Numbers | 5 minutes | **ONLINE** |
| **LEARN** Divide Whole Numbers and Decimals | 25 minutes | **OFFLINE** |
| **LEARN** Divide a Decimal by a Decimal | 15 minutes | **OFFLINE** |
| **TRY IT** Practice Dividing Decimals | 15 minutes | **OFFLINE** |

### ▶ Lesson Objectives
Solve a multiplication or division problem that involves decimal numbers.

### ▶ Prerequisite Skills
Estimate or calculate a product or a quotient in a whole-number problem.

### ▶ Content Background
Decimal numbers and whole numbers can be dividends and divisors when students are finding quotients. Students will continue to learn to use a step-by-step algorithm to divide decimal numbers by whole numbers, whole numbers by decimal numbers, and decimal numbers by decimal numbers.

When students write and compute with decimal numbers, they often use numbers that are between 0 and 1—for example, 0.1. While it is acceptable to write this number as .1, mathematicians usually write the leading zero, to show that the whole-number value for the decimal number is zero and to avoid confusion about the value of the number.

### ▶ Advance Preparation
Print three copies of the Hundredths Decimal Squares printout.

### ▶ Safety
Make sure students handle the scissors carefully and be sure to store them in a safe place.

### Materials to Gather

**SUPPLIED**

Hundredths Decimal Squares (printout)

Divide Whole Numbers and Decimals activity page

Divide a Decimal by a Decimal activity page

Practice Dividing Decimals activity page

**ALSO NEEDED**

markers, coloring

scissors, pointed-end safety

## GET READY Divide Whole Numbers

*ONLINE 5 min*

Students will practice estimating and computing quotients of whole numbers. They will use rounding to the nearest ten and friendly numbers to estimate the quotients.

### Objectives
- Estimate or calculate a product or a quotient in a whole-number problem.

## LEARN  Divide Whole Numbers and Decimals

**OFFLINE 25 min**

### Objectives

- Solve a multiplication or division problem that involves decimal numbers.

Students will estimate quotients, use models, and learn a step-by-step approach to divide whole numbers by decimal numbers and decimal numbers by whole numbers. They will compare the exact answers to their estimates to check the reasonableness of their answers.

Gather the Hundredths Decimal Squares printouts, markers, and scissors.

Have students turn to the Divide Whole Numbers and Decimals activity page in their Activity Book. Students should copy the problems from the Activity Book into their Math Notebook as necessary and solve them there. Throughout this activity, have students write the problem in their Math Notebook so they can refer to it as they estimate and work with the models.

In some problems in this activity, the decimal number will be the divisor and in other problems, the decimal number will be the dividend. Students will see other problems where the dividend and the divisor are both decimal numbers.

1. Tell students they will use models and a step-by-step process to divide whole numbers by decimal numbers and decimal numbers by whole numbers.

**1.8 ÷ 2 = ?**

2. Give students a copy of the printout. Tell them they will estimate the quotient of 1.8 ÷ 2 so they can check the reasonableness of their answer when they divide and find the exact answer.

   **Ask:** How do you estimate 1.8 ÷ 2 rounding both numbers to the nearest whole number? Round 1.8 to 2. The divisor, 2, is already a whole number.

   **Say:** Write the number sentence to estimate the quotient in your Math Notebook. What is the estimate? Estimate: 2 ÷ 2 = 1

3. Have students follow these steps to model 1.8 ÷ 2 on the printout.
   - Write 1.8 ÷ 2 = ? above two grids.
   - Shade 1.8.

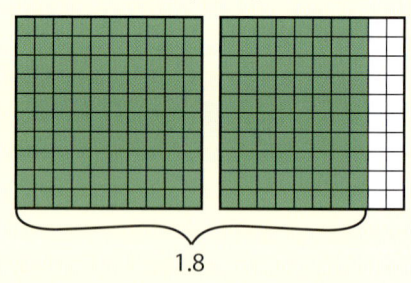

     1.8 ÷ 2 = ?

     1.8

   - Cut the model of 1.8 into tenths.

**262** DECIMALS: MULTIPLICATION AND DIVISION

- Divide the tenths into 2 equal groups.

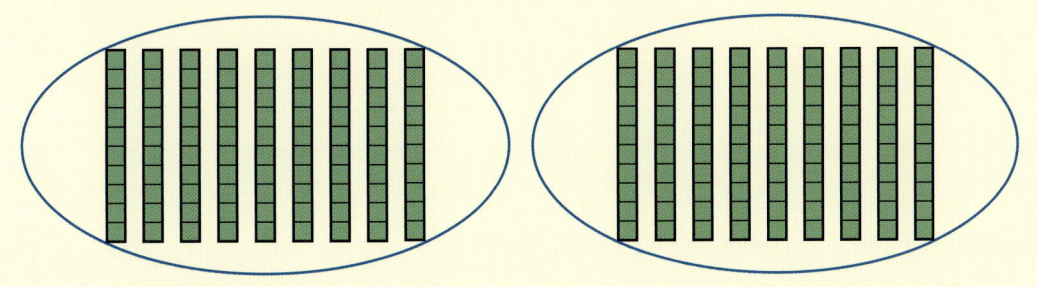

4. Discuss the model with students.
   **Ask:** How many tenths are in each group? 9 tenths
   **Ask:** What is 1.8 ÷ 2? 9 tenths
5. Tell students they can also use a step-by-step approach, or an algorithm, to find 1.8 ÷ 2. Have students read the first problem in the Worked Examples on the activity page. Guide them to follow the steps for dividing a decimal number by a whole number.
6. **Ask:** How does the model relate to the division? One whole decimal grid and $\frac{8}{10}$ of another decimal grid represents the number you divide. The dividend, 2, shows that you divide one whole decimal grid and $\frac{8}{10}$ of another grid into 2 equal groups. The quotient is 0.9.

   Have students compare their estimate of 1.8 ÷ 2 to the exact quotient.

   **Ask:** How do you know that your exact answer, 0.9, is reasonable? The exact answer, 0.9, rounded to the nearest whole number, is 1, which is the same as the estimated answer. So the exact answer, 0.9, is reasonable.

**0.21 ÷ 7 = ?**

7. Tell students that the next problem is 0.21 ÷ 7. Have them first estimate the quotient.

   **Ask:** How do you estimate 0.21 ÷ 7 by rounding both numbers to the nearest whole number? 0.21 rounded to the nearest whole number is 0. 7 is already a whole number.

   **Say:** Write the number sentence to estimate the quotient in your Math Notebook. What is the estimate? Estimate: 0 ÷ 7 = 0
8. Have students follow these steps to model 0.21 ÷ 7 on another printout.
   - Write 0.21 ÷ 7 = ? above one grid.
   - Shade 0.21.

MULTIPLY AND DIVIDE DECIMALS (B) 263

- Cut the shaded strips, which are 21 hundredths.

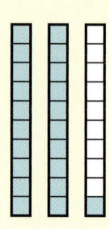

- Divide the 21 hundredths into 7 equal groups with 3 hundredths in each group.

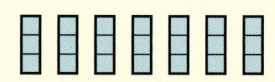

9. Tell students they can also use an algorithm to find the quotient of 0.21 ÷ 7. Have them read the second problem in the Worked Examples on the activity page. Guide them to follow the steps for dividing a decimal number by a whole number.

10. **Ask:** How does the model relate to the division? The dividend, 0.21, represents the number you divide on the decimal grid. The divisor, 7, divides 0.21 into 7 groups. Each square represents $\frac{1}{100}$, and there are 3 squares in each of the 7 equal groups. 0.03 is the quotient.

    Have students compare their exact quotient of 0.21 ÷ 7 = 0.03 to the estimate.

    **Ask:** Is 0.03 close to 0? Yes

    **Say:** The exact answer, 0.03, is close to 0, so 0.03 is a reasonable answer.

## 6 ÷ 1.2 = ?

11. Give students another copy of the printout. Tell them they will divide a whole number by a decimal: 6 ÷ 1.2.

    **Ask:** How do you estimate 6 ÷ 1.2 by rounding both numbers to the nearest whole number? 6 is already a whole number. 1.2 rounded to the nearest whole number is 1.

    **Say:** Write the number sentence to estimate the quotient in your Math Notebook. Estimate: 6 ÷ 1 = 6

12. Tell them to follow these steps to model 6 ÷ 1.2 on the printout.
    - Write 6 ÷ 1.2 = ? above the grids.
    - Shade 6 whole grids. The grids represent the dividend.

    6 ÷ 1.2 = ?

**DECIMALS: MULTIPLICATION AND DIVISION**

- Cut 1 grid into groups of 2 tenths (20 hundredths) to prepare to show 1.2, the divisor.

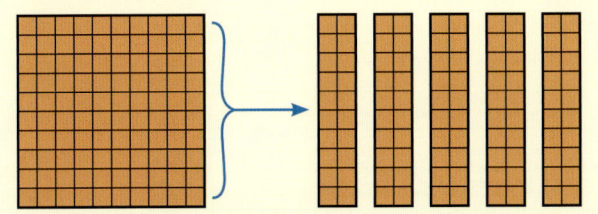

- Divide the 5 whole grids and tenths into groups of 1.2.

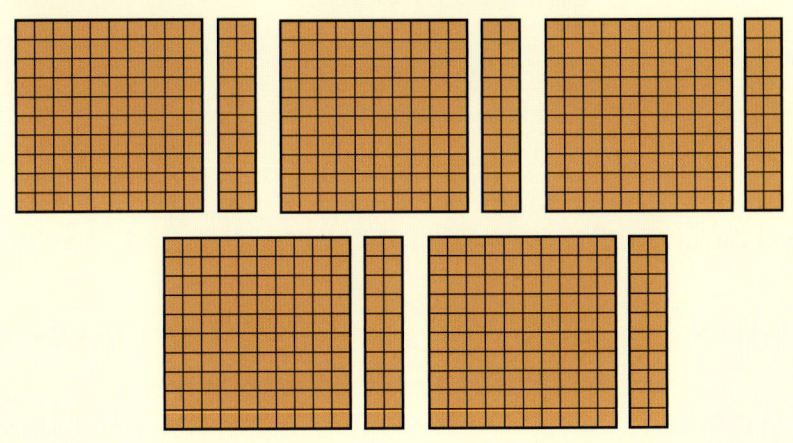

13. Have students read the third problem in the Worked Examples on the activity page. Guide them to follow the steps for dividing a whole number by a decimal number.

14. Discuss the model with students.

    **Ask:** How many groups of 1.2 are there? 5

    **Ask:** What is 6 ÷ 1.2? 5

    **Ask:** How does the model relate to the quotient? There are 5 groups of 12 in 60, or there are 5 groups of 1.2 in 6.

15. Have students compare their estimate of 6 ÷ 1.2 to the actual quotient.

    **Ask:** Is 5 close to 6? Yes

    **Say:** The estimate of the quotient, 6, is close to 5, so 5 is a reasonable answer.

## 20 ÷ 1.25 = ?

16. Tell students that they won't model the following problem. In the fouth problem in the Worked Examples, have students estimate the quotient.

    **Ask:** How do you estimate 20 ÷ 1.25 by rounding both numbers to the nearest whole number? 20 is already a whole number. 1.25 rounded to the nearest whole number is 1.

    **Say:** Write the number sentence to estimate the quotient in your Math Notebook. Estimate: 20 ÷ 1 = 20

17. Have students read the fouth problem. Guide them to follow the steps for dividing a whole number by a decimal number.

18. Have students compare the estimate of 20 with the exact quotient of 16.

    **Ask:** How do you know that your exact answer, 16, is reasonable? The exact answer, 16, rounded to the nearest ten is 20, which is the same as the estimated answer. So the exact answer, 16, is reasonable.

19. Have students complete the activity page problems in their Math Notebook.

**MULTIPLY AND DIVIDE DECIMALS (B)**

## Multiply and Divide Decimals (B)
### Divide Whole Numbers and Decimals

**Worked Examples**

You can use a step-by-step approach, or algorithm, to divide a decimal number by a whole number and to divide a whole number by a decimal number.

**PROBLEM 1** $1.8 \div 2 = ?$

**SOLUTION** Follow the steps to divide a number in tenths by a whole number.

1. Use the long-division symbol to write the problem. → $2\overline{)1.8}$
   Dividing 1.8 by 2 is similar to dividing a whole number by 2.
2. Line up all place values in the dividend and quotient. The 9 in the quotient should be placed above the 8. You can see that 1.8 divided by 2 is 0.9. → $2\overline{)1.8}^{0.9}$
3. Use fractions to make sure tenths are correct for expressing the answer.
   $1\frac{8}{10} \div 2 = \frac{18}{10} \div \frac{2}{1} = \frac{18}{10} \times \frac{1}{2} = \frac{9}{10}$

**ANSWER** $1.8 \div 2 = 0.9$

**PROBLEM 2** $0.21 \div 7 = ?$

**SOLUTION** Follow the steps to divide a number in hundredths by a whole number.

1. Use the long-division symbol to write the problem. → $7\overline{)0.21}$
   Dividing 0.21 by 7 is similar to dividing a whole number by 7. Lining up place values is important here, too.
2. Line up all place values in the dividend and quotient. The 3 in the quotient needs to be above the 1, so if you place a 0 between the decimal point and the 3, you create the two places that are needed. → $7\overline{)0.21}^{0.03}$
3. Use fractions to make sure hundredths are correct for expressing the answer.
   $\frac{21}{100} \div 7 = \frac{21}{100} \div \frac{7}{1} = \frac{21}{100} \times \frac{1}{7} = \frac{3}{100}$

**ANSWER** $0.21 \div 7 = 0.03$

---

**PROBLEM 3** $6 \div 1.2 = ?$

**SOLUTION** Follow the steps to divide a whole number by a number in tenths.

1. Use the long-division symbol to write the problem. Dividing by a decimal number is easier if you multiply to change the divisor into a whole number. Multiply the dividend by the same number. Look at the problem as a fraction, even though it looks a little strange: $\frac{6.0}{1.2}$. Create an equivalent fraction so that 1.2 becomes a whole number. Multiply 1.2 by 10 to get 12. Both the numerator and denominator must be multiplied by the same value. Multiply 6.0 by 10. → $1.2\overline{)6.0}$
   $\frac{6.0}{1.2} \times \frac{10}{10} = \frac{60}{12}$
2. Line up all place values in the dividend and quotient, so the 5 in the quotient should be placed above the 0. You can see that $60 \div 12 = 5$. Because $60 \div 12$ is equivalent to $6.0 \div 1.2$, the quotient of $6.0 \div 1.2$ is also 5. → $12\overline{)60}^{5}$
3. Use fractions to make sure that a whole number is correct for expressing the answer.
   $6.0 \div 1.2 = \frac{6}{1} \div 1\frac{2}{10} = 6 \div \frac{12}{10} = \frac{6}{1} \times \frac{10}{12} = \frac{10}{2} = 5$

**ANSWER** $6 \div 1.2 = 5$

**PROBLEM 4** $20 \div 1.25 = ?$

**SOLUTION** Follow the steps to divide a whole number by a number in hundredths.

1. Use the long-division symbol to write the problem. Multiply to change the divisor into a whole number. Multiply the dividend by the same number. Look at the problem as a fraction: $\frac{20}{1.25}$. Multiply the numerator and denominator by 1 in the form of $\frac{100}{100}$. Change your original fraction to an equivalent fraction that will be easier for your division problem. → $1.25\overline{)20}$
   $\frac{20}{1.25} \times \frac{100}{100} = \frac{2,000}{125}$
2. Line up all place values in the dividend and quotient. You can see that $2,000 \div 125 = 16$. Because $2,000 \div 125$ is equivalent to $20 \div 1.25$, the quotient of $20 \div 1.25$ is also 16.
   $125\overline{)2,000}$ → $16$; $-1,250$; $750$; $-750$; $0$

**ANSWER** $20 \div 1.25 = 16$

---

Estimate the quotient. Find the exact answer by using an algorithm. Compare the exact answer to the estimated answer to see if the exact answer is reasonable.

1. $0.25 \div 5 = ?$ **Estimated answers will vary.**
   **Estimate: 0.06; Exact answer: 0.05**
2. $6 \div 1.5 = ?$
   **Estimated answers will vary.**
   **Estimate: 3; Exact answer: 4**

---

## LEARN Divide a Decimal by a Decimal

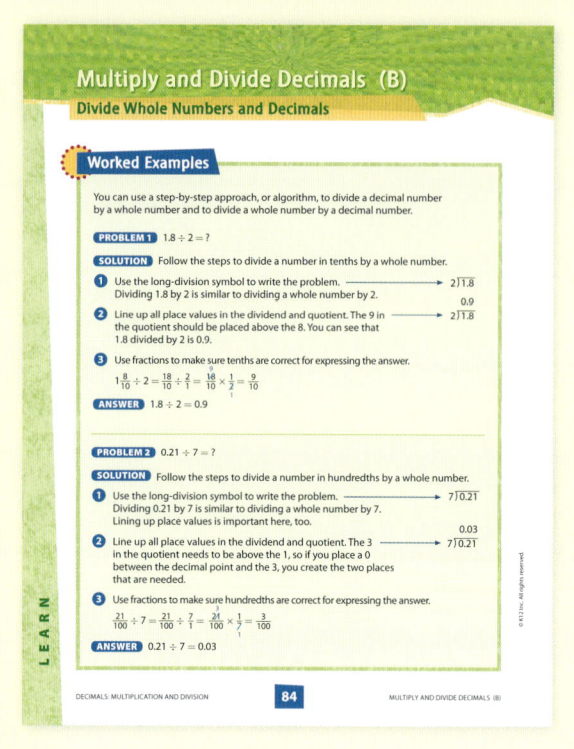

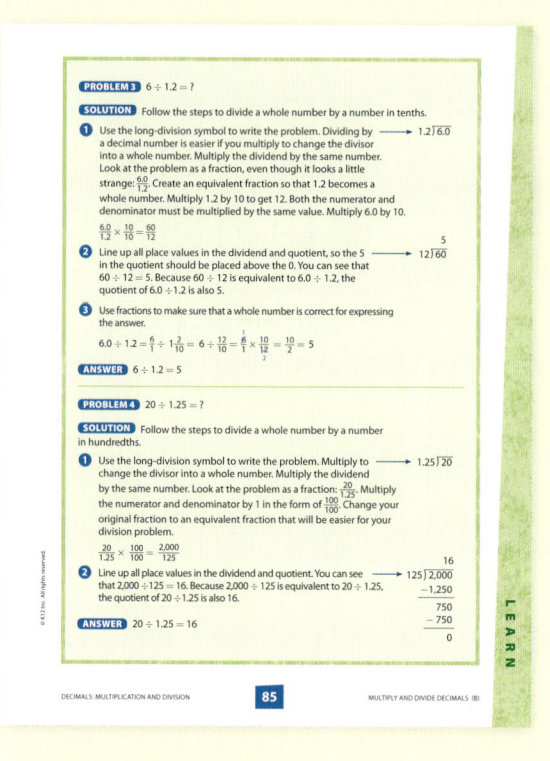

OFFLINE 15 min

Students will estimate quotients and use a step-by-step approach, or an algorithm, to divide decimal numbers by decimal numbers.

### Objectives
- Solve a multiplication or division problem that involves decimal numbers.

**266 DECIMALS: MULTIPLICATION AND DIVISION**

Have students turn to the Divide a Decimal by a Decimal activity page in their Activity Book and read the directions with them. Students should copy the problems from the Activity Book into their Math Notebook as necessary and solve them there.

> **Tips**
>
> Have students describe each step they take as they use an algorithm to divide.

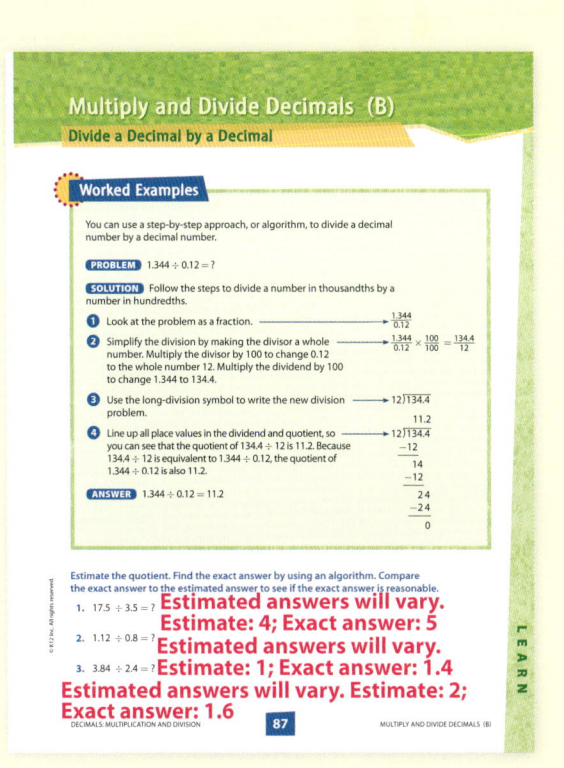

1. Tell students they will use an algorithm to find 3.9 ÷ 1.3. Have them write 3.9 ÷ 1.3 = ? in their Math Notebook. First they will estimate the quotient.

   **Ask:** How do you estimate 3.9 ÷ 1.3 rounding both numbers to the nearest whole number? Round 3.9 to 4. Round 1.3 to 1.

   **Say:** Write the number sentence to estimate the quotient in your Math Notebook. Estimate: 4 ÷ 1 = 4

2. **Say:** To find the exact answer, make the divisor, 1.3, a whole number to simplify the division. The division problem is the same as this fraction: $\frac{3.9}{1.3}$.

   Have students write $\frac{3.9}{1.3}$ = ? in their Math Notebook.

   **Say:** To make the denominator a whole number, multiply it by 10. You need to multiply the numerator by the same number, 10. When you multiply $\frac{3.9}{1.3}$ by $\frac{10}{10}$, you are multiplying $\frac{3.9}{1.3}$ by 1, so you aren't changing the value of the numbers in this problem.

   Have students write $\frac{3.9}{1.3} = \frac{3.9}{1.3} \times \frac{10}{10} = ?$ in their Math Notebook.

   **Ask:** What is $\frac{3.9}{1.3} \times \frac{10}{10}$? $\frac{39}{13}$

   Have students write $\frac{3.9}{1.3} = \frac{3.9}{1.3} \times \frac{10}{10} = \frac{39}{13} = ?$ in their Math Notebook.

   **Say:** $\frac{39}{13}$ equals $\frac{3.9}{1.3}$.

   **Ask:** What is 39 ÷ 13? 3

   **Ask:** So what is 3.9 ÷ 1.3? 3

   Have students write $\frac{3.9}{1.3} = \frac{3.9}{1.3} \times \frac{10}{10} = \frac{39}{13} = 3$.

3. Have students compare their exact answer to 3.9 ÷ 1.3 to their estimate.

   **Ask:** How do you know that your exact answer, 3, is reasonable? The exact answer, 3, is close to the estimate, 4, so 3 is a reasonable answer.

4. Have students estimate the quotient of 1.344 ÷ 0.12.

   **Ask:** How do you estimate 1.344 ÷ 0.12 rounding the dividend to the nearest whole number and the divisor to the nearest tenth? Round 1.344 to 1. Round 0.12 to 0.1.

   **Say:** Write the number sentence to estimate the quotient in your Math Notebook. Estimate: 1 ÷ 0.1 = 10

5. Read the problem in the Worked Examples on the activity page with students. Guide them to follow the steps for dividing a decimal number by a decimal number.

6. Have students compare the exact answer to 1.344 ÷ 0.12 to their estimate. The exact answer, 11.2, rounded to the nearest whole number, is 10, which is the same as the estimated answer. So the exact answer, 11.2, is reasonable.

7. Have students complete the activity page problems in their Math Notebook using a step-by-step approach. Remind them to estimate the quotients first, either by rounding the dividend and divisor or by using friendly numbers, and to use the estimates to check the reasonableness of the exact answers.

---

**Multiply and Divide Decimals (B)**
**Divide a Decimal by a Decimal**

**Worked Examples**

You can use a step-by-step approach, or algorithm, to divide a decimal number by a decimal number.

**PROBLEM** 1.344 ÷ 0.12 = ?

**SOLUTION** Follow the steps to divide a number in thousandths by a number in hundredths.

1. Look at the problem as a fraction. → $\frac{1.344}{0.12}$

2. Simplify the division by making the divisor a whole number. Multiply the divisor by 100 to change 0.12 to the whole number 12. Multiply the dividend by 100 to change 1.344 to 134.4. → $\frac{1.344}{0.12} \times \frac{100}{100} = \frac{134.4}{12}$

3. Use the long-division symbol to write the new division problem. → 12)134.4

4. Line up all place values in the dividend and quotient, so you can see that the quotient of 134.4 ÷ 12 is 11.2. Because 134.4 ÷ 12 is equivalent to 1.344 ÷ 0.12, the quotient of 1.344 ÷ 0.12 is also 11.2.

   ```
        11.2
   12)134.4
      -12
       14
      -12
        24
       -24
         0
   ```

**ANSWER** 1.344 ÷ 0.12 = 11.2

Estimate the quotient. Find the exact answer by using an algorithm. Compare the exact answer to the estimated answer to see if the exact answer is reasonable.

1. 17.5 ÷ 3.5 = ? Estimated answers will vary. Estimate: 4; Exact answer: 5
2. 1.12 ÷ 0.8 = ? Estimated answers will vary. Estimate: 1; Exact answer: 1.4
3. 3.84 ÷ 2.4 = ? Estimated answers will vary. Estimate: 2; Exact answer: 1.6

MULTIPLY AND DIVIDE DECIMALS (B)

# TRY IT  Practice Dividing Decimals

**OFFLINE 10 min**

Students will practice using a step-by-step approach to divide decimal numbers. Have students turn to the Practice Dividing Decimals activity page in their Activity Book and read the directions with them.

Students should copy the problems from the Activity Book into their Math Notebook as necessary and solve them there.

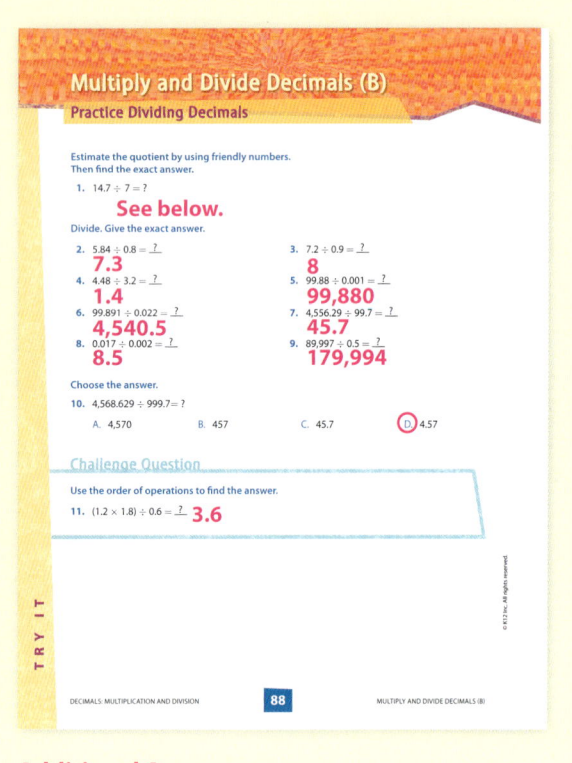

## Objectives

- Solve a multiplication or division problem that involves decimal numbers.

## Tips

Remind students that they can change a division problem to a fraction to make it simpler to find the answer. By multiplying the numerator and the denominator by a fraction that is equivalent to 1, they can change the divisor to a whole number.

### Multiply and Divide Decimals (B)
**Practice Dividing Decimals**

Estimate the quotient by using friendly numbers. Then find the exact answer.
1. $14.7 \div 7 = ?$
   **See below.**

Divide. Give the exact answer.
2. $5.84 \div 0.8 = ?$ **7.3**
3. $7.2 \div 0.9 = ?$ **8**
4. $4.48 \div 3.2 = ?$ **1.4**
5. $99.88 \div 0.001 = ?$ **99,880**
6. $99.891 \div 0.022 = ?$ **4,540.5**
7. $4,556.29 \div 99.7 = ?$ **45.7**
8. $0.017 \div 0.002 = ?$ **8.5**
9. $89,997 \div 0.5 = ?$ **179,994**

Choose the answer.
10. $4,568.629 \div 999.7 = ?$
    A. 4,570   B. 457   C. 45.7   (D.) 4.57

**Challenge Question**

Use the order of operations to find the answer.
11. $(1.2 \times 1.8) \div 0.6 = ?$ **3.6**

## Additional Answers

1. **Estimate:** Use 14 as a friendly number for the dividend, 14.7. Keep 7 as the divisor, since it is already a friendly number. $14 \div 7 = 2$
   **Exact answer:** 2.1

# Multiply and Divide Decimals (C)

## Lesson Overview

| | | |
|---|---|---|
| **LEARN** Decimal Quotients | 15 minutes | **OFFLINE** |
| **LEARN** Divide and Check | 15 minutes | **ONLINE** |
| **TRY IT** Practice Multiplying and Dividing | 20 minutes | **OFFLINE** |
| **CHECKPOINT** | 10 minutes | **ONLINE** |

### ▶ Lesson Objectives
- Solve a multiplication or division problem that involves decimal numbers.
- Verify that the calculated result of a problem involving multiplication or division of decimal numbers is reasonable.

### ▶ Prerequisite Skills
Estimate or calculate a product or a quotient in a whole-number problem.

### ▶ Content Background
Decimal numbers and whole numbers can be factors in multiplication problems, and they can be dividends and divisors in division problems. Students will learn to use a step-by-step algorithm to divide a whole number by a greater whole number, resulting in a decimal quotient.

Students build number-sense skills when they verify the reasonableness of answers. One way to determine whether an exact answer is reasonable is to estimate the answer before finding the exact answer and solving the problem. Students can compare the estimate to the exact answer to determine if the answer is reasonable.

When students write and compute with decimal numbers, they often use numbers that are between 0 and 1—for example, 0.1. While it is acceptable to write this number as .1, mathematicians usually write the leading zero, to show that the whole-number value for the decimal number is zero and to avoid confusion about the value of the number.

### ▶ Advance Preparation
Print the Hundredths Decimal Squares printout.

### ▶ Safety
Make sure students handle the scissors carefully and be sure to store them in a safe place.

### Materials to Gather

**SUPPLIED**
Hundredths Decimal Squares (printout)
Decimal Quotients activity page
Practice Multiplying and Dividing activity page

**ALSO NEEDED**
markers, coloring
scissors, pointed-end safety

---

## LEARN Decimal Quotients  *OFFLINE 15 min*

**Objectives**
- Solve a multiplication or division problem that involves decimal numbers.

Students will divide a whole number by a greater whole number, resulting in a decimal quotient. They will use a model and then a step-by-step approach.

Gather the Hundredths Decimal Squares printout, markers and scissors.

Have students turn to the Decimal Quotients activity page in their Activity Book and read the directions with them. Students should copy the problems from the Activity Book into their Math Notebook as necessary and solve them there.

1. Tell students they will use a model and then a step-by-step approach to divide whole numbers that have a decimal quotient. Give students the printout.

2. Tell students they will model 3 ÷ 10. Have them follow these steps to model 3 ÷ 10.

   • Shade 3 whole grids.

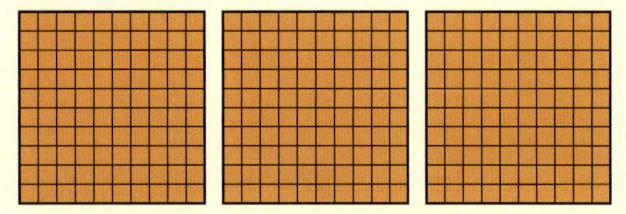

   • Cut each shaded grid into tenths.

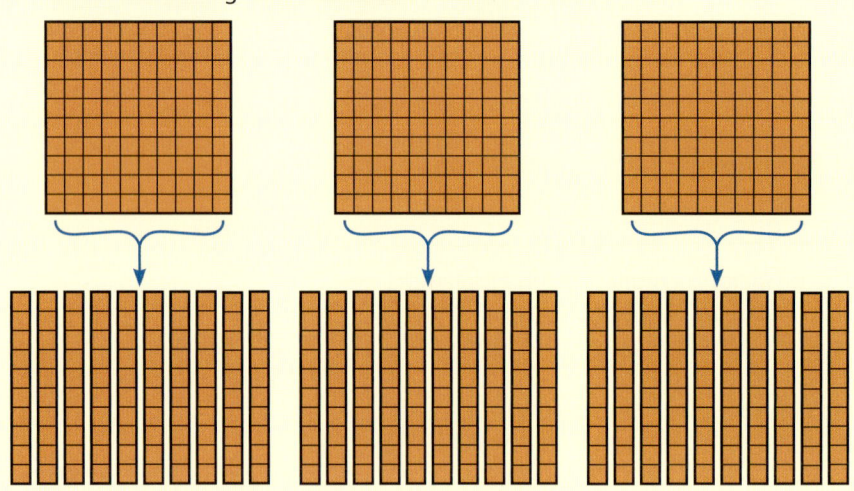

   • Divide the tenths into 10 equal groups.

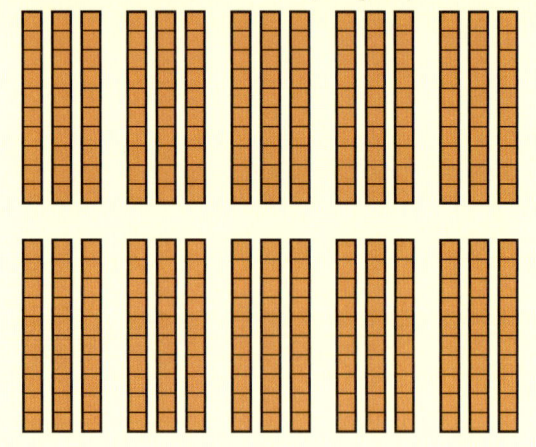

3. Discuss the final model with students.

   **Ask:** How many tenths of an entire grid are in each group? 3 tenths

   **Ask:** What is 3 ÷ 10? 3 tenths

   **Ask:** How does the model relate to the division? Three whole decimal grids represent the number you divide. Three tenths in each of 10 equal groups represents the quotient.

**270** DECIMALS: MULTIPLICATION AND DIVISION

4. Tell students they can also use a step-by-step approach, or an algorithm, to divide 3 by 10.

5. Have students read the first problem in the Worked Examples on the activity page. Explain that if students don't know how many zeros to add to the dividend, they can add one zero at a time until the division comes out evenly (or shows a pattern). Have students write 0.3 or $\frac{3}{10}$ as the answer to the problem in their Math Notebook.

6. Have students read the second problem in the Worked Examples. Guide them to follow the steps for dividing a whole number by a greater whole number, resulting in a decimal quotient in the tenths place.

7. Have students read the third problem in the Worked Examples. Guide them to follow the steps for dividing a whole number by a greater whole number, resulting in a decimal quotient in the hundredths place.

8. Have them complete the activity page problems in their Math Notbook, using a step-by-step approach.

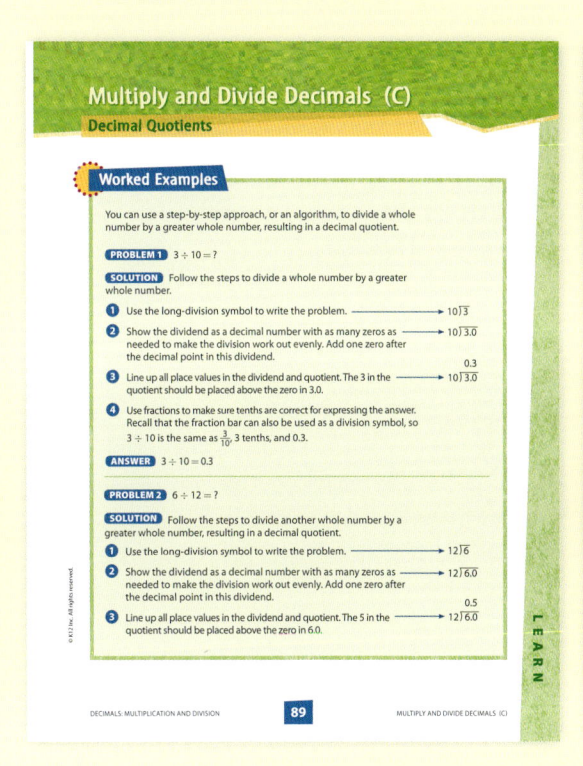

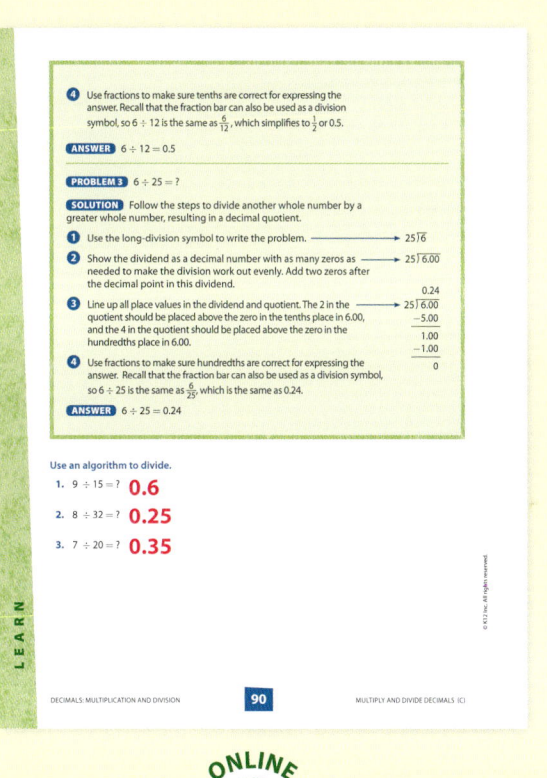

## LEARN Divide and Check

**ONLINE 15 min**

Students will divide decimals and verify the reasonableness of the answers. They will see how to compare the exact answer to the estimate to decide if it is reasonable. They will also use multiplication to check their division.

### Objectives

- Solve a multiplication or division problem that involves decimal numbers.
- Verify that the calculated result of a problem involving multiplication or division of decimal numbers is reasonable.

MULTIPLY AND DIVIDE DECIMALS (C) **271**

## TRY IT Practice Multiplying and Dividing

**OFFLINE 20 min**

Students will practice multiplying and dividing decimal numbers. Have students turn to the Practice Multiplying and Dividing activity page in their Activity Book and read the directions with them.

Students should copy the problems from the Activity Book into their Math Notebook as necessary and solve them there.

**Tips** Have students choose two problems and explain how they found the answers. Ask students to also explain how they know the exact answers are reasonable compared to the estimated answers.

### Objectives
- Solve a multiplication or division problem that involves decimal numbers.
- Verify that the calculated result of a problem involving multiplication or division of decimal numbers is reasonable.

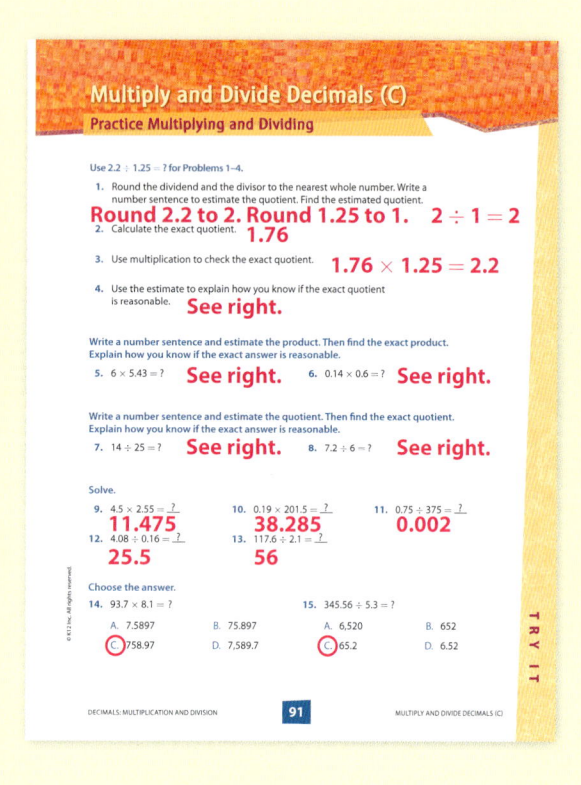

### Additional Answers

4. The exact quotient, 1.76, rounded to the nearest whole number is 2, which is the same as the estimated answer. So the exact answer, 1.76, is reasonable.

5. Answers will vary. **Estimate:** 30, rounding to the nearest whole number; **Exact:** 32.58
   The exact answer, 32.58, rounded to the nearest ten is 30, which is the same as the estimated answer. So the exact answer is reasonable.

6. Answers will vary. **Estimate:** 0.06, using friendly numbers 0.1 and 0.6; **Exact:** 0.084
   The exact answer, 0.084, and the estimated answer, 0.06, can both be rounded to the friendly number 0.075. So the exact answer is reasonable.

7. Answers will vary. **Estimate:** 0.6, using friendly numbers 15 and 25; **Exact:** 0.56
   The exact answer, 0.56, rounded to the nearest tenth is 0.6, which is the same as the estimated answer. So the exact answer is reasonable.

8. Answers will vary. **Estimate:** 1.25, using friendly numbers 7.5 and 6; **Exact:** 1.2
   The exact answer, 1.2, can be rounded to the friendly number 1.25, which is the same as the estimated answer. So the exact answer is reasonable.

## CHECKPOINT

**ONLINE 10 min**

Students will complete an online Checkpoint. If necessary, read the directions, problems, and answer choices to students and help them with keyboard or mouse operations.

### Objectives
- Solve a multiplication or division problem that involves decimal numbers.
- Verify that the calculated result of a problem involving multiplication or division of decimal numbers is reasonable.

272 DECIMALS: MULTIPLICATION AND DIVISION

# Compute Decimal Story Problems (A)

## Lesson Overview

| | | |
|---|---|---|
| **GET READY** Multiply Decimals | 5 minutes | **ONLINE** |
| **LEARN** Multiply Decimals in Story Problems | 20 minutes | **ONLINE** |
| **LEARN** Bicycle Race Decimal Story Problems | 20 minutes | **OFFLINE** |
| **TRY IT** Multiply Decimals to Solve Problems | 15 minutes | **ONLINE** |

### ▶ Lesson Objectives
Solve a story problem that involves multiplication or division of decimal numbers.

### ▶ Prerequisite Skills
Solve a multiplication or division problem that involves decimal numbers.

### ▶ Content Background
Students will calculate the answers to multiplication story problems involving decimal numbers and whole numbers.

When students write and compute with decimal numbers, they often use numbers that are between 0 and 1—for example, 0.1. While it is acceptable to write this number as .1, mathematicians usually write the leading zero, to show that the whole-number value for the decimal number is zero and to avoid confusion about the value of the number.

**Materials to Gather**

**SUPPLIED**
Bicycle Race Decimal Story Problems activity page

## GET READY  Multiply Decimals
*ONLINE 5 min*

Students will multiply decimal numbers and whole numbers to find products.

**Objectives**
- Solve a multiplication or division problem that involves decimal numbers.

## LEARN  Multiply Decimals in Story Problems
*ONLINE 20 min*

In this activity, students will multiply decimal numbers and whole numbers to solve story problems about bicycle races.

**Objectives**
- Solve a story problem that involves multiplication or division of decimal numbers.

## LEARN Bicycle Race Decimal Story Problems

**OFFLINE 20 min**

### Objectives
- Solve a story problem that involves multiplication or division of decimal numbers.

Students will set up and then solve multiplication problems with decimal numbers and whole numbers as factors.

Have students turn to the Bicycle Race Decimal Story Problems activity page in their Activity Book and read the directions with them. Students should copy the problems from the Activity Book into their Math Notebook as necessary and solve them there.

1. Have students read the problems in the Worked Examples.
2. Tell students that they will find exact products.
3. Note that some problems require students to multiply decimal numbers by whole numbers, and other problems require students to multiply decimal numbers by decimal numbers.
4. Make sure students understand where the place the decimal when they multiply a decimal number by a decimal number.
5. **Ask:** In Problem 2 of the problem set, what are the two factors? 134.4 and 0.62

   **Ask:** What decimal place will the answer be in? thousandths

   **Ask:** How do you know it will be in the thousandths place? 10 times 100 is 1,000, so tenths multiplied by hundredths will give an answer in the thousandths.

   Have students use a step-by-step process to solve.

$$\begin{array}{r} \overset{2\ 2\ 2}{134.4} \\ \times\ 0.62 \\ \hline 2688 \\ +\ 80640 \\ \hline 83.328 \end{array}$$

6. Have students solve Problem 1 and Problems 3–10 on their own.

### Tips
Encourage students to estimate the product before they find the exact answer. The estimate will help them determine if their exact answer is reasonable.

## Compute Decimal Story Problems (A)
### Bicycle Race Decimal Story Problems

**Worked Examples**

You can write a number sentence with decimal numbers and solve it to find the answer to the following story problem.
- A book about bicycle racing costs $12.95. What is the cost of 4 books?

**PROBLEM 1** Write a number sentence that you can use to solve the story problem.

**SOLUTION**
1. Read the problem.
2. Decide what question needs to be answered. For this problem, you need to find the cost of 4 books that cost $12.95 each.
3. Decide what operation to use. For this problem, you need to use multiplication to find what $12.95 per book for 4 books equals.
4. Write a number sentence that finds the product of the factors 12.95 and 4.

**ANSWER** $12.95 \times 4 = ?$

**PROBLEM 2** Solve the number sentence you wrote for Problem 1. Answer the question in a complete sentence.

**SOLUTION**
1. Write the number sentence that solves the problem. → $12.95 \times 4 = ?$
2. Write the problem vertically. Use a step-by-step process to solve the problem.
   $\quad 12.95$
   $\times \quad 4$
3. Multiply. You are multiplying hundredths by a whole number, so the answer is in hundredths.
   $\quad\; 1\,3\,2$
   $\quad 12.95$
   $\times \quad\;\; 4$
   $\overline{\quad 51.80}$

**ANSWER** The cost of 4 books on bicycle racing is $51.80.

---

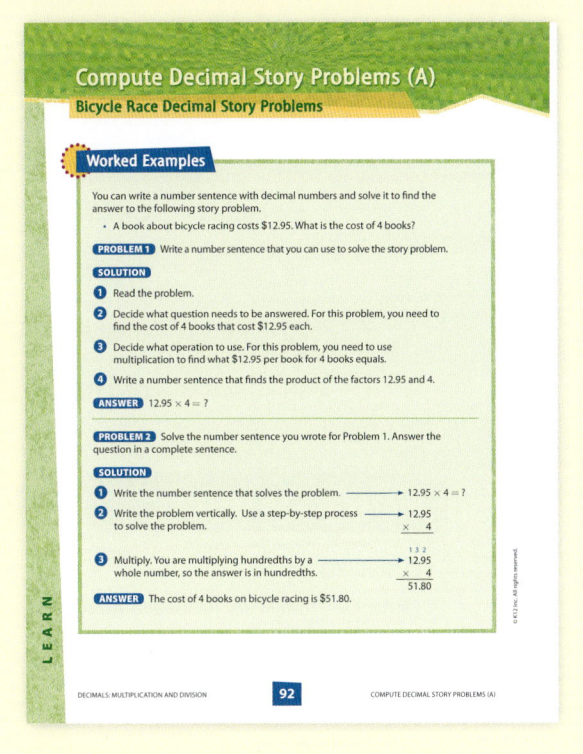

Write a multiplication number sentence. Solve. Answer the question in a complete sentence.

1. The Tour with Us bicycle race takes place over 3 days. If cyclists ride 23.76 kilometers a day, how many kilometers long is the race?
   **$23.76 \times 3 = 71.28$; The race is 71.28 km long.**
2. One kilometer is equal to 0.62 of a mile. If a race is 134.4 kilometers, how many miles is it equivalent to?
   **See below.**
3. Along the race route, vendors sell T-shirts for $11.55. How much will it cost to buy 8 T-shirts? **$11.55 \times 8 = 92.40$**
   **The 8 T-shirts will cost $92.40.**
4. Vendors also have sun visors for $5.15. How much will it cost to buy 20 sun visors? **$5.15 \times 20 = 103$**
   **The 20 visors will cost $103.**
5. On average, a cyclist can bike 24 kilometers in an hour. How many kilometers will he bike in 8.6 hours? **$24 \times 8.6 = 206.4$**
   **A cyclist will bike 206.4 km in 8.6 hours.**
6. The average weight of a bicycle is 27.8 pounds. What is the combined weight of 11 bicycles? **See below.**
7. The Race with Me bicycle race takes place over 8 days. If cyclists ride 45.85 kilometers a day, how many kilometers long is the race? **See below.**
8. One meter is equal to 3.28 feet. If a time trial is 19.6 meters long, how many feet is it equivalent to? **See below.**
9. At the end of the race, vendors sell T-shirts with the winner's name on them. If each T-shirts costs $16.30, how much will 6 T-shirts cost? **See below.**
10. The leader of the race is averaging 28.3 kilometers an hour. If she rides at the same speed for the entire time, how many kilometers will she bike in 5.7 hours? **See below.**

### Additional Answers

2. $134.4 \times 0.62 = 83.328$
   134.4 kilometers is equivalent to 83.328 miles.
6. $27.8 \times 11 = 305.8$
   The combined weight of 11 bicycles is 305.8 pounds.
7. $45.85 \times 8 = 366.8$
   Cyclists ride 366.8 km during the 8 days of the Race with Me race.
8. $3.28 \times 19.6 = 64.288$
   A time trial that is 19.6 meters long is equivalent to 64.288 feet.
9. $16.30 \times 6 = 97.80$
   The 6 T-shirts will cost $97.80.
10. $28.3 \times 5.7 = 161.31$
    The rider will ride 161.31 kilometers in 5.7 hours.

### TRY IT Multiply Decimals to Solve Problems

ONLINE 15 min

### Objectives

Students will complete an online Try It. If necessary, read the directions, problems, and answer choices to students and help them with keyboard or mouse operations.

- Solve a story problem that involves multiplication or division of decimal numbers.

# Compute Decimal Story Problems (B)

## Lesson Overview

| | | |
|---|---|---|
| **GET READY** Divide Decimals | 5 minutes | **ONLINE** |
| **LEARN** Divide Decimals in Story Problems | 20 minutes | **ONLINE** |
| **LEARN** Picnic Decimal Story Problems | 20 minutes | **OFFLINE** |
| **TRY IT** Divide Decimals to Solve Story Problems | 15 minutes | **ONLINE** |

### ▶ Lesson Objectives
Solve a story problem that involves multiplication or division of decimal numbers.

### ▶ Prerequisite Skills
Solve a multiplication or division problem that involves decimal numbers.

### ▶ Content Background
Students will calculate the answers to division story problems involving decimal numbers and whole numbers.

When students write and compute with decimal numbers, they often use numbers that are between 0 and 1—for example, 0.1. While it is acceptable to write this number as .1, mathematicians usually write the leading zero, to show that the whole-number value for the decimal number is zero and to avoid confusion about the value of the number.

### Materials to Gather
**SUPPLIED**
Picnic Decimal Story Problems activity page

---

## GET READY  Divide Decimals  ONLINE 5 min

Students will divide decimal numbers and whole numbers to find quotients.

**Tips** Allow students to use multiplication as another way to verify the reasonableness of their answers.

### Objectives
- Solve a multiplication or division problem that involves decimal numbers.

---

## LEARN  Divide Decimals in Story Problems  ONLINE 20 min

Students will divide decimal numbers by decimal numbers and decimal numbers by whole numbers to solve story problems about a picnic.

### Objectives
- Solve a story problem that involves multiplication or division of decimal numbers.

276  DECIMALS: MULTIPLICATION AND DIVISION

## LEARN Picnic Decimal Story Problems

**OFFLINE 20 min**

### Objectives
- Solve a story problem that involves multiplication or division of decimal numbers.

### Tips
Encourage students to estimate the quotient before they find the exact quotient. The estimate will help them verify the reasonableness of their exact answer.

Students will set up and then solve division problems in which decimal numbers are divided by whole numbers and decimal numbers.

Have students turn to the Picnic Decimal Story Problems activity page in their Activity Book and read the directions with them. Students should copy the problems from the Activity Book into their Math Notebook as necessary and solve them there.

1. Have students read the problems in the Worked Examples.
2. Tell students that they will find exact quotients.
3. Note that some problems require students to divide decimal numbers by whole numbers, and other problems require students to divide decimal numbers by decimal numbers.
4. In Problem 2 of the problem set, remind students that when they divide a decimal number by another decimal number, the divisor needs to be changed to a whole number.
5. Guide students to multiply both the dividend and the divisor by the same number. Remind them that they are actually multiplying a fraction (the dividend over the divisor) by a fraction that is the equivalent of 1.
6. **Ask:** What will you multiply 36.5 by to make it into a whole number? **10**

   **Ask:** What will you then multiply 54.75 by? **10**

   **Ask:** What will the division problem be after you multiply the divisor and dividend by 10? **547.5 divided by 365 or $\frac{547.5}{365}$**

   Have students use a step-by-step process to solve.

   $$36.5 \overline{)54.75} = 365 \overline{)547.5}$$

   ```
              1.5
       365 ) 547.5
           - 365.0
             -----
             182.5
           - 182.5
             -----
                 0
   ```

7. Have students solve Problem 1 and Problems 3–10 on their own.

**COMPUTE DECIMAL STORY PROBLEMS (B)** 277

## Compute Decimal Story Problems (B)
### Picnic Decimal Story Problems

**Worked Examples**

You can write a number sentence with decimal numbers and solve it to find the answer to the following story problem.
- Children at a picnic sang the same song 4 times in a row. They sang for a total of 10.4 minutes. If singing the song takes the same number of minutes each time, how many minutes does it take to sing the song?

**PROBLEM 1** Write a number sentence that you can use to solve the story problem.

**SOLUTION**
1. Read the problem.
2. Decide what question needs to be answered. For this problem, you need to find the number of minutes children would spend if they sang the song one time.
3. Decide what operation to use. For this problem, you need to use division to find the quotient of 10.4 minutes divided by 4 times.
4. Write a number sentence that finds the quotient of the dividend 10.4 and the divisor 4.

**ANSWER** 10.4 ÷ 4 = ?

**PROBLEM 2** Solve the number sentence you wrote for Problem 1. Answer the question in a complete sentence.

**SOLUTION**
1. Write the number sentence that solves the problem. → 10.4 ÷ 4 = ?
2. Use the long-division symbol to write the problem. → 4)10.4
   Use a step-by-step process to solve the problem.

---

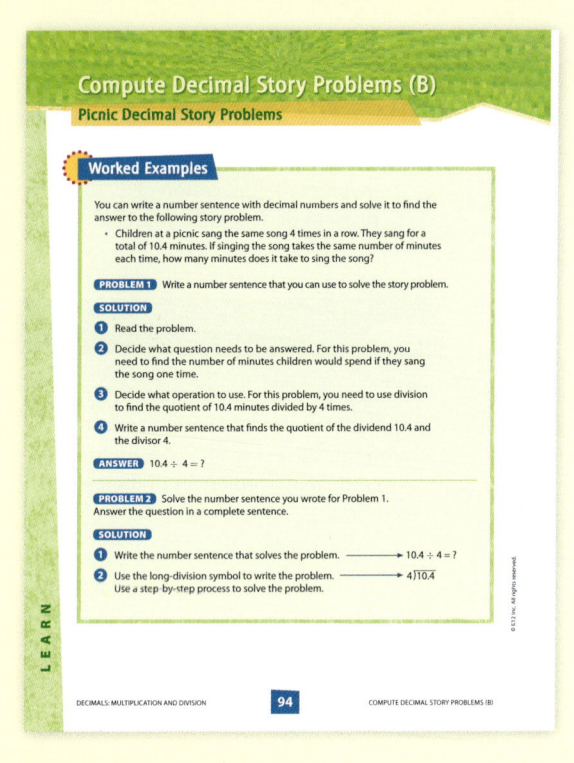

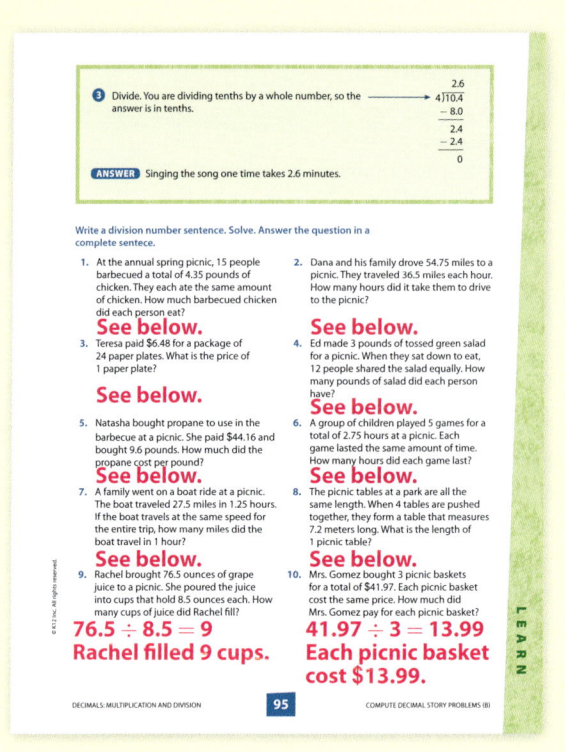

3. Divide. You are dividing tenths by a whole number, so the answer is in tenths.

```
      2.6
   4)10.4
    - 8.0
      2.4
    - 2.4
        0
```

**ANSWER** Singing the song one time takes 2.6 minutes.

Write a division number sentence. Solve. Answer the question in a complete sentence.

1. At the annual spring picnic, 15 people barbecued a total of 4.35 pounds of chicken. They each ate the same amount of chicken. How much barbecued chicken did each person eat?
   **See below.**

2. Dana and his family drove 54.75 miles to a picnic. They traveled 36.5 miles each hour. How many hours did it take them to drive to the picnic?
   **See below.**

3. Teresa paid $6.48 for a package of 24 paper plates. What is the price of 1 paper plate?
   **See below.**

4. Ed made 3 pounds of tossed green salad for a picnic. When they sat down to eat, 12 people shared the salad equally. How many pounds of salad did each person have?
   **See below.**

5. Natasha bought propane to use in the barbecue at a picnic. She paid $44.16 and bought 9.6 pounds. How much did the propane cost per pound?
   **See below.**

6. A group of children played 5 games for a total of 2.75 hours at a picnic. Each game lasted the same amount of time. How many hours did each game last?
   **See below.**

7. A family went on a boat ride at a picnic. The boat traveled 27.5 miles in 1.25 hours. If the boat travels at the same speed for the entire trip, how many miles did the boat travel in 1 hour?
   **See below.**

8. The picnic tables at a park are all the same length. When 4 tables are pushed together, they form a table that measures 7.2 meters long. What is the length of 1 picnic table?
   **See below.**

9. Rachel brought 76.5 ounces of grape juice to a picnic. She poured the juice into cups that hold 8.5 ounces each. How many cups of juice did Rachel fill?
   **76.5 ÷ 8.5 = 9**
   **Rachel filled 9 cups.**

10. Mrs. Gomez bought 3 picnic baskets for a total of $41.97. Each picnic basket cost the same price. How much did Mrs. Gomez pay for each picnic basket?
    **41.97 ÷ 3 = 13.99**
    **Each picnic basket cost $13.99.**

### Additional Answers

1. 4.35 ÷ 15 = 0.29
   Each person ate 0.29 pounds of chicken.

2. 54.75 ÷ 36.5 = 1.5
   It took 1.5 hours to drive to the picnic.

3. 6.48 ÷ 24 = 0.27
   Each plate costs $0.27.

4. 3 ÷ 12 = 0.25
   Each person had 0.25 pounds of salad.

5. 44.16 ÷ 9.6 = 4.6
   The propane cost $4.60 per pound.

6. 2.75 ÷ 5 = 0.55
   Each game lasted 0.55 of an hour.

7. 27.5 ÷ 1.25 = 22
   The boat traveled 22 miles in 1 hour.

8. 7.2 ÷ 4 = 1.8
   Each table is 1.8 meters long.

---

## TRY IT  Divide Decimals to Solve Story Problems

**ONLINE 15 min**

Students will complete an online Try It. If necessary, read the directions, problems, and answer choices to students and help them with keyboard or mouse operations.

### Objectives
- Solve a story problem that involves multiplication or division of decimal numbers.

# Compute Decimal Story Problems (C)

## Lesson Overview

| | | |
|---|---|---|
| **LEARN** Hidden Picture Story Problems | 15 minutes | ONLINE |
| **LEARN** Camping Trip Story Problems | 15 minutes | ONLINE |
| **LEARN** More Camping Trip Story Problems | 15 minutes | OFFLINE |
| **TRY IT** Multiply and Divide Decimals | 5 minutes | ONLINE |
| **CHECKPOINT** | 10 minutes | ONLINE |

### ▶ Lesson Objectives
Solve a story problem that involves multiplication or division of decimal numbers.

### ▶ Prerequisite Skills
Solve a multiplication or division problem that involves decimal numbers.

### ▶ Content Background
Students will calculate the answers to multiplication and division story problems involving decimal numbers and whole numbers.

When students write and compute with decimal numbers, they often use numbers that are between 0 and 1—for example, 0.1. While it is acceptable to write this number as .1, mathematicians usually write the leading zero, to show that the whole-number value for the decimal number is zero and to avoid confusion about the value of the number.

**Materials to Gather**

SUPPLIED
More Camping Trip Story Problems activity page

## LEARN Hidden Picture Story Problems — ONLINE 15 min

Students will solve story problems involving multiplication and division of decimal numbers to unveil a hidden picture.

**Objectives**
- Solve a story problem that involves multiplication or division of decimal numbers.

## LEARN Camping Trip Story Problems — ONLINE 15 min

Students will multiply and divide using decimal numbers. They will solve story problems about activities people do on camping trips.

**Objectives**
- Solve a story problem that involves multiplication or division of decimal numbers.

COMPUTE DECIMAL STORY PROBLEMS (C) **279**

## LEARN More Camping Trip Story Problems

**OFFLINE 15 min**

### Objectives
- Solve a story problem that involves multiplication or division of decimal numbers.

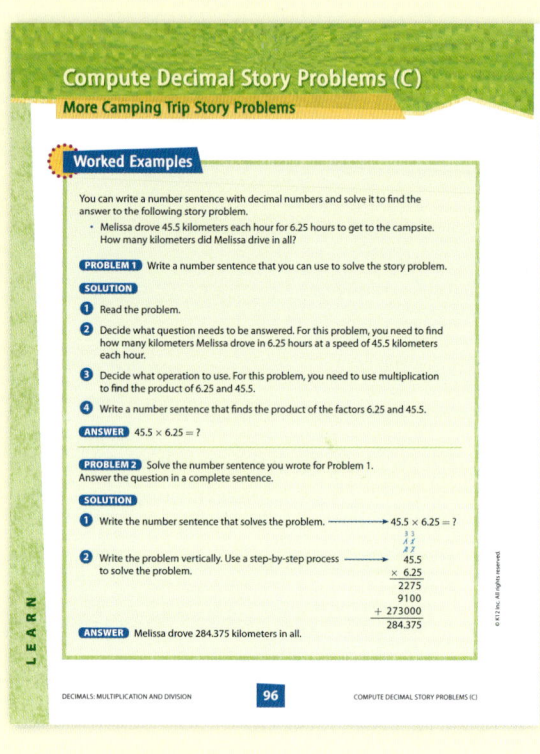

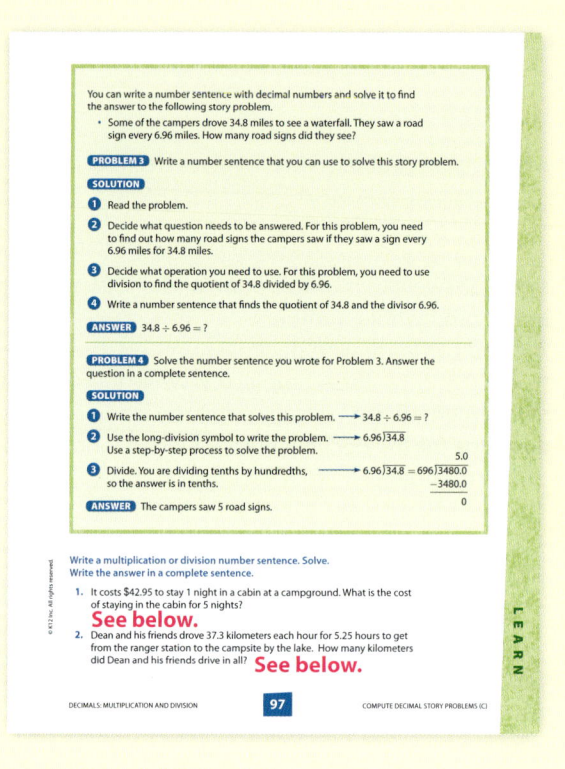

Students will set up and then solve multiplication problems and division problems involving decimal numbers and whole numbers.

Have students turn to the More Camping Trip Story Problems activity page in their Activity Book and read the directions with them. Students should copy the problems from the Activity Book into their Math Notebook as necessary and solve them there.

1. Have students read the Worked Examples.
2. Tell students they will find the exact products and quotients.
3. Note that some problems require students to multiply and divide decimal numbers by whole numbers, and other problems require students to multiply and divide decimal numbers by decimal numbers.

**Additional Answers**
1. $42.95 \times 5 = 214.75$; It costs $214.75 to stay 5 nights in the cabin.
2. $37.3 \times 5.25 = 195.825$; Dean and his friends drove 195.825 kilometers in all.

**280** DECIMALS: MULTIPLICATION AND DIVISION

3. The distance from the campsite to the lake is 0.6 of the distance from the campsite to the hiking trails. The distance from the campsite to the hiking trails is 1.4 kilometers. What is the distance from the campsite to the lake?
**See below.**

4. Ryan brought 6 bags of marshmallows to roast over a campfire. Each bag weighs 0.625 pound. How many pounds do the bags of marshmallows weigh in all? **See below.**

5. Rick and his family spent 1.25 hours setting up their tent. They spent 1.04 as much time unpacking their camping supplies. How much time did Rick and his family spend unpacking their camping supplies? **See below.**

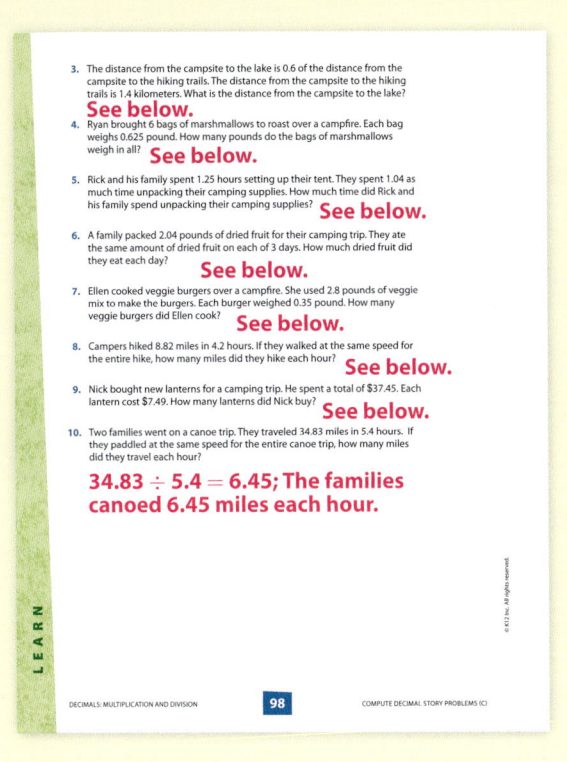

6. A family packed 2.04 pounds of dried fruit for their camping trip. They ate the same amount of dried fruit on each of 3 days. How much dried fruit did they eat each day? **See below.**

7. Ellen cooked veggie burgers over a campfire. She used 2.8 pounds of veggie mix to make the burgers. Each burger weighed 0.35 pound. How many veggie burgers did Ellen cook? **See below.**

8. Campers hiked 8.82 miles in 4.2 hours. If they walked at the same speed for the entire hike, how many miles did they hike each hour? **See below.**

9. Nick bought new lanterns for a camping trip. He spent a total of $37.45. Each lantern cost $7.49. How many lanterns did Nick buy? **See below.**

10. Two families went on a canoe trip. They traveled 34.83 miles in 5.4 hours. If they paddled at the same speed for the entire canoe trip, how many miles did they travel each hour?
**34.83 ÷ 5.4 = 6.45; The families canoed 6.45 miles each hour.**

## Additional Answers

3. 0.6 × 1.4 = 0.84; The distance from the campsite to the lake is 0.84 kilometers.
4. 6 × 0.625 = 3.75; The 6 bags of marshmallows weigh 3.75 pounds in all.
5. 1.25 × 1.04 = 1.3; Rick and his family spent 1.3 hours unpacking their camping supplies.
6. 2.04 ÷ 3 = 0.68; The family ate 0.68 pound of dried fruit each day.
7. 2.8 ÷ 0.35 = 8; Ellen cooked 8 veggie burgers.
8. 8.82 ÷ 4.2 = 2.1; The campers hiked 2.1 miles each hour.
9. 37.45 ÷ 7.49 = 5; Nick bought 5 lanterns.

### TRY IT  Multiply and Divide Decimals

**ONLINE 5 min**

Students will complete an online Try It. If necessary, read the directions, problems, and answer choices to students and help them with keyboard or mouse operations.

**Objectives**
- Solve a story problem that involves multiplication or division of decimal numbers.

### CHECKPOINT

**ONLINE 10 min**

Students will complete an online Checkpoint. If necessary, read the directions, problems, and answer choices to students and help them with keyboard or mouse operations.

**Objectives**
- Solve a story problem that involves multiplication or division of decimal numbers.

# Unit Review

## Lesson Overview

| | | |
|---|---|---|
| **UNIT REVIEW** Look Back | 10 minutes | **ONLINE** |
| **UNIT REVIEW** Checkpoint Practice | 50 minutes | **ONLINE** |
| ▶ **UNIT REVIEW** Prepare for the Checkpoint | | |

## ▶ Unit Objectives

This lesson reviews the following objectives:

- Estimate the product or quotient of a computation problem involving decimal numbers.
- Solve a multiplication or division problem that involves decimal numbers.
- Verify that the calculated result of a problem involving multiplication or division of decimal numbers is reasonable.
- Solve a story problem that involves multiplication or division of decimal numbers.

### Materials to Gather

There are no materials to gather for this lesson.

## ▶ Advance Preparation

In this lesson, students will have an opportunity to review previous activities in the Decimals: Multiplication and Division unit. Look at the suggested activities in Unit Review: Prepare for the Checkpoint online and gather any needed materials.

### UNIT REVIEW  Look Back   *ONLINE 10 min*

**Objectives**
- Review unit objectives.

Students will review key concepts from the unit to prepare for the Unit Checkpoint.

### UNIT REVIEW  Checkpoint Practice   *ONLINE 50 min*

**Objectives**
- Review unit objectives.

Students will complete an online Checkpoint Practice to prepare for the Unit Checkpoint. If necessary, read the directions, problems, and answer choices to students. Have students answer the problems on their own. Review any missed problems with students.

### ▶ UNIT REVIEW  Prepare for the Checkpoint

What you do next depends on how students performed in the previous activity, Unit Review: Checkpoint Practice. If students had difficulty with any of the problems, complete the appropriate review activity listed in the table online.

# Unit Checkpoint

## Lesson Overview

**UNIT CHECKPOINT** Online | 60 minutes | **ONLINE**

### ▶ Unit Objectives

This lesson assesses the following objectives:
- Estimate the product or quotient of a computation problem involving decimal numbers.
- Solve a multiplication or division problem that involves decimal numbers.
- Verify that the calculated result of a problem involving multiplication or division of decimal numbers is reasonable.
- Solve a story problem that involves multiplication or division of decimal numbers.

### Materials to Gather

There are no materials to gather for this lesson.

## UNIT CHECKPOINT  Online

ONLINE 60 min

### Objectives
- Assess unit objectives.

Students will complete the Unit Checkpoint online. If necessary, read the directions, problems, and answer choices to students and help them with keyboard or mouse operations.

# Integers

## ▶ Unit Objectives

- Identify and represent decimal numbers, fractions, mixed numbers, and positive and negative integers on a number line.
- Solve a problem involving addition or subtraction of integers.
- Verify that the calculated result of a problem involving addition or subtraction of integers is reasonable.

## ▶ Big Ideas

Any integer or rational number can be plotted on a number line.

## ▶ Unit Introduction

In this unit, students will be introduced to integers, which is the set of whole numbers, such as 1, 2, 3, and so on, and their opposites, ⁻1, ⁻2, ⁻3, and so on. The number 0 is also considered an integer. Activities in this unit focus on relating integers to decimal numbers, fractions, and mixed numbers. These numbers will be identified and compared by the use of a number line. Other activities will engage students using addition and subtraction to solve computation and story problems with integers. While solving problems, students will check that their answers are reasonable.

## ▶ Keywords

absolute value
integer

negative sign
opposites

positive sign

# Explore Rational Numbers (A)

## Lesson Overview

| | | |
|---|---|---|
| **GET READY** Compare Fractions and Decimals | 5 minutes | **ONLINE** |
| **LEARN** Identify Opposites | 15 minutes | **ONLINE** |
| **LEARN** Find Absolute Value | 10 minutes | **ONLINE** |
| **LEARN** Compare Integers | 10 minutes | **ONLINE** |
| **TRY IT** Number Lines and Opposite Integers | 20 minutes | **OFFLINE** |

### ▶ Lesson Objectives
Identify and represent decimal numbers, fractions, mixed numbers, and positive and negative integers on a number line.

### ▶ Prerequisite Skills
Identify relative positions of rational numbers on a number line.

### ▶ Content Background
Students will be introduced to integers. They will use number lines to identify opposites, find the absolute value of integers, and compare integers.

*Natural numbers* are also called counting numbers. Natural numbers are 1, 2, 3, 4, and so on.

*Whole numbers* are zero and the natural numbers. Whole numbers are 0, 1, 2, 3, 4, and so on.

An *integer* is the set of whole numbers and the opposites of the whole numbers. Integers are…$^-4, ^-3, ^-2, ^-1, 0, ^+1, ^+2, ^+3, ^+4,$…and so on. When working with integers, be sure to say "negative 5" instead of "minus 5," which would mean to subtract 5. In the same way, say "positive 5" instead of "plus 5," which would mean to add 5.

Sometimes, positive integers will be written with a raised positive sign, like this: $^+4$. Other times, positive integers will be written without a raised positive sign, like this: 4. Both $^+4$ and 4 are the same. However, when students first begin working with positive and negative integers, positive integers will have a raised positive sign so that there is no confusion.

A *rational number* is a number that can be expressed, or written, as a fraction of two integers. Some examples of rational numbers are fractions, integers, decimal numbers, whole numbers, and natural numbers.

The *absolute value* of a number is its distance from 0 on a number line. For example, the absolute value of $^+3$, written as $|^+3|$, is 3. The absolute value of $^-7$, written as $|^-7|$, is 7. The absolute value of a number is always positive, even if the number is negative.

Although students will most often see fractions written with a horizontal fraction bar in math, such as $\frac{2}{3}$ or $5\frac{5}{6}$, they will occasionally see a diagonal fraction bar, such as 2/3 or 5 5/6. They will very likely see the diagonal fraction bar in everyday experiences, but be sure they understand that using the horizontal fraction bar in their work will make problems involving fractions easier to interpret and solve.

### Materials to Gather

**SUPPLIED**

Number Lines and Opposite Integers activity page

**EXPLORE RATIONAL NUMBERS (A)** 287

## GET READY  Compare Fractions and Decimals
**ONLINE 5 min**

Students will use a number line to compare fractions, mixed numbers, and decimal numbers.

**Objectives**
- Identify relative positions of rational numbers on a number line.

## LEARN  Identify Opposites
**ONLINE 15 min**

Students will be introduced to negative numbers. They will learn about positive and negative integers. They will find the opposites of positive and negative numbers by using a number line.

**Objectives**
- Identify and represent decimal numbers, fractions, mixed numbers, and positive and negative integers on a number line.

## LEARN  Find Absolute Value
**ONLINE 10 min**

Students will learn that the absolute value of a number is its distance from 0. They will practice finding the absolute value of positive and negative numbers by using a number line.

**Objectives**
- Identify and represent decimal numbers, fractions, mixed numbers, and positive and negative integers on a number line.

**Tips**  Explain to students that the absolute value of a number is the number of units the number is from 0, not whether the number is to the left or right of 0.

## LEARN  Compare Integers
**ONLINE 10 min**

Students will practice comparing integers by using a number line.

**Objectives**
- Identify and represent decimal numbers, fractions, mixed numbers, and positive and negative integers on a number line.

## TRY IT  Number Lines and Opposite Integers
**OFFLINE 20 min**

Students will practice using a number line to identify opposite integers, find the absolute value of integers, and compare integers. Have students turn to the Number Lines and Opposite Integers activity page in their Activity Book and read the directions with them.

Students should copy the problems from the Activity Book into their Math Notebook as necessary and solve them there.

**Objectives**
- Identify and represent decimal numbers, fractions, mixed numbers, and positive and negative integers on a number line.

**Tips**  Allow students to use a blank number line, label the tick marks, and put dots on the number line for the numbers in each problem, if they wish.

**288  INTEGERS**

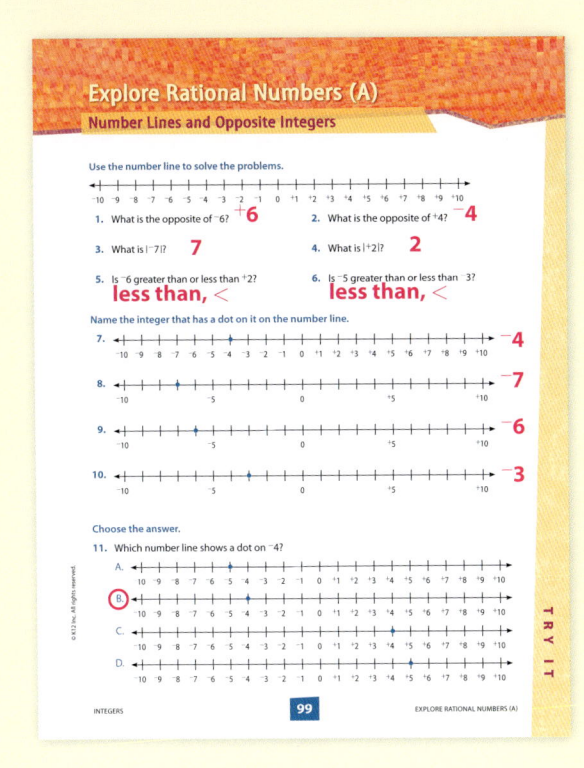

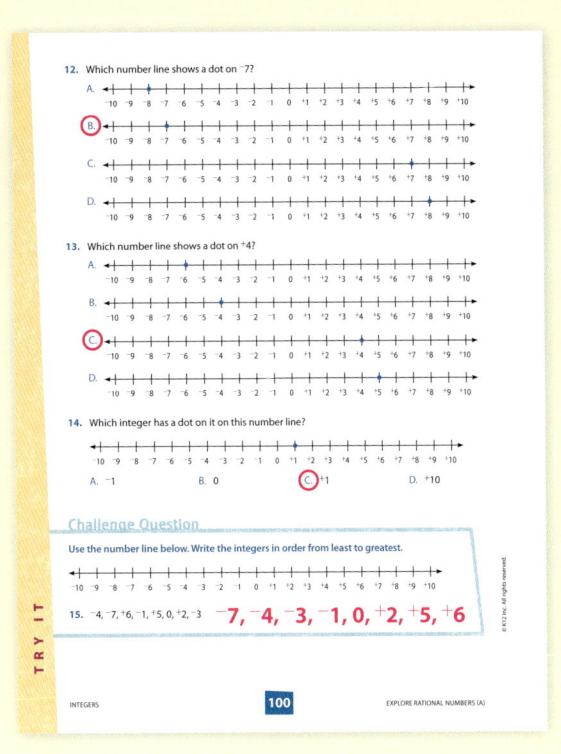

# Explore Rational Numbers (A)
## Number Lines and Opposite Integers

Use the number line to solve the problems.

1. What is the opposite of ⁻6? **⁺6**
2. What is the opposite of ⁺4? **⁻4**
3. What is |⁻7|? **7**
4. What is |⁺2|? **2**
5. Is ⁻6 greater than or less than ⁺2? **less than, <**
6. Is ⁻5 greater than or less than ⁻3? **less than, <**

Name the integer that has a dot on it on the number line.

7. **⁻4**
8. **⁺7**
9. **⁻6**
10. **⁻3**

Choose the answer.

11. Which number line shows a dot on ⁻4?
    **B**

12. Which number line shows a dot on ⁻7?
    **B**

13. Which number line shows a dot on ⁺4?
    **C**

14. Which integer has a dot on it on this number line?
    A. ⁻1  B. 0  **C. ⁺1**  D. ⁺10

### Challenge Question

Use the number line below. Write the integers in order from least to greatest.

15. ⁻4, ⁻7, ⁺6, ⁻1, ⁺5, 0, ⁺2, ⁻3    **⁻7, ⁻4, ⁻3, ⁻1, 0, ⁺2, ⁺5, ⁺6**

# Explore Rational Numbers (B)

## Lesson Overview

| | | |
|---|---|---|
| **GET READY** Numbers on a Number Line | 10 minutes | ONLINE |
| **LEARN** Opposite Fractions | 15 minutes | ONLINE |
| **LEARN** Decimals on a Number Line | 15 minutes | ONLINE |
| **TRY IT** Fractions and Decimals on a Number Line | 20 minutes | OFFLINE |

### ▶ Lesson Objectives

Identify and represent decimal numbers, fractions, mixed numbers, and positive and negative integers on a number line.

### ▶ Prerequisite Skills

Identify relative positions of rational numbers on a number line.

### ▶ Content Background

Students will continue to learn about integers. They will also learn about decimal numbers, fractions, mixed numbers, and their opposites. They will use number lines to identify opposites and compare numbers.

*Natural numbers* are also called counting numbers. Natural numbers are 1, 2, 3, 4, and so on.

*Whole numbers* are zero and the natural numbers. Whole numbers are 0, 1, 2, 3, 4, and so on.

An *integer* is the set of whole numbers and the opposites of the whole numbers. Integers are…$^-4, ^-3, ^-2, ^-1, 0, ^+1, ^+2, ^+3, ^+4,$…and so on. When working with integers, be sure to say "negative 5" instead of "minus 5," which would mean to subtract 5. In the same way, say "positive 5" instead of "plus 5," which would mean to add 5.

Sometimes, positive integers will be written with a raised positive sign, like this: $^+4$. Other times, positive integers will be written without a raised positive sign, like this: 4. Both $^+4$ and 4 are the same. However, when students first begin working with positive and negative integers, positive integers will have a raised positive sign so that there is no confusion.

A *rational number* is a number that can be expressed, or written, as a fraction of two integers. Some examples of rational numbers are fractions, integers, decimal numbers, whole numbers, and natural numbers.

The *absolute value* of a number is its distance from 0 on a number line. For example, the absolute value of $^+3$, written as $|^+3|$, is 3. The absolute value of $^-7$, written as $|^-7|$, is 7. The absolute value of a number is always positive, even if the number is negative.

Although students will most often see fractions written with a horizontal fraction bar in math, such as $\frac{2}{3}$ or $5\frac{5}{6}$, they will occasionally see a diagonal fraction bar, such as 2/3 or 5 5/6. They will very likely see the diagonal fraction bar in everyday experiences, but be sure they understand that using the horizontal fraction bar in their work will make problems involving fractions easier to interpret and solve.

### Materials to Gather

**SUPPLIED**

Fractions and Decimals on a Number Line activity page

When students write and compute with decimal numbers, they often use numbers that are between 0 and 1—for example, 0.1. While it is acceptable to write this number as .1, mathematicians usually write the leading zero, to show that the whole number value for the decimal number is zero and to avoid confusion about the value of the number.

When students write and compute with positive and negative rational numbers, they may see numbers such as $^+8$ and $^-8$, with the positive and negative signs raised slightly higher next to the number. They may also see numbers such as $+8$ and $-8$, with the positive and negative signs in line next to the number. When students use the keyboard to type positive and negative rational numbers, have them use the in-line positive or negative sign and the number, without a space between the sign and the number. For positive rational numbers, correct answers use the "+" sign and the number, or just the number. For negative rational numbers, correct answers use the "−" sign and the number.

## GET READY  Numbers on a Number Line

**ONLINE 10 min**

### Objectives
- Identify relative positions of rational numbers on a number line.

Students will use a number line to locate and compare positive fractions, mixed numbers, decimal numbers, and positive and negative integers.

**Tips** Explain to students that positive numbers are always greater than negative numbers.

## LEARN  Opposite Fractions

**ONLINE 15 min**

### Objectives
- Identify and represent decimal numbers, fractions, mixed numbers, and positive and negative integers on a number line.

Students will practice finding opposites of positive and negative fractions and mixed numbers on number lines. Integers are also shown on the number lines. Remind students that opposite numbers are the same distance from 0 on the number line, but they are on opposite sides of 0. Lead students to make the connection between opposites and the absolute value of numbers. The absolute value of a number is its distance from 0 on a number line, so opposite numbers, such as $^+1\frac{3}{4}$ and $^-1\frac{3}{4}$, have the same absolute value. Guide students to understand that the value of the fractions and mixed numbers on the number line decreases as they move to the left and increases as they move to the right.

## LEARN  Decimals on a Number Line

**ONLINE 15 min**

### Objectives
- Identify and represent decimal numbers, fractions, mixed numbers, and positive and negative integers on a number line.

Students will identify positive and negative decimal numbers using a number line. They will also find the positive or negative decimal number that is the same as a positive or negative fraction.

EXPLORE RATIONAL NUMBERS (B)  **291**

# TRY IT  Fractions and Decimals on a Number Line

**OFFLINE 20 min**

## Objectives

- Identify and represent decimal numbers, fractions, mixed numbers, and positive and negative integers on a number line.

Students will practice using a number line to identify positive and negative fractions and decimal numbers. Have students turn to the Fractions and Decimals on a Number Line activity page in their Activity Book and read the directions with them.

Students should copy the problems from the Activity Book into their Math Notebook as necessary and solve them there.

**Tips**  Allow students to copy the number lines for the first eight problems and mark dots for numbers in the problems, if they wish.

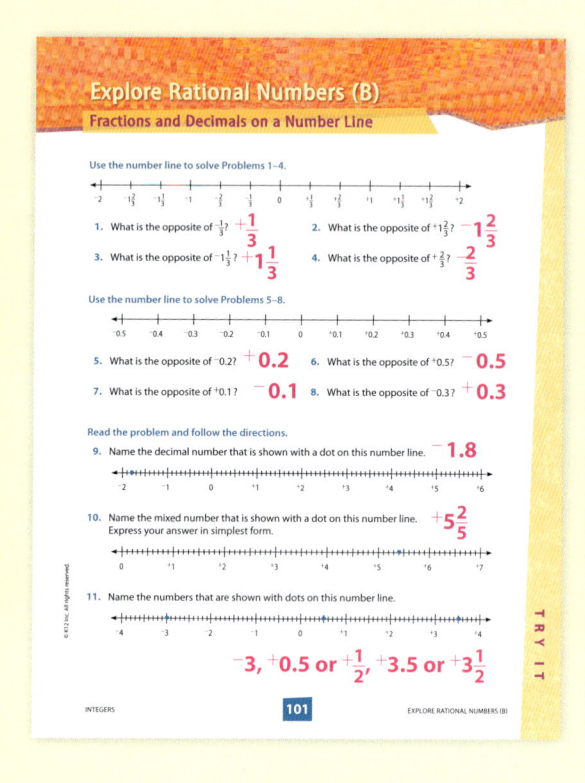

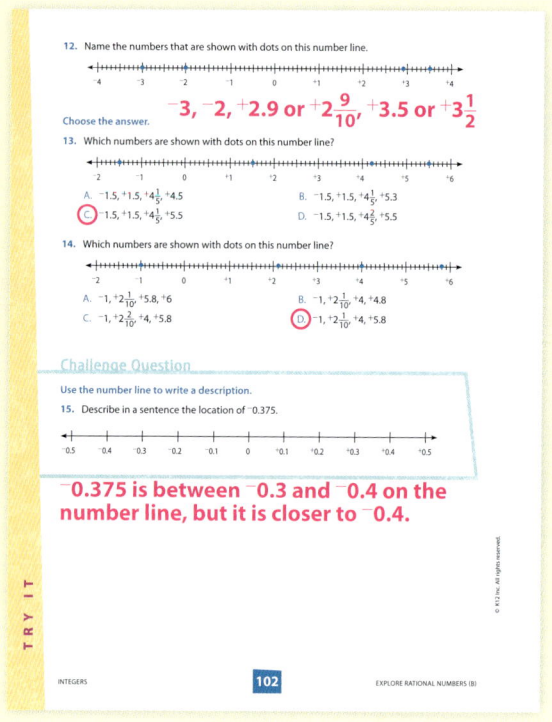

### Explore Rational Numbers (B)
**Fractions and Decimals on a Number Line**

Use the number line to solve Problems 1–4.

1. What is the opposite of $^-\frac{1}{3}$?  $^+\frac{1}{3}$
2. What is the opposite of $^+1\frac{2}{3}$?  $^-1\frac{2}{3}$
3. What is the opposite of $^-1\frac{1}{3}$?  $^+1\frac{1}{3}$
4. What is the opposite of $^+\frac{2}{3}$?  $^-\frac{2}{3}$

Use the number line to solve Problems 5–8.

5. What is the opposite of $^-0.2$?  $^+0.2$
6. What is the opposite of $^+0.5$?  $^-0.5$
7. What is the opposite of $^+0.1$?  $^-0.1$
8. What is the opposite of $^-0.3$?  $^+0.3$

Read the problem and follow the directions.

9. Name the decimal number that is shown with a dot on this number line.  $^-1.8$

10. Name the mixed number that is shown with a dot on this number line. Express your answer in simplest form.  $^+5\frac{2}{5}$

11. Name the numbers that are shown with dots on this number line.
$^-3$, $^+0.5$ or $^+\frac{1}{2}$, $^+3.5$ or $^+3\frac{1}{2}$

12. Name the numbers that are shown with dots on this number line.
$^-3$, $^-2$, $^+2.9$ or $^+2\frac{9}{10}$, $^+3.5$ or $^+3\frac{1}{2}$

**Choose the answer.**

13. Which numbers are shown with dots on this number line?
   - A. $^-1.5$, $^+1.5$, $^+4\frac{1}{5}$, $^+4.5$
   - B. $^-1.5$, $^+1.5$, $^+4\frac{1}{5}$, $^+5.3$
   - (C) $^-1.5$, $^+1.5$, $^+4\frac{1}{5}$, $^+5.5$
   - D. $^-1.5$, $^+1.5$, $^+4\frac{2}{5}$, $^+5.5$

14. Which numbers are shown with dots on this number line?
   - A. $^-1$, $^+2\frac{1}{10}$, $^+5.8$, $^+6$
   - B. $^-1$, $^+2\frac{1}{10}$, $^+4$, $^+4.8$
   - C. $^-1$, $^+2\frac{2}{10}$, $^+4$, $^+5.8$
   - (D) $^-1$, $^+2\frac{1}{10}$, $^+4$, $^+5.8$

### Challenge Question

Use the number line to write a description.

15. Describe in a sentence the location of $^-0.375$.

$^-0.375$ is between $^-0.3$ and $^-0.4$ on the number line, but it is closer to $^-0.4$.

# Explore Rational Numbers (C)

## Lesson Overview

| | | |
|---|---|---|
| **GET READY** Negative Numbers on a Number Line | 5 minutes | ONLINE |
| **LEARN** Locate Numbers on a Number Line | 10 minutes | OFFLINE |
| **LEARN** Make a Number Line | 20 minutes | OFFLINE |
| **TRY IT** Practice Locating Numbers | 15 minutes | OFFLINE |
| **CHECKPOINT** | 10 minutes | OFFLINE |

### ▶ Lesson Objectives
Identify and represent decimal numbers, fractions, mixed numbers, and positive and negative integers on a number line.

### ▶ Prerequisite Skills
Identify relative positions of rational numbers on a number line.

### ▶ Content Background
Students will make and use number lines to identify and show relationships between positive and negative integers, fractions, mixed numbers, and decimals.

An *integer* is the set of whole numbers and the opposites of the whole numbers. Integers are …$^-4$, $^-3$, $^-2$, $^-1$, 0, $^+1$, $^+2$, $^+3$, $^+4$,…and so on. When working with integers, be sure to say "negative 5" instead of "minus 5," which would mean to subtract 5. In the same way, say "positive 5" instead of "plus 5," which would mean to add 5.

Sometimes, positive integers will be written with a raised positive sign, like this: $^+4$. Other times, positive integers will be written without a raised positive sign, like this: 4. Both $^+4$ and 4 are the same. However, when students first begin working with positive and negative integers, positive integers will have a raised positive sign, so that there is no confusion.

A *rational number* is a number that can be expressed, or written, as a fraction of two integers. Some examples of rational numbers are fractions, integers, decimal numbers, whole numbers, and natural numbers.

Although students will most often see fractions written with a horizontal fraction bar in math, such as $\frac{2}{3}$ or $5\frac{5}{6}$, they will occasionally see a diagonal fraction bar, such as 2/3 or 5 5/6. They will very likely see the diagonal fraction bar in everyday experiences, but be sure they understand that using the horizontal fraction bar in their work will make problems involving fractions easier to interpret and solve.

### Materials to Gather

**SUPPLIED**
Blank Decimal Number Lines (printout)
Locate Numbers on a Number Line activity page
Practice Locating Numbers activity page
Checkpoint (printout)

**ALSO NEEDED**
ruler

EXPLORE RATIONAL NUMBERS (C)

▶ **Advance Preparation**

Print one copy of the Blank Decimal Number Lines printout. On one of the number lines, put a short tick mark halfway between each printed tick mark. Label the number line as shown. Do not write the numbers that are red. Students will label those tick marks in the Learn: Locate Numbers on a Number Line.

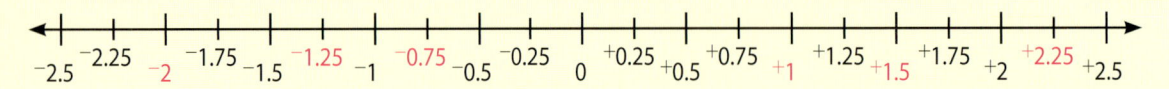

$$\longleftarrow|\underset{-2.5}{\phantom{x}}\underset{-2.25}{\phantom{x}}|\underset{-2}{\phantom{x}}\underset{-1.75}{\phantom{x}}|\underset{-1.5}{\phantom{x}}\underset{-1.25}{\phantom{x}}|\underset{-1}{\phantom{x}}\underset{-0.75}{\phantom{x}}|\underset{-0.5}{\phantom{x}}\underset{-0.25}{\phantom{x}}|\underset{0}{\phantom{x}}\underset{+0.25}{\phantom{x}}|\underset{+0.5}{\phantom{x}}\underset{+0.75}{\phantom{x}}|\underset{+1}{\phantom{x}}\underset{+1.25}{\phantom{x}}|\underset{+1.5}{\phantom{x}}\underset{+1.75}{\phantom{x}}|\underset{+2}{\phantom{x}}\underset{+2.25}{\phantom{x}}|\underset{+2.5}{\phantom{x}}\longrightarrow$$

## GET READY  Negative Numbers on a Number Line   ONLINE 5 min

Students will use a number line to compare positive and negative integers, fractions, and decimal numbers. Explain to students that positive numbers are always greater than negative numbers, whether the numbers being compared are fractions, mixed numbers, decimal numbers, or integers.

**Objectives**
- Identify relative positions of rational numbers on a number line.

## LEARN  Locate Numbers on a Number Line   OFFLINE 10 min

Students will use a number line to show relationships between positive and negative integers, fractions, mixed numbers, and decimals. Give students the labeled Blank Decimal Number Lines printout. Have students turn to the Locate Numbers on a Number Line activity page in their Activity Book and read the directions with them.

Students should copy the problems from the Activity Book into their Math Notebook as necessary and solve them there.

1. On the printout, have students label the following points: $^-2, ^-1.25, ^-0.75, ^+1, ^+1.5,$ and $^+2.25$.
2. Read the problem in the Worked Examples on the activity page with students.

    **Ask:** What is the greatest mixed number and decimal on the number line?
    $^+2\frac{1}{2}, ^+2.5$

    **Ask:** What is the least mixed number and decimal on the number line?
    $^-2\frac{1}{2}, ^-2.5$

    **Ask:** What fraction and decimal intervals is the number line divided into?
    intervals of $\frac{1}{4}$, or 0.25

3. Have students complete Problems 1–9 on their own.

**Objectives**
- Identify and represent decimal numbers, fractions, mixed numbers, and positive and negative integers on a number line.

**Tips**

Have students describe their reasoning as they locate and compare numbers on the number line.

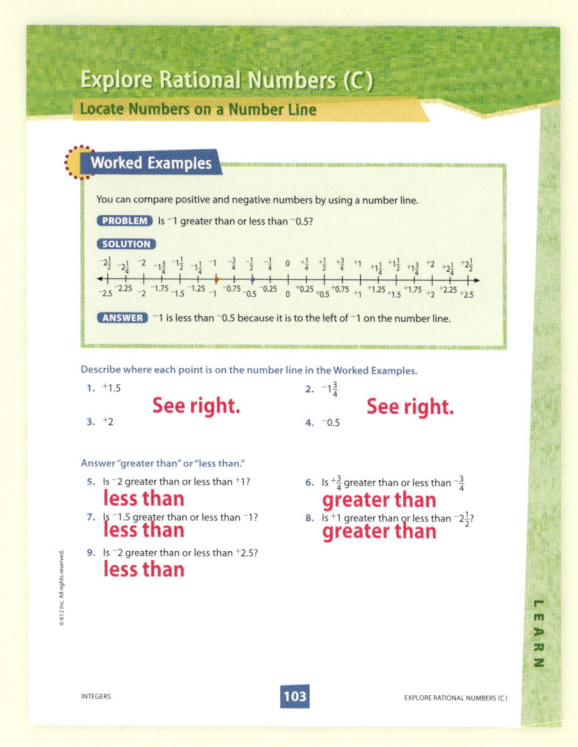

## Additional Answers

1. halfway between $^+1.25$ or $^+1\frac{1}{4}$ and $^+1.75$ or $^+1\frac{3}{4}$
2. halfway between $^-2$ and $^-1\frac{1}{2}$ or $^-1.5$
3. halfway between $^+1\frac{3}{4}$ or $^+1.75$ and $^+2\frac{1}{4}$ or $^+2.25$
4. halfway between $^-0.75$ or $^-\frac{3}{4}$ and $^-0.25$ or $^-\frac{1}{4}$

## LEARN  Make a Number Line

**OFFLINE 20 min**

### Objectives

- Identify and represent decimal numbers, fractions, mixed numbers, and positive and negative integers on a number line.

Students will make a number line and plot positive and negative integers, fractions, mixed numbers, and decimal numbers on it. Give students a ruler.

Evaluate students' work throughout the activity by ensuring that all negative numbers are to the left of 0 on the number line and all positive numbers are to the right of 0, and that student explanations are reasonable. Number lines may have a range between $^-10$ and $^+10$.

1. Tell students they will make a number line and mark dots on the number line to show the locations of positive and negative integers, fractions, mixed numbers, and decimal numbers.

2. Have students turn their Math Notebook horizontally so they can draw a long number line. Have them use a ruler to draw a number line with an arrow at each end.

3. Have students draw a tick mark and label a dot for 0 in the middle of the number line.

4. Tell students to draw 3 or 4 evenly spaced tick marks (without numbers) between 0 and the positive end of the number line. Do the same on the negative end. The purpose of the number line is to show that greater integers, decimal numbers, fractions, and mixed numbers are to the right of lesser numbers on the number line. Students don't need to draw a highly detailed number line.

5. Have students think of a positive integer. Have them use their number line to make a tick mark, write the number below the number line, and mark the positive integer with a dot.

   **Say:** Name one integer, one decimal number, and one fraction or mixed number that your integer is greater than. Answers will vary.

**EXPLORE RATIONAL NUMBERS (C)  295**

**Say:** Name one integer, one decimal number, and one fraction or mixed number that your integer is less than. Answers will vary.

6. Repeat Step 5 with a negative integer.
7. Have students think of a positive decimal number that is between the positive and negative integers they marked on their number line in Steps 5 and 6. Have them use their number line to make a tick mark, write the number below the number line, and mark the positive decimal number with a dot.

   **Say:** Name two decimal numbers that are less than the decimal number you just labeled and marked. Answers will vary.

   **Say:** Name two decimal numbers that are greater than the decimal number you just labeled and marked. Answers will vary.

8. Repeat Step 7 with a negative decimal number.
9. Have students think of a negative fraction or mixed number. Have them use their number line to make a tick mark, write the number above the number line, and mark the negative fraction or mixed number with a dot.

   **Say:** Make a tick mark, number it, and mark a dot to show the location of the opposite of the fraction or mixed number you just put on the number line.

10. Repeat Step 9 with a positive fraction or mixed number.
11. Have students make tick marks, write the numbers, and mark them with dots to show three more numbers. The numbers can be positive or negative integers, fractions, mixed numbers, or decimal numbers.
12. Have students describe the location of the three numbers using words such as *greater than*, *less than*, or *between*.
13. Use this number line as an example of what students might create:

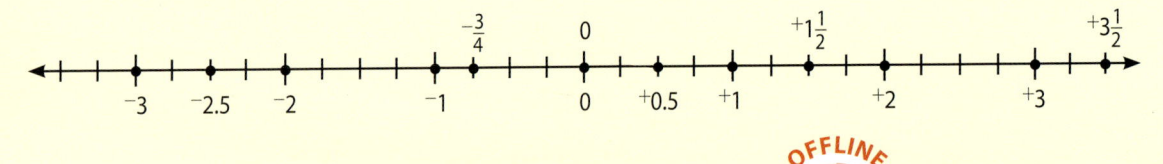

## TRY IT  Practice Locating Numbers

**OFFLINE 15 min**

### Objectives

- Identify and represent decimal numbers, fractions, mixed numbers, and positive and negative integers on a number line.

Students will practice locating positive and negative integers, fractions, mixed numbers, and decimal numbers on a number line they make. Have students turn to the Practice Locating Numbers activity page in their Activity Book and read the directions with them.

Students should copy the problems from the Activity Book into their Math Notebook as necessary and solve them there.

**INTEGERS**

## CHECKPOINT

**OFFLINE 10 min**

Have students complete the first set of items on their own. If necessary, read the directions, problems, and answer choices to students. Record students' responses to observational items on the Learning Coach Recording Sheet. Use the answer key to score the Checkpoint, and then enter the results online.

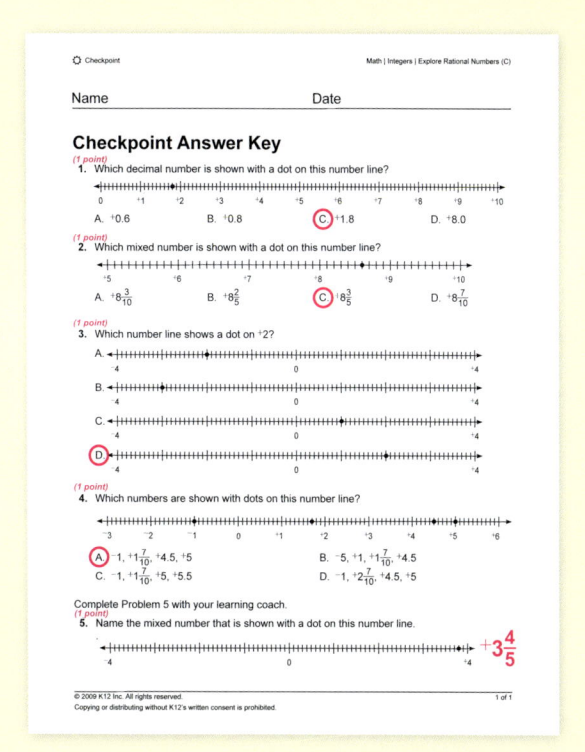

### Objectives

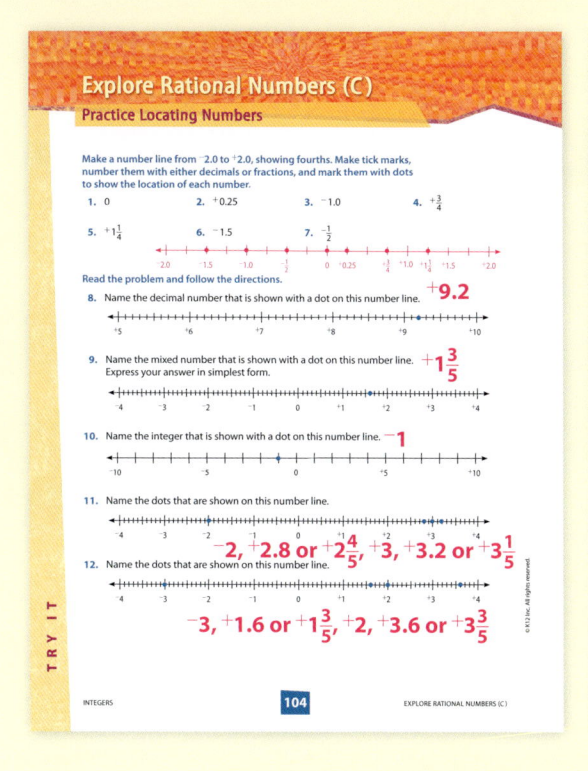

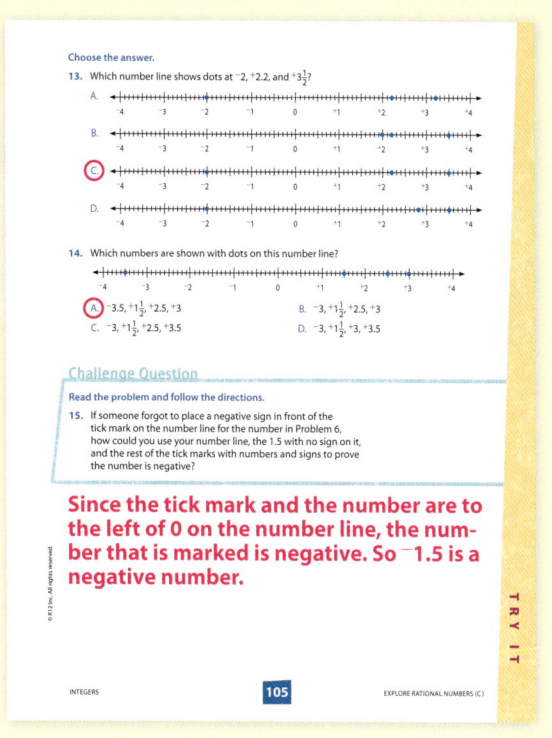

- Identify and represent decimal numbers, fractions, mixed numbers, and positive and negative integers on a number line.

**EXPLORE RATIONAL NUMBERS (C)** 297

# Add and Subtract Integers (A)

## Lesson Overview

| | | |
|---|---|---|
| **GET READY** Greater and Lesser on a Number Line | 5 minutes | **OFFLINE** |
| **LEARN** Use Tiles to Understand Integers | 20 minutes | **OFFLINE** |
| **LEARN** Add Negatives and Subtract Positives | 20 minutes | **OFFLINE** |
| **TRY IT** Practice Adding and Subtracting | 15 minutes | **OFFLINE** |

### ▶ Lesson Objectives
Solve a problem involving addition or subtraction of integers.

### ▶ Prerequisite Skills
- Identify and place negative numbers on a number line.
- Estimate or calculate a sum or a difference in a whole-number problem.
- Estimate or calculate a sum or a difference in a whole-number story problem.

### ▶ Content Background
Students will learn how to use addition and subtraction with integers to solve computation and story problems. They will add two negative integers, add two positive integers, subtract a positive from a negative, and subtract a positive from a positive.

An *integer* is any number in the set of whole numbers and the opposites of the whole numbers. Integers are …$^-4, ^-3, ^-2, ^-1, 0, ^+1, ^+2, ^+3, ^+4,$…and so on. When working with integers, be sure to say "negative 5" instead of "minus 5," which would mean to subtract 5. In the same way, say "positive 5" instead of "plus 5," which would mean to add 5.

Sometimes, positive integers will be written with a raised positive sign, like this: $^+4$. Other times, positive integers will be written without a raised positive sign, like this: 4. Both $^+4$ and 4 are the same. However, when students first begin working with positive and negative integers, positive integers will have a raised positive sign so that there is no confusion.

Although students will most often see fractions written with a horizontal fraction bar in math, such as $\frac{2}{3}$ or $5\frac{5}{6}$, they will occasionally see a diagonal fraction bar, such as 2/3 or 5 5/6. They will very likely see the diagonal fraction bar in everyday experiences, but be sure they understand that using the horizontal fraction bar in their work will make problems involving fractions easier to interpret and solve.

### ▶ Advance Preparation
- For the Get Ready activity, print a number line without labels from the Number Line Creator Tool. Label the number line as shown. Do not write the numbers that are red. Students will label those tick marks.

### Materials to Gather

**SUPPLIED**

Negative Tiles (printout)

Positive Tiles (printout)

number line from Number Line Creator Tool

Add Negatives and Subtract Positives activity page

Practice Adding and Subtracting activity page

**ALSO NEEDED**

scissors, adult

**298 INTEGERS**

$^-8\ ^-7\ ^-6\ ^-5\ ^-4\ ^-3\ ^-2\ ^-1\ 0\ ^+1\ ^+2\ ^+3\ ^+4\ ^+5\ ^+6\ ^+7\ ^+8$

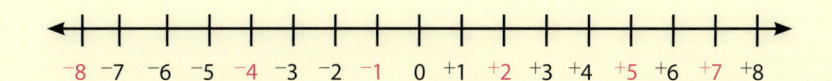

| DIRECTIONS FOR USING THE NUMBER LINE CREATOR TOOL |||
|---|---|---|
| To Create an Unlabeled Number Line from $^-8$ to $^+8$: |||
| 1. Set Range:<br>• Start Number Line at: $^-8$<br>• End Number Line at: $^+8$ | 2. Select Options:<br>• Tick Marks: ones<br>• Labels: Don't select any labels. Unclick any clicked choices. | 3. Print Number Line:<br>• Page Orientation: landscape<br>• Number Lines per Sheet: 1 |

- For the Learn activities, print one copy each of the Negative Tiles and Positive Tiles printouts. Cut out each of the tiles.

## GET READY  Greater and Lesser on a Number Line

**OFFLINE 5 min**

Students will label a number line with positive and negative integers. Then they will decide which of two integers is greater or lesser.

Gather the number line you printed from the Number Line Creator Tool and that you labeled with some tick marks.

1. Have students label $^-8$, $^-4$, $^-1$, $^+2$, $^+5$, and $^+7$ on the number line. Students should start at zero and move to the left for negative numbers. They should start at zero and move to the right for positive numbers.

2. Tell students they can use their number line to compare numbers. Discuss with them how they would know if 0 or $^-4$ is the greater number. The greater number is farther to the right on the number line; therefore, 0 is greater than $^-4$.

3. Ask students to identify the greater number in each pair. Students may use the number line to help them.
   - $^-8$ or $^-1$? $^-1$
   - $^-2$ or $^+1$? $^+1$
   - $^-5$ or $^-4$? $^-4$
   - $^-7$ or $^+6$? $^+6$

4. Discuss with students how they would know if $^-6$ or $^+2$ is the lesser number. Discussion should include that the lesser number is farther to the left on the number line; therefore, $^-6$ is less than $^+2$.

5. Ask students to identify the lesser number in each pair. Students may use the number line to help them.
   - 0 or $^+4$? 0
   - $^+1$ or $^+8$? $^+1$
   - $^-4$ or $^+3$? $^-4$
   - $^+5$ or $^-2$? $^-2$

### Objectives
- Identify and place negative numbers on a number line.

### Tips
Have students use the number line. Have them place an index finger on each integer in the pair in the question without crossing one hand over the other. Tell students that the integer they are touching with their left index finger is the lesser integer. A way to remember this is the left integer is the lesser integer.

**ADD AND SUBTRACT INTEGERS (A)**

## LEARN  Use Tiles to Understand Integers

**OFFLINE 20 min**

### Objectives
- Solve a problem involving addition or subtraction of integers.

### Tips
Save the positive and negative tiles for use throughout the lesson. Place the tiles in an envelope or resealable bag to keep them together.

Students will solve these types of computation problems:
- Add negative integers.
- Subtract a positive integer from a negative integer.
- Subtract a positive integer from a positive integer.

They will use positive and negative tiles to help them understand the values of the sums and differences.

Gather the positive and negative tiles you cut out. Students will answer problems in their Math Notebook.

1. Explain to students that there are many everyday situations when they might add and subtract integers. Discuss some examples, such as keeping score in golf, calculating temperature changes, and calculating heights above or below sea level.

2. Have students model $3 + 5$ using the positive tiles. Students should combine 3 positive tiles and 5 positive tiles. Have students write the number sentence. $3 + 5 = 8$

3. **Ask:** What if I asked you to add $^-3 + {}^-5$? How would you find that sum?

4. Tell students that they can use positive and negative tiles to model problems involving addition and subtraction of integers.

5. Have students model 3 negative tiles. Then have students model 5 negative tiles.

   **Ask:** How many negative tiles are there? There are 8 negative tiles.

6. Have students write the number sentence $^-3 + {}^-5 = {}^-8$.

   **Ask:** Explain how the number sentence is related to the negative tiles. The number sentence uses integers to show that 3 negative tiles plus 5 negative tiles equals 8 negative tiles.

7. Have students repeat Steps 5 and 6 for the following problems:
   - $^-2 + {}^-8 = \underline{\phantom{xx}}$  $^-10$
   - $^-4 + {}^-12 = \underline{\phantom{xx}}$  $^-16$
   - $^-6 + {}^-7 = \underline{\phantom{xx}}$  $^-13$

8. **Say:** Think about when you added $3 + 5 = 8$ and $^-3 + {}^-5 = {}^-8$. When you add negative integers, you use a process that is similar to the process you use when you add positive integers.

9. Tell students to look at the problems they solved and decide if adding negative integers gives a positive or negative sum. Students should see that adding two negative integers results in a negative sum.

10. **Say:** The value of the sum of negative integers is actually less than either addend. For example, in $^-3 + {}^-5 = {}^-8$, $^-8$ is a lesser number than either $^-3$ or $^-5$.

11. **Say:** Now subtract a positive integer from a negative integer.

    Have students write $^-5 - {}^+2 = \underline{\phantom{xx}}$ in their Math Notebook.

12. Model 5 negative tiles. Then model 2 positive tiles and 2 negative tiles. Explain to students that the pair with 2 positive and negative tiles is equal to 0 and is considered "zeroing out" from the total number of tiles. Using pairs of positive and negative tiles does not affect the total. In this problem,

300  INTEGERS

2 pairs of positive and negative tiles were chosen because of the positive integer being subtracted, $^+2$.

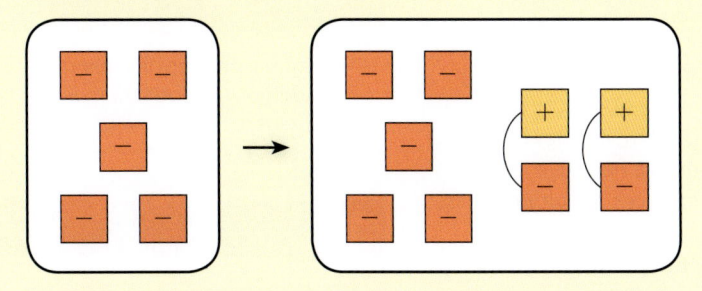

**13.** Remove 2 positive tiles, to correspond to $^+2$ in the number sentence. Students should find that $^-5 - {^+2} = {^-7}$. Write the difference in the number sentence.

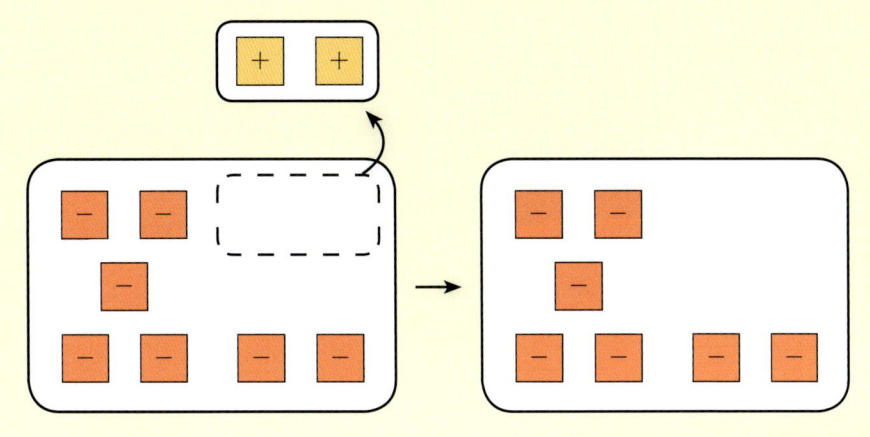

**14.** Guide students to repeat Steps 11–13 for the following problems:
- $^-7 - {^+6} =$ ___ $^-13$
- $^-9 - {^+3} =$ ___ $^-12$
- $^-11 - {^+5} =$ ___ $^-16$

**15.** Have students write the following number sentences, one below the other:
- $^-5 - {^+2} = {^-7}$
- $^-5 + {^-2} = {^-7}$

**16. Say:** Subtracting a positive integer from a negative integer is actually like adding a negative integer to a negative integer.

**Say:** Look at the two number sentences. Think about this: The difference when a positive integer is subtracted from a negative integer is always less than the minuend and subtrahend. For example, in $^-5 - {^+2} = {^-7}$, $^-7$ is a lesser number than either $^-5$ or $^+2$.

**17. Say:** Now subtract a positive integer from a positive integer.

Model 12 positive tiles and then move 8 of them away from the group.

**Ask:** What number sentence can you write for the tiles I've modeled? $^+12 - {^+8} = {^+4}$

**18.** Have students use tiles to model and write the difference to the following problems:
- $^+9 - {^+7} =$ ___ $^+2$
- $^+17 - {^+11} =$ ___ $^+6$

**ADD AND SUBTRACT INTEGERS (A)** **301**

# LEARN  Add Negatives and Subtract Positives

**OFFLINE 20 min**

## Objectives
- Solve a problem involving addition or subtraction of integers.

Students will add two negative integers. Then they will subtract a positive integer from a negative integer. They will solve computation problems and story problems. This activity will reinforce the concept that subtracting a positive integer from a negative integer is equivalent to adding a negative integer to a negative integer. Have students turn to the Add Negatives and Subtract Positives activity page in their Activity Book and read the directions with them.

Students should copy the problems from the Activity Book into their Math Notebook as necessary and solve them there.

1. Read the first problem in the Worked Examples with students. Make sure students understand it.
2. Have students solve Problems 1–3.
3. Read the second problem in the Worked Examples with students.

   **Say:** We added 0 when we added the 4 pairs of negative and positive tiles. We chose to add 4 pairs because we wanted to take away 4 positive tiles to solve the problem. But we had no positive tiles to begin with. We had only negative tiles. When we added 4 positive tiles and 4 negative tiles, or 0, we then had 4 positive tiles that we could take away to find the difference.

4. Have students solve Problems 4–6. Assist them as needed. If they have difficulty, first encourage them to look at the Worked Examples and follow the process shown. If they still have difficulty, help them apply the process shown in the Worked Examples.

## Tips
Allow students to use positive and negative tiles to help them understand how the values change, if needed.

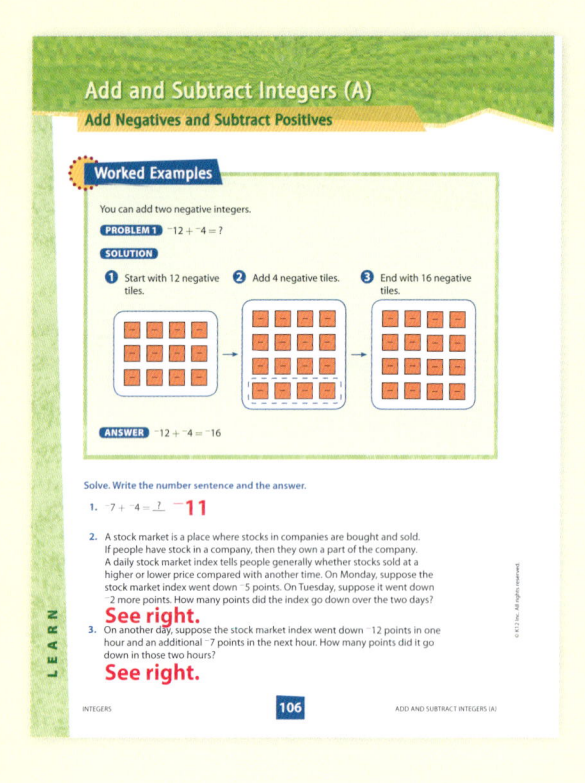

## Additional Answers

2. $^-5 + {^-2} = {^-7}$
   The index went down 7 points during the two days.
3. $^-12 + {^-7} = {^-19}$
   The index went down 19 points during the two hours.

302  INTEGERS

## Worked Examples

You can subtract a positive integer from a negative integer. When you subtract a positive integer from a negative integer, the problem is the same as adding a negative integer to a negative integer.

**PROBLEM 2** $^-15 - {^+4} = ?$

**SOLUTION**

1. Start with $^-15$.
2. Add $^-4$ and $^+4$. You have added 0. By the zero property of addition, $^-15 + 0 = {^-15}$. The total value of the tiles has not changed.
3. Subtract $^+4$.
4. End with $^-19$.

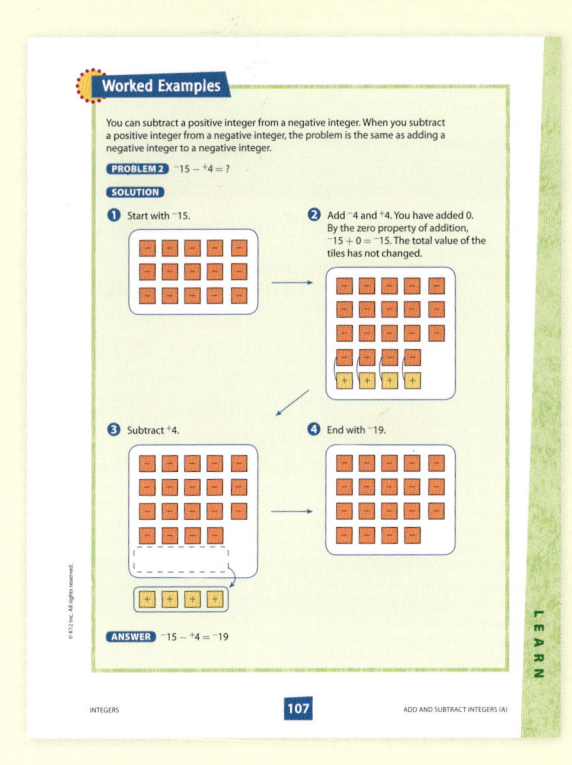

**ANSWER** $^-15 - {^+4} = {^-19}$

---

Solve. Write the number sentence and the answer.

4. $^-13 - {^+4} = \underline{?}$   $^-17$
5. $^-4 - {^+9} = \underline{?}$   $^-13$
6. You are playing a quiz game with your friends. You have answered a number of questions incorrectly. Your score is $^-8$ points. You answer the next question incorrectly and lose 4 more points. What is your new score?

$^-8 - {^+4} = {^-12}$
**Your new score is $^-12$ points.**

---

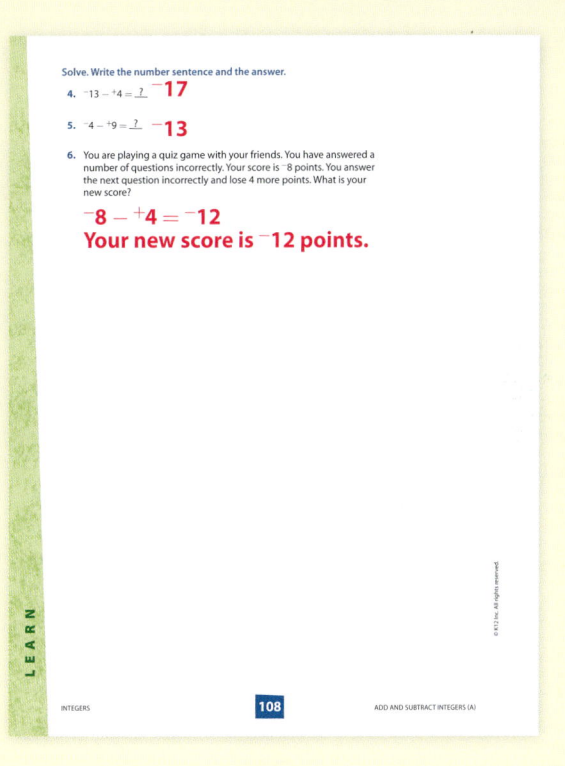

# TRY IT  Practice Adding and Subtracting

**OFFLINE 15 min**

## Objectives
- Solve a problem involving addition or subtraction of integers.

Students will practice adding and subtracting with positive and negative integers. Have students turn to the Practice Adding and Subtracting activity page in their Activity Book and read the directions with them.

Students should copy the problems from the Activity Book into their Math Notebook as necessary and solve them there.

---

### Add and Subtract Integers (A)
**Practice Adding and Subtracting**

Add.
1. $^-10 + {^-6} = \underline{?}$   $^-16$
2. $^-12 + {^-15} = \underline{?}$   $^-27$
3. $^-8 + {^-6} = \underline{?}$   $^-14$

Subtract.
4. $^+23 - {^+18} = \underline{?}$   $^+5$
5. $^+67 - {^+28} = \underline{?}$   $^+39$
6. $^-2 - {^+8} = \underline{?}$   $^-10$
7. $^-12 - {^+13} = \underline{?}$   $^-25$
8. $^-54 - {^+43} = \underline{?}$   $^-97$

Choose the answer.

9. $^-6 + {^-2} = ?$
   A. $^+4$
   B. $^-4$
   C. $^-8$ (circled)
   D. $^+8$

10. $^+5 + {^+3} = ?$
    A. $^+8$ (circled)
    B. $^-8$
    C. $^-2$
    D. $^+2$

11. $^-43 - {^+10} = ?$
    A. $^-53$ (circled)
    B. $^-33$
    C. $^+33$
    D. $^+53$

12. $^+83 - {^+9} = ?$
    A. $^-91$
    B. $^-74$
    C. $^+74$ (circled)
    D. $^+91$

**ADD AND SUBTRACT INTEGERS (A)** 303

# Add and Subtract Integers (B)

## Lesson Overview

| | | |
|---|---|---|
| **GET READY** Add and Subtract Whole Numbers | 10 minutes | **ONLINE** |
| **LEARN** Add and Subtract with Number Lines | 15 minutes | **ONLINE** |
| **LEARN** Draw Number Lines to Add or Subtract | 10 minutes | **OFFLINE** |
| **LEARN** Temperature and Golf Story Problems | 15 minutes | **OFFLINE** |
| **TRY IT** Practice with Integers | 10 minutes | **OFFLINE** |

### ▶ Lesson Objectives
Solve a problem involving addition or subtraction of integers.

### ▶ Prerequisite Skills
- Identify and place negative numbers on a number line.
- Estimate or calculate a sum or a difference in a whole-number problem.
- Estimate or calculate a sum or a difference in a whole-number story problem.

### ▶ Content Background
Students will use number lines as models to learn how to add and subtract integers. They will solve computation problems as well as story problems. They will solve these types of problems:
- Add two negative integers.
- Add two positive integers.
- Subtract a positive integer from a positive integer.
- Subtract a positive integer from a negative integer.

An *integer* is any number in the set of whole numbers and the opposites of the whole numbers. Integers are… $^-4$, $^-3$, $^-2$, $^-1$, 0, $^+1$, $^+2$, $^+3$, $^+4$,… and so on. When working with integers, be sure to say "negative 5" instead of "minus 5," which would mean to subtract 5. In the same way, say "positive 5" instead of "plus 5," which would mean to add 5.

Sometimes, positive integers will be written with a raised positive sign, like this: $^+4$. Other times, positive integers will be written without a raised positive sign, like this: 4. Both $^+4$ and 4 are the same. However, when students first begin working with positive and negative integers, positive integers will have a raised positive sign so that there is no confusion.

### Materials to Gather

**SUPPLIED**
Temperature and Golf Story Problems activity page
Practice with Integers activity page

**ALSO NEEDED**
pencils, coloring

---

## GET READY  Add and Subtract Whole Numbers   ONLINE 10 min

Students will practice adding and subtracting whole numbers to find the estimated and exact sum or difference.

### Objectives
- Estimate or calculate a sum or a difference in a whole-number problem.

**304** INTEGERS

## LEARN  Add and Subtract with Number Lines

**ONLINE 15 min**

**Objectives**
- Solve a problem involving addition or subtraction of integers.

Students will use number lines as models to learn how to add and subtract with positive and negative integers. They will solve these types of problems:
- Add two positive integers.
- Subtract a positive integer from a positive integer.
- Add two negative integers.
- Subtract a positive integer from a negative integer.

## LEARN  Draw Number Lines to Add or Subtract

**OFFLINE 10 min**

**Objectives**
- Solve a problem involving addition or subtraction of integers.

Students will learn to sketch number lines to model how to add and subtract positive and negative integers. Tell students that the number lines that they will draw are more like quick sketches. They do not need to be exact, since the number lines are being used to model how to solve problems.

Students will sketch number lines and solve problems in their Math Notebook. Gather the coloring pencils.

1. Have students write $^-3 + {}^-5 = $ ___ in their Math Notebook.

2. Have students select pencils of three different colors for sketching a number line. Have them use one color to draw a line with an arrow pointing left and label it $^-3$. Have them put a short vertical line on the right end of the arrow and label it 0. Have students write $^-3$ below the arrow, to represent the first addend. Then have them begin writing a number sentence above the number line.

    **Say:** The first addend in this number sentence is a negative integer, $^-3$. The arrow to show that number points left.

3. Have students use a different color to draw an arrow pointing left, starting at the left end of the first arrow, and about twice the length of the first arrow. Have them write $^-5$ below the arrow, to represent the second addend. Then have them finish writing the number sentence above the arrow.

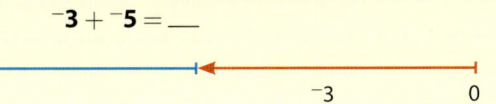

$$^-3 + {}^-5 = \underline{\phantom{00}}$$

4. **Ask:** Use the sketched number line of the two arrows. What is the answer to $^-3 + {}^-5$? $^-8$

5. Have students use a third color to draw one long arrow above the other two arrows and label the long arrow $^-8$. Put a short vertical line on the right end of the arrow and label it 0. This arrow is the same length as the two arrows below. The top arrow shows the answer to the problem. Also have students write $^-8$ to complete the number sentence.

    **Say:** The top number line shows that the sum of the two number lines below it is $^-8$, and the answer to the number sentence is $^-8$.

ADD AND SUBTRACT INTEGERS (B)  **305**

$$^-3 + {}^-5 = {}^-8$$

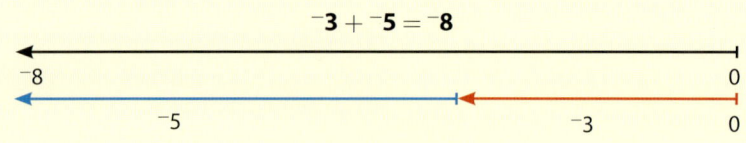

6. Work with students to solve the following problem by sketching number line and writing and answering the two different number sentences presented in this step: $^-5 - {}^+7 =$ ___.

   **Say:** To find the difference, show $^-5$ with an arrow that points to the left. Even though $^+7$ is a positive number, you will subtract it from $^-5$ in this problem. The arrow for $^+7$ starts at the end of the arrow for $^-5$ but it is on the left and shows that you moved left. The difference is $^-12$.

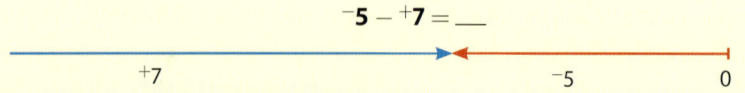

   $$^-5 - {}^+7 = \underline{\phantom{00}}$$

   **Say:** Remember that subtracting a positive integer from a negative integer is the same as adding a negative integer to a negative integer. Sketch a number line for this new number sentence, write the problem, and solve it: $^-5 + {}^-7 =$ ___.

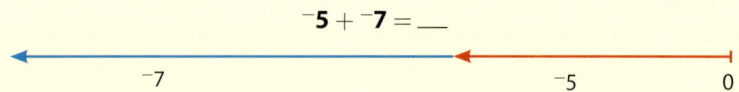

   $$^-5 + {}^-7 = \underline{\phantom{00}}$$

7. **Ask:** What is $^-5 - {}^+7$? $^-12$

   Have students write $^-12$ to complete the number sentence above the first sketched number line. Have them add an arrow, pointing left, above the two arrows, labeled $^-12$.

8. **Ask:** What is $^-5 + {}^-7$? $^-12$

   Have students write $^-12$ to complete the number sentence above the second sketched number line. Have them add an arrow, pointing left, above the two arrows, labeled $^-12$.

9. Using sketched number lines and writing and answering number sentences, have students use the strategy of subtracting a positive integer from a negative integer being equivalent to adding a negative integer to a negative integer to solve the following problem: $^-2 - {}^+7 =$ ___. $^-9$

## LEARN  Temperature and Golf Story Problems

**OFFLINE 15 min**

Students will first review how to add and subtract negative and positive integers. Then they will use those operations to solve story problems about temperature and golf. Have students turn to the Temperature and Golf Story Problems activity page in their Activity Book and read the directions with them.

Students should copy the problems from the Activity Book into their Math Notebook as necessary and solve them there.

1. Read the first problem in the Worked Examples with students. Then have them complete Problems 1 and 2. Throughout the activity, if students have difficulty finding the answers, first encourage them to look at the Worked Examples and follow the process shown. If they still have difficulty, help them apply the process shown in the Worked Examples.

### Objectives

- Solve a problem involving addition or subtraction of integers.

### Tips

Allow students to sketch number lines to help them solve the problems, if they wish.

**306** INTEGERS

Remind students that when they subtract a positive integer from a negative integer, it is the same as adding a negative integer to a negative integer.

2. Have students read the second problem in the Worked Examples. Then have them answer Problems 3–8.

3. Have students read the third problem in the Worked Examples. Then have them answer Problems 9–13.

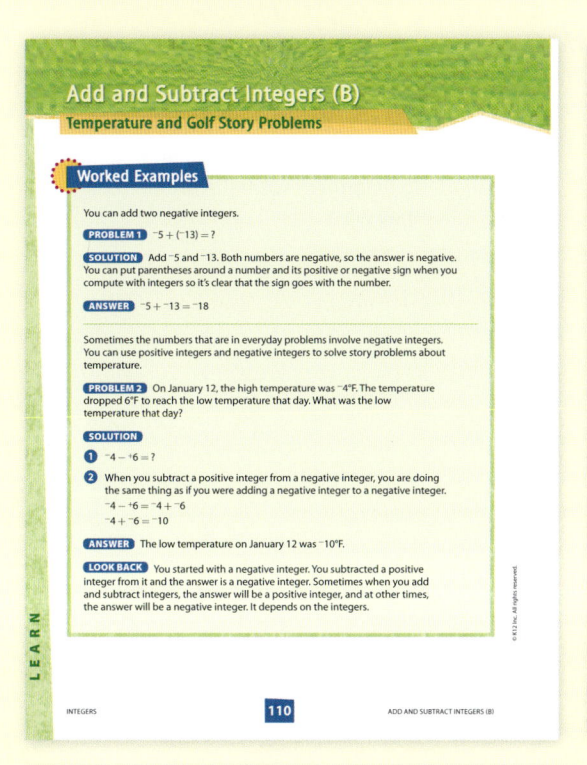

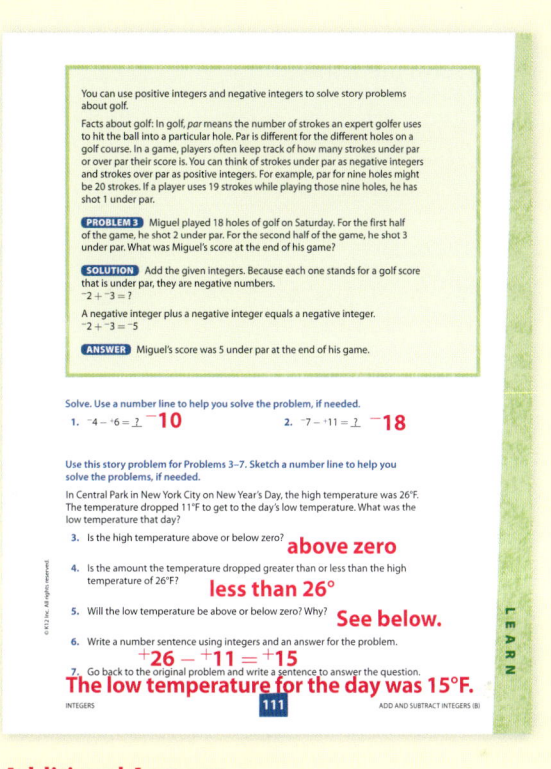

### Student page 110 — Add and Subtract Integers (B): Temperature and Golf Story Problems

**Worked Examples**

You can add two negative integers.

**PROBLEM 1** $^-5 + (^-13) = ?$

**SOLUTION** Add $^-5$ and $^-13$. Both numbers are negative, so the answer is negative. You can put parentheses around a number and its positive or negative sign when you compute with integers so it's clear that the sign goes with the number.

**ANSWER** $^-5 + ^-13 = ^-18$

Sometimes the numbers that are in everyday problems involve negative integers. You can use positive integers and negative integers to solve story problems about temperature.

**PROBLEM 2** On January 12, the high temperature was $^-4°F$. The temperature dropped 6°F to reach the low temperature that day. What was the low temperature that day?

**SOLUTION**

① $^-4 - ^+6 = ?$

② When you subtract a positive integer from a negative integer, you are doing the same thing as if you were adding a negative integer to a negative integer.
$^-4 - ^+6 = ^-4 + ^-6$
$^-4 + ^-6 = ^-10$

**ANSWER** The low temperature on January 12 was $^-10°F$.

**LOOK BACK** You started with a negative integer. You subtracted a positive integer from it and the answer is a negative integer. Sometimes when you add and subtract integers, the answer will be a positive integer, and at other times, the answer will be a negative integer. It depends on the integers.

### Student page 111

You can use positive integers and negative integers to solve story problems about golf.

Facts about golf: In golf, *par* means the number of strokes an expert golfer uses to hit the ball into a particular hole. Par is different for the different holes on a golf course. In a game, players often keep track of how many strokes under par or over par their score is. You can think of strokes under par as negative integers and strokes over par as positive integers. For example, par for nine holes might be 20 strokes. If a player uses 19 strokes while playing those nine holes, he has shot 1 under par.

**PROBLEM 3** Miguel played 18 holes of golf on Saturday. For the first half of the game, he shot 2 under par. For the second half of the game, he shot 3 under par. What was Miguel's score at the end of his game?

**SOLUTION** Add the given integers. Because each one stands for a golf score that is under par, they are negative numbers.
$^-2 + ^-3 = ?$

A negative integer plus a negative integer equals a negative integer.
$^-2 + ^-3 = ^-5$

**ANSWER** Miguel's score was 5 under par at the end of his game.

Solve. Use a number line to help you solve the problem, if needed.

1. $^-4 - ^+6 = \underline{?}\ ^-10$
2. $^-7 - ^+11 = \underline{?}\ ^-18$

Use this story problem for Problems 3–7. Sketch a number line to help you solve the problems, if needed.

In Central Park in New York City on New Year's Day, the high temperature was 26°F. The temperature dropped 11°F to get to the day's low temperature. What was the low temperature that day?

3. Is the high temperature above or below zero? **above zero**
4. Is the amount the temperature dropped greater than or less than the high temperature of 26°F? **less than 26°**
5. Will the low temperature be above or below zero? Why? **See below.**
6. Write a number sentence using integers and an answer for the problem.
$^+26 - ^+11 = ^+15$
7. Go back to the original problem and write a sentence to answer the question.
**The low temperature for the day was 15°F.**

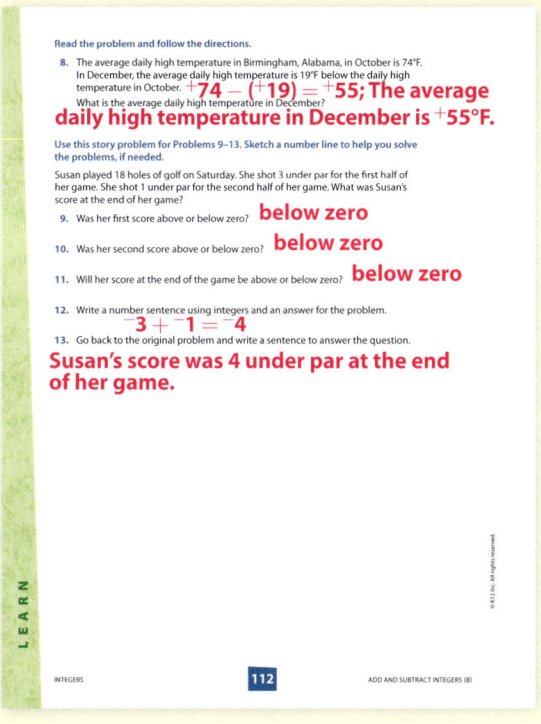

### Additional Answers

5. It will be above zero, because the temperature starts at 26°F and drops 11°F. The temperature would have to drop an additional 15 or more degrees Fahrenheit for the low temperature to be zero or below zero.

### Student page 112

Read the problem and follow the directions.

8. The average daily high temperature in Birmingham, Alabama, in October is 74°F. In December, the average daily high temperature is 19°F below the daily high temperature in October. What is the average daily high temperature in December?
$^+74 - (^+19) = ^+55$; **The average daily high temperature in December is $^+55°F$.**

Use this story problem for Problems 9–13. Sketch a number line to help you solve the problems, if needed.

Susan played 18 holes of golf on Saturday. She shot 3 under par for the first half of her game. She shot 1 under par for the second half of her game. What was Susan's score at the end of her game?

9. Was her first score above or below zero? **below zero**
10. Was her second score above or below zero? **below zero**
11. Will her score at the end of the game be above or below zero? **below zero**
12. Write a number sentence using integers and an answer for the problem.
$^-3 + ^-1 = ^-4$
13. Go back to the original problem and write a sentence to answer the question.
**Susan's score was 4 under par at the end of her game.**

## TRY IT  Practice with Integers

**OFFLINE 10 min**

### Objectives

- Solve a problem involving addition or subtraction of integers.

Students will practice adding and subtracting integers. Have students turn to the Practice with Integers activity page in their Activity Book and read the directions with them.

Students should copy the problems from the Activity Book into their Math Notebook as necessary and solve them there.

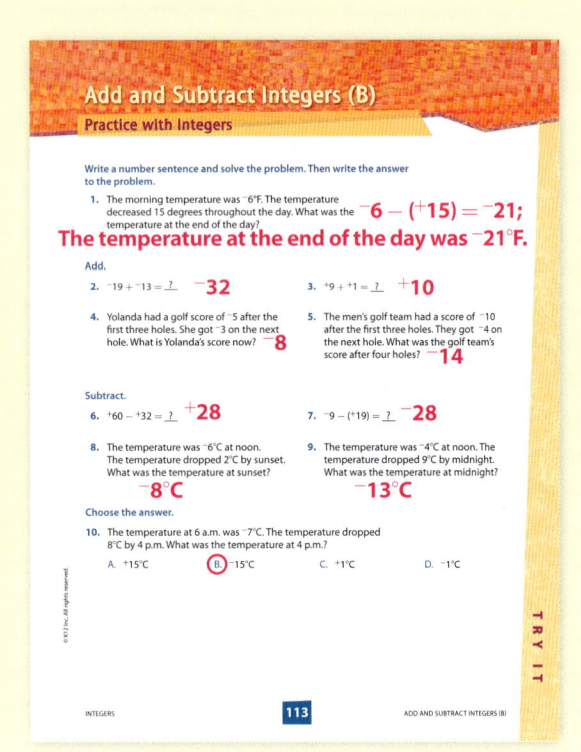

### Tips

Allow students to sketch number lines to help them solve the problems, if they wish.

### Add and Subtract Integers (B)
**Practice with Integers**

Write a number sentence and solve the problem. Then write the answer to the problem.

1. The morning temperature was ⁻6°F. The temperature decreased 15 degrees throughout the day. What was the temperature at the end of the day?  ⁻6 − (⁺15) = ⁻21;
**The temperature at the end of the day was ⁻21°F.**

Add.

2. ⁻19 + ⁻13 = ?   ⁻32
3. ⁺9 + ⁺1 = ?   ⁺10

4. Yolanda had a golf score of ⁻5 after the first three holes. She got ⁻3 on the next hole. What is Yolanda's score now?  ⁻8

5. The men's golf team had a score of ⁻10 after the first three holes. They got ⁻4 on the next hole. What was the golf team's score after four holes?  ⁻14

Subtract.

6. ⁺60 − ⁺32 = ?   ⁺28
7. ⁻9 − (⁺19) = ?   ⁻28

8. The temperature was ⁻6°C at noon. The temperature dropped 2°C by sunset. What was the temperature at sunset?  ⁻8°C

9. The temperature was ⁻4°C at noon. The temperature dropped 9°C by midnight. What was the temperature at midnight?  ⁻13°C

Choose the answer.

10. The temperature at 6 a.m. was ⁻7°C. The temperature dropped 8°C by 4 p.m. What was the temperature at 4 p.m.?

    A. ⁺15°C   (B.) ⁻15°C   C. ⁺1°C   D. ⁻1°C

# Add and Subtract Integers (C)

## Lesson Overview

| | | |
|---|---|---|
| **GET READY** Football Whole-Number Story Problems | 10 minutes | **ONLINE** |
| **LEARN** Add or Subtract Integers to See the Picture | 15 minutes | **ONLINE** |
| **LEARN** Write and Solve Ocean Story Problems | 15 minutes | **OFFLINE** |
| **TRY IT** Add and Subtract with Integers | 10 minutes | **ONLINE** |
| **CHECKPOINT** | 10 minutes | **ONLINE** |

### ▶ Lesson Objectives
Solve a problem involving addition or subtraction of integers.

### ▶ Prerequisite Skills
- Identify and place negative numbers on a number line.
- Estimate or calculate a sum or a difference in a whole-number problem.
- Estimate or calculate a sum or a difference in a whole-number story problem.

### ▶ Content Background
Students will solve computation problems and story problems in which they will add and subtract positive and negative integers. They will solve these types of problems:
- Add two negative integers.
- Add two positive integers.
- Subtract a positive integer from a positive integer.
- Subtract a positive integer from a negative integer.

An *integer* is any number in the set of whole numbers and the opposites of the whole numbers. Integers are…$^-4, ^-3, ^-2, ^-1, 0, ^+1, ^+2, ^+3$…and so on. When working with integers, be sure to say "negative 5" instead of "minus 5," which would mean to subtract 5. In the same way, say "positive 5" instead of "plus 5," which would mean to add 5.

Sometimes, positive integers will be written with a raised positive sign, like this: $^+4$. Other times, positive integers will be written without a raised positive sign, like this: 4. Both $^+4$ and 4 are the same. However, when students first begin working with positive and negative integers, positive integers will have a raised positive sign so that there is no confusion.

When students write and compute with positive and negative rational numbers, they may see numbers such as $^+8$ and $^-8$, with the positive and negative signs raised slightly higher next to the number. They may also see numbers such as $+8$ and $-8$, with the positive and negative signs in line next to the number. When students use the keyboard to type positive and negative rational numbers, have them use the in-line positive or negative sign and the number, without a space between the sign and the number. For positive rational numbers, correct answers use the "$+$" sign and the number, or just the number. For negative rational numbers, correct answers use the "$-$" sign and the number.

### Materials to Gather

**SUPPLIED**
Negative Tiles (printout, optional)
Positive Tiles (printout, optional)
Write and Solve Ocean Story Problems activity page

**ALSO NEEDED**
scissors, adult (optional)

▶ **Advance Preparation**

The Negative Tiles and Positive Tiles printouts are optional materials. Print and cut out the tiles if you think students will want to use them to solve story problems.

---

**GET READY** Football Whole-Number Story Problems

ONLINE 10 min

**Objectives**

- Estimate or calculate a sum or a difference in a whole-number story problem.

Students will estimate and then calculate the exact sum or difference in a whole-number story problem.
   Check that students are estimating before they add or subtract to find the exact answer.

---

**LEARN** Add or Subtract Integers to See the Picture

ONLINE 15 min

**Objectives**

- Solve a problem involving addition or subtraction of integers.

Students will solve addition and subtraction problems with positive and negative integers to reveal a hidden picture.

**Tips** Allow students to sketch number lines to help them solve the problems, if they wish.

---

**LEARN** Write and Solve Ocean Story Problems

OFFLINE 15 min

**Objectives**

- Solve a problem involving addition or subtraction of integers.

Students will use information about ocean animals to write and solve addition and subtraction story problems with integers. Have students turn to the Write and Solve Ocean Story Problems activity page in their Activity Book and read the directions with them.
   Students should copy the problems from their Activity Book into their Math Notebook as necessary and solve them there.

**Tips**

Allow students to use number line sketches or the negative and positive tiles to help them solve the problems, if they wish.

1. Look at the activity page with students. Explain that sea level is the level of the surface of the ocean. Scientists measure depths in the ocean from sea level. They also measure heights, or elevations, on the land from sea level. Show students the line that is the surface of the water, or sea level.

   **Say:** The picture shows approximately where these animals live, either below, at, or above sea level. These measurements are approximations, and each animal has a range of elevation or depth. The dolphin is a mammal and comes to the surface to breathe, but it mostly lives below sea level.

2. Tell students that sea level has a measure of 0 meters. Use the idea that sea level is somewhat like 0 on a number line or a thermometer.

3. Explain that students will write and solve addition and subtraction story problems in their Math Notebook about the ocean animals. Distances below sea level will be negative numbers, and distances above sea level will be positive numbers.

**310** INTEGERS

4. Point to the anglerfish and the giant squid.

   **Say:** Write a story problem that states the depths where the anglerfish and the giant squid live and asks how much farther below sea level the giant squid lives than the anglerfish. The anglerfish lives about 200 meters below sea level. The giant squid lives about 550 feet below sea level. About many meters below the anglerfish does the giant squid live?

5. **Say:** Write a number sentence to use to solve the problem. Then write a number sentence including the answer.
   $^-200 + \_\_\_ = {}^-550; {}^-200 + {}^-350 = {}^-550$

6. Tell students to write a sentence that answers the question in the story problem. The giant squid lives about 350 meters below the anglerfish.

7. **Ask:** When you add two negative integers, is the sum positive or negative? negative

8. Describe another problem: Suppose an animal that lives below the surface swims down 20 meters. Have students write a story problem to find out how far below sea level the animal is after it swims down. **Example:** The Atlantic spotted dolphin lives about 12 meters below the surface. If it swims down another 20 meters, about how far below sea level is it?

9. **Say:** This problem can be written using positive and negative integers. The depth below sea level, minus the distance the dolphin swims down, gives the total distance of the dive below sea level. Subtracting a positive number from a negative number is the same as adding a negative number to a negative number.

10. Have students write the number sentence, solve the problem, and write a sentence that answers the question. $^-12 - {}^+20 = \_\_\_$; $^-12 - {}^+20 = {}^-32$; After swimming down, the dolphin is about 32 meters below sea level.

11. **Ask:** When you subtract a positive integer from a negative integer, is the difference positive or negative? negative

12. Have students write one or more story problems about the animals above, at, or below sea level. Problems should be of the following types:
    - Add two negative integers.
    - Add two positive integers.
    - Subtract a positive integer from a positive integer.
    - Subtract a positive integer from a negative integer.

13. For each story problem, students should do the following:
    - Write a question.
    - Write the number sentence needed to solve the problem.
    - Find the answer to the number sentence.
    - Write a sentence that answers the question.

**ADD AND SUBTRACT INTEGERS (C)**

## TRY IT  Add and Subtract with Integers

**ONLINE 10 min**

### Objectives
- Solve a problem involving addition or subtraction of integers.

Students will complete an online Try It. If necessary, read the directions, problems, and answer choices to students and help them with keyboard or mouse operations.

## CHECKPOINT

**ONLINE 10 min**

### Objectives
- Solve a problem involving addition or subtraction of integers.

Students will complete an online Checkpoint. If necessary, read the directions, problems, and answer choices to students and help them with keyboard or mouse operations.

# Integer Answers: Reasonable or Not?

## Lesson Overview

| | | |
|---|---|---|
| Skills Update | 5 minutes | **ONLINE** |
| **GET READY** Integer Flash Cards | 5 minutes | **ONLINE** |
| **LEARN** General Statements About Integer Math | 15 minutes | **OFFLINE** |
| **LEARN** Verify Reasonableness | 15 minutes | **OFFLINE** |
| **TRY IT** Check Integers for Reasonableness | 10 minutes | **ONLINE** |
| **CHECKPOINT** | 10 minutes | **ONLINE** |

### ▶ Lesson Objectives
Verify that the calculated result of a problem involving addition or subtraction of integers is reasonable.

### ▶ Prerequisite Skills
Solve a problem involving addition or subtraction of integers.

### ▶ Content Background
Students will learn to verify the reasonableness of their answers to problems involving the addition or subtraction of integers. They will solve these types of problems:
- Add two negative integers.
- Add two positive integers.
- Subtract a positive integer from a positive integer.
- Subtract a positive integer from a negative integer.

An *integer* is any number in the set of whole numbers and their opposites. Integers are…$^-4, ^-3, ^-2, ^-1, 0, ^+1, ^+2, ^+3, ^+4$…and so on. When working with integers, be sure to say "negative 5" instead of "minus 5," which would mean to subtract 5. In the same way, say "positive 5" instead of "plus 5," which would mean to add 5.

Sometimes, positive integers will be written with a raised positive sign, like this: $^+4$. Other times, positive integers will be written without a raised positive sign, like this: 4. Both $^+4$ and 4 are the same. However, when students first begin working with positive and negative integers, positive integers will have a raised positive sign so that there is no confusion.

### ▶ Common Errors and Misconceptions
- Students might become so concerned about getting the correct answer when estimating that they first find the exact answer, and then round it. For example, when asked to estimate $348 + 176$, students might find the sum (524), and then round it to the nearest hundred (500).
- Students might have difficulty accepting that there is more than one correct approach and answer to an estimation problem.

### Materials to Gather

**SUPPLIED**

Negative Tiles (printout, optional)
Positive Tiles (printout, optional)
General Statements About Integer Math activity page
Verify Reasonableness activity page

**ALSO NEEDED**

scissors, adult (optional)

**INTEGER ANSWERS: REASONABLE OR NOT?** 313

▶ **Advance Preparation**

The Negative Tiles and Positive Tiles printouts are optional materials. Print and cut out the tiles if you think students will want to use them to solve problems.

## GET READY  Integer Flash Cards

**ONLINE 5 min**

Students will use online flash cards to practice adding and subtracting integers.

### Objectives
- Solve a problem involving addition or subtraction of integers.

## LEARN  General Statements About Integer Math

**OFFLINE 15 min**

Students will learn some general statements that are true about adding and subtracting positive and negative integers. They will use those general statements to verify the reasonableness of integer answers. Have students turn to the General Statements About Integer Math activity page in their Activity Book and read the directions with them.

Students should copy the problems from the Activity Book into their Math Notebook as necessary and solve them there.

1. Read the problems in the Worked Examples with students. Make sure students understand the problems and the general statement about each type of problem. They should also verify that the answer to the problem is reasonable based on the general statements in the solutions.

2. Have students write the following general statements in their Math Notebook:
   - When you subtract a positive integer from a greater positive integer, the difference will always be a positive integer less than the first number in the number sentence. The difference is 0 if the minuend and subtrahend are the same number.
   - When you add two positive integers, the sum will be a positive integer greater than either of the two addends.
   - When you add two negative integers, the sum is a negative integer less than either of the two addends.
   - When you subtract a positive integer from a negative integer, the difference is a negative integer less than either of the other numbers in the number sentence.

3. Have students solve Problems 1–8. See the Additional Answers for some statements that students may write to support the reasonableness of their answers.

### Objectives
- Verify that the calculated result of a problem involving addition or subtraction of integers is reasonable.

### Tips
Allow students to use number lines to solve the problems and verify reasonableness, if they wish.

## Integer Answers: Reasonable or Not?
### General Statements About Integer Math

**Worked Examples**

You can make general statements about the kinds of answers you will get when you add and subtract positive and negative integers in certain ways. You can use the general statements to verify the reasonableness of answers.

**PROBLEM 1** $^+8 - {^+5} = ?$

**SOLUTION** When you subtract a positive integer from a greater positive integer, the difference will always be a positive integer less than the first number in the number sentence. The difference is 0 if the minuend and subtrahend are the same number.

It is reasonable that the answer will be a positive integer less than the first number in the number sentence.

**ANSWER** $^+8 - {^+5} = {^+3}$

**PROBLEM 2** $^+4 + {^+5} = ?$

**SOLUTION** When you add two positive integers, the sum will be a positive integer greater than either of the two addends.

It is reasonable that the answer will be a positive integer greater than either of the two addends.

**ANSWER** $^+4 + {^+5} = {^+9}$

**PROBLEM 3** $^-2 + {^-6} = ?$

**SOLUTION** When you add two negative integers, the sum is a negative integer less than either of the two addends.

It is reasonable that the answer will be a negative integer less than either of the two addends.

**ANSWER** $^-2 + {^-6} = {^-8}$

**PROBLEM 4** $^-5 - {^+2} = ?$

**SOLUTION** When you subtract a positive integer from a negative integer, the difference is a negative integer less than either of the other numbers in the number sentence.

It is reasonable that the answer will be a negative integer that is less than either of the other numbers in the number sentence.

**ANSWER** $^-5 - {^+2} = {^-7}$

Solve each number sentence. Then decide if your answer is reasonable.

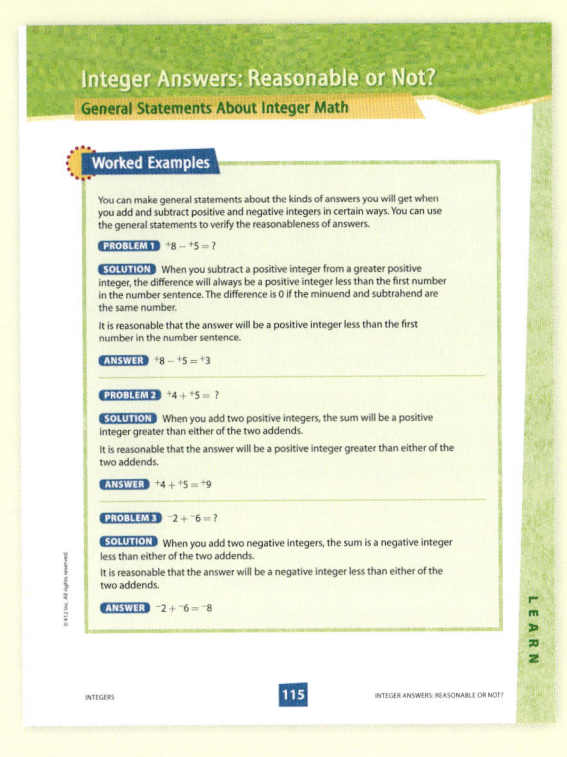

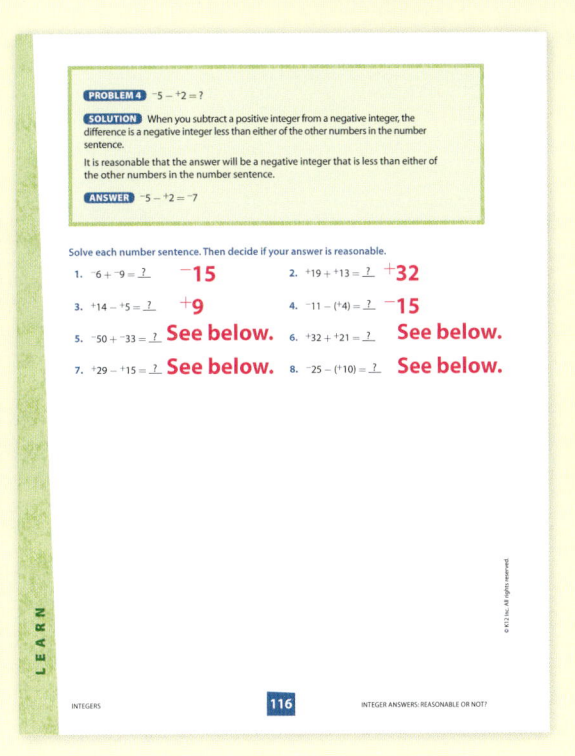

1. $^-6 + {^-9} = ?$    $^-15$
2. $^+19 + {^+13} = ?$    $^+32$
3. $^+14 + {^-5} = ?$    $^+9$
4. $^-11 - ({^+4}) = ?$    $^-15$
5. $^-50 + {^-33} = ?$    See below.
6. $^+32 + {^+21} = ?$    See below.
7. $^+29 - {^+15} = ?$    See below.
8. $^-25 - ({^+10}) = ?$    See below.

**Additional Answers**

5. $^-83$; It is reasonable that the answer will be a negative integer less than either of the two addends.

6. $^+53$; It is reasonable that the answer will be a positive integer greater than either of the two addends.

7. $^+14$; It is reasonable that the answer will be a positive integer less than either of the other numbers in the number sentence.

8. $^-35$; It is reasonable that the answer will be a negative integer less than either of the other numbers in the number sentence.

## LEARN Verify Reasonableness

**OFFLINE 15 min**

Students will verify that the calculated answers to integer addition and subtraction computation and story problems are reasonable. They will verify the reasonableness of the answers by checking the calculation and applying what they know about general statements that are true about adding and subtracting positive and negative integers. Have students turn to the Verify Reasonableness activity page in their Activity Book and read the directions with them.

Students should copy the problems from the Activity Book into their Math Notebook as necessary and solve them there.

1. Read the problems in the Worked Examples with students. Make sure students find the answer to the problem and use the general statements about adding and subtracting positive and negative integers to verify the reasonableness of the answer.

2. Have students solve Problems 1–4.

### Objectives

- Verify that the calculated result of a problem involving addition or subtraction of integers is reasonable.

### Tips

Allow students to use number lines, the positive and negative tiles, and sketched number lines to help them verify the reasonableness of the answers, if needed.

**INTEGER ANSWERS: REASONABLE OR NOT?**   315

## Integer Answers: Reasonable or Not?
**Verify Reasonableness**

### Worked Examples

You can verify that the answer to an integer addition or subtraction problem is reasonable by applying general statements that are true about adding and subtracting positive and negative integers.

- When you subtract a positive integer from a greater positive integer, the difference will always be a positive integer less than the first number in the number sentence. The difference is 0 if the minuend and subtrahend are the same number.
- When you add two positive integers, the sum will be a positive integer greater than either of the two addends.
- When you add two negative integers, the sum is a negative integer less than either of the two addends.
- When you subtract a positive integer from a negative integer, the difference is a negative integer less than either of the other numbers in the number sentence.

**PROBLEM 1** Martin said that $^-43 + {}^-47$ equals $^-90$. Is Martin's answer reasonable?

**SOLUTION** The problem asks you to add two negative integers and decide if the sum, a negative integer, is reasonable. When you add two negative integers, the sum is a negative integer less than either of the two addends.

If you think about starting at $^-43$ on the number line and moving 47 spaces to the left (to add $^-47$), you will get $^-90$.

**ANSWER** Yes, Martin's answer is reasonable. He correctly found that $^-43 + {}^-47 = {}^-90$. He correctly answered that the sum of two negative integers is a negative integer that is less than either of the two addends.

**PROBLEM 2** Sierra solved this problem: Elian's score in a quiz game was $^+52$ points. Elian answered his next question correctly and got $^+13$ points. How many points does Elian have now? Sierra thought the answer was $^-65$ points. Is Sierra's answer reasonable?

**SOLUTION** The problem asks you to add two positive integers and decide if the given sum, a negative integer, is reasonable. When you add two positive integers, the sum will be a positive integer greater than either of the two addends.

If you think about starting with 52 positive tiles and adding 13 positive tiles, you get a total of 65 positive tiles.

**ANSWER** No, Sierra's answer is not reasonable. She found an incorrect answer to the problem. $^+52 + {}^+13 = {}^+65$, not $^-65$. Her answer should have shown that the sum of two positive integers is a positive integer that is greater than either of the two addends. Elian has $^+65$ points.

**PROBLEM 3** Jabar solved this problem: The temperature was $^-4°C$ at midnight. The temperature dropped $3°C$ by 5 a.m. What was the temperature at 5 a.m.? Jabar thought the answer was $^-1°C$. Is Jabar's answer reasonable?

**SOLUTION** The problem asks you to subtract a positive integer from a negative integer and decide if the given difference, a negative integer greater than the first number in the subtraction problem, is reasonable. When you subtract a positive integer from a negative integer, the difference is a negative integer less than either of the other numbers in the number sentence.

If you think about making an arrow to show $^-4$ on a number line and adding an arrow that shows $^+3$, the sketched arrows will show the difference is $^-7$.

**ANSWER** No, Jabar's answer is not reasonable. He found an incorrect answer to the problem. $^-4 - {}^+3 = {}^-7$, not $^-1$. His answer should have shown that when you subtract a positive integer from a negative integer, the difference is a negative integer less than either of the other numbers in the number sentence. The temperature at 5 a.m. was $^-7°C$.

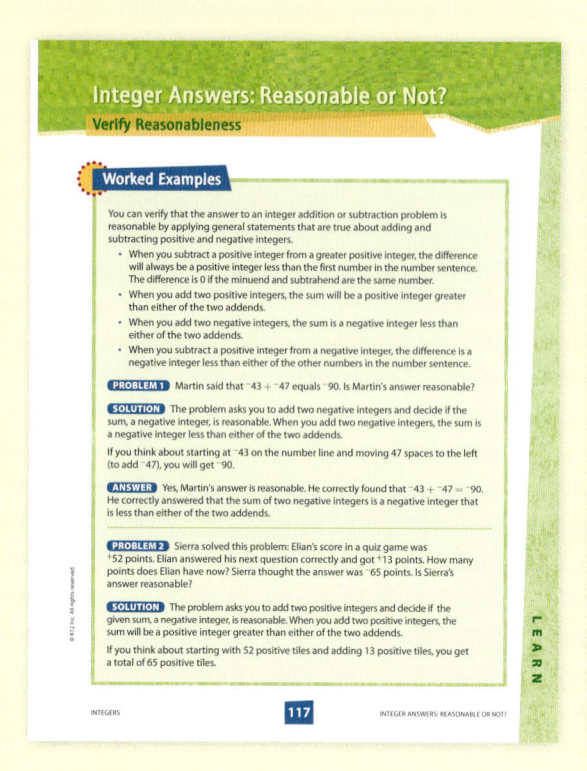

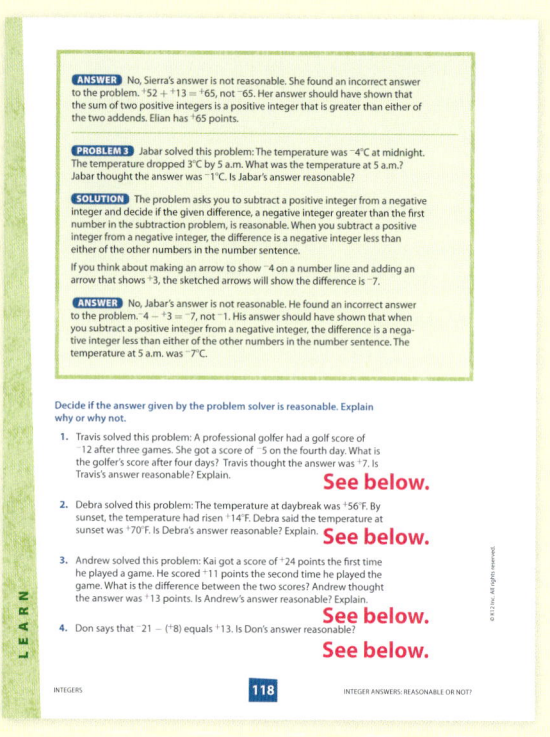

Decide if the answer given by the problem solver is reasonable. Explain why or why not.

1. Travis solved this problem: A professional golfer had a golf score of $^-12$ after three games. She got a score of $^-5$ on the fourth day. What is the golfer's score after four days? Travis thought the answer was $^+7$. Is Travis's answer reasonable? Explain. **See below.**

2. Debra solved this problem: The temperature at daybreak was $^+56°F$. By sunset, the temperature had risen $^+14°F$. Debra said the temperature at sunset was $^+70°F$. Is Debra's answer reasonable? Explain. **See below.**

3. Andrew solved this problem: Kai got a score of $^+24$ points the first time he played a game. He scored $^+11$ points the second time he played the game. What is the difference between the two scores? Andrew thought the answer was $^+13$ points. Is Andrew's answer reasonable? Explain. **See below.**

4. Don says that $^-21 - ({}^+8)$ equals $^+13$. Is Don's answer reasonable? **See below.**

### Additional Answers

1. No, Travis's answer is not reasonable. He found an incorrect answer to the problem. $^-12 + {}^-5 = {}^-17$, not $^+7$. When you add two negative integers, the sum is a negative integer less than either of the two addends. The golfer's score should be $^-17$.

2. Yes, Debra's answer is reasonable. She correctly found that $^+56 + {}^+14 = {}^+70$. She correctly answered that the sum of two positive integers is a positive integer that is greater than either of the two addends. The temperature at sunset was $^+70°F$.

3. Yes, Andrew's answer is reasonable. He correctly found that $^+24 - {}^+11 = {}^+13$. He correctly answered that when you subtract a positive integer from a greater positive integer, the difference will always be a positive integer less than the first number in the number sentence. The difference between the two scores is $^+13$ points.

4. No, Don's answer is not reasonable. He found an incorrect answer to the problem. $^-21 - ({}^+8) = {}^-29$, not $^+13$. When you subtract a positive integer from a negative integer, the difference is a negative integer less than either of the other numbers in the number sentence.

### TRY IT  Check Integers for Reasonableness
**ONLINE 10 min**

Students will complete an online Try It. If necessary, read the directions, problems, and answer choices to students and help them with keyboard or mouse operations.

**Objectives**
- Verify that the calculated result of a problem involving addition or subtraction of integers is reasonable.

### CHECKPOINT
**ONLINE 10 min**

Students will complete an online Checkpoint. If necessary, read the directions, problems, and answer choices to students and help them with keyboard or mouse operations.

**Objectives**
- Verify that the calculated result of a problem involving addition or subtraction of integers is reasonable.

# Unit Review

| **Lesson Overview** | | |
|---|---|---|
| **UNIT REVIEW** Look Back | 10 minutes | **ONLINE** |
| **UNIT REVIEW** Checkpoint Practice | 25 minutes | **ONLINE** |
| **UNIT REVIEW** Checkpoint Practice | 25 minutes | **OFFLINE** |
| ▶ **UNIT REVIEW** Prepare for the Checkpoint | | |

## ▶ Unit Objectives

This lesson reviews the following objectives:

- Identify and represent decimal numbers, fractions, mixed numbers, and positive and negative integers on a number line.
- Solve a problem involving addition or subtraction of integers.
- Verify that the calculated result of a problem involving addition or subtraction of integers is reasonable.

## ▶ Advance Preparation

In this lesson, students will have an opportunity to review previous activities in the Integers unit. Look at the suggested activities in Unit Review: Prepare for the Checkpoint online and gather any needed materials.

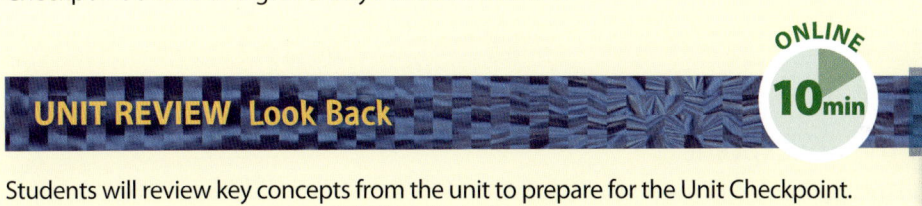

### Materials to Gather

**SUPPLIED**
Checkpoint Practice activity page

---

### UNIT REVIEW  Look Back

**ONLINE 10 min**

Students will review key concepts from the unit to prepare for the Unit Checkpoint.

**Objectives**
- Review unit objectives.

---

### UNIT REVIEW  Checkpoint Practice

**ONLINE 25 min**

Students will complete this part of the Checkpoint Practice online. Read the directions, problems, and answer choices to students. If necessary, help students with keyboard or mouse operations.

**Objectives**
- Review unit objectives.

# UNIT REVIEW Checkpoint Practice

**OFFLINE 25 min**

## Objectives
- Review unit objectives.

Students will complete this part of the Checkpoint Practice offline. If necessary, read the directions, problems, and answer choices to students. Have students answer the problems on their own. Carefully review the answers with students.

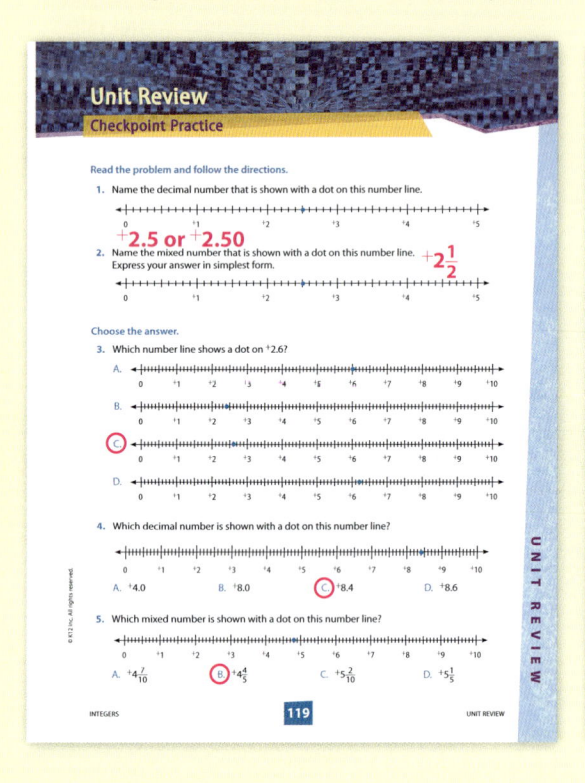

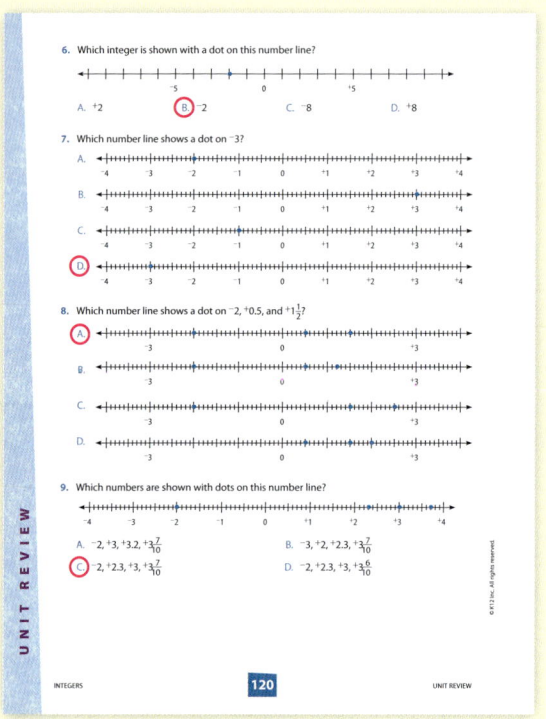

# UNIT REVIEW Prepare for the Checkpoint

What you do next depends on how students performed in the previous activity, Unit Review: Checkpoint Practice. If students had difficulty with any of the problems, complete the appropriate review activity listed in the table online.

318 INTEGERS

# Unit Checkpoint

## Lesson Overview

| | | |
|---|---|---|
| **UNIT CHECKPOINT** Online | 30 minutes | **ONLINE** |
| **UNIT CHECKPOINT** Offline | 30 minutes | **OFFLINE** |

### ▶ Unit Objectives

This lesson assesses the following objectives:

- Identify and represent decimal numbers, fractions, mixed numbers, and positive and negative integers on a number line.
- Solve a problem involving addition or subtraction of integers.
- Verify that the calculated result of a problem involving addition or subtraction of integers is reasonable.

**Materials to Gather**

**SUPPLIED**
Unit Checkpoint (printout)

## UNIT CHECKPOINT Online

**ONLINE 30 min**

### Objectives

- Assess unit objectives.

Students will complete this part of the Unit Checkpoint online. Read the directions, problems, and answer choices to students. If necessary, help students with keyboard or mouse operations.

# UNIT CHECKPOINT  Offline

**OFFLINE 30 min**

## Objectives

- Assess unit objectives.

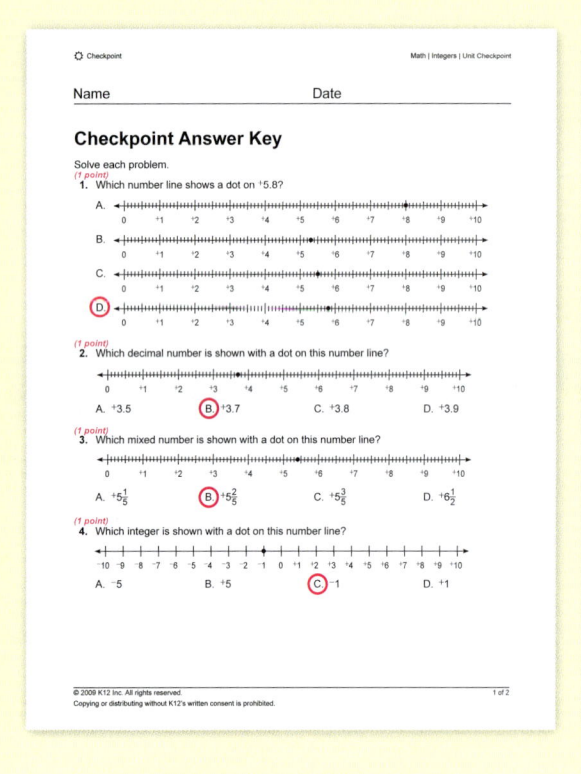

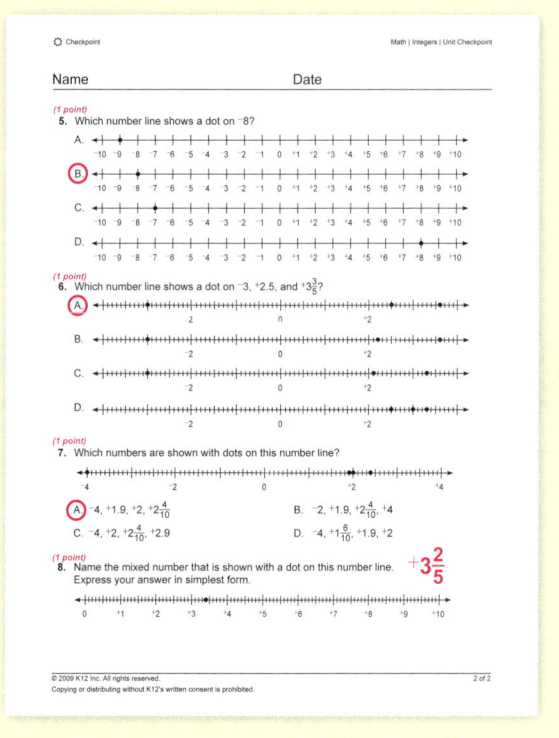

Students will complete this part of the Unit Checkpoint offline. Print the Unit Checkpoint. Read the directions, problems, and answer choices to students, if necessary. Use the answer key to score the Unit Checkpoint. Use the Learning Coach Recording Sheet to keep track of answers to observational questions. Then enter the results online.

# Semester Review

## Lesson Overview

| | | |
|---|---|---|
| **SEMESTER REVIEW** Look Back | 10 minutes | **ONLINE** |
| **SEMESTER REVIEW** Checkpoint Practice | 50 minutes | **ONLINE** |
| ▶ **SEMESTER REVIEW** Prepare for the Checkpoint | | |

### ▶ Semester Objectives

This lesson reviews the following objectives:

- Estimate or calculate a sum or a difference in a whole-number story problem.
- Estimate or calculate a product or quotient in a whole-number story problem.
- Represent and compute a power by using repeated multiplication.
- Solve a problem that involves powers.
- Determine the prime factorization of a composite number.
- Identify, measure, and draw angles with appropriate math tools.
- Identify and draw perpendicular or parallel lines with appropriate math tools.
- Identify that the sum of the interior angles of any triangle is 180° and solve related problems.
- Identify that the sum of the interior angles of any quadrilateral is 360° and solve related problems.
- Divide fractions and explain a step-by-step approach.
- Solve a story problem involving multiplication or division of fractions.
- Solve a simple problem involving addition or subtraction of fractions.
- Round a decimal number to any place through hundredths.
- Estimate the sum or difference in a problem involving decimal numbers.
- Solve a story problem involving addition or subtraction of decimal numbers.
- Estimate the product or quotient of a computation problem involving decimal numbers.
- Solve a story problem that involves multiplication or division of decimal numbers.
- Identify and represent decimal numbers, fractions, mixed numbers, and positive and negative integers on a number line.
- Solve a problem involving addition or subtraction of integers.

### Materials to Gather

There are no materials to gather for this lesson.

▶ **Advance Preparation**

In this lesson, students will have an opportunity to review previous activities from the semester. Look at the suggested activities in Semester Review: Prepare for the Checkpoint online and be prepared to gather any needed materials.

## SEMESTER REVIEW  Look Back

**ONLINE 10 min**

**Objectives**

- Review semester objectives.

As students prepare to complete the semester, they should refresh their knowledge of the math they have learned thus far. You may notice that some of the objectives in the Semester Review are not necessarily included in the Semester Checkpoint. Some of these concepts are particularly important to review in order to be successful with the upcoming topics students will encounter, and others contribute to a greater understanding of the concepts that are being assessed. Therefore, a complete review of the objectives in this lesson is recommended.

To review, students will play a Super Genius game. If students answer a problem incorrectly, the correct answer will display. Be sure to help students understand why the answer is correct before students move on to the next problem. If they miss several problems, have students play the game again.

## SEMESTER REVIEW  Checkpoint Practice

**ONLINE 50 min**

**Objectives**

- Review semester objectives.

Students will complete an online Checkpoint Practice to prepare for the Semester Checkpoint. If necessary, read the directions, problems, and answer choices to students. Have students answer the problems on their own. Review any missed problems with students.

⇄ **SEMESTER REVIEW  Prepare for the Checkpoint**

What you do next depends on how students performed in the previous activity, Semester Review: Checkpoint Practice. If students had difficulty with any of the problems, complete the appropriate review activity listed in the Unit Review tables online.

Because there are many concepts to review, consider using the Your Choice day to continue preparing for the Semester Checkpoint.

# Semester Checkpoint

## Lesson Overview

**SEMESTER CHECKPOINT** Online | 60 minutes | **ONLINE**

### ▶ Semester Objectives

This lesson assesses the following objectives:

- Estimate or calculate a sum or a difference in a whole-number story problem.
- Estimate or calculate a product or quotient in a whole-number story problem.
- Represent and compute a power by using repeated multiplication.
- Solve a problem that involves powers.
- Determine the prime factorization of a composite number.
- Identify that the sum of the interior angles of any triangle is 180° and solve related problems.
- Identify that the sum of the interior angles of any quadrilateral is 360° and solve related problems.
- Solve a story problem involving multiplication or division of fractions.
- Solve a simple problem involving addition or subtraction of fractions.
- Estimate the sum or difference in a problem involving decimal numbers.
- Solve a story problem involving addition or subtraction of decimal numbers.
- Estimate the product or quotient of a computation problem involving decimal numbers.
- Solve a story problem that involves multiplication or division of decimal numbers.
- Identify and represent decimal numbers, fractions, mixed numbers, and positive and negative integers on a number line.
- Solve a problem involving addition or subtraction of integers.

### Materials to Gather

There are no materials to gather for this lesson.

## SEMESTER CHECKPOINT Online

ONLINE 60 min

### Objectives

- Assess semester objectives.

Students will complete the Semester Checkpoint online. Read the directions, problems, and answer choices to students. If necessary, help students with keyboard or mouse operations.

# Percents and Probability

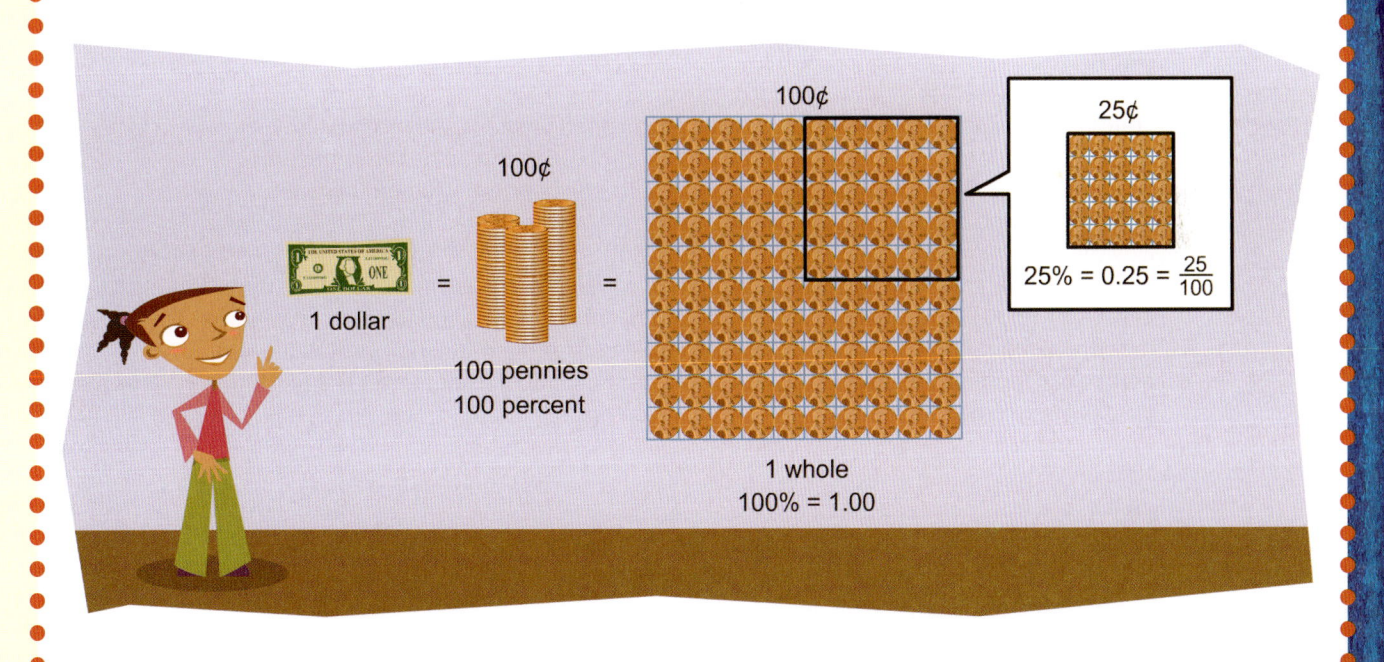

1 dollar = 100¢ = 100 pennies / 100 percent

100¢ — 1 whole, 100% = 1.00

25¢

$25\% = 0.25 = \frac{25}{100}$

## ▶ Unit Objectives

- Interpret a percent as a part of a hundred.
- Determine the decimal and percent equivalents for a common fraction and explain why they represent the same value.
- Compute a given percent of a whole number.
- Represent probabilities as fractions, decimals, and percents.
- Identify events that are dependent or independent.
- Use probability to predict future events.

## ▶ Big Ideas

- Ratios, fractions, percents, and decimals can be used to compare one value to another, or, through models, to compare properties of two things or situations.
- Equivalence is a fundamental property of rational numbers; equivalent fractions, percents, and decimals all name the same relationship between two values.
- Independent events are events in which the occurrence of one event does not affect the occurrence of the other.
- Knowing the probability of an event can help you predict the likelihood that it will occur again.

## ▶ Unit Introduction

Students will explore two topics in this unit: percents of numbers and probability. First students will relate percents to parts of one hundred, connecting a penny as one hundredth of one dollar to one part of one hundred. To build on understanding percents, students will find decimal-number and percent equivalents for fractions while describing why the three representations show the same value.

Students will then find a percent (less than or equal to one hundred) of a whole number. Next they will investigate probability, using fractions, decimal numbers, and percents to connect to probability, the study of the possibility of an event taking place. Work with probability continues with investigating dependent and independent events and using probability to predict the possibility of future events.

## ▶ Keywords

arrangement
combination
dependent event
equally likely
equivalent

experimental probability
independent event
justify conclusions
line plot
outcomes

percent (%)
predict
probability
theoretical probability
tree diagram

# Understand Percents (A)

## Lesson Overview

| | | |
|---|---|---|
| Skills Update | 5 minutes | ONLINE |
| **GET READY** Represent Decimals and Fractions | 5 minutes | OFFLINE |
| **LEARN** Use Grids to Understand Percents | 20 minutes | OFFLINE |
| **LEARN** Grids That Show a Percent | 20 minutes | ONLINE |
| **TRY IT** Practice Identifying Percents | 10 minutes | ONLINE |

### ▶ Lesson Objectives
Interpret a percent as a part of a hundred.

### ▶ Prerequisite Skills
Write tenths and hundredths in decimal and fraction notation and show that the representations are equivalent.

### ▶ Content Background
Students will learn the meaning of *percent*. They will learn about the relationship between decimal numbers, fractions, and percents. Students will shade representations of percents and match them with equivalent decimal numbers and fractions. They will also identify which shaded grids represent a given percent and decide what percent a shaded grid represents.

*Percent* is a Latin word meaning "of each hundred." Percents connect with fractions and decimal numbers to mean one part in a hundred, $\frac{1}{100}$, or one hundredth, 0.01. It may be helpful to connect percent to 1 penny, or 1 cent, as 1 percent of a dollar, since 1 dollar equals 100 cents. A benchmark is a reference number. Percents such as 5%, 10%, 25%, 50%, 75%, and 100% are benchmark percents that can be used to find relationships with other percents. For example, when students understand 10%, they can use it to have a sense for how much 13% is. Knowing that 10% is 10 parts of 100 helps them know that 13% would be slightly more than 10%.

Although students will most often see fractions written with a horizontal fraction bar in math, such as $\frac{2}{3}$ or $5\frac{5}{6}$, they will occasionally see a diagonal fraction bar, such as 2/3 or 5 5/6. Students will very likely see the diagonal fraction bar in everyday experiences, but be sure they understand that using the horizontal fraction bar in their work will make problems involving fractions easier to interpret and solve.

When students write and compute with decimal numbers, they often use numbers that are between 0 and 1, for example, 0.1. While it is acceptable to write this number as .1, mathematicians usually write the leading zero, to show that the whole-number value for the decimal number is zero and to avoid confusion about the value of the number.

### Materials to Gather

**SUPPLIED**
Centimeter Grid Paper (printout)
10 by 10 Penny Grid (printout)

**ALSO NEEDED**
pencils, coloring

▶ **Advance Preparation**

Print one copy of the Centimeter Grid Paper and two copies of the 10 by 10 Penny Grid.

## GET READY Represent Decimals and Fractions  *OFFLINE 5 min*

### Objectives

- Write tenths and hundredths in decimal and fraction notation and show that the representations are equivalent.

Students will use grid paper to model equivalent decimal numbers and fractions. Gather the Centimeter Grid Paper.

1. Have students write this number sentence at the top of the grid paper: $0.79 = \frac{79}{100}$. Remind students that 0.79 is read as "seventy-nine hundredths."
2. Tell students to outline a 10 by 10 square on the top half of the grid paper.
3. Explain that the square is divided into 100 equal-sized small squares. Each small square represents one hundredth.
4. Have students shade 7 columns or rows and 9 squares to show 79 of the small squares shaded. Explain that this model represents 79 hundredths because they shaded 79 parts of a whole that is divided into 100 equal parts.
5. Explain that students can write 79 hundredths as a fraction or a decimal number. Both the fraction $\frac{79}{100}$ and the decimal number 0.79 represent 79 of 100 parts of the one large square.
6. Repeat Steps 1–5 with this number sentence: $0.37 = \frac{37}{100}$. This time, however, have students explain how the model represents both the decimal number and the fraction. Students can use the bottom half of the Centimeter Grid Paper for that 10 by 10 square. They can write $0.37 = \frac{37}{100}$ next to or above the square.

## LEARN Use Grids to Understand Percents  *OFFLINE 20 min*

### Objectives

- Interpret a percent as a part of a hundred.

Students will learn the term *percent* and will relate percents to decimal numbers and fractions. They will then connect percents to pennies shown on the grid and learn that 1¢ is the same as 1%.

Gather two copies of the 10 by 10 Penny Grid and the coloring pencils. Students will shade colors on the grid and will write answers in their Math Notebook. Have them use one color on a grid for the first set of problems (5%, 10%, 25%, 50%, 100%) and a second color on the other grid for the second set of problems (3%, 15%, 33%, 75%).

1. Give students one copy of the grid. Tell them the grid shows 100 pennies, and it represents 100 cents, or $1.00.
2. Have students shade the top left penny on the grid with any color. Explain that because 1 of 100 pennies is shaded, one hundredth of the grid is shaded. Ask them to write one hundredth in decimal number and fraction forms in their notebook. 0.01 and $\frac{1}{100}$

**Say:** There is another way you can describe this shaded penny in the grid. You can say it is *1 percent* of the entire grid.

### Tips

If students have difficulty remembering how related fractions, decimal numbers, and percents are written, put sets of the three representations on separate index cards and have students match them.

**328** PERCENTS AND PROBABILITY

3. **Ask:** In what everyday situations have you heard the word *percent*? Examples: a weather report, a discount price, voting results

   Explain that *percent* comes from Latin and means "of each hundred." Have students write 1% next to 0.01 and $\frac{1}{100}$ and read aloud "1 percent."

4. **Say:** Each penny is one of the 100 parts of a dollar, so 1 penny is 1% of 100 cents, or 1% of a dollar.

5. Now guide students to understand 5%, 10%, 25%, 50%, and 100%. They will shade the grid with the same color they used for 1%.

6. Have students shade 4 more pennies on the grid (so that $\frac{1}{2}$ of one row is shaded). Ask them to write five hundredths in decimal number and fraction form. 0.05 and $\frac{5}{100}$

   Have them write 5% and read aloud "5 percent."

   **Say:** Since 5 of 100 pennies are shaded, 5% of the grid is shaded. So 5% of a dollar is 5 cents.

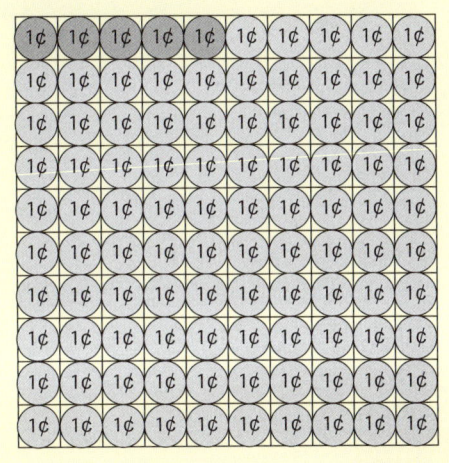

7. Have students shade 5 more pennies on the grid (so that $\frac{1}{2}$ of the row directly below the first one is shaded). Ask them to write 10 hundredths in decimal number and fraction form. 0.10 and $\frac{10}{100}$

   Then have them write 10% and read aloud "10 percent."

   **Say:** Since 10 of 100 pennies are shaded, 10% of the grid is shaded. So 10% of a dollar is 10 cents.

8. Have students shade 3 more $\frac{1}{2}$-rows of pennies directly below the first two, so that five rows have 5 pennies shaded in each row. A total of 25 pennies are shaded on the grid. Ask them to count the shaded pennies, and write the decimal number and fraction that tell how many pennies out of 100 are shaded. Have students read aloud the number. 0.25; $\frac{25}{100}$; twenty-five hundredths

   **Ask:** What percent of the grid is shaded? 25%

   Explain that 25% is one-fourth of the grid and that one-fourth is also called a quarter. Now students know why the 25-cent coin is known as a quarter. They should write 25% by the equivalent numerals.

9. Have students shade 5 more $\frac{1}{2}$-rows directly below the first five, so that 10 rows have 5 pennies shaded in each row. Ask them to count the shaded pennies, write the fraction that tells how many pennies are shaded, and read aloud the fraction. $\frac{50}{100}$; fifty-hundredths

**UNDERSTAND PERCENTS (A)** 329

Have them write the equivalent decimal number. 0.50

**Ask:** What percent of the grid is shaded? 50%

**Say:** Fifty cents is fifty hundredths, or 50%, or one half, of a dollar.

10. Have students shade the rest of the grid. Explain that when 100 of 100 pennies are shaded, 100% of the grid is shaded.

11. Give students the second copy of the grid. Have them select a different color to shade this grid. Using a second color reminds them that the second grid represents the second set of problems. Repeat the activity with the following percents, using one color of shading for 3%, 15%, 33%, and 75%.

    Tell students that the shaded pennies in the grid don't have to be next to each other. For example, single pennies in 3 different corners or rows could be shaded and those 3 pennies would represent 3%.

## LEARN Grids That Show a Percent

**ONLINE 20 min**

### Objectives
- Interpret a percent as a part of a hundred.

Students will visualize percents by identifying the grid that shows a given percent shaded and by identifying the percent that is filled in on a grid. They will then use the Grid Learning Tool to represent a given percent.

### DIRECTIONS FOR USING THE GRID LEARNING TOOL

1. Have students choose a color and then click one square. Tell them that each shaded square represents 1% of the 100 squares in the grid.

2. Have students shade the grid for the following percents, clearing the squares after each problem. Sample answers are shown. Students can fill in other squares to show each percent.

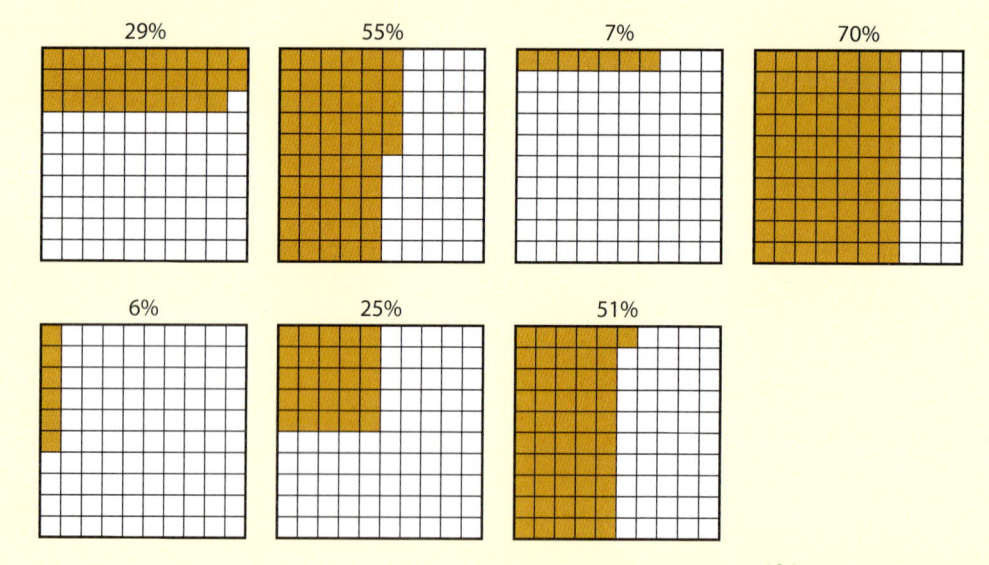

    29%   55%   7%   70%

    6%   25%   51%

## TRY IT Practice Identifying Percents

**ONLINE 10 min**

### Objectives
- Interpret a percent as a part of a hundred.

Students will complete an online Try It. If necessary, read the directions, problems, and answer choices to students and help them with keyboard or mouse operations.

**330** PERCENTS AND PROBABILITY

# Understand Percents (B)

## Lesson Overview

| | | |
|---|---|---|
| **LEARN** Percents, Decimals, and Fractions | 15 minutes | **ONLINE** |
| **LEARN** Show Percents on Grids | 10 minutes | **OFFLINE** |
| **LEARN** Find Percents in Story Problems | 20 minutes | **OFFLINE** |
| **TRY IT** Practice Percent as Part of a Hundred | 5 minutes | **ONLINE** |
| **CHECKPOINT** | 10 minutes | **ONLINE** |

## ▶ Lesson Objectives
Interpret a percent as a part of a hundred.

## ▶ Prerequisite Skills
Write tenths and hundredths in decimal and fraction notation and show that the representations are equivalent.

## ▶ Content Background
Students will review the meaning of *percent*. They will find the equivalent percent, fraction, or decimal number for a given amount and solve story problems involving parts of a hundred.

*Percent* is a Latin word meaning "of each hundred." Percents connect with fractions and decimal numbers to mean one part in a hundred, $\frac{1}{100}$, or one hundredth, 0.01. It may be helpful to connect percent to 1 penny, or 1 cent, as 1 percent of a dollar, since 1 dollar equals 100 cents. A benchmark is a reference number. Percents such as 5%, 10%, 25%, 50%, 75%, and 100% are benchmark percents that can be used to find relationships with other percents. For example, when students understand 10%, they can use it to have a sense for how much 13% is. Knowing that 10% is 10 parts of 100 helps them know that 13% would be slightly more than 10%.

Although students will most often see fractions written with a horizontal fraction bar in math, such as $\frac{2}{3}$ or $5\frac{5}{6}$, they will occasionally see a diagonal fraction bar, such as 2/3 or 5 5/6. Students will very likely see the diagonal fraction bar in everyday experiences, but be sure they understand that using the horizontal fraction bar in their work will make problems involving fractions easier to interpret and solve.

When students write and compute with decimal numbers, they often use numbers that are between 0 and 1, for example, 0.1. While it is acceptable to write this number as .1, mathematicians usually write the leading zero, to show that the whole-number value for the decimal number is zero and to avoid confusion about the value of the number.

## ▶ Advance Preparation
Print three copies of the Centimeter Grid Paper.

### Materials to Gather

**SUPPLIED**
Centimeter Grid Paper (printout) – 3
Find Percents in Story Problems activity page

## LEARN  Percents, Decimals, and Fractions

ONLINE 15 min

**Objectives**
- Interpret a percent as a part of a hundred.

Students will review equivalent fractions, decimal numbers, and percents for parts of a hundred by matching percents, decimal numbers, or fractions for a given amount.

## LEARN  Show Percents on Grids

OFFLINE 10 min

**Objectives**
- Interpret a percent as a part of a hundred.

Students will be given some percents. They will shade grid paper to represent the equivalent squares out of 100 for each given percent.

Gather the Centimeter Grid Paper. Have students outline two 10 by 10 grids of 100 squares on each of the three copies.

**Say:** Shade one 10 by 10 grid to represent an equivalent number for each of the following percents:

- 4%  4 squares shaded
- 12%  12 squares shaded
- 33%  33 squares shaded
- 47%  47 squares shaded
- 65%  65 squares shaded
- 75%  75 squares shaded

These examples show how students may shade each grid.

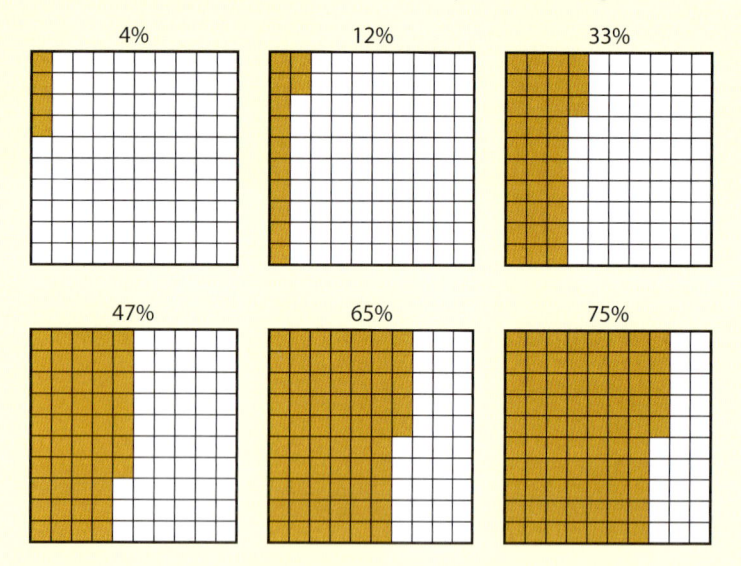

4%           12%           33%

47%           65%           75%

## LEARN  Find Percents in Story Problems

OFFLINE 20 min

**Objectives**
- Interpret a percent as a part of a hundred.

Students will solve story problems that either ask for percents or ask for the number of items when the percent is given. Have students turn to the Find Percents in Story Problems activity page in their Activity Book and read the directions with them.

Students should copy the problems from the Activity Book into their Math Notebook as necessary and solve them there.

1. Read the Worked Example with students and make sure they understand it.
2. Review the following with students before they solve the problems. Remind students that percent means "out of a hundred."

   **Ask:** One dollar is 100 cents. What are three ways you can show 30 cents besides using the word *cents*? 0.30, $\frac{30}{100}$, or 30%

   **Ask:** If 29 out of 100 children prefer green apples to red apples, what percent prefer green apples to red apples? 29%

3. Have students solve Problem 1. Make sure they have answered it correctly before they move on to the next problem. Assist students as needed with the remaining problems.

### Tips

If students have difficulty understanding the connection between percent and parts of a hundred, have them write and solve some story problems of their own.

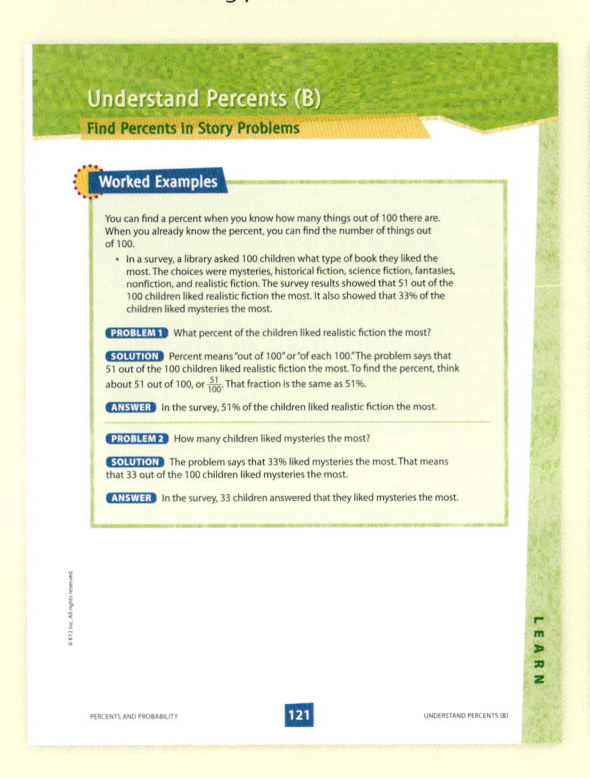

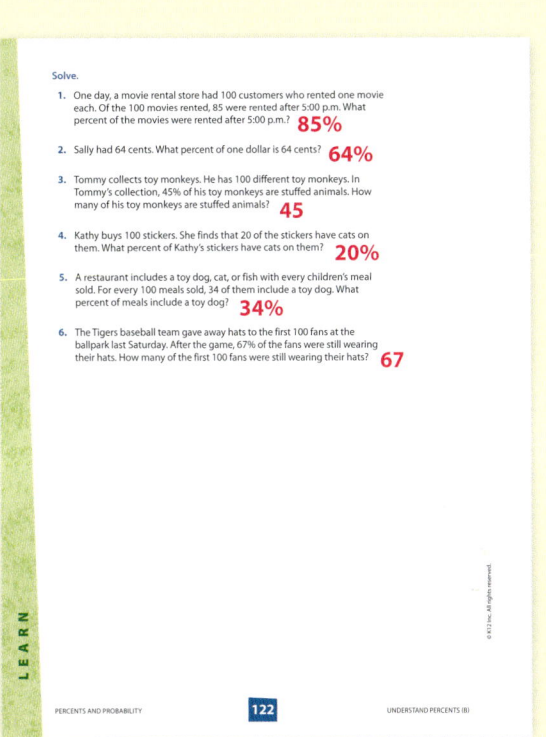

---

**Understand Percents (B)**
**Find Percents in Story Problems**

**Worked Examples**

You can find a percent when you know how many things out of 100 there are. When you already know the percent, you can find the number of things out of 100.

- In a survey, a library asked 100 children what type of book they liked the most. The choices were mysteries, historical fiction, science fiction, fantasies, nonfiction, and realistic fiction. The survey results showed that 51 out of the 100 children liked realistic fiction the most. It also showed that 33% of the children liked mysteries the most.

**PROBLEM 1** What percent of the children liked realistic fiction the most?

**SOLUTION** Percent means "out of 100" or "of each 100." The problem says that 51 out of the 100 children liked realistic fiction the most. To find the percent, think about 51 out of 100, or $\frac{51}{100}$. That fraction is the same as 51%.

**ANSWER** In the survey, 51% of the children liked realistic fiction the most.

**PROBLEM 2** How many children liked mysteries the most?

**SOLUTION** The problem says that 33% liked mysteries the most. That means that 33 out of the 100 children liked mysteries the most.

**ANSWER** In the survey, 33 children answered that they liked mysteries the most.

---

**Solve.**

1. One day, a movie rental store had 100 customers who rented one movie each. Of the 100 movies rented, 85 were rented after 5:00 p.m. What percent of the movies were rented after 5:00 p.m.? **85%**

2. Sally had 64 cents. What percent of one dollar is 64 cents? **64%**

3. Tommy collects toy monkeys. He has 100 different toy monkeys. In Tommy's collection, 45% of his toy monkeys are stuffed animals. How many of his toy monkeys are stuffed animals? **45**

4. Kathy buys 100 stickers. She finds that 20 of the stickers have cats on them. What percent of Kathy's stickers have cats on them? **20%**

5. A restaurant includes a toy dog, cat, or fish with every children's meal sold. For every 100 meals sold, 34 of them include a toy dog. What percent of meals include a toy dog? **34%**

6. The Tigers baseball team gave away hats to the first 100 fans at the ballpark last Saturday. After the game, 67% of the fans were still wearing their hats. How many of the first 100 fans were still wearing their hats? **67**

---

### TRY IT  Practice Percent as Part of a Hundred

**ONLINE 5 min**

**Objectives**
- Interpret a percent as a part of a hundred.

Students will complete an online Try It. If necessary, read the directions, problems, and answer choices to students and help them with keyboard or mouse operations.

### CHECKPOINT

**ONLINE 10 min**

**Objectives**
- Interpret a percent as a part of a hundred.

Students will complete an online Checkpoint. If necessary, read the directions, problems, and answer choices to students and help them with keyboard or mouse operations.

**UNDERSTAND PERCENTS (B)** 333

# Find Equivalents to Percents (A)

## Lesson Overview

| | | |
|---|---|---|
| Skills Update | 5 minutes | ONLINE |
| **GET READY** Match Fractions and Decimals | 5 minutes | ONLINE |
| **LEARN** Equivalent Fractions and Decimals | 15 minutes | OFFLINE |
| **LEARN** Find Decimals Equal to a Fraction | 10 minutes | OFFLINE |
| **LEARN** Fraction and Decimal Story Problems | 15 minutes | OFFLINE |
| **TRY IT** Practice with Equivalents | 10 minutes | ONLINE |

### ▶ Lesson Objectives

Determine the decimal and percent equivalents for a common fraction and explain why they represent the same value.

### ▶ Prerequisite Skills

- Write tenths and hundredths in decimal and fraction notation and show that the representations are equivalent.
- Identify fraction and decimal-number equivalents for halves and fourths.

### ▶ Content Background

Students will learn to identify the decimal-number equivalent for a fraction by finding an equivalent fraction with a denominator of 10, 100, or 1,000 and then naming the decimal number with the same value.

*Percent* is a Latin word meaning "of each hundred." Percents connect with fractions and decimal numbers to mean one part in a hundred, $\frac{1}{100}$, or one hundredth, 0.01. It may be helpful to connect percent to 1 penny, or 1 cent, as 1 percent of a dollar, since 1 dollar equals 100 cents.

Although students will most often see fractions written with a horizontal fraction bar in math, such as $\frac{2}{3}$ or $5\frac{5}{6}$, they will occasionally see a diagonal fraction bar, such as 2/3 or 5 5/6. Students will very likely see the diagonal fraction bar in everyday experiences, but be sure they understand that using the horizontal fraction bar in their work will make problems involving fractions easier to interpret and solve.

When students write and compute with decimal numbers, they often use numbers that are between 0 and 1, for example, 0.1. While it is acceptable to write this number as .1, mathematicians usually write the leading zero, to show that the whole-number value for the decimal number is zero and to avoid confusion about the value of the number.

### ▶ Advance Preparation

Print the Centimeter Grid Paper.

### Materials to Gather

**SUPPLIED**

Centimeter Grid Paper (printout)
Fraction and Decimal Story Problems activity page

**ALSO NEEDED**

pencils, coloring

## GET READY  Match Fractions and Decimals

**ONLINE 5 min**

Students will match equivalent decimal numbers and fractions to reveal a hidden picture.

### Objectives
- Write tenths and hundredths in decimal and fraction notation and show that the representations are equivalent.
- Identify fraction and decimal-number equivalents for halves and fourths.

## LEARN  Equivalent Fractions and Decimals

**OFFLINE 15 min**

Students will shade representations of fractions and decimal numbers and write the equivalent numbers. They will learn how to change fractions to decimal numbers by changing the denominator to 10 or 100. Students will write the equivalent fractions and decimal numbers in their Math Notebook. As needed, have them write their answers as they say them, because equivalent fraction and decimal numbers are pronounced the same. You can point to fractions and decimal numbers as you discuss them.

Note that the term *decimal number* means a number with a decimal point in it. Sometimes, the term *decimal* is used here as another way to say *decimal number*. An *equivalent decimal* is an *equivalent decimal number*.

Gather the Centimeter Grid Paper and the coloring pencils.

### Objectives
- Determine the decimal and percent equivalents for a common fraction and explain why they represent the same value.

1. Have students outline a row of 10 squares at the top of the Centimeter Grid Paper. Have them shade 3 of the squares with any color.

   **Ask:** What fraction with a denominator of 10 represents the shaded squares? Write and say your answers. $\frac{3}{10}$

   **Ask:** What decimal number can also represent the shaded squares? 0.3

   **Say:** Remember that the decimal number 0.3 is pronounced "three tenths."

   Have students write $\frac{3}{10} = 0.3$. Explain that $\frac{3}{10}$ and 0.3 are equivalent because they both represent the same value.

2. Have students outline a 10 by 10 area on the grid paper and shade 32 of the squares with a different color from the 3 of 10 squares.

   **Ask:** What fraction with a denominator of 100 can represent the shaded squares? $\frac{32}{100}$

   **Ask:** What decimal number can also represent the shaded squares? 0.32

   **Say:** Remember that 0.32 is pronounced "thirty-two hundredths."

   Have students write $\frac{32}{100} = 0.32$. Explain that $\frac{32}{100}$ and 0.32 are equivalent because they both represent the same value.

3. Tell students that they will now learn to write and name the decimal equivalent for the fraction $\frac{3}{5}$.

   **Say:** You already know how to express, or show, a fraction with a denominator of 10 or 100 as a decimal number. Now you will find the equivalent decimal number for $\frac{3}{5}$ by first finding an equivalent fraction with a denominator of 10.

FIND EQUIVALENTS TO PERCENTS (A)

4. Write $\frac{3}{5} = \frac{?}{10}$. Remind students that when they create an equivalent fraction, they have to multiply the numerator and denominator by the same value.

   **Ask:** To change the denominator to 10, what will you multiply 5 by? **2**

   **Ask:** Now you'll multiply the numerator by 2. What is the product? **6**

   Explain that students multiplied 5 × 2 because they needed to change the denominator from fifths to tenths. They then needed to multiply the numerator by 2 as well, so they multiplied 3 × 2.

   Have students write the following:

   $\frac{3}{5} = \frac{6}{10}$

   $\frac{6}{10} = 0.6$

   $\frac{3}{5} = 0.6$

   Explain that now they can write the decimal equivalent because $\frac{6}{10} = 0.6$. Tell them that since $\frac{3}{5} = \frac{6}{10}$ and $\frac{6}{10} = 0.6$, then $\frac{3}{5} = 0.6$.

5. Tell students that they will now learn to name the decimal equivalent for the fraction $\frac{2}{25}$. Have students write $\frac{2}{25} = \frac{?}{100}$.

   Tell them the process is similar to the one they used for $\frac{3}{5}$, but this time, they will change a fraction to a decimal number in hundredths.

   Guide students to find that 4 multiplied by the denominator 25 gives them the denominator 100. Guide them to find that 4 multiplied by the numerator 2 gives them the numerator 8. Have students write the following:

   $\frac{2}{25} = \frac{8}{100}$

   $\frac{8}{100} = 0.08$

   $\frac{2}{25} = 0.08$

   **Say:** The decimal equivalent for $\frac{2}{25}$ is 0.08, which is pronounced "eight hundredths."

   Write 0.80 and 0.08 next to each other.

   **Say:** If you made a mistake and thought that eight hundredths is written 0.80, remember that 0.80 is eighty hundredths, or $\frac{80}{100}$, or 80 parts out of 100, and 0.08 is eight hundredths, or $\frac{8}{100}$, or 8 parts out of 100.

6. Tell students they will now name the decimal equivalent for the fraction $\frac{1}{2}$. Have them find an equivalent fraction with a denominator of 10, asking them to provide the missing number and showing how they found it. Their work should be as follows:

   - Write $\frac{1}{2} = \frac{?}{10}$.
   - Multiply 5 times 2 to change the denominator to 10.
   - Multiply 5 times 1 because the numerator needs to be multiplied by the same number as was used to multiply the denominator.
   - $\frac{1}{2} = \frac{5}{10}$

   Have students write the following:

   $\frac{1}{2} = \frac{5}{10}$

   $\frac{5}{10} = 0.5$

   $\frac{1}{2} = 0.5$

PERCENTS AND PROBABILITY

**Ask:** What is the decimal equivalent of $\frac{5}{10}$? 0.5

**Ask:** What is the decimal equivalent of $\frac{1}{2}$? 0.5

7. Have students name the decimal equivalent for $\frac{6}{20}$. See if they can write the following steps on their own. Guide them if necessary.

    $\frac{6}{20} = \frac{30}{100}$

    $\frac{30}{100} = 0.30$

    $\frac{6}{20} = 0.30$

8. Have students name the decimal equivalent for $\frac{23}{50}$. See if they can write the following steps on their own. Guide them if necessary.

    $\frac{23}{50} = \frac{46}{100}$

    $\frac{46}{100} = 0.46$

    $\frac{23}{50} = 0.46$

9. Summarize how to find an equivalent decimal number for a fraction:
    - Start with a fraction.
    - Find an equivalent fraction with a denominator of 10 or 100.
    - Change the fraction with a denominator of 10 or 100 to an equivalent decimal number.
    - Write a number sentence to show the fraction and the equivalent decimal number.

## LEARN Find Decimals Equal to a Fraction

OFFLINE 10 min

### Objectives
- Determine the decimal and percent equivalents for a common fraction and explain why they represent the same value.

Students will learn that more than one decimal number can be equivalent to a given fraction. Have students write their answers, including all equivalent fraction and decimal numbers, in their Math Notebook.

1. Guide students to find two decimal numbers that are equivalent to $\frac{6}{10}$.

    **Ask:** What is a decimal number that is equivalent to $\frac{6}{10}$? 0.6

2. Have students write $\frac{6}{10} = 0.6 = \frac{60}{100}$. Remind them that $\frac{6}{10}$ and $\frac{60}{100}$ have the same value because $\frac{6}{10}$ can be multiplied by $\frac{10}{10}$, a fraction that is equivalent to 1, to write a fraction with a denominator of 100.

    **Ask:** What is the decimal equivalent of $\frac{60}{100}$? 0.60

    Have students write "= 0.60" next to their $\frac{60}{100}$ in the number sentence.

3. Explain to students why these fractions and decimals are equivalent by making the following points:
    - The decimal equivalent for $\frac{6}{10}$ is 0.6.
    - The fraction $\frac{6}{10}$ has the same value as $\frac{60}{100}$ because $\frac{60}{100}$ also means 6 parts out of every 10.
    - The number 0.60 is the equivalent decimal for $\frac{60}{100}$.
    - $\frac{6}{10}$ is equivalent to 0.6. It's also true that $\frac{6}{10}$ is equivalent to $\frac{60}{100}$ and 0.60. That means that $\frac{6}{10}$, 0.6, $\frac{60}{100}$, and 0.60 all have the same value.

**FIND EQUIVALENTS TO PERCENTS (A)** 337

4. Have students repeat the steps in this activity to find two decimal equivalents for each of the following fractions and then explain why the fractions and decimals are equivalent. Remind students to start by changing their fraction to a denominator of 10 if necessary.

- $\frac{7}{10}$  $\frac{7}{10} = 0.7 = \frac{70}{100} = 0.70$
- $\frac{3}{10}$  $\frac{3}{10} = 0.3 = \frac{30}{100} = 0.30$
- $\frac{9}{10}$  $\frac{9}{10} = 0.9 = \frac{90}{100} = 0.90$
- $\frac{1}{2}$  $\frac{1}{2} = \frac{5}{10} = 0.5 = \frac{50}{100} = 0.50$

**Tips**  If students have difficulty finding equivalent decimals and fractions, create index cards with a decimal number or fraction on each one and have them match pairs.

## LEARN  Fraction and Decimal Story Problems

OFFLINE 15 min

### Objectives

- Determine the decimal and percent equivalents for a common fraction and explain why they represent the same value.

Students will practice solving story problems that provide fractions and ask for the equivalent decimals. Have students turn to the Fraction and Decimals Story Problems activity page in their Activity Book and read the directions with them.

Students should copy the problems from the Activity Book into their Math Notebook as necessary and solve them there.

1. Read the first Worked Example with students. Remind them that when they create an equivalent fraction, they have to multiply the numerator and denominator by the same value.

2. Have students complete Problems 1–4. For Problem 2, remind students that since the fraction is already expressed using tenths, they can write the decimal equivalent without first finding the equivalent fraction.

   **Say:** Name two decimal equivalents for $\frac{4}{10}$. 0.4 and 0.40

3. Read the second Worked Example with students. Explain that since the fraction is already written as a fraction with a denominator of 1,000, the decimal equivalent can be written without first finding an equivalent fraction.

4. Have students complete Problems 5–7.

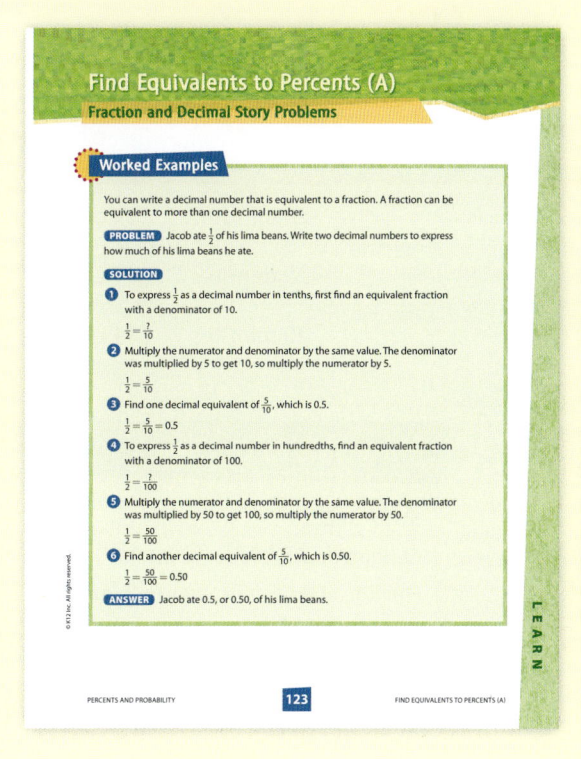

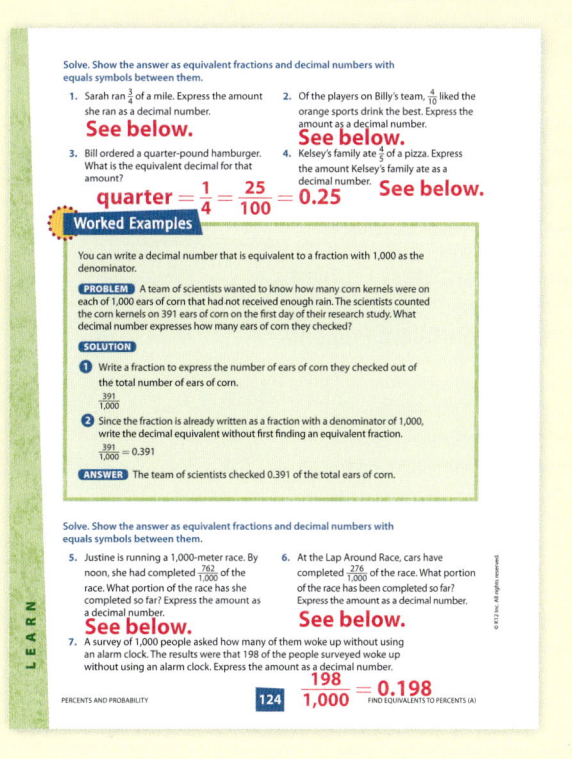

## Additional Answers

1. $\frac{3}{4} = \frac{75}{100} = 0.75$

2. $\frac{4}{10} = 0.4$

4. $\frac{4}{5} = \frac{8}{10} = 0.8$ or $0.80$

5. $\frac{762}{1,000} = 0.762$

6. $\frac{276}{1,000} = 0.276$

## TRY IT  Practice with Equivalents

ONLINE 10 min

Students will complete an online Try It. If necessary, read the directions, problems, and answer choices to students and help them with keyboard or mouse operations.

### Objectives

- Determine the decimal and percent equivalents for a common fraction and explain why they represent the same value.

**FIND EQUIVALENTS TO PERCENTS (A)** 339

# Find Equivalents to Percents (B)

## Lesson Overview

| | | |
|---|---|---|
| **LEARN** Equivalent Fractions and Percents | 20 minutes | **OFFLINE** |
| **LEARN** Fraction and Percent Story Problems | 20 minutes | **OFFLINE** |
| **TRY IT** Practice Finding Equivalent Percents | 20 minutes | **OFFLINE** |

### ▶ Lesson Objectives
Determine the decimal and percent equivalents for a common fraction and explain why they represent the same value.

### ▶ Prerequisite Skills
- Write tenths and hundredths in decimal and fraction notation and show that the representations are equivalent.
- Identify fraction and decimal-number equivalents for halves and fourths.

### ▶ Content Background
Students will learn to identify a percent that is equivalent to a fraction. They will explain how to find equivalent fractions with denominators of 100 and then use these fractions to name a percent with the same value as the original fraction.

*Percent* is a Latin word meaning "of each hundred." Percents connect with fractions and decimal numbers to mean one part in a hundred, $\frac{1}{100}$, or one hundredth, 0.01. It may be helpful to connect percent to 1 penny, or 1 cent, as 1 percent of a dollar, since 1 dollar equals 100 cents.

Although students will most often see fractions written with a horizontal fraction bar in math, such as $\frac{2}{3}$ or $5\frac{5}{6}$, they will occasionally see a diagonal fraction bar, such as 2/3 or 5 5/6. Students will very likely see the diagonal fraction bar in everyday experiences, but be sure they understand that using the horizontal fraction bar in their work will make problems involving fractions easier to interpret and solve.

When students write and compute with decimal numbers, they often use numbers that are between 0 and 1, for example, 0.1. While it is acceptable to write this number as .1, mathematicians usually write the leading zero, to show that the whole-number value for the decimal number is zero and to avoid confusion about the value of the number.

### ▶ Advance Preparation
Print the Centimeter Grid Paper.

---

**Materials to Gather**

**SUPPLIED**
Centimeter Grid Paper (printout)
Fraction and Percent Story Problems activity page
Practice Finding Equivalent Percents activity page

**ALSO NEEDED**
pencils, coloring

## LEARN Equivalent Fractions and Percents

**OFFLINE 20 min**

### Objectives
- Determine the decimal and percent equivalents for a common fraction and explain why they represent the same value.

Students will shade representations of equivalent fractions and percents and learn how to find percents that are equivalent to fractions. They will write their equivalent fractions and percents in their Math Notebook.

Gather the Centimeter Grid Paper and the coloring pencils.

1. Have students outline a 10 by 10 area at the top of the grid paper. Have them shade 20 of the squares with any color.

   **Ask:** What fraction with a denominator of 100 represents the shaded squares? $\frac{20}{100}$

   **Ask:** What decimal represents the shaded squares? 0.20

   **Ask:** If 20 squares are shaded out of 100 squares, what percent of the squares are shaded? 20%

   Have students write $\frac{20}{100} = 0.20 = 20\%$. Explain that the fraction, decimal number, and percent are equivalent, which means they represent the same value.

2. Have students outline a 10 by 10 area on the grid paper and shade 17 of the squares with a different color. Repeat Step 1 for students to find the equivalent percent of $\frac{17}{100}$. Have students write $\frac{17}{100} = 0.17 = 17\%$.

3. Tell students you will ask them to name the equivalent percent for various fractions, starting with $\frac{5}{10}$. Have them write $\frac{5}{10} = \frac{?}{100}$. Tell them that they can find the equivalent percent for $\frac{5}{10}$ by first finding an equivalent fraction with a denominator of 100.

   **Ask:** What number times 10 equals the denominator 100? 10

   **Ask:** Now you need to multiply the numerator by the same value to create an equivalent fraction. If you multiply the numerator 5 by 10, what is the missing numerator? 50

   **Say:** You can write the fraction $\frac{50}{100}$, which is equivalent to $\frac{5}{10}$, as 50%.

   Have students write $\frac{5}{10} = \frac{50}{100} = 50\%$.

4. Have students follow the same process in Step 3 to find the equivalent percent for $\frac{12}{25}$. If necessary, remind them that they need to begin by writing a fraction with a denominator of 100 and an unknown numerator. Their process should work like the following:

   - $\frac{12}{25} = \frac{?}{100}$
   - Multiply the numerator by 4 because the denominator was multiplied by 4 to get 100.
   - $\frac{12}{25} = \frac{48}{100} = 48\%$

   **Ask:** What is the equivalent percent for $\frac{48}{100}$? 48%

5. Tell students they will name the equivalent percent for $\frac{9}{50}$.

   **Ask:** What is the equivalent fraction for $\frac{9}{50}$ that has a denominator of 100? $\frac{18}{100}$

   **Ask:** What is the equivalent percent for $\frac{9}{50}$? 18%

   Have students write $\frac{9}{50} = \frac{18}{100} = 18\%$.

FIND EQUIVALENTS TO PERCENTS (B) 341

6. Have students repeat Step 5 to name equivalent percents for the following fractions. Have them explain why the fractions and percents are equivalent by writing the chain of equivalent fractions and percents.

   - $\frac{47}{100}$   $\frac{47}{100} = 47\%$
   - $\frac{9}{10}$   $\frac{9}{10} = \frac{90}{100} = 90\%$
   - $\frac{3}{5}$   $\frac{3}{5} = \frac{60}{100} = 60\%$
   - $\frac{37}{50}$   $\frac{37}{50} = \frac{74}{100} = 74\%$
   - $\frac{11}{25}$   $\frac{11}{25} = \frac{44}{100} = 44\%$
   - $\frac{17}{20}$   $\frac{17}{20} = \frac{85}{100} = 85\%$

## LEARN Fraction and Percent Story Problems

**OFFLINE 20 min**

### Objectives

- Determine the decimal and percent equivalents for a common fraction and explain why they represent the same value.

Students will practice solving story problems that give a fraction and ask for the equivalent percent. They will also practice solving problems that give a percent and ask for the equivalent fraction with a denominator of 100. Have students turn to the Fraction and Percent Story Problems activity page in their Activity Book and read the directions with them.

Students should copy the problems from the Activity Book into their Math Notebook as necessary and solve them there.

1. Read the first Worked Example with students.

   **Ask:** Why do you need to write the fraction $\frac{1}{2}$ as a fraction with 100 as the denominator? To write a percent, which is part of 100, I want a fraction with a denominator of 100, so I can write the decimal number in the hundredths.

   Remind students that when they create an equivalent fraction, they have to multiply the numerator and denominator by the same value, as shown in the example.

2. Read the second Worked Example with students. Explain that they can write a percent as an equivalent fraction with a denominator of 100.

3. Have students read Problem 1.

   **Ask:** What does the story problem ask? Write $\frac{3}{5}$ as a percent.

   **Ask:** What number times 5 equals the denominator 100? 20
   If you multiply the numerator 3 by 20, what is the new numerator? 60

   **Ask:** What is the equivalent fraction for $\frac{3}{5}$ with a denominator of 100? $\frac{60}{100}$

   **Ask:** What is the equivalent percent for $\frac{60}{100}$? 60%

   **Say:** State the answer to the story problem in a complete sentence. Larry spends 60% of his exercise time jogging.

4. Have students complete the rest of the problems. After they have found the percent or fraction for each problem, have them state the answer by relating the percent or fraction to the original question in the story problem.

**342** PERCENTS AND PROBABILITY

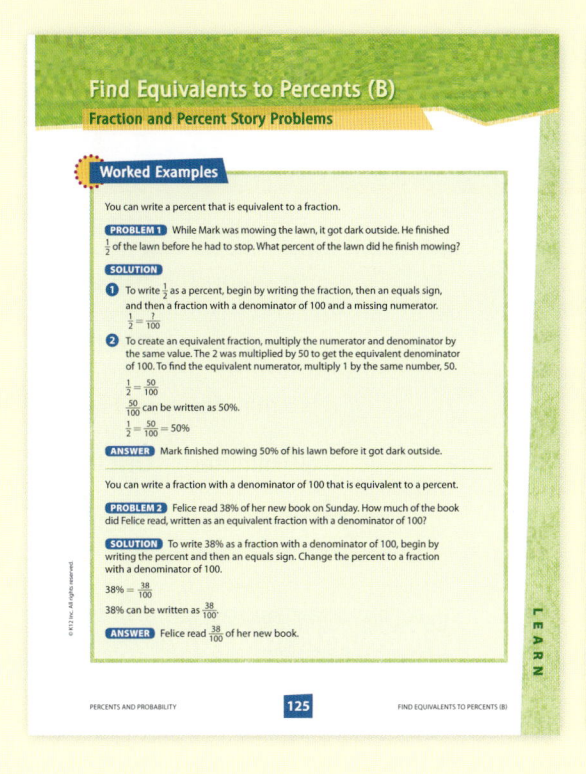

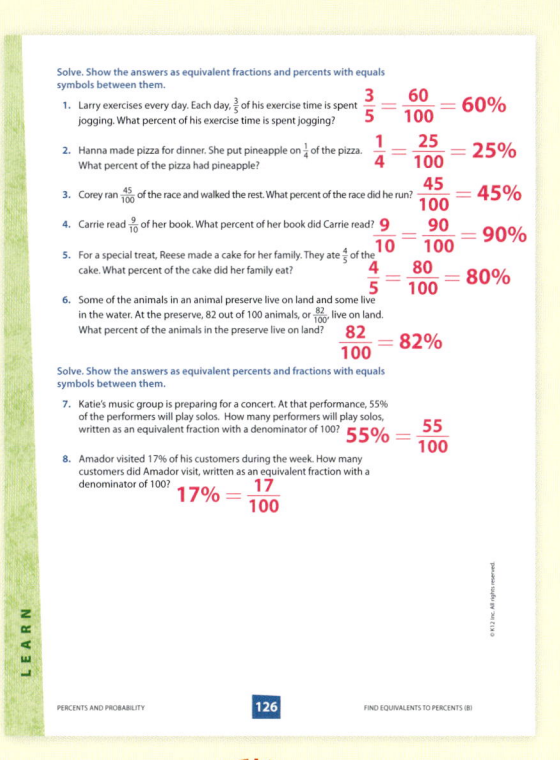

## TRY IT  Practice Finding Equivalent Percents

Students will practice calculating equivalent fractions and percents. Have students turn to the Practice Finding Equivalent Percents activity page in their Activity Book and read the directions with them.

Students should copy the problems from the Activity Book into their Math Notebook as necessary and solve them there.

**OFFLINE 20 min**

### Objectives

- Determine the decimal and percent equivalents for a common fraction and explain why they represent the same value.

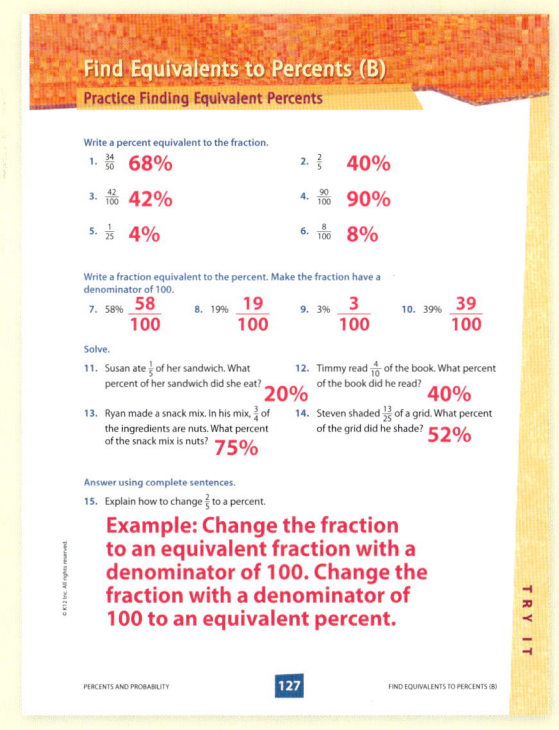

---

### Find Equivalents to Percents (B)
**Practice Finding Equivalent Percents**

Write a percent equivalent to the fraction.

1. $\frac{34}{50}$  **68%**
2. $\frac{2}{5}$  **40%**
3. $\frac{42}{100}$  **42%**
4. $\frac{90}{100}$  **90%**
5. $\frac{1}{25}$  **4%**
6. $\frac{8}{100}$  **8%**

Write a fraction equivalent to the percent. Make the fraction have a denominator of 100.

7. 58%  $\frac{58}{100}$
8. 19%  $\frac{19}{100}$
9. 3%  $\frac{3}{100}$
10. 39%  $\frac{39}{100}$

Solve.

11. Susan ate $\frac{1}{5}$ of her sandwich. What percent of her sandwich did she eat? **20%**
12. Timmy read $\frac{4}{10}$ of the book. What percent of the book did he read? **40%**
13. Ryan made a snack mix. In his mix, $\frac{3}{4}$ of the ingredients are nuts. What percent of the snack mix is nuts? **75%**
14. Steven shaded $\frac{13}{25}$ of a grid. What percent of the grid did he shade? **52%**

Answer using complete sentences.

15. Explain how to change $\frac{2}{5}$ to a percent.

**Example: Change the fraction to an equivalent fraction with a denominator of 100. Change the fraction with a denominator of 100 to an equivalent percent.**

---

**FIND EQUIVALENTS TO PERCENTS (B)  343**

# Find Equivalents to Percents (C)

## Lesson Overview

| | | |
|---|---|---|
| **GET READY** Match Decimals and Fractions | 5 minutes | **ONLINE** |
| **LEARN** Show Fractions, Decimals, and Percents | 10 minutes | **ONLINE** |
| **LEARN** Match Fraction, Decimal, and Percent | 10 minutes | **ONLINE** |
| **LEARN** Story Problems with Equivalents | 15 minutes | **OFFLINE** |
| **TRY IT** Practice Finding the Same Value | 10 minutes | **ONLINE** |
| **CHECKPOINT** | 10 minutes | **ONLINE** |

### ▶ Lesson Objectives
Determine the decimal and percent equivalents for a common fraction and explain why they represent the same value.

### ▶ Prerequisite Skills
- Write tenths and hundredths in decimal and fraction notation and show that the representations are equivalent.
- Identify fraction and decimal-number equivalents for halves and fourths.

### ▶ Content Background
Students will match and name equivalent fractions, decimal numbers, and percents. They will solve story problems that ask them to find equivalent fractions, decimal numbers, or percents.

*Percent* is a Latin word meaning "of each hundred." Percents connect with fractions and decimal numbers to mean one part in one hundred, $\frac{1}{100}$, or one hundredth, 0.01. It may be helpful to connect percent to 1 penny, or 1 cent, as 1 percent of a dollar, since 1 dollar equals 100 cents.

Although students will most often see fractions written with a horizontal fraction bar in math, such as $\frac{2}{3}$ or $5\frac{5}{6}$, they will occasionally see a diagonal fraction bar, such as 2/3 or 5 5/6. Students will very likely see the diagonal fraction bar in everyday experiences, but be sure they understand that using the horizontal fraction bar in their work will make problems involving fractions easier to interpret and solve.

When students write and compute with decimal numbers, they often use numbers that are between 0 and 1, for example, 0.1. While it is acceptable to write this number as .1, mathematicians usually write the leading zero, to show that the whole-number value for the decimal number is zero and to avoid confusion about the value of the number.

### Materials to Gather

**SUPPLIED**

Centimeter Grid Paper (optional printout)

Story Problems with Equivalents activity page

## GET READY  Match Decimals and Fractions

**ONLINE 5 min**

Students will match the fraction and decimal number that have the same value.

**Tips**  If students have trouble finding fractions and decimal numbers that are equivalent, use Centimeter Grid Paper and have students represent each one.

### Objectives

- Write tenths and hundredths in decimal and fraction notation and show that the representations are equivalent.
- Identify fraction and decimal-number equivalents for halves and fourths.

## LEARN  Show Fractions, Decimals, and Percents

**ONLINE 10 min**

Students will use the Fractions, Decimal Numbers, & Percents Learning Tool to represent equivalent values of fractions, decimal numbers, and percents.

**DIRECTIONS FOR USING THE FRACTIONS, DECIMAL NUMBERS, & PERCENTS LEARNING TOOL**

1. Read the instructions, and click Start.
2. **Say:** You will use fraction strips, decimal-number strips, and percent strips to represent a value. The problems you'll solve will not always start with a fraction. Some problems will start with a decimal number or a percent.
3. Have students review the sets of fraction, decimal-number, and percent strips at the top of the screen. They should also open the equivalent chart and review the fractions, decimals, and percents charts.
4. Have students drag one $\frac{1}{4}$ strip from the top bar to the left section of the screen. Using the decimal-number and percent sets of strips, have them show the decimal and percent equivalents for $\frac{1}{4}$ under the fraction strip. Students should use only one strip from each set. Make sure that each strip is in its own row, and be sure the left ends of the strips are lined up.

   **Ask:** How do you know that the decimal-number strip and percent strip show the same value as the $\frac{1}{4}$ fraction strip? When you show the fraction, decimal-number, and percent strip for $\frac{1}{4}$, one on top of another, with the left ends lined up, the right ends of all three strips also line up, even though each strip is a different representation.

   **Ask:** What decimal number and percent have the same value as $\frac{1}{4}$? 0.25 and 25%
5. Have students clear the left section of the screen. Have them drag one 0.2 strip from the top bar to the left section of the screen. Using the fraction and percent sets of strips, have them show the fraction and percent equivalents for 0.2 under the decimal-number strip. Students should use only one strip from each set. Make sure that each strip is in its own row and the left ends of the strips are lined up.

### Objectives

- Determine the decimal and percent equivalents for a common fraction and explain why they represent the same value.

**Tips**

If students have difficulty with changing values between fractions, decimal numbers, and percents, have them use their Math Notebook to write one representation and find the other two values.

**FIND EQUIVALENTS TO PERCENTS (C)**  345

**Ask:** How do you know that the fraction strip and percent strip show the same value as the 0.2 decimal-number strip? When you show the fraction, decimal-number, and percent strip for 0.2, one on top of another, with the left ends lined up, the right ends of all three strips also line up, even though each strip is a different representation.

**Ask:** What fraction and percent have the same value as 0.2? $\frac{1}{5}$ and 20%

6. Repeat Step 5 for the decimal number 0.70. Students will need to use more than one strip to represent the value.

    **Ask:** What fraction and percent have the same value as 0.70? $\frac{7}{10}$ and 70%

7. Repeat Step 5 for the percent 10%.

    **Ask:** What fraction and decimal number have the same value as 10%?
    $\frac{1}{10}$ and 0.1

8. Repeat Step 5 for the percent 45%. Students will need to use more than one strip to represent the value.

    **Ask:** What fraction and decimal number have the same value as 45%?
    $\frac{45}{100}$ and 0.45

9. For extra practice, have students choose a fraction, decimal number, or percent, and show all three representations of that value using all three sets of strips.

## LEARN  Match Fraction, Decimal, and Percent

*ONLINE 10 min*

**Objectives**

- Determine the decimal and percent equivalents for a common fraction and explain why they represent the same value.

Students will match the fraction, decimal number, and percent that have the same value. They will connect the three representations by changing between fractions, decimal numbers, and percents.

**Tips** If students have trouble finding fractions, decimal numbers, and percents that are equivalent, use Centimeter Grid Paper and have students represent each one.

## LEARN  Story Problems with Equivalents

*OFFLINE 15 min*

**Objectives**

- Determine the decimal and percent equivalents for a common fraction and explain why they represent the same value.

Students will use their knowledge of the equivalent forms of fractions, decimal numbers, and percents to solve story problems. Have students turn to the Story Problems with Equivalents activity page in their Activity Book and read the directions with them.

Students should copy the problems from the Activity Book into their Math-Notebook as necessary and solve them there.

1. Read Problem 1 of Worked Examples with students.

    Make sure students understand how the equivalent fraction $\frac{40}{100}$ was found by multiplying the numerator and denominator of $\frac{20}{50}$ by 2.

2. Read Problem 2 of Worked Examples with students.

    **Ask:** When you know a percent that is less than 100%, how can you write it as a decimal number? A percent that is less than 100% can be written as a decimal number by writing 0 in the whole-number place, then the decimal point, and the parts of 100 in the decimal places to the right of the decimal point.

**346** PERCENTS AND PROBABILITY

3. Read Problem 3 of Worked Examples with students.

   **Say:** The numerator and denominator needed to be divided, instead of multiplied. You needed an equivalent fraction with a denominator of 100, and the denominator was 400. In these types of story problems, you will need to use the information in the problem to decide whether you will multiply or divide to get an equivalent fraction with a denominator of 100.

4. Have students look at Problem 1 in the problem set.

   **Ask:** What is the fraction you will write to represent the information in the problem? $\frac{120}{400}$

   **Ask:** Do you need to multiply or divide to write an equivalent fraction with a denominator of 100? divide

   **Ask:** What will you divide 400 by? 4

   **Ask:** What will you divide 120 by? 4

   Have students finish solving the problem, referring to the Worked Examples as needed.

5. Have students complete Problems 2–8, using the Worked Examples as needed.

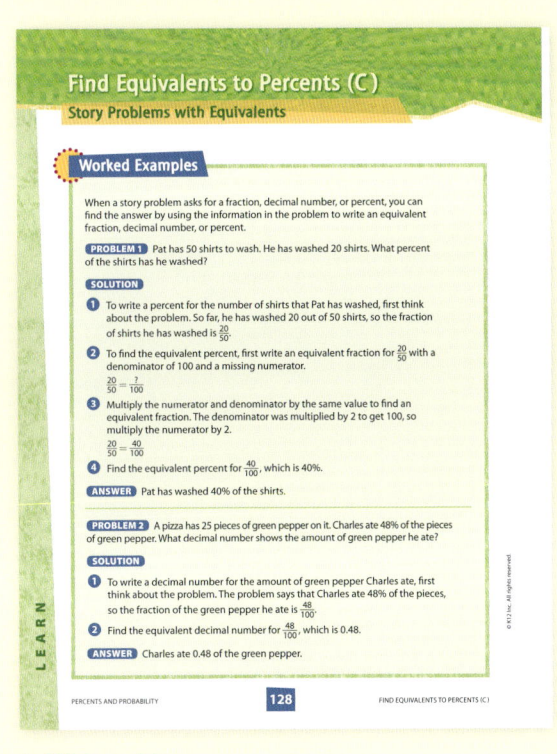

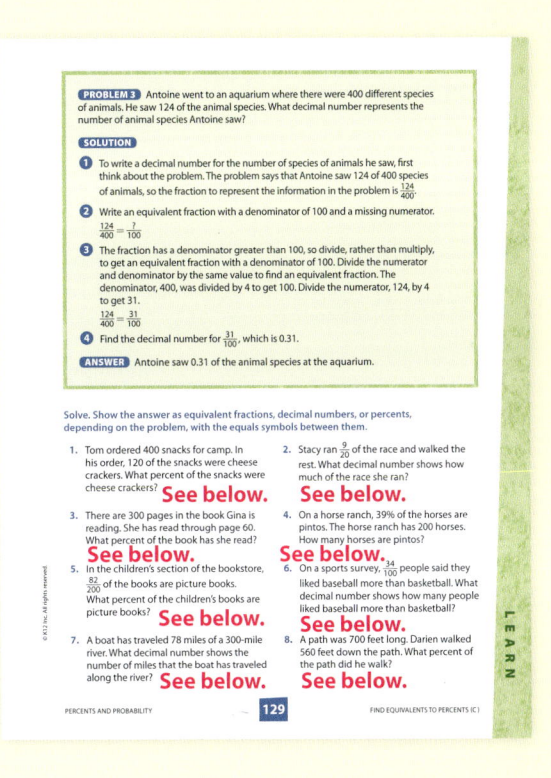

### Additional Answers

1. $\frac{120}{400} = \frac{30}{100} = 30\%$
2. $\frac{9}{20} = \frac{45}{100} = 0.45$
3. $\frac{60}{300} = \frac{20}{100} = 20\%$
4. $39\% = \frac{39}{100} = \frac{78}{200}$; 78 horses are pintos.
5. $\frac{82}{200} = \frac{41}{100} = 41\%$
6. $\frac{34}{100} = 0.34$
7. $\frac{78}{300} = \frac{26}{100} = 0.26$
8. $\frac{560}{700} = \frac{80}{100} = 80\%$

**FIND EQUIVALENTS TO PERCENTS (C)** 347

## TRY IT  Practice Finding the Same Value

**ONLINE 10 min**

Students will complete an online Try It. If necessary, read the directions, problems, and answer choices to students and help them with keyboard or mouse operations.

**Objectives**

- Determine the decimal and percent equivalents for a common fraction and explain why they represent the same value.

## CHECKPOINT

**ONLINE 10 min**

Students will complete an online Checkpoint. If necessary, read the directions, problems, and answer choices to students and help them with keyboard or mouse operations.

**Objectives**

- Determine the decimal and percent equivalents for a common fraction and explain why they represent the same value.

# Percent of a Number (A)

## Lesson Overview

| | | |
|---|---|---|
| Skills Update | 5 minutes | **ONLINE** |
| **GET READY** Percent Models | 5 minutes | **ONLINE** |
| **LEARN** Find the Percent | 10 minutes | **ONLINE** |
| **LEARN** Percent of 100 | 10 minutes | **OFFLINE** |
| **LEARN** Percent Story Problems | 15 minutes | **ONLINE** |
| **TRY IT** Practice Finding Percents | 15 minutes | **OFFLINE** |

### ▶ Lesson Objectives
Compute a given percent of a whole number.

### ▶ Prerequisite Skills
Interpret a percent as a part of a hundred.

### ▶ Content Background
Students will learn to find the number that is a given percent of 100 and also find the percent that a given number is of 100.

*Percent* is a Latin word meaning "of each hundred." Percents connect with fractions and decimal numbers to mean one part in one hundred, $\frac{1}{100}$, or one hundredth, 0.01. It may be helpful to connect percent to 1 penny, or 1 cent, as 1 percent of a dollar, since 1 dollar equals 100 cents.

Although students will most often see fractions written with a horizontal fraction bar in math, such as $\frac{2}{3}$ or $5\frac{5}{6}$, they will occasionally see a diagonal fraction bar, such as 2/3 or 5 5/6. Students will very likely see the diagonal fraction bar in everyday experiences, but be sure they understand that using the horizontal fraction bar in their work will make problems involving fractions easier to interpret and solve.

When students write and compute with decimal numbers, they often use numbers that are between 0 and 1, for example, 0.1. While it is acceptable to write this number as .1, mathematicians usually write the leading zero, to show that the whole-number value for the decimal number is zero and to avoid confusion about the value of the number.

### Materials to Gather

**SUPPLIED**
Percent of 100 activity page
Practice Finding Percents activity page

## GET READY Percent Models

**ONLINE** 5 min

### Objectives
- Interpret a percent as a part of a hundred.

Students will view and count shaded squares on 10 by 10 grids to name percents of 100 that are shown.

## LEARN  Find the Percent

**ONLINE 10 min**

Students will learn to find the part of the whole by using the given percent and the whole. They will also learn to find the percent of 100 by using the given part of the whole and the whole.

### Objectives
- Compute a given percent of a whole number.

## LEARN  Percent of 100

**OFFLINE 10 min**

Students will practice finding percents of 100. Have students turn to the Percent of 100 activity page in their Activity Book and read the directions with them.
Students should copy the problems from the Activity Book into their Math Notebook as necessary and solve them there.

1. Read both problems in Worked Examples with students. Make sure students understand that the decimal number 0.79 is the same as $\frac{79}{100}$. The decimal number shows how many of 100, and the percent also shows how many of 100. Also review how to change 27 of 100 to a fraction, a decimal number, and then to a percent.
2. Have students complete Problems 1–9.
3. If students know the answers without computing, have them multiply 100 by the decimal equivalent of each percent to verify that their answers are correct.

### Objectives
- Compute a given percent of a whole number.

### Tips
Point out to students that if a percent is a single-digit number, it is still part of 100, not part of 10. For example, 6% is 6 parts of 100.

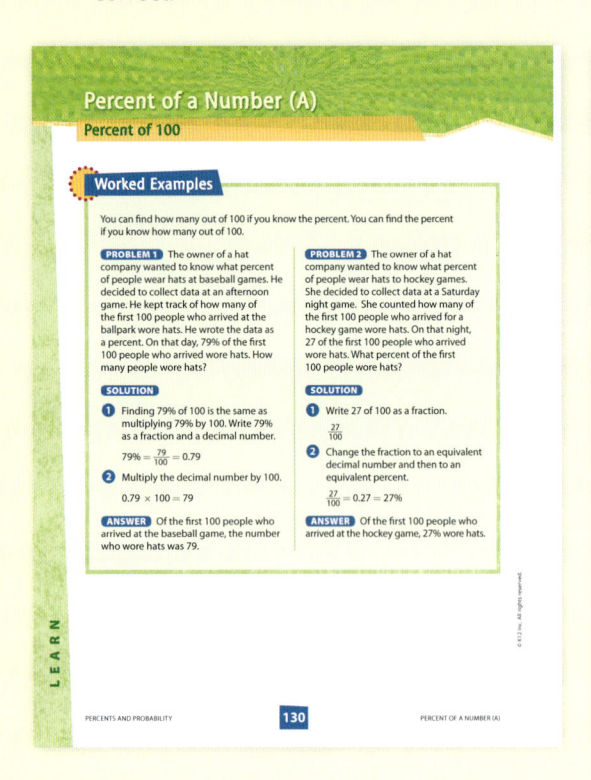

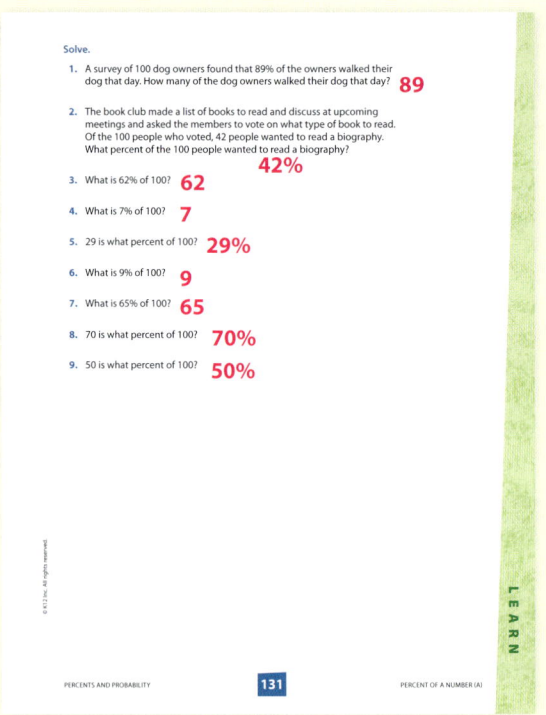

---

**Percent of a Number (A)**
**Percent of 100**

**Worked Examples**

You can find how many out of 100 if you know the percent. You can find the percent if you know how many out of 100.

**PROBLEM 1**  The owner of a hat company wanted to know what percent of people wear hats at baseball games. He decided to collect data at an afternoon game. He kept track of how many of the first 100 people who arrived at the ballpark wore hats. He wrote the data as a percent. On that day, 79% of the first 100 people who arrived wore hats. How many people wore hats?

**SOLUTION**
1. Finding 79% of 100 is the same as multiplying 79% by 100. Write 79% as a fraction and a decimal number.
$79\% = \frac{79}{100} = 0.79$
2. Multiply the decimal number by 100.
$0.79 \times 100 = 79$

**ANSWER**  Of the first 100 people who arrived at the baseball game, the number who wore hats was 79.

**PROBLEM 2**  The owner of a hat company wanted to know what percent of people wear hats at hockey games. She decided to collect data at a Saturday night game. She counted how many of the first 100 people who arrived for a hockey game wore hats. On that night, 27 of the first 100 people who arrived wore hats. What percent of the first 100 people wore hats?

**SOLUTION**
1. Write 27 of 100 as a fraction.
$\frac{27}{100}$
2. Change the fraction to an equivalent decimal number and then to an equivalent percent.
$\frac{27}{100} = 0.27 = 27\%$

**ANSWER**  Of the first 100 people who arrived at the hockey game, 27% wore hats.

---

**Solve.**

1. A survey of 100 dog owners found that 89% of the owners walked their dog that day. How many of the dog owners walked their dog that day?  **89**
2. The book club made a list of books to read and discuss at upcoming meetings and asked the members to vote on what type of book to read. Of the 100 people who voted, 42 people wanted to read a biography. What percent of the 100 people wanted to read a biography?  **42%**
3. What is 62% of 100?  **62**
4. What is 7% of 100?  **7**
5. 29 is what percent of 100?  **29%**
6. What is 9% of 100?  **9**
7. What is 65% of 100?  **65**
8. 70 is what percent of 100?  **70%**
9. 50 is what percent of 100?  **50%**

---

**350**  PERCENTS AND PROBABILITY

## LEARN Percent Story Problems

Students will find what percent of $100 a family spent on different items at the grocery store.

## TRY IT Practice Finding Percents

Students will practice finding percents of 100. Have students turn to the Practice Finding Percents activity page in their Activity Book and read the directions with them.

Students should copy the problems from the Activity Book into their Math Notebook as necessary and solve them there.

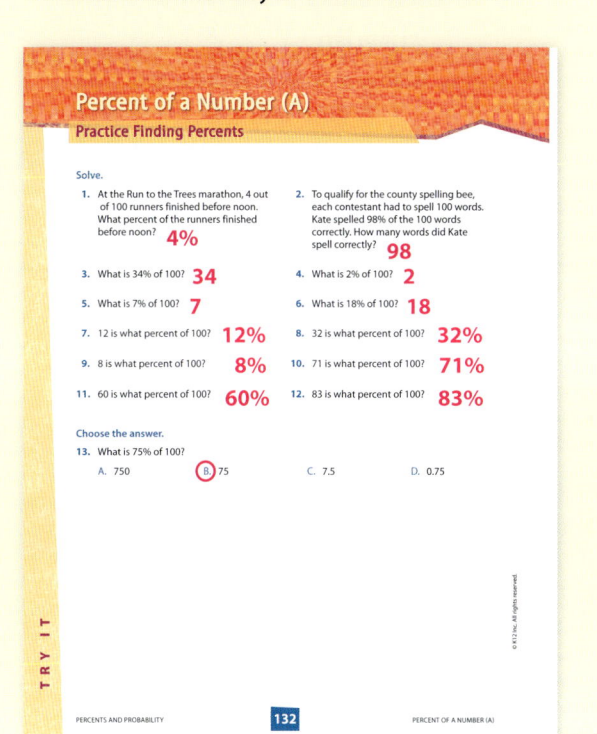

### Objectives
- Compute a given percent of a whole number.

### Objectives
- Compute a given percent of a whole number.

### Tips

Have students use computation to solve one problem and explain their solution. Remind students that a fraction or its equivalent decimal number that shows a part of 100 also has an equivalent percent.

### Percent of a Number (A)
**Practice Finding Percents**

Solve.

1. At the Run to the Trees marathon, 4 out of 100 runners finished before noon. What percent of the runners finished before noon? **4%**

2. To qualify for the county spelling bee, each contestant had to spell 100 words. Kate spelled 98% of the 100 words correctly. How many words did Kate spell correctly? **98**

3. What is 34% of 100? **34**
4. What is 2% of 100? **2**
5. What is 7% of 100? **7**
6. What is 18% of 100? **18**
7. 12 is what percent of 100? **12%**
8. 32 is what percent of 100? **32%**
9. 8 is what percent of 100? **8%**
10. 71 is what percent of 100? **71%**
11. 60 is what percent of 100? **60%**
12. 83 is what percent of 100? **83%**

Choose the answer.
13. What is 75% of 100?
    A. 750   (B.) 75   C. 7.5   D. 0.75

PERCENT OF A NUMBER (A) **351**

# Percent of a Number (B)

## Lesson Overview

| | | |
|---|---|---|
| Skills Update | 5 minutes | **ONLINE** |
| **LEARN** Percent of Numbers < 100 or > 100 | 15 minutes | **ONLINE** |
| **LEARN** Different Ways to Find Percent | 25 minutes | **OFFLINE** |
| **TRY IT** Find Percents of Numbers | 15 minutes | **OFFLINE** |

### ▶ Lesson Objectives
Compute a given percent of a whole number.

### ▶ Prerequisite Skills
Interpret a percent as a part of a hundred.

### ▶ Content Background
Students will continue to learn to find the number that is a given percent of 100 and also find the percent that a given number is of 100.

*Percent* is a Latin word meaning "of each hundred." Percents connect with fractions and decimal numbers to mean one part in one hundred, $\frac{1}{100}$, or one hundredth, 0.01. It may be helpful to connect percent to 1 penny, or 1 cent, as 1 percent of a dollar, since 1 dollar equals 100 cents.

Although students will most often see fractions written with a horizontal fraction bar in math, such as $\frac{2}{3}$ or $5\frac{5}{6}$, they will occasionally see a diagonal fraction bar, such as 2/3 or 5 5/6. Students will very likely see the diagonal fraction bar in everyday experiences, but be sure they understand that using the horizontal fraction bar in their work will make problems involving fractions easier to interpret and solve.

When students write and compute with decimal numbers, they often use numbers that are between 0 and 1, for example, 0.1. While it is acceptable to write this number as .1, mathematicians usually write the leading zero, to show that the whole-number value for the decimal number is zero and to avoid confusion about the value of the number.

### Materials to Gather

**SUPPLIED**

Different Ways to Find Percent activity page

Find Percents of Numbers activity page

---

**LEARN** Percent of Numbers < 100 or > 100  **ONLINE 15min**

### Objectives

- Compute a given percent of a whole number.

Students will learn how to find percents of numbers less than 100 or greater than 100.

## LEARN  Different Ways to Find Percent

**OFFLINE 25 min**

Students will use different methods to find percents of numbers less than 100 and greater than 100. Have students turn to the Different Ways to Find Percent activity page in their Activity Book and read the directions with them.

Students should copy the problems from the Activity Book into their Math Notebook as necessary and solve them there.

1. Tell students that no matter what size the whole is that they're finding a percent of, they can multiply the decimal form of the percent by the whole to find the part.
   - A percent is part of 100.
   - Any percent can be changed to a fraction with a denominator of 100. Then the fraction can be changed to a decimal number.

2. Read the five problems in Worked Examples with students. Make sure students understand all the shortcuts in the solutions.

   **Say:** You can use different shortcuts for different problems. The shortcut you use depends on the problem and your way of working with the numbers. For some problems, it will be easier to think of the percent as a decimal number or a fraction. For other problems, it will be easier to start by thinking of the percent as a half, a fourth, twice as much, or another part of the whole. And other problems will be easier to solve using a step-by-step approach.

3. Expand Solution 1 of Problem 1 in the Worked Examples by telling students that when they know 10% of any number, they can find 30% of the number by multiplying the answer by 3, and with 40%, multiply by 4, and so on.

4. Tell students that sometimes a percent of a number can be a decimal number, as shown in Problem 4 of the Worked Examples, in which the answer is 9.5. Make sure students understand Shortcut 2 to find 10% of a number. Explain that 0.10 is the same as $\frac{1}{10}$. So another way to find 10% of 95 is by using fractions: $\frac{1}{10} \times 95 = 9.5$

5. Tell students that sometimes they can use an algorithm to find the answer to a percent story problem, as shown in Problem 5 of the Worked Examples.

6. Have students complete Problems 1–11.

### Objectives

- Compute a given percent of a whole number.

### Tips

Have students check their answers to 20% of 72 and 30% of 202 by changing the percents to decimal numbers and multiplying.

**PERCENT OF A NUMBER (B)**

## Percent of a Number (B)
### Different Ways to Find Percent

**Worked Examples**

You can use different methods to find percents of numbers less than 100 and greater than 100.

**PROBLEM 1** What is 20% of 60?
**SOLUTION 1** $0.20 \times 60 = ?$
$0.20 \times 60 = 12$

**SOLUTION 2**
1. Shortcut: Start by multiplying 10% by 60. 10% is equivalent to 0.10.
$0.10 \times 60 = 6$
2. Remember that the original problem asked for 20% of 60, and you just found 10% of 60. To find 20% of a number, find 10% of the number and multiply the answer by 2, because 20% is twice as much as 10%.
$6 \times 2 = 12$

**ANSWER** 20% of 60 is 12.

**PROBLEM 2** What is 50% of 80?
**SOLUTION 1** $0.50 \times 80 = ?$
$0.50 \times 80 = 40$

**SOLUTION 2**
1. Shortcut: Think of 50% as $\frac{50}{100}$, which is $\frac{1}{2}$. Another way to think of $\frac{1}{2}$ is that it is the same as half.
2. Find that half of 80 is 40.

**ANSWER** 50% of 80 is 40.

**PROBLEM 3** What is 25% of 200?
**SOLUTION**
1. Shortcut: Since the factor 200 has zeros in the ones and tens places, place 2 zeros in the answer and then multiply by 2, the first nonzero digit in that factor. Finish by placing the decimal point.
2. $\phantom{x}0.25$
$\underline{\times\, 2\,00}$
$\phantom{x}50.00$

**ANSWER** 25% of 200 is 50.

---

**PROBLEM 4** What is 10% of 95?
**SOLUTION**
1. $0.10 \times 95 = ?$
$0.10 \times 95 = 9.5$
2. Shortcut: Multiply the fraction for 0.10 by 95.
$\frac{1}{10} \times 95 = \frac{95}{10} = 9.5$

**ANSWER** 10% of 95 is 9.5.

**PROBLEM 5** Of the 450 people at the lake one day, 22% were fishing. How many people were fishing?
**SOLUTION**
1. Shortcut: Multiply the fraction for 22% by 450.
$\frac{22}{100} \times 450 = \frac{9,900}{100} = 99$
2. Multiply 450 by 0.22, the decimal number for 22%.
$\phantom{xx}\overset{\phantom{x}7}{450}$
$\underline{\times\,\, 0.22}$
$\phantom{xx}900$
$\underline{+\,\,9,000}$
$\phantom{xx}99.00$

**ANSWER** 22% of 450 is 99, so 99 people were fishing at the lake.

Use the methods from the Worked Examples to solve.
1. What is 10% of 55? **5.5**
2. What is 20% of 55? **11**
3. What is 30% of 55? **16.5**
4. What is 50% of 350? **175**
5. What is 20% of 72? **14.4**
6. What is 10% of 72? **7.2**
7. What is 30% of 400? **120**
8. What is 10% of 202? **20.2**
9. What is 20% of 202? **40.4**
10. What is 30% of 202? **60.6**
11. There are 350 campsites by the river. One day, the ranger reported that 14% of the campsites were vacant. How many campsites were vacant?
**49 campsites were vacant.**

---

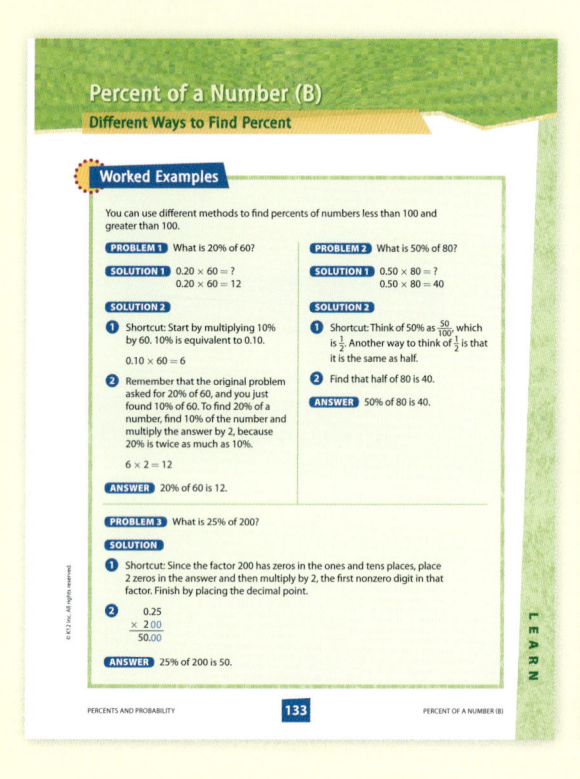

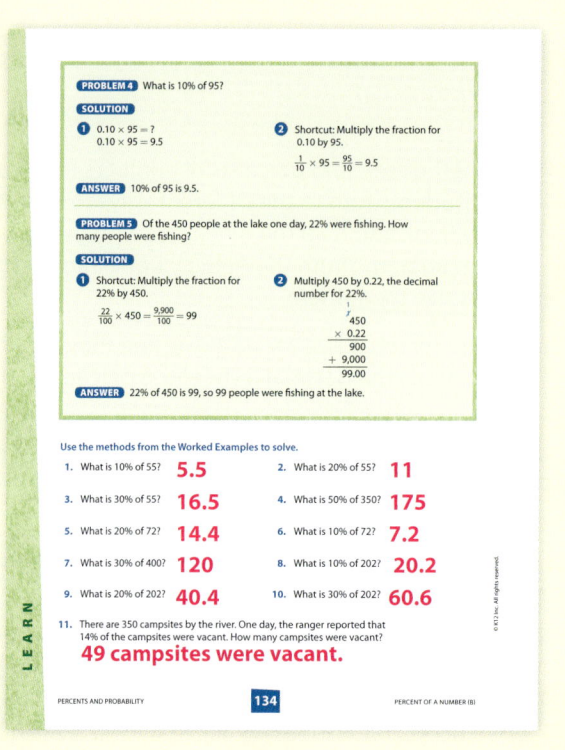

## TRY IT  Find Percents of Numbers
OFFLINE 15 min

### Objectives
- Compute a given percent of a whole number.

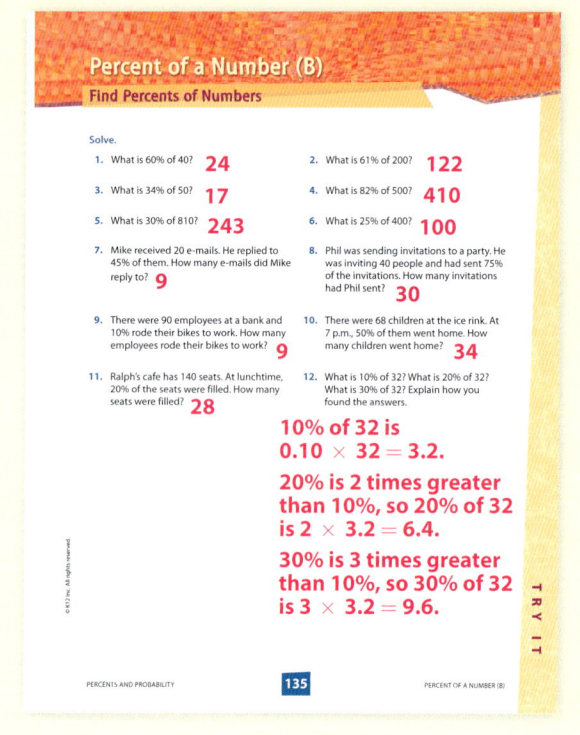

Students will practice finding percents of numbers less than 100 or greater than 100. Have students turn to the Find Percents of Numbers activity page in their Activity Book and read the directions with them.

Students should copy the problems from the Activity Book into their Math Notebook as necessary and solve them there.

---

### Percent of a Number (B)
**Find Percents of Numbers**

Solve.
1. What is 60% of 40? **24**
2. What is 61% of 200? **122**
3. What is 34% of 50? **17**
4. What is 82% of 500? **410**
5. What is 30% of 810? **243**
6. What is 25% of 400? **100**
7. Mike received 20 e-mails. He replied to 45% of them. How many e-mails did Mike reply to? **9**
8. Phil was sending invitations to a party. He was inviting 40 people and had sent 75% of the invitations. How many invitations had Phil sent? **30**
9. There were 90 employees at a bank and 10% rode their bikes to work. How many employees rode their bikes to work? **9**
10. There were 68 children at the ice rink. At 7 p.m., 50% of them went home. How many children went home? **34**
11. Ralph's cafe has 140 seats. At lunchtime, 20% of the seats were filled. How many seats were filled? **28**
12. What is 10% of 32? What is 20% of 32? What is 30% of 32? Explain how you found the answers.

**10% of 32 is**
$0.10 \times 32 = 3.2.$

**20% is 2 times greater than 10%, so 20% of 32 is $2 \times 3.2 = 6.4.$**

**30% is 3 times greater than 10%, so 30% of 32 is $3 \times 3.2 = 9.6.$**

# Percent of a Number (C)

## Lesson Overview

| | | |
|---|---|---|
| **LEARN** Calculate Tips | 20 minutes | OFFLINE |
| **LEARN** Calculate Taxes | 20 minutes | OFFLINE |
| **TRY IT** Practice Calculating Tips and Taxes | 10 minutes | ONLINE |
| **CHECKPOINT** | 10 minutes | ONLINE |

### ▶ Lesson Objectives
Compute a given percent of a whole number.

### ▶ Prerequisite Skills
Interpret a percent as a part of a hundred.

### ▶ Content Background
Students will practice finding the number that is a given percent of 100 and also finding the percent that a given number is of 100 in the context of story problems.

*Percent* is a Latin word meaning "of each hundred." Percents connect with fractions and decimal numbers to mean one part in one hundred, $\frac{1}{100}$, or one hundredth, 0.01. It may be helpful to connect percent to 1 penny, or 1 cent, as 1 percent of a dollar, since 1 dollar equals 100 cents.

Although students will most often see fractions written with a horizontal fraction bar in math, such as $\frac{2}{3}$ or $5\frac{5}{6}$, they will occasionally see a diagonal fraction bar, such as 2/3 or 5 5/6. Students will very likely see the diagonal fraction bar in everyday experiences, but be sure they understand that using the horizontal fraction bar in their work will make problems involving fractions easier to interpret and solve.

When students write and compute with decimal numbers, they often use numbers that are between 0 and 1, for example, 0.1. While it is acceptable to write this number as .1, mathematicians usually write the leading zero, to show that the whole-number value for the decimal number is zero and to avoid confusion about the value of the number.

### Materials to Gather

**SUPPLIED**
Calculate Tips activity page
Calculate Taxes activity page

## LEARN Calculate Tips
**OFFLINE 20 min**

### Objectives
- Compute a given percent of a whole number.

Students will find percents of dollar amounts to calculate tips. They will not add the tip to the cost, but they should understand that the total cost would be the cost of service plus the cost of the tip. Have students turn to the Calculate Tips activity page in their Activity Book and read the directions with them.

Students should copy the problems from the Activity Book into their Math Notebook as necessary and solve them there.

1. Read the background information on tips with students. Be sure they understand tips as a money amount.
2. Read Problem 1 in Worked Examples with students.

   **Ask:** Why is it correct to calculate 10% and 5% of the cost and then add the two amounts for a 15% tip? *If you calculate 10% and 5% of a number and add the two percents together, you will get the same answer as if you had calculated 15% of the number.*
3. Read Problem 2 in Worked Examples with students.
4. Remind students that the answer to a problem about tips must be a money amount because a tip is a money amount. Remind them to label the amounts with the dollar sign.
5. Have students use the methods shown in the Worked Examples to answer Problems 1–6.

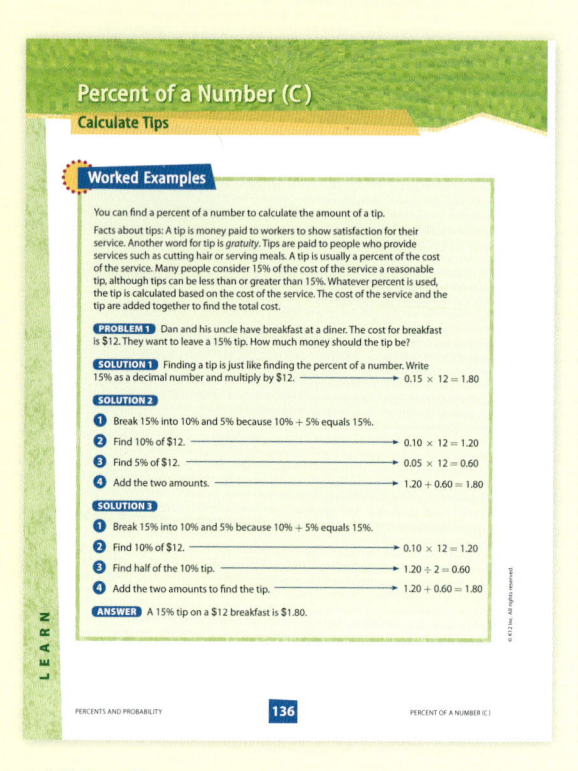

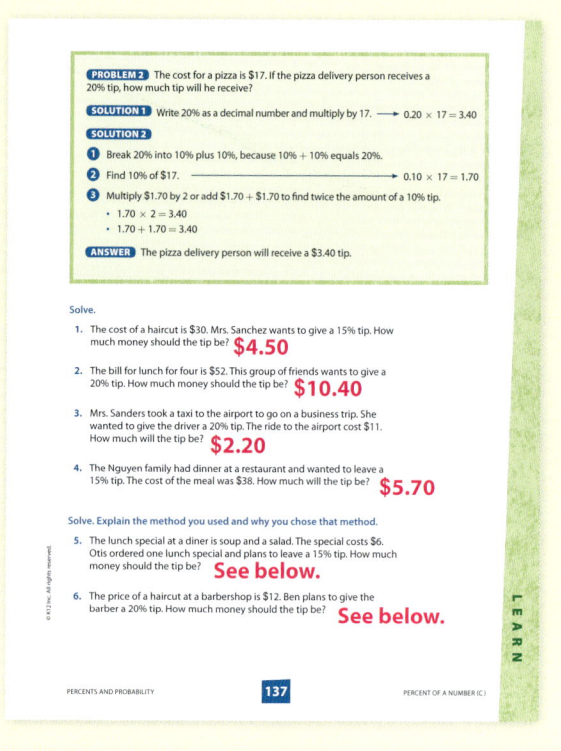

### Additional Answers

5. $0.90; **Example explanation:** I multiplied 0.10 by $6 to get $0.60. I took half of $0.60 to get $0.30. I added $0.60 and $0.30 to get $0.90. Finding 10% of $6 was an easy way to begin figuring it out.

6. $2.40; **Example explanation:** I found 10% of $12 to be $1.20. I knew that 20% is 2 times 10%, so 20% of $12 is 2 × $1.20, or $2.40. It was easy to double the answer of 10% of $12 to find a 20% tip.

**356** PERCENTS AND PROBABILITY

## LEARN  Calculate Taxes

**OFFLINE 20 min**

### Objectives
- Compute a given percent of a whole number.

Students will find percents of dollar amounts to calculate taxes. Have students turn to the Calculate Taxes activity page in their Activity Book and read the directions with them.

Students should copy the problems from the Activity Book into their Math Notebook as necessary and solve them there.

1. Read the background information on taxes with students. Be sure they understand basic information about sales taxes.

2. Read Problems 1 and 2 in the Worked Examples with students. Remind them that 4% is four hundredths, written as the decimal number 0.04, and not four tenths, written as the decimal number 0.4.

   **Ask:** In Problem 2, why did you add $29 to our first answer, $1.16? *You had to add the cost of the shoes to the cost of the sales tax to find the total that Janelle would pay.*

3. Have students read Problem 1 in the problem set. Explain that to solve this problem, they need to find 10% of $20.

   **Ask:** How would you calculate 10% of $20? $0.10 \times 20 = 2$

   **Ask:** What is the sales tax for the $20 sweatshirt? *$2*

4. Have students read Problem 2 in the problem set.

   **Ask:** How are the directions different for this problem than for the first problem about the sales tax on a sweatshirt? *The directions ask me to add the sales tax to the purchase price of the books.*

   Have students solve Problem 2. Check to see that they solved it correctly and that they added the sales tax to the purchase price.

5. Remind students that the answer to a problem about taxes must be a money amount because a tax is a money amount. Remind them to label the money amounts with the dollar sign.

6. Have students solve the rest of the problems. Make sure they carefully read the directions in the problems to see whether to calculate only the sales tax or the entire purchase price with the sales tax included.

> **Tips**  Have students explain how calculating tips and calculating sales taxes are similar. (You find the percent of a dollar amount when you calculate each one.)

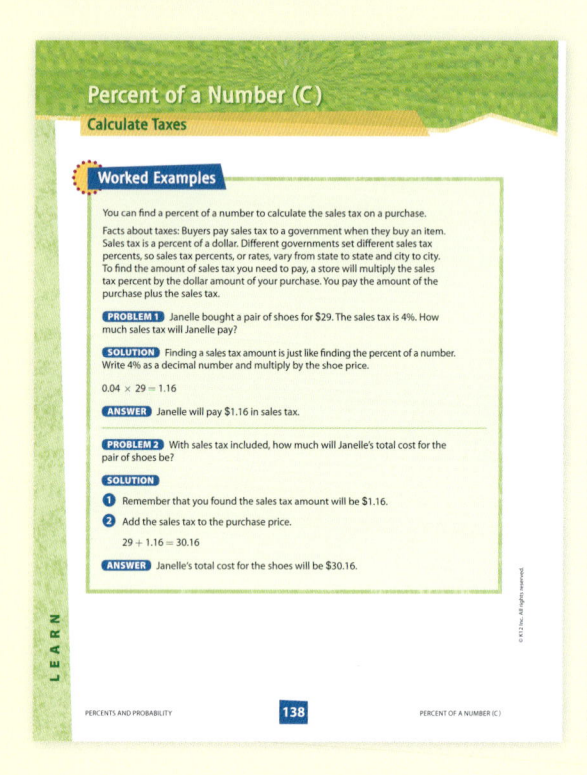

## Percent of a Number (C)
### Calculate Taxes

**Worked Examples**

You can find a percent of a number to calculate the sales tax on a purchase.

Facts about taxes: Buyers pay sales tax to a government when they buy an item. Sales tax is a percent of a dollar. Different governments set different sales tax percents, so sales tax percents, or rates, vary from state to state and city to city. To find the amount of sales tax you need to pay, a store will multiply the sales tax percent by the dollar amount of your purchase. You pay the amount of the purchase plus the sales tax.

**PROBLEM 1** Janelle bought a pair of shoes for $29. The sales tax is 4%. How much sales tax will Janelle pay?

**SOLUTION** Finding a sales tax amount is just like finding the percent of a number. Write 4% as a decimal number and multiply by the shoe price.

$0.04 \times 29 = 1.16$

**ANSWER** Janelle will pay $1.16 in sales tax.

**PROBLEM 2** With sales tax included, how much will Janelle's total cost for the pair of shoes be?

**SOLUTION**
1. Remember that you found the sales tax amount will be $1.16.
2. Add the sales tax to the purchase price.

$29 + 1.16 = 30.16$

**ANSWER** Janelle's total cost for the shoes will be $30.16.

---

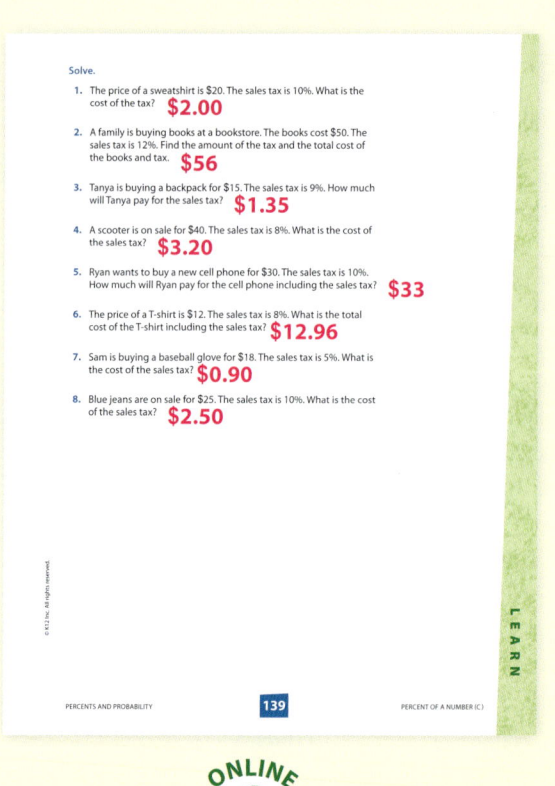

Solve.

1. The price of a sweatshirt is $20. The sales tax is 10%. What is the cost of the tax? **$2.00**

2. A family is buying books at a bookstore. The books cost $50. The sales tax is 12%. Find the amount of the tax and the total cost of the books and tax. **$56**

3. Tanya is buying a backpack for $15. The sales tax is 9%. How much will Tanya pay for the sales tax? **$1.35**

4. A scooter is on sale for $40. The sales tax is 8%. What is the cost of the sales tax? **$3.20**

5. Ryan wants to buy a new cell phone for $30. The sales tax is 10%. How much will Ryan pay for the cell phone including the sales tax? **$33**

6. The price of a T-shirt is $12. The sales tax is 8%. What is the total cost of the T-shirt including the sales tax? **$12.96**

7. Sam is buying a baseball glove for $18. The sales tax is 5%. What is the cost of the sales tax? **$0.90**

8. Blue jeans are on sale for $25. The sales tax is 10%. What is the cost of the sales tax? **$2.50**

---

## TRY IT   Practice Calculating Tips and Taxes

**ONLINE 10 min**

Students will complete an online Try It. If necessary, read the directions, problems, and answer choices to students and help them with keyboard or mouse operations.

**Objectives**
- Compute a given percent of a whole number.

## CHECKPOINT

**ONLINE 10 min**

Students will complete an online Checkpoint. If necessary, read the directions, problems, and answer choices to students and help them with keyboard or mouse operations.

**Objectives**
- Compute a given percent of a whole number.

**PERCENTS AND PROBABILITY**

# Represent Probabilities

## Lesson Overview

| | | |
|---|---|---|
| **GET READY** Name the Probability | 10 minutes | ONLINE |
| **LEARN** Probability: Outcomes and Events | 10 minutes | ONLINE |
| **LEARN** Different Ways to Show Probability | 20 minutes | OFFLINE |
| **TRY IT** Practice Writing Probability Three Ways | 10 minutes | ONLINE |
| **CHECKPOINT** | 10 minutes | ONLINE |

## ▶ Lesson Objectives
Represent probabilities as fractions, decimals, and percents.

## ▶ Prerequisite Skills
- Represent a probability as a fraction.
- Determine the decimal and percent equivalents for a common fraction and explain why they represent the same value.

## ▶ Content Background
Students will learn how to represent the probability of an event as a fraction, a decimal number, and a percent.

Probability is the area of mathematics that studies the chance, or possibility, of an event taking place. One example of probability is tossing a two-sided coin that has heads and tails. For a coin, the probability of tossing heads is $\frac{1}{2}$ because heads is one side of a two-sided coin.

An outcome is one of the possible results of an experiment. For example, a spinner that is divided into three equal sections, with a red section, a blue section, and a green section, has three possible outcomes:
- Landing on red
- Landing on blue
- Landing on green

An event is one or more outcomes to which a probability is assigned. In the spinner example, the event of spinning red has a probability of $\frac{1}{3}$, because there is 1 red section out of 3 equal sections on the spinner. Spinning blue also has a probability of $\frac{1}{3}$. Spinning a green has a probability of $\frac{1}{3}$ as well.

Although students will most often see fractions written with a horizontal fraction bar in math, such as $\frac{2}{3}$ or $5\frac{5}{6}$, they will occasionally see a diagonal fraction bar, such as 2/3 or 5 5/6. Students will very likely see the diagonal fraction bar in everyday experiences, but be sure they understand that using the horizontal fraction bar in their work will make problems involving fractions easier to interpret and solve.

## Materials to Gather

**SUPPLIED**

Different Ways to Show Probability activity page

When students write and compute with decimal numbers, they often use numbers that are between 0 and 1, for example, 0.1. While it is acceptable to write this number as .1, mathematicians usually write the leading zero, to show that the whole-number value for the decimal number is zero and to avoid confusion about the value of the number.

## GET READY  Name the Probability

**ONLINE 10 min**

### Objectives
- Represent a probability as a fraction.

Students will describe the probability of of pulling circles of particular colors from a bag. They will give answers as fractions and explain what the probability for each event is.

## LEARN  Probability: Outcomes and Events

**ONLINE 10 min**

### Objectives
- Represent probabilities as fractions, decimals, and percents.

Students will learn the meaning of an outcome and an event by seeing a demonstration of tossing a coin and examples of spinning a spinner. They will also answer questions about the probabilities of a variety of experiments.

**Tips**  To help students keep track of the vocabulary related to probability, have them create a foldable book about probability. Each page could include the term, its definition, and an example.

## LEARN  Different Ways to Show Probability

**OFFLINE 20 min**

### Objectives
- Represent probabilities as fractions, decimals, and percents.

Students will learn to represent probability as a fraction, a decimal number, and a percent. Have students turn to the Different Ways to Show Probability activity page in their Activity Book and read the directions with them.

Students should copy the problems from the Activity Book into their Math Notebook as necessary and solve them there.

1. Have students read Problem 1 in the Worked Examples.

    **Ask:** Why would the fraction that expresses the probability be written as $\frac{3}{3}$? There are 3 blue sections and 3 total sections, so the probability is 3 out of 3, or $\frac{3}{3}$.

    Remind students that $\frac{3}{3}$ is the same as the decimal number 1.0 because $\frac{3}{3}$ is equal to 1 whole. It is also true that 1.0 is the same as 100%.

2. Have students read Problem 2 in the Worked Examples.

    **Ask:** How is the spinner in this problem different from the previous spinner? The previous spinner was divided into 3 equal sections, and they were all blue. This spinner is divided into 2 equal sections: 1 blue, 1 red.

    Discuss why the probability of spinning blue is $\frac{1}{2}$. If necessary, help students change $\frac{1}{2}$ to $\frac{50}{100}$ to the decimal number 0.50 and then to 50%.

PERCENTS AND PROBABILITY

3. Have students solve Problem 1 in the problem set and check that they answered correctly.

   **Ask:** You've found the probability of landing on red. What is the probability of landing on blue? 50%

   **Ask:** Why is the probability the same for landing on red or blue? The spinner is divided into 2 equal sections: 1 red and 1 blue. So the probability of landing on red or landing on blue is $\frac{1}{2}$.

4. Have students look at Problem 2 in the problem set. Explain that this spinner has 4 equal sections: 2 green, 1 blue, 1 purple. The probability of landing on purple is 1 purple section divided by the 4 total sections of the circle. Discuss how to change $\frac{1}{4}$ to a decimal number and a percent.

5. Have students solve Problems 3 and 4.

6. Have students read Problem 5.

   **Ask:** How many socks are in the basket? 10

   **Ask:** How many socks are purple? 3

   Have students solve the problem and express the probability as a fraction, decimal number, and percent.

7. Read the number cube problem in the second Worked Examples box with students. Make sure they understand that each of the numbers 1 through 6 are shown only once on the sides of the number cube shown.

   **Ask:** What are all of the possible outcomes when you roll the cube? There are 6 possible outcomes, rolling 1, 2, 3, 4, 5, or 6.

   Discuss with students why the probability of landing on 3 is $\frac{1}{6}$.

   **Ask:** What is the probability of landing on the number 5? Explain your answer. $\frac{1}{6}$; Because each number is shown on only one side, the chance of rolling the number cube and landing on any side is the same.

8. Have students read Problem 6 of the problem set. Tell them to count the number of odd numbers on the number cube, and then divide by the total number of sides to find the probability of the number cube landing on an odd number. They can then express the probability as a decimal number and a fraction.

9. Have students complete the rest of the problems. Have them refer to the Worked Example as needed.

**Tips**
If students are struggling to write probability as a fraction, remind them that the numerator is the number of favorable outcomes (meaning the number of outcomes that answers the question) and the denominator is the total number of outcomes.

## Additional Answers

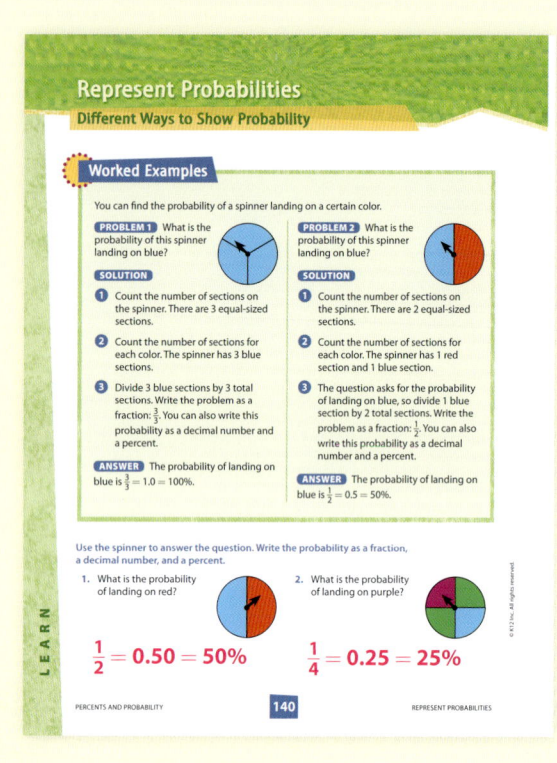

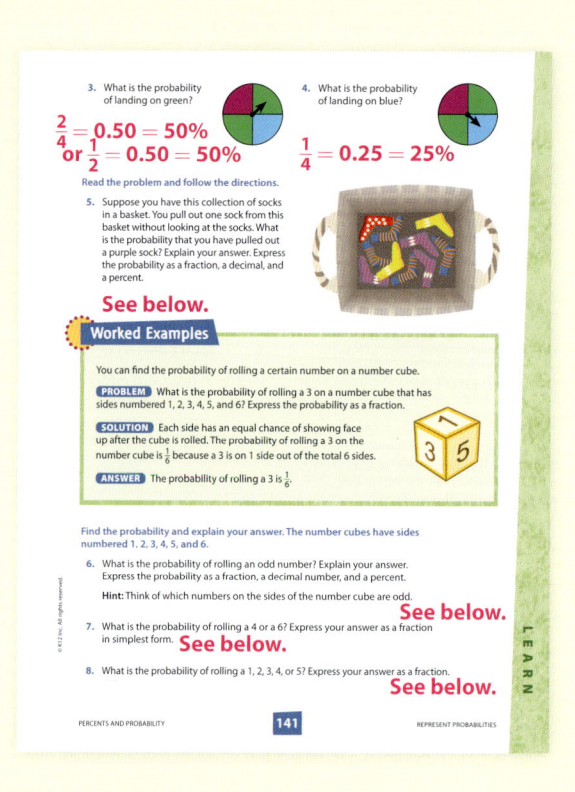

**5.** The basket contained 10 socks, including 3 purple socks. To find the probability of pulling out a purple sock, divide the number of purple socks by the total number of socks (3 ÷ 10). The probability is $\frac{3}{10} = 0.30 = 30\%$.

**7.** The number cube has 6 numbers on its sides, and the 4 and 6 are 2 out of the 6 numbers. The probability of rolling a 4 or a 6 is $\frac{2}{6}$, which is $\frac{1}{3}$ in simplest form.

**6.** The number cube has 3 odd numbers on its sides: 1, 3, and 5. The number cube has 6 sides. The probability of landing on an odd number is the number of odd numbers divided by the total number of sides (3 ÷ 6). The probability is written as $\frac{3}{6} = \frac{1}{2} = 0.50 = 50\%$.

**8.** The number cube has 6 numbers on its sides, and the 1, 2, 3, 4, and 5 are 5 out of the 6 numbers. The probability of rolling 1, 2, 3, 4, or 5 out of 6 is $\frac{5}{6}$.

## TRY IT  Practice Writing Probability Three Ways

**ONLINE 10 min**

Students will complete an online Try It. If necessary, read the directions, problems, and answer choices to students and help them with keyboard or mouse operations.

### Objectives
- Represent probabilities as fractions, decimals, and percents.

## CHECKPOINT

**ONLINE 10 min**

Students will complete an online Checkpoint. If necessary, read the directions, problems, and answer choices to students and help them with keyboard or mouse operations.

### Objectives
- Represent probabilities as fractions, decimals, and percents.

# Identify Dependent and Independent Events

## Lesson Overview

| | | |
|---|---|---|
| **LEARN** Model Events | 20 minutes | **OFFLINE** |
| **LEARN** Identify Events | 15 minutes | **ONLINE** |
| **TRY IT** Dependent and Independent Events | 15 minutes | **OFFLINE** |
| **CHECKPOINT** | 10 minutes | **ONLINE** |

### ▶ Lesson Objectives
Identify events that are dependent or independent.

### ▶ Content Background
Students will learn to identify dependent events and independent events. They will learn how to represent the probability of an event as a fraction, a decimal number, and a percent.

Probability is the area of mathematics that studies the chance, or possibility, of an event taking place. One example of probability is tossing a two-sided coin that has heads and tails. For a coin, the probability of tossing heads is $\frac{1}{2}$ because heads is one side of a two-sided coin.

An outcome is one of the possible results of an experiment. For example, a spinner that is divided into three equal sections, with a red section, a blue section, and a green section, has three possible outcomes:

- Landing on red
- Landing on blue
- Landing on green

Independent events are two or more events in which the outcome of the second event in the sequence does **not** depend on the outcome of the first event. Suppose there is a bag with 3 marbles in it: 2 red ones and 1 blue one. On the first draw from the bag, a red marble is drawn and then replaced in the bag. The second draw from the bag is independent from the first draw because the red marble was put back after the first draw. In both draws, the probability of drawing a red marble is $\frac{2}{3}$.

Dependent events are two or more events in which the outcome of the second event in the sequence depends on the outcome of the first event. Suppose there is a bag with 3 marbles in it: 2 red ones and 1 blue one. On the first draw from the bag, a red marble is drawn and **not** put back in the bag. The second draw from the bag is dependent on the first draw because the marble was not put back after the first draw. In other words, the chance of getting a red marble on the first draw is $\frac{2}{3}$. But on the second draw, the chance of getting a red marble changed to $\frac{1}{2}$.

Although students will most often see fractions written with a horizontal fraction bar in math, such as $\frac{2}{3}$ or $5\frac{5}{6}$, they will occasionally see a diagonal fraction bar, such as 2/3 or 5 5/6. Students will very likely see the diagonal fraction bar in everyday experiences, but be sure they understand that using the horizontal

### Materials to Gather

**SUPPLIED**
Dependent and Independent Events activity page

**ALSO NEEDED**
pipe cleaners – 3 red, 3 blue
index cards – 8 labeled

IDENTIFY DEPENDENT AND INDEPENDENT EVENTS **363**

fraction bar in their work will make problems involving fractions easier to interpret and solve.

When students write and compute with decimal numbers, they often use numbers that are between 0 and 1, for example, 0.1. While it is acceptable to write this number as .1, mathematicians usually write the leading zero, to show that the whole-number value for the decimal number is zero and to avoid confusion about the value of the number.

## ▶ Common Errors and Misconceptions

Students might develop misconceptions and misleading intuitions about probability situations. For example, in a "fair game" activity in which a coin is flipped two times, students might assume that these following three events are equally likely: heads on both flips of the coin, heads on only one of the flips, and no heads on either flip.

## ▶ Advance Preparation

Label index cards with the letters **A** through **H**, one per card.

## LEARN Model Events   OFFLINE 20 min

### Objectives
- Identify events that are dependent or independent.

Students will use common materials to model dependent and independent events.
Gather the pipe cleaners and prepared index cards. Have students write descriptions of the events and explain why the events are dependent or independent in their Math Notebook.

1. Place the group of six pipe cleaners in front of students.
   **Ask:** If I asked you to close your eyes and choose a pipe cleaner, what is the probability that you would pick a blue pipe cleaner? Why? $\frac{1}{2}$ or 50%; because there are 3 blue pipe cleaners and a total of 6 pipe cleaners
   
   **Say:** Now take away 1 blue pipe cleaner. You randomly chose a blue pipe cleaner. You demonstrated the probability idea of picking an object at random.
   
   **Ask:** Now put the pipe cleaner back into the group. What is the probability of picking a blue pipe cleaner now? $\frac{1}{2}$ or 50%
   
   **Ask:** Did the probability of picking a blue pipe cleaner change? Why? No; because the blue pipe cleaner was put back with the group; The probability of picking a blue pipe cleaner is still $\frac{1}{2}$, 0.5, or 50%.

2. Explain to students that in the events in Step 1, they started with a group of objects, then an object was picked from the group at random, and then it was replaced in the group. When there are two or more events such as the events in Step 1, and the outcome of the second event in the sequence does not depend on the outcome of the first event, the events are called *independent events*. The probability of picking a blue pipe cleaner the first time was the same as the probability of picking a blue pipe cleaner the second time.
   
   **Say:** Describe other independent events. tossing a coin or rolling a number cube; picking a feather out of a bag, replacing it, and picking again

3. Use the same group of pipe cleaners.

   **Ask:** If I asked you to close your eyes and choose a pipe cleaner, what is the probability that you would pick a red pipe cleaner? Why? $\frac{1}{2}$, 0.5, or 50%; because there are 3 red pipe cleaners and and a total of 6 pipe cleaners

   **Say:** Take away 1 red pipe cleaner from the group. Again, you demonstrated the probability idea of picking an object at random. In this case, a red pipe cleaner was chosen at random from the group of 6 pipe cleaners.

   **Ask:** This time, do **not** put the red pipe cleaner back into the group. What is the probability of picking a red pipe cleaner now? $\frac{2}{5}$, 0.4, or 40%

   **Ask:** Did the probability of picking a red pipe cleaner change? Why? Yes; because the red pipe cleaner was **not** put back with the group; Taking the red pipe cleaner out of the group and not putting it back changed the total number of possible outcomes, therefore changing the probability.

4. Explain to students that in the events in Step 3, they started with a group of objects, then an object was picked from the group at random, and then it was **not** replaced in the group. When there are 2 or more events such as the events in Step 3, and the outcome of the second event in the sequence depends on the outcome of the first event, the events are called *dependent events*. The probability of picking a red pipe cleaner the second time was different from the probability of picking a red pipe cleaner the first time.

   **Say:** With dependent events, the probability of a certain outcome changes depending on the outcomes that come before it. Describe other dependent events. picking a feather out of a bag, not replacing it, and picking again

5. Next have students use the labeled index cards to model one example of dependent events and one example of independent events.

   **Say:** Place the labeled index cards face down in a row. Take one card from the group. The probability of drawing any one card is $\frac{1}{8}$. Do not put the card back. Then take another card from the row. Now the probability of drawing any one of the remaining cards is $\frac{1}{7}$. Were the two events dependent or independent? Why? The two events were dependent. Since one card was taken from the group and not put back, the outcome of the second event depends on the outcome of the first event. Taking one card out of the group and not putting it back changed the total number of possible outcomes, therefore changing the probability.

6. Use the same group of index cards.

   **Say:** Place the labeled index cards face down in a row. Take one card from the group. The probability of drawing any one card is $\frac{1}{8}$. Put the card back. Then take another card from the row. The probability of drawing any one of the remaining cards stays the same, $\frac{1}{8}$. Were the two events dependent or independent? Why? The two events were independent. Since one card was taken from the group, and then put back, the outcome of the second event does not depend on the outcome of the first event. Taking one card out of the group and putting it back did not change the total number of possible outcomes and did not change the probability.

7. **Say:** Think about the independent events you modeled with the pipe cleaners. Describe independent events that you could model with a bag that had 5 green marbles and 5 yellow marbles. Choose 1 marble out of the bag. Look at the marble to see that it is a green marble. Put the green marble back in the bag. Choose 1 marble out of the bag. Look at the marble to see that it is a green marble.

8. **Say:** Think about the dependent events you modeled with the labeled index cards. Describe dependent events that you could model with a box of crayons that has 4 orange crayons, 3 pink crayons, 2 green crayons, and 1 black crayon. Choose 1 crayon out of the box. Look to see that it is an orange crayon. Do not put the orange crayon back in the box. Choose 1 crayon out of the box. Look to see that it is a pink crayon.

9. **Say:** You can also use number cubes to model events. Think about rolling a number cube that has the numbers 1, 2, 3, 4, 5, and 6 on the sides. Suppose you roll a 4 on the number cube. Then you roll the number cube again and it shows a 5. The events are independent because the second outcome, rolling a 5, does not depend on the first outcome, rolling a 4.

## LEARN  Identify Events

**ONLINE 15 min**

Students will identify events that are dependent and independent.

**Tips** — If students have difficulty distinguishing between dependent and independent events, copy the definitions from the Content Background for the students. Have students act out the events in the descriptions.

**Objectives**
- Identify events that are dependent or independent.

## TRY IT  Dependent and Independent Events

**OFFLINE 15 min**

Students will practice identifying dependent and independent events. Have students turn to the Dependent and Independent Events activity page in their Activity Book and read the directions with them.

Students should copy the problems from the Activity Book into their Math Notebook as necessary and solve them there.

**Objectives**
- Identify events that are dependent or independent.

## Additional Answers

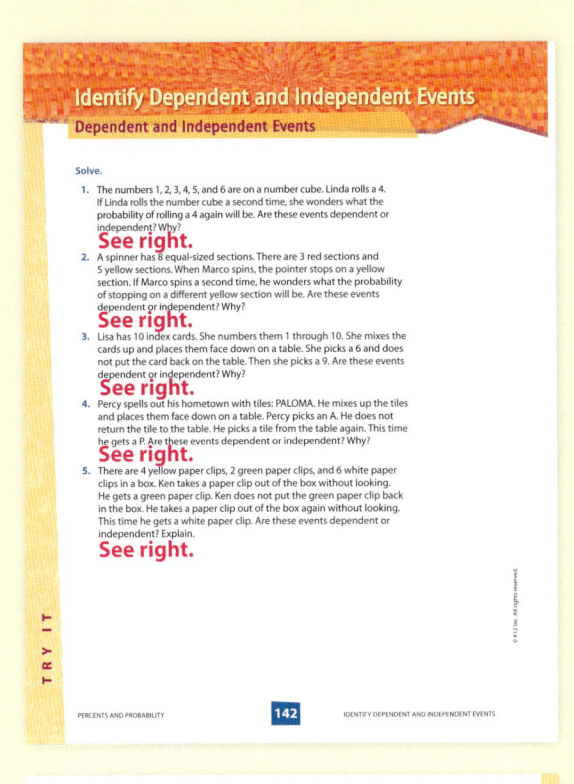

1. independent; The second outcome, rolling a 4, is not dependent on the first, rolling a 4, so the events are independent.

2. independent; The second outcome, spinning yellow, is not dependent on the first, spinning yellow, so the events are independent.

3. dependent; The second outcome, picking a 9, is dependent on the first, picking a 6 and not returning it to the table, so the events are dependent.

4. dependent; The second outcome, picking a P, is dependent on the first, picking an A and not returning it to the table, so the events are dependent.

5. dependent; The second outcome, picking a white paper clip, is dependent on the first, picking a green paper clip and not returning it to the box, so the events are dependent.

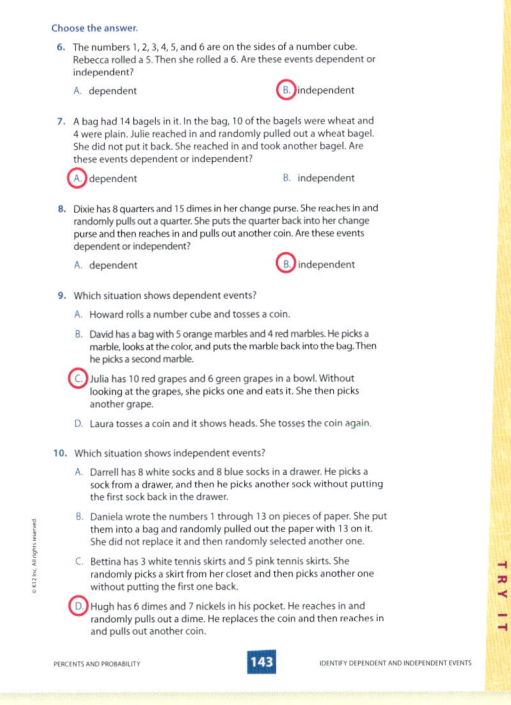

## CHECKPOINT

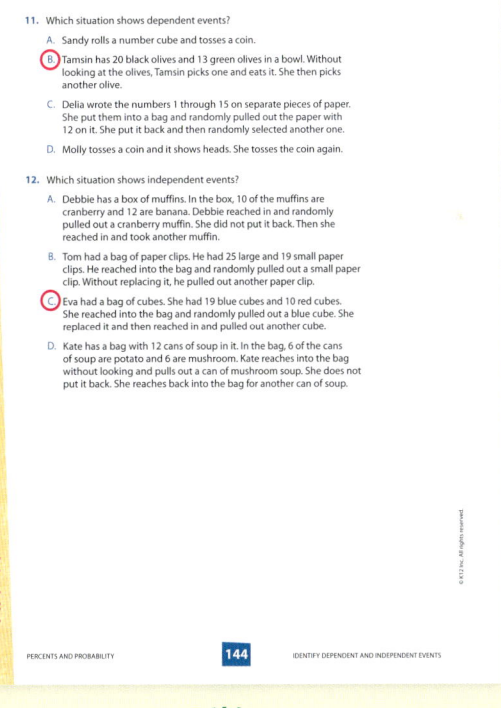

**ONLINE 10 min**

Students will complete an online Checkpoint. If necessary read the directions, problems, and answer choices to students and help them with keyboard or mouse operations.

### Objectives

- Identify events that are dependent or independent.

**IDENTIFY DEPENDENT AND INDEPENDENT EVENTS** 367

# Probability and Predictions

## Lesson Overview

| | | |
|---|---|---|
| **GET READY** Use a Spinner | 10 minutes | **OFFLINE** |
| **LEARN** Coin Toss | 10 minutes | **OFFLINE** |
| **LEARN** Make Predictions | 20 minutes | **OFFLINE** |
| **TRY IT** Prediction Problems | 10 minutes | **OFFLINE** |
| **CHECKPOINT** | 10 minutes | **ONLINE** |

▶ ### Lesson Objectives
Use probability to predict future events.

▶ ### Prerequisite Skills
Identify and systematically record the possible outcomes for a simple event.

▶ ### Content Background
Students will learn to use probability to predict future events.

Probability is the area of mathematics that studies the chance, or possibility, of an event taking place. One example of probability is tossing a two-sided coin that has heads and tails. For a coin, the probability of tossing heads is $\frac{1}{2}$ because heads is one side of a two-sided coin.

An outcome is one of the possible results of an experiment. For example, a spinner that is divided into three equal sections, with a red section, a blue section, and a green section, has three possible outcomes:

- Landing on red
- Landing on blue
- Landing on green

*Experimental probability* is the term given to the kind of probability involved when measuring the chance of an event happening based on data collected during an actual experiment. Experimental probability is a number between and including 0 and 1. For example, Kevin won 8 out of 15 chess games, so the experimental probability of Kevin winning a chess game is $\frac{8}{15}$.

*Theoretical probability* is the term given to the kind of probability involved when measuring the chance of an event happening based on calculating the probability. Theoretical probability is also a number between and including 0 and 1. For example, when someone spins a spinner with 4 congruent sections labeled A, B, C, and D, the theoretical probability of landing on B is $\frac{1}{4}$ because B is 1 of 4 equally likely outcomes for the spinner.

Although students will most often see fractions written with a horizontal fraction bar in math, such as $\frac{2}{3}$ or $5\frac{5}{6}$, they will occasionally see a diagonal fraction bar, such as 2/3 or 5 5/6. Students will very likely see the diagonal fraction bar in everyday experiences, but be sure they understand that using the horizontal

### Materials to Gather

**SUPPLIED**
Spinner – 4 and 5 Parts (printout)
Make Predictions activity page
Prediction Problems activity page

**ALSO NEEDED**
paper clip
coin
scissors, adult

fraction bar in their work will make problems involving fractions easier to interpret and solve.

When students write and compute with decimal numbers, they often use numbers that are between 0 and 1, for example, 0.1. While it is acceptable to write this number as .1, mathematicians usually write the leading zero, to show that the whole-number value for the decimal number is zero and to avoid confusion about the value of the number.

## ▶ Advance Preparation

Print the Spinner – 4 and 5 Parts and cut out the 5-part spinner. Bend open one part of the paper clip as a pointer for the spinning part of a spinner. The closed loop of the paper clip will sit over the dot on the spinner.

## GET READY  Use a Spinner

**OFFLINE — 10 min**

### Objectives

- Identify and systematically record the possible outcomes for a simple event.

Students will identify and record the outcomes of spinning a spinner. Help students if they need assistance in making the spinner. Gather the 5-part spinner that you printed and cut out.

1. Place the spinner in front of students. Have them label each section of the spinner with a letter from A to E. Tell students they will use the spinner to collect data.

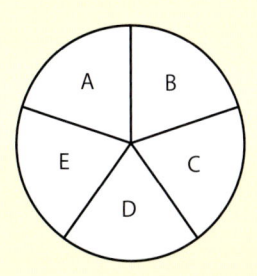

### Tips

Allow students to find the total number of tally marks for each letter and write the totals next to the tally marks.

2. Tell students they will record the data in a tally chart. Have them make a tally chart with 6 rows and 3 columns in their Math Notebook. The first row is for the column labels. In that row, tell students to write "Outcome" in the left box, "Tally" in the middle box, and "Total" in the right box. Tell them to label the remaining left boxes A–E. Have them title the chart "Spins for the Letter Spinner."

**Spins for the Letter Spinner**

| Outcome | Tally | Total |
|---|---|---|
| A | | |
| B | | |
| C | | |
| D | | |
| E | | |

PROBABILITY AND PREDICTIONS

3. Discuss the spinner with students.

   **Ask:** What are the possible outcomes for this spinner? A, B, C, D, or E

   **Ask:** What is the probability of landing on B? Why? $\frac{1}{5}$; The letter B is on 1 section of the spinner and the spinner has 5 equal-sized sections.

   **Ask:** Is the probability of landing on any other letter the same as the probability of landing on B? Why? Yes. Each letter on the spinner is a possible outcome and each letter has the same probability of $\frac{1}{5}$.

   **Ask:** If you spun the spinner 20 times, how many times would you **expect** the spinner to land on each letter? Why? Answers may vary. **Example:** 4 times for each letter. Each letter has the same probability. If I spin 20 times and have 5 sections, 20 spins divided by 5 sections is 4 spins. I expect the spinner to land on each section 4 times.

4. Show students how to use the spinner.
   - Place the closed loop of the paper clip over the dot in the center of the spinner.
   - Place the tip of a pencil on the dot. The straight part of the paper clip acts as the pointer.
   - Flick the paper clip with your finger while holding the pencil steady. It should spin around a few times and stop on one of the sections of the spinner.
   - Have students practice using the spinner before proceeding with the activity.

5. Have students spin the spinner a total of 20 times and record the results of each spin in the center column of the tally chart. Review with students how to make tally marks.
   - Tell them a single tally mark represents 1. |
   - Tell them a group of four tally marks with a fifth tally mark on the diagonal from the upper left to lower right represents 5. ||||

6. When students have finished the spins, have them count the number of tallies for each letter. Record the number of tallies for each letter in the Total column. Then have students name the letter the spinner landed on the greatest number of times, the fewest number of times, and any letters the spinner landed on an equal number of times. (These answers will vary depending on the data students collect.)

7. Ask students if their data numbers show what they may have expected—4 spins landing on each section. Chances are the experiment did not work out exactly as expected.

   **Say:** The expectation of 4 spins landing on each section is called the *theoretical probability*, or what would happen in the perfect experiment. However, the data tallies you collected show the *experimental probability* for each section, or what actually happened.

## LEARN Coin Toss

**OFFLINE 10 min**

### Objectives
- Use probability to predict future events.

Students will flip a coin and use probability to predict future events. Gather the coin.

1. Give students the coin. Ask students these questions.
   - What is the probability of landing on heads? $\frac{1}{2}$, 0.5, or 50%
   - What is the probability of landing on tails? $\frac{1}{2}$, 0.5, or 50%
   - Explain how to find these probabilities. The coin has 2 sides. One side is heads and one side is tails, so the probability of landing on heads is $\frac{1}{2}$, and the probability of landing on tails is also $\frac{1}{2}$.

2. Have students make a tally chart with 3 rows and 3 columns in their Math Notebook. The first row is for the column labels. Tell students to write "Outcome" in the left box, "Tally" in the middle box, and "Total" in the right box. Tell students to label the remaining left boxes "Heads" and "Tails." Have them title the chart "Coin Tosses."

3. Have students predict the outcome of tossing the coin 10 times.

   **Say:** The *theoretical probability* is that the coin would land heads up 5 times and tails up 5 times. Do an experiment so you can compare the theoretical probability with the *experimental probability*. Toss the coin 10 times and record the data in a tally chart.

   | Coin Tosses |||
   |---|---|---|
   | **Outcome** | **Tally** | **Total** |
   | Heads | | |
   | Tails | | |

4. After the 10 tosses, discuss the tally results. Ask students if the outcomes match their prediction. Have them explain why or why not. Then ask students if they want to change their prediction for the next 10 coin tosses based on the results of the first 10 coin tosses. Have them explain their reasoning.

5. Have students toss the coin 10 more times and record the tally results. Repeat Step 4 for 20 tosses.

6. Have students toss the coin 10 more times and record the tally results. After 30 coin tosses, have them count the number of tallies for each outcome. Record the number of tallies for each outcome in the Total column. Ask students to explain how their original prediction compares to the results of 30 coin tosses. Then have them explain how the probabilities of the experiment compare to the probabilities they found in Step 3. Students should discover that as the number of coin tosses increases, the closer the results are to the probability.

7. Remind students again that the first probability prediction they made is called theoretical probability. *Theoretical probability* is the kind of probability involved when measuring the chance of an event happening based on calculating the probability as it should work out. In this case, there were 2 possible outcomes, so the probability of landing on heads or tails was $\frac{1}{2}$, or 5 heads and 5 tails in 10 tosses.

PROBABILITY AND PREDICTIONS

8. Remind students that the probability predictions they made by looking at the data they had collected is called experimental probability. *Experimental probability* is the kind of probability given to events that occur during an actual experiment, like the one they conducted with the coin toss.

## LEARN Make Predictions

**OFFLINE 20 min**

### Objectives

- Use probability to predict future events.

Students will solve probability problems about predicting future events. Students will see problems that use theoretical and experimental probability. Have students turn to the Make Predictions activity page in their Activity Book and read the directions with them.

Students should copy the problems from the Activity Book into their Math Notebook as necessary and solve them there.

1. Read Problem 1 in the Worked Examples with students. Tell them they should carefully read the facts in problems that ask them to describe whether the probability is one of the following: *certain, likely, unlikely,* or *impossible*. Make sure they understand from the Worked Example that if there had been no yellow eraser in the group, then they would have answered *impossible*. If all the erasers had been yellow, then they would have answered *certain*.

2. Remind students that this type of probability is called theoretical probability. *Theoretical probability* is the kind of probability given to events that should occur in a perfect experiment.

3. Tell students that another example of theoretical probability is Problem 2 of the Worked Examples.

4. Have students read Problem 3 in the Worked Examples. Then have students complete Problems 1–6 in the problem set.

    **Ask:** Why is it most likely that the spinner will land on blue the most? There are more blue sections on the spinner than any other sections.

5. Read Problem 4 in the Worked Examples with students.

    **Ask:** What situations might occur that would make the outcome different from the predicted outcome? Answers will vary. **Example:** Many of the ducks could move to another area because their food supply ran out in the area where the counting happens every year.

6. Have students read and solve Problem 7 in the problem set.

    **Ask:** Why did you answer that adventure movies would be the most rented ones? More customers rented adventure movies in Weeks 1–4 than any other type of movie, so it is likely that the greatest number of customers will rent adventure movies in Week 5.

    Have students think about situations that might cause some different movie-rental outcome to occur than predicted. Answers will vary. **Example:** A popular comedy that people are eager to see is released for rental in Week 5.

7. Have students solve Problem 8.

## Additional Answers

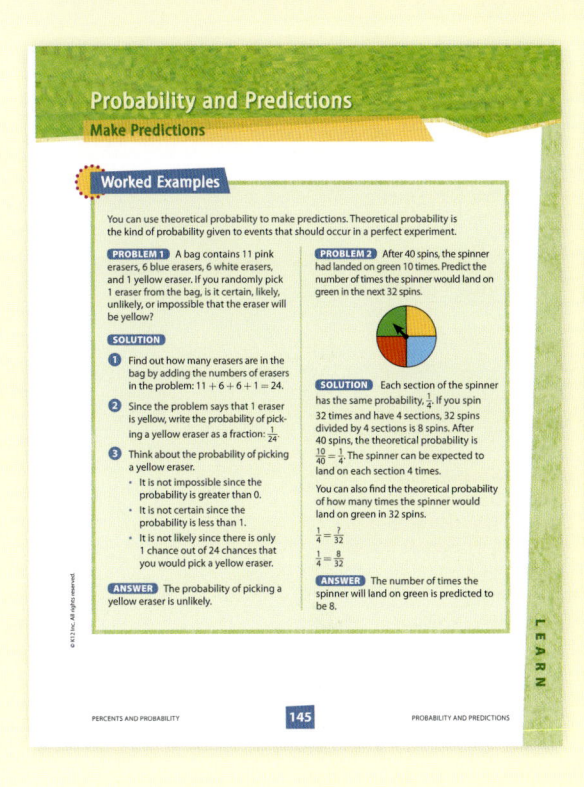

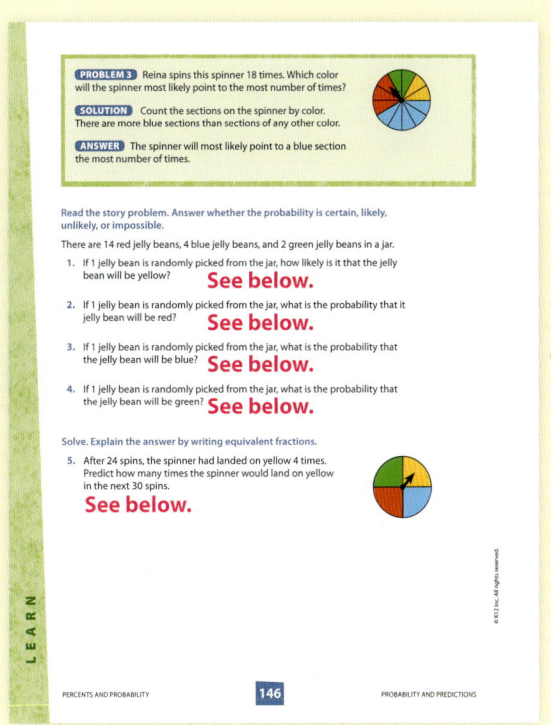

1. The probability of picking a yellow jelly bean is impossible. There are no yellow jelly beans in the jar.

3. Since 4 out of 20 jelly beans are blue, the probability of picking a blue jelly bean is $\frac{1}{5}$. A 20% chance is an unlikely probability.

5. After 24 spins, the experimental probability is $\frac{4}{24} = \frac{1}{6}$.

   You can also use the probability of landing on yellow to find the theoretical probability of how many times the spinner would land on yellow in 30 spins.

   $\frac{1}{6} = \frac{?}{30}$

   $\frac{1}{6} = \frac{5}{30}$

   The number of times the spinner will land on yellow is predicted to be 5.

2. Since 14 out of 20 jelly beans are red, the probability of picking a red jelly bean is $\frac{7}{10}$. A 70% chance is a likely probability.

4. Since 2 out of 20 jelly beans are green, the probability of picking a green jelly bean is $\frac{1}{10}$. A 10% chance is an unlikely probability.

### Worked Examples (Page 147)

**Choose the answer.**

6. Abby has a bag of blocks. She knows that each block is either purple or green. She pulls a block from the bag and records the color on a chart. She puts the block back into the bag and pulls out another block. After Abby has pulled out 10 blocks, her tally chart looks like this. Which prediction about the blocks in the bag is likely?

   **Blocks in Abby's Bag**

   | Purple | Green |
   |--------|-------|
   | ||||| || | ||| |

   A. There are more green blocks than purple blocks in the bag.
   **B. There are more purple blocks than green blocks in the bag.** (circled)
   C. The number of purple blocks in the bag is equal to the number of green blocks.

#### Worked Examples

You can use experimental probability to make predictions. Experimental probability is the kind of probability given to events that occur during an actual experiment. You use data to measure the chance of an event happening.

**PROBLEM** The chart shows the type and number of birds that scientists counted near a river and lake on a one-day bird-counting project each year for 5 years. Predict which type of bird would be the most numerous in Year 6.

**Bird Survey**

| Type of Bird | Year 1 | Year 2 | Year 3 | Year 4 | Year 5 | Year 6 |
|--------------|--------|--------|--------|--------|--------|--------|
| Sparrow | 12 | 14 | 10 | 15 | 13 | ? |
| Woodpecker | 2 | 4 | 5 | 5 | 4 | ? |
| Duck | 10 | 8 | 16 | 18 | 19 | ? |
| Hawk | 3 | 2 | 1 | 3 | 4 | ? |

**SOLUTION** Observe the trends in the chart.

**ANSWER** You can predict that ducks will be the most numerous birds in the sixth year of the bird-counting project because the greatest number of birds in the first 5 years are ducks. The number of ducks has also increased for the past 3 years.

---

### Page 148

**Read the problem and follow the directions.**

7. The owner of a movie rental business made this chart to show the different types of movies rented each week by customers. Using the results from Weeks 1–4, predict the type of movie that the greatest number of customers will likely rent in Week 5. **See below.**

   **Movie Rentals**

   | Type | Week 1 | Week 2 | Week 3 | Week 4 | Week 5 |
   |------|--------|--------|--------|--------|--------|
   | Drama | 83 | 78 | 91 | 75 | ? |
   | Comedy | 56 | 79 | 49 | 53 | ? |
   | Adventure | 156 | 139 | 147 | 155 | ? |
   | Mystery | 22 | 31 | 28 | 33 | ? |

8. The chart shows the number of points a basketball team scored in Games 1–4. Predict the number of points the team will likely score in Game 5 and explain your reasoning.

   **Basketball Scores**

   | | Game 1 | Game 2 | Game 3 | Game 4 | Game 5 |
   |---|--------|--------|--------|--------|--------|
   | Points | 78 | 82 | 73 | 80 | ? |

   **Answers may vary. Example: The numbers of points in Games 1–4 are in the 70s and 80s, so the number of points the team scores in Game 5 will likely be in the 70s or 80s.**

---

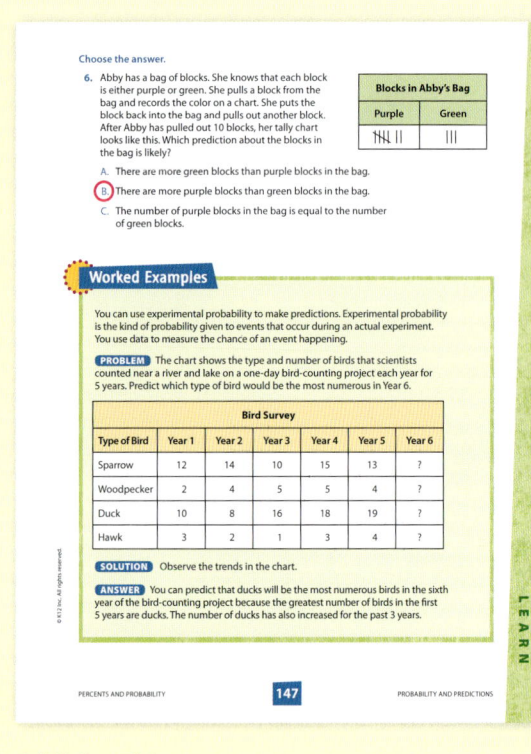

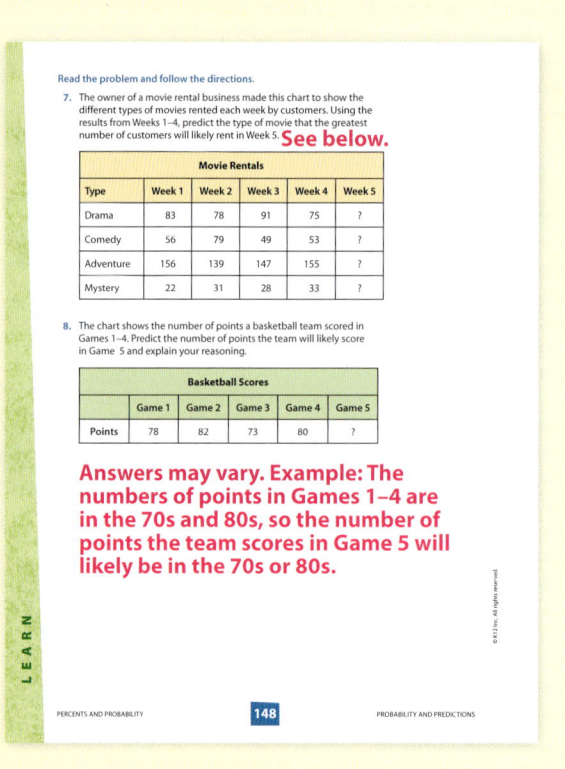

### Additional Answers

7. If you add the total number of rentals for movie type, adventure movies are rented the most. Adventure movies will likely be rented by the greatest number of customers in Week 5.

---

### TRY IT  Prediction Problems

**OFFLINE 10 min**

### Objectives

- Use probability to predict future events.

Students will use probability to make predictions. Have students turn to the Prediction Problems activity page in their Activity Book and read the directions with them.

Students should copy the problems from the Activity Book into their Math Notebook as necessary and solve them there.

## Probability and Predictions
### Prediction Problems

**Read the problem and follow the directions.**

1. A spinner has 4 equal-sized sections. One section is orange; one section is blue; one section is green; and one section is red. After 24 spins, the spinner had landed on red 6 times. Predict the number of times the spinner will land on red in the next 8 spins. Explain your answer.

   **See below.**

2. A spinner has 3 equal-sized sections. One section is orange; one section is green; and one section is blue. After 36 spins, the spinner had landed on green 12 times. Predict the number of times the spinner will land on green in the next 15 spins. Explain your answer.

   **See below.**

3. The owner of an online T-shirt store made this chart to show the number of customers who bought different sizes of T-shirts. Based on the results from Weeks 1–4, predict the size of T-shirts that the fewest number of customers will buy in Week 5.

   **T-Shirt Sales**

   | Size | Week 1 | Week 2 | Week 3 | Week 4 | Week 5 |
   |---|---|---|---|---|---|
   | Small | 114 | 120 | 99 | 125 | ? |
   | Medium | 34 | 37 | 33 | 41 | ? |
   | Large | 225 | 218 | 199 | 189 | ? |
   | X-Large | 150 | 177 | 179 | 164 | ? |

   **medium**

**Choose the answer.**

4. There are 25 gold stars, 15 red stars, and 3 blue stars in a box. If Fiona randomly picks 1 star from the box, what is the probability that the star will be gold?
   A. certain  **B. likely**  C. unlikely  D. impossible

5. There are 20 orange balls and 3 green balls in a bag. Paige reaches into the bag and pulls out a ball. What is the probability that the ball is green?
   A. certain  B. likely  **C. unlikely**  D. impossible

6. There are exactly 12 cranberry muffins and no other types of muffins in a box. Tara randomly picks 1 muffin from the box. What is the probability that the muffin will be a bran muffin?
   A. certain  B. likely  C. unlikely  **D. impossible**

7. The owner of a bakery made this chart showing the number of muffins she sold each week. Predict which type of muffin would sell the most in Week 4.

   **Muffins Sold**

   | Flavor | Week 1 | Week 2 | Week 3 | Week 4 |
   |---|---|---|---|---|
   | Orange | 88 | 82 | 79 | ? |
   | Bran | 56 | 50 | 51 | ? |
   | Blueberry | 38 | 40 | 37 | ? |
   | Banana Nut | 11 | 10 | 13 | ? |

   **A. orange**  B. bran  C. blueberry  D. banana nut

8. Olivia spun a spinner 30 times and recorded the results. If Olivia spins her spinner another 15 times, which color will the spinner most likely land on? Base your answer on the information in the chart.

   **Spinner Results**

   | Red | 6 |
   |---|---|
   | Green | 12 |
   | Yellow | 5 |
   | Orange | 7 |

   A. red  **B. green**  C. yellow  D. orange

---

### Additional Answers

1. **Example:** The probability of landing on red is 1 out of 4. So in the next 8 spins, the probability of landing on red would be 2 out of 8.

2. **Example:** The probability of landing on green is 1 out of 3. So in the next 15 spins, the probability of landing on green would be 5 out of 15.

---

## CHECKPOINT  ONLINE 10 min

Students will complete an online Checkpoint. If necessary, read the directions, problems, and answer choices to students and help them with keyboard or mouse operations.

### Objectives
- Use probability to predict future events.

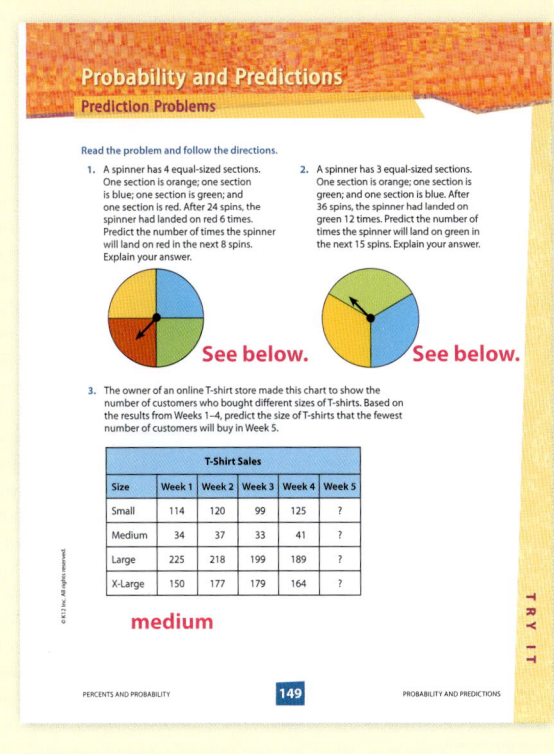

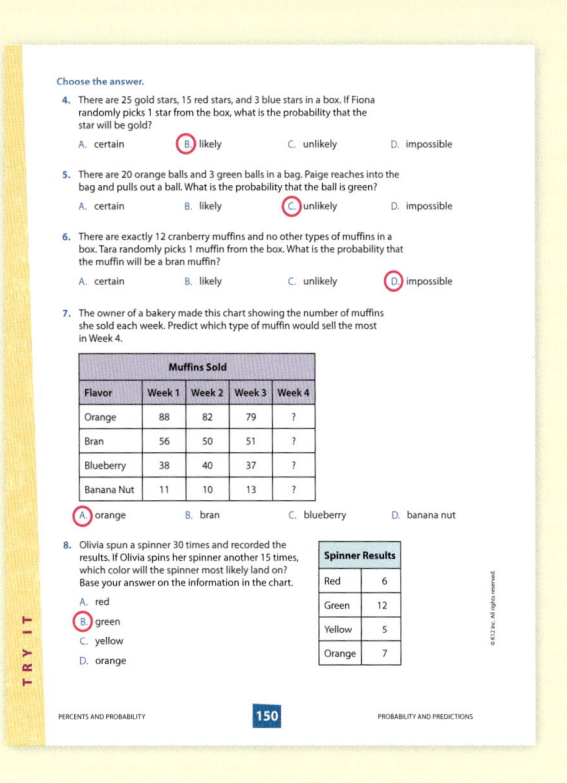

# Unit Review

## Lesson Overview

| | | |
|---|---|---|
| **UNIT REVIEW** Look Back | 10 minutes | **ONLINE** |
| **UNIT REVIEW** Checkpoint Practice | 50 minutes | **ONLINE** |
| ▶ **UNIT REVIEW** Prepare for the Checkpoint | | |

### ▶ Unit Objectives

This lesson reviews the following objectives:

- Interpret a percent as a part of a hundred.
- Determine the decimal and percent equivalents for a common fraction and explain why they represent the same value.
- Compute a given percent of a whole number.
- Represent probabilities as fractions, decimals, and percents.
- Identify events that are dependent or independent.
- Use probability to predict future events.

**Materials to Gather**

There are no materials to gather for this lesson.

### ▶ Advance Preparation

In this lesson, students will have an opportunity to review previous activities in the Percents and Probability unit. Look at the suggested activities in Unit Review: Prepare for the Checkpoint online and gather any needed materials.

## UNIT REVIEW  Look Back

**ONLINE 10 min**

Students will review key concepts from the unit to prepare for the Unit Checkpoint.

**Objectives**
- Review unit objectives.

## UNIT REVIEW  Checkpoint Practice

**ONLINE 50 min**

Students will complete an online Checkpoint Practice to prepare for the Unit Checkpoint. If necessary, read the directions, problems, and answer choices to students. Have students answer the problems on their own. Review any missed problems with students.

**Objectives**
- Review unit objectives.

### ▶ **UNIT REVIEW** Prepare for the Checkpoint

What you do next depends on how students performed in the previous activity, Unit Review: Checkpoint Practice. If students had difficulty with any of the problems, complete the appropriate review activity listed in the table online.

**376** PERCENTS AND PROBABILITY

# Unit Checkpoint

## Lesson Overview

**UNIT CHECKPOINT** Online | 60 minutes | **ONLINE**

### ▶ Unit Objectives

This lesson assesses the following objectives:
- Interpret a percent as a part of a hundred.
- Determine the decimal and percent equivalents for a common fraction and explain why they represent the same value.
- Compute a given percent of a whole number.
- Represent probabilities as fractions, decimals, and percents.
- Identify events that are dependent or independent.
- Use probability to predict future events.

### Materials to Gather

There are no materials to gather for this lesson.

### UNIT CHECKPOINT Online

Students will complete the Unit Checkpoint online. If necessary, read the directions, problems, and answer choices to students and help them with keyboard or mouse operations.

### Objectives

- Assess unit objectives.

# Algebra

$25 = p + 17$

$m + 5$

$18 - w$

$18 - y$

$4 \times 9 = n$

$72 \div \triangle = 12$

$10 + d$

$x + 5 = 9$

## ▶ Unit Objectives

- Use a letter to represent an unknown value in an expression or an equation.
- Identify and apply the distributive property in an equation or an expression with variables.
- Evaluate a simple algebraic expression in one variable by using substitution.
- Identify or use an expression or an equation to answer questions about a problem.

## ▶ Big Ideas

- A variable is a symbol, usually a letter, that is used to stand for a number or a set of numbers.
- The distributive property illustrates how to multiply a specific multiplier by a series of numbers being added or subtracted.
- An expression represents a value that can be a number, a variable, or a group of numbers, variables, and operation symbols. Some examples of expressions are $10 - 4 + 1$, $3 + x$, $5y + 2$, $b$, and 5.

## ▶ Unit Introduction

Students will begin the Algebra unit with an introduction to using letters to represent variables in both expressions and equations. To extend their investigation of variables, they will explore examples of how the distributive property is correctly applied in expressions and equations. Students will use substitution to evaluate an expression with one variable. The unit culminates with identifying expressions or equations that answer questions about a story problem. Another way to think about a story problems is as a situation. Students will work with story problems in many activities in this unit.

## ▶ Keywords

| distributive property | expression | substitution |
| equation | order of operations | term |
| evaluate | solve | variable |

# Understand Variables in Algebra (A)

## Lesson Overview

| | | |
|---|---|---|
| **GET READY** Build Expressions and Equations | 5 minutes | **ONLINE** |
| **LEARN** Variables | 15 minutes | **ONLINE** |
| **LEARN** Find the Value of Expressions | 15 minutes | **OFFLINE** |
| **LEARN** Variables in Situations: Add, Subtract | 15 minutes | **ONLINE** |
| **TRY IT** Variables in Expressions and Equations | 10 minutes | **ONLINE** |

### ▶ Lesson Objectives
Use a letter to represent an unknown value in an expression or an equation.

### ▶ Prerequisite Skills
Use symbols to stand for variables in simple expressions or equations.

### ▶ Content Background
Students will learn the meaning of a variable and use it to represent an unknown value in an expression or an equation. They will also relate expressions and equations to different situations.

- An *expression* is a part of a number sentence and can have numbers, operation symbols (such as $+$, $-$, $\cdot$, or $\div$), and variables. An expression does **not** have a relational symbol, such as $<$, $>$, or $=$, in it. Some examples of expressions are $m + 7$, $12 - 2w$, $11 \cdot 6$, and $100 \div 4$.

- An *equation* is a number sentence that shows that two quantities are equal. Equations can include numbers, variables, and operation symbols (such as $+$, $-$, $\cdot$, or $\div$). Some examples of equations are $2r - 3 = 9$ and $16 = 2 + 4$.

- A *variable* is a symbol that stands for a quantity. For example, in the equation $2 + m = 5$, $m$ stands for the number that makes the equation true. So in $2 + m = 5$, $m = 3$, since $2 + 3 = 5$. Sometimes the variable stands for many possible quantities. One reason the symbols are called *variables* is that the amount they represent can vary. For example, in the expression $52 - p$, you can replace $p$ with any number and find the value of the expression. You may often see $x$ and $y$ used as variables in expressions and equations, but any letter can be used as a variable.

When students multiply in expressions and equations in this lesson, they will not always see the $\times$ symbol. They might see the dot that represents multiplication: $\cdot$. Students might also see implied multiplication, where no multiplication symbol is used. For example, they will see $3n$ instead of $3 \cdot n$.

### Materials to Gather

**SUPPLIED**
There are no materials to gather for this lesson.

## ▶ Common Errors and Misconceptions

- Students might have a difficult time understanding that a letter can represent varying values or that different letters can represent the same value. They commonly interpret a letter as representing a specific number. For example, students might think that $7w + 22 = 109$ and $7n + 22 = 109$ have different answers because they don't understand that $w$ and $n$ represent the same number.
- Students might not understand that arithmetic and algebra treat the placement of symbols differently. For example, $8y$ means $8 \cdot y$ while 54 means $50 + 4$. So when solving for $x$ in $2x = 24$, students often think that $x = 4$.

## ▶ Advance Preparation

In the Math Notebook, create the charts shown below.

| $z$ | $z + 4$ | Value of the expression |
|---|---|---|
|  |  |  |
|  |  |  |
|  |  |  |
|  |  |  |

| $x$ | $5 - x$ | Value of the expression |
|---|---|---|
| 1 |  |  |
| 2 |  |  |
| 3 |  |  |
| 4 |  |  |

## GET READY  Build Expressions and Equations

ONLINE 5 min

Students will read a description of an expression or an equation. They will then use numbers and symbols to build the expression or equation.

**Objectives**
- Use symbols to stand for variables in simple expressions or equations.

## LEARN  Variables

ONLINE 15 min

Students will learn what a variable is and how it is used in expressions and equations. They will also practice reading expressions and equations with variables.

**Objectives**
- Use a letter to represent an unknown value in an expression or an equation.

## LEARN  Find the Value of Expressions

**OFFLINE 15 min**

### Objectives
- Use a letter to represent an unknown value in an expression or an equation.

Students will complete charts to write expressions and find values for each expression.
Gather the two charts you created in the Math Notebook.

1. Tell students that when they write expressions and equations that have addition, there can be more than one way to write them because the addends can switch places and still represent the same expression or equation.

   **Ask:** In subtraction expressions and equations, why can't you switch around the numbers and variables as you can in addition expressions and equations? Addition has the commutative property, which means the order of the addends can be changed and the sum will remain the same. Subtraction doesn't have the commutative property.

2. Give students the addition chart.

   **Say:** The chart shows values for the variable $z$. It also has the expression $z + 4$. Read the expression as "an unknown number, $z$, combined with 4." You will fill in the chart to write four values for the variable $z$ and find the value of four expressions for those values of $z$.

3. Read the column headings and the values of $z$ on the chart.

   **Say:** Find out what values you can get for the expression $z + 4$. You will write the values for the expression in the third column, Value of the Expression.

4. Have students look at the first row. Tell them that in this row, $z$ has a value of 1. That means they can rewrite the expression $z + 4$ as $1 + 4$.

   **Say:** Add $1 + 4$. For $z$ equal to 1, the value of the expression $z + 4$ is 5.

   On the chart, have students write $1 + 4$ in the second column, $z + 4$. Have them write 5 in the third column, Value of the Expression.

5. Have students fill in the other rows of the chart as they did with the first row. The completed chart is shown here.

| $z$ | $z + 4$ | Value of the expression |
|---|---|---|
| 1 | $1 + 4$ | 5 |
| 2 | $2 + 4$ | 6 |
| 3 | $3 + 4$ | 7 |
| 4 | $4 + 4$ | 8 |

6. Have students read aloud and explain each row in the chart. They should say the variable, the expression with the value of the variable, and the value of the expression. For example, students would read the first row as, "For the variable $z$ with the value of 1, the value of the expression $z + 4$ equals $1 + 4$, which equals 5."

UNDERSTAND VARIABLES IN ALGEBRA (A)

7. Give students the subtraction chart and have them complete it, using their experience from the addition chart. Repeat Step 6 with this chart. The completed chart is shown here.

| x | 5 − x | Value of the expression |
|---|---|---|
| 1 | 5 − 1 | 4 |
| 2 | 5 − 2 | 3 |
| 3 | 5 − 3 | 2 |
| 4 | 5 − 4 | 1 |

### LEARN  Variables in Situations: Add, Subtract

ONLINE 15 min

Students will hear a discussion between two characters about how to write expressions and equations to match story problems. Then they will match expressions and equations to story problems that involve addition and subtraction.

**Objectives**
- Use a letter to represent an unknown value in an expression or an equation.

### TRY IT  Variables in Expressions and Equations

ONLINE 10 min

Students will complete an online Try It. If necessary, read the directions, problems, and answer choices to students and help them with keyboard or mouse operations.

**Objectives**
- Use a letter to represent an unknown value in an expression or an equation.

**Tips**

It may be helpful for students to read the expressions and equations aloud to help them match the expressions and equations with story problems.

# Understand Variables in Algebra (B)

## Lesson Overview

| | | |
|---|---|---|
| Skills Update | 5 minutes | **ONLINE** |
| **LEARN** Other Ways to Show Multiplication | 20 minutes | **ONLINE** |
| **LEARN** Variables in Situations: Multiply, Divide | 15 minutes | **ONLINE** |
| **TRY IT** Find Expressions and Equations | 10 minutes | **ONLINE** |
| **CHECKPOINT** | 10 minutes | **ONLINE** |

### ▶ Lesson Objectives
Use a letter to represent an unknown value in an expression or an equation.

### ▶ Prerequisite Skills
Use symbols to stand for variables in simple expressions or equations.

### ▶ Content Background
Students will continue to learn the meaning of a variable and use it to represent an unknown value in an expression or an equation. They will also relate expressions and equations to different situations.

- An *expression* is a part of a number sentence and can have numbers, operation symbols (such as $+$, $-$, $\cdot$, or $\div$), and variables. An expression does **not** have a relational symbol, such as $<$, $>$, or $=$, in it. Some examples of expressions are $m + 7$, $12 - 2w$, $11 \cdot 6$, and $100 \div 4$.

- An *equation* is a number sentence that shows that two quantities are equal. Equations can include numbers, variables, and operation symbols (such as $+$, $-$, $\cdot$, or $\div$). Some examples of equations are $2r - 3 = 9$ and $16 = 12 + 4$.

- A *variable* is a symbol that stands for a quantity. For example, in the equation $2 + m = 5$, $m$ stands for the number that makes the equation true. So in $2 + m = 5$, $m = 3$, since $2 + 3 = 5$. Sometimes the variable stands for many possible quantities. One reason the symbols are called *variables* is that the amount they represent can vary. For example, in the expression $52 - p$, you can replace $p$ with any number and find the value of the expression. You may often see $x$ and $y$ used as variables in expressions and equations, but any letter can be used as a variable.

When students multiply in expressions and equations in this lesson, they will not always see the $\times$ symbol. They might see the dot that represents multiplication: $\cdot$ . Students might also see implied multiplication, where no multiplication symbol is used. For example, they will see $3n$ instead of $3 \cdot n$.

### Materials to Gather

**SUPPLIED**
There are no materials to gather for this lesson.

### ▶ Common Errors and Misconceptions

- Students might have a difficult time understanding that a letter can represent varying values or that different letters can represent the same value. They commonly interpret a letter as representing a specific number. For example, students might think that $7w + 22 = 109$ and $7n + 22 = 109$ have different answers because they don't understand that $w$ and $n$ represent the same number.

- Students might not understand that arithmetic and algebra treat the placement of symbols differently. For example, $8y$ means $8 \cdot y$ while 54 means $50 + 4$. So when solving for $x$ in $2x = 24$, students often think that $x = 4$.

## LEARN  Other Ways to Show Multiplication
**ONLINE 20 min**

Students will learn different ways to represent multiplication expressions and equations with numbers and variables.

**Objectives**
- Use a letter to represent an unknown value in an expression or an equation.

## LEARN  Variables in Situations: Multiply, Divide
**ONLINE 15 min**

Students will hear a discussion between two characters about how to write multiplication and division expressions and equations to match situations. Then they will match expressions and equations to situations.

**Objectives**
- Use a letter to represent an unknown value in an expression or an equation.

## TRY IT  Find Expressions and Equations
**ONLINE 10 min**

Students will complete an online Try It. If necessary, read the directions, problems, and answer choices to students and help them with keyboard or mouse operations.

**Objectives**
- Use a letter to represent an unknown value in an expression or an equation.

## CHECKPOINT
**ONLINE 10 min**

Students will complete an online Checkpoint. If necessary, read the directions, problems, and answer choices to students and help them with keyboard or mouse operations.

**Objectives**
- Use a letter to represent an unknown value in an expression or an equation.

# Use the Distributive Property (A)

## Lesson Overview

| | | |
|---|---|---|
| **GET READY** Solve Distributive Property Problems | 10 minutes | ONLINE |
| **LEARN** Model and Use Variables | 10 minutes | ONLINE |
| **LEARN** Apply the Distributive Property | 15 minutes | OFFLINE |
| **LEARN** Proper Use of the Distributive Property | 15 minutes | ONLINE |
| **TRY IT** Practice the Distributive Property | 10 minutes | ONLINE |

### ▶ Lesson Objectives
Identify and apply the distributive property in an equation or an expression with variables.

### ▶ Prerequisite Skills
Demonstrate how and when to use the distributive property.

### ▶ Content Background
Students will use the distributive property to evaluate expressions and equations with numbers and variables. They will begin with models and then move to symbols.

The distributive property applied to addition says that the same answer is obtained under either of the following methods: (1) add the addends and then multiply the sum by another amount, or (2) multiply each addend separately by the same amount and then add those products. Similarly, the distributive property allows multiplication of a difference in two ways. This property can make it easier for students to mentally multiply numbers, to check the reasonableness of products, and to achieve success with future algebraic topics.

When students are using the distributive property to evaluate expressions and equations that include subtraction, emphasize that they need to evaluate the numbers in the given order. For example, when evaluating $(5 \cdot 50) - (5 \cdot 2) = 250 - 10$, students need to subtract the products in the given order to get the result 240, since subtraction is not commutative.

The order of operations is a set of rules that states the order in which students need to perform computation problems that are written horizontally and include more than one operation. If students don't follow the correct order, they will not calculate the answer correctly. The order of operations is used to find the value of the expression or equation, or to evaluate the expression or equation. The order of operations follows a step-by-step priority:

- First, if there are parentheses, complete the computations inside the parentheses. There are other grouping symbols that could be within the parentheses. If two or more computations are within parentheses or grouping symbols, the following order is also used there.
- Simplify exponents.

**Materials to Gather**

**SUPPLIED**
Apply the Distributive Property activity page

- Multiply or divide from left to right, starting with the operation that comes first (either division or multiplication) and perform those two operations consecutively.
- Finally subtract or add from left to right, starting with the operation that comes first (either addition or subtraction) and perform those two operations consecutively.

### ▶ Common Errors and Misconceptions

- Students might have a difficult time understanding that a letter can represent varying values or that different letters can represent the same value. They commonly interpret a letter as representing a specific number. For example, students might think that $7w + 22 = 109$ and $7n + 22 = 109$ have different answers because they don't understand that $w$ and $n$ represent the same number.
- Students might not understand that arithmetic and algebra treat the placement of symbols differently. For example, $8y$ means $8 \cdot y$ while 54 means $50 + 4$. So when solving for $x$ in $2x = 24$, students often think that $x = 4$.
- Students might use wrong arithmetic principles when trying to apply the distributive property, such as in the following examples:
Incorrectly distributing:
$a(b + c) = (a \times b) + (b \times c)$
Incorrectly generalizing the distributive property to addition:
$a + (b \times c) = (a + b) \times (a + c)$
Incorrectly applying the distributive property to three factors:
$2(ab) = 2a \times 2b$

## GET READY  Solve Distributive Property Problems  10 min

Students will use the distributive property to solve problems that do not have variables.

**Objectives**
- Demonstrate how and when to use the distributive property.

## LEARN  Model and Use Variables  10 min

Students will see grids that model the distributive property. They will use the distributive property to solve equations that have variables.

**Objectives**
- Identify and apply the distributive property in an equation or an expression with variables.

## LEARN Apply the Distributive Property

**Objectives**
- Identify and apply the distributive property in an equation or an expression with variables.

Students will apply the distributive property to evaluate expressions. Have students turn to the Apply the Distributive Property activity page in their Activity Book and read the directions with them.

Students should copy the problems from the Activity Book into their Math Notebook as necessary and solve them there.

1. Read Problem 1 of the Worked Examples with students.

   **Ask:** What property allows you to write 3 · (40 + 2) as (3 · 40) + (3 · 2)? **the distributive property**

2. Read Problem 2 of the Worked Examples with students.

   **Say:** In this problem, the distributive property has already been applied, but you don't know the value of the variable $f$. The number 78 can be written as an expression with two addends, 8 and an unknown addend. The unknown addend is represented by the variable $f$.

   **Ask:** Why does the variable $f$ equal 70? **Sample answer:** The variable $f$ represents the number that you add to 8 to get 78. When you add 70 to 8, you get 78, so $f$ equals 70.

3. Have students work the first three problems in the problem set.

   **Say:** In Problem 3, the answer $54 + 9b$ is the same as $54 + 9 · b$. The implied multiplication, $9b$, is equal to $9 · b$. Using implied multiplication can sometimes be easier to work with when you are evaluating expressions.

4. Have students complete the rest of the problems in the problem set. If students have difficulty, first encourage them to look at the problems in the Worked Examples and follow the processes shown. If they still have difficulty, help them apply the processes shown in the Worked Examples.

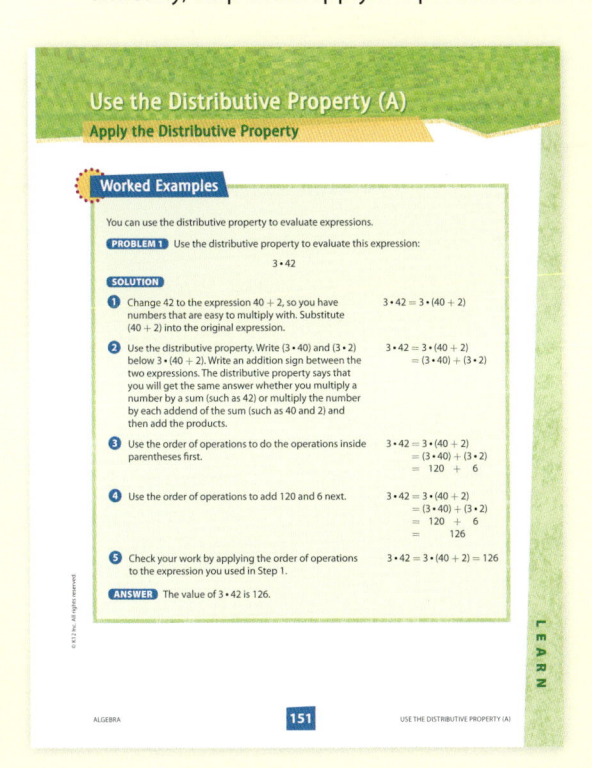

USE THE DISTRIBUTIVE PROPERTY (A) **389**

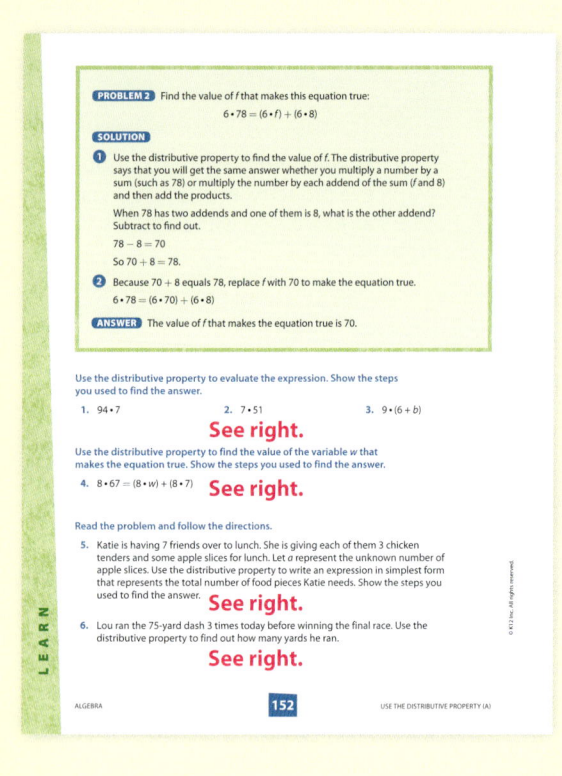

## Additional Answers

1. $94 \cdot 7 = (90 \cdot 7) + (4 \cdot 7)$
   $\phantom{94 \cdot 7} = 630 + 28$
   $\phantom{94 \cdot 7} = 658$

2. $7 \cdot 51 = (7 \cdot 50) + (7 \cdot 1)$
   $\phantom{7 \cdot 51} = 350 + 7$
   $\phantom{7 \cdot 51} = 357$

3. $9 \cdot (6 + b) = (9 \cdot 6) + (9 \cdot b)$
   $\phantom{9 \cdot (6 + b)} = 54 + 9b$

4. Answers will vary. Students should show steps that indicate that they understand how to find the value of the variable.

   | Use the distributive property. Write an equation to find the value of $w$ | $67 = w + 7$ |
   | --- | --- |
   | Solve the equation for $w$. | $67 - 7 = w + 7 - 7$ |
   | | $60 = w$ |
   | Replace 60 for $w$ in the original equation. | $8 \cdot 67 = (8 \cdot 60) + (8 \cdot 7)$ |
   | The value of $w$ that makes the equation true is 60. | |

5. $7 \cdot (3 + a) = (7 \cdot 3) + (7 \cdot a)$
   $\phantom{7 \cdot (3 + a)} = 21 + 7a$

6. $75 \cdot 3 = (70 \cdot 3) + (5 \cdot 3)$
   $\phantom{75 \cdot 3} = 210 + 15$
   $\phantom{75 \cdot 3} = 225$
   Lou ran 225 yards today.

## LEARN  Proper Use of the Distributive Property

**ONLINE 15 min**

Students will study examples of the distributive property to learn how it can be properly applied. They will then apply the distributive property to find the value of expressions.

### Objectives
- Identify and apply the distributive property in an equation or an expression with variables.

## TRY IT  Practice the Distributive Property

**ONLINE 10 min**

Students will complete an online Try It. If necessary, read the directions, problems, and answer choices to students and help them with keyboard or mouse operations.

### Objectives
- Identify and apply the distributive property in an equation or an expression with variables.

# Use the Distributive Property (B)

## Lesson Overview

| | | |
|---|---|---|
| **GET READY** Use the Distributive Property | 10 minutes | ONLINE |
| **LEARN** Distributive Property Subtraction | 15 minutes | ONLINE |
| **LEARN** Simplify with Distributive Property | 15 minutes | OFFLINE |
| **TRY IT** Solve with the Distributive Property | 10 minutes | ONLINE |
| **CHECKPOINT** | 10 minutes | ONLINE |

### ▶ Lesson Objectives
Identify and apply the distributive property in an equation or an expression with variables.

### ▶ Prerequisite Skills
Demonstrate how and when to use the distributive property.

### ▶ Content Background
Students will further explore the distributive property. They will also use the distributive property with subtraction and fill in examples of its use.

    The distributive property applied to addition says that the same answer is obtained under either of the following methods: (1) add the addends and then multiply the sum by another amount, or (2) multiply each addend separately by the same amount and then add those products. Similarly, the distributive property allows multiplication of a difference in two ways. This property can make it easier for students to mentally multiply numbers, to check the reasonableness of products, and to achieve success with future algebraic topics.

    When students are using the distributive property to evaluate expressions and equations that include subtraction, emphasize that they need to evaluate the numbers in the given order. For example, when evaluating $(5 \cdot 50) - (5 \cdot 2) = 250 - 10$, students need to subtract the products in the given order to get the result 240, since subtraction is not commutative.

    The order of operations is a set of rules that states the order in which students need to perform computation problems that are written horizontally and include more than one operation. If students don't follow the correct order, they will not calculate the answer correctly. The order of operations is used to find the value of the expression or equation, or to evaluate the expression or equation. The order of operations follows a step-by-step priority:

- First, if there are parentheses, complete the computations inside the parentheses. There are other grouping symbols that could be within the parentheses. If two or more computations are within parentheses or grouping symbols, the following order is also used there.
- Simplify exponents.
- Multiply or divide from left to right, starting with the operation that comes first (either division or multiplication) and perform those two operations consecutively.

### Materials to Gather

**SUPPLIED**

Simplify with Distributive Property activity page

- Finally subtract or add from left to right, starting with the operation that comes first (either addition or subtraction) and perform those two operations consecutively.

## ▶ Common Errors and Misconceptions

- Students might have a difficult time understanding that a letter can represent varying values or that different letters can represent the same value. They commonly interpret a letter as representing a specific number. For example, students might think that $7w + 22 = 109$ and $7n + 22 = 109$ have different answers because they don't understand that $w$ and $n$ represent the same number.
- Students might not understand that arithmetic and algebra treat the placement of symbols differently. For example, $8y$ means $8 \cdot y$ while 54 means $50 + 4$. So when solving for $x$ in $2x = 24$, students often think that $x = 4$.
- Students might use wrong arithmetic principles when trying to apply the distributive property, such as in the following examples:
Incorrectly distributing:
$a(b + c) = (a \times b) + (b \times c)$
Incorrectly generalizing the distributive property to addition:
$a + (b \times c) = (a + b) \times (a + c)$
Incorrectly applying the distributive property to three factors:
$2(ab) = 2a \times 2b$

### GET READY  Use the Distributive Property

ONLINE 10 min

**Objectives**
- Identify and apply the distributive property in an equation or an expression with variables.

Students will select the correct way to apply the distributive property to find the value of expressions and to solve equations.

### LEARN  Distributive Property Subtraction

ONLINE 15 min

**Objectives**
- Identify and apply the distributive property in an equation or an expression with variables.

Students will study examples of expressions with subtraction that can be simplified by using the distributive property. They will then apply the distributive property to simplify multiplication and subtraction expressions that include variables.

**Tips** — If students have trouble understanding how to apply the distributive property with subtraction, have them show all the steps to evaluate an addition expression. Then have them evaluate a subtraction expression, using their work on the addition expression for guidance.

## LEARN  Simplify with Distributive Property

**OFFLINE 15 min**

### Objectives
- Identify and apply the distributive property in an equation or an expression with variables.

Students will start by filling in the steps in problems that apply the distributive property. Then they will use the distributive property to simplify expressions. Some of the expressions will use variables. Have students turn to the Simplify with Distributive Property activity page in their Activity Book and read the directions with them.

Students should copy the problems from the Activity Book into their Math Notebook as necessary and solve them there.

1. Read Problem 1 of the Worked Examples with students and make sure they understand the steps.

    **Say:** Remember that the expression on the right shows how the distributive property is applied to the expression on the left.

    **Ask:** What does the final step, 30 = 30, tell you about whether the distributive property was applied correctly or not? *Because you have an equation with both sides equal to the same number, you know that the distributive property was applied correctly.*

2. Read Problems 2 and 3 in the Worked Examples with students and make sure they understand the solutions.

    **Ask:** What steps did you use to replace the question mark with the variable $m$ on the right side of the equation in Problem 3? *The expression $(m - 2)$ needs to be multiplied by 4. To do that, first multiply 4 times $m$. Then multiply 4 times 2. After that, subtract the second product from the first product. The variable $m$ represents a number in the expression.*

3. Read Problem 4 in the Worked Examples with students. Make sure they understand the solution.

4. Have students complete the problems in the problem set. Tell them to review the Worked Examples if they need help understanding the problems, and help them as needed.

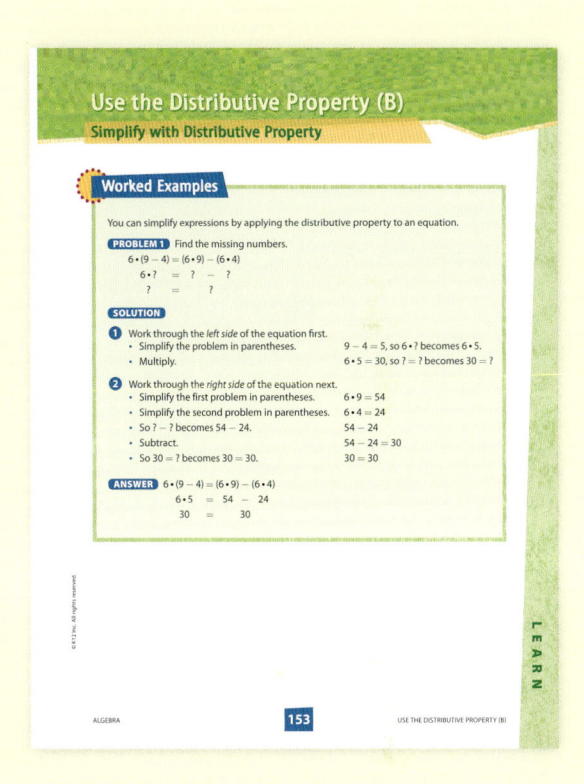

**USE THE DISTRIBUTIVE PROPERTY (B)  393**

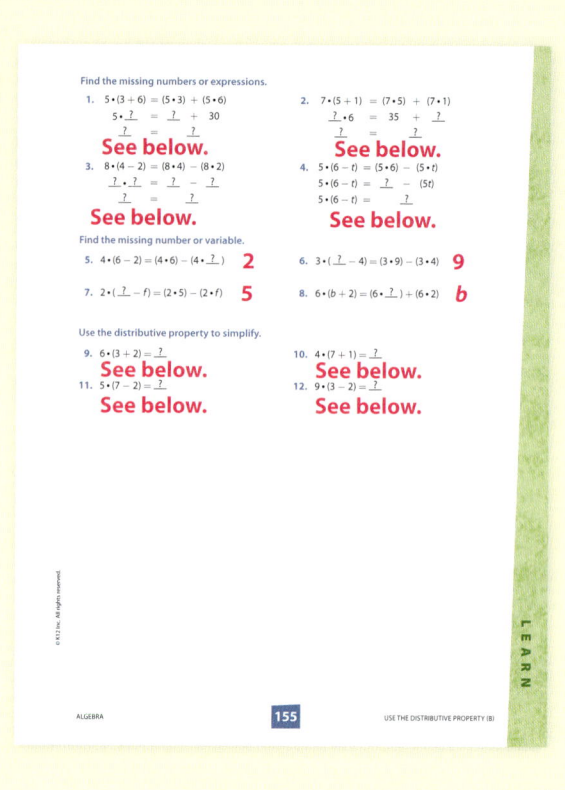

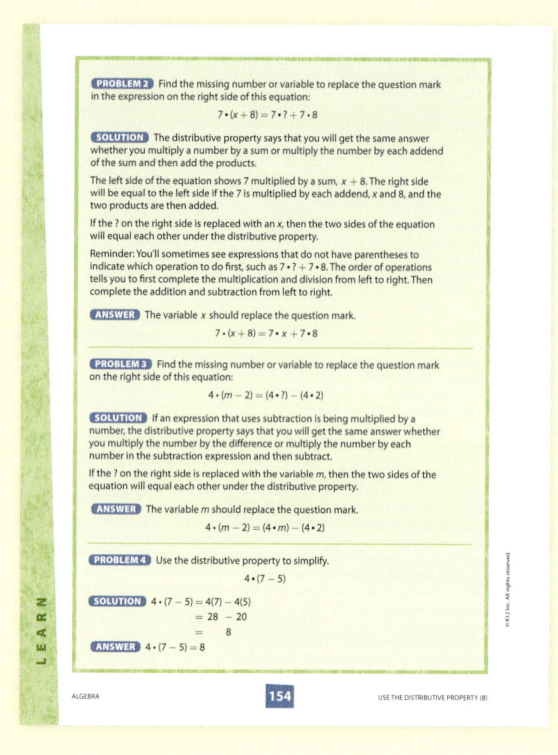

## Additional Answers

1. $5 \cdot 9 = 15 + 30$
   $45 = 45$

2. $7 \cdot 6 = 35 + 7$
   $42 = 42$

3. $8 \cdot 2 = 32 - 16$
   $16 = 16$

4. $5 \cdot (6 - t) = 30 - (5t)$
   $5 \cdot (6 - t) = 30 - 5t$

9. $(6 \cdot 3) + (6 \cdot 2) = 18 + 12 = 30$
10. $(4 \cdot 7) + (4 \cdot 1) = 28 + 4 = 32$
11. $(5 \cdot 7) - (5 \cdot 2) = 35 - 10 = 25$
12. $(9 \cdot 3) - (9 \cdot 2) = 27 - 18 = 9$

## TRY IT  Solve with the Distributive Property

Students will complete an online Try It. If necessary, read the directions, problems, and answer choices to students and help them with keyboard or mouse operations.

**Objectives**
- Identify and apply the distributive property in an equation or an expression with variables.

## CHECKPOINT

Students will complete an online Checkpoint. If necessary, read the directions, problems, and answer choices to students and help them with keyboard or mouse operations.

**Objectives**
- Identify and apply the distributive property in an equation or an expression with variables.

# One Variable in Algebraic Expressions

| **Lesson Overview** | | |
|---|---|---|
| **GET READY** Order of Operations in Expressions | 10 minutes | **ONLINE** |
| **LEARN** Use Substitution in Expressions | 15 minutes | **OFFLINE** |
| **LEARN** Distributive Property Substitution | 15 minutes | **ONLINE** |
| **TRY IT** Practice with Variable Expressions | 10 minutes | **ONLINE** |
| **CHECKPOINT** | 10 minutes | **ONLINE** |

## ▶ Lesson Objectives
Evaluate a simple algebraic expression in one variable by using substitution.

## ▶ Prerequisite Skills
Use parentheses and the order of operations to write or evaluate an expression.

## ▶ Content Background
Students will learn to evaluate simple algebraic expressions with one variable using substitution. They will evaluate one-, two-, and three-step expressions. They will also use the distributive property to evaluate expressions with one variable.

A *variable* is a symbol that stands for a quantity. For example, in the equation $2 + m = 5$, $m$ stands for the number that makes the equation true. So in $2 + m = 5$, $m = 3$, since $2 + 3 = 5$. Sometimes the variable stands for many possible quantities. One reason the symbols are called *variables* is that the amount they represent can vary. For example, in the expression $52 - p$, you can replace $p$ with any number and find the value of the expression. The letters $x$ and $y$ are often used as variables in expressions and equations, but any letter can be used as a variable.

## ▶ Common Errors and Misconceptions
- Students might have a difficult time understanding that a letter can represent varying values or that different letters can represent the same value. They commonly interpret a letter as representing a specific number. For example, students might think that $7w + 22 = 109$ and $7n + 22 = 109$ have different answers because they don't understand that $w$ and $n$ represent the same number.
- Students might not understand variables partly because there are limited examples of variables in the elementary grades. For example, they see equations such as $52 = 5$ tens $\square$ ones in which the unknown has a specific value. They also see boxes and letters that represent a specific unknown such as $7 + \square = 10$ or $7 + a = 10$. Students rarely see cases where letters represent general unknown values or patterns.
- Students might see equations such as $5 + a = 12$ as merely abstract symbols with little or no connection to everyday situations.
- Students might not understand that letters in algebraic expressions and equations represent different values.

### Materials to Gather
**SUPPLIED**
Use Substitution in Expressions activity page

# GET READY  Order of Operations in Expressions

**ONLINE 10 min**

### Objectives
- Use parentheses and the order of operations to write or evaluate an expression.

Students will follow the order of operations, including parentheses, to evaluate expressions.

# LEARN  Use Substitution in Expressions

**OFFLINE 15 min**

### Objectives
- Evaluate a simple algebraic expression in one variable by using substitution.

Students will learn how to use substitution to evaluate a simple algebraic expression with one variable. Some of the expressions they will evaluate will have more than one operation, giving them practice with using the order of operations. Have students turn to the Use Substitution in Expressions activity page in their Activity Book and read the directions with them.

Students should copy the problems from the Activity Book into their Math Notebook as necessary and solve them there.

### Tips

If students have trouble understanding how to substitute a value for the variable, have them practice substituting different values in Problem 1 of the Worked Examples.

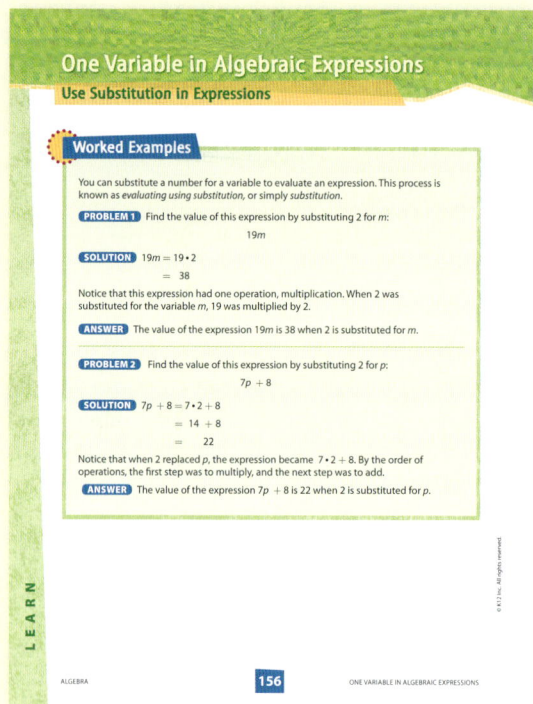

1. Read Problem 1 of the Worked Examples with students. Explain that to find the value of an expression that has a variable, students can replace the variable with any number. This process is known as evaluating using substitution. The value of the expression will depend on the number that replaces the variable.

   **Ask:** What operation was used to evaluate the expression in Problem 1? multiplication

   **Ask:** How would you know to use 2 to multiply by 19? The directions said to substitute 2 for the variable $m$, so that's how I would know to multiply 19 by 2.

2. Read Problem 2 of the Worked Examples with students.

   **Ask:** Why was 7 multiplied by 2 before 8 was added? The order of operations requires that multiplication be calculated before addition.

3. Read Problem 3 of the Worked Examples with students. Note that this problem has two operations. The expression in parentheses is calculated first. Operations within parentheses are calculated first in the order of operations.

4. Read Problem 4 of the Worked Examples with students. Note that this problem has three operations. Make sure students read and understand how to use the correct order of operations to calculate the addition first, then the multiplication, and then the division.

   **Say:** These problems all have one variable each. As you study mathematics more, you may evaluate expressions and equations that have more than one variable.

5. Have students complete the problems in the problem set.

---

### One Variable in Algebraic Expressions
#### Use Substitution in Expressions

**Worked Examples**

You can substitute a number for a variable to evaluate an expression. This process is known as *evaluating using substitution*, or simply *substitution*.

**PROBLEM 1**  Find the value of this expression by substituting 2 for $m$:

$$19m$$

**SOLUTION**  $19m = 19 \cdot 2$
$\phantom{19m} = 38$

Notice that this expression had one operation, multiplication. When 2 was substituted for the variable $m$, 19 was multiplied by 2.

**ANSWER**  The value of the expression $19m$ is 38 when 2 is substituted for $m$.

**PROBLEM 2**  Find the value of this expression by substituting 2 for $p$:

$$7p + 8$$

**SOLUTION**  $7p + 8 = 7 \cdot 2 + 8$
$\phantom{7p + 8} = 14 + 8$
$\phantom{7p + 8} = 22$

Notice that when 2 replaced $p$, the expression became $7 \cdot 2 + 8$. By the order of operations, the first step was to multiply, and the next step was to add.

**ANSWER**  The value of the expression $7p + 8$ is 22 when 2 is substituted for $p$.

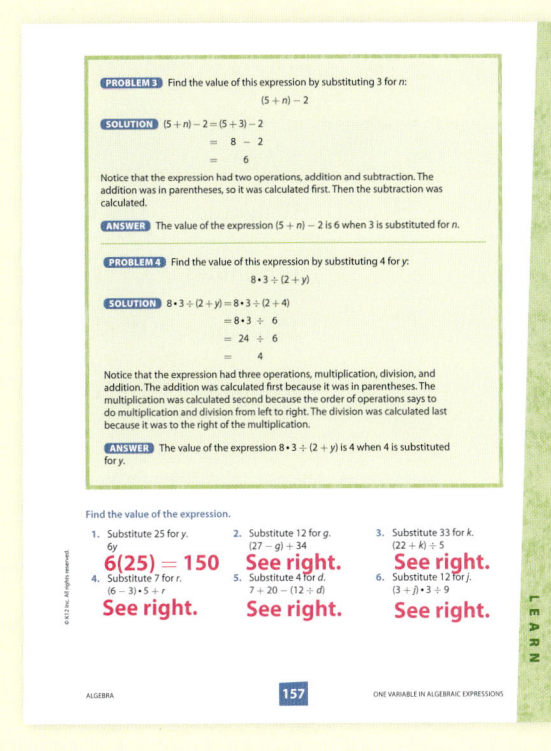

### Additional Answers

2. $(27 - 12) + 34 = 15 + 34$
   $= 49$

3. $(22 + 33) \div 5 = 55 \div 5$
   $= 11$

4. $(6 - 3) \cdot 5 + 7 = 3 \cdot 5 + 7$
   $= 15 + 7$
   $= 22$

5. $7 + 20 - (12 \div 4) = 7 + 20 - 3$
   $= 27 - 3$
   $= 24$

6. $(3 + 12) \cdot 3 \div 9 = 15 \cdot 3 \div 9$
   $= 45 \div 9$
   $= 5$

## LEARN  Distributive Property Substitution

**ONLINE 15 min**

Students will see worked examples and then use substitution with one variable to evaluate algebraic expressions. They will use the distributive property and order of operations to find the value of expressions.

**Objectives**
- Evaluate a simple algebraic expression in one variable by using substitution.

## TRY IT  Practice with Variable Expressions

**ONLINE 10 min**

Students will complete an online Try It. If necessary, read the directions, problems, and answer choices to students and help them with keyboard or mouse operations.

**Objectives**
- Evaluate a simple algebraic expression in one variable by using substitution.

## CHECKPOINT

**ONLINE 10 min**

Students will complete an online Checkpoint. If necessary, read the directions, problems, and answer choices to students and help them with keyboard or mouse operations.

**Objectives**
- Evaluate a simple algebraic expression in one variable by using substitution.

**ONE VARIABLE IN ALGEBRAIC EXPRESSIONS**

# Expression and Equation Problems (A)

## Lesson Overview

| | | |
|---|---|---|
| **GET READY** Evaluate Expressions | 10 minutes | **ONLINE** |
| **LEARN** Expressions and Story Problems | 10 minutes | **OFFLINE** |
| **LEARN** Match Expressions and Story Problems | 20 minutes | **OFFLINE** |
| **TRY IT** Practice with Expressions | 20 minutes | **OFFLINE** |

### ▶ Lesson Objectives

Identify or use an expression or an equation to answer questions about a problem.

### ▶ Prerequisite Skills

- Evaluate a simple algebraic expression in one variable by using substitution.
- Solve for one variable in a two-variable equation when the value of the other variable is given.

### ▶ Content Background

Students will learn to connect expressions to story problems.

### ▶ Common Errors and Misconceptions

- Students might not understand variables partly because there are limited examples of variables in the elementary grades. For example, they see equations such as $52 = 5$ tens $\square$ ones in which the unknown has a specific value. They also see boxes and letters that represent a specific unknown such as $7 + \square = 10$ or $7 + a = 10$. Students rarely see cases where letters represent general unknown values or patterns.
- Students might not understand that letters in algebraic expressions and equations represent different values.
- Students might see equations such as $5 + a = 12$ as merely abstract symbols with little or no connection to everyday situations.

### Materials to Gather

**SUPPLIED**

Expressions and Story Problems activity page

Match Expressions and Story Problems activity page

Practice with Expressions activity page

---

## GET READY  Evaluate Expressions

**ONLINE 10 min**

Students will use substitution to evaluate expressions that have one variable.

### Objectives

- Evaluate a simple algebraic expression in one variable by using substitution.

## LEARN Expressions and Story Problems

**OFFLINE 10 min**

### Objectives
- Identify or use an expression or an equation to answer questions about a problem.

Students will write expressions that represent story problems. Students may use letters for variables that are different from the letters shown in answers in the story problems. Have students turn to the Expressions and Story Problems activity page in their Activity Book and read the directions with them.

Students should copy the problems from the Activity Book into their Math Notebook as necessary and solve them there.

1. Read the Worked Example with students.

   **Ask:** Instead of the answer, 3c, what addition expression could have been used? $c + c + c$

   **Ask:** What expression would have been the answer if Anna's mom bought only 2 bags of cheese? The expression would have been 2c.

   **Say:** At this point, you know an expression that helps you answer a question about a problem. The expression is $3 \cdot c$, which you can also write as 3c. As you continue to study mathematics, you'll take further steps to find the value of an expression like this or others in this activity.

2. Have students read Problem 1 in the problem set.

   **Ask:** What do you know? I know Percy earned $16 mowing lawns.

   **Ask:** What don't you know? I don't know how much Percy will spend at the county fair.

   **Ask:** Pick a letter for a variable. What expression stands for how much money Percy will have left after he goes to the county fair? Answers will vary, depending on the variable students pick. **Example:** $16 - m$

3. Have students complete the rest of the problems.

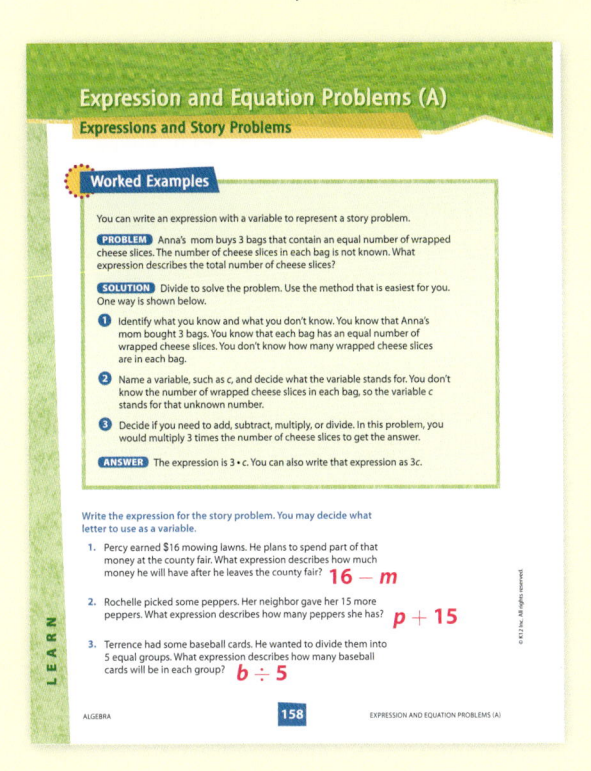

# LEARN Match Expressions and Story Problems

**OFFLINE 20 min**

## Objectives
- Identify or use an expression or an equation to answer questions about a problem.

Students will match expressions to story problems and story problems to expressions. They also will change an expression to match a changed story problem. Have students turn to the Match Expressions and Story Problems activity page in their Activity Book and read the directions with them.

Students should copy the problems from the Activity Book into their Math Notebook as necessary and solve them there.

1. Read the problem in the first Worked Examples box with students.
2. Explain to students that an important step in understanding the relationship between a story problem and an expression is figuring out what information the story problem includes and doesn't include.
3. Have students complete Problems 1–3 in the problem set.
4. Point out that students won't solve the story problems now. Instead, they will learn how to write expressions. As they continue to study mathematics, they will learn how to solve story problems by writing and evaluating expressions.
5. Read all problems in the second Worked Examples box with students.

   **Ask:** In Problem 2 of the Worked Examples, why did the expression change to $b - 9$? The story problem changed. Bill sold 2 more baseball cards.

   **Ask:** In Problem 3 of the Worked Examples, how do you know to add 13? Caron bought 4 milk boxes and 9 milk boxes, so the expression needs to represent $4 + 9$.

6. Have students complete Problems 4–6 in the problem set. Encourage them to look at the Worked Examples if they need help with the problems.

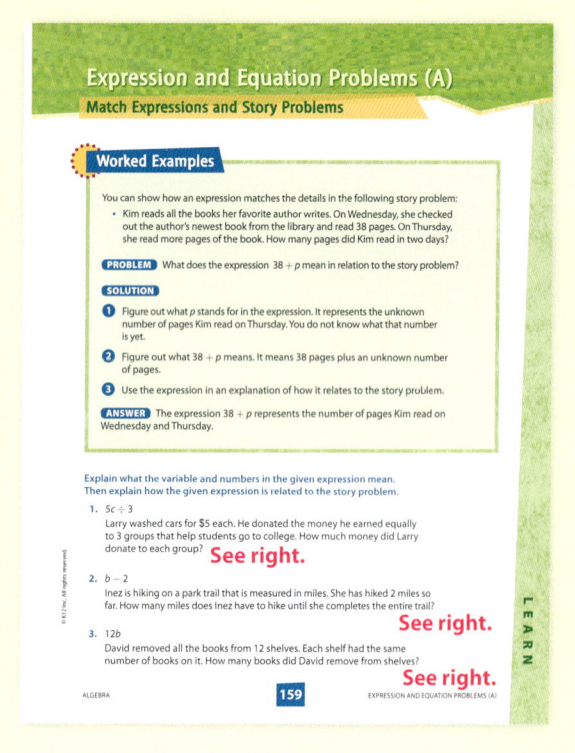

### Additional Answers

1. The 5 stands for the $5 that Larry received for each car he washed. The $c$ represents the unknown number of cars Larry washed. The 3 stands for the 3 groups he donated money to. The expression $5c \div 3$ represents the amount of money Larry donated to each of the 3 groups.

2. The $b$ represents the unknown length of the trail in miles. The 2 stands for the 2 miles of the trail Inez has hiked so far. The expression $b - 2$ represents the number of remaining miles Inez will hike.

3. The 12 stands for the number of bookshelves. The $b$ represents the unknown number of books on each shelf. The expression $12b$ represents the number of books David removed from the shelves.

400 ALGEBRA

## Worked Examples

You can write an expression to represent a story problem and then change the expression when the story problem changes.

- Bill brought an unknown number of baseball cards to a sports card show. He sold 7 baseball cards. What expression represents the number of baseball cards Bill has left?

**PROBLEM 1** Write an expression for the story problem.

**SOLUTION**

1. Identify what you know. You know that Bill sold 7 baseball cards.
2. Identify what you don't know. You don't know how many baseball cards Bill brought to the sports card show. That unknown amount can be represented by the variable $b$.
3. Decide what operation you should use and write an expression with the variable $b$ and the information you know.

**ANSWER** $b - 7$

**PROBLEM 2** Extend Problem 1. What expression represents the number of baseball cards Bill has left if he sells 2 more cards?

**SOLUTION**

1. Add $7 + 2$ because he sold 7 cards and then 2 more cards.
2. Replace the 7 with a 9 in the expression.

**ANSWER** $b - 9$

**PROBLEM 3** Caron had some milk boxes at home. She bought 4 more milk boxes. She could represent the number of milk boxes she has now by using the expression $m + 4$. What expression represents the number of milk boxes she has if she buys another 9 milk boxes?

**SOLUTION**

1. Write $4 + 9$ because you know that Caron bought 4 milk boxes and then 9 more milk boxes. Add.
$4 + 9 = 13$
2. Replace the 4 in the original expression, $m + 4$, with 13.

**ANSWER** $m + 13$

---

Explain what information you know and what information you don't know from reading the story problem. Then write an expression that represents the story problem.

4. Adam has 5 baskets and a pile of onions. He wants to put the same number of onions in each basket. What expression represents how many onions he should put in each basket? **See below.**

Write an expression that represents the changed story problem.

5. Jerry has some ears of corn from his corn plants. He gave away 10 ears of corn. He could use the expression $c - 10$ for the amount of corn he gave away. If he then ate 3 ears of corn, what expression represents the number of ears of corn remaining? **$c - 13$**

6. A garden had some rows of beans. A deer ate 2 rows of beans. An expression that represents how many rows of beans were left is $g - 2$. If another deer ate 2 more rows of beans, what expression represents the number of rows of beans remaining? **$g - 4$**

---

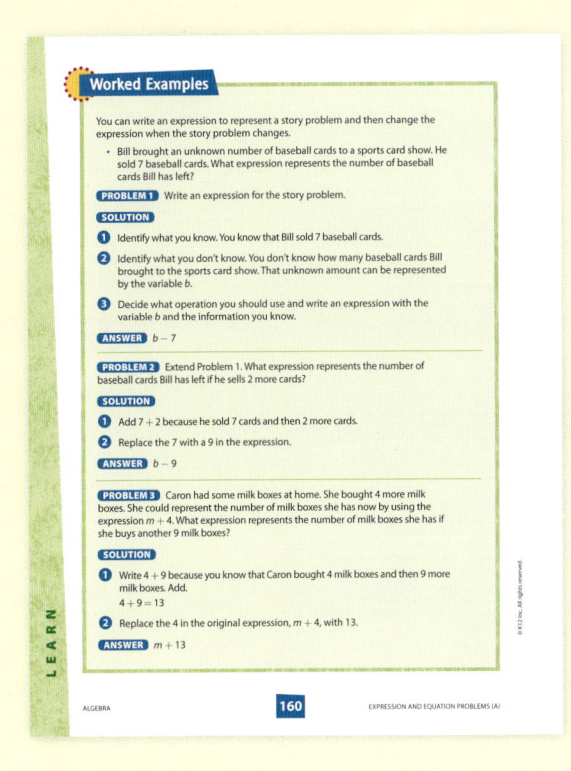

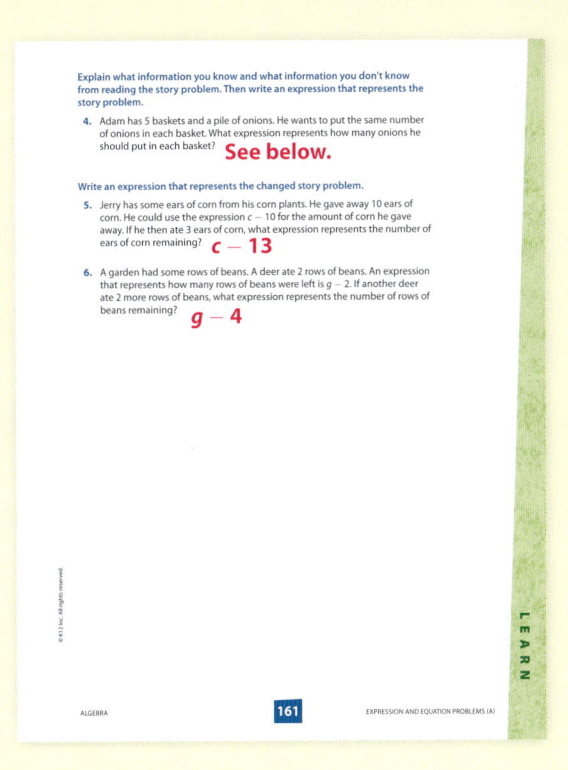

### Additional Answers

4. I know that Adam has 5 baskets. I don't know how many onions he has. The variable $n$ can stand for the onions Adam has. An expression that represents the story problem is $n \div 5$.

## TRY IT  Practice with Expressions

**OFFLINE 20 min**

### Objectives

- Identify or use an expression or an equation to answer questions about a problem.

Students will choose expressions that represent story problems. Have students turn to the Practice with Expressions activity page in their Activity Book and read the directions with them.

Students should copy the problems from the Activity Book into their Math Notebook as necessary and solve them there.

**EXPRESSION AND EQUATION PROBLEMS (A)** 401

# Expression and Equation Problems (A)
## Practice with Expressions

Choose the answer.

1. Becky made beaded necklaces. She put 8 beads on each necklace. She could use the expression 8 · n to represent the number of beads she used to make each necklace.

   Which expression represents the number of beads Becky could use if she put 4 more beads on each necklace?

   A. 12 · 4
   B. 8 · 4
   C. 4 · n
   D. (12 · n)

2. Randy bought several postcards when he was on vacation. He mailed 5 of the postcards to his friends. He could use the expression $p - 5$ to represent the number of postcards he has left.

   Which expression represents the number of postcards Randy has left if he sends 3 more postcards to friends?

   A. $p - 3$
   B. ($p - 8$)
   C. $5 - 3$
   D. $8 - 5$

3. Jennifer can do 6 fewer sit-ups than Michelle. Jennifer described the number of sit-ups she can do using the expression $m - 6$.

   One day Jennifer was tired and did 2 fewer sit-ups than usual. Which expression represents the number of sit-ups Jennifer did that day?

   A. $6 - 2$
   B. $m - 4$
   C. $m - 6$
   D. ($m - 8$)

4. Beth bought 2 packages of coloring markers. She could use the expression $2m$ to represent the total number of coloring markers she bought.

   Which expression represents the total number of coloring markers Beth would have if she bought 5 more packages of coloring markers?

   A. $2 \times 7$
   B. $2 \times 5$
   C. ($7m$)
   D. $5m$

5. Pedro rented some movies on Saturday. He returned 1 movie on Monday. He could use the expression $m - 1$ to represent the number of movies he has left.

   Which expression represents the number of movies Pedro has left if he returns 2 more movies?

   A. $m - 2$
   B. ($m - 3$)
   C. $3 - 2$
   D. $2 - 1$

6. Jeffrey had some apples at home. He bought 6 more apples. He could represent the number of apples that he now has by using the expression $a + 6$.

   Which expression represents the number of apples Jeffrey has if he buys another 8 apples?

   A. $u + 6$
   B. ($a + 14$)
   C. $6 + 8$
   D. $6 + 14$

7. Megan worked 10 hours overtime in one month. She could use the expression $t + 10$ to represent the total time she worked.

   Which expression represents the total number of hours Megan worked if she had worked an additional 12 hours overtime?

   A. $t + 2$
   B. $t + 10$
   C. $2 + 12$
   D. ($t + 22$)

8. Peter has 4 fewer trophies than Jack. Peter can represent the number of trophies he has with the expression $t - 4$.

   Peter won another 2 trophies. Which expression represents the number of trophies Peter has now?

   A. ($t - 2$)
   B. $t - 4$
   C. $t - 6$
   D. $t - 10$

9. Carla had several jigsaw puzzles. She bought 6 more jigsaw puzzles. She could use the expression $p + 6$ to represent the number of jigsaw puzzles she has now.

   Which expression represents the number of jigsaw puzzles Carla has if she buys 4 more jigsaw puzzles?

   A. $10 + 4$
   B. $p + 4$
   C. $6 + 4$
   D. ($p + 10$)

10. Anna had some peaches at home. She bought 5 more peaches. She could represent the number of peaches that she now has by using the expression $p + 5$.

    Which expression represents the number of peaches Anna has if she buys another 3 peaches?

    A. $p + 3$
    B. $p + 5$
    C. ($p + 8$)
    D. $3 + 5$

11. Jason bought a number of packages of buns. There are 8 buns in each package. He could use the expression $8b$ to represent the number of buns he bought.

    Which expression would represent the number of buns Jason bought if the store had put an additional 2 buns into each package?

    A. $10 \times 8$
    B. $2b$
    C. $2 \times 8$
    D. ($10b$)

12. Edgar has a pack of stickers to share with his 4 friends. He could represent the number of stickers each friend would get using the expression $s \div 4$.

    Edgar is thinking of sharing his stickers with 1 additional friend. Which expression would represent the number of stickers each person would get now?

    A. $s \div 1$
    B. $s \div 3$
    C. ($s \div 5$)
    D. $4 \div 1$

13. Paul paid $5 per ticket for a number of tickets to the baseball game on Wednesday. He could represent the total he spent on baseball tickets by using the expression $5t$.

    On Saturday, Paul bought the same number of tickets. However, the price of these tickets was $2 more per ticket. Which expression represents the amount Paul paid for tickets on Saturday?

    A. $5 \times 2$
    B. $2t$
    C. ($7t$)
    D. $10t$

14. Eddie has a set of football cards he wants to put in an album. He is planning on putting 9 cards per page. He could represent the number of pages he would need by using the expression $b \div 9$.

    Eddie is thinking of putting 5 fewer cards on each page. Which expression would represent the number of pages he would need?

    A. ($b \div 4$)
    B. $b \div 5$
    C. $b \div 14$
    D. $b \div 45$

# Expression and Equation Problems (B)

## Lesson Overview

| | | |
|---|---|---|
| **GET READY** Solve Equations | 10 minutes | **ONLINE** |
| **LEARN** Equations and Story Problems | 10 minutes | **OFFLINE** |
| **LEARN** Match Equations and Story Problems | 20 minutes | **OFFLINE** |
| **TRY IT** Practice with Equations | 20 minutes | **OFFLINE** |

▶ ### Lesson Objectives
Identify or use an expression or an equation to answer questions about a problem.

▶ ### Prerequisite Skills
- Evaluate a simple algebraic expression in one variable by using substitution.
- Solve for one variable in a two-variable equation when the value of the other variable is given.

▶ ### Content Background
Students will continue to learn to connect equations to story problems.

▶ ### Common Errors and Misconceptions
- Students might not understand variables partly because there are limited examples of variables in the elementary grades. For example, they see equations such as $52 = 5$ tens $\square$ ones in which the unknown has a specific value. They also see boxes and letters that represent a specific unknown such as $7 + \square = 10$ or $7 + a = 10$. Students rarely see cases where letters represent general unknown values or patterns.
- Students might not understand that letters in algebraic expressions and equations represent different values.
- Students might see equations such as $5 + a = 12$ as merely abstract symbols with little or no connection to everyday situations.

### Materials to Gather

**SUPPLIED**

Equations and Story Problems activity page

Match Equations and Story Problems activity page

Practice with Equations activity page

## GET READY  Solve Equations

**ONLINE 10 min**

Students will find the solution to two-variable equations when given the value of one variable.

**Tips** Remind students that when they solve equations, they want the values on the left and right sides to be equal.

### Objectives
- Solve for one variable in a two-variable equation when the value of the other variable is given.

## LEARN  Equations and Story Problems

**Objectives**

- Identify or use an expression or an equation to answer questions about a problem.

Students will write equations that represent story problems. They will not solve the equations at this stage in their study of mathematics. Instead they will read story problems and write equations that use a variable to represent the unknown fact. Students may use letters for variables that are different from the letters shown in answers in the story problems. Have students turn to the Equations and Story Problems activity page in their Activity Book and read the directions with them.

Students should copy the problems from the Activity Book into their Math Notebook as necessary and solve them there.

1. Read the Worked Example with students.

    **Ask:** If the painter needs 2.5 gallons to paint 1 room, what expression with numbers stands for the number of gallons the painter needs for 2 rooms? $2.5 \cdot 2$ or $2 \cdot 2.5$

    **Ask:** What does the variable $p$ stand for? It stands for the unknown number of gallons of paint the painter needs to complete the entire job.

    **Ask:** What does $2.5 \cdot 6 = p$ mean in relation to the story problem? It means that 2.5 gallons of paint times 6 rooms equals an unknown number of gallons of paint.

    **Say:** At this point, you know an equation that helps answer a question in a story problem. As you continue to study mathematics, you'll take further steps to solve an equation for the value of a variable.

2. Have students read Problem 1 in the problem set.

    **Ask:** What do you know and what don't you know? I know that Meredith used 54 seashells to decorate 6 picture frames, and she put an equal number of seashells on each picture frame. I don't know the number of seashells Meredith put on each picture frame.

    **Ask:** Choose a letter for a variable. What equation represents the number of seashells Meredith put on each picture frame? $54 \div n = 6$

3. Make sure students understand that equations have an equals symbols. Expressions have numbers, variables, and operation signs, but they don't have equals symbols.

4. Have students complete Problem 2. Help them refer to Worked Examples for help if needed.

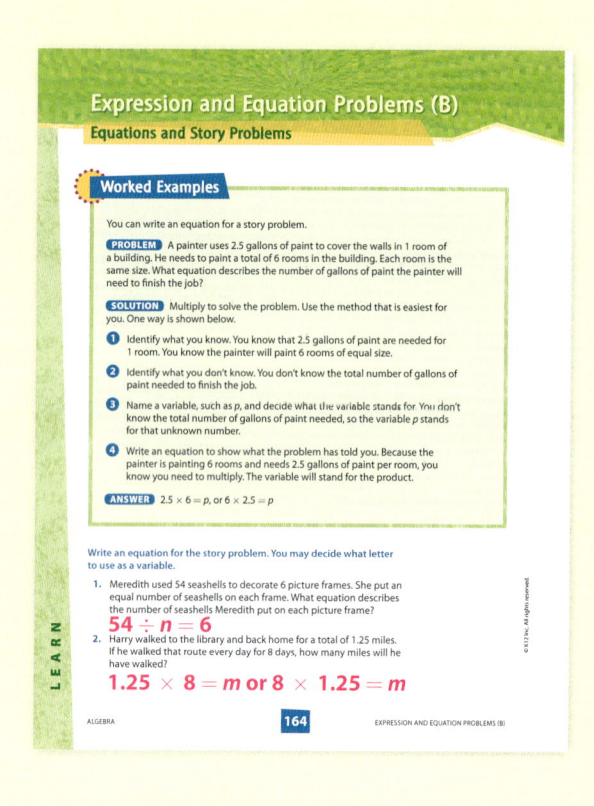

**404  ALGEBRA**

## LEARN Match Equations and Story Problems

**OFFLINE 20 min**

### Objectives
- Identify or use an expression or an equation to answer questions about a problem.

Students will match equations to story problems and story problems to equations. They will also write an equation to match a changed story problem. Have students turn to the Math Equations and Story Problems activity page in their Activity Book and read the directions with them.

Students should copy the problems from their Activity Book into their Math Notebook as necessary and solve them there.

1. Tell students that they will show how an equation can match the details in a story problem. Another way to describe story problems is *situations*.
2. Read the problem in the first Worked Examples box with students.
3. Explain that it is important to carefully read a problem and decide what information is known and unknown. Those steps will help students understand the relationship between the story problem and the equation that represents the problem.
4. Point out that students won't solve the problems now; they will do that as they continue to study mathematics. Don't discourage students who want to solve the equation and find the number of wolves that were not at the pond that day. Rather, focus their attention on connecting the equation to the details of the story problem.
5. Have students complete the Problems 1 and 2 in the problem set.
6. Read all problems in the second Worked Examples box with students.

    **Ask:** In Problem 2 of the Worked Examples, why is the expression $6 + 8$ multiplied by 3? The problem was extended to have Raul plant 3 rows of flowers.

    **Ask:** In Problem 3 of the Worked Examples, why is the expression $9 + 6$ divided by 3? The problem was extended to have Sherman divide the items into 3 equal groups.

7. Have students complete Problems 3–5 in the problem set. Encourage them to look at the Worked Examples if they need help with the problems.

EXPRESSION AND EQUATION PROBLEMS (B)

## Expression and Equation Problems (B)
### Match Equations and Story Problems

**Worked Examples**

You can show how an equation matches the details in the following story problem:
- A scientist records data about wolves she's tracking. She knows there are 45 wolves in the area. She observes 22 of the wolves at a pond one day. The scientist wants to know how many wolves were not at the pond that day.

**PROBLEM** How can $45 - w = 22$ be matched with the details in the story problem?

**SOLUTION**
1. Decide what $w$ stands for in the equation. It stands for the unknown number of wolves that weren't at the pond that day.
2. Decide what $45 - w$ means. It means 45 minus an unknown number of wolves.
3. Decide what 22 means. It means the number of wolves the scientist observed at the pond.

**ANSWER** The equation $45 - w = 22$ represents the number of wolves that weren't at the pond that day.

---

Explain what the variable and numbers in the given equation mean. Then explain how the given equation is related to the story problem.

1. $10 + 3c = 34$

   Linda had 10 comic books. She bought 3 boxes of comic books at a yard sale. Each box has the same number of comic books. Now Linda has 34 comic books. How many comic books are in each box? **See below.**

2. $60 \div d = 3$

   Kelly bought 60 pounds of dry dog food. The dog food is in 3 equal-sized bags. How many pounds of dog food are in each bag? **See below.**

---

**Worked Examples**

You can write an equation to represent a story problem and then change the equation when the story problem changes.
- Raul planted a flower garden. He planted 6 geraniums and 8 petunias in one row. How many flowers did Raul plant in one row?

**PROBLEM 1** Write an equation for the story problem.

**SOLUTION**
1. Identify what you know. You know that Raul planted 6 geraniums and 8 petunias in one row.
2. Identify what you don't know. You don't know how many flowers Raul planted in one row. That unknown amount can be called variable $f$.
3. Decide which operation you should use, and write an equation with the variable $f$ and the information you know.

**ANSWER** $6 + 8 = f$

**PROBLEM 2** Extend the problem. What equation represents the total number of flowers Raul planted if he planted 3 rows that had 6 geraniums and 8 petunias in each row?

**SOLUTION**
1. Let the variable $f$ represent the total number.
2. Show that $6 + 8$ is being multiplied by 3 by writing $3 \cdot (6 + 8)$.
3. Replace the expression $6 + 8$ with $3 \cdot (6 + 8)$ in the equation.

**ANSWER** $3 \cdot (6 + 8) = f$

**PROBLEM 3** Sherman helped on park cleanup day and collected 9 pounds of cans and 6 pounds of bottles. He wrote this equation to represent the unknown total number of pounds of items he collected.

$9 + 6 = p$

He wanted to divide those items into 3 equal groups. Write an equation that represents the number of items in each group.

**SOLUTION** Show $9 + 6$ as an expression that is divided by 3.

**ANSWER** $(9 + 6) \div 3 = p$

---

Explain what information you know and what information you don't know from reading the story problem. Then write an equation that represents the story problem.

3. Aisha wrote 12 poems during the summer. If she wrote 12 poems each in the fall, spring, and winter, how many poems will she have written altogether? **See right.**

Write an equation that represents the changed story problem.

4. Colton had 30 T-shirts and pairs of pants. He gave away 14 of those items that were too small. He wrote this equation to represent the items of clothing he gave away: $30 - 14 = c$.

   He then found another T-shirt and didn't give it away. What equation represents the total number of items of clothing he had after he gave away some items and found the T-shirt? **$(30 + 1) - 14 = c$**

5. Annie had 17 notebooks and gave 5 of the notebooks to her sister. She wrote this equation to represent the number of notebooks she had left: $17 - 5 = n$.

   She decided to sort her notebooks into 3 stacks. What equation represents the number of notebooks in each stack? **$(17 - 5) \div 3 = n$**

---

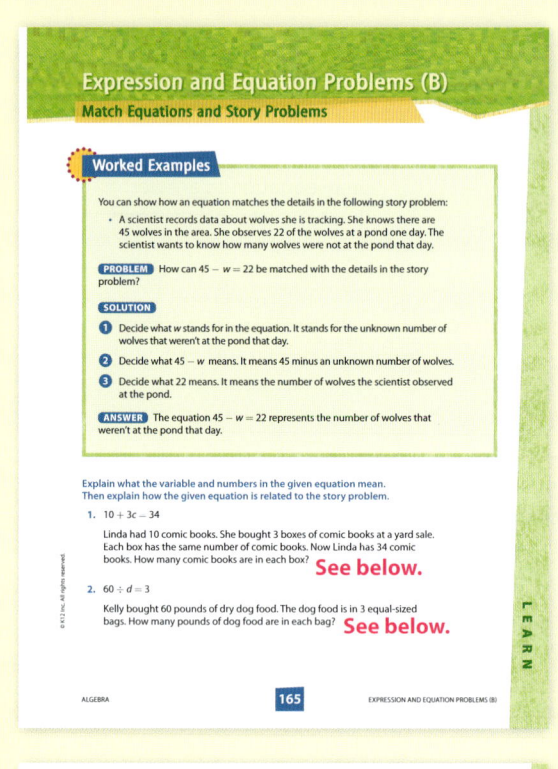

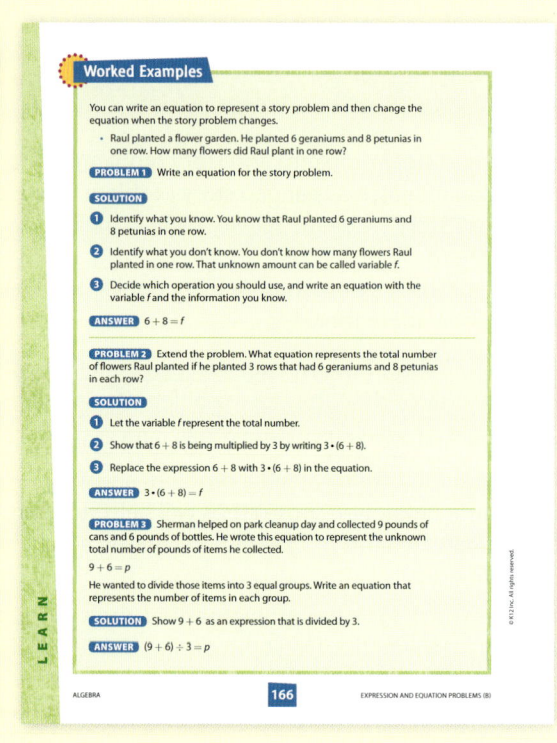

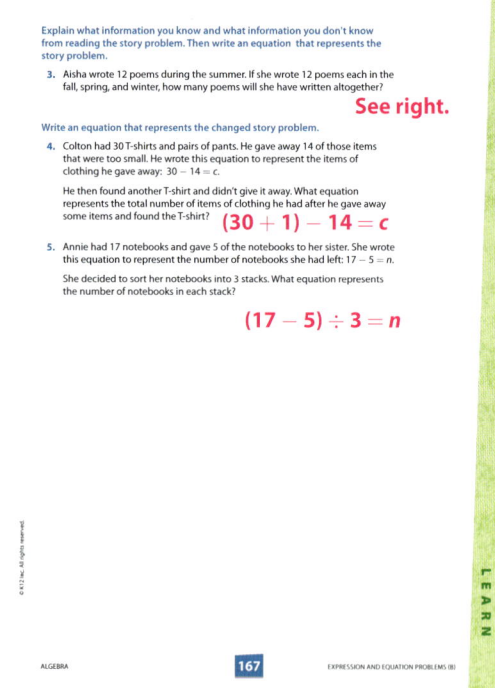

### Additional Answers

1. The 10 stands for the number of comic books Linda started with. The 3 stands for the 3 boxes she bought. Each box has the same number of comic books in it. The $c$ represents the unknown number of comic books in each box. The 34 stands for the total number of comic books she has. The equation $10 + 3c = 34$ represents one way to find the number of comic books in each box.

2. The 60 stands for the total pounds of dry dog food. The $d$ represents the unknown number of pounds of dog food in each bag. The 3 stands for the number of bags of dog food. The equation $60 \div d = 3$ represents one way to find the amount of food in each bag.

3. I know how many poems Aisha wrote in the summer. She wrote the same number of poems in 4 seasons. I don't know how many poems she will have written altogether. Let $a$ represent the unknown number of poems Aisha will write. $12 \cdot 4 = a$

# TRY IT  Practice with Equations

**OFFLINE 20 min**

## Objectives

- Identify or use an expression or an equation to answer questions about a problem.

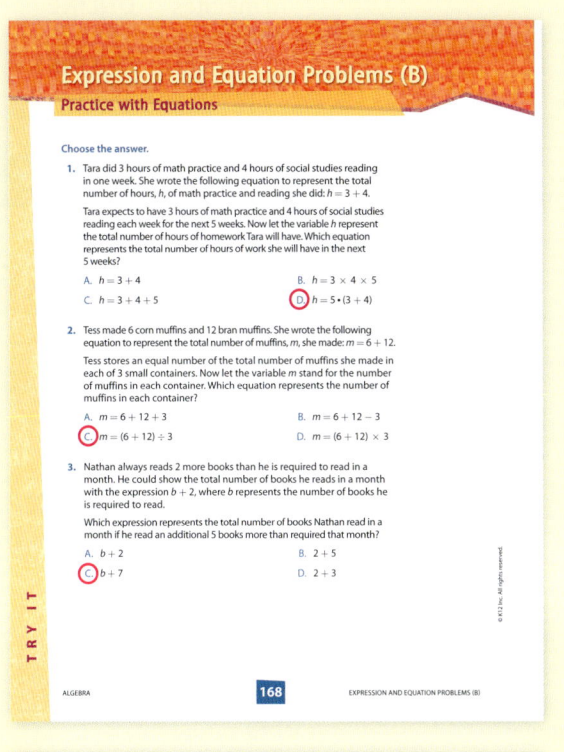

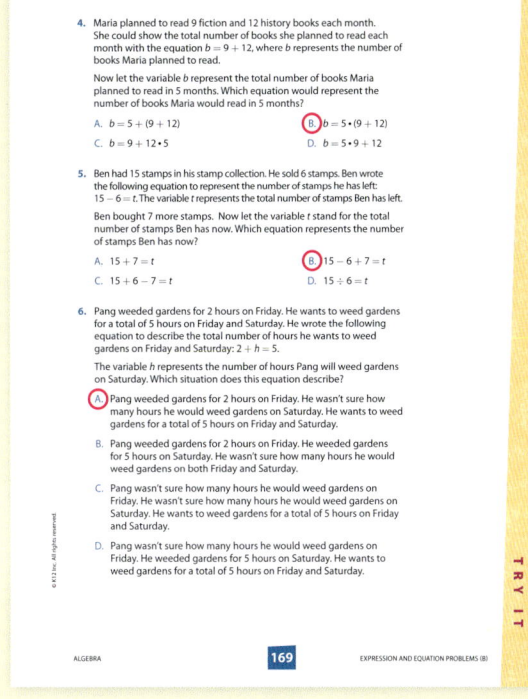

Students will choose equations that match story problems and choose situations that match equations. Have students turn to the Practice with Equations activity page in their Activity Book and read the directions with them.

Students should copy the problems from the Activity Book into their Math Notebook as necessary and solve them there.

---

### Expression and Equation Problems (B)
#### Practice with Equations

Choose the answer.

1. Tara did 3 hours of math practice and 4 hours of social studies reading in one week. She wrote the following equation to represent the total number of hours, $h$, of math practice and reading she did: $h = 3 + 4$.

   Tara expects to have 3 hours of math practice and 4 hours of social studies reading each week for the next 5 weeks. Now let the variable $h$ represent the total number of hours of homework Tara will have. Which equation represents the total number of hours of work she will have in the next 5 weeks?

   A. $h = 3 + 4$
   B. $h = 3 \times 4 \times 5$
   C. $h = 3 + 4 + 5$
   **D. $h = 5 \cdot (3 + 4)$**

2. Tess made 6 corn muffins and 12 bran muffins. She wrote the following equation to represent the total number of muffins, $m$, she made: $m = 6 + 12$.

   Tess stores an equal number of the total number of muffins she made in each of 3 small containers. Now let the variable $m$ stand for the number of muffins in each container. Which equation represents the number of muffins in each container?

   A. $m = 6 + 12 + 3$
   B. $m = 6 + 12 - 3$
   **C. $m = (6 + 12) \div 3$**
   D. $m = (6 + 12) \times 3$

3. Nathan always reads 2 more books than he is required to read in a month. He could show the total number of books he reads in a month with the expression $b + 2$, where $b$ represents the number of books he is required to read.

   Which expression represents the total number of books Nathan read in a month if he read an additional 5 books more than required that month?

   A. $b + 2$
   B. $2 + 5$
   **C. $b + 7$**
   D. $2 + 3$

---

4. Maria planned to read 9 fiction and 12 history books each month. She could show the total number of books she planned to read each month with the equation $b = 9 + 12$, where $b$ represents the number of books Maria planned to read.

   Now let the variable $b$ represent the total number of books Maria planned to read in 5 months. Which equation would represent the number of books Maria would read in 5 months?

   A. $b = 5 + (9 + 12)$
   **B. $b = 5 \cdot (9 + 12)$**
   C. $b = 9 + 12 \cdot 5$
   D. $b = 5 \cdot 9 + 12$

5. Ben had 15 stamps in his stamp collection. He sold 6 stamps. Ben wrote the following equation to represent the number of stamps he has left: $15 - 6 = t$. The variable $t$ represents the total number of stamps Ben has left.

   Ben bought 7 more stamps. Now let the variable $t$ stand for the total number of stamps Ben has now. Which equation represents the number of stamps Ben has now?

   A. $15 + 7 = t$
   **B. $15 - 6 + 7 = t$**
   C. $15 + 6 - 7 = t$
   D. $15 \div 6 = t$

6. Pang weeded gardens for 2 hours on Friday. He wants to weed gardens for a total of 5 hours on Friday and Saturday. He wrote the following equation to describe the total number of hours he wants to weed gardens on Friday and Saturday: $2 + h = 5$.

   The variable $h$ represents the number of hours Pang will weed gardens on Saturday. Which situation does this equation describe?

   **A. Pang weeded gardens for 2 hours on Friday. He wasn't sure how many hours he would weed gardens on Saturday. He wants to weed gardens for a total of 5 hours on Friday and Saturday.**
   B. Pang weeded gardens for 2 hours on Friday. He weeded gardens for 5 hours on Saturday. He wasn't sure how many hours he would weed gardens on both Friday and Saturday.
   C. Pang wasn't sure how many hours he would weed gardens on Friday. He wasn't sure how many hours he would weed gardens on Saturday. He wants to weed gardens for a total of 5 hours on Friday and Saturday.
   D. Pang wasn't sure how many hours he would weed gardens on Friday. He weeded gardens for 5 hours on Saturday. He wants to weed gardens for a total of 5 hours on Friday and Saturday.

---

7. A farmer wants to plant a total of 80 stalks of corn. He plants 8 cornstalks in each row. He wrote the following equation to describe the number of rows of cornstalks he will plant: $80 = 8r$.

   The variable $r$ represents the number of rows of cornstalks the farmer wants to plant. Which situation does this equation describe?

   A. A farmer wants to plant a total of 80 stalks of corn. He isn't sure how many rows of cornstalks he will plant. He isn't sure how many cornstalks he will plant in each row.
   B. A farmer wants to plant a total of 80 stalks of corn. He plants 72 rows of cornstalks. He isn't sure how many cornstalks he will plant in each row.
   **C. A farmer wants to plant a total of 80 stalks of corn. He plants 8 cornstalks in each row. He isn't sure how many rows of cornstalks he will plant.**
   D. A farmer wants to plant a total of 80 stalks of corn. He plants 8 cornstalks in each row. He will plant 8 rows of cornstalks.

8. April read 5 newspaper articles and 3 magazine articles every week. She wrote the following equation to represent the number of articles she read in a week: $r = 3 + 5$. The variable $r$ represents the total number of books April reads every week.

   Now let the variable $r$ represents the total number of articles April reads in 6 weeks. Which equation would represent the total number of articles April would read in 6 weeks?

   A. $r = 6 + (3 + 5)$
   B. $r = 3 + (6 \cdot 5)$
   C. $r = (6 \cdot 3) + 5$
   **D. $r = 6 \cdot (3 + 5)$**

9. Claudia bought some apples. She gave away 16 of them. She could represent the total number of apples she has left with the expression $a - 16$, where the variable $a$ represents the total number of apples Claudia has left.

   Claudia then gave away another 5 apples. Which expression represents the number of apples that Claudia has now?

   A. $16 - 5$
   B. $a - 5$
   C. $a - 16$
   **D. $a - 21$**

10. Benny spends $3 a day on bus fare. He can represent the total amount he spends riding the bus with the expression $3b$, where $b$ represents the number of days Benny rides the bus.

    The bus company is thinking of increasing the fares by $1 a day. Which expression would represent the amount Benny would spend at the new rate?

    **A. $4b$**
    B. $12b$
    C. $4 \times 3$
    D. $1 \times 3$

---

11. Zoe sends letters to her pen pal by mail. She spends 42¢ on a stamp and 55¢ on an envelope. She wrote this equation to represent the total cost for sending a letter to her pen pal: $c = 42 + 55$. The variable $c$ represents the total cost for sending a letter.

    Zoe writes to her pen pal 8 times a year. Now let the variable $c$ represent the total cost of sending her pen pals letters. Which equation would represent the total cost of sending her pen pal letters for a year?

    A. $c = 8 + (42 + 55)$
    B. $c = 42 + (8 \cdot 55)$
    **C. $c = 8 \cdot (42 + 55)$**
    D. $c = (8 \cdot 42) + 55$

12. Veronica had some cherries to give to 3 friends. She could represent the total number of cherries each friend would get with the expression $g \div 3$, where the variable $g$ represents the total number of cherries Veronica has.

    Veronica is thinking about giving cherries to 2 additional friends. Which expression represents the number of cherries each friend would now get?

    A. $g \div 2$
    **B. $g \div 5$**
    C. $g \div 6$

13. Ms. Tania is planning the seating arrangements for her concert. She is dividing the seats equally into 6 rows. She could represent the total number of seats in each row with the expression $s \div 6$, where the variable $s$ represents the total number of seats.

    Ms. Tania is thinking about dividing all of the seats into 2 fewer rows than the original plan. Which expression would represent the number of seats in each row now?

    **A. $s \div 4$**
    B. $s \div 8$
    C. $s \div 12$
    D. $s \div 36$

14. John is planning the seating arrangements for the music show. He is dividing the total number of seats equally into 8 rows. He could represent the total number of seats in each row with the expression $t \div 8$, where the variable $t$ represents the total number of seats.

    John is thinking of dividing the seats into 2 more rows than the original plan. Which expression represents the total number of seats in each row now?

    A. $t \div 6$
    **B. $t \div 10$**
    C. $t \div 16$
    D. $8 + 2$

---

**EXPRESSION AND EQUATION PROBLEMS (B)  407**

# Expression and Equation Problems (C)

## Lesson Overview

| | | |
|---|---|---|
| **LEARN** Examples of Story Problems | 15 minutes | **ONLINE** |
| **LEARN** Write Story Problems | 25 minutes | **OFFLINE** |
| **TRY IT** Practice with Story Problems | 10 minutes | **ONLINE** |
| **CHECKPOINT** | 10 minutes | **ONLINE** |

### ▶ Lesson Objectives
Identify or use an expression or an equation to answer questions about a problem.

### ▶ Prerequisite Skills
- Evaluate a simple algebraic expression in one variable by using substitution.
- Solve for one variable in a two-variable equation when the value of the other variable is given.

### ▶ Content Background
Students will learn to write story problems about expressions and equations.

### ▶ Common Errors and Misconceptions:
- Students might not understand variables partly because there are limited examples of variables in the elementary grades. For example, they see equations such as $52 = 5$ tens $\square$ ones in which the unknown has a specific value. They also see boxes and letters that represent a specific unknown such as $7 + \square = 10$ or $7 + a = 10$. Students rarely see cases where letters represent general unknown values or patterns.
- Students might not understand that letters in algebraic expressions and equations represent different values.
- Students might see equations such as $5 + a = 12$ as merely abstract symbols with little or no connection to everyday situations.

**Materials to Gather**

**SUPPLIED**
Write Story Problems activity page

## LEARN  Examples of Story Problems

**ONLINE 15 min**

Students will see examples of expressions and equations that can be used to answer questions about a story problem. Then they will see an example of a changed story problem and the equation that answers it. Students will also match story problems to equations and expressions.

**Objectives**
- Identify or use an expression or an equation to answer questions about a problem.

## LEARN Write Story Problems

OFFLINE 25 min

Students will be given expressions and equations and will write story problems about them. They also will write changed expressions and equations for story problems that have changes. Have students turn to the Write Story Problems activity page in their Activity Book and read the directions with them.

Students should copy the problems from the Activity Book into their Math Notebook as necessary and solve them there.

1. Read the problems in the first Worked Examples box with students.
2. Have students complete Problems 1–6 in the problem set. Answers will vary. The given answers are examples.
3. Read the problems in the second Worked Examples box with students.
4. Have students complete Problems 7–9 in the problem set. Encourage students to use the Worked Examples for reference if needed.
5. As time permits, have students write their own story problem and an expression or equation that represents it.

### Objectives

- Identify or use an expression or an equation to answer questions about a problem.

### Tips

Have students illustrate their favorite problem and its matching expression or equation in their Math Notebook.

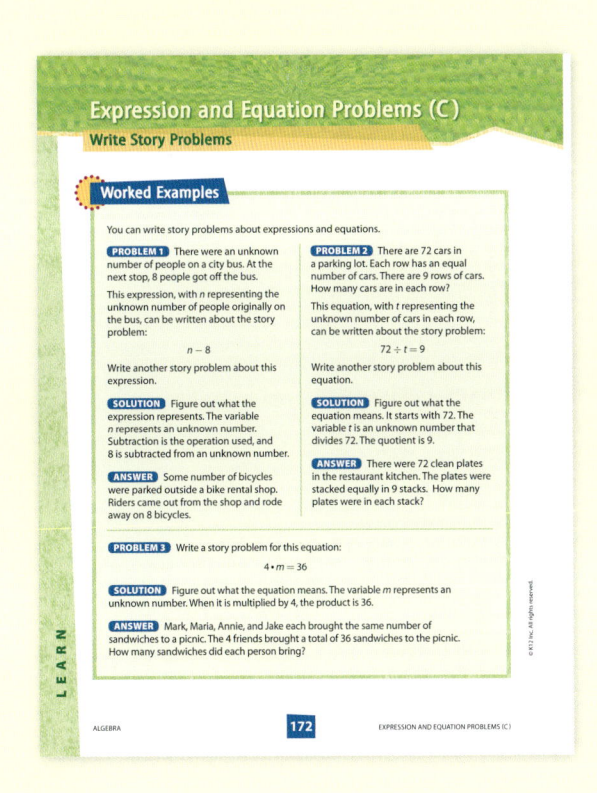

---

**Expression and Equation Problems (C)**
Write Story Problems

**Worked Examples**

You can write story problems about expressions and equations.

**PROBLEM 1** There were an unknown number of people on a city bus. At the next stop, 8 people got off the bus.

This expression, with $n$ representing the unknown number of people originally on the bus, can be written about the story problem:

$$n - 8$$

Write another story problem about this expression.

**SOLUTION** Figure out what the expression represents. The variable $n$ represents an unknown number. Subtraction is the operation used, and 8 is subtracted from an unknown number.

**ANSWER** Some number of bicycles were parked outside a bike rental shop. Riders came out from the shop and rode away on 8 bicycles.

**PROBLEM 2** There are 72 cars in a parking lot. Each row has an equal number of cars. There are 9 rows of cars. How many cars are in each row?

This equation, with $t$ representing the unknown number of cars in each row, can be written about the story problem:

$$72 \div t = 9$$

Write another story problem about this equation.

**SOLUTION** Figure out what the equation means. It starts with 72. The variable $t$ is an unknown number that divides 72. The quotient is 9.

**ANSWER** There were 72 clean plates in the restaurant kitchen. The plates were stacked equally in 9 stacks. How many plates were in each stack?

**PROBLEM 3** Write a story problem for this equation:

$$4 \cdot m = 36$$

**SOLUTION** Figure out what the equation means. The variable $m$ represents an unknown number. When it is multiplied by 4, the product is 36.

**ANSWER** Mark, Maria, Annie, and Jake each brought the same number of sandwiches to a picnic. The 4 friends brought a total of 36 sandwiches to the picnic. How many sandwiches did each person bring?

EXPRESSION AND EQUATION PROBLEMS (C)

### Worked Examples page (173)

Write a story problem for each expression or equation.

1. $6 + p$ — See below.
2. $2a$ — See below.
3. $b \div 4$ — See below.
4. $f = 3 + 5$ — See below.
5. $m - 4 = 6$ — See below.
6. $18 = 6h$ — See below.

**Worked Examples**

When a story problem changes, you can write a changed expression or a changed equation.

**PROBLEM 1** Andrea rode the bus for a number of miles. She then walked for 1.5 miles. She could represent the miles she traveled by the expression $b + 1.5$. The variable $b$ represents the number of miles Andrea rode on the bus.

She then rode in a taxi for twice as many miles as she rode on the bus and walked. Which expression represents the total number of miles she traveled?

In the new expression, let the variable $b$ represent the total number of miles Andrea rode in a bus and a taxi and walked.

**SOLUTION** Start with the expression from the original problem. Figure out how to represent "twice as many" from the changed story problem. For "twice as many," multiply by 2.

**ANSWER** $2 \cdot (b + 1.5)$

**PROBLEM 2** Chip hiked on a lakeside trail for 3 miles. He then hiked up a mountain trail for 2 miles. He could represent the total miles he hiked with the variable $m$ in the equation $3 + 2 = m$.

What equation would represent the miles he hiked if he then hiked down the mountain trail for 2 miles?

In the new equation, let the variable $m$ represent the total miles hiked on the trail and up and down the mountain.

**SOLUTION** Start with the equation from the original problem. Figure out how to represent an additional 2 miles from the changed story problem. For an additional 2 miles, add 2.

**ANSWER** $3 + 2 + 2 = m$

### Page 174

Write a changed expression or changed equation.

7. Marty had 7 books checked out from the library. He returned 3 of the books. He could represent the books he still had with the variable $p$ in the equation $7 - 3 = p$. If he then checked out 6 more books, what equation would represent how many books he had? In the new equation, let the variable $p$ represent the total number of books Marty had after he checked out 6 more books.

   $(7 - 3) + 6 = p$

8. Annette planted 20 sunflower seeds and some watermelon seeds. She could represent the number of seeds she planted with the expression $20 + w$, where $w$ represents the number of watermelon seeds Annette planted. If Annette planted 4 times as many of the same seeds, what expression would represent the number of seeds she planted? In the new expression, let the variable $w$ represent the number of watermelon seeds Annette originally planted.

   $4 \cdot (20 + w)$

9. On Monday, Wendi collected 28 grass samples for a science project. The next day she collected 8 more grass samples. She could represent the number of grass samples she collected with the variable $g$ in the equation $28 + 8 = g$. If she then discarded 4 grass samples, what equation would represent the number of grass samples she had? In the new equation, let the variable $g$ represent the total number of grass samples Wendi had after she discarded 4 samples.

   $(28 + 8) - 4 = g$

---

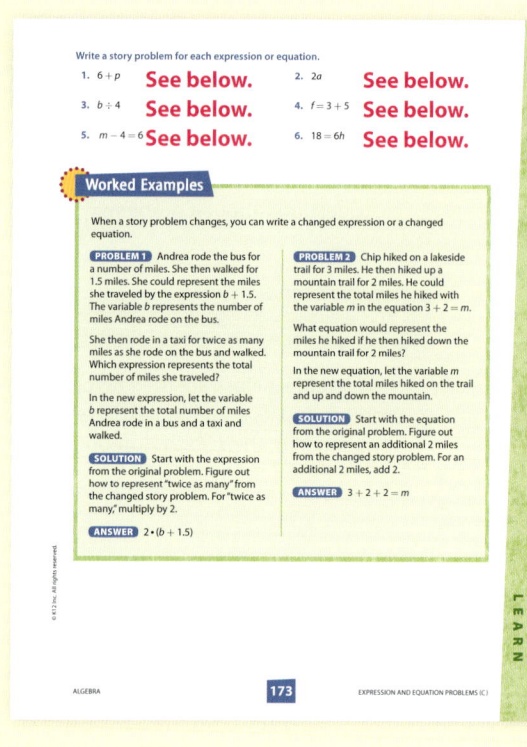

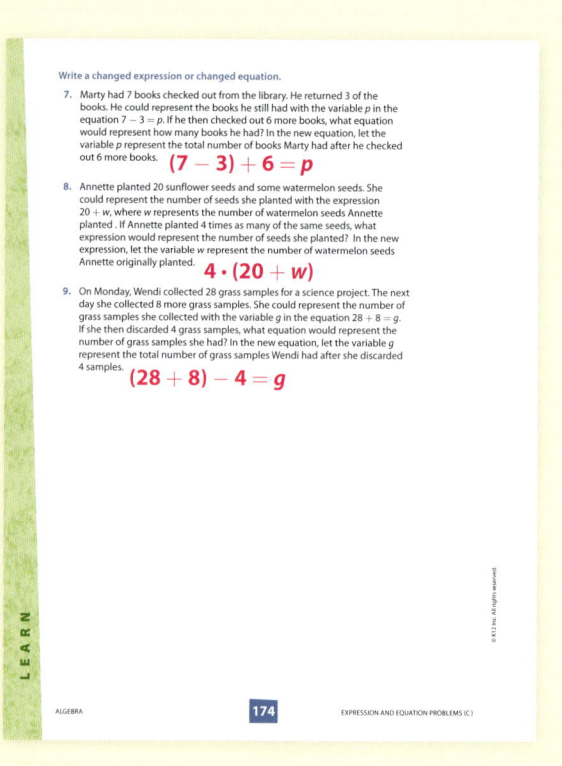

### Additional Answers

1. **Example:** There were 6 people in line at the movie theater. More people got in line.
2. **Example:** The distance around the track is 2 miles. Gary walked around the track multiple times.
3. **Example:** Cass made muffins. She shared the muffins she made equally among 4 friends.
4. **Example:** One afternoon, Ron sent 3 e-mails to his friends and 5 e-mails to his family. How many e-mails did he send in all?
5. **Example:** Ling knitted scarves to sell at the fair. She sold 4 scarves and has 6 scarves left. How many scarves did Ling knit to sell at the fair?
6. **Example:** A clerk at a store unpacked 18 snow globes from boxes. Each box contained 6 snow globes. How many boxes of snow globes did the clerk unpack?

---

### TRY IT  Practice with Story Problems  ONLINE 10 min

Students will complete an online Try It. If necessary, read the directions, problems, and answer choices to students and help them with keyboard or mouse operations.

**Objectives**
- Identify or use an expression or an equation to answer questions about a problem.

### CHECKPOINT  ONLINE 10 min

Students will complete an online Checkpoint. If necessary, read the directions, problems, and answer choices to students and help them with keyboard or mouse operations.

**Objectives**
- Identify or use an expression or an equation to answer questions about a problem.

# Unit Review

## Lesson Overview

| | | |
|---|---|---|
| **UNIT REVIEW** Look Back | 10 minutes | **ONLINE** |
| **UNIT REVIEW** Checkpoint Practice | 50 minutes | **ONLINE** |
| ▶ **UNIT REVIEW** Prepare for the Checkpoint | | |

### ▶ Unit Objectives

This lesson reviews the following objectives:

- Use a letter to represent an unknown value in an expression or an equation.
- Identify and apply the distributive property in an equation or an expression with variables.
- Evaluate a simple algebraic expression in one variable by using substitution.
- Identify or use an expression or an equation to answer questions about a problem.

**Materials to Gather**

There are no materials to gather for this lesson.

### ▶ Advance Preparation

In this lesson, students will have an opportunity to review previous activities in the Algebra unit. Look at the suggested activities in Unit Review: Prepare for the Checkpoint online and gather any needed materials.

## UNIT REVIEW  Look Back

**ONLINE 10 min**

**Objectives**

- Review unit objectives.

Students will review key concepts from the unit to prepare for the Unit Checkpoint.

## UNIT REVIEW  Checkpoint Practice

**ONLINE 50 min**

**Objectives**

- Review unit objectives.

Students will complete an online Checkpoint Practice to prepare for the Unit Checkpoint. If necessary, read the directions, problems, and answer choices to students. Have students answer the problems on their own. Review any missed problems with students.

### ▶ UNIT REVIEW  Prepare for the Checkpoint

What you do next depends on how students performed in the previous activity, Unit Review: Checkpoint Practice. If students had difficulty with any of the problems, complete the appropriate review activity listed in the table online.

# Unit Checkpoint

## Lesson Overview

**UNIT CHECKPOINT** Online                                60 minutes | ONLINE

### ▶ Unit Objectives

This lesson assesses the following objectives:

- Use a letter to represent an unknown value in an expression or an equation.
- Identify and apply the distributive property in an equation or an expression with variables.
- Evaluate a simple algebraic expression in one variable by using substitution.
- Identify or use an expression or an equation to answer questions about a problem.

### Materials to Gather

There are no materials to gather for this lesson.

## UNIT CHECKPOINT  Online

ONLINE 60min

### Objectives

- Assess unit objectives.

Students will complete the Unit Checkpoint online. If necessary, read the directions, problems, and answer choices to students and help them with keyboard or mouse operations.

ALGEBRA

# Coordinate Planes

## Unit Objectives

- Identify and graph ordered pairs in all quadrants of a coordinate plane.
- Use the situation presented in a problem to describe the meaning of each coordinate of an ordered pair displayed on a graph.
- Graph or write an equation to solve a problem that involves a linear function.

## Big Ideas

Any point in a coordinate plane can be described by an ordered pair of coordinates.

## Unit Introduction

In this unit, students will explore all four quadrants of the coordinate plane. They will relate ordered pairs and their locations in the plane to problem situations. They will continue their investigation of coordinate planes by graphing as well as writing equations to solve a story problem. Students will work with linear functions, which are equations whose graphs are straight lines in the coordinate plane.

In this unit's lessons, students will sometimes see that the axes on the coordinate plane show only even numbers. It is sometimes necessary to skip labels of numbers on the coordinate plane to make it easier to read the numbers on each axis. The origin is still located at (0, 0), and odd-numbered coordinates can still be plotted and labeled.

## Keywords

| | | |
|---|---|---|
| axis (plural: axes) | integers | quadrants |
| coordinate | line | quantity |
| coordinate plane | linear function | variable |
| equation | ordered pair | $x$-axis |
| function table | origin | $y$-axis |
| graph | output | |
| input | point on a coordinate plane | |

# Quadrants in the Coordinate Plane

## Lesson Overview

| | | |
|---|---|---|
| **GET READY** Locate and Plot Ordered Pairs | 5 minutes | **OFFLINE** |
| **LEARN** Coordinate Plane and Quadrants | 15 minutes | **ONLINE** |
| **LEARN** Positives and Negatives in Quadrants | 10 minutes | **ONLINE** |
| **LEARN** Complete Shapes with Coordinates | 10 minutes | **OFFLINE** |
| **TRY IT** Practice with Coordinates | 10 minutes | **OFFLINE** |
| **CHECKPOINT** | 10 minutes | **ONLINE** |

### ▶ Lesson Objectives
Identify and graph ordered pairs in all quadrants of a coordinate plane.

### ▶ Prerequisite Skills
Locate and plot points on a coordinate plane.

### ▶ Content Background
Students will learn how to identify and graph ordered pairs in all quadrants of a coordinate plane.

A *coordinate* is a position along a number line or within the *coordinate plane*, the coordinate grid formed by two number lines, called *axes*. The *x*-axis is the horizontal number line, and the *y*-axis is the vertical number line. The two axes are perpendicular. Other names for the coordinate plane are *coordinate grid* and *Cartesian plane*.

The point where the *x*- and *y*-axes meet is called the *origin*. When labeling points on the coordinate plane, you label the origin with the ordered pair (0, 0).

One way to describe the coordinate plane is to talk about each of the four sections, or *quadrants*. The sections are usually labeled using roman numerals. Starting in the upper-right section and moving counterclockwise, the sections are called Quadrant I, Quadrant II, Quadrant III, and Quadrant IV.

A pair of numbers, shown inside parentheses with a comma separating the numbers, is one way to describe the position of a point on a plane. This pair of numbers is known as an *ordered pair*. On the coordinate plane, the way to label all points is to write the horizontal distance from the origin, moving along the *x*-axis, as the first coordinate, and the vertical distance, moving parallel to the *y*-axis, as the second coordinate. Examples of ordered pairs are (*x*, *y*) and ($^+2$, $^+3$). In the latter example, the ordered pair ($^+2$, $^+3$) is 2 steps to the right from the origin, then 3 steps above that point. Coordinates in an ordered pair can be both positive, both negative, or one positive and one negative.

### ▶ Advance Preparation
Print four copies of the Coordinate Grid.

### Materials to Gather

**SUPPLIED**
Coordinate Grid (printout) – 4
Complete Shapes with Coordinates activity page
Practice with Coordinates activity page

**ALSO NEEDED**
ruler, dual-scale

## GET READY  Locate and Plot Ordered Pairs

**OFFLINE 5 min**

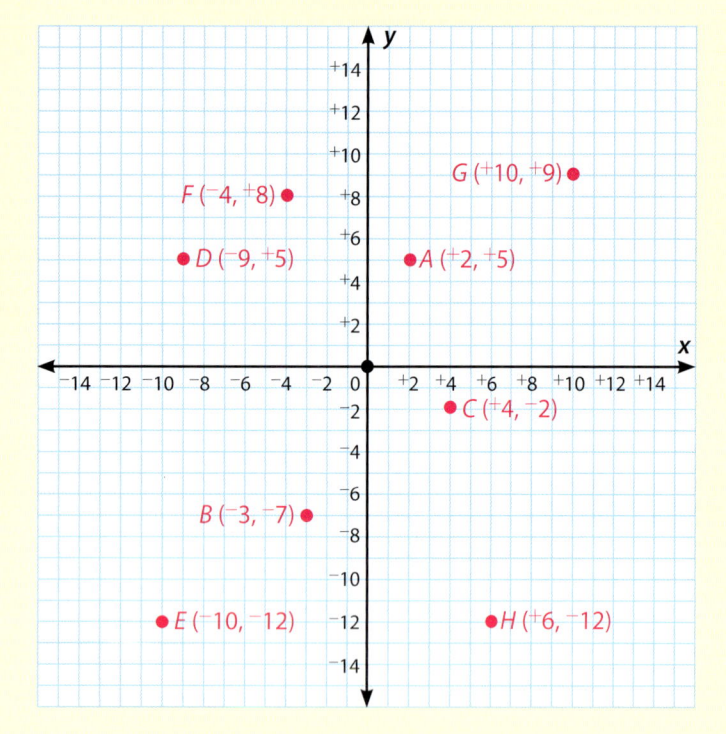

### Objectives
- Locate and plot points on a coordinate plane.

Students will locate and plot eight points on a coordinate plane. They also will label the coordinates of the points with the ordered pair and letter. Gather one copy of the Coordinate Grid printout.

Direct students to locate the point ($^+2$, $^+5$). Tell students to start at the origin and move to the right along the *x*-axis from the origin to $^+2$. From that point, tell them to move 5 units up. Have them place a dot at that point, and then label that point using the ordered pair ($^+2$, $^+5$) as well as the letter *A*.

Have students continue the activity by plotting the following points with a dot and labeling each point with the ordered pair and letter:

- ($^-3$, $^-7$); B
- ($^+4$, $^-2$); C
- ($^-9$, $^+5$); D
- ($^-10$, $^-12$); E
- ($^-4$, $^+8$); F
- ($^+10$, $^+9$); G
- ($^+6$, $^-12$); H

**416  COORDINATE PLANES**

## LEARN Coordinate Plane and Quadrants

**ONLINE 15 min**

**Objectives**
- Identify and graph ordered pairs in all quadrants of a coordinate plane.

Students will review parts of a coordinate plane and learn about quadrants. They will also learn how to label and find coordinates of ordered pairs in all four quadrants.

**Tips** If students have difficulty remembering where the quadrants are in the coordinate plane, have students draw $x$- and $y$-axes on a piece of paper to form a coordinate plane. Have them label the axes $x$ and $y$ but not number the units on the axes. Guide students to correctly label the quadrants.

## LEARN Positives and Negatives in Quadrants

**ONLINE 10 min**

**Objectives**
- Identify and graph ordered pairs in all quadrants of a coordinate plane.

Students will graph ordered pairs in all four quadrants of a coordinate plane. They will also learn to identify which quadrant a point is in by looking at whether its $x$- and $y$-coordinates are positive or negative.

## LEARN Complete Shapes with Coordinates

**OFFLINE 10 min**

**Objectives**
- Identify and graph ordered pairs in all quadrants of a coordinate plane.

Students will work in everyday contexts to plot points and locate a point that will create a given shape on the coordinate plane. Story problems will give them the location of three points. Students will then find the fourth point.

Gather the ruler and two copies of the Coordinate Grid. Have students turn to the Complete Shapes with Coordinates activity page in their Activity Book and read the directions with them.

1. Read only the Problem (not the Solution or Answer) in the Worked Examples with students.

   **Ask:** What are the characteristics of a square? All sides of a square have equal length. A square has 4 right angles.

2. Read the Solution and Answer with students.

   **Ask:** How can you use reflection to know that the answer of point $D$ (⁻3, 0) is correct? Point $A$ is reflected across the $y$-axis to make point $B$, so point $C$ must be reflected across the $y$-axis to make the answer, point $D$, because the sides of the square need to be all the same length.

3. Have students follow the Solution steps to plot and locate the three given points in the problem and find the location of the fourth booth.

4. Give students the ruler and a copy of the Coordinate Grid. Have them read and solve Problem 1 of the problem set on the printout. Encourage them to refer to the Worked Example as needed to help them plot the points and decide where point $H$ should be placed.

**QUADRANTS IN THE COORDINATE PLANE**

## Quadrants in the Coordinate Plane
### Complete Shapes with Coordinates

**Worked Examples**

You can figure out where to place a point on the coordinate plane to complete a given shape.

**PROBLEM** Tom's job is to plan where the four food booths at an upcoming town festival will be located. He wants the booths to be in the four corners of a square. He is using a coordinate plane to plan the location of the booths.

Here are the locations for three of the four food booths on Tom's coordinate plane:
- point A ($^+$3, $^+$6)
- point B ($^-$3, $^+$6)
- point C ($^+$3, 0)

Where will Tom locate the fourth booth, point D, to form a square on the coordinate plane?

**SOLUTION**

1. On the coordinate plane, locate points A, B, and C. Label each point with the point name and its ordered pair.
2. Connect the three points. Note that points A and B are 6 units apart. Note that points A and C are 6 units apart.
3. Note that point A is reflected across the y-axis to make point B.
4. Figure out the coordinates of the ordered pair for point D. Count from the origin. On the x-axis, count 3 units left from the origin. On the y-axis, count zero units up from the origin. The ordered pair is ($^-$3, 0).
5. Connect the four points with a ruler to make a square.

**ANSWER** Tom will locate the fourth booth at point D ($^-$3, 0).

Locate and plot ordered pairs on the coordinate plane to solve.

1. Betty is planning a city vacation with her family. The family members have specific places they want to see in the city. Betty is using a coordinate plane to decide the best way for family members to visit the following sites:
   - Her sister wants to see the City Zoo at point C ($^-$6, $^-$4).
   - Her dad wants to see the Jazz Museum at point J ($^-$4, $^+$3).
   - Her mom wants to see the Waterfront Art Gallery at point W ($^+$6, $^+$3).

   Betty wants to visit the History Museum. The location of the History Museum and the locations of the other sites make a parallelogram.
   - Name the ordered pair that describes the location of the History Museum.
   - Mark the point on a coordinate plane.
   - Label the point with its ordered pair and the letter H.
   - Connect the four points with a ruler to make a parallelogram.

   **See below.**

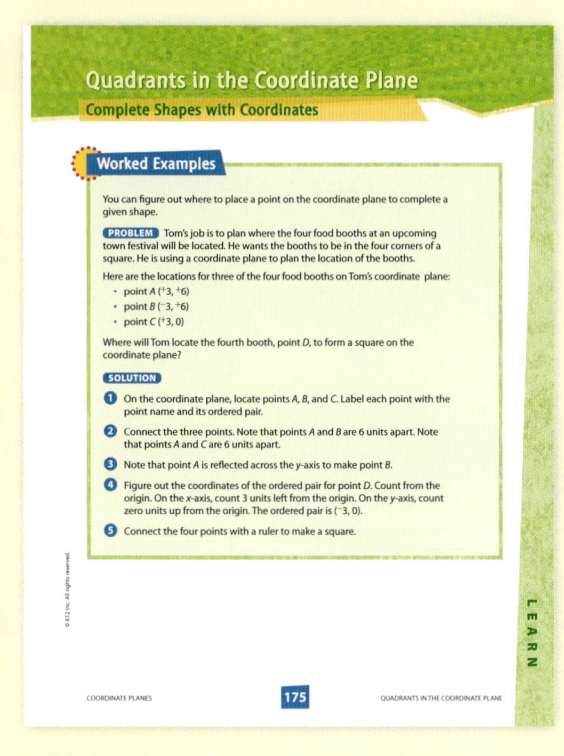

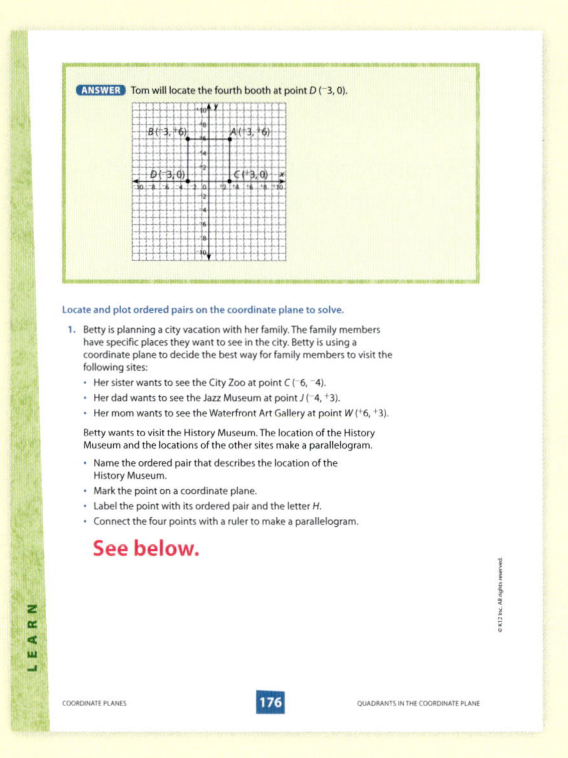

### Additional Answers

1. ($^+$4, $^-$4)

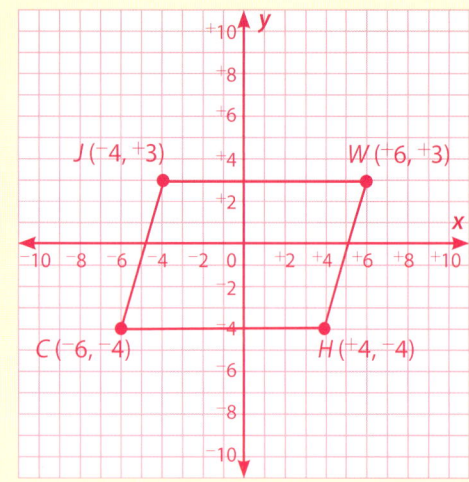

### TRY IT Practice with Coordinates

**OFFLINE 10 min**

Students will identify and graph ordered pairs in the four quadrants in a coordinate plane. Gather a copy of the Coordinate Grid for students to use for Problem 8. Have students turn to the Practice with Coordinates activity page in their Activity Book and read the directions with them.

Students should copy the problems from the Activity Book into their Math Notebook as necessary and solve them there.

**Objectives**
- Identify and graph ordered pairs in all quadrants of a coordinate plane.

# Quadrants in the Coordinate Plane
## Practice with Coordinates

**Choose the answer.**

1. Which point on the graph shows a coordinate of $(^-3, ^+8)$?
   A. A
   B. B
   C. C
   D. **D** ✓

2. Which point on the graph shows a coordinate of $(^+2, ^+6)$?
   A. **A** ✓
   B. B
   C. C
   D. D

3. Which point on the graph shows a coordinate of $(^-3, ^-4)$?
   A. A
   B. B
   C. **C** ✓
   D. D

4. Which point on the graph shows a coordinate of $(^+4, ^-2)$?
   A. **A** ✓
   B. B
   C. C
   D. D

5. Which point on the graph shows a coordinate of $(^+4, ^+2)$?
   A. **A** ✓
   B. B
   C. C
   D. D

6. Which graph shows a point with a coordinate of $(^-5, ^-8)$?
   A.
   B. ✓
   C.
   D.

7. Which ordered pair is graphed?
   A. $(^-5, ^+4)$
   B. $(^+5, ^-4)$
   C. $(^+4, ^-5)$
   D. **$(^-4, ^+5)$** ✓

**Solve.**

8. Plot the following points with a dot and label each point with the ordered pair and letter.
   A $(^+2, ^+3)$
   B $(^-10, ^-4)$
   C $(^+9, ^-5)$
   D $(0, ^+3)$
   E $(^-6, ^+8)$

# CHECKPOINT

**ONLINE 10 min**

Students will complete an online Checkpoint. If necessary, read the directions, problems, and answer choices to students and help them with keyboard or mouse operations.

## Objectives

- Identify and graph ordered pairs in all quadrants of a coordinate plane.

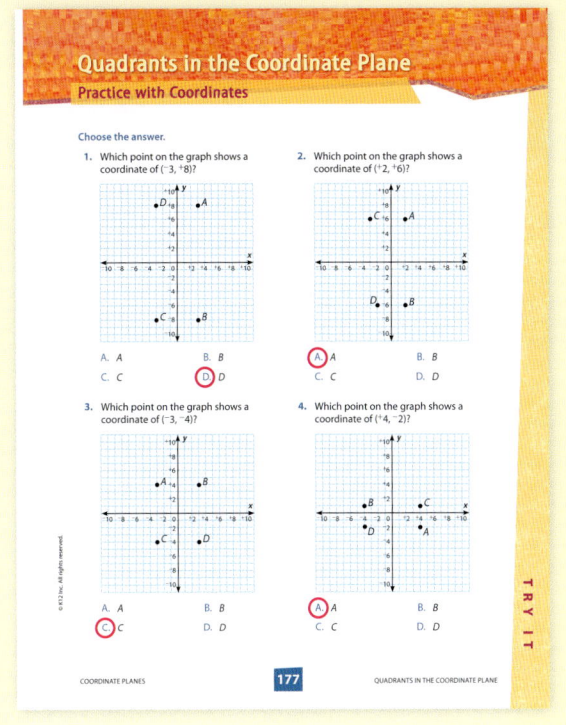

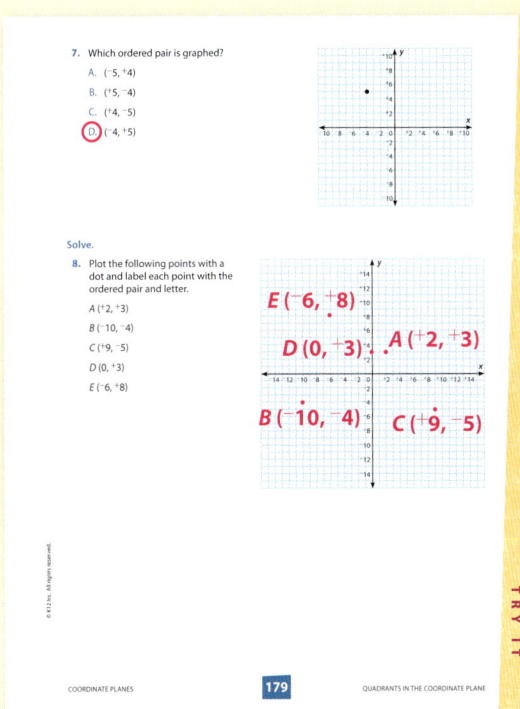

**QUADRANTS IN THE COORDINATE PLANE** 419

# Ordered Pairs

## Lesson Overview

| | | |
|---|---|---|
| **LEARN** Increase (x, y) Coordinates | 15 minutes | **ONLINE** |
| **LEARN** Coordinates Increase or Decrease | 10 minutes | **ONLINE** |
| **LEARN** Interpret Coordinates on a Graph | 10 minutes | **OFFLINE** |
| **TRY IT** Practice to Understand Coordinates | 15 minutes | **OFFLINE** |
| **CHECKPOINT** | 10 minutes | **ONLINE** |

### ▶ Lesson Objectives
Use the situation presented in a problem to describe the meaning of each coordinate of an ordered pair displayed on a graph.

### ▶ Prerequisite Skills
Identify and graph ordered pairs in all quadrants of a coordinate plane.

### ▶ Content Background
Students will explore the relationship of story problems to their graphs. Often students plot points related to story problems without understanding the meaning of the points and the significance of their locations on the coordinate plane. For example, suppose they plot points to show the cost of multiple DVDs. In this case, points in the second, third, and fourth quadrants make no sense, since a negative number of DVDs or negative cost is impossible. Understanding the meaning of coordinates can be a difficult idea for students to grasp in their early experiences with story problems and graphs on the coordinate plane, so this lesson concentrates on problems with data graphed in Quadrant I only. Because students focus on positive values of *x* and *y*, there are no positive signs in front of the coordinates.

This lesson introduces students to two types of data on the graphs. Although they will not learn these terms, the two types of data are called *discrete data* and *continuous data*. With discrete data, only the coordinates plotted make sense in the problem. For example, plotting points to show the cost of multiple DVDs is discrete data, since points in between the data points are irrelevant. Fractions of DVDs are not for sale, so a point showing the cost of $1\frac{1}{2}$ DVDs would make no sense. So with discrete data, points remain separate. They are not connected with a line. With continuous data, however, even the points along the line between the plotted points make sense to consider in the problem. For example, plotting points that show how much gas is used over several miles of driving is continuous data. Fractions of a mile and fractions of a gallon of gas exist, so connecting plotted points with a line in this case does make sense. In some problems, students will see an arrow on the end of the line. The arrow means that the data for this situation could continue beyond the points that are plotted.

Although the terms *positive correlation* and *negative correlation* (also known as *direct* and *inverse relationships*) are not part of this lesson, it is important for students to notice these relationships on their graphs. A positive correlation, or direct

### Materials to Gather

**SUPPLIED**

Quadrant I Coordinate Grid (printout) – 2

Interpret Coordinates on a Graph activity page

Practice to Understand Coordinates activity page

relationship, is one where the *y*-coordinates increase as the *x*-coordinates increase, so the path of the points moves up to the right on the graph. A negative correlation, or inverse relationship, is one where the *y*-coordinates decrease as the *x*-coordinates increase, so the path of the points moves down to the right on the graph.

A *coordinate* is a position along a number line or within the coordinate plane.

An *ordered pair* is a pair of numbers, shown inside parentheses, with a comma separating the numbers. It is one way to describe the position of a point on a plane. On the coordinate plane, all points can be labeled by writing the horizontal distance from the origin, moving along the *x*-axis, as the first coordinate, and the vertical distance, moving parallel to the *y*-axis, as the second coordinate, such as $(x, y)$ or $(^+2, ^+3)$. For example, the ordered pair $(^+2, ^+3)$ is 2 steps to the right of the origin, then 3 steps above that point. Even though this lesson concentrates on problems with data graphed in Quadrant I only, coordinates in an ordered pair can be positive and negative, depending on the quadrant in which they are located.

## ▶ Advance Preparation
Print two copies of the Quadrant I Coordinate Grid.

### LEARN  Increase (x, y) Coordinates
**ONLINE 15 min**

Students will graph and describe the meaning of ordered pairs on the coordinate plane. They will work with story problems from everyday situations. The data that students will see in the problems have a positive correlation.

**Objectives**
- Use the situation presented in a problem to describe the meaning of each coordinate of an ordered pair displayed on a graph.

**Tips**  If students have difficulty understanding why sometimes the data in a problem can be graphed so a line can connect the points, have them think of another example like the bike-riding problem, where the data between graphed points make sense in the context of the problem. Then have students think of another example like the zoo problem, where the data between the graphed points do not make sense in the context of the problem.

### LEARN  Coordinates Increase or Decrease
**ONLINE 10 min**

Students will graph and describe the meaning of ordered pairs on the coordinate plane. They will work with a story problem from an everyday situation. The data that students will see in the problem have a negative correlation.

**Objectives**
- Use the situation presented in a problem to describe the meaning of each coordinate of an ordered pair displayed on a graph.

# LEARN Interpret Coordinates on a Graph

**OFFLINE 10 min**

## Objectives

- Use the situation presented in a problem to describe the meaning of each coordinate of an ordered pair displayed on a graph.

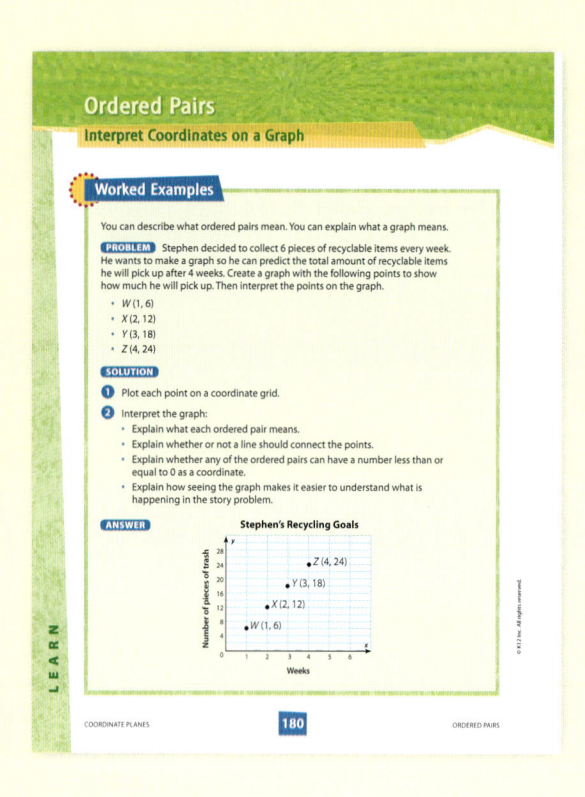

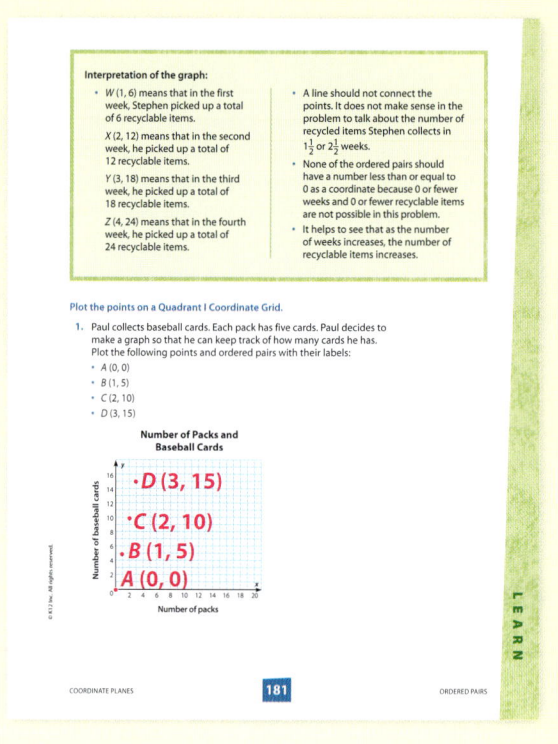

Students will graph and describe the meaning of ordered pairs on the coordinate plane. Gather the Quadrant I Coordinate Grid. Have students turn to the Interpret Coordinates on a Graph activity page in their Activity Book and read the directions with them.

Students should copy the problems from the Activity Book into their Math Notebook as necessary and solve them there.

1. Read the problem in the Worked Examples box with students. Make sure they understand the graph and how the graph was interpreted.

2. Have students read Problem 1. Have them plot the points on the Quadrant I Coordinate Grid. Check that they plotted the points correctly.

3. Have students complete Problems 2–11. Check that they answered the problems correctly. If they have trouble, go over the Worked Example again and then have them look at the problems again.

422 COORDINATE PLANES

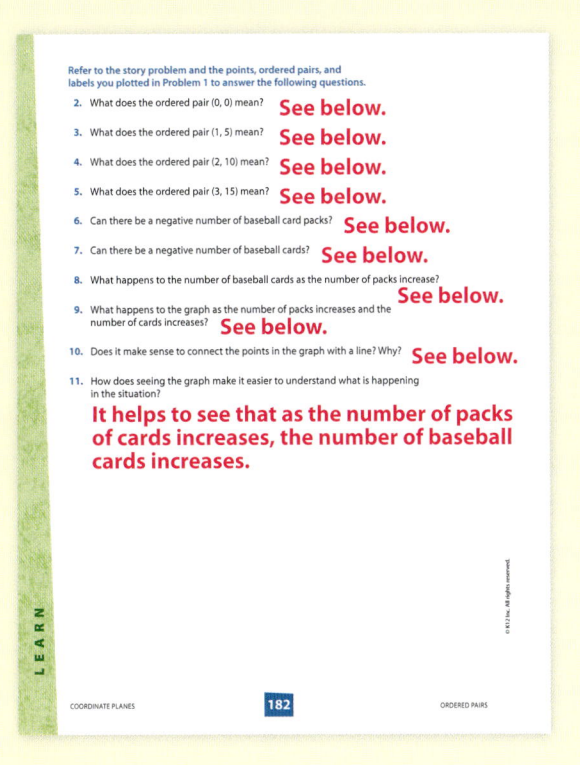

> Refer to the story problem and the points, ordered pairs, and labels you plotted in Problem 1 to answer the following questions.
>
> 2. What does the ordered pair (0, 0) mean? **See below.**
> 3. What does the ordered pair (1, 5) mean? **See below.**
> 4. What does the ordered pair (2, 10) mean? **See below.**
> 5. What does the ordered pair (3, 15) mean? **See below.**
> 6. Can there be a negative number of baseball card packs? **See below.**
> 7. Can there be a negative number of baseball cards? **See below.**
> 8. What happens to the number of baseball cards as the number of packs increase? **See below.**
> 9. What happens to the graph as the number of packs increases and the number of cards increases? **See below.**
> 10. Does it make sense to connect the points in the graph with a line? Why? **See below.**
> 11. How does seeing the graph make it easier to understand what is happening in the situation?
>     **It helps to see that as the number of packs of cards increases, the number of baseball cards increases.**

### Additional Answers

2. Paul has 0 packs and 0 baseball cards.
3. Paul has 1 pack with 5 baseball cards.
4. Paul has 2 packs with 10 baseball cards.
5. Paul has 3 packs with 15 baseball cards.
6. No. There are 0 or more packs of baseball cards. Fewer than 0 packs is not possible in this problem.
7. No. There are 0 or more baseball cards. Fewer than 0 baseball cards is not possible in this problem.
8. The number of baseball cards increases as the number of packs increases.
9. The ordered pairs move up and to the right of the origin.
10. No. In this problem, there are only whole packs of baseball cards.

## TRY IT  Practice to Understand Coordinates

**OFFLINE 15 min**

### Objectives
- Use the situation presented in a problem to describe the meaning of each coordinate of an ordered pair displayed on a graph.

Students will plot points on a coordinate grid. They will describe what the coordinates on a graph of an everyday situation mean. And they'll answer questions based on graphs. Gather the Quadrant I Coordinate Grid. Have students turn to the Practice to Understand Coordinates activity page in their Activity Book and read the directions with them.

Students should copy the problems from the Activity Book into their Math Notebook as necessary and solve them there.

## Ordered Pairs
### Practice to Understand Coordinates

**Plot the points on a Quadrant I Coordinate Grid.**

1. Tim's family went on vacation to Yellowstone National Park. When they left, they had 15 gallons of gas. After 1 hour, they had 12 gallons of gas left. Tim made a graph of how much gas they had left after each hour so his mother could plan when she would need to stop for gas. Plot the following points, ordered pairs, and labels, and connect the points with a line:
   - A (0, 15)
   - B (1, 12)
   - C (2, 9)
   - D (3, 6)
   - E (4, 3)
   - F (5, 0)

*See below.*

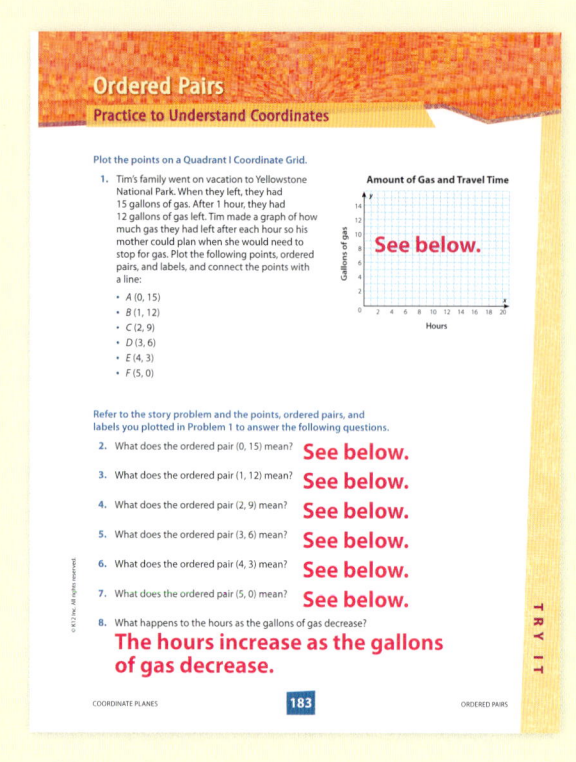

**Refer to the story problem and the points, ordered pairs, and labels you plotted in Problem 1 to answer the following questions.**

2. What does the ordered pair (0, 15) mean?  *See below.*
3. What does the ordered pair (1, 12) mean?  *See below.*
4. What does the ordered pair (2, 9) mean?  *See below.*
5. What does the ordered pair (3, 6) mean?  *See below.*
6. What does the ordered pair (4, 3) mean?  *See below.*
7. What does the ordered pair (5, 0) mean?  *See below.*
8. What happens to the hours as the gallons of gas decrease?
   **The hours increase as the gallons of gas decrease.**

**Choose the answer.**

9. Ben's graph shows that the total number of medals won by Team USA on day 3 was 8. How many medals were won by day 5?
   - A. 2
   - B. 5
   - **C. 11**
   - D. 15

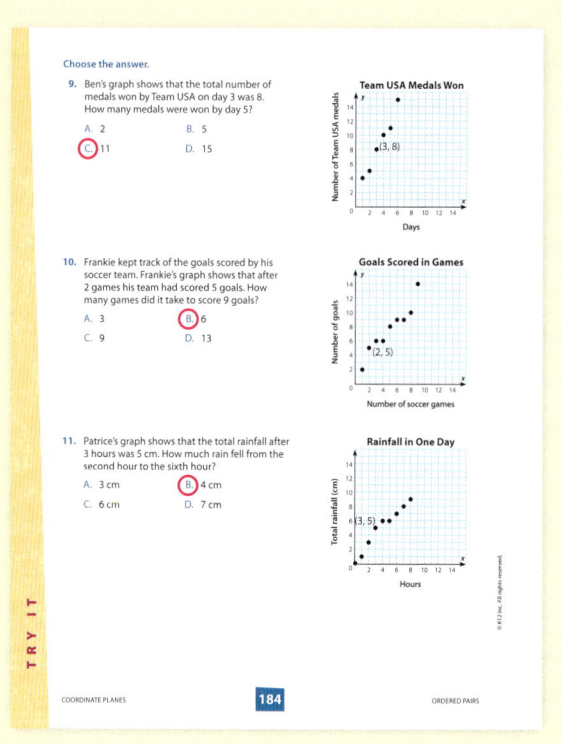

10. Frankie kept track of the goals scored by his soccer team. Frankie's graph shows that after 2 games his team had scored 5 goals. How many games did it take to score 9 goals?
    - A. 3
    - **B. 6**
    - C. 9
    - D. 13

11. Patrice's graph shows that the total rainfall after 3 hours was 5 cm. How much rain fell from the second hour to the sixth hour?
    - A. 3 cm
    - **B. 4 cm**
    - C. 6 cm
    - D. 7 cm

### Additional Answers

1. **Amount of Gas and Travel Time** — graph showing points A (0, 15), B (1, 12), C (2, 9), D (3, 6), E (4, 3), F (5, 0) connected by a line; x-axis: Hours, y-axis: Gallons of gas.

2. Tim's family traveled for 0 hours and has 15 gallons of gas left.
3. Tim's family traveled for 1 hour and has 12 gallons of gas left.
4. Tim's family traveled for 2 hours and has 9 gallons of gas left.
5. Tim's family traveled for 3 hours and has 6 gallons of gas left.
6. Tim's family traveled for 4 hours and has 3 gallons of gas left.
7. Tim's family traveled for 5 hours and has 0 gallons of gas left.

## CHECKPOINT

ONLINE 10 min

Students will complete an online Checkpoint. If necessary, read the directions, problems, and answer choices to students and help them with keyboard or mouse operations.

### Objectives

- Use the situation presented in a problem to describe the meaning of each coordinate of an ordered pair displayed on a graph.

# Graph or Write an Equation (A)

## Lesson Overview

| | | |
|---|---|---|
| Skills Update | 5 minutes | **ONLINE** |
| **LEARN** Inputs and Outputs of Function Tables | 15 minutes | **ONLINE** |
| **LEARN** Equations and Function Tables | 15 minutes | **OFFLINE** |
| **LEARN** Find Equations for Function Tables | 15 minutes | **OFFLINE** |
| **TRY IT** Practice Completing Function Tables | 10 minutes | **ONLINE** |

### ▶ Lesson Objectives
Graph or write an equation to solve a problem that involves a linear function.

### ▶ Prerequisite Skills
- Use an equation to represent a relationship between quantities.
- Use the situation presented in a problem to describe the meaning of each coordinate of an ordered pair displayed on a graph.
- Plot a linear relationship in the first quadrant of a coordinate plane.

### ▶ Content Background
Students will complete the *x*- and *y*-values of a function table and learn to write an equation based on a linear function.

An *equation* is a number sentence that shows that two quantities are equal. Equations can include numbers, variables, and operation signs (such as $+$, $-$, $\cdot$, or $\div$). Some examples of equations are $2r - 3 = 9$ and $16 = 12 + 4$.

A *linear function* is a relationship between two quantities in which one variable depends on another. One reason this type of function is called linear is that the graph of the equation has points that fall on a straight line. Most often, linear equations are written in the form of $y = mx + b$, where *x* and *y* are the two quantities. In that linear equation, the variable *m* stands for any number that is multiplied by *x*. When you multiply *m* by *x*, you have a linear function. The variable *b* stands for any number that is added to the expression *mx*. The equation $y = mx + b$ is a linear function. It's also the case that *b* can be a negative number, so that $y = mx - b$ is also a linear function.

### Materials to Gather

**SUPPLIED**
Equations and Function Tables activity page
Find Equations for Function Tables activity page

**ALSO NEEDED**
ruler, dual-scale

## LEARN Inputs and Outputs of Function Tables

**ONLINE 15 min**

Students will learn about input-output tables. They will apply a rule to an input to get an output. They also will find missing values in input-output tables. They will learn that input-output tables can also be called function tables.

### Objectives
- Graph or write an equation to solve a problem that involves a linear function.

## LEARN Equations and Function Tables

**OFFLINE 15 min**

### Objectives

- Graph or write an equation to solve a problem that involves a linear function.

Students will learn that a function table lists input and output values for a function, which is an equation. A function table uses one variable to represent input and another variable to represent output. Students will find missing values for variables in function tables. Gather a ruler. Have students turn to the Equations and Function Tables activity page in their Activity Book and read the directions with them.

Students should copy the problems from the Activity Book into their Math Notebook as necessary and solve them there. Have them use a ruler to help them draw the function tables in their Math Notebook.

1. Read the Problem and Solution in the Worked Examples box with students.

2. Make sure students understand the function table.

   **Ask:** How would you read the rows in this incomplete function table? Read a few rows. **Sample answer:** In the third row, the value of *x* is 7 and the value of *y* isn't known. Next row: The value of *x* isn't known and the value of *y* is 13. Next row: The value of *x* is 9 and the value of *y* is 14.

3. Point to the rule at the top of the function table. Explain that instead of writing a rule with words such as "add 5" or "subtract 1," the rule of a function table is written as an equation. Remind students that while the tables in this activity use *x* and *y*, other letters can also be used as variables.

4. Read the Answer in the Worked Examples box with students. Make sure they understand how the table was completed.

5. Have students look at Problem 1 in the problem set. Point to the first row of function values. Tell students that the value for *x* is 3 and they should substitute 3 in the equation for *x*.

   **Ask:** What will you write as the first value for *y* in the function table? **6**

   Have students continue to substitute the values of *x* into the equation to fill in the missing values for *y*.

6. Have students complete Problem 2 on their own. If they have difficulty, first encourage them to look at the Worked Example and follow the process shown.

7. Have students look at the function table in Problem 3. Tell them that some of the values for *x* and *y* are missing.

   **Say:** In the fourth row of function values in the function table, both values are missing. Look for a pattern in the values for *x* to find the missing value. The three numbers before the missing value are 10, 11, and 12 and the number after the missing value is 14.

   **Ask:** What is the missing value for *x*? **13**

   Have students complete the remaining rows on the function table.

8. Have students complete Problem 4 on their own. If they have difficulty, have them review the steps they took to complete the function table in Problem 3.

9. Discuss with students that in these examples, the *x*-values have always been numbers that are in counting order. Tell them that as they continue to study mathematics, *x*-values may not always be in counting order. In fact, *x*-values may be in a random order or may include other types of numbers, such as negative numbers. To find missing *x*-values, think about the equation and the *y*-value. Then work backward.

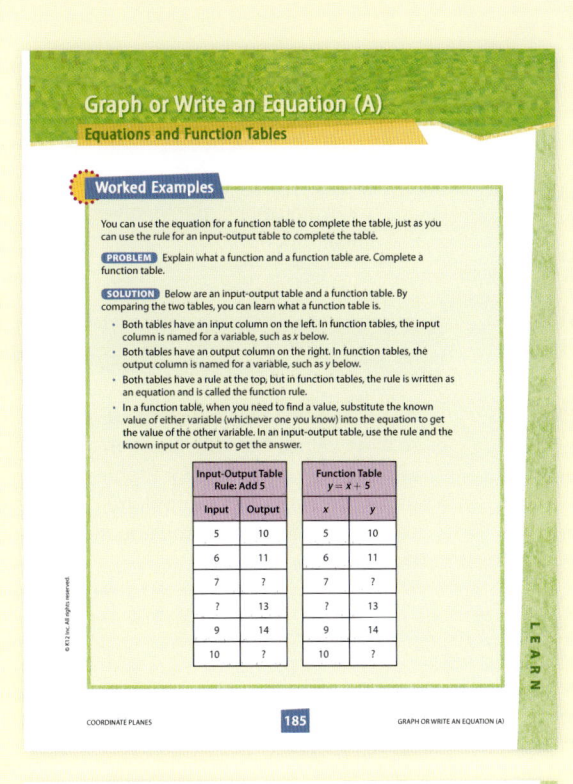

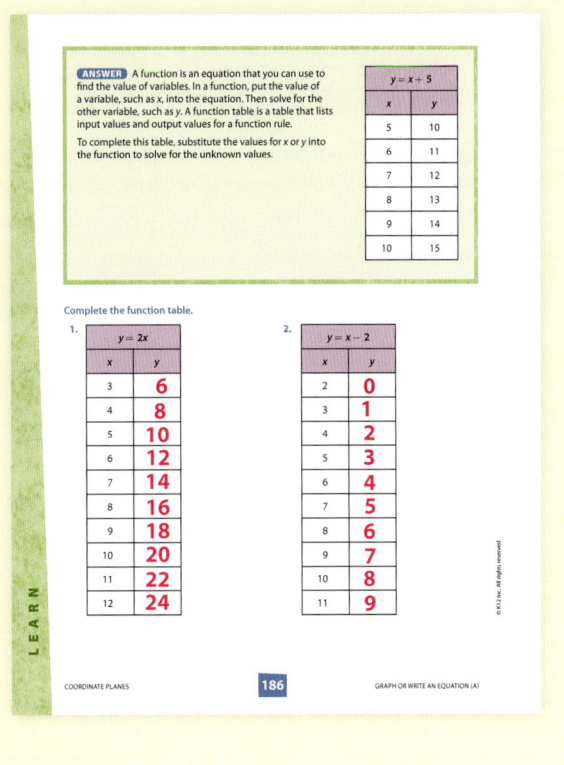

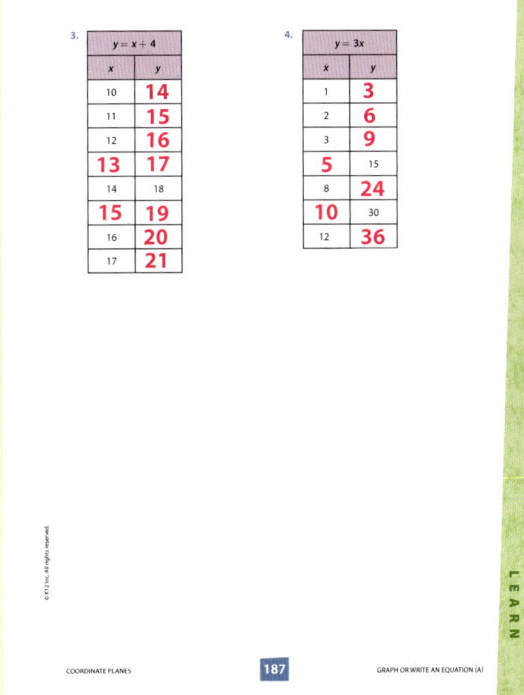

# Graph or Write an Equation (A)
## Equations and Function Tables

### Worked Examples

You can use the equation for a function table to complete the table, just as you can use the rule for an input-output table to complete the table.

**PROBLEM** Explain what a function and a function table are. Complete a function table.

**SOLUTION** Below are an input-output table and a function table. By comparing the two tables, you can learn what a function table is.

- Both tables have an input column on the left. In function tables, the input column is named for a variable, such as $x$ below.
- Both tables have an output column on the right. In function tables, the output column is named for a variable, such as $y$ below.
- Both tables have a rule at the top, but in function tables, the rule is written as an equation and is called the function rule.
- In a function table, when you need to find a value, substitute the known value of either variable (whichever one you know) into the equation to get the value of the other variable. In an input-output table, use the rule and the known input or output to get the answer.

Input-Output Table Rule: Add 5

| Input | Output |
|---|---|
| 5 | 10 |
| 6 | 11 |
| 7 | ? |
| ? | 13 |
| 9 | 14 |
| 10 | ? |

Function Table $y = x + 5$

| x | y |
|---|---|
| 5 | 10 |
| 6 | 11 |
| 7 | ? |
| ? | 13 |
| 9 | 14 |
| 10 | ? |

**ANSWER** A function is an equation that you can use to find the value of variables. In a function, put the value of a variable, such as $x$, into the equation. Then solve for the other variable, such as $y$. A function table is a table that lists input values and output values for a function rule.

To complete this table, substitute the values for $x$ or $y$ into the function to solve for the unknown values.

$y = x + 5$

| x | y |
|---|---|
| 5 | 10 |
| 6 | 11 |
| 7 | 12 |
| 8 | 13 |
| 9 | 14 |
| 10 | 15 |

**Complete the function table.**

1. $y = 2x$

| x | y |
|---|---|
| 3 | 6 |
| 4 | 8 |
| 5 | 10 |
| 6 | 12 |
| 7 | 14 |
| 8 | 16 |
| 9 | 18 |
| 10 | 20 |
| 11 | 22 |
| 12 | 24 |

2. $y = x - 2$

| x | y |
|---|---|
| 2 | 0 |
| 3 | 1 |
| 4 | 2 |
| 5 | 3 |
| 6 | 4 |
| 7 | 5 |
| 8 | 6 |
| 9 | 7 |
| 10 | 8 |
| 11 | 9 |

3. $y = x + 4$

| x | y |
|---|---|
| 10 | 14 |
| 11 | 15 |
| 12 | 16 |
| 13 | 17 |
| 14 | 18 |
| 15 | 19 |
| 16 | 20 |
| 17 | 21 |

4. $y = 3x$

| x | y |
|---|---|
| 1 | 3 |
| 2 | 6 |
| 3 | 9 |
| 5 | 15 |
| 8 | 24 |
| 10 | 30 |
| 12 | 36 |

## LEARN  Find Equations for Function Tables

**OFFLINE 15 min**

### Objectives
- Graph or write an equation to solve a problem that involves a linear function.

Students will use the values for variables in a function table to find the equation that matches all the values. Gather a ruler. Have students turn to the Find Equations for Function Tables activity page in their Activity Book and read the directions with them.

Students should copy the problems from the Activity Book into their Math Notebook as necessary and solve them there. Have them use the ruler to help them copy the function tables into their Math Notebook. They will need to use function tables in their Math Notebook to work out the answers to the problems in the problem set.

1. Read Problem 1 of the Worked Examples with students.

   **Ask:** Why did you substitute the values for *x* and *y* in the two equations? *I wanted to find out if the equations were true for the x- and y-values in the two function tables.*

   **Ask:** What happened when 2 was substituted for *x* and 6 for *y* in the two equations? *For those values, one equation, $y = 3x$, was true. The other equation, $y = x + 2$, was not true.*

2. Explain that students always need to check each row of values in the function table with the equation that they believe is correct. They need to be sure that the equation works for all pairs of *x*- and *y*-values.

3. Read Problem 2 of the Worked Examples with students.

   **Ask:** Why did the Solution try out the equation $y = x + 1$? *The numbers for x and y showed a pattern of each y-value being 1 greater than its matching x-value.*

4. Summarize the strategy used in the Worked Examples problems.

   **Say:** If you are asked to write an equation for a function table with given *x*- and *y*-values, look at all the numbers to find a pattern and to find what operation you might need to use in the equation. Check all the values in the function table to see if they all work in the equation you are trying.

5. Have students complete Problems 1–3 in the problem set. Note that for all the problems in this set, the equation that matches a function table needs only one operation, such as add a number or multiply by a number. If students have difficulty, first encourage them to look at the Worked Examples and follow the process shown. Help them as needed.

### Tips
Allow students to use paper and pencil to write values from the function table and possible equations for Problem 3, using a guess-and-test problem-solving strategy to find the equation that matches the values.

# Graph or Write an Equation (A)
## Find Equations for Function Tables

### Worked Examples

You can identify the equation that matches the x- and y-values in a function table.

**PROBLEM 1** Which of these two equations matches the values in the function table?
$y = x + 2$ or $y = 3x$

| ? | |
|---|---|
| x | y |
| 1 | 3 |
| 2 | 6 |
| 3 | 9 |

**SOLUTION**

1. Substitute the x- and y-values into each equation, starting with the values in the first row.

2. Start with $y = x + 2$. Substitute 1 for x and 3 for y in that equation. Then substitute 1 for x and 3 for y in $y = 3x$.

   The first and second equations are true when the values of 1 and 3 from the function table are substituted for x and y.

   | $y = x + 2$ | |
   |---|---|
   | x | y |
   | 1 | 3 |

   It is true that $3 = 1 + 2$.

   | $y = 3x$ | |
   |---|---|
   | x | y |
   | 1 | 3 |

   It is true that $3 = 3(1)$.

3. Substitute the values in the second row into each equation.

   Only the equation $y = 3x$ is true when 2 and 6 are substituted for x and y.

   | $y = x + 2$ | |
   |---|---|
   | x | y |
   | 1 | 3 |
   | 2 | 6 |

   It is **not** true that $6 = 2 + 2$.

   | $y = 3x$ | |
   |---|---|
   | x | y |
   | 1 | 3 |
   | 2 | 6 |

   It is true that $6 = 3(2)$.

4. Check the rest of the values in the function table to make sure the equation is true for those values.

   $9 = 3(3)$, so $y = 3x$ is true for all values in the function table.

**ANSWER** The equation $y = 3x$ matches the values in the function table.

| $y = 3x$ | |
|---|---|
| x | y |
| 1 | 3 |
| 2 | 6 |
| 3 | 9 |

**PROBLEM 2** Which equation matches the function table?

| ? | |
|---|---|
| x | y |
| 1 | 2 |
| 2 | 3 |
| 3 | 4 |
| 4 | 5 |
| 5 | 6 |
| 6 | 7 |

**SOLUTION**

1. Look carefully at all the x- and y-values in the function table.

2. Note that each y-value is greater than the x-value on the same row. That fact helps you know which operation is used in the function. Because the y-value is greater than the x-value in each row, the equation that matches the function table must use either addition or multiplication.

3. Note that the y-value increases by 1 in all rows of the function table. Because it increases by 1, "+ 1" might be in the equation.

4. Try $y = x + 1$ as the equation that matches the function table. When you substitute 1 for x and 2 for y, the equation is true. Substitute the rest of the values into the equation.

5. When you substitute the values in each row of the function table in the equation $y = x + 1$, find that the following equations are true:

   $2 = 1 + 1$   $3 = 2 + 1$   $4 = 3 + 1$
   $5 = 4 + 1$   $6 = 5 + 1$   $7 = 6 + 1$

**ANSWER** The equation that matches the function table is $y = x + 1$.

| $y = x + 1$ | |
|---|---|
| x | y |
| 1 | 2 |
| 2 | 3 |
| 3 | 4 |
| 4 | 5 |
| 5 | 6 |
| 6 | 7 |

Choose the equation for the function table.

1.

| ? | |
|---|---|
| x | y |
| 0 | 4 |
| 1 | 5 |
| 2 | 6 |
| 3 | 7 |
| 4 | 8 |
| 5 | 9 |
| 6 | 10 |

(A) $y = x + 4$
B. $y = 2x$

2.

| ? | |
|---|---|
| x | y |
| 0 | 0 |
| 1 | 1 |
| 2 | 2 |
| 3 | 3 |
| 4 | 4 |
| 5 | 5 |
| 6 | 6 |

A. $y = x - 2$
(B) $y = x$

Write the equation that matches the function table.

3.

| ? | |
|---|---|
| x | y |
| 1 | 0 |
| 2 | 1 |
| 3 | 2 |
| 4 | 3 |
| 5 | 4 |
| 6 | 5 |

$y = x - 1$

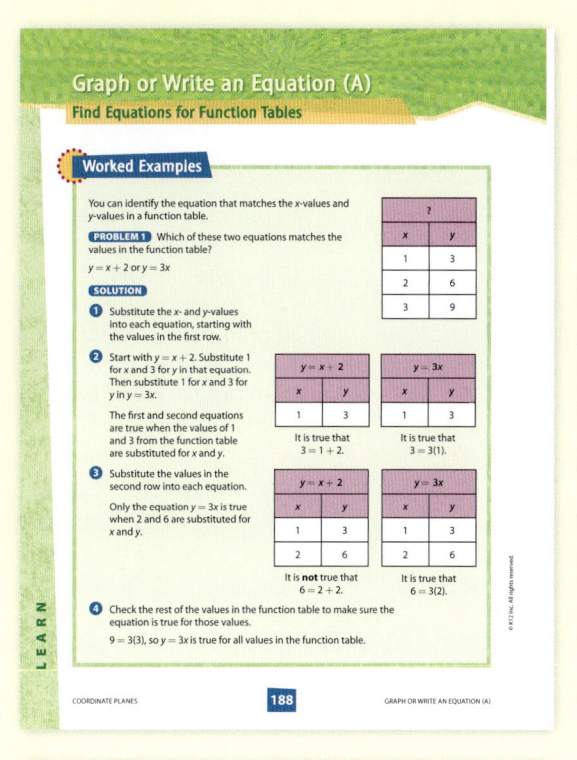

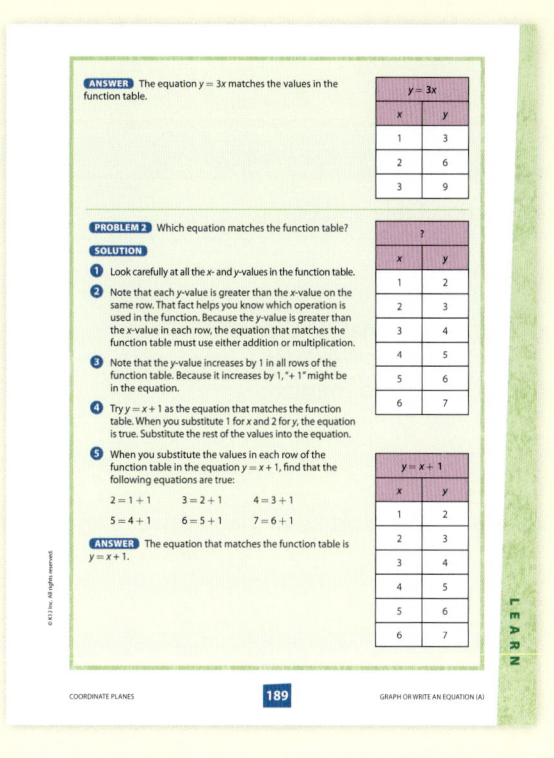

## TRY IT Practice Completing Function Tables
**ONLINE 10 min**

Students will complete an online Try It. If necessary, read the directions, problems, and answer choices to students and help them with keyboard or mouse operations.

### Objectives
- Graph or write an equation to solve a problem that involves a linear function.

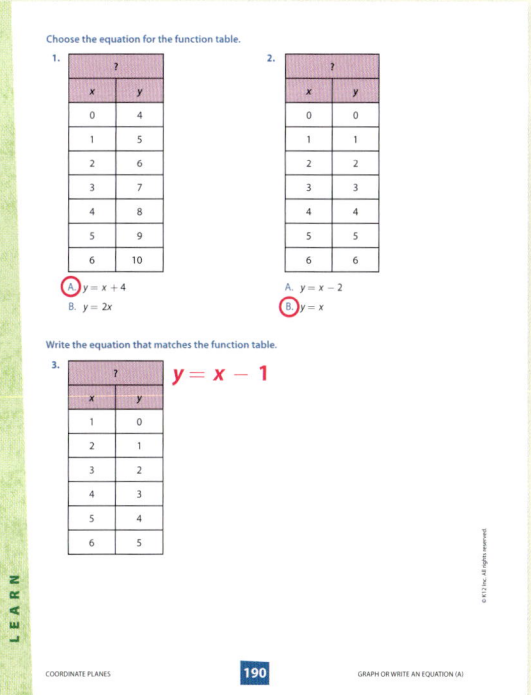

# Graph or Write an Equation (B)

## Lesson Overview

| | | |
|---|---|---|
| **LEARN** Complete a Function Table and Graph | 15 minutes | **ONLINE** |
| **LEARN** Graph Linear Functions | 10 minutes | **ONLINE** |
| **LEARN** Find an Equation Used to Make a Graph | 20 minutes | **OFFLINE** |
| **TRY IT** Practice Function Tables and Graphs | 15 minutes | **OFFLINE** |

### ▶ Lesson Objectives
Graph or write an equation to solve a problem that involves a linear function.

### ▶ Prerequisite Skills
- Use an equation to represent a relationship between quantities.
- Use the situation presented in a problem to describe the meaning of each coordinate of an ordered pair displayed on a graph.
- Plot a linear relationship in the first quadrant of a coordinate plane.

### ▶ Content Background
Students will learn to graph a set of points from a function table that has an equation and data for $x$- and $y$-values.

An *equation* is a number sentence that shows that two quantities are equal. Equations can include numbers, variables, and operation signs (such as $+$, $-$, $\cdot$, or $\div$). Some examples of equations are $2r - 3 = 9$ and $16 = 12 + 4$.

A *linear function* is a relationship between two quantities in which one variable depends on another. One reason this type of function is called linear is that the graph of the equation has points that fall on a straight line. Most often linear equations are written in the form of $y = mx + b$, where $x$ and $y$ are the two quantities. In that linear equation, the variable $m$ stands for any number that is multiplied by $x$. When you multiply $m$ by $x$, you have a linear function. The variable $b$ stands for any number that is added to the expression $mx$. The equation $y = mx + b$ is a linear function. It's also the case that $b$ can be a negative number, so that $y = mx - b$ is also a linear function.

### ▶ Advance Preparation
Print two copies of Graphing Equations.

### Materials to Gather

**SUPPLIED**
Graphing Equations (printout) – 2
Find an Equation Used to Make a Graph activity page
Practice Function Tables and Graphs activity page

**430** COORDINATE PLANES

## LEARN  Complete a Function Table and Graph  ONLINE 15 min

### Objectives
- Graph or write an equation to solve a problem that involves a linear function.

Students will complete a function table and plot the values from the table on a graph. The function table values, graph, and equation represent a linear function.

**Tips**  Tell students that an infinite number of points can be plotted for any linear function.

## LEARN  Graph Linear Functions  ONLINE 10 min

### Objectives
- Graph or write an equation to solve a problem that involves a linear function.

Students will use the Coordinate Grid Learning Tool to graph a linear function.

**DIRECTIONS FOR USING THE COORDINATE GRID LEARNING TOOL**

1. Explain to students that they will be graphing a type of equation called a linear function.

   **Say:** A linear function is a relationship between two quantities. The two quantities will be the *x*- and *y*-values in a function table with *y* dependent on *x*.

2. Tell students to select Stage 2: $^-15$ to $^+15$ and click Next.
3. Then have students select Linear Equations and click Next. Have them read the Help text.
4. Explain that the function table shows an equation and *x*- and *y*-values. Have students read the equation and the *x*- and *y*-values before they graph the points.
5. To graph the linear function, have students plot a point on the coordinate plane for each pair of *x*- and *y*-values in the function table.
6. Have students graph the remaining functions in the problem set.

## LEARN  Find an Equation Used to Make a Graph  OFFLINE 20 min

### Objectives
- Graph or write an equation to solve a problem that involves a linear function.

Students will look at the graph of a linear function and use the information in it to write the equation that was used to create the graph. Gather two copies of the Graphing Equations printout. Have students turn to the Find an Equation Used to Make a Graph activity page in their Activity Book and read the directions with them.

Students will solve the problems in this activity on the Graphing Equations printouts. They also may copy the problems from the Activity Book into their Math Notebook.

1. Read all the text, the graph, and the tables in Worked Examples with students.

   **Ask:** How was the function table completed? It was completed by entering each *x*-value and *y*-value in the ordered pairs on the graph into the function table.

**GRAPH OR WRITE AN EQUATION (B)  431**

2. Tell students that they can enter *x*- and *y*-values into the function table out of sequential order. The equation would still be correct and, if the graph were created again with this table, it would still look the same. When the values appear in sequential order, plotting points is easier. But as long as the values in the function table are correct with the equation, it does not matter if the values are in sequential order.

3. Remind students that when they find an equation that works with some of the variables in a function table, they need to substitute the remaining *x*- and *y*-values in the function table. They need to check that the equation is correct for all *x*- and *y*-values in the table.

4. Discuss with students that in these examples, the *x*-values have always been positive numbers that are in counting order. Tell students that as they continue to study graphing and other topics in mathematics, *x*-values may not always be in counting order. In fact, the *x*-values may be in a random order or may include other types of numbers, such as negative numbers.

5. Before they begin, discuss the problem set with students.

    **Ask:** The Worked Examples box shows a graph and function table for an addition equation. What other operations could be used in equations for graphed lines? subtraction, multiplication, or division

    **Say:** Even if the problem had an operation other than addition, you would still follow the same process by taking the information from the graph to write the equation that was used to create the graph.

6. Have students complete both problems in the problem set.

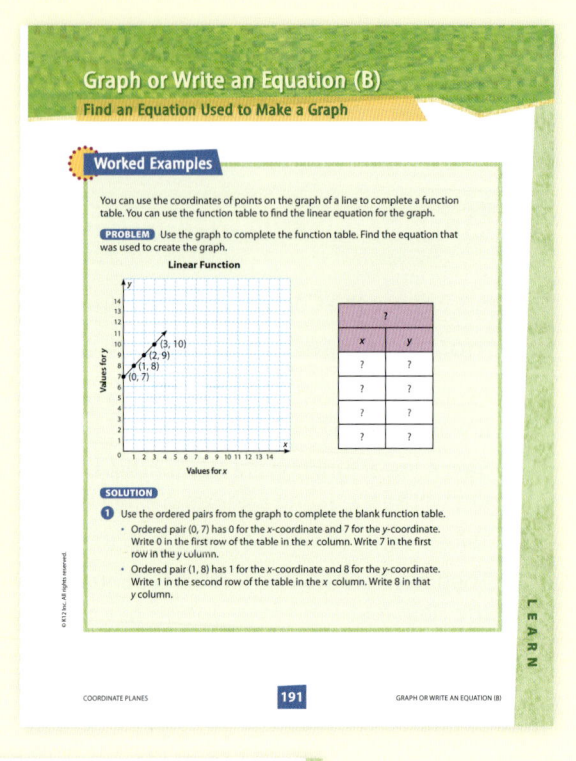

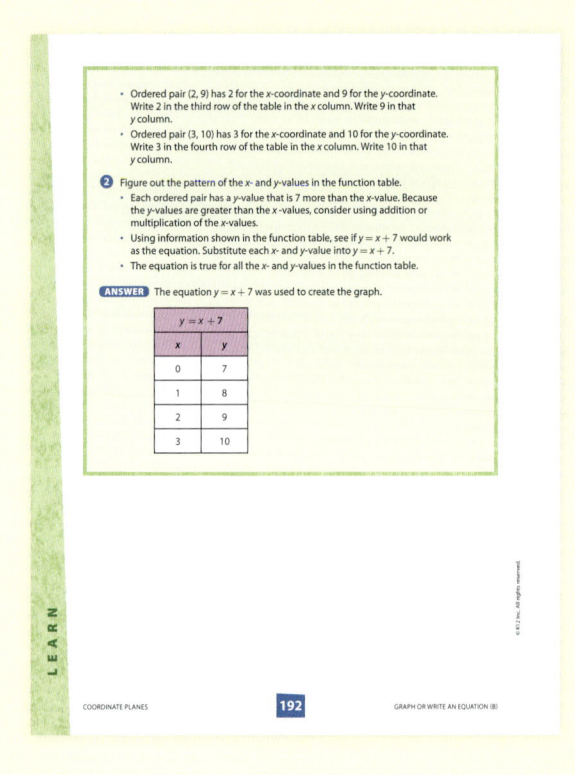

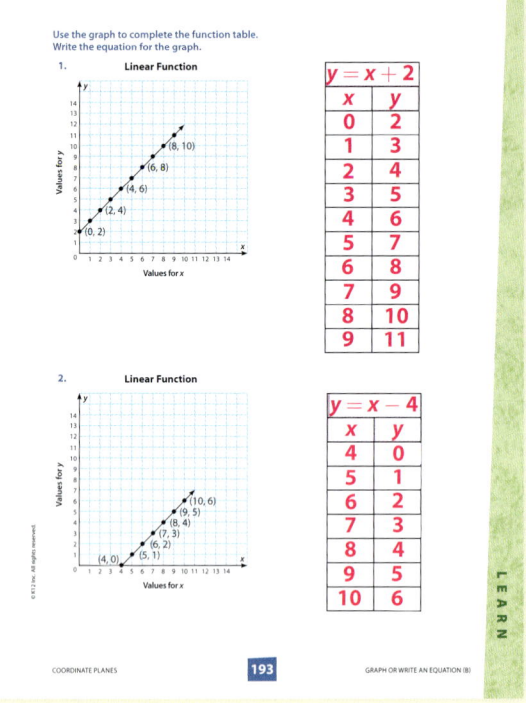

**432**  COORDINATE PLANES

# TRY IT Practice Function Tables and Graphs

**OFFLINE 15 min**

## Objectives

- Graph or write an equation to solve a problem that involves a linear function.

Students will practice finding the graph that matches an equation and writing the equation that matches a graph. Have students turn to the Practice Function Tables and Graphs activity page in their Activity Book and read the directions with them.

Students should copy the problems from the Activity Book into their Math Notebook as necessary and solve them there.

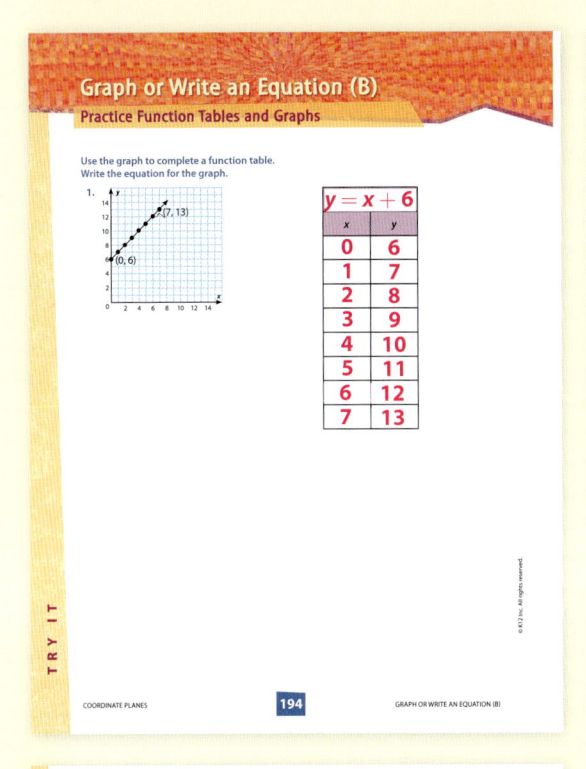

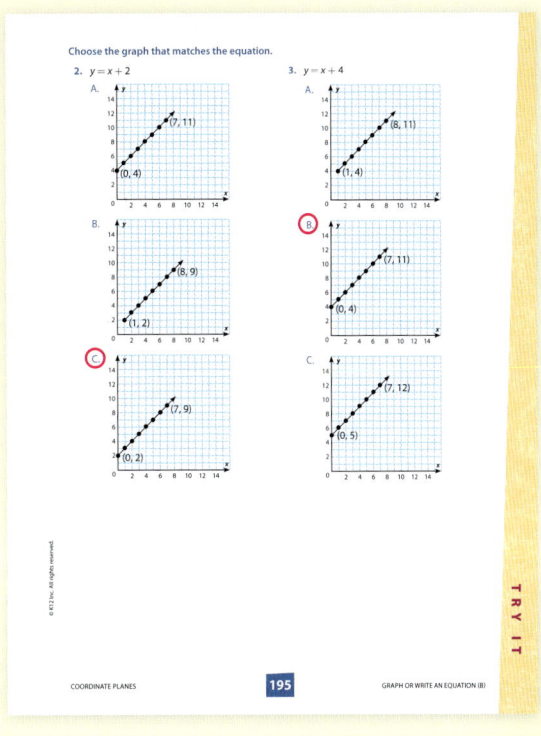

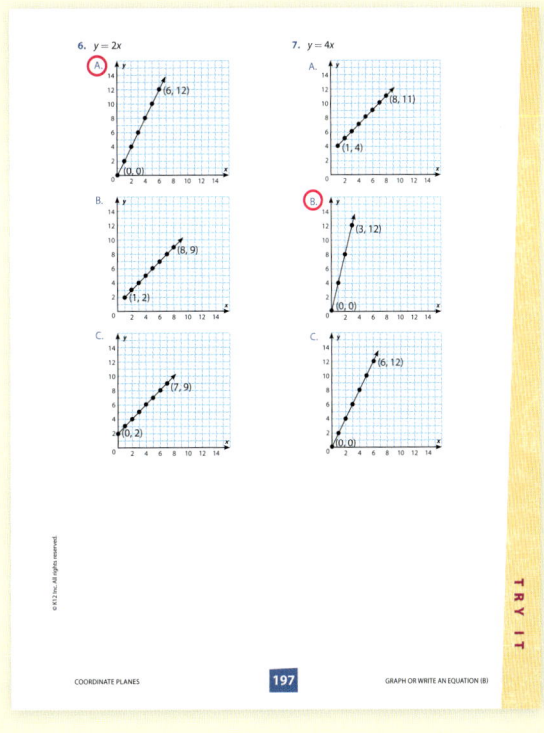

GRAPH OR WRITE AN EQUATION (B) 433

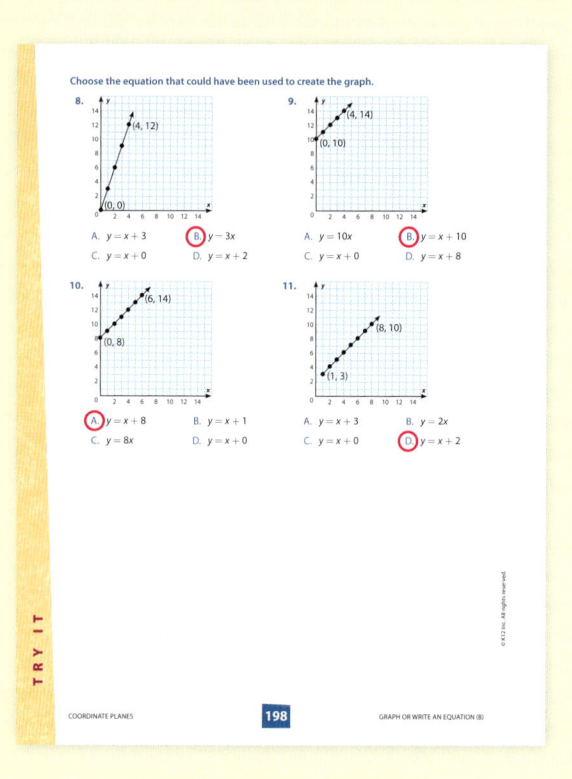

**Choose the equation that could have been used to create the graph.**

8.

A. $y = x + 3$    B. $y = 3x$ ✓
C. $y = x + 0$    D. $y = x + 2$

9.

A. $y = 10x$    B. $y = x + 10$ ✓
C. $y = x + 0$    D. $y = x + 8$

10.

A. $y = x + 8$ ✓    B. $y = x + 1$
C. $y = 8x$    D. $y = x + 0$

11.

A. $y = x + 3$    B. $y = 2x$
C. $y = x + 0$    D. $y = x + 2$ ✓

COORDINATE PLANES        GRAPH OR WRITE AN EQUATION (B)

**434 COORDINATE PLANES**

# Graph or Write an Equation (C)

## Lesson Overview

| | | |
|---|---|---|
| **LEARN** Graph Equations for Story Problems | 15 minutes | **ONLINE** |
| **LEARN** Graph Circumference Equations | 20 minutes | **ONLINE** |
| **LEARN** Graph Equations About Animals | 15 minutes | **OFFLINE** |
| **TRY IT** Practice with Graphs of Equations | 10 minutes | **OFFLINE** |

### ▶ Lesson Objectives
Graph or write an equation to solve a problem that involves a linear function.

### ▶ Prerequisite Skills
- Use an equation to represent a relationship between quantities.
- Use the situation presented in a problem to describe the meaning of each coordinate of an ordered pair displayed on a graph.
- Plot a linear relationship in the first quadrant of a coordinate plane.

### Materials to Gather

**SUPPLIED**
Graphing Equations (printout)
Graph Equations About Animals activity page
Practice with Graphs of Equations activity page

### ▶ Content Background
Students will continue to complete the *x*- and *y*-values of a function table and learn to write an equation based on a linear function.

An *equation* is a number sentence that shows that two quantities are equal. Equations can include numbers, variables, and operation signs (such as +, −, •, or ÷). Some examples of equations are $2r - 3 = 9$ and $16 = 12 + 4$.

A *linear function* is a relationship between two quantities in which one variable depends on another. One reason this type of function is called linear is that the graph of the equation has points that fall on a straight line. Most often, linear equations are written in the form of $y = mx + b$, where *x* and *y* are the two quantities. In that linear equation, the variable *m* stands for any number that is multiplied by *x*. When you multiply *m* by *x*, you have a linear function. The variable *b* stands for any number that is added to the expression *mx*. The equation $y = mx + b$ is a linear function. It's also the case that *b* can be a negative number, so that $y = mx - b$ is also a linear function.

### ▶ Advance Preparation
Print one copy of Graphing Equations.

## LEARN  Graph Equations for Story Problems
**ONLINE 15 min**

Students will create a function table, write an equation, and graph data for a linear function that represents a story problem. They will work with data about the rate of speed that shorebirds fly.

### Objectives
- Graph or write an equation to solve a problem that involves a linear function.

## LEARN  Graph Circumference Equations
**ONLINE 20 min**

Students will create a function table, write an equation, and graph data for a linear function that represents a story problem. They will work with data about the circumference of circles with different diameter lengths.

### Objectives
- Graph or write an equation to solve a problem that involves a linear function.

## LEARN  Graph Equations About Animals
**OFFLINE 15 min**

Students will create a function table, write an equation, and graph data for a linear function representing a story problem about animals. Gather the Graphing Equations printout. Have students turn to the Graph Equations About Animals activity page in their Activity Book and read the directions with them.

### Objectives
- Graph or write an equation to solve a problem that involves a linear function.

1. Have students read the Worked Example.

   **Say:** The value of variable $r$ depends on variable $m$ in this problem because to find the number of meters the tortoise walked, represented by $r$, you multiply the minutes, represented by $m$, by 5. Also remember that other letters could have been used for the variables. When you find an equation to solve a story problem, you can choose the variables you want to use.

2. Ask students to explain the graph in the answer. Their explanation should include the axes, the graphed points, and the equation used to determine the points. **Sample answer:** The $m$-axis is labeled "Minutes" because it shows each minute the tortoise walked. The $r$-axis is labeled "Distance walked (meters)" because it shows the number of meters the tortoise walked. The point (1, 5) means that the tortoise walked 1 minute and went 5 meters. The point (2, 10) means it walked 2 minutes and went 10 meters, the point (3, 15) means it walked 3 minutes and went 15 meters, and so on. The equation in the function table, $r = 5m$, was used to find the ordered pairs. The problem asked about 2, 3, 4, and 5 minutes. Those numbers were substituted for the variable $m$ in the equation.

3. Discuss with students how they could use the graph to figure out how many meters the tortoise would walk in $2\frac{1}{2}$ minutes. On the $m$-axis, locate $2\frac{1}{2}$ halfway between 2 and 3. Then move up to the graphed line. On the graphed line, the $r$-axis shows that you are at $12\frac{1}{2}$ meters. The tortoise would walk $12\frac{1}{2}$ meters in $2\frac{1}{2}$ minutes.

4. Point out to students that they are using a different interval on the $r$-axis than they are using on the $m$-axis but that the data can still be accurately graphed.

5. Have students complete Problem 1 in the problem set. Give them the Graphing Equations printout and have them create a function table and plot the data on the graph. Have students refer to the Worked Examples for assistance and help them as needed.

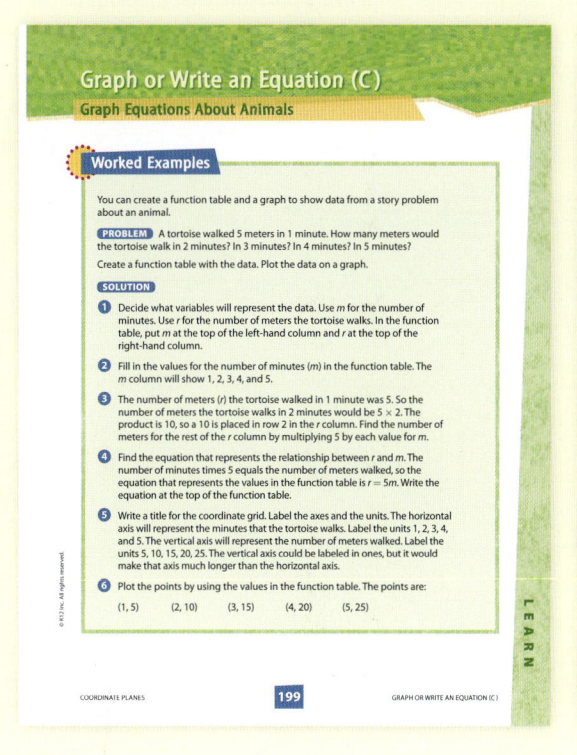

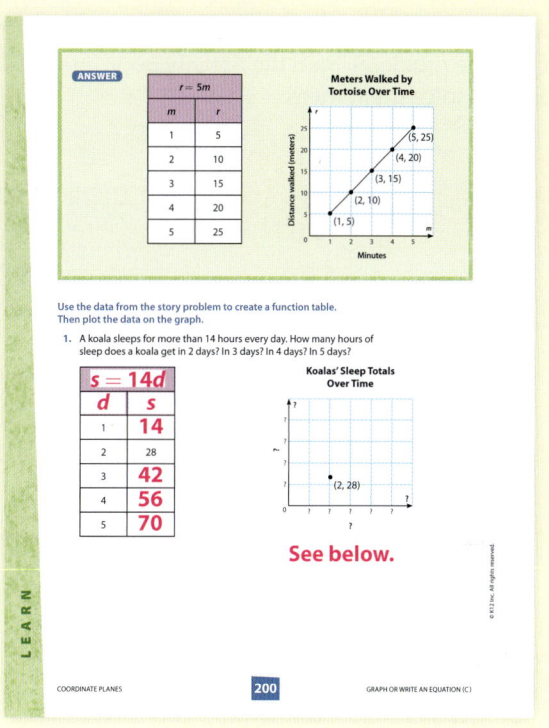

## Additional Answers

1.

**Koalas' Sleep Totals Over Time**

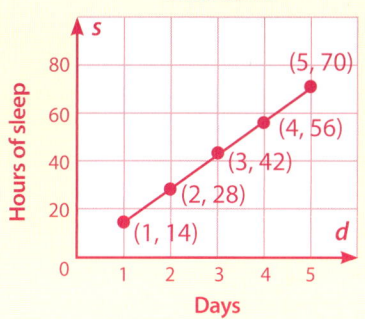

Days = 1 and Hours of Sleep = 14
Days = 2 and Hours of Sleep = 28
Days = 3 and Hours of Sleep = 42
Days = 4 and Hours of Sleep = 56
Days = 5 and Hours of Sleep = 70

**GRAPH OR WRITE AN EQUATION (C)** 437

## TRY IT Practice with Graphs of Equations

**OFFLINE 10 min**

### Objectives
- Graph or write an equation to solve a problem that involves a linear function.

Students will choose the graph or equation that matches the given story problem. Have students turn to the Practice with Graphs of Equations activity page in their Activity Book and read the directions with them.

Students should copy the problems from the Activity Book into their Math Notebook as necessary and solve them there.

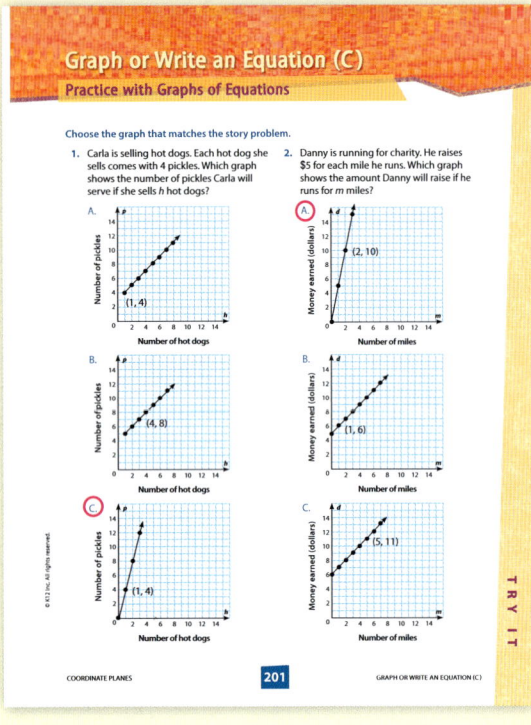

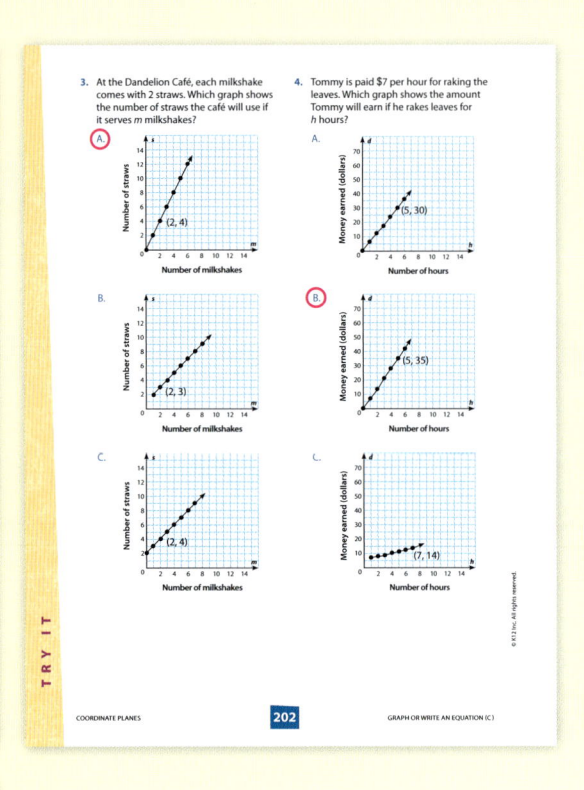

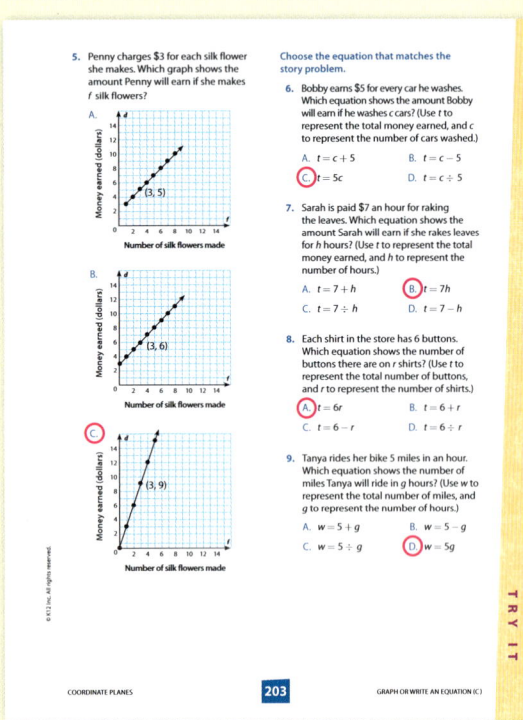

438  COORDINATE PLANES

# Graph or Write an Equation (D)

## Lesson Overview

| | | |
|---|---|---|
| **LEARN** Graph Equations About a DVD Club | 10 minutes | **ONLINE** |
| **LEARN** Graph Equations About Plants | 15 minutes | **ONLINE** |
| **LEARN** Graph Equations About Purchases | 15 minutes | **OFFLINE** |
| **TRY IT** Graph Two-Step Equations | 10 minutes | **OFFLINE** |
| **CHECKPOINT** | 10 minutes | **ONLINE** |

### ▶ Lesson Objectives
Graph or write an equation to solve a problem that involves a linear function.

### ▶ Prerequisite Skills
- Use an equation to represent a relationship between quantities.
- Use the situation presented in a problem to describe the meaning of each coordinate of an ordered pair displayed on a graph.
- Plot a linear relationship in the first quadrant of a coordinate plane.

### ▶ Content Background
Students will continue to complete the *x*- and *y*-values of a function table and learn to write an equation based on a linear function.

An *equation* is a number sentence that shows that two quantities are equal. Equations can include numbers, variables, and operation signs (such as $+$, $-$, $\cdot$, or $\div$). Some examples of equations are $2r - 3 = 9$ and $16 = 12 + 4$.

A *linear function* is a relationship between two quantities in which one variable depends on another. One reason this type of function is called linear is that the graph of the equation has points that fall on a straight line. Most often, linear equations are written in the form of $y = mx + b$, where *x* and *y* are the two quantities. In that linear equation, the variable *m* stands for any number that is multiplied by *x*. When you multiply *m* by *x*, you have a linear function. The variable *b* stands for any number that is added to the expression *mx*. The equation $y = mx + b$ is a linear function. It's also the case that *b* can be a negative number, so that $y = mx - b$ is also a linear function.

### ▶ Advance Preparation
Print one copy of Graphing Equations.

### Materials to Gather

**SUPPLIED**
Graphing Equations (printout)
Graph Equations About Purchases activity page
Graph Two-Step Equations activity page

### LEARN Graph Equations About a DVD Club

**ONLINE 10 min**

Students will create a function table, write a two-step equation, and graph data for a linear function that represents a story problem. They will work with data about the costs of renting DVDs.

**Objectives**
- Graph or write an equation to solve a problem that involves a linear function.

**Tips** Allow some students to use the variables *x* and *y* in the function table, equation, and graph, if they wish. Tell them they can choose any variables they want to represent unknown values in a story problem, but they should decide which variables to use as they begin to solve the problem and use those same variables as they complete all the steps to solve the problem.

### LEARN Graph Equations About Plants

**ONLINE 15 min**

Students will create a function table, write a two-step equation, and graph data for a linear function that represents a story problem. They will work with data about the growth of bamboo plants.

**Objectives**
- Graph or write an equation to solve a problem that involves a linear function.

### LEARN Graph Equations About Purchases

**OFFLINE 15 min**

Students will create a function table, write a two-step equation, and graph data from a story problem. Gather a copy of the Graphing Equations printout. Have students turn to the Graph Equations About Purchases activity page in their Activity Book and read the directions with them.

**Objectives**
- Graph or write an equation to solve a problem that involves a linear function.

1. Read the Worked Example with students.

   **Ask:** How would you know by reading the problem that you would use multiplication and addition in the equation? **Sample answer:** The problem says "4 bags of vegetables for $2.50 each," which means I need to multiply 4 by 2.5. It says Daniella bought 1 loaf of bread for $2.00. That means I need to add 2 to the product of 4 times 2.5.

2. Tell students that because multiplication and addition are used, there are two steps needed to solve this equation. The function table shows solutions after both steps have been completed.

3. Have students read Problem 1 about the lemonade stand. Give them the Graphing Equations printout.

4. Have students choose variables they will use. They should choose variables for the number of jumbo cups sold and the amount of the profit. They should put the variables at the top of the columns in the function table, with the jumbo cups variable on the left and the profit variable on the right.

   **Note:** The remaining steps in this activity will refer to *j* for the left-hand column and *p* for the right-hand column.

   **Ask:** Which variable depends on the other variable. Why? The variable *p* depends on *j* because the amount of profit depends on the number of jumbo cups of lemonade sold.

COORDINATE PLANES

5. Work with students as they develop the equation. Ask them which two operations the equation will have. It will have multiplication to find the amount of money Ralph earns selling jumbo cups of lemonade and subtraction to find the profit after the $9 cost of setting up the lemonade stand.

   After students come up with the equation, have them write it at the top of the function table: $p = 1.50j - 9$.

6. Have students use the equation and function table to find the profit after selling 7, 8, 9, 10, and 11 jumbo cups of lemonade.

   **Ask:** How much profit did Ralph make when he sold 11 jumbo cups of lemonade? $7.50

7. Discuss with students what they think the profit will be when Ralph sells 14 jumbo cups of lemonade. Have them use the equation and function table to check their prediction. $12

8. Have students complete the function table on the Graphing Equations printout by putting *j*-values in each row they haven't yet completed and solving for *p*-values.

9. Have students use the ordered pairs to plot points on the coordinate grid. Tell them that the broken line between 0 and 7 on the *j*-axis indicates that data are not shown for 1 through 6 cups. They should show the same broken line on the graph they are making.

   **Say:** In other activities, the *x*-axis has been labeled with an *x*. The axes are labeled for the variables in this problem. The horizontal axis is labeled with a *j*, rather than an *x*. The vertical axis is labeled with a *p*, rather than a *y*.

   - Have students label the *j*-axis from 0 to 16 with an interval of 1 and the *p*-axis from 0 to 20 with an interval of 2.
   - Remind students that because the numbers on the *p*-axis are in intervals of 2, the points they plot on the graph will fall between the *p*-values.

10. Ask students if it would make sense to draw a line through the points they graphed. Lead students to conclude that it wouldn't make sense to talk about the data between the points they graphed. In this problem, Ralph is unlikely to sell a part of a jumbo cup of lemonade and charge only part of $1.50 for the drink.

11. After they complete the problem, ask students the following questions about the data in the function table and the graph:

    **Ask:** How many jumbo cups of lemonade does Ralph need to sell to make at least $10 in profit? 13

    **Ask:** Why is there no profit until Ralph sells 7 jumbo cups of lemonade? The cost of supplies is $9. Until Ralph earns more than $9 selling lemonade, he will not make any profit. There is no profit after Ralph sells 1 through 5 jumbo cups of lemonade. After Ralph sells 6 jumbo cups of lemonade, he has earned $9.00. There is still no profit. After Ralph sells 7 cups, he has earned $10.50. The profit at this point is $1.50.

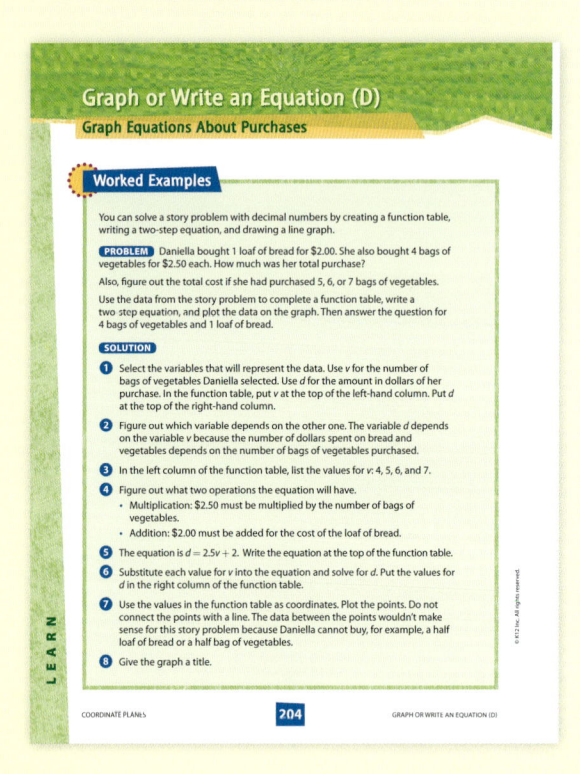

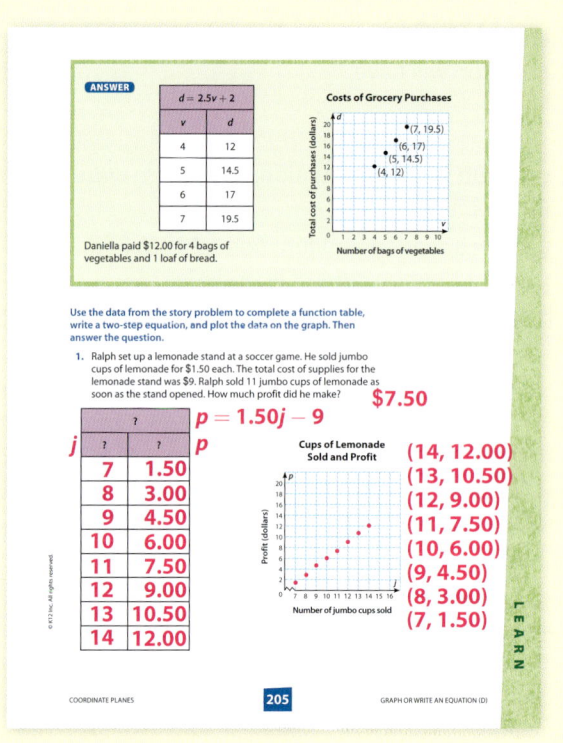

## TRY IT  Graph Two-Step Equations

**OFFLINE 10 min**

### Objectives
- Graph or write an equation to solve a problem that involves a linear function.

Students will choose the graph or equation that matches the given story problem that is solved with a two-step equation. Have students turn to the Graph Two-Step Equations activity page in their Activity Book and read the directions with them.

Students should copy the problems from the Activity Book into their Math Notebook as necessary and solve them there.

**442  COORDINATE PLANES**

# Graph or Write an Equation (D)
## Graph Two-Step Equations

**Choose the graph that matches the story problem.**

1. Annie is saving money. Her dad said that whatever she saves, he will give her $5 more. Which graph shows the amount Annie will have if she saves *v* dollars?

   A. (5, 10) ✓
   B. (5, 11)
   C. (5, 9)

2. Gerald is saving money. His mom said that whatever he saves, she will give him $10 more. Which graph shows the amount Gerald will have if he saves *d* dollars?

   A. (3, 11)
   B. (3, 12)
   C. (3, 13) ✓

3. Taz is running for charity. He gets $1 for each mile he runs, and a fixed amount of $12. Which graph shows how much Taz will raise if he runs for *p* miles?

   A. (1, 13) ✓
   B. (1, 11)
   C. (1, 12)

4. Raquel is collecting magazines to recycle. She gets $1 per pound and another $7 for taking the whole amount to the recycling facility. Which graph shows how many dollars Raquel will earn if she drops off *k* pounds of magazines?

   A. (5, 35)
   B. (7, 14) ✓
   C. (7, 13)

**Choose the equation that solves the problem.**

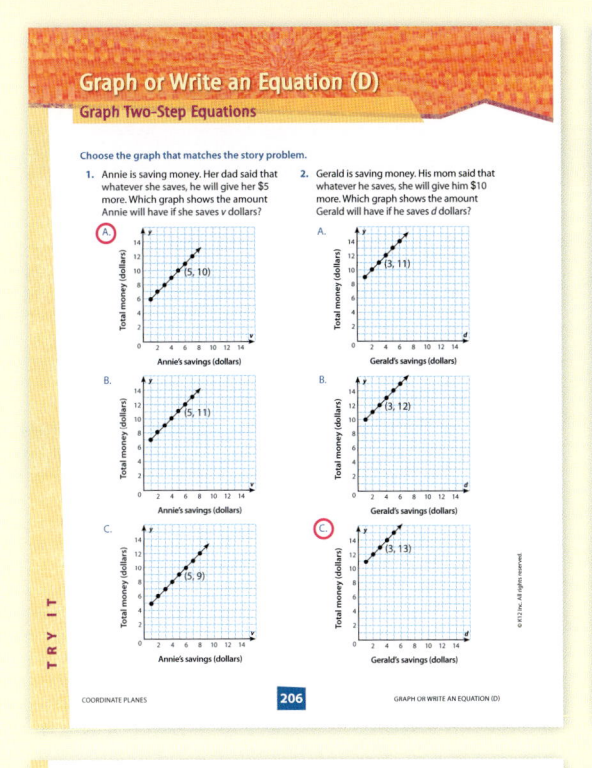

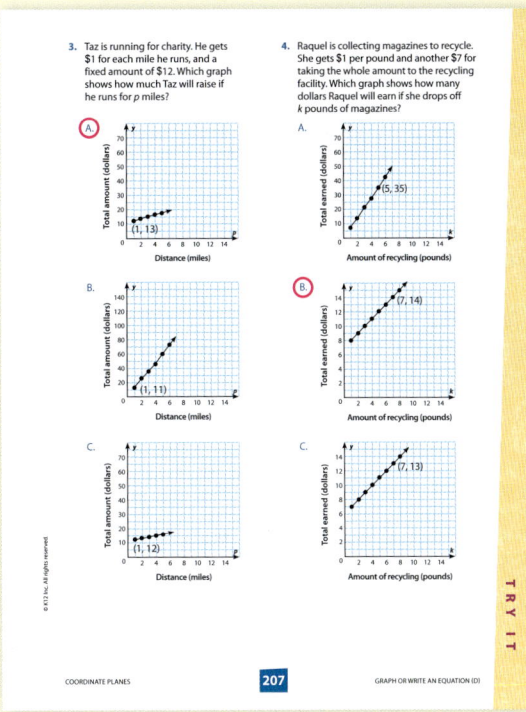

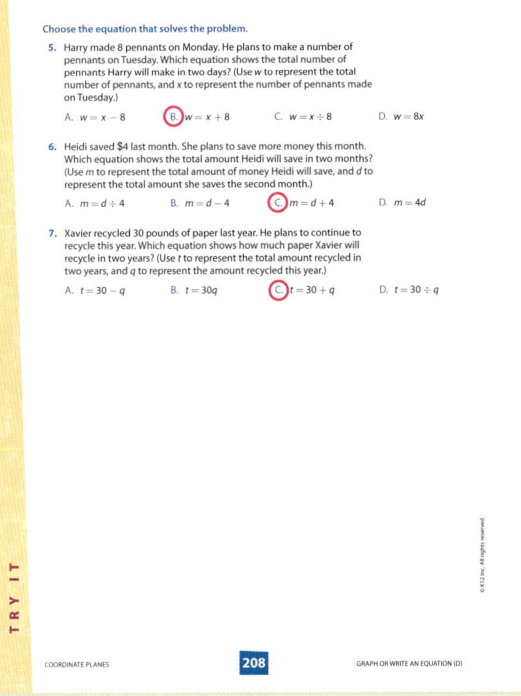

5. Harry made 8 pennants on Monday. He plans to make a number of pennants on Tuesday. Which equation shows the total number of pennants Harry will make in two days? (Use *w* to represent the total number of pennants, and *x* to represent the number of pennants made on Tuesday.)

   A. $w = x - 8$   B. $w = x + 8$ ✓   C. $w = x \div 8$   D. $w = 8x$

6. Heidi saved $4 last month. She plans to save more money this month. Which equation shows the total amount Heidi will save in two months? (Use *m* to represent the total amount of money Heidi will save, and *d* to represent the total amount she saves the second month.)

   A. $m = d \div 4$   B. $m = d - 4$   C. $m = d + 4$ ✓   D. $m = 4d$

7. Xavier recycled 30 pounds of paper last year. He plans to continue to recycle this year. Which equation shows how much paper Xavier will recycle in two years? (Use *t* to represent the total amount recycled in two years, and *q* to represent the amount recycled this year.)

   A. $t = 30 - q$   B. $t = 30q$   C. $t = 30 + q$ ✓   D. $t = 30 \div q$

# CHECKPOINT

**ONLINE 10 min**

Students will complete an online Checkpoint. If necessary, read the directions, problems, and answer choices to students and help them with keyboard or mouse operations.

## Objectives

- Graph or write an equation to solve a problem that involves a linear function.

# Unit Review

## Lesson Overview

| UNIT REVIEW Look Back | 10 minutes | ONLINE |
| UNIT REVIEW Checkpoint Practice | 50 minutes | ONLINE |
| ▶ UNIT REVIEW Prepare for the Checkpoint | | |

### ▶ Unit Objectives

This lesson reviews the following objectives:
- Identify and graph ordered pairs in all quadrants of a coordinate plane.
- Use the situation presented in a problem to describe the meaning of each coordinate of an ordered pair displayed on a graph.
- Graph or write an equation to solve a problem that involves a linear function.

**Materials to Gather**

There are no materials to gather for this lesson.

### ▶ Advance Preparation

In this lesson, students will have an opportunity to review previous activities in the Coordinate Planes unit. Look at the suggested activities in Unit Review: Prepare for the Checkpoint online and gather any needed materials.

## UNIT REVIEW Look Back

ONLINE 10 min

**Objectives**
- Review unit objectives.

Students will review key concepts from the unit to prepare for the Unit Checkpoint.

## UNIT REVIEW Checkpoint Practice

ONLINE 50 min

**Objectives**
- Review unit objectives.

Students will complete an online Checkpoint Practice to prepare for the Unit Checkpoint. If necessary, read the directions, problems, and answer choices to students. Have students answer the problems on their own. Review any missed problems with students.

## ▶ UNIT REVIEW Prepare for the Checkpoint

What you do next depends on how students performed in the previous activity, Unit Review: Checkpoint Practice. If students had difficulty with any of the problems, complete the appropriate review activity listed in the table online.

# Unit Checkpoint

## Lesson Overview

**UNIT CHECKPOINT** Online — 60 minutes — **ONLINE**

### ▶ Unit Objectives

This lesson assesses the following objectives:

- Identify and graph ordered pairs in all quadrants of a coordinate plane.
- Use the situation presented in a problem to describe the meaning of each coordinate of an ordered pair displayed on a graph.
- Graph or write an equation to solve a problem that involves a linear function.

### Materials to Gather

There are no materials to gather for this lesson.

### UNIT CHECKPOINT Online

ONLINE 60 min

Students will complete the Unit Checkpoint online. If necessary, read the directions, problems, and answer choices to students and help them with keyboard or mouse operations.

### Objectives

- Assess unit objectives.

# Perimeter, Area, and Volume

## ▶ Unit Objectives

- Determine the perimeter of a plane figure and use appropriate units.
- Derive and use the formula for the area of a parallelogram and use appropriate units.
- Derive and use the formula for the area of a triangle and use appropriate units.
- Construct a cube or a rectangular box from a two-dimensional pattern and determine the surface area.
- Use squares to approximate the area of an irregular shape.
- Explain and determine the volume of a solid figure and use appropriate units.
- Differentiate among appropriate units to measure perimeter, area, and volume.

## ▶ Big Ideas

- The perimeter of any polygon is the sum of the lengths of its sides.
- Area is a measure of how much material is needed to cover a plane figure.
- Volume is a measure of the amount of space a solid figure occupies.
- Measurement is the process of repeatedly using a unit over a quantity to determine how much you have.

## ▶ Unit Introduction

The focus of this unit is exploring perimeter and area of two-dimensional shapes and surface area and volume of three-dimensional figures. Students first will find perimeter of regular and irregular plane figures. They will use their prior knowledge of finding the area of a square or rectangle as a reference for finding the area of a parallelogram or triangle. They will see how the formulas for finding the areas of parallelograms and triangles are developed, or derived. After exploring area of two-dimensional objects, students will construct a three-dimensional figure using a pattern and find the surface area of that object. They will extend their understanding of finding the area of regular shapes to use a square to find the approximate area of an irregular two-dimensional shape. Once students have a foundation in area and surface area, they will explain the meaning of the volume of solid figures and compute the volume. To conclude the unit, students will compare and contrast the different units used to measure perimeter, area, and volume to better understand linear, square, and cubic measurements with respect to dimensions.

## ▶ Keywords

| | | |
|---|---|---|
| area | irregular shape | surface area |
| base of a figure | linear unit | two-dimensional pattern |
| cubic unit | net | unit |
| formula | perimeter | volume |
| height | square unit | |

# Find the Perimeter of Plane Figures

## Lesson Overview

| | | |
|---|---|---|
| **GET READY** Rectangle and Square Perimeters | 5 minutes | **OFFLINE** |
| **LEARN** Rectangles with the Same Perimeter | 10 minutes | **OFFLINE** |
| **LEARN** Perimeter of Plane Figures | 15 minutes | **OFFLINE** |
| **LEARN** Perimeter of Everyday Objects | 10 minutes | **OFFLINE** |
| **TRY IT** Practice Finding Perimeter | 10 minutes | **ONLINE** |
| **CHECKPOINT** | 10 minutes | **ONLINE** |

### ▶ Lesson Objectives
Determine the perimeter of a plane figure and use appropriate units.

### ▶ Prerequisite Skills
- Define and demonstrate understanding of the perimeter of any polygon.
- Use a formula to find the perimeter of a rectangle or a square.

### ▶ Content Background
Students will find the perimeter of plane figures and use appropriate units of measure.

*Perimeter* is the distance around a geometric figure or an everyday object. Perimeter is a linear measurement since it measures length, so the units used to measure perimeter have an understood exponent of 1. That is, the units for perimeter measures are written without the exponent. For example, you might see perimeter measured in centimeters (cm), meters (m), kilometers (km), inches (in.), feet (ft), yards (yd), or miles (mi).

### ▶ Advance Preparation
For the Get Ready: Rectangle and Square Perimeters activity, print one copy of the Rectangle and Square Perimeters printout.
For the Learn: Rectangles with the Same Perimeter activity,
- Print one copy of the Centimeter Grid Paper.
- Gather a string such as yarn, kite string, or lightweight cord. Measure 36 centimeters (see Hints), form a loop with that length, and tie a knot to make a loop of 36 centimeters in circumference.

  **Hints:** Use string or cord that will stretch very little and that has been kept on a roll or in a ball so it will lie flat on paper. When you measure 36 centimeters, add a few centimeters to allow for the knot. Leave a short length of yarn beyond the loop and the knot. On the Centimeter Grid Paper, form and hold the loop in a 9 cm by 9 cm shape to make sure the loop will measure the perimeter of a 36-centimeter rectangle. Cut the loop from the roll of string.

### Materials to Gather

**SUPPLIED**

Rectangle and Square Perimeters (printout)
Centimeter Grid Paper (printout)
Perimeter of Plane Figures activity page

**ALSO NEEDED**

string
ruler, dual-scale
paper, 8.5 in. by 11 in.
index card, 3 in. by 5 in.
paper, drawing
scissors, adult

For the Learn: Perimeter of Everyday Objects activity, use a ruler and a pencil to draw a 3-inch square on drawing paper and cut it out.

▶ **Safety**
Make sure students do not place the loop of string around their neck.

## GET READY  Rectangle and Square Perimeters

**OFFLINE 5 min**

### Objectives
- Define and demonstrate understanding of the perimeter of any polygon.
- Use a formula to find the perimeter of a rectangle or a square.

Students will use the correct formula to find the perimeter of a rectangle and a square.
Gather the Rectangle and Square Perimeters printout.

1. Point to the rectangle at the top of the page. Ask students to describe how to measure the perimeter of a rectangle. Add the measurements of the 4 sides.
2. Have students add the side measurements to find the perimeter. $8 + 5 + 8 + 5 = 26$; The perimeter is 26 cm.
3. Ask students if the measurement is in linear or square units. linear
4. Tell students to use the formula $P = 2l + 2w$ to calculate the perimeter of the rectangle. 26 cm

   Have students compare the results of the two methods of finding the perimeter. Guide them to see that both ways led them to find the correct perimeter. Tell them that they may find that using a perimeter formula will be quicker when they need to find the perimeter of a figure with many sides.
5. Repeat Steps 1 and 2 to find the perimeter of the square. $6 + 6 + 6 + 6 = 24$; The perimeter is 24 cm.
6. Repeat Steps 3 and 4 using the formula $P = 4s$ to find the perimeter of the square. 24 cm

## LEARN  Rectangles with the Same Perimeter

**OFFLINE 10 min**

### Objectives
- Determine the perimeter of a plane figure and use appropriate units.

Students will use a loop of string to form rectangles with different lengths and widths on grid paper to show that many different rectangles can have the same perimeter.
Gather the Centimeter Grid Paper and the loop of string you made.

1. Tell students that they are going to make different rectangles with perimeters of 36 centimeters and record the rectangles' measurements in a table.
2. Have students make a table in their Math Notebook with 6 rows and 4 columns. The top row is for the column headings. Have them write the column headings as follows: "Shape name," "Length of 1 side," "Width of 1 side," and "Perimeter."

### Tips

If students have difficulty with the string moving before they find the perimeter of the rectangle, help them use a pencil to trace along the string. They can then remove the string to find the perimeter of the rectangle.

PERIMETER, AREA, AND VOLUME

3. Under "Shape name" for each row, have them write "rectangle." Under "Perimeter" for each row, have them write "36 cm."

| Rectangles with Perimeter of 36 cm | | | |
| --- | --- | --- | --- |
| Shape name | Length of 1 side | Width of 1 side | Perimeter |
| rectangle | | | 36 cm |
| rectangle | | | 36 cm |
| rectangle | | | 36 cm |
| rectangle | | | 36 cm |
| rectangle | | | 36 cm |

4. Show students how to lay the loop of string on the grid paper so that it forms a rectangle with a length of 12 centimeters and a width of 6 centimeters. Show them how to use their thumbs to hold the bottom 2 corners in place and their fingers to hold the top 2 corners in place.

5. Have students count the outer edges of the squares (the perimeter) on the grid paper to check that the rectangle has a perimeter of 36 centimeters. You may need to help them count as they hold the string, or you can hold the string while they count the squares. Note that as they count in the corners, they are not counting number of squares but number of outer edges of squares that make up the perimeter. So each square in a corner has 2 edges that are counted.

6. Guide students to complete their table for that row. The row of the table should have this information: rectangle, 12 cm, 6 cm, 36 cm.

7. Tell students that they can find many more rectangles with a perimeter of 36 centimeters. Help them make at least 4 more rectangles. Remind them to record their findings in their table. They may add more rows to the table if needed.

8. Guide students to include one rectangle that has dimensions of 9 centimeters per side.

9. After students have found 5 rectangles, have them use the information they recorded in their table to answer the following questions:

   **Ask:** Describe the dimensions of two of the different rectangles. How were the rectangles alike? How were they different? **Sample answer:** One rectangle had a length of 14 centimeters and a width of 4 centimeters, so the length was greater than the width. The other rectangle had a length of 7 centimeters and a width of 11 centimeters, so the width was greater than the length.

   **Ask:** If you were to make another rectangle with the same dimensions as one of the rectangles you made, but oriented differently on the paper, would the perimeter still be the same? Why? The way a shape is oriented does not change its dimensions, so the perimeter would still be the same.

   **Ask:** What special kind of rectangle did you make that had a perimeter of 36 centimeters? What were its dimensions? One rectangle was a square. Each side was 9 centimeters long.

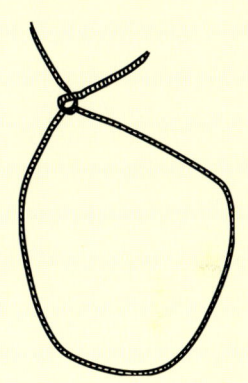

FIND THE PERIMETER OF PLANE FIGURES 451

## LEARN Perimeter of Plane Figures

**OFFLINE 15 min**

### Objectives
- Determine the perimeter of a plane figure and use appropriate units.

### Tips
Extend the activity by having students write and solve a word problem about measuring and finding the perimeter of an everyday object or in an everyday setting.

Students will use two methods to find perimeter. They will find the perimeter of regular and irregular plane figures. Have students turn to the Perimeter of Plane Figures activity page in their Activity Book and read the directions with them.

Students should copy the problems from the Activity Book into their Math Notebook as necessary and solve them there.

1. Tell students that they will find the perimeter of plane figures in these two ways: adding the measures of the sides and using a formula.
2. Tell students that both methods are reasonable ways to find the perimeter of a plane figure. Using the formula may simplify the process, but adding the side lengths might be easier for some figures.
3. Read the Worked Examples box with students.

   **Say:** The tick marks on the octagon mean that all 8 sides have the same length. When tick marks on a plane figure match each other, then the sides marked by those ticks have the same length.

   **Say:** Because all sides are the same length, you were able to solve this problem with the formula $P = 8s$.

4. Have students focus on the equations in Solution 1 and Solution 2.

   **Ask:** What operation was used in Solution 1 and what was the answer? addition; 16

   **Ask:** What operation was used in Solution 2 and what was the answer? multiplication; 16

5. Have students look at Problem 1 in the problem set.

   **Ask:** What formula can you use to find the perimeter of the hexagon? Use the variables $P$ and $s$ and tell what the variables mean. The formula for finding the perimeter of a hexagon is $P = 6s$, where the variable $s$ stands for the length of a side of the hexagon. The variable $P$ stands for the perimeter.

6. Have students solve the problem. They should substitute 12 for $s$ in the perimeter formula to find a perimeter of 72 cm. Be sure students write the formulas, steps they used, and answers in their Math Notebook.

7. Repeat Steps 5 and 6 for Problem 2.

8. Tell students that they can write a formula to find the perimeter of any plane figure. Explain that a formula can even be written for irregular shapes like the ones in Problems 3 and 4.

   **Say:** In Problem 3, the sides of the pentagon are not all the same length. The base has one length. The vertical sides have a different length from the base. The slanted sides have a different length from the base and the vertical sides. The vertical sides are marked with a single tick mark to show that their lengths are the same. The slanted sides are marked with double tick marks to show that their lengths are the same but are a different length from the vertical sides.

9. Guide students to see that a formula can be written to find the perimeter of the pentagon. Have them substitute the measurements into the formula and solve.

PERIMETER, AREA, AND VOLUME

10. Have students read Problem 4.

    **Ask:** How many different lengths do you see for the sides of this shape?
    5 different lengths

    Guide students to use 5 different variables for the lengths as they write the formula. Have them substitute values for the variables and solve the problem.

11. Have students look at Problem 5 in the problem set.

    **Ask:** What formula can you use to find the perimeter of the square? Use the variables *P* and *s* and tell what the variables mean. The formula for finding the perimeter of a square is $P = 4s$, where the variable *s* stands for the length of a side of the square. The variable *P* stands for the perimeter.

12. Have students solve the problem. They should substitute 9.4 for *s* in the perimeter formula to find a perimeter of 37.6 cm. Be sure students write the formulas, steps they used, and answers in their Math Notebook.

13. Repeat Steps 11 and 12 for Problem 6. Students will find the perimeter of a rectangle and use the formula $P = 2a + 2b$.

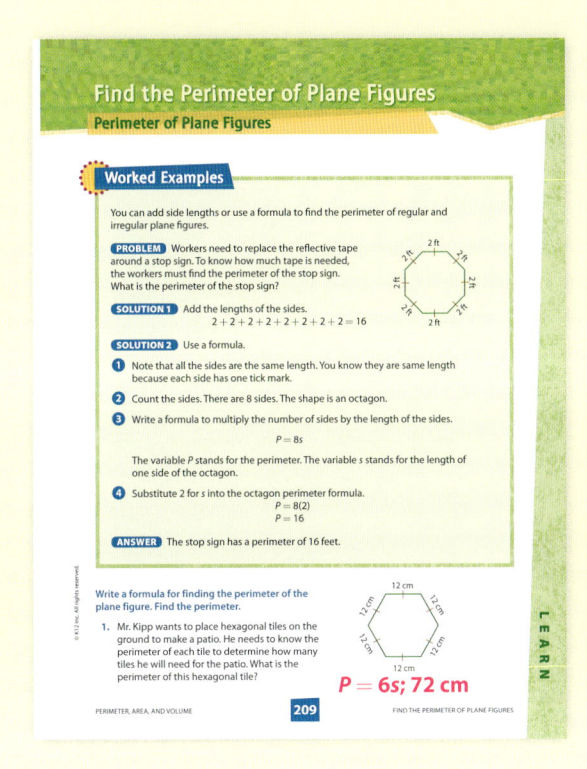

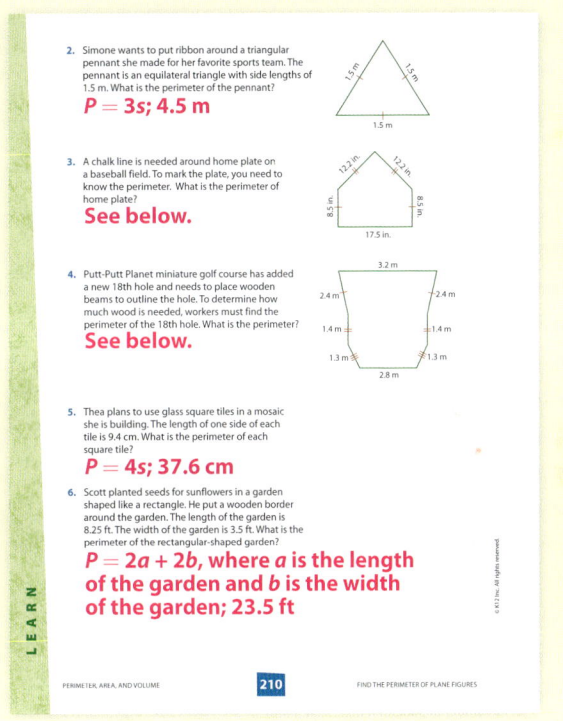

### Additional Answers

**3.** $P = a + 2b + 2c$, where *a* is the length of the base, *b* is the length of the vertical sides, and *c* is the length of the slanted sides; 58.9 in.

**4.** $P = a + 2b + 2c + 2d + e$, where *a* is the length of the top of the figure; *b*, *c*, and *d* are the lengths of the pairs of equal sides of the figure; and *e* is the length of the base of the figure; 16.2 m

**FIND THE PERIMETER OF PLANE FIGURES** 453

## LEARN  Perimeter of Everyday Objects

**OFFLINE 10 min**

### Objectives
- Determine the perimeter of a plane figure and use appropriate units.

Students will measure and find the perimeter of three everyday objects. Gather the ruler, index card, sheet of paper, and 3-inch square of paper. Don't tell students the measurements of any of the objects.

1. Tell students that they are going to measure and find the perimeter of an index card, a sheet of paper, and the piece of square paper you cut out. Explain to students that they will record their findings in a table.

2. Have students make a table in their Math Notebook with 4 rows and 4 columns. The top row is for the column headings. Have them write the column headings as follows: "Object name," "Length of 1 side," "Width of 1 side," and "Perimeter." Under "Object name" for each row, have them write the name of each of the three objects.

**Measures and Perimeters of Objects**

| Object name | Length of 1 side | Width of 1 side | Perimeter |
|---|---|---|---|
| index card | | | |
| sheet of paper | | | |
| square paper | | | |

3. Give students the index card. Have them use the ruler to measure its length and record the measurement in inches on their table. Remind students to include the unit of measure. 5 in.

    Have students measure the width and record the measurement on their table. 3 in.

4. Have students add all 4 side measurements to find the perimeter of the index card. 16 in.

    **Ask:** What shape is the index card? rectangle

    **Ask:** What is the formula for finding the perimeter of a rectangle? $P = 2l + 2w$

5. Have students find the perimeter of the index card again, this time using the formula. Talk about whether students found the same perimeter each time.

6. Have students place the index card to the side and pick up the square of paper.

7. Have students use the ruler to measure the length and width of the square of paper and record the measurements in inches on their table. length of 1 side is 3 in.; width of 1 side is 3 in.

    Have students add all 4 side measurements to find the perimeter of the square of paper. 12 in.

    **Ask:** What is the formula for finding the perimeter of a square? $P = 4s$

8. Have students use the formula to find the perimeter of the square of paper. Discuss whether students found the same perimeter each time.

9. Have students place the square of paper to the side and pick up the full sheet of paper.

**454  PERIMETER, AREA, AND VOLUME**

10. Have students use the ruler to measure the sheet of paper and record the measurements on their table. Length of 1 side is 11 in.; width of 1 side is 8.5 in.

    Have students add the measurements together to find the perimeter of the sheet of paper. 39 in.

11. Tell students to substitute the measurements into the rectangle perimeter formula $P = 2l + 2w$ and solve.

    **Ask:** Why does the formula for finding a rectangle's perimeter work, such as when you used it to find the perimeter of the index card and the sheet of paper? The formula $P = 2l + 2w$ works because the perimeter is the total distance around the rectangle. Since there are 2 sides that are $l$ units long and 2 sides that are $w$ units long, I add the lengths of the sides to find the perimeter of the rectangle.

## TRY IT  Practice Finding Perimeter

ONLINE 10 min

**Objectives**

- Determine the perimeter of a plane figure and use appropriate units.

Students will complete an online Try It. If necessary, read the directions, problems, and answer choices to students and help them with keyboard or mouse operations.

## CHECKPOINT

ONLINE 10 min

**Objectives**

- Determine the perimeter of a plane figure and use appropriate units.

Students will complete an online Checkpoint. If necessary, read the directions, problems, and answer choices to students and help them with keyboard or mouse operations.

# Area of Parallelograms (A)

## Lesson Overview

| | | |
|---|---|---|
| **GET READY** Area of Rectangles | 10 minutes | ONLINE |
| **LEARN** Base and Height Formula for Area | 10 minutes | ONLINE |
| **LEARN** Connect Parallelograms and Rectangles | 15 minutes | ONLINE |
| **LEARN** Make Shapes with the Same Area | 15 minutes | ONLINE |
| **TRY IT** Practice Finding Parallelogram Area | 10 minutes | OFFLINE |

### ▶ Lesson Objectives
Derive and use the formula for the area of a parallelogram and use appropriate units.

### ▶ Prerequisite Skills
Use a formula to find the area of a rectangle, a square, or a figure that can be divided into rectangles or squares.

### ▶ Content Background
Students will learn to calculate the area of a parallelogram by transforming the parallelogram into a rectangle and finding the area of a rectangle. They will also learn that the area of a rectangle and the area of a parallelogram both equal base times height.

*Area* is the measure of the region inside a two-dimensional figure or the surface of a three-dimensional figure. Since it measures length and width, area is a square measurement. Area is measured by finding the number of square units within a region. The units used to measure area have an exponent of 2. For example, you might see area measured in square meters ($m^2$), square inches ($in^2$), square miles ($mi^2$), or square centimeters ($cm^2$).

To *derive* a formula, mathematicians follow a sequence of steps, with one step leading logically from the previous step. In this lesson, students will do an activity that will lead them through a sequence of steps to derive the formula for finding the area of a parallelogram.

### ▶ Common Errors and Misconceptions
- Students might think of all measurements as length. For example, they might perceive area as a distance—something that they can measure with a ruler. Consequently, they often measure the perimeter (the path around the figure).
- Students might believe that it doesn't matter if units are all identical. They may believe that if they can fill a region (such as a box) with units of measure (such as beans), it doesn't matter if some of the units of measure (beans) are of a different size. They will simply count the number of objects contained within the region (box).
- Students might believe that although the units of measure should be identical, it doesn't matter if they do not completely cover a region.

### Materials to Gather

**SUPPLIED**
Practice Finding Parallelogram Area activity page

## GET READY  Area of Rectangles

**ONLINE 10 min**

Students will be reminded that area is a square measure, rather than a linear measure. They will find the area of several rectangles that are measured and are described by various units squared.

**Objectives**

- Use a formula to find the area of a rectangle, a square, or a figure that can be divided into rectangles or squares.

## LEARN  Base and Height Formula for Area

**ONLINE 10 min**

Students will learn that the formula for the area of a rectangle, $A = lw$, can also be written as Area = base • height, or $A = bh$.

**Objectives**

- Derive and use the formula for the area of a parallelogram and use appropriate units.

**Tips** If students have difficulty relating length and width to base and height, draw several rectangles. Have them label each figure's length and width, and connect those dimensions to the base and height.

## LEARN  Connect Parallelograms and Rectangles

**ONLINE 15 min**

Students will learn how a parallelogram can transform into a rectangle. They will learn that the formula for the area of a parallelogram is the same as the formula for the area of a rectangle, $A = bh$.

**Objectives**

- Derive and use the formula for the area of a parallelogram and use appropriate units.

**Tips** If students have difficulty understanding how a parallelogram transforms into a rectangle, have them cut out a parallelogram from paper and transform it into a rectangle by following the steps in the activity.

## LEARN  Make Shapes with the Same Area

**ONLINE 15 min**

Students will use the Geoboard Learning Tool to create parallelograms and rectangles with the same areas.

**Objectives**

- Derive and use the formula for the area of a parallelogram and use appropriate units.

### DIRECTIONS FOR USING THE GEOBOARD LEARNING TOOL

1. Click Lesson Mode. If necessary, click Menu and Help to review the instructions for the learning tool.
2. Have students follow these steps:
   - Click the ruler on the left-hand side of the screen to show the measurements of the sides of the shape they are creating.
   - Click Show Info at the bottom of the screen to display information about the shape they are creating.
   - Click the rubber band and drag it through a color to make a rectangle with an area of 32 square units.
   - Note the area information at the bottom of the Geoboard.

AREA OF PARALLELOGRAMS (A)  **457**

A rectangle that is 8 units by 4 units is one example of a rectangle with an area of 32 square units.

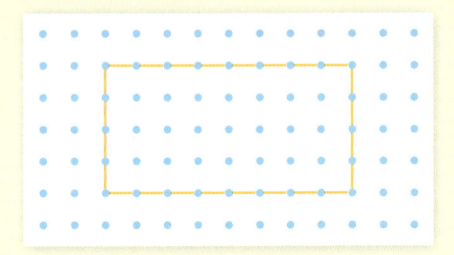

3. Once students have made the rectangle, have them adjust its corners to make a parallelogram. They can see the shape information at the bottom of the Geoboard to confirm that they have made a parallelogram.

   Remind students to make sure the area of the parallelogram is also 32 square units. The parallelogram also has a length of 8 units and height of 4 units. The height can be found by counting units from the top to the bottom of the shape in a vertical line.

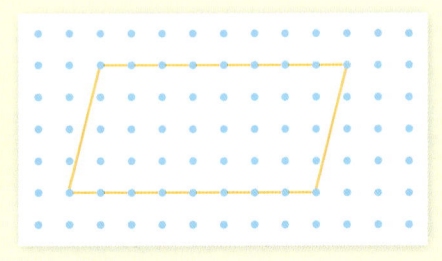

4. Have students repeat Step 3 to transform rectangles with the following areas into parallelograms:
   - 104 square units
   - 84 square units
   - 49 square units

5. Have students make a parallelogram with an area of 28 square units.
   - Tell students that the description at the bottom of the screen will help them know what the area of the parallelogram is. A parallelogram with a base of 7 units and a height of 4 units is an example of a 28-square-unit parallelogram.
   - Once students have a parallelogram with an area of 28 square units, have them adjust its corners to make a rectangle.
   - Remind students to make sure the area of the rectangle is also 28 square units. The rectangle also has a length of 7 units and a width of 4 units.

6. Have students repeat Step 5 to transform parallelograms with the following areas into rectangles:
   - 77 square units
   - 56 square units

## TRY IT  Practice Finding Parallelogram Area

**OFFLINE 10 min**

Students will use the formula $A = bh$ to find the area of a parallelogram. Have students turn to the Practice Finding Parallelogram Area activity page in their Activity Book and read the directions with them.

Students should copy the problems from the Activity Book into their Math Notebook as necessary and solve them there.

### Objectives

- Derive and use the formula for the area of a parallelogram and use appropriate units.

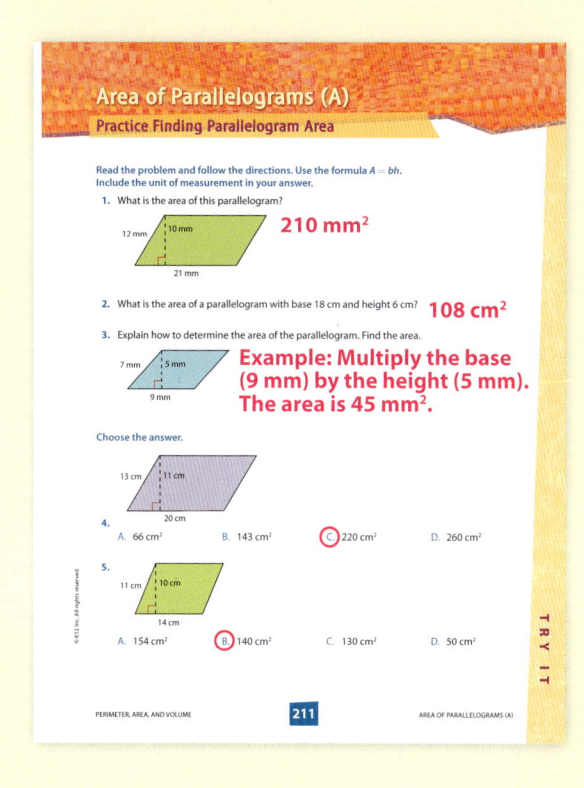

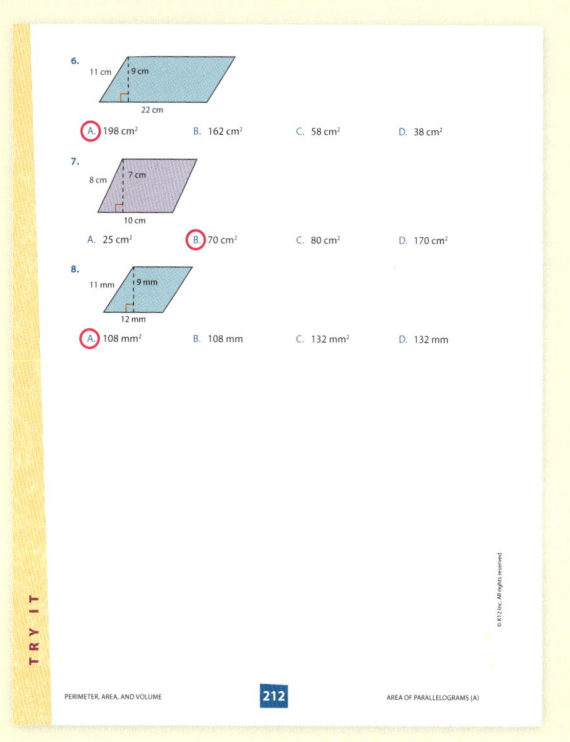

### Area of Parallelograms (A)
**Practice Finding Parallelogram Area**

Read the problem and follow the directions. Use the formula $A = bh$. Include the unit of measurement in your answer.

1. What is the area of this parallelogram?
   (12 mm, 10 mm, 21 mm) — **210 mm²**

2. What is the area of a parallelogram with base 18 cm and height 6 cm? — **108 cm²**

3. Explain how to determine the area of the parallelogram. Find the area.
   (7 mm, 5 mm, 9 mm) — **Example: Multiply the base (9 mm) by the height (5 mm). The area is 45 mm².**

Choose the answer.

4. (13 cm, 11 cm, 20 cm)
   A. 66 cm²   B. 143 cm²   **C. 220 cm²**   D. 260 cm²

5. (11 cm, 10 cm, 14 cm)
   A. 154 cm²   **B. 140 cm²**   C. 130 cm²   D. 50 cm²

6. (11 cm, 9 cm, 22 cm)
   **A. 198 cm²**   B. 162 cm²   C. 58 cm²   D. 38 cm²

7. (8 cm, 7 cm, 10 cm)
   A. 25 cm²   **B. 70 cm²**   C. 80 cm²   D. 170 cm²

8. (11 mm, 9 mm, 12 mm)
   **A. 108 mm²**   B. 108 mm   C. 132 mm²   D. 132 mm

**AREA OF PARALLELOGRAMS (A)** 459

# Area of Parallelograms (B)

## Lesson Overview

| | | |
|---|---|---|
| **LEARN** Formula for Area of a Parallelogram | 10 minutes | **ONLINE** |
| **LEARN** Substitute Values to Find Area | 15 minutes | **OFFLINE** |
| **LEARN** Story Problems on Parallelogram Area | 10 minutes | **OFFLINE** |
| **TRY IT** Solve Parallelogram Area Problems | 15 minutes | **OFFLINE** |
| **CHECKPOINT** | 10 minutes | **ONLINE** |

### ▶ Lesson Objectives
Derive and use the formula for the area of a parallelogram and use appropriate units.

### ▶ Prerequisite Skills
Use a formula to find the area of a rectangle, a square, or a figure that can be divided into rectangles or squares.

### ▶ Content Background
Students will learn to calculate the area of a parallelogram by transforming a rectangle into a parallelogram. They will relate the formula for finding the area of a rectangle ($A = bh$) to the formula for finding the area of a parallelogram. They will practice finding the base or height of a parallelogram when they know the area and solving story problems about the area of parallelograms.

 *Area* is the measure of the region inside a two-dimensional figure or the surface of a three-dimensional figure. Since it measures length and width, area is a square measurement. Area is measured by finding the number of square units within a region. The units used to measure area have an exponent of 2. For example, you might see area measured in square meters ($m^2$), square inches ($in^2$), square miles ($mi^2$), or square centimeters ($cm^2$).

 To *derive* a formula, mathematicians follow a sequence of steps, with one step leading logically from the previous step. In this lesson, students will do an activity that will lead them through a sequence of steps to derive the formula for finding the area of a parallelogram.

### ▶ Common Errors and Misconceptions
- Students might think of all measurements as length. For example, they might perceive area as a distance—something that they can measure with a ruler. Consequently, they often measure the perimeter (the path around the figure).
- Students might believe that it doesn't matter if units are all identical. They may believe that if they can fill a region (such as a box) with units of measure (such as beans), it doesn't matter if some of the units of measure (beans) are of a different size. They will simply count the number of objects contained within the region (box).
- Students might believe that although the units of measure should be identical, it doesn't matter if they do not completely cover a region.

### Materials to Gather

**SUPPLIED**

Substitute Values to Find Area activity page

Story Problems on Parallelogram Area activity page

Solve Parallelogram Area Problems activity page

## LEARN  Formula for Area of a Parallelogram

**ONLINE 10 min**

### Objectives
- Derive and use the formula for the area of a parallelogram and use appropriate units.

Students will see how a rectangle can transform into a parallelogram and understand why the formula for the area of both rectangles and parallelograms is $A = bh$. They will also use the formula to find the area of parallelograms.

**Tips**  If students have difficulty understanding how a rectangle transforms into a parallelogram, have them cut out a rectangle from paper and transform it into a parallelogram by following the steps in the activity.

## LEARN  Substitute Values to Find Area

**OFFLINE 15 min**

### Objectives
- Derive and use the formula for the area of a parallelogram and use appropriate units.

Students will practice finding the height or base of a parallelogram when they know the area and one of the measurements. They also will practice substituting values into the area formula $A = bh$. They will learn to find the area of a parallelogram when they know the area of a triangle created by diagonally dividing the parallelogram into two equal parts. Have students turn to the Substitute Values to Find Area activity page in their Activity Book and read the directions with them.

Students should copy the problems from the Activity Book into their Math Notebook as necessary and solve them there.

1. Tell students that in this activity they will focus on substituting values for the base and height into the area formula. Remind them that the area formula is Area = length • width, or $A = bh$.

2. Remind students that they have used this formula to find the area of parallelograms that have whole-number and decimal-number base and height measurements. Remind them that a parallelogram can transform into a rectangle, and the area of a rectangle is always $A = bh$, or Area = length • width.

3. Read the first Worked Examples box with students.

   **Ask:** Why was 144 substituted for the area and 9 substituted for the height in the formula, and how did it help you solve the problem? *The problem gave me those two measurements. To use the formula and solve the problem, I needed to substitute the given values for the variables and solve for the unknown value, b, the length of the base.*

4. Have students complete Problems 1–6 in the problem set, referring to the first Worked Examples box if they need help.

5. Read the second Worked Examples box with students.

6. Have students complete Problem 7. If students have difficulty, encourage them to look at the second Worked Examples box and follow the process shown. If they still have difficulty, help them apply the process shown in the Worked Example.

AREA OF PARALLELOGRAMS (B)

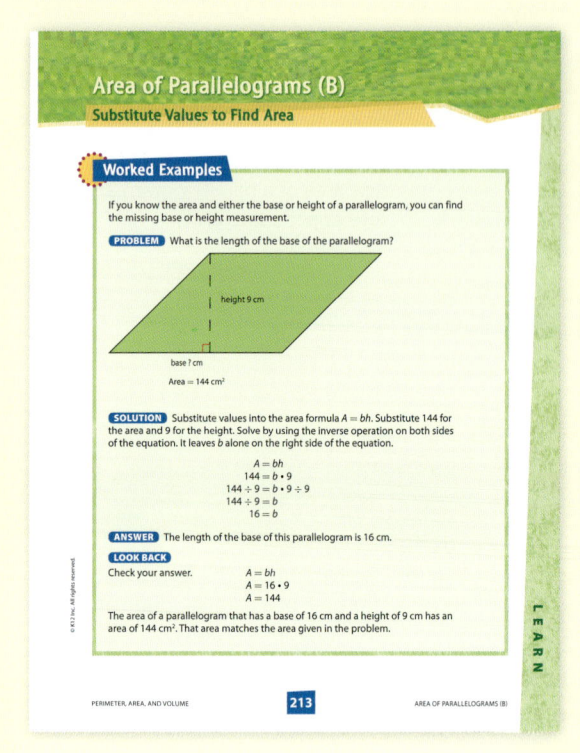

## Area of Parallelograms (B)
### Substitute Values to Find Area

**Worked Examples**

If you know the area and either the base or height of a parallelogram, you can find the missing base or height measurement.

**PROBLEM** What is the length of the base of the parallelogram?

height 9 cm
base ? cm
Area = 144 cm²

**SOLUTION** Substitute values into the area formula $A = bh$. Substitute 144 for the area and 9 for the height. Solve by using the inverse operation on both sides of the equation. It leaves $b$ alone on the right side of the equation.

$A = bh$
$144 = b \cdot 9$
$144 \div 9 = b \cdot 9 \div 9$
$144 \div 9 = b$
$16 = b$

**ANSWER** The length of the base of this parallelogram is 16 cm.

**LOOK BACK** Check your answer.
$A = bh$
$A = 16 \cdot 9$
$A = 144$

The area of a parallelogram that has a base of 16 cm and a height of 9 cm has an area of 144 cm². That area matches the area given in the problem.

---

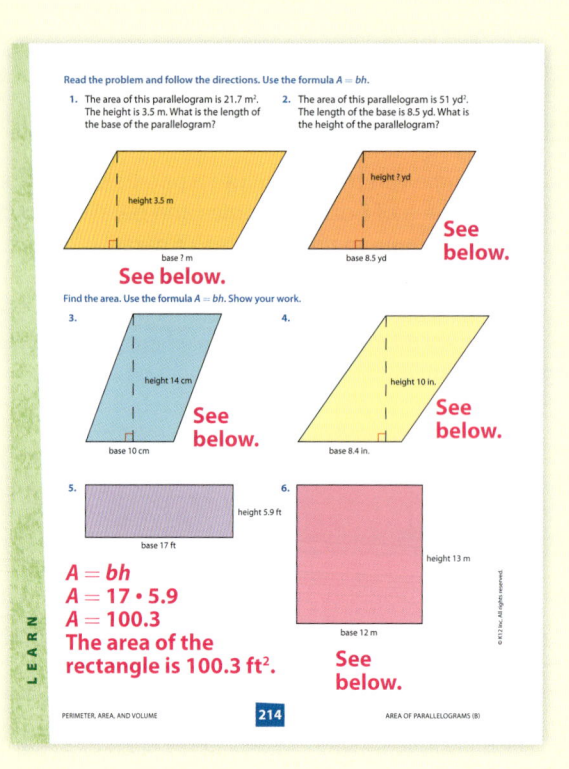

Read the problem and follow the directions. Use the formula $A = bh$.

1. The area of this parallelogram is 21.7 m². The height is 3.5 m. What is the length of the base of the parallelogram?

   height 3.5 m
   base ? m
   **See below.**

2. The area of this parallelogram is 51 yd². The length of the base is 8.5 yd. What is the height of the parallelogram?

   height ? yd
   base 8.5 yd
   **See below.**

Find the area. Use the formula $A = bh$. Show your work.

3. height 14 cm, base 10 cm — **See below.**
4. height 10 in., base 8.4 in. — **See below.**
5. height 5.9 ft, base 17 ft
   $A = bh$
   $A = 17 \cdot 5.9$
   $A = 100.3$
   The area of the rectangle is 100.3 ft².
6. height 13 m, base 12 m — **See below.**

---

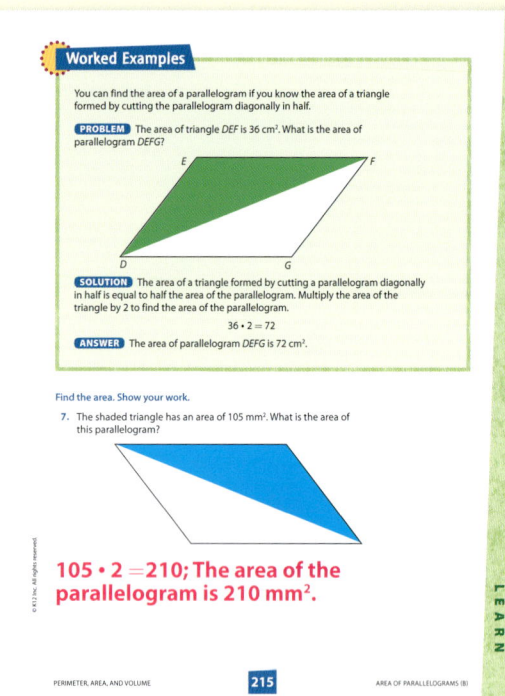

**Worked Examples**

You can find the area of a parallelogram if you know the area of a triangle formed by cutting the parallelogram diagonally in half.

**PROBLEM** The area of triangle DEF is 36 cm². What is the area of parallelogram DEFG?

**SOLUTION** The area of a triangle formed by cutting a parallelogram diagonally in half is equal to half the area of the parallelogram. Multiply the area of the triangle by 2 to find the area of the parallelogram.

$36 \cdot 2 = 72$

**ANSWER** The area of parallelogram DEFG is 72 cm².

Find the area. Show your work.

7. The shaded triangle has an area of 105 mm². What is the area of this parallelogram?

   $105 \cdot 2 = 210$; The area of the parallelogram is 210 mm².

---

### Additional Answers

1. $A = bh$
   $21.7 = b \cdot 3.5$
   $21.7 \div 3.5 = b \cdot 3.5 \div 3.5$
   $21.7 \div 3.5 = b$
   $6.2 = b$
   The base of the parallelogram measures 6.2 m.

2. $A = bh$
   $51 = 8.5 \cdot h$
   $51 \div 8.5 = 8.5 \div 8.5 \cdot h$
   $51 \div 8.5 = h$
   $6 = h$
   The height of the parallelogram measures 6 yd.

3. $A = bh$
   $A = 10 \cdot 14$
   $A = 140$
   The area of the parallelogram is 140 cm².

4. $A = bh$
   $A = 8.4 \cdot 10$
   $A = 84$
   The area of the parallelogram is 84 in².

6. $A = bh$
   $A = 12 \cdot 13$
   $A = 156$
   The area of the rectangle is 156 m².

**462** PERIMETER, AREA, AND VOLUME

## LEARN  Story Problems on Parallelogram Area

**OFFLINE 10 min**

### Objectives
- Derive and use the formula for the area of a parallelogram and use appropriate units.

Students will solve story problems about the area of parallelograms. They will use the formula $A = bh$ to solve the problems. Some problems will give a measurement that is related to another measurement (such as "the base is 3 times the height") and ask students to find the area of a parallelogram. Have students turn to the Story Problems on Parallelogram Area activity page in their Activity Book and read the directions with them.

Students should copy the problems from the Activity Book into their Math Notebook as necessary and solve them there.

1. Read the Worked Examples box with students.

    **Ask:** How was the height calculated? The height was calculated by adding 5.4 to 12 because the problem said that the height was 5.4 cm more than the base, which was 12 cm.

2. Have students complete Problem 1 in the problem set. Make sure they have answered Problem 1 correctly before they move on to the next problem.

3. Guide students to solve Problem 2. If students have difficulty, ask them what pairs of numbers, when multiplied, equal 72. Tell them that those pairs of numbers could be the base and height of a parallelogram with an area of 72.

4. Extend the activity by asking students to find a pair of decimal numbers that could be possible lengths of the base and height of a parallelogram with an area of 72 m². Remind students that it is important for the base and height measurements to each have a unit label. **Examples:** 4.5 m and 16 m; 3.6 m and 20 m

5. Have students complete Problem 3.

    **Ask:** Does your answer make sense in the story problem? Yes, the patio is a parallelogram, and the area makes sense as 143 ft² because I could estimate the area of the patio as 15 • 10 = 150, or 150 ft². The number 143 rounded to the greater ten is 150.

6. Have students complete Problem 4. Guide them as necessary to understand that the area of the triangle should be multiplied by 2 to get the area of the park.

AREA OF PARALLELOGRAMS (B)

### Area of a Parallelograms (B)
**Story Problems on Parallelogram Area**

#### Worked Examples

You can solve story problems about the area of parallelograms. You can find the area of a parallelogram when the base and height are given as measurements related to each other.

**PROBLEM** The height of a parallelogram-shaped tile is 5.4 cm more than the length of its base. If the base is 12 cm, what is the area of the tile in centimeters squared?

**SOLUTION** Use the area formula $A = bh$.

1. State the measurements you know. You know that the base is 12 cm and the height is 5.4 cm more than the base.
2. Since the height is more than the base by 5.4 cm, add 5.4 cm to the measurement of the base. Then you'll have the height measurement.
$12 + 5.4 = 17.4$
3. Substitute the base and height measurements into the area formula. Use order of operations to find the area.
$A = bh$
$A = 12 \cdot (12 + 5.4)$
$A = 12 \cdot 17.4$
$A = 208.8$

**ANSWER** The area of the tile is 208.8 cm².

Find the area. Use the formula $A = bh$. Show your work.

1. Charlene has a poster that is shaped like a parallelogram. The height of the poster is 3 times the length of its base. If the base is 18 inches, what is the area of the poster in inches squared?
$A = bh$; $A = 18 \cdot (18 \cdot 3)$; $A = 18 \cdot 54$;
$A = 972$; The area of the poster is 972 in².

2. A garden is in the shape of a parallelogram. The garden has an area of 72 m². Give 4 possible whole-number measurements for the base and height.
**Answers may include 2 m and 36 m, 3 m and 24 m, 4 m and 18 m, 6 m and 12 m, and 8 m and 9 m.**

3. Mr. Donne is going to build a patio in the shape of a parallelogram. The base of the patio will be 13 feet. The height of the patio will be 11 feet. He needs to know the area of the patio so he can order concrete. What will the area of the patio be?
$A = bh$; $A = 13 \cdot 11$; $A = 143$;
The area will be 143 ft².

4. A park in the shape of a parallelogram had a path that crossed it diagonally, dividing it in half. A triangle bordered by the path and 2 sides of the park had an area of 225 yd². What was the area of the park?
$225 \cdot 2 = 450$; The area of the triangle is 450 yd².

---

### TRY IT  Solve Parallelogram Area Problems
OFFLINE 15 min

**Objectives**
- Derive and use the formula for the area of a parallelogram and use appropriate units.

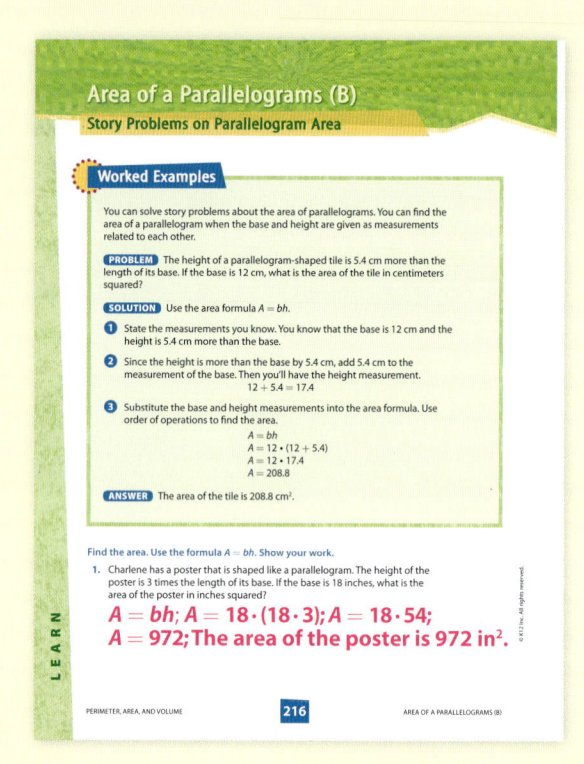

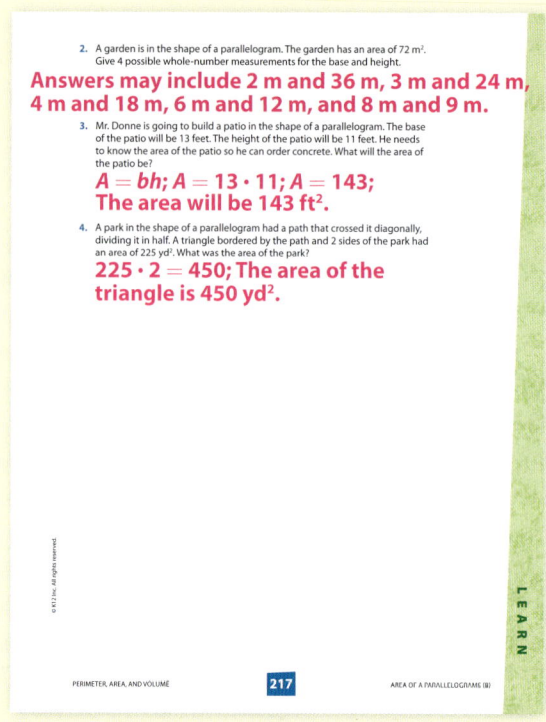

Students will practice finding the area of parallelograms by using the formula $A = bh$ for the area of a parallelogram. Have students turn to the Solve Parallelogram Area Problems activity page in their Activity Book and read the directions with them.

Students should copy the problems from the Activity Book into their Math Notebook as necessary and solve them there.

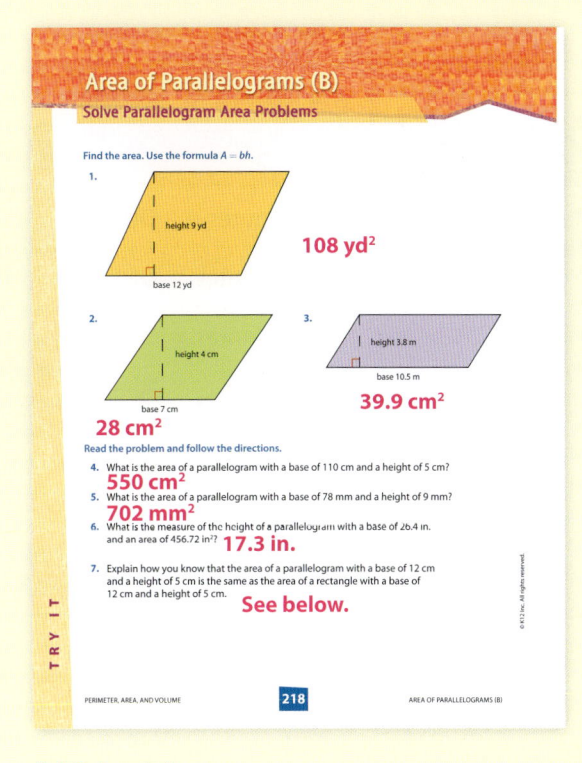

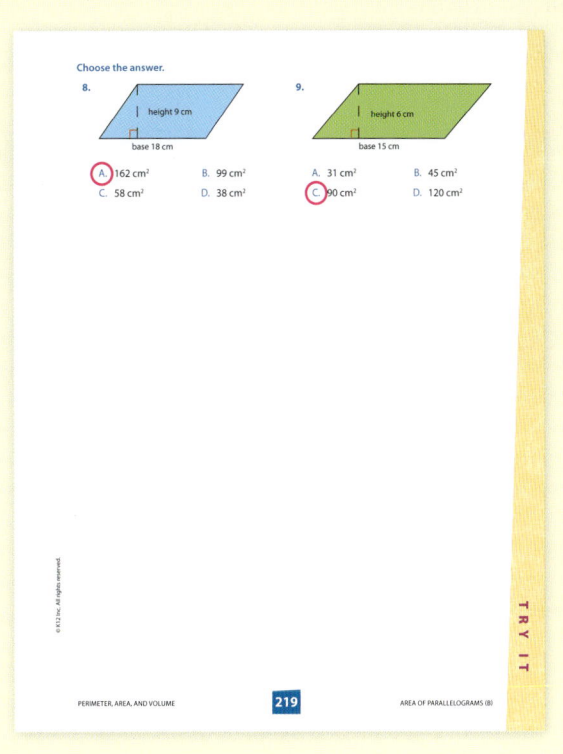

## Additional Answers

**7. Example:** You can cut a triangle off one side of the parallelogram and slide it to the other side of the parallelogram and make a rectangle with a base of 12 cm and a height of 5 cm.

## CHECKPOINT

Students will complete an online Checkpoint. If necessary, read the directions, problems, and answer choices to students and help them with keyboard or mouse operations.

## Objectives

- Derive and use the formula for the area of a parallelogram and use appropriate units.

AREA OF PARALLELOGRAMS (B)   465

# Area of Triangles (A)

## Lesson Overview

| | | |
|---|---|---|
| **GET READY** Find the Area of Parallelograms | 5 minutes | ONLINE |
| **LEARN** Parallelograms and Triangles | 15 minutes | ONLINE |
| **LEARN** Area on a Geoboard | 20 minutes | ONLINE |
| **LEARN** Compare Areas | 10 minutes | OFFLINE |
| **TRY IT** Area of Parallelograms and Triangles | 10 minutes | OFFLINE |

### ▶ Lesson Objectives
Derive and use the formula for the area of a triangle and use appropriate units.

### ▶ Prerequisite Skills
Derive and use the formula for the area of a parallelogram and use appropriate units.

### ▶ Content Background
Students will learn to derive the formula for the area of a triangle by finding the area of a parallelogram and dividing the parallelogram into two congruent triangles.

*Area* is the measure of the region inside a two-dimensional figure or the surface of a three-dimensional figure. Since it measures length and width, area is a square measurement. Area is measured by finding the number of square units within a region. The units used to measure area have an exponent of 2. For example, you might see area measured in square meters ($m^2$), square inches ($in^2$), square miles ($mi^2$), or square centimeters ($cm^2$).

To *derive* a formula, mathematicians follow a sequence of steps, with one step leading logically from the previous step. In this lesson, students will do an activity that will lead them through a sequence of steps to derive the formula for finding the area of a triangle.

### ▶ Common Errors and Misconceptions
- Students might think of all measurements as length. For example, they might perceive area as a distance—something that they can measure with a ruler. Consequently, they often measure the perimeter (the path around the figure).
- Students might believe that it doesn't matter if units are all identical. They may believe that if they can fill a region (such as a box) with units of measure (such as beans), it doesn't matter if some of the units of measure (beans) are of a different size. They will simply count the number of objects contained within the region (box).
- Students might believe that although the units of measure should be identical, it doesn't matter if the units do not completely cover a region.

### ▶ Advance Preparation
Print the Compare Parallelogram and Triangle Areas printout.

### Materials to Gather

**SUPPLIED**
Compare Parallelogram and Triangle Areas (printout)
Area of Parallelograms and Triangles activity page

**ALSO NEEDED**
scissors, pointed-end safety

▶ **Safety**

Make sure students handle the scissors carefully and be sure to store them in a safe place.

## GET READY  Find the Area of Parallelograms

ONLINE 5 min

### Objectives
- Derive and use the formula for the area of a parallelogram and use appropriate units.

Students will practice finding the area of parallelograms given the measurements of the base and height. They will also practice finding the height of a parallelogram given the measurements of the area and the base. The dimensions of the parallelograms have different units of measurement.

**Tips**  Point out to students that the parallelograms in the first two problems each show a measurement that they don't need for finding the area.

## LEARN  Parallelograms and Triangles

ONLINE 15 min

### Objectives
- Derive and use the formula for the area of a triangle and use appropriate units.

Students will learn how to use the formula for the area of a parallelogram to derive the formula for the area of a triangle. They will explore parallelograms that can be divided into two congruent right, obtuse, or acute triangles.

## LEARN  Area on a Geoboard

ONLINE 20 min

### Objectives
- Derive and use the formula for the area of a triangle and use appropriate units.

Students will use the Geoboard Learning Tool to show the relationship between the area of a parallelogram and the area of two congruent triangles that can be formed from the parallelogram.

**DIRECTIONS FOR USING THE GEOBOARD LEARNING TOOL**

1. Click Lesson Mode. If necessary, click Menu and Help to review the instructions for the learning tool.
2. Have students follow these steps:
   - Click the ruler on the left-hand side of the screen to show the measurements of the sides.
   - Click Show Info in the lower right to display information about the shape they are creating. They will be able to read the area of each figure they make.
   - Tell students they will make parallelograms and triangles. As they create these figures, lead students to observe that the area of each triangle is half the area of the parallelogram. Remind students that when they are making obtuse and acute triangles, the height of the triangle is not equal to the length of one of the legs of the triangle.
   - Make a rectangle with 18 square units.
   - Make two congruent right triangles that cover the rectangle. Use a different color of rubber band for each triangle. Ask students for the area of each right triangle in the rectangle. The area of each right triangle is 9 square units

**AREA OF TRIANGLES (A)**  467

This is an example of a rectangle with an area of 18 square units and two right triangles that each has an area of 9 square units:

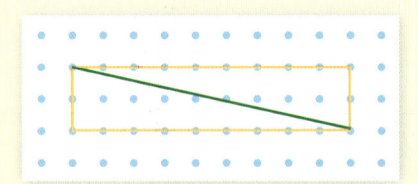

- Make a parallelogram with an area of 12 square units. Then make two congruent obtuse triangles that cover the parallelogram. Ask students for the area of each obtuse triangle. The area of each obtuse triangle is 6 square units.

This is an example of a parallelogram with an area of 12 square units and two obtuse triangles that each has an area of 6 square units:

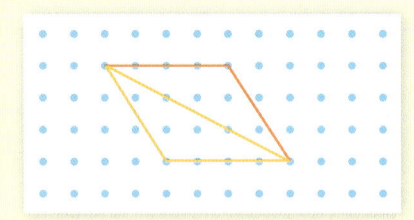

- Make a parallelogram with an area of 28 square units. Then make two congruent acute triangles that cover the parallelogram. Ask students for the area of each acute triangle. The area of each acute triangle is 14 square units.

This is an example of a parallelogram with an area of 28 square units and two acute triangles that each has an area of 14 square units:

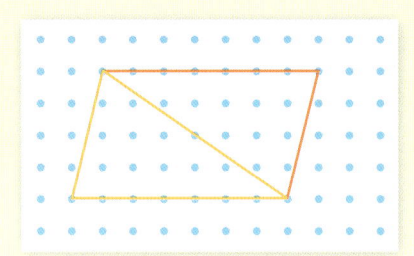

3. Next have students use the following pairs of congruent triangles to make parallelograms of any size. Remind students that when they are making obtuse and acute triangles, the height of the triangle is not equal to the length of one of the legs of the triangle.
   - Make two congruent right triangles that form a rectangle.
   - Make two congruent obtuse triangles that form a parallelogram.
   - Make two congruent acute triangles that form a parallelogram.

   **Ask:** How does the area of each triangle compare to the area of the parallelogram? The area of each triangle is half the area of the parallelogram.

## LEARN Compare Areas

**OFFLINE 10 min**

### Objectives
- Derive and use the formula for the area of a triangle and use appropriate units.

Students will use the formula for the area of a parallelogram to find the area of a triangle.

Gather the Compare Parallelogram and Triangle Areas printout and scissors.

1. Have students use the formula $A = bh$ to find the area of the rectangle on the printout. Have them solve the problem in their Math Notebook.

   $A = bh$
   $A = 10 \cdot 15$
   $A = 150$
   The area of the rectangle is 150 cm².

   Then have students cut out the rectangle and cut on the dotted line to make two congruent triangles. Place one triangle on top of the other to determine if they are congruent. Have students find the area of one of the triangles. Have them solve the problem in their Math Notebook.

   $A = \frac{bh}{2}$
   $A = \frac{10 \cdot 15}{2}$
   $A = 75$
   The area of one triangle is 75 cm².

2. Repeat Step 1 for the parallelogram.

   $A = bh$
   $A = 8 \cdot 2$
   $A = 16$
   The area of the parallelogram is 16 cm².

   $A = \frac{bh}{2}$
   $A = \frac{8 \cdot 2}{2}$
   $A = 8$
   The area of one triangle is 8 cm².

AREA OF TRIANGLES (A)

## TRY IT  Area of Parallelograms and Triangles

**OFFLINE 10 min**

### Objectives
- Derive and use the formula for the area of a triangle and use appropriate units.

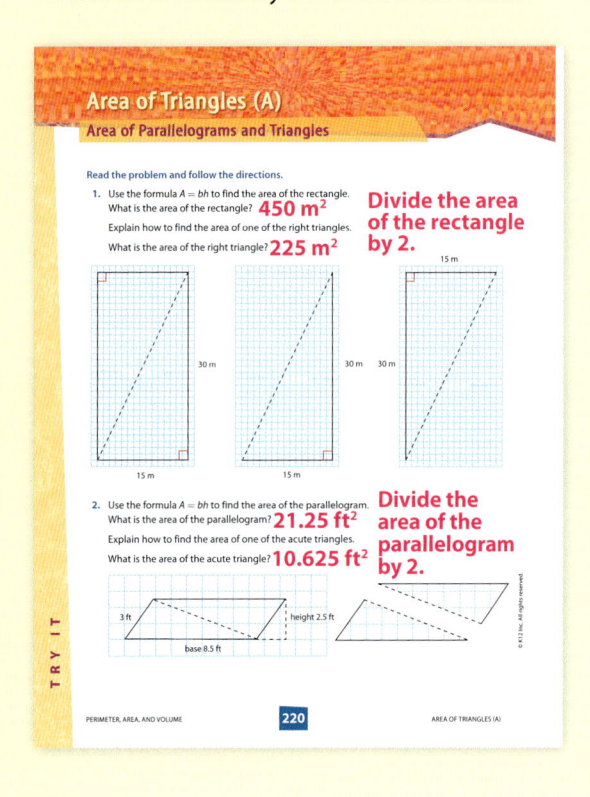

Students will use the formula for the area of a parallelogram to find the area of a triangle. Have students turn to the Area of Parallelograms and Triangles activity page in their Activity Book and read the directions with them.

Students should copy the problems from the Activity Book into their Math Notebook as necessary and solve them there.

---

**Area of Triangles (A)**
Area of Parallelograms and Triangles

Read the problem and follow the directions.

1. Use the formula $A = bh$ to find the area of the rectangle. What is the area of the rectangle? **450 m²**
   Explain how to find the area of one of the right triangles.
   What is the area of the right triangle? **225 m²**

   **Divide the area of the rectangle by 2.**

   (30 m × 15 m rectangles and triangles)

2. Use the formula $A = bh$ to find the area of the parallelogram. What is the area of the parallelogram? **21.25 ft²**
   Explain how to find the area of one of the acute triangles.
   What is the area of the acute triangle? **10.625 ft²**

   **Divide the area of the parallelogram by 2.**

   (base 8.5 ft, height 2.5 ft, 3 ft)

220   AREA OF TRIANGLES (A)
PERIMETER, AREA, AND VOLUME

---

**470**  PERIMETER, AREA, AND VOLUME

# Area of Triangles (B)

## Lesson Overview

| | | |
|---|---|---|
| Skills Update | 5 minutes | ONLINE |
| **LEARN** Base and Height | 10 minutes | ONLINE |
| **LEARN** Area and Triangles | 15 minutes | ONLINE |
| **LEARN** Area of Triangles Story Problems | 10 minutes | ONLINE |
| **TRY IT** Practice Finding Area of Triangles | 10 minutes | ONLINE |
| **CHECKPOINT** | 10 minutes | ONLINE |

### ▶ Lesson Objectives
Derive and use the formula for the area of a triangle and use appropriate units.

### ▶ Prerequisite Skills
Derive and use the formula for the area of a parallelogram and use appropriate units.

### ▶ Content Background
Students will continue to learn to derive the formula for the area of a triangle by finding the area of a parallelogram and dividing the parallelogram into two congruent triangles.

*Area* is the measure of the region inside a two-dimensional figure or the surface of a three-dimensional figure. Since it measures length and width, area is a square measurement. Area is measured by finding the number of square units within a region. The units used to measure area have an exponent of 2. For example, you might see area measured in square meters ($m^2$), square inches ($in^2$), square miles ($mi^2$), or square centimeters ($cm^2$).

To *derive* a formula, mathematicians follow a sequence of steps, with one step leading logically from the previous step. In this lesson, students will do an activity that will lead them through a sequence of steps to derive the formula for finding the area of a triangle.

### ▶ Common Errors and Misconceptions
- Students might think of all measurements as length. For example, they might perceive area as a distance—something that they can measure with a ruler. Consequently, they often measure the perimeter (the path around the figure).
- Students might believe that it doesn't matter if units are all identical. They may believe that if they can fill a region (such as a box) with units of measure (such as beans), it doesn't matter if some of the units of measure (beans) are of a different size. They will simply count the number of objects contained within the region (box).
- Students might believe that although the units of measure should be identical, it doesn't matter if the units do not completely cover a region.

### Materials to Gather
There are no materials to gather for this lesson.

## LEARN  Base and Height

**ONLINE 10 min**

Students will learn to identify the base and height of different types of triangles. They will see that the base and height of triangles meet at a right angle.

### Objectives
- Derive and use the formula for the area of a triangle and use appropriate units.

## LEARN  Area and Triangles

**ONLINE 15 min**

Students will use the formula $A = \frac{bh}{2}$ to find the area of triangles. They can use the formula to find the measure of the base of a triangle when they know the area and measure of the height. They can also use the formula to find the measure of the height of a triangle when they know the area and measure of the base.

**Tips** Tell students that the formula $A = \frac{bh}{2}$ works for any type of number (including whole numbers or decimal numbers) and for any type of triangle (acute, obtuse, or right), no matter how it is oriented.

### Objectives
- Derive and use the formula for the area of a triangle and use appropriate units.

## LEARN  Area of Triangles Story Problems

**ONLINE 10 min**

Students will find the base, height, or area of triangles to solve story problems.

**Tips** Tell students they can sketch diagrams of triangles and label the measurements to help them solve these problems.

### Objectives
- Derive and use the formula for the area of a triangle and use appropriate units.

## TRY IT  Practice Finding Area of Triangles

**ONLINE 10 min**

Students will complete an online Try It. If necessary, read the directions, problems, and answer choices to students and help them with keyboard or mouse operations.

### Objectives
- Derive and use the formula for the area of a triangle and use appropriate units.

## CHECKPOINT

**ONLINE 10 min**

Students will complete an online Checkpoint. If necessary, read the directions, problems, and answer choices to students and help them with keyboard or mouse operations.

### Objectives
- Derive and use the formula for the area of a triangle and use appropriate units.

# Nets, Solids, and Surface Area

## Lesson Overview

| | | |
|---|---|---|
| **GET READY** Views of Solid Objects | 5 minutes | **OFFLINE** |
| **LEARN** Nets and Solid Figures | 10 minutes | **OFFLINE** |
| **LEARN** Nets and Surface Area | 10 minutes | **OFFLINE** |
| **LEARN** Solve Surface Area Problems | 10 minutes | **OFFLINE** |
| **TRY IT** Find Surface Area | 15 minutes | **OFFLINE** |
| **CHECKPOINT** | 10 minutes | **ONLINE** |

### ▶ Lesson Objectives
Construct a cube or a rectangular box from a two-dimensional pattern and determine the surface area.

### ▶ Prerequisite Skills
- Identify or draw a two-dimensional view of a three-dimensional object.
- Find the area of a rectangular shape and use the appropriate unit.

### ▶ Content Background
Students will learn how to construct a cube and a rectangular prism from a net and how to find the surface area of a cube and a rectangular prism.

*Surface area* is the sum of the areas of all the faces, bases, and curved surfaces of a solid figure. Surface area is not the same as volume, which measures the space inside a solid figure. One way to find the surface area of a solid figure is to make a two-dimensional pattern called a *net*, calculate the area of each surface of the figure, and then find the sum of the areas. For example, to find the surface area of a cube, first find the area of one of the 6 faces, and then multiply that area by 6 because a cube has 6 congruent faces. Surface area is a square-unit measurement because it is a measure of the length times the width of each face of a solid figure. The units that measure surface area have an exponent of 2. For example, the units for the surface area of a solid figure might be square meters ($m^2$), square inches ($in^2$), square miles ($mi^2$), or square centimeters ($cm^2$).

A *net* is a two-dimensional pattern that folds to make a three-dimensional solid.
This is a two-dimensional net and the three-dimensional result for a rectangular prism.

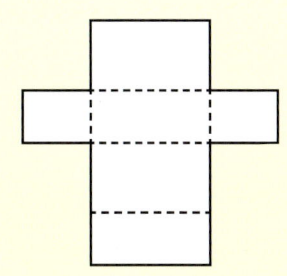

Net for a rectangular prism

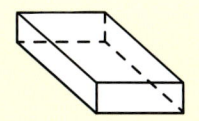

The result of folding a net for a rectangular prism

### Materials to Gather

**SUPPLIED**

Net for Cube (printout) – 2
Net for Rectangular Prism (printout) – 2
Centimeter Grid Paper (printout) – 2
Solve Surface Area Problems activity page
Find Surface Area activity page

**ALSO NEEDED**

household objects that are the shape of cubes and rectangular prisms (such as cereal boxes, tissue boxes, books, pads of sticky notes)
scissors, pointed-end safety
tape, clear

**NETS, SOLIDS, AND SURFACE AREA** 473

This is the two-dimensional net and the three-dimensional result for a cube.

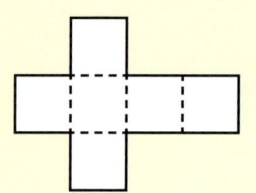

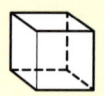

Net for a cube

The result of folding a net for a cube

## ▶ Common Errors and Misconceptions

- Students might think of all measurements as length. For example, they might perceive area as a distance—something that they can measure with a ruler. Consequently, they often measure the perimeter (the path around the figure).
- Students might believe that it doesn't matter if units are all identical. They may believe that if they can fill a region (such as a box) with units of measure (such as beans), it doesn't matter if some of the units of measure (beans) are of a different size. They will simply count the number of objects contained within the region (box).
- Students might believe that although the units of measure should be identical, it doesn't matter if the units do not completely cover a region.

## ▶ Advance Preparation

Print two copies each of Net for Cube printout, Net for Rectangular Prism printout, and Centimeter Grid Paper.

## ▶ Safety

Make sure students handle the scissors carefully and be sure to store them in a safe place.

## GET READY  Views of Solid Objects     OFFLINE 5 min

### Objectives

- Identify or draw a two-dimensional view of a three-dimensional object.

Students will view various household objects shaped like cubes or rectangular prisms from different perspectives to draw the top, bottom, front, and side views. Each view of the three-dimensional object will show a two-dimensional shape.

Gather two copies of the Centimeter Grid Paper and the household objects that are cubes and rectangular prisms.

1. Have students choose one household object and identify it as the shape of a cube or a rectangular prism. Then have them identify the top, bottom, side, and front views of the object.
2. Tell students to draw and label each view on Centimeter Grid Paper. For example, if the object is a rectangular prism, they might draw a large rectangle for the front view and a small rectangle for the side view.

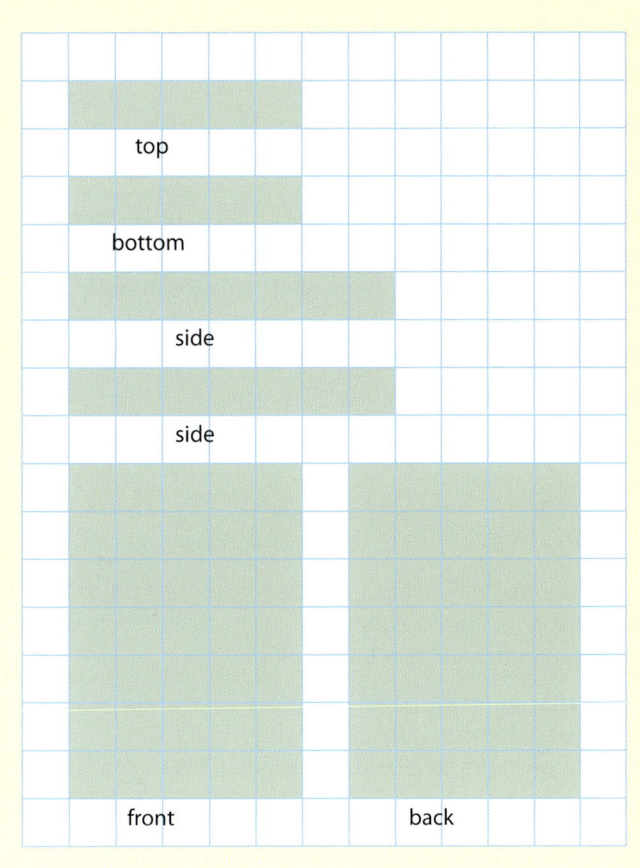

3. Have students use the object to describe what they drew for each view.
4. Repeat Steps 1–3 with the second copy of the grid paper for another household object.

## LEARN  Nets and Solid Figures

OFFLINE 10 min

### Objectives
- Construct a cube or a rectangular box from a two-dimensional pattern and determine the surface area.

Students will make a cube and a rectangular prism from nets.
Gather the Net for Cube and Net for Rectangular Prism printouts, scissors, and tape.

1. Place the Net for Cube printout, scissors, and tape in front of students. Tell students the net is a pattern for making a cube.
2. Discuss the Net for Cube printout with students.
   
   **Ask:** What is the shape of each two-dimensional figure in the net? square
   
   **Ask:** What is the shape of each face of a cube? square
   
   **Ask:** How many squares are in the net? 6
   
   **Ask:** How many faces does a cube have? 6

3. Give students the Net for Rectangular Prism printout. Tell students the net is a pattern for making a rectangular prism.

NETS, SOLIDS, AND SURFACE AREA

4. Discuss the Net for Rectangular Prism printout with students.

   **Ask:** What is the shape of each two-dimensional figure in the net? rectangle

   **Ask:** What is the shape of each face of a rectangular prism? rectangle

   **Ask:** How many rectangles are in the net? 6

   **Ask:** How many faces does a rectangular prism have? 6

   **Ask:** Are all the faces on a rectangular prism congruent? no

5. Have students cut out the net for the cube and the net for the rectangular prism on the solid lines.

   Then have students fold each net on the fold lines and tape each net together to make a cube and a rectangular prism.

## LEARN Nets and Surface Area

OFFLINE 10 min

### Objectives

- Construct a cube or a rectangular box from a two-dimensional pattern and determine the surface area.

Students will use nets to find the surface area of a cube and a rectangular prism. Students will calculate surface area in their Math Notebook.

Gather the Net for Cube and Net for Rectangular Prism printouts.

1. Tell students they can use nets to find the surface area of a cube and a rectangular prism. Explain to students that the surface area of a solid figure is the sum of the areas of all the faces, bases, and curved surfaces of a solid figure.
   - To find the surface area of a cube, first find the area of one of the 6 faces, and then multiply that area by 6 because a cube has 6 congruent faces.
   - To find the surface area of a rectangular prism, find the area of each of the 6 faces, and then find the sum of the areas.

2. Place the Net for Cube printout in front of students. Have students find the area of one face of the cube by counting the square units. 16 square units

   **Ask:** How many square faces does a cube have? 6

   **Ask:** Are all the faces congruent? Yes

3. Remind students that surface area is a square-unit measurement because it is a measure of the length times the width of each face of a solid figure. The units that measure surface area have an exponent of 2.

   Explain to students that since the 6 faces are congruent, they can multiply the area of one face, 16 square units, by 6, to find the surface area of the entire cube.

   Have students find the surface area of the cube. 96 units squared or 96 units$^2$

4. Now place the Net for Rectangular Prism printout in front of students.

   **Ask:** How many faces does a rectangular prism have? 6

   **Ask:** Are all the faces congruent? No

   Lead students to understand that because all the faces are not congruent, they cannot find the area of one face and multiply that area by 6 to find the surface area of a rectangular prism, as they did when they found the surface area of a cube.

5. Have students count square units to find the area of each face of the rectangular prism and add the areas together to find the surface area.
   $28 + 12 + 21 + 12 + 28 + 21 = 122$; The surface area is 122 units$^2$.

### Tips

Suggest to students that they write the number of square units on each face of the net and mark off each face when they find its area in Step 5. This will prevent them from skipping or duplicating the area of any faces.

**476** PERIMETER, AREA, AND VOLUME

6. Guide students to discover a quicker way to find the surface area of the rectangular prism.

   **Ask:** How many different sizes of faces are there? 3 sizes

   **Say:** Multiply the area of each size by 2, and then add the products.

7. Tell students they can also use the distributive property to find the surface area of the rectangular prism. Write the following equation in the Math Notebook and discuss how the distributive property is applied:

   2(area of face 1 + area of face 2 + area of face 3) = 2(area of face 1) + 2(area of face 2) + 2(area of face 3) = surface area

   Guide students to fill in the values in the equation to find the surface area as follows:

   $2(28 + 21 + 12) = 2(28) + 2(21) + 2(12) = 56 + 42 + 24 = 122$

   Have students solve both sides of the equation to show that the surface area is still 122 square units or 122 units$^2$.

## LEARN Solve Surface Area Problems

**OFFLINE 10 min**

### Objectives
- Construct a cube or a rectangular box from a two-dimensional pattern and determine the surface area.

### Tips
Encourage students to find the surface area of rectangular prisms two ways: add the areas of the 6 faces, and apply the distributive property.

Students will find the surface area of rectangular prisms and cubes to solve problems. Have students turn to the Solve Surface Area Problems activity page in their Activity Book and read the directions with them.

Students should copy the problems from the Activity Book into their Math Notebook as necessary and solve them there.

1. Read Problem 1 of the Worked Examples with students. Tell students that some rectangular prisms have only 2 different rectangular faces because 4 of the faces are congruent. Faces that are congruent have the same shape and size. Point out on the net the 2 different sizes of rectangular faces.

2. Point out to students that they will use both multiplication and addition in the equation to find surface area. The first equation shows addition of the area of each face. The following equations work through the math until the answer is reached.

3. Read Problem 2 of the Worked Examples with students. Tell them that some rectangular prisms have 3 different rectangular faces. Point out on the net the 3 different sizes of rectangular faces and the 3 pairs of faces that are the same, that is, are congruent.

4. Again point out to students that both multiplication and addition should be used in the equation to find surface area.

   **Say:** To find surface area, multiply the number of faces by the area of a face. Do the same for each different face. Then add the products.

5. Have students complete Problems 1 and 2 in the problem set.

6. Read the second Worked Examples box with students. In this problem, students find the surface area of a cube. They do not use a net to help them write the equation.

   **Ask:** How many congruent faces does a cube have? 6

**NETS, SOLIDS, AND SURFACE AREA**

7. Have students complete Problems 3 and 4 in the problem set. Have them refer to the Worked Example as needed.

8. Have students complete Problems 5 and 6 in which they solve story problems about surface area. When they write the equations, have them refer to the Worked Examples boxes for help as needed.

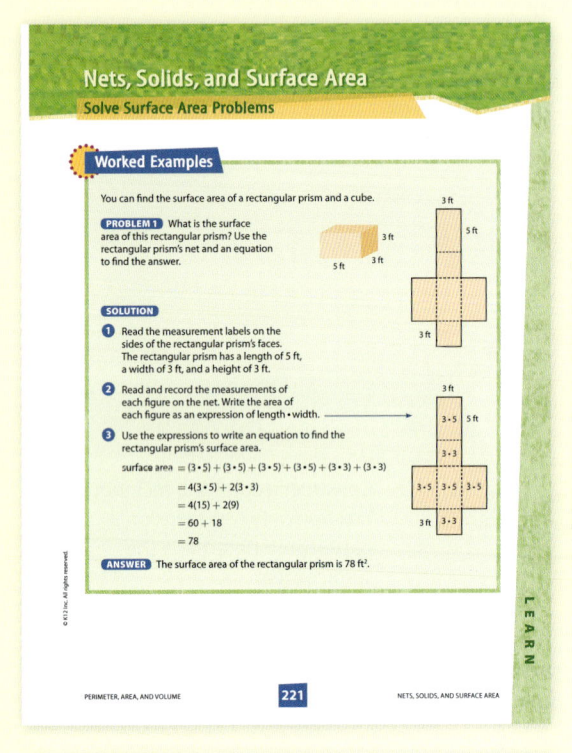

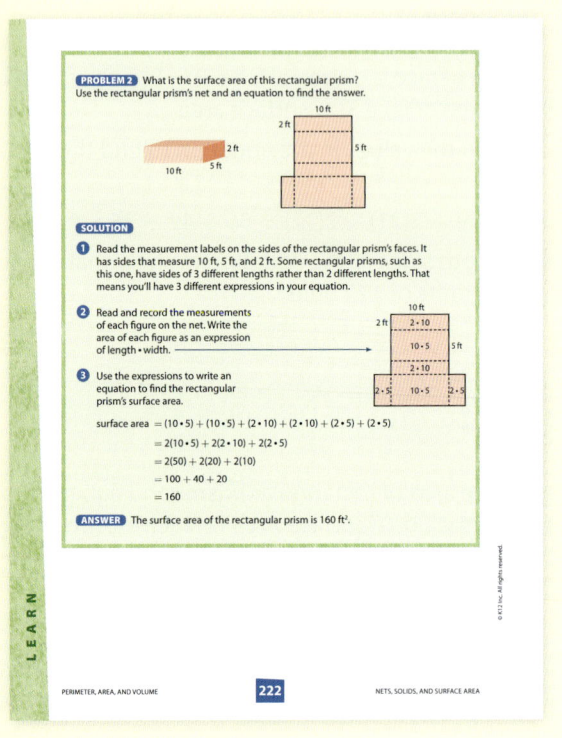

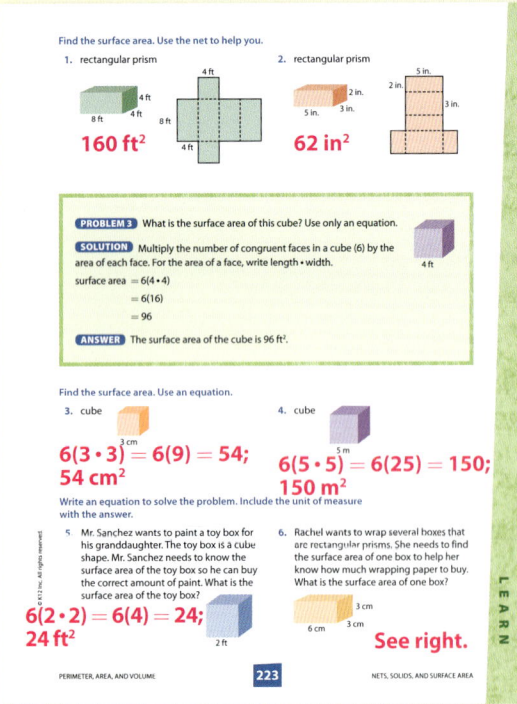

**Additional Answers**

6. $4(6 \cdot 3) + 2(3 \cdot 3) = 4(18) + 2(9) = 90$; 90 cm²

**478** PERIMETER, AREA, AND VOLUME

## TRY IT  Find Surface Area

**OFFLINE 15 min**

### Objectives
- Construct a cube or a rectangular box from a two-dimensional pattern and determine the surface area.

Students will practice finding the surface area of cubes and rectangular prisms. Have students turn to the Find Surface Area activity page in their Activity Book and read the directions with them.

Students should copy the problems from the Activity Book into their Math Notebook as necessary and solve them there.

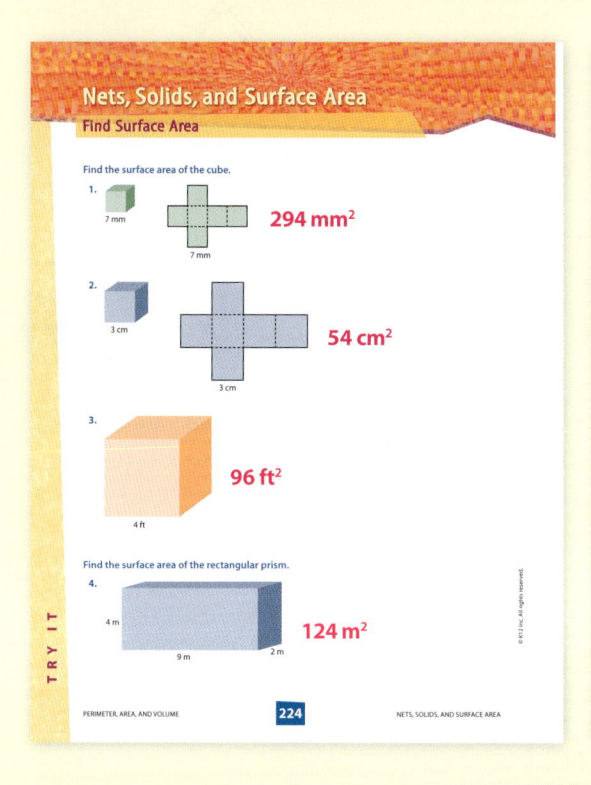

**Nets, Solids, and Surface Area**
**Find Surface Area**

Find the surface area of the cube.

1. 7 mm — **294 mm²**
2. 3 cm — **54 cm²**
3. 4 ft — **96 ft²**

Find the surface area of the rectangular prism.

4. 4 m, 9 m, 2 m — **124 m²**

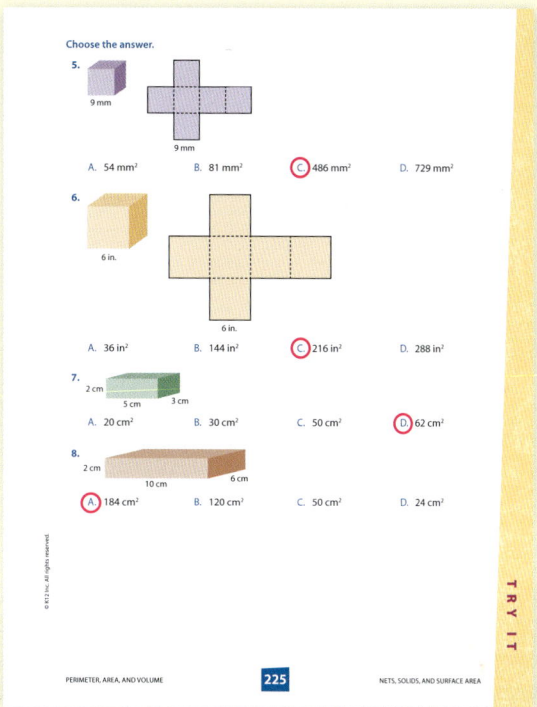

Choose the answer.

5. 9 mm
   - A. 54 mm²
   - B. 81 mm²
   - C. 486 mm² ✓
   - D. 729 mm²

6. 6 in.
   - A. 36 in²
   - B. 144 in²
   - C. 216 in² ✓
   - D. 288 in²

7. 2 cm, 5 cm, 3 cm
   - A. 20 cm²
   - B. 30 cm²
   - C. 50 cm²
   - D. 62 cm² ✓

8. 2 cm, 10 cm, 6 cm
   - A. 184 cm² ✓
   - B. 120 cm²
   - C. 50 cm²
   - D. 24 cm²

## CHECKPOINT

**ONLINE 10 min**

### Objectives
- Construct a cube or a rectangular box from a two-dimensional pattern and determine the surface area.

Students will complete an online Checkpoint. If necessary, read the directions, problems, and answer choices to students and help them with keyboard or mouse operations.

NETS, SOLIDS, AND SURFACE AREA

# Area of Irregular Shapes

## Lesson Overview

| | | |
|---|---|---|
| Skills Update | 5 minutes | ONLINE |
| **GET READY** Area of Rectangles | 10 minutes | OFFLINE |
| **LEARN** Whole Squares and Partial Squares | 10 minutes | ONLINE |
| **LEARN** Solve Area Problems | 15 minutes | OFFLINE |
| **TRY IT** Area and Irregular Shapes | 15 minutes | OFFLINE |
| **CHECKPOINT** | 5 minutes | ONLINE |

### ▶ Lesson Objectives
Use squares to approximate the area of an irregular shape.

### ▶ Prerequisite Skills
- Define and demonstrate understanding of the area of any plane figure.
- Find the area of a rectangular shape and use the appropriate unit.

### ▶ Content Background
Students will learn to approximate the area of irregular shapes in square units.
   *Area* is the measure of the region inside a two-dimensional figure or the surface of a three-dimensional figure. Since it measures length and width, area is a square measurement. Area is measured by finding the number of square units within a region. The units used to measure area have an exponent of 2. For example, you might see area measured in square meters ($m^2$), square inches ($in^2$), square miles ($mi^2$), or square centimeters ($cm^2$).

### ▶ Common Errors and Misconceptions
- Students might think of all measurements as length. For example, they might perceive area as a distance—something that they can measure with a ruler. Consequently, they often measure the perimeter (the path around the figure).
- Students might believe that it doesn't matter if units are all identical. They may believe that if they can fill a region (such as a box) with units of measure (such as beans), it doesn't matter if some of the units of measure (beans) are of a different size. They will simply count the number of objects contained within the region (box).
- Students might believe that although the units of measure should be identical, it doesn't matter if they do not completely cover a region.

### ▶ Advance Preparation
Print one copy of the Centimeter Grid Paper.

### Materials to Gather

**SUPPLIED**
Centimeter Grid Paper (printout)
Solve Area Problems activity page
Area and Irregular Shapes activity page

PERIMETER, AREA, AND VOLUME

## GET READY  Area of Rectangles

**OFFLINE 10 min**

### Objectives
- Define and demonstrate understanding of the area of any plane figure.
- Find the area of a rectangular shape and use the appropriate unit.

Students will draw rectangles, label the dimensions, and use the area formula to find the area of each rectangle.

Gather the Centimeter Grid Paper.

1. Remind students that a formula is a standard equation used to compute values, such as area, perimeter, or volume.

   **Say:** Write the formula for finding the area of a rectangle, $A = bh$, at the top of the grid paper.

   **Say:** Explain what the variables in the formula mean. *A stands for area, which is equal to the measure of the base (b) times the measure of the height (h).*

2. Have students use a scale of 1 foot per square centimeter to draw a rectangle on the grid paper with a base of 12 and height of 8. Have them label the base 12 ft and the height 8 ft.

3. Have students use the formula to find the area of the rectangle.

   $A = bh$

   $A = 12 \cdot 8$

   $A = 96$

   The area of the rectangle is 96 ft².

   **Ask:** Why is the area measured in square feet, rather than in linear feet that aren't squared? *Since area measures length and width, area is a square measurement.*

4. Have students check their calculation by counting the centimeter squares inside the rectangle. Remind students that each square on the grid paper has a scale of 1 foot per centimeter.

5. Repeat Steps 2–4 for a rectangle that has a base of 6 meters and a height of 14 meters using a scale of 1 meter per centimeter.

   $A = bh$

   $A = 6 \cdot 14$

   $A = 84$

   The area of the rectangle is 84 m².

## LEARN  Whole Squares and Partial Squares

**ONLINE 10 min**

### Objectives
- Use squares to approximate the area of an irregular shape.

Students will count whole squares and partial squares on a grid to find the approximate area of an irregular shape.

AREA OF IRREGULAR SHAPES

## LEARN Solve Area Problems

**OFFLINE 15 min**

### Objectives
- Use squares to approximate the area of an irregular shape.

Students will solve story problems by estimating the area of irregular shapes. Have students turn to the Solve Area Problems activity page in their Activity Book and read the directions with them.

Students should copy the problems from the Activity Book into their Math Notebook as necessary and solve them there.

1. Read the Worked Examples box with students. Help them count the 5 whole squares and the 11 partial squares on the grid.
2. Help them estimate as they mentally combine the partial squares to form about 4 whole squares.
3. Remind students that area is a square measure, so they need to write their answers to area problems with square-unit measures, such as square miles.
4. Tell students that answers to questions about the area of irregular shapes can vary. The estimated area can range from the number of whole squares without any partial squares counted to the number of all squares covered and partially covered by the irregular shape. In this activity, the acceptable answers include those ranges.
5. Help students systematically record their work to help eliminate simple tracking or counting errors. One method is to have students draw a grid and mark "P" for a partial square and "W" for a whole square as they look at the irregular shape they are measuring. Then they can count the whole squares, estimate the area of partial squares, and add them together.
6. Have students complete Problem 1 in the problem set. They should discover that there are no whole squares covered by the shape of the rug. They will mentally combine the partial squares to reach their answer.
7. Have students complete Problem 2 in the problem set.
8. When students reach Problem 3, have them pay close attention to the fact that each square on the grid represents more than 1 square unit. Each square represents 4 ft². Tell them they will need to multiply to find the approximate area.

   **Ask:** This problem uses squares that equal 4 square feet each. After you count the squares in the area, what will you do to get the estimate? Multiply the number of estimated squares by 4.

   Have students complete Problem 3.

9. Make sure students see that Problem 4 uses squares that represent 10,000 mi².

   **Ask:** After you count the squares in the area, what will you do to get the estimate? Multiply the number of estimated squares by 10,000.

10. After students solve Problem 4, challenge them to use a different way to estimate the area of Nevada.
    - Have students divide the Nevada shape into a rectangle and a triangle, use formulas to estimate the area of each shape, and then add the areas.
      The formula for finding the area of a rectangle is $A = bh$.
      The formula for finding the area of a triangle is $A = \frac{bh}{2}$.
    - Remind students that each square on the grid represents 10,000 mi².
    - Have students compare their answer to the answer they got when they used the whole and partial squares method. See the following illustration and solution equations.

### Tips
The formula for the area of a rectangle is $A = bh$. The formula for the area of a triangle is $A = \frac{bh}{2}$. Extend the activity by investigating the actual area of the state of Nevada.

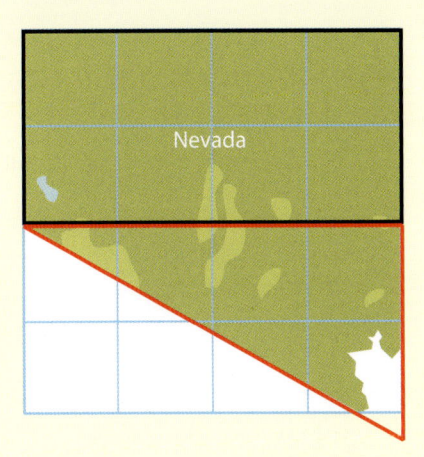

Find the area of the rectangle.

$A = bh$
$A = 4 \cdot 2$
$A = 8$

Find the area of the triangle.

$A = \dfrac{bh}{2}$
$A = \dfrac{4 \cdot 2}{2}$
$A = 4$

$10{,}000\,(8 + 4) = 10{,}000\,(12) = 120{,}000$

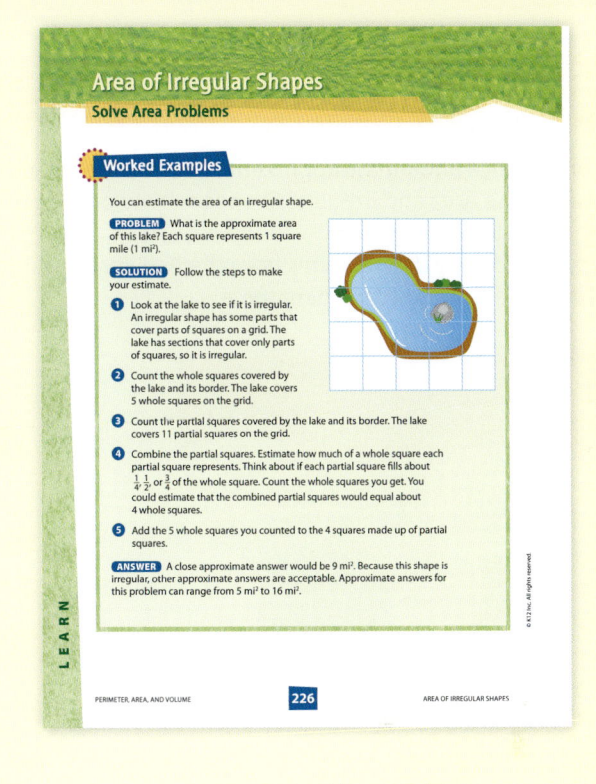

The approximate area of the shape, calculated by adding the area of the rectangle and the triangle, is 120,000 mi².

11. Discuss that the answer reached by using formulas and the answer reached by counting squares are both estimates of the exact area.

**Additional Answers**

1. A close estimate would be 6 ft². Accept any answer between 6 ft² and 10 ft².

2. A close estimate would be 26 yd². Accept any answer between 18 yd² and 36 yd².

4. A close estimate would be 120,000 mi². Accept any answer between 100,000 mi² and 140,000 mi².

AREA OF IRREGULAR SHAPES

## TRY IT  Area and Irregular Shapes

**OFFLINE 15 min**

### Objectives
- Use squares to approximate the area of an irregular shape.

Students will practice finding the approximate area of irregular shapes. Have students turn to the Area and Irregular Shapes activity page in their Activity Book and read the directions with them.

Students should copy the problems from the Activity Book into their Math Notebook as necessary and solve them there.

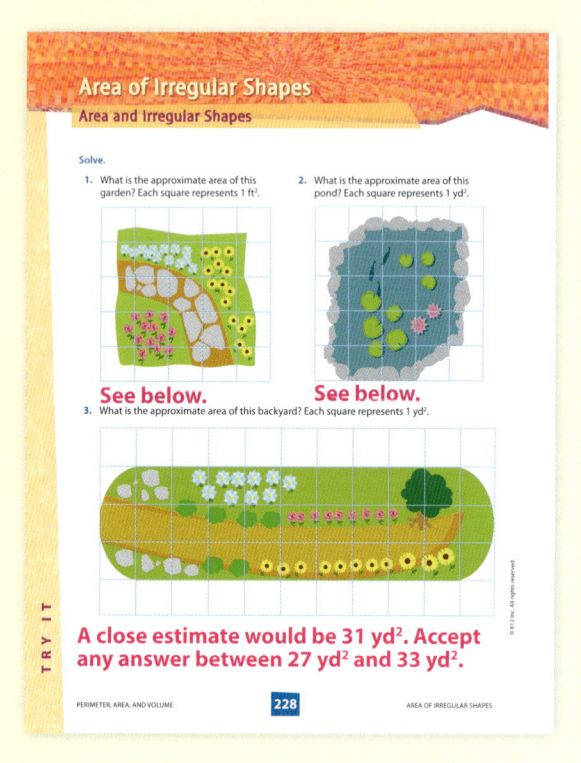

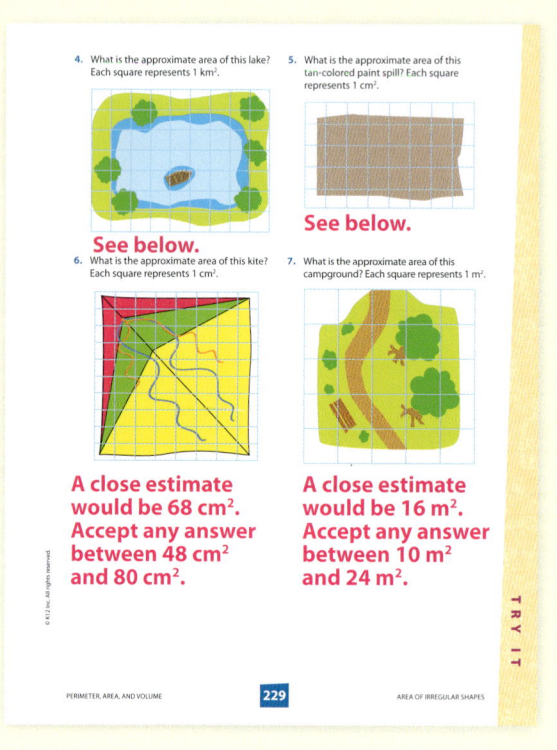

### Additional Answers
1. A close estimate would be 17 ft². Accept any answer between 9 ft² and 25 ft².
2. A close estimate would be 18 yd². Accept any answer between 11 yd² and 25 yd².
4. A close estimate would be 54 km². Accept any answer between 39 km² and 63 km².
5. A close estimate would be 26 cm². Accept any answer between 18 cm² and 40 cm².

## CHECKPOINT

**ONLINE 5 min**

### Objectives
- Use squares to approximate the area of an irregular shape.

Students will complete an online Checkpoint. If necessary, read the directions, problems, and answer choices to students and help them with keyboard or mouse operations.

484  PERIMETER, AREA, AND VOLUME

# Volume of Solid Figures (A)

## Lesson Overview

| | | |
|---|---|---|
| **GET READY** Estimate Cubes in a Solid Figure | 10 minutes | **OFFLINE** |
| **LEARN** Build in Three Dimensions for Volume | 15 minutes | **OFFLINE** |
| **LEARN** Different Shapes with the Same Volume | 15 minutes | **ONLINE** |
| **LEARN** Choose Reasonable Units for Volume | 10 minutes | **ONLINE** |
| **TRY IT** Practice Volume of Solid Figures | 10 minutes | **OFFLINE** |

### ▶ Lesson Objectives
Explain and determine the volume of a solid figure and use appropriate units.

### ▶ Prerequisite Skills
Estimate or determine the number of cubes required to fill a solid figure.

### ▶ Content Background
Students will learn how to find the volume of three-dimensional objects by counting cubes that fit inside an object. They will explore that the same volume measurement can represent different shapes and sizes. They will also learn how to decide which unit of measurement is reasonable to measure the volume of an object.

*Volume* is the measure of the number of cubic units that a space occupies. Volume is a cubic-unit measurement (since it measures the three dimensions of length, width, and height), so the units used to measure volume have an exponent of 3. For example, you might see volume measured in cubic meters ($m^3$), cubic inches ($in^3$), cubic miles ($mi^3$), or cubic centimeters ($cm^3$).

### ▶ Common Errors and Misconceptions
Students might think that volume is a two-dimensional concept since they have worked with representations of three-dimensional figures on a two-dimensional textbook page.

### ▶ Advance Preparation
Gather two rectangular boxes of different sizes and some small cubes, such as sugar cubes or toy blocks. Gather enough cubes to fill the boxes. Try filling each box with the cubes, and then remove the cubes so students don't see how many cubes the boxes will hold. Students will measure the boxes separately by putting cubes into them. They will use small cubes in two activities in this lesson.

### Materials to Gather

**SUPPLIED**
Practice Volume of Solid Figures activity page

**ALSO NEEDED**
household objects – 27 small cubes of the same size (such as sugar cubes or toy blocks); 2 small rectangular boxes of different sizes (such as a gelatin box, rice box, cereal box, or reusable plastic container)

ruler, dual-scale

## GET READY  Estimate Cubes in a Solid Figure

**OFFLINE 10 min**

### Objectives
- Estimate or determine the number of cubes required to fill a solid figure.

Students will estimate how many cubes fill different small boxes. Then they will find out if their estimate was close to the exact answer. They will write measurements of volume in units cubed (units³).

Gather the small cubes, ruler, and two small rectangular boxes of different sizes.

1. Tell students that they are going to estimate the number of cubes that will fit in each box. Have them write a description of one of the small boxes in their Math Notebook and predict the number of cubes that will fill it. Have them use units³ as the unit of measurement for each cube and for the volume of cubes that fill the box. An example would be "gelatin box, estimated volume: 12 units³."

2. Tell students to use the cubes to fill the box. Explain that they may not get an exact "tight fit" of their cubes in the box, but they should come as close as they can. Have them count the number of cubes they put in the box.

3. Have students compare their prediction to the actual number of cubes in the box. They should write the actual volume in units cubed in their notebook under their prediction. An example would be "gelatin box, actual volume: 15 units³."

4. Have students discuss whether their estimate was close to the actual volume.

5. Repeat Steps 1–4 with the box that is a different size.

## LEARN  Build in Three Dimensions for Volume

**OFFLINE 15 min**

### Objectives
- Explain and determine the volume of a solid figure and use appropriate units.

Students will learn about the volume of a rectangular prism by counting units as they build prisms. They will also multiply measurements.

Gather 27 small cubes.

1. Ask students what the dimensions of one cube are. **1 unit by 1 unit by 1 unit**
    - Have students make a layer of cubes that is 2 by 3.
    - Make sure their layer looks like the diagram to the right. It is 2 cubes across (or long), 3 cubes wide (or down), and 1 cube high. Another way to think of it is 2 units by 3 units by 1 unit.
    - Explain to students that this first layer has a volume of 6 units³ because the layer is 2 units long, 3 units wide, and 1 unit high.
    - Have students count the cubes in the layer to confirm that 6 units³ is the volume.
    - Tell them they can count cubes to calculate the volume, or the measure of the number of cubic units a space occupies.
    - Tell students that the length of the first layer is 2 units and the width is 3 units.
    - Remind students that the area of a rectangle is $A = lw$. The area of this rectangle is $2 \cdot 3 = 6$.
    - Explain to students that because this is the first layer, 6 units³ is the volume and 6 units² is the area. Point out that the units of measure for the volume are cubic units and the units of measure for the area are square units.

### Tips
Note that dimensions of solids, such as 2 by 3 by 5, are sometimes written as $2 \times 3 \times 5$.

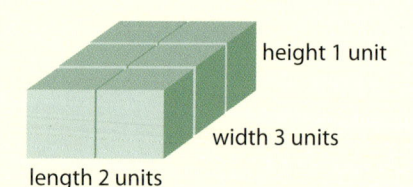

height 1 unit
width 3 units
length 2 units

**486**  PERIMETER, AREA, AND VOLUME

2. Have students add another 2 by 3 layer on top of the first layer.
   - Tell students that adding this layer doubles the volume of the solid figure.
   - Explain to students that they can count the cubes in the second layer just like they counted the cubes in the first layer.
   - Have students count the second layer's cubes.
   - Ask students what the volume of the second layer is. 6 units$^3$

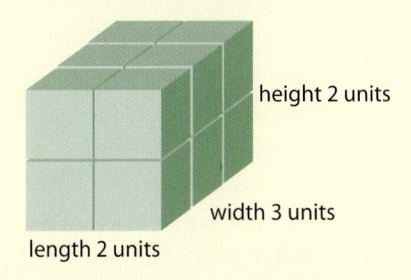

   **Ask:** If you know that the volume of the second layer is 6 units$^3$ and you know that the volume of the first layer was also 6 units$^3$, then what is the volume of the two layers together? 2 units long times 3 units wide times 2 layers, which is (2 • 3) • 2 = 12. (2 • 3 is in parentheses to indicate the volume of the first layer.) The volume of the two layers of the solid is 12 units$^3$.

3. Have students add another 2 by 3 layer on top of the second layer.
   - Explain to students that they can count the cubes in the third layer just like they counted the cubes in the first and second layers.
   - Have them count the third layer's cubes.
   - Ask students what the volume of the third layer is. 6 units$^3$

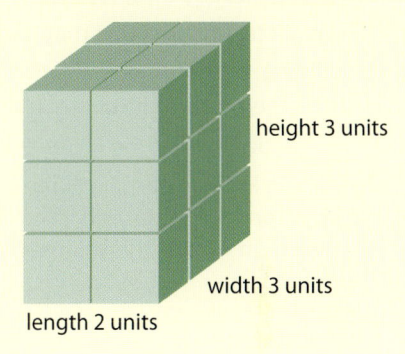

   **Ask:** If you know that the volume of the third layer is 6 units$^3$, the volume of the second layer is 6 units$^3$, and the volume of the first layer was also 6 units$^3$, then what is the volume of all three layers together? 2 units long times 3 units wide times 3 layers, which is (2 • 3) • 3 = 18. (2 • 3 is in parentheses to indicate the volume of the first layer.) The volume of the three layers of the rectangular solid is 18 units$^3$.

4. Tell students they will now use the cubes to build another three-dimensional rectangular prism. This time, they will build a special case of the rectangular prism, a cube.

   **Ask:** If you are building a special-case rectangular prism, a cube, what do you know about the number of cubes in the first layer? There must be the same number of cubes in the length and the width.

5. Tell students they are going to build a special-case rectangular prism, a cube, that is 3 cubes long and 3 cubes wide.

   **Ask:** If you are building a cube with a bottom layer that is 3 cubes long and 3 cubes wide, what do you know about the number of layers that will be in the cube? There will be 3 layers, because a cube has the same dimension for the height—in this case, 3 cubes—as for the length and width.

6. Have students make a layer of cubes that is 3 by 3.
   - Ask students to count the cubes in the layer to find the volume. 9 units$^3$
   - Tell students that the length of the first layer is 3, the width is 3, and the height is 1.
   - Remind students that the area of a square is $A = lw$. The area of this square is 3 • 3 = 9.
   - Explain to students that because this is the first layer, 9 units$^3$ is the volume and 9 units$^2$ is the area. Remind students that the units of measure for the volume are cubic units and the units of measure for the area are square units.

**VOLUME OF SOLID FIGURES (A)** 487

7. Have students add another 3 by 3 layer on top of the cubes in the first layer.
   - Tell them that they've doubled the volume of the solid figure.
   - Ask students to count the cubes in the second layer just like they counted the cubes in the first layer.
   - Ask students what the volume of the second layer is. 9 units$^3$

   **Ask:** If you know that the volume of the second layer is 9 units$^3$ and the volume of the first layer was also 9 units$^3$, then what is the volume of the two layers together? 3 units long times 3 units wide times 2 layers, which is (3 • 3) • 2 = 18. (3 • 3 is in parentheses to indicate the volume of the first layer.) The volume of the two layers is 18 units$^3$.

8. Have students add another 3 by 3 layer on top of the second layer.
   - Explain to students that they can count the cubes in the third layer just like they counted the cubes in the first and second layers.
   - Have them count the cubes in the third layer.
   - Ask students what the volume of the third layer is. 9 units$^3$

   **Ask:** If you know that the volume of the third layer is 9 units$^3$, the volume of the second layer is 9 units$^3$, and the volume of the first layer was also 9 units$^3$, then what is the volume of all three layers together? 3 units long times 3 units wide times 3 layers, which is (3 • 3) • 3 = 27. (3 • 3 is in parentheses to indicate the volume of the first layer.) The volume of the three layers that form the cube is 27 units$^3$.

9. **Ask:** Why would the process you just used work for finding the volume of any rectangular prism, including a cube? A rectangular prism is built with layers that all have the same length and width. So I can repeat the process of finding the volume of each layer and adding the layers' volumes to find the total volume for the prism.

**Tips** If students have difficulty understanding how to find volume this way, have them repeat the activity, making rectangular prisms that have layers with different lengths and widths.

## LEARN Different Shapes with the Same Volume

ONLINE 15 min

### Objectives
- Explain and determine the volume of a solid figure and use appropriate units.

Students will explore different rectangular prisms that have the same volume. Then they will use the Volume Lab Learning Tool to make different rectangular prisms with the same volume.

### DIRECTIONS FOR USING THE VOLUME LAB LEARNING TOOL

1. Click Explore.

   **Say:** Not all rectangular prisms have 2 or more layers. Move the sliders to make a rectangular prism that has 1 layer, is 10 cm long, and has a volume of 30 cm$^3$. The number of layers of a rectangular prism is the same thing as the measurement of height.

   **Ask:** What is the width of the rectangular prism? 3 cm

   **Ask:** How many cubes are in the rectangular prism? 30

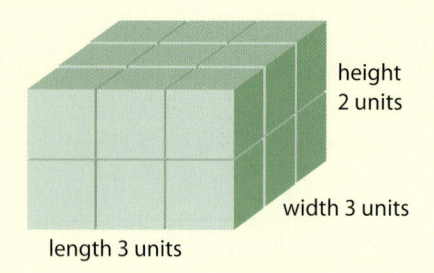

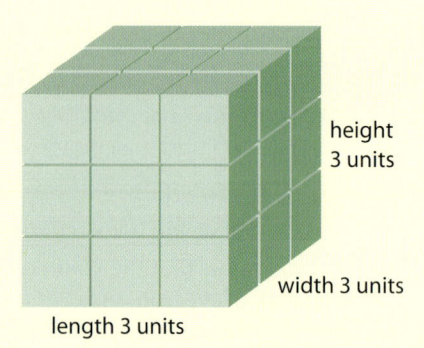

488 PERIMETER, AREA, AND VOLUME

2. Have students move the sliders to make a rectangular prism with the same number of cubes but with multiple layers. Their rectangular prism should be 2 by 3 by 5 (or any combination of those numbers). Tell students to keep reading the changing volume on the learning tool to help them. The volume should be 30 cm$^3$ when they've finished building their rectangular prism.

3. Tell students they'll now make rectangular prisms with another volume. Have them make a rectangular prism with 1 layer and a volume of 8 cm$^3$. The rectangular prism may be 1 by 8 by 1 (or any combination of those numbers) or 2 by 4 by 1 (or any combination of those numbers).

4. Have students move sliders to make another rectangular prism with a volume of 8 cm$^3$ but with 2 layers. Students should make a 2 × 2 × 2 rectangular prism.

    **Ask:** Can a rectangular prism with a volume of 8 cm$^3$ be a cube and why? Yes, if a rectangular prism has equal length, width, and height, it is a cube. A rectangular prism with a length, width, and height of 2 cm has a volume of 8 cm$^3$ and is a cube.

5. Tell students they'll now make rectangular prisms with another volume. Have them make two different rectangular prisms with a volume of 24 cm$^3$. Possible dimensions (or combinations within these dimensions) for their two solids include the following:
    - 1 by 24 by 1
    - 2 by 12 by 1
    - 3 by 8 by 1
    - 4 by 6 by 1
    - 2 by 3 by 4
    - 2 by 6 by 2

### Tips

If students have difficulty understanding that different rectangular prisms can have the same volume, have them build several different rectangular prisms with a volume of 10 units$^3$. Possible dimensions include 1 × 1 × 10, 1 × 2 × 5, 1 × 5 × 2, and 2 × 1 × 5.

## LEARN Choose Reasonable Units for Volume
**ONLINE 10 min**

Students will choose reasonable units for measuring the volume of various everyday objects shaped like rectangular prisms. Before starting the activity,

**Say:** You can use cubes to build rectangular prisms and find the volume of three-dimensional common objects. Those cubes are often described as having a volume of 1 unit$^3$.

**Ask:** What are some common units of measurement that might be used to measure volume? Answers will vary but may include cubic meters, cubic centimeters, cubic inches, cubic feet, and cubic yards.

### Objectives
- Explain and determine the volume of a solid figure and use appropriate units.

## TRY IT Practice Volume of Solid Figures
**OFFLINE 10 min**

Students will count the cubes in each layer to find the volume of rectangular prisms. Have students turn to the Practice Volume of Solid Figures activity page in their Activity Book and read the directions with them.

Students should copy the problems from the Activity Book into their Math Notebook as necessary and solve them there.

### Objectives
- Explain and determine the volume of a solid figure and use appropriate units.

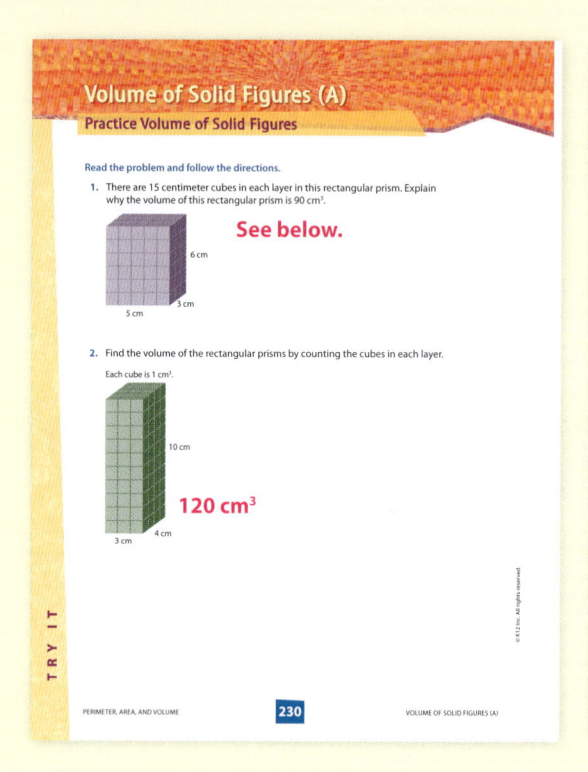

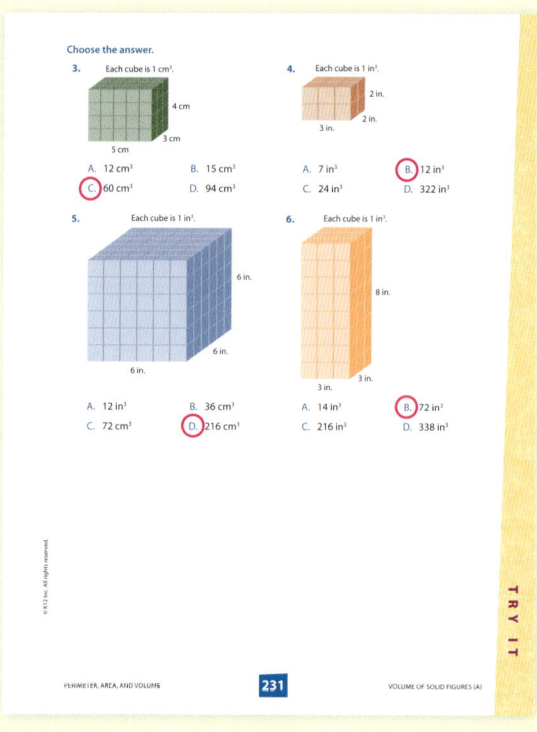

## Additional Answers

1. **Example:** Volume means how many cubes the rectangular prism will hold. The top layer has 15 cm cubes, and there are 6 layers, so there would be 15 by 6 centimeter cubes, or 90 centimeter cubes, in the rectangular prism. The rectangular prism's volume is 90 cm³.

**490** PERIMETER, AREA, AND VOLUME

# Volume of Solid Figures (B)

## Lesson Overview

| | | |
|---|---|---|
| Skills Update | 5 minutes | **ONLINE** |
| **LEARN** Derive the Formula for Volume | 15 minutes | **ONLINE** |
| **LEARN** Use the Volume Formula | 20 minutes | **OFFLINE** |
| **TRY IT** Practice the Formula for Volume | 10 minutes | **OFFLINE** |
| **CHECKPOINT** | 10 minutes | **ONLINE** |

### ▶ Lesson Objectives
Explain and determine the volume of a solid figure and use appropriate units.

### ▶ Prerequisite Skills
Estimate or determine the number of cubes required to fill a solid figure.

### ▶ Content Background
Students will derive the formula and practice using the formula to find the volume of rectangular prisms. A cube is a special case of a rectangular prism.

*Volume* is the measure of the number of cubic units that a space occupies. Volume is a cubic-unit measurement (since it measures the three dimensions of length, width, and height), so the units used to measure volume have an exponent of 3. For example, you might see volume measured in cubic meters ($m^3$), cubic inches ($in^3$), cubic miles ($mi^3$), or cubic centimeters ($cm^3$).

### ▶ Common Errors and Misconceptions
Students might think that volume is a two-dimensional concept since they have worked with representations of three-dimensional figures on a two-dimensional textbook page.

### Materials to Gather

**SUPPLIED**
Use the Volume Formula activity page
Practice the Formula for Volume activity page

## LEARN Derive the Formula for Volume

**ONLINE 15 min**

Students will see how volume measures the cubic units that a space occupies and derive the formula for calculating the volume of a rectangular prism.

### Objectives
- Explain and determine the volume of a solid figure and use appropriate units.

**VOLUME OF SOLID FIGURES (B)** 491

# LEARN  Use the Volume Formula

**OFFLINE 20 min**

Students will solve problems by using the formula $V = lwh$ for finding the volume of a rectangular prism. They will also find missing measurements when the volume is given. Have students turn to the Use the Volume Formula activity page in their Activity Book and read the directions with them.

Students should copy the problems from the Activity Book into their Math Notebook as necessary and solve them there.

1. Read Problem 1 of the Worked Examples with students. Remind them that volume is a cubic measurement, so their answers will be in units cubed.
2. Read Problem 2 of the Worked Examples with students.

   **Ask:** What is the inverse of multiplication by 280? **division by 280**
3. Remind students that dividing 280 by 280 equals 1, so the right side of the equation for that step will end up with $1 \cdot h$, or just $h$.
4. Have students solve the problems in the problem set. Make sure they write the formula, correctly substitute the values, and write the volume in a cubic measurement.
5. If students have difficulty, first encourage them to look at the Worked Examples and follow the process shown. If they still have difficulty, help them apply the process shown in the Worked Examples.

## Objectives

- Explain and determine the volume of a solid figure and use appropriate units.

## Tips

If students have difficulty understanding how to substitute measurements for variables in the formula for volume, have them write the variable and corresponding measurement. For example, in Problem 1 in the problem set, students would write $l = 7$ inches, $w = 9$ inches, and $h = 4$ inches.

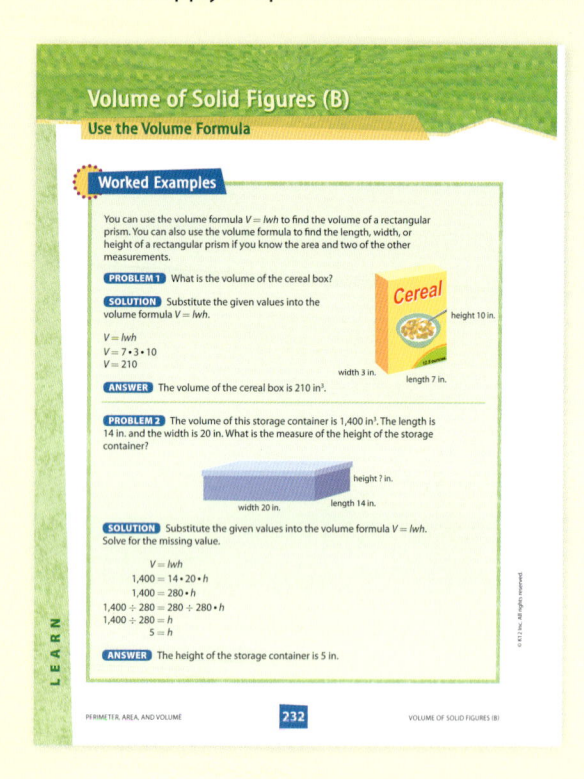

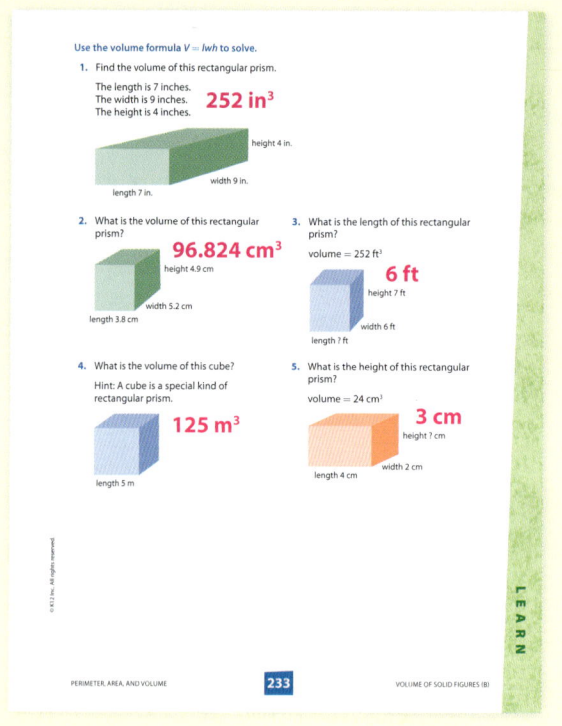

492  PERIMETER, AREA, AND VOLUME

## TRY IT  Practice the Formula for Volume

**OFFLINE 10 min**

### Objectives
- Explain and determine the volume of a solid figure and use appropriate units.

Students will use the formula $V = lwh$ to find the volume of rectangular prisms. They will also use the formula to find the width of a rectangular prism given its length and height. Have students turn to the Practice the Formula for Volume activity page in their Activity Book and read the directions with them.

Students should copy the problems from the Activity Book into their Math Notebook as necessary and solve them there.

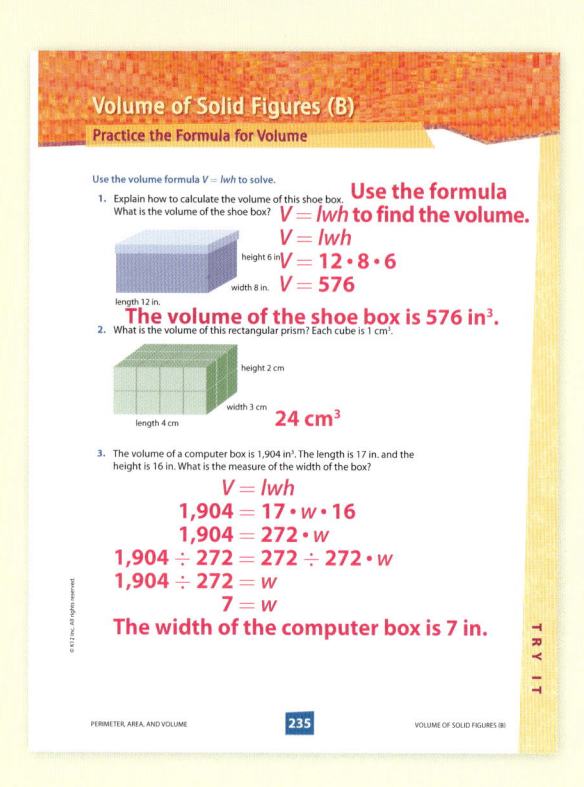

### Volume of Solid Figures (B)
**Practice the Formula for Volume**

Use the volume formula $V = lwh$ to solve.

1. Explain how to calculate the volume of this shoe box. What is the volume of the shoe box?

   height 6 in, width 8 in, length 12 in.

   **Use the formula $V = lwh$ to find the volume.**
   $V = lwh$
   $V = 12 \cdot 8 \cdot 6$
   $V = 576$
   **The volume of the shoe box is 576 in³.**

2. What is the volume of this rectangular prism? Each cube is 1 cm³.

   height 2 cm, width 3 cm, length 4 cm

   **24 cm³**

3. The volume of a computer box is 1,904 in³. The length is 17 in. and the height is 16 in. What is the measure of the width of the box?

   $V = lwh$
   $1,904 = 17 \cdot w \cdot 16$
   $1,904 = 272 \cdot w$
   $1,904 \div 272 = 272 \div 272 \cdot w$
   $1,904 \div 272 = w$
   $7 = w$
   **The width of the computer box is 7 in.**

TRY IT

235

PERIMETER, AREA, AND VOLUME — VOLUME OF SOLID FIGURES (B)

## CHECKPOINT

ONLINE 10 min

Students will complete an online Checkpoint. If necessary, read the directions, problems, and answer choices to students and help them with keyboard or mouse operations.

### Objectives
- Explain and determine the volume of a solid figure and use appropriate units.

**PERIMETER, AREA, AND VOLUME**

# Units of Perimeter, Area, and Volume

| **Lesson Overview** | | |
|---|---|---|
| **LEARN** Units for Perimeter | 5 minutes | **OFFLINE** |
| **LEARN** Units for Area | 15 minutes | **OFFLINE** |
| **LEARN** Units for Volume | 10 minutes | **ONLINE** |
| **LEARN** Differentiate Among Appropriate Units | 10 minutes | **ONLINE** |
| **TRY IT** Practice with Appropriate Units | 10 minutes | **ONLINE** |
| **CHECKPOINT** | 10 minutes | **ONLINE** |

## ▶ Lesson Objectives
Differentiate among appropriate units to measure perimeter, area, and volume.

## ▶ Prerequisite Skills
- Determine the perimeter of a plane figure and use appropriate units.
- Derive and use the formula for the area of a parallelogram and use appropriate units.
- Derive and use the formula for the area of a triangle and use appropriate units.
- Explain and determine the volume of a solid figure and use appropriate units.

### Materials to Gather

**SUPPLIED**
Centimeter Grid Paper (printout) – 4
Net for Rectangular Prism (printout)

## ▶ Content Background
Students will learn to differentiate among appropriate units to measure perimeter, area, and volume in the context of architecture.

*Perimeter* is the distance around a geometric shape or figure, or an everyday object. Perimeter is a linear measurement (since it measures length), so the units used to measure perimeter have an understood exponent of 1. That is, the units for perimeter measures are written without the exponent. For example, you might see perimeter measured in centimeters (cm), meters (m), kilometers (km), inches (in.), feet (ft), yards (yd), or miles (mi).

*Area* is the measure of the region inside a two-dimensional figure or the surface of a three-dimensional figure. Area is a square-unit measurement (since it measures length and width), so the units used to measure area have an exponent of 2. For example, you might see area measured in square meters ($m^2$), square inches ($in^2$), square miles ($mi^2$), or square centimeters ($cm^2$).

*Volume* is the measure of the number of cubic units that a space occupies. Volume is a cubic-unit measurement (since it measures the three dimensions of length, width, and height), so the units used to measure volume have an exponent of 3. For example, you might see volume measured in cubic meters ($m^3$), cubic inches ($in^3$), cubic miles ($mi^3$), or cubic centimeters ($cm^3$).

## ▶ Common Errors and Misconceptions

- Students might think of all measurements as length. For example, they might perceive area as a distance—something that they can measure with a ruler. Consequently, they often measure the perimeter (the path around the figure).
- Students might believe that it doesn't matter if units are all identical. They may believe that if they can fill a region (such as a box) with units of measure (such as beans), it doesn't matter if some of the units of measure (beans) are of a different size. They will simply count the number of objects contained within the region (box).
- Students might believe that although the units of measure should be identical, it doesn't matter if they do not completely cover a region.

## ▶ Advance Preparation

Print four copies of the Centimeter Grid Paper.

- For the Learn: Units for Perimeter activity, draw a 14 by 14 square on one copy of the Centimeter Grid Paper. The square will represent the floor plan of a building. Students will use a second printout to design their own floor plan.
- For the Learn: Units for Area activity, use one copy of the Centimeter Grid Paper to draw the following figures: a square, a parallelogram, and a triangle (see the sample figure at right). The square represents a house, and the parallelogram and triangle represent the house's front yard. Students will use a second printout to design the house's backyard.

Print one copy of the Net for Rectangular Prism printout.

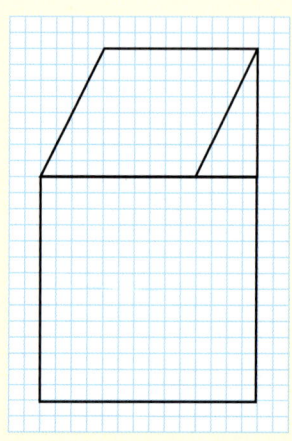

## LEARN  Units for Perimeter

**OFFLINE 5 min**

### Objectives

- Differentiate among appropriate units to measure perimeter, area, and volume.

Students will discuss the perimeter of a building. They will decide the appropriate unit for measuring perimeter.

Gather the Centimeter Grid Paper on which you drew a 14 by 14 square, plus a second copy of the grid paper.

1. Tell students they will apply geometry and measurement concepts to architecture. Explain that one of the first steps in designing a building is to create a floor plan. A floor plan shows the dimensions of the building as if viewed from above the building.

2. Show students the square you drew on Centimeter Grid Paper. Tell students that the square is the floor plan of a building.

   **Say:** A builder wants to install drainage pipes around the perimeter of the building. Water will then drain away from the building. The builder wants to know the perimeter of the building.

   **Ask:** What unit of measurement would you use to describe the perimeter of the building and why? *Answers will vary. Answers may include meters, feet, or yards. Answers about why the unit was chosen will vary but should include that the unit chosen is a type of unit used for measuring length. Students may also say that inches, centimeters, and certain other units are too small to use for measuring the building's perimeter, while miles and kilometers are too large to use for measuring the building's perimeter.*

3. Have students draw a floor plan of a building on another sheet of grid paper. They can decide what type of building it is, such as an office building, a community center, or a museum.
   - Tell students the building can be a square, a rectangle, or a parallelogram, or a shape with edges that vary, such as a large square connected to a small square.
   - Have them label the dimensions, including the unit of measure, such as feet or meters.
   - Have students find the perimeter of the building and write it, using an appropriate unit of measure. Answers will vary. Make sure students have chosen a linear unit in the perimeter measurement.

## LEARN Units for Area

**OFFLINE 15 min**

### Objectives
- Differentiate among appropriate units to measure perimeter, area, and volume.

Students will identify appropriate units to measure area of a parallelogram, area of a triangle, and surface area of a rectangular prism and cube in the context of a house plan.

Gather the Centimeter Grid Paper on which you drew the square, triangle, and parallelogram. Also gather a second copy of the grid paper and the Net for Rectangular Prism printout.

1. Show students the figures you drew on Centimeter Grid Paper. Tell students that a design for a house frequently includes a plan for the yard.

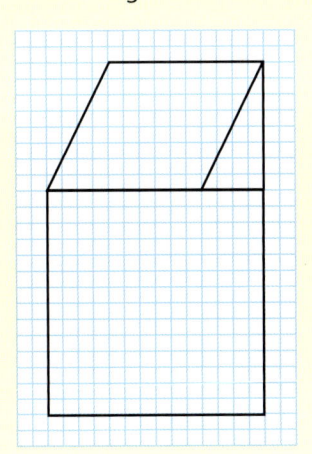

### Tips

These are the formulas for area for different plane figures:
square: $A = bh$
rectangle: $A = bh$
parallelogram: $A = bh$
triangle: $A = \frac{bh}{2}$

2. Discuss the plan for the yard.

   **Say:** The square represents a house and the parallelogram and triangle represent the front yard. If the homeowners want to plant grass in the front yard, they need to find the area of the parallelogram and triangle to determine how much grass seed to buy.

   **Ask:** What type of unit—linear, squared, or cubed—would you use to describe the area of the parallelogram and why? Square units, because area is a measure of two dimensions, base and height. Area is the number of square units that cover a shape.

   **Ask:** What type of unit would you use to describe the area of the triangle and why? Square units, because area is a measure of two dimensions, base and height. Area is the number of square units that cover a shape.

3. Have students draw and label the dimensions (including the unit of measure, such as feet or meters) of the backyard of a house on another sheet of grid paper.
   - Tell students the backyard can be a square, rectangle, parallelogram, or triangle.
   - Have students find the area of the yard and use an appropriate unit to record the area. Have them write the formula and substitute the value of each dimension in the formula to find the area. An example of finding the area of a triangle with base 12 m and height 10 m is shown below.

   $A = \frac{bh}{2}$

   $A = \frac{12 \cdot 10}{2}$

   $A = \frac{120}{2}$

   $A = 60$

   The area of the triangle is 60 m².

4. Tell students they can also use surface area to solve problems about other rectangular prisms.

   **Say:** Surface area is the sum of the areas of all the faces, bases, and curved surfaces of a solid figure. These are two examples of problems you could solve by finding surface area:
   - If you want to cover the outside of a box with wrapping paper, the surface area of the outside of the box determines the amount of paper you need.
   - If you want to paint the inside of the box, the surface area of the inside of the box determines the amount of paint you need.

5. Give students the Net for Rectangular Prism printout. Tell them that the net represents the living room of a house.

   **Say:** Suppose the homeowners want to cover the floor with carpeting, the walls with wallpaper, and the ceiling with paint. Use the printout to label the walls, floor, and ceiling of the net.

6. Discuss the net and the labeled parts of the living room.

   **Ask:** What unit of measurement would you use to find the area of the ceiling if each unit in the net is 1 foot? Square feet, or ft², because area is a square measure of two dimensions: base and height.

   **Ask:** What unit of measurement would you use to find the area of the floor and the walls if each unit in the net is 1 foot? Would it be the same unit of measurement as the area of the ceiling? Why? Square feet, or ft², because area is a square measure of two dimensions: base and height. Each square in the net represents 1 foot, so I would use a square measure for the area of the floor and walls, just like the area of the ceiling.

7. Use the net to discuss surface area.

   **Ask:** How would you calculate the surface area of all the surfaces in the room that would be covered with carpeting, paint, or wallpaper? Add the areas of the surfaces of the rectangular prism together.

   **Ask:** If each square in the net represents 1 foot, what unit of measurement would you use for the surface area and why? Square feet, or ft², because surface area is a square-unit measurement. It measures the length times the width of each face of a solid figure.

PERIMETER, AREA, AND VOLUME

## LEARN  Units for Volume

**ONLINE 10 min**

Students will identify appropriate units to measure the volume of rectangular prisms and cubes in the context of different types of buildings.

**Tips** Allow students to sketch each building and label the dimensions (including the unit of measure, such as feet or meters) before finding the volume.

### Objectives
- Differentiate among appropriate units to measure perimeter, area, and volume.

## LEARN  Differentiate Among Appropriate Units

**ONLINE 10 min**

Students will differentiate among appropriate units to measure perimeter, area, surface area, and volume of two notable buildings in New York City.

### Objectives
- Differentiate among appropriate units to measure perimeter, area, and volume.

## TRY IT  Practice with Appropriate Units

**ONLINE 10 min**

Students will complete an online Try It. If necessary, read the directions, problems, and answer choices to students and help them with keyboard or mouse operations.

### Objectives
- Differentiate among appropriate units to measure perimeter, area, and volume.

## CHECKPOINT

**ONLINE 10 min**

Students will complete an online Checkpoint. If necessary, read the directions, problems, and answer choices to students and help them with keyboard or mouse operations.

### Objectives
- Differentiate among appropriate units to measure perimeter, area, and volume.

# Unit Review

## Lesson Overview

| | | |
|---|---|---|
| **UNIT REVIEW** Look Back | 10 minutes | **ONLINE** |
| **UNIT REVIEW** Checkpoint Practice | 50 minutes | **ONLINE** |
| **UNIT REVIEW** Prepare for the Checkpoint | | |

## ▶ Unit Objectives

This lesson reviews the following objectives:

- Determine the perimeter of a plane figure and use appropriate units.
- Derive and use the formula for the area of a parallelogram and use appropriate units.
- Derive and use the formula for the area of a triangle and use appropriate units.
- Construct a cube or a rectangular box from a two-dimensional pattern and determine the surface area.
- Use squares to approximate the area of an irregular shape.
- Explain and determine the volume of a solid figure and use appropriate units.
- Differentiate among appropriate units to measure perimeter, area, and volume.

### Materials to Gather

There are no materials to gather for this lesson.

## ▶ Advance Preparation

In this lesson, students will have an opportunity to review previous activities in the Perimeter, Area, and Volume unit. Look at the suggested activities in Unit Review: Prepare for the Checkpoint online and gather any needed materials.

### UNIT REVIEW  Look Back — ONLINE 10 min

Students will review key concepts from the unit to prepare for the Unit Checkpoint.

**Objectives**
- Review unit objectives.

### UNIT REVIEW  Checkpoint Practice — ONLINE 50 min

Students will complete an online Checkpoint Practice to prepare for the Unit Checkpoint. If necessary, read the directions, problems, and answer choices to students. Have students answer the problems on their own. Review any missed problems with students.

**Objectives**
- Review unit objectives.

### ➡ UNIT REVIEW  Prepare for the Checkpoint

What you do next depends on how students performed in the previous activity, Unit Review: Checkpoint Practice. If students had difficulty with any of the problems, complete the appropriate review activity listed in the table online.

**500** PERIMETER, AREA, AND VOLUME

# Unit Checkpoint

## Lesson Overview

**UNIT CHECKPOINT** Online                                    60 minutes  |  ONLINE

### ▶ Unit Objectives

This lesson assesses the following objectives:
- Determine the perimeter of a plane figure and use appropriate units.
- Derive and use the formula for the area of a parallelogram and use appropriate units.
- Derive and use the formula for the area of a triangle and use appropriate units.
- Construct a cube or a rectangular box from a two-dimensional pattern and determine the surface area.
- Use squares to approximate the area of an irregular shape.
- Explain and determine the volume of a solid figure and use appropriate units.
- Differentiate among appropriate units to measure perimeter, area, and volume.

### Materials to Gather

There are no materials to gather for this lesson.

### UNIT CHECKPOINT Online

ONLINE 60 min

Students will complete the Unit Checkpoint online. If necessary, read the directions, problems, and answer choices to students and help them with keyboard or mouse operations.

### Objectives

- Assess unit objectives.

# Math Reasoning: Methods and Strategies

## Unit Objectives

- Prioritize and sequence the information in a story problem that involves multiplication or division of decimal numbers.
- Determine when and how to break a multistep whole-number story problem or money problem into simpler parts.
- Use a variety of methods, such as words, numbers, symbols, charts, graphs, tables, diagrams, and models, to explain mathematical reasoning in nonroutine or complex problems.
- Identify and generalize methods for solving problems that are similar to each other.
- Apply strategies and results from simple story problems involving fractions to more complex problems.

## Unit Introduction

In this unit, students will develop ways to solve story problems. They will list by priority and will sequence the information in the problem. They will determine when and how to break a multistep problem into simpler parts. They will use methods such as words, numbers, graphs, tables, and models to explain their problem-solving reasoning with complex problem situations.

Students will identify and generalize the methods they use to solve problems so they can apply these procedures to problems that are similar to one another. They will also apply the strategies and results used to answer simple problems to solve more complex problems. As they study problem solving in this unit, students will work with whole numbers, fractions, multiplication and division of decimal numbers, and money amounts.

## Keywords

conjecture
reasoning

representation
sequence information

solution
strategy

# Steps to Solve Story Problems (A)

## Lesson Overview

| | | |
|---|---|---|
| **GET READY** Explain Steps to Solve a Problem | 10 minutes | **ONLINE** |
| **LEARN** Sequence Steps to Solve Problems | 15 minutes | **ONLINE** |
| **LEARN** Correct Order to Solve Story Problems | 15 minutes | **ONLINE** |
| **LEARN** Order Steps to Solve Story Problems | 10 minutes | **ONLINE** |
| **TRY IT** Determine Steps to Solve Problems | 10 minutes | **ONLINE** |

### ▶ Lesson Objectives
Prioritize and sequence the information in a story problem that involves multiplication or division of decimal numbers.

### ▶ Prerequisite Skills
Analyze a story problem by identifying the question, recognizing relevant information, sequencing and prioritizing information, and developing a solution strategy.

### ▶ Content Background
Students will determine and sequence steps to find solutions to story problems that involve multiplication or division of decimal numbers.

Solving a story problem is a strategic process that is not always straightforward. The following problem-solving method was developed by George Pólya and is an effective way to solve a variety of story problems: (1) understand the problem; (2) devise a plan; (3) carry out the plan; and (4) look back.

The first step of this process, "understand the problem," often interferes with students' ability to follow a problem to its solution. The secret to success is in the ability to carefully read the problem, reword the problem, analyze the question, and figure out relationships among the given pieces of information. Only then can students recognize an effective strategy for solving the problem.

Students should also realize that there are often different ways to solve a problem and different strategies that will work. By using many different strategies, they learn to be flexible in their problem solving and learn that some strategies are more efficient than others.

### Materials to Gather
There are no materials to gather for this lesson.

## GET READY  Explain Steps to Solve a Problem

**ONLINE 10 min**

### Objectives
- Analyze a story problem by identifying the question, recognizing relevant information, sequencing and prioritizing information, and developing a solution strategy.

Students will walk through the steps to solve a problem involving decimal numbers and find the solution.

**Tips** Have students solve the problem a different way to show them that they can arrive at the same solution in more than one way.

## LEARN  Sequence Steps to Solve Problems

**ONLINE 15 min**

### Objectives
- Prioritize and sequence the information in a story problem that involves multiplication or division of decimal numbers.

Students will sequence the steps to solve a multistep problem involving finding the cost of purchases.

**Tips** Ask students what would happen if they reversed the order of solving the first two smaller problems, finding the cost of the strawberries before finding the cost of the apples. Have them discuss whether or not the order of solving these two smaller problems makes a difference in finding the solution to the original problem.

## LEARN  Correct Order to Solve Story Problems

**ONLINE 15 min**

### Objectives
- Prioritize and sequence the information in a story problem that involves multiplication or division of decimal numbers.

Students will determine the steps needed to solve multistep problems involving multiplication of decimal numbers, including money amounts.

## LEARN  Order Steps to Solve Story Problems

**ONLINE 10 min**

### Objectives
- Prioritize and sequence the information in a story problem that involves multiplication or division of decimal numbers.

Students will determine the steps needed to solve multistep problems involving division of decimal numbers, including money amounts.

## TRY IT  Determine Steps to Solve Problems

**ONLINE 10 min**

### Objectives
- Prioritize and sequence the information in a story problem that involves multiplication or division of decimal numbers.

Students will complete an online Try It. If necessary, read the directions, problems, and answer choices to students and help them with keyboard or mouse operations.

# Steps to Solve Story Problems (B)

## Lesson Overview

| | | |
|---|---|---|
| **GET READY** Relevant and Irrelevant Numbers | 10 minutes | ONLINE |
| **LEARN** Analyze Problems and Make Steps | 20 minutes | OFFLINE |
| **LEARN** Make a Plan to Solve Story Problems | 10 minutes | ONLINE |
| **TRY IT** Steps for Multistep Problems | 10 minutes | ONLINE |
| **CHECKPOINT** | 10 minutes | ONLINE |

### ▶ Lesson Objectives

Prioritize and sequence the information in a story problem that involves multiplication or division of decimal numbers.

### ▶ Prerequisite Skills

Analyze a story problem by identifying the question, recognizing relevant information, sequencing and prioritizing information, and developing a solution strategy.

### ▶ Content Background

Students will continue to determine and sequence steps to find solutions to story problems that involve multiplication or division of decimal numbers.

Solving a story problem is a strategic process that is not always straightforward. The following problem-solving plan was developed by George Pólya and is an effective way to solve a variety of story problems: (1) understand the problem; (2) devise a plan; (3) carry out the plan; and (4) look back.

### ▶ Advance Preparation

Print the Problem-Solving Plan.

**Materials to Gather**

**SUPPLIED**
Problem-Solving Plan (printout)
Analyze Problems and Make Steps activity page

## GET READY  Relevant and Irrelevant Numbers   ONLINE 10 min

Students will determine what information is needed to solve a problem and what information is irrelevant.

**Objectives**

- Analyze a story problem by identifying the question, recognizing relevant information, sequencing and prioritizing information, and developing a solution strategy.

# LEARN  Analyze Problems and Make Steps

**OFFLINE 20 min**

## Objectives

- Prioritize and sequence the information in a story problem that involves multiplication or division of decimal numbers.

## Tips

Have students rewrite their plan reversing the first three steps to show that the order of those steps do not matter in finding the solution.

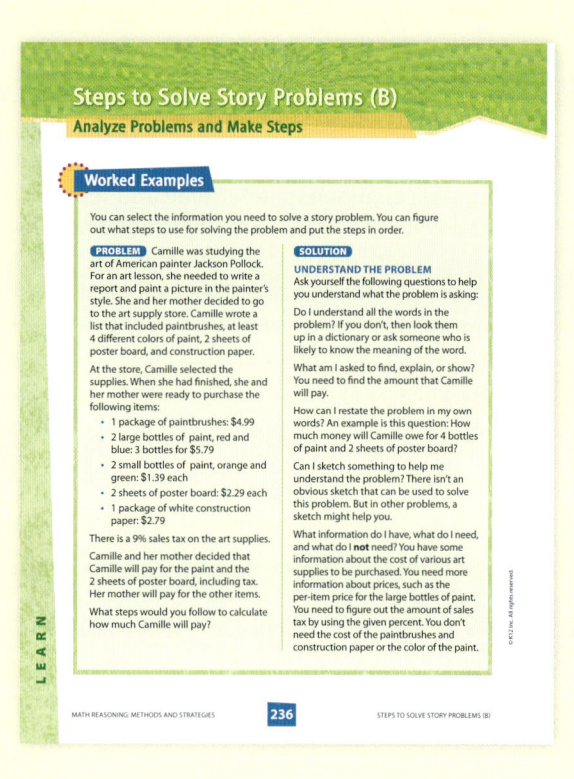

Students will see how Pólya's 4-step problem-solving plan can be used to solve a story problem. They will make sure they understand the problem and will put steps in a correct order for solving it. Gather the Problem-Solving Plan. Have students turn to the Analyze Problems and Make Steps activity page in their activity book and read the directions with them.

Students should copy the problems from the Activity Book into their Math Notebook as necessary and solve them there.

1. Give students the Problem-Solving Plan. Read the information about George Pólya with students. Read the four numbered steps on the printout with students.

2. Tell students that the first step, "understand the problem," is critical to solving a problem correctly.

3. Read the Worked Examples box with students through the section called "understand the problem." Point out the questions in that section on the printout.

4. Read the rest of the Worked Examples box with students. Explain that there is more than one way to solve most problems.

    **Ask:** Why doesn't the order of the first three steps matter? **I can figure the costs of items in any order because the costs will be added together when I take the fourth step to find the answer.**

    **Ask:** Why does the order of the final three steps matter? **I can't add the costs of the supplies without knowing each item's cost. I can't figure out the sales tax before knowing the total cost of the items. I can't add the tax to the total cost without figuring out the tax amount.**

    **Ask:** How do you know if this path was the right one for solving this problem? **Example:** In the last section, "look back," the questions and answers supported the answer that I found for the story problem. The question in the story problem has been answered. The answer makes sense when compared with an estimate.

5. Have students complete the problems in the problem set. Have them refer to the Problem-Solving Plan and the Worked Example as needed.

6. After students finish Problem 3, ask the following question:

    **Ask:** What information in the problem wasn't needed for solving it? **Don has 7 neighbors. A neighbor has 3 dogs. Another neighbor has 4 cars.**

**508  MATH REASONING: METHODS AND STRATEGIES**

## Page 237

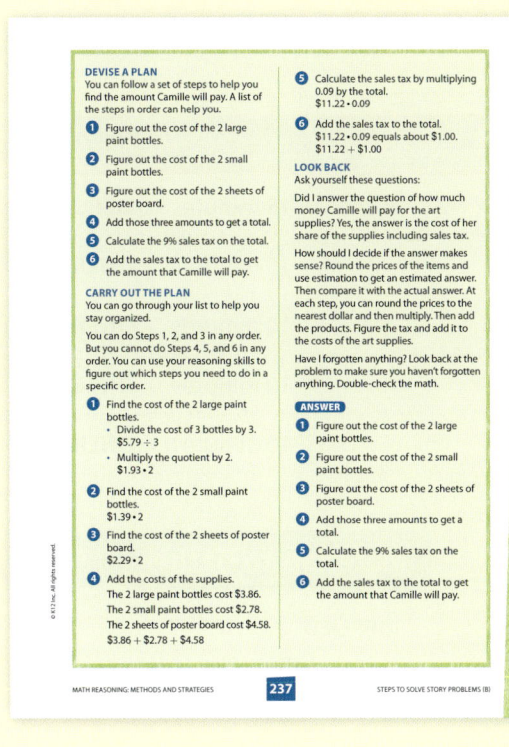

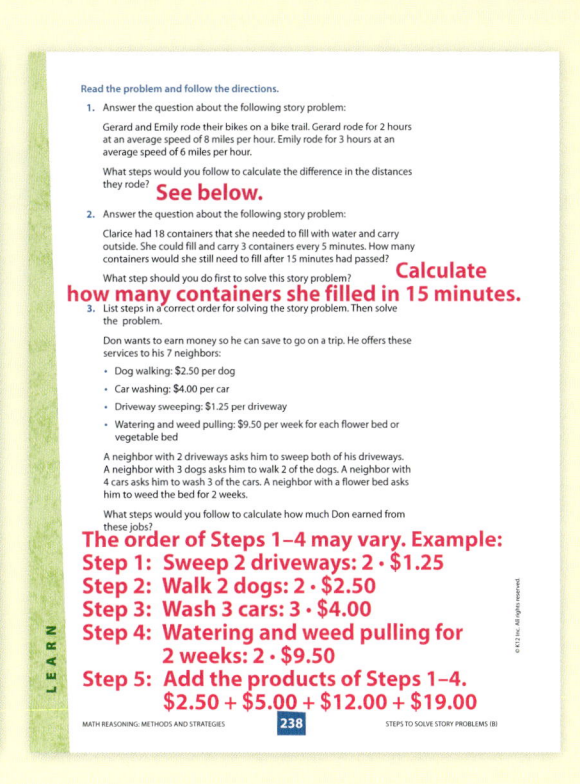

**DEVISE A PLAN**
You can follow a set of steps to help you find the amount Camille will pay. A list of the steps in order can help you.

1. Figure out the cost of the 2 large paint bottles.
2. Figure out the cost of the 2 small paint bottles.
3. Figure out the cost of the 2 sheets of poster board.
4. Add those three amounts to get a total.
5. Calculate the 9% sales tax on the total.
6. Add the sales tax to the total to get the amount that Camille will pay.

**CARRY OUT THE PLAN**
You can go through your list to help you stay organized.
You can do Steps 1, 2, and 3 in any order. But you cannot do Steps 4, 5, and 6 in any order. You can use your reasoning skills to figure out which steps you need to do in a specific order.

1. Find the cost of the 2 large paint bottles.
   - Divide the cost of 3 bottles by 3. $5.79 ÷ 3$
   - Multiply the quotient by 2. $1.93 · 2$
2. Find the cost of the 2 small paint bottles. $1.39 · 2$
3. Find the cost of the 2 sheets of poster board. $2.29 · 2$
4. Add the costs of the supplies.
   The 2 large paint bottles cost $3.86.
   The 2 small paint bottles cost $2.78.
   The 2 sheets of poster board cost $4.58.
   $3.86 + $2.78 + $4.58

5. Calculate the sales tax by multiplying 0.09 by the total. $11.22 · 0.09
6. Add the sales tax to the total. $11.22 · 0.09 equals about $1.00. $11.22 + $1.00

**LOOK BACK**
Ask yourself these questions:
Did I answer the question of how much money Camille will pay for the art supplies? Yes, the answer is the cost of her share of the supplies including sales tax.
How should I decide if the answer makes sense? Round the prices of the items and use estimation to get an estimated answer. Then compare it with the actual answer. At each step, you can round the prices to the nearest dollar and then multiply. Then add the products. Figure the tax and add it to the costs of the art supplies.
Have I forgotten anything? Look back at the problem to make sure you haven't forgotten anything. Double-check the math.

**ANSWER**
1. Figure out the cost of the 2 large paint bottles.
2. Figure out the cost of the 2 small paint bottles.
3. Figure out the cost of the 2 sheets of poster board.
4. Add those three amounts to get a total.
5. Calculate the 9% sales tax on the total.
6. Add the sales tax to the total to get the amount that Camille will pay.

## Page 238

Read the problem and follow the directions.

1. Answer the question about the following story problem:
   Gerard and Emily rode their bikes on a bike trail. Gerard rode for 2 hours at an average speed of 8 miles per hour. Emily rode for 3 hours at an average speed of 6 miles per hour.
   What steps would you follow to calculate the difference in the distances they rode? **See below.**

2. Answer the question about the following story problem:
   Clarice had 18 containers that she needed to fill with water and carry outside. She could fill and carry 3 containers every 5 minutes. How many containers would she still need to fill after 15 minutes had passed?
   What step should you do first to solve this story problem? **Calculate how many containers she filled in 15 minutes.**

3. List steps in a correct order for solving the story problem. Then solve the problem.
   Don wants to earn money so he can save to go on a trip. He offers these services to his 7 neighbors:
   - Dog walking: $2.50 per dog
   - Car washing: $4.00 per car
   - Driveway sweeping: $1.25 per driveway
   - Watering and weed pulling: $9.50 per week for each flower bed or vegetable bed
   A neighbor with 2 driveways asks him to sweep both of his driveways. A neighbor with 3 dogs asks him to walk 2 of the dogs. A neighbor with 4 cars asks him to wash 3 of the cars. A neighbor with a flower bed asks him to weed the bed for 2 weeks.
   What steps would you follow to calculate how much Don earned from these jobs?
   **The order of Steps 1–4 may vary. Example:**
   **Step 1: Sweep 2 driveways: 2 · $1.25**
   **Step 2: Walk 2 dogs: 2 · $2.50**
   **Step 3: Wash 3 cars: 3 · $4.00**
   **Step 4: Watering and weed pulling for 2 weeks: 2 · $9.50**
   **Step 5: Add the products of Steps 1–4. $2.50 + $5.00 + $12.00 + $19.00**

---

**Additional Answers**
1. **Step 1:** Multiply 2 by 8.
   **Step 2:** Multiply 3 by 6.
   **Step 3:** Subtract the lesser product from the greater product.

## LEARN  Make a Plan to Solve Story Problems — ONLINE 10 min

Students will determine the steps needed to solve multistep problems involving multiplication or division of decimal amounts, including money.

**Objectives**
- Prioritize and sequence the information in a story problem that involves multiplication or division of decimal numbers.

## TRY IT  Steps for Multistep Problems — ONLINE 10 min

Students will complete an online Try It. If necessary, read the directions, problems, and answer choices to students and help them with keyboard or mouse operations.

**Objectives**
- Prioritize and sequence the information in a story problem that involves multiplication or division of decimal numbers.

## CHECKPOINT — ONLINE 10 min

Students will complete an online Checkpoint. If necessary, read the directions, problems, and answer choices to students and help them with keyboard or mouse operations.

**Objectives**
- Prioritize and sequence the information in a story problem that involves multiplication or division of decimal numbers.

STEPS TO SOLVE STORY PROBLEMS (B)

# Break Down Multistep Problems

## Lesson Overview

| | | |
|---|---|---|
| **LEARN** Simpler Parts | 15 minutes | **OFFLINE** |
| **LEARN** More Than One Way | 15 minutes | **ONLINE** |
| **LEARN** Who Owes Whom? | 10 minutes | **ONLINE** |
| **TRY IT** Find the Simpler Parts of a Problem | 10 minutes | **ONLINE** |
| **CHECKPOINT** | 10 minutes | **ONLINE** |

### ▶ Lesson Objectives
Determine when and how to break a multistep whole-number story problem or money problem into simpler parts.

### ▶ Prerequisite Skills
- Solve a story problem involving addition or subtraction of money amounts in decimal notation.
- Solve a story problem involving multiplication or division of money amounts in decimal notation.
- Use negative numbers in story problems that involve owing money.

### Materials to Gather

**SUPPLIED**
Problem-Solving Plan (printout)
Simpler Parts activity page

### ▶ Content Background
Students will determine and sequence steps to find solutions to story problems that involve multiplication or division of decimal numbers.

Solving a story problem is a strategic process that is not always straightforward. The following problem-solving method was developed by George Pólya and is an effective way to solve a variety of story problems: (1) understand the problem; (2) devise a plan; (3) carry out the plan; and (4) look back.

The first step of this process, "understand the problem," often interferes with students' ability to follow a problem to its solution. The secret to success is in the ability to carefully read the problem, reword the problem, analyze the question, and figure out relationships among the given pieces of information. Only then can students recognize an effective strategy for solving the problem.

Students should also realize that there are often different ways to solve a problem and different strategies that will work. By using many different strategies, they learn to be flexible in their problem solving and learn that some strategies are more efficient than others.

### ▶ Advance Preparation
Print the Problem-Solving Plan.

## LEARN  Simpler Parts

**OFFLINE 15 min**

### Objectives

- Determine when and how to break a multistep whole-number story problem or money problem into simpler parts.

Students will determine when and how to break a multistep whole-number story problem or decimal money problem into simpler parts. Gather the Problem-Solving Plan. Have students turn to the Simpler Parts activity page in their Activity Book and read the directions with them.

Students should copy the problems from the Activity Book into their Math Notebook as necessary and solve them there.

1. Give students the Problem-Solving Plan. Review the first step, "understand the problem," by having students read the questions aloud.

2. Explain that this activity focuses on determining how and when breaking a problem into simpler parts will help solve the problem.

3. Read the Worked Examples box with students.

   **Ask:** What is another way of restating the problem? Answers will vary.

   **Example:** How much money does Eduardo have left after spending $\frac{3}{4}$ on a baseball glove and then later spending $\frac{1}{3}$ of the money he had left on a baseball book?

   **Ask:** Can any of the steps in the plan for solving this problem be done in any other order? No. This problem has a certain order for the steps because of the information given in the problem and because of the question that is asked.

4. Have students answer Problem 1 in the problem set.

   **Ask:** How would you break the problem into simpler parts? Find the total number of people who attended the first 4 performances. Add that amount to the number of people who attended the last performance.

5. Have students read Problem 2.

   **Ask:** How would you break the problem into simpler parts? Find the number of coins in each jar. Then find the number of coins in each jar that are not gold coins.

6. Have students answer Problem 3.

   **Ask:** Why didn't this problem need to be broken into simpler parts? There is only one part and one calculation in the problem: multiply $3.45 by 8 to find the cost of 8 packages of stickers.

7. Have students answer Problem 4.

   **Ask:** If you divide first and then subtract, will you solve the simpler problems in the correct order? Explain your reasoning. No; the answer would be incorrect unless the subtraction is done first to find the number of cans that both Nancy and Elaine collected.

# Break Down Multistep Problems
## Simpler Parts

### Worked Examples

You can determine when and how to break a story problem into simpler parts.

**PROBLEM** Answer the questions about this story problem:

Eduardo saved $3.00 from his allowance every week for 12 weeks. He spent $\frac{3}{4}$ of the saved amount on a baseball glove. Later, he spent $\frac{1}{3}$ of the remaining amount on a baseball book. How much money does he have left?

Should the problem be broken into simpler problems? If so, how should it be done?

**SOLUTION**

**UNDERSTAND THE PROBLEM**
To figure out if the problem should be broken into simpler parts, ask yourself these questions:

What am I asked to find, explain, or show? You are asked to find how much of Eduardo's savings of 12 weeks he has left.

How can I restate the problem in my own words? Eduardo saved a sum of money. He spent a fraction of the money. Then later he spent another fraction of the remaining money.

What information do I have, what do I need, and what do I **not** need? You know how much he saved each week for 12 weeks. You know the fractional amounts he spent on a baseball glove and a book. You know he spent the money at different times. You need to calculate how much he saved, each amount he spent, and how much he has left.

Yes, the problem requires several calculations, so it should be broken into simpler parts. To break it into simpler problems, devise a plan.

**DEVISE A PLAN**
To break the problem into simpler parts, make a list of the calculations you need to do.
1. Calculate how much Eduardo saved in 12 weeks.
2. Calculate how much he spent on the baseball glove.
3. Subtract that amount from his savings.
4. Calculate how much of his remaining savings he spent on the baseball book.
5. Subtract that amount from his remaining savings.

**CARRY OUT THE PLAN**
1. Multiply to find out how much Eduardo saved in 12 weeks.
2. Multiply the amount of money he saved by $\frac{3}{4}$ to find out how much he spent on the glove.
3. Subtract that amount from his savings.
4. Multiply the difference by $\frac{1}{3}$ to find out how much he spent on the book.
5. Subtract that amount from his remaining savings.

**LOOK BACK**
Ask yourself these questions:
Did I answer the question of whether to break the problem into simpler parts? Yes.
Did I answer the question of how to break the problem into simpler parts? Yes. You made a list of the calculations needed for solving the problem.

**ANSWER** Yes, the problem should be broken into simpler parts. The simpler parts are the calculations needed to find the final answer.

Read the problem and follow the directions.

1. What calculations could be used to solve this problem?

   A popular singer was on a concert tour. Attendance at the concerts was 7,845 for each of the first 4 performances and 6,920 for the final performance. How many people in all attended the concerts?

   Choose the answer.

   **Multiply 7,845 by 4.
   Add 6,920 to the product.**

2. Which describes the calculations that could be used to solve this problem?

   A coin collector keeps 1,482 coins in 6 jars. Each jar contains an equal number of coins. Nine coins in each jar are gold coins. How many coins in each jar are **not** gold coins?

   A. Subtract 6 from 1,482. Then divide by 9.
   B. Add 6 to 1,482. Then divide by 9.
   **C. Divide 1,482 by 6. Then subtract 9.**
   D. Multiply 1,482 by 6. Then subtract 9.

3. Read the problem and review the data in the table. What calculations could be used to solve the following problem?

   What is the cost of 8 packages of stickers?

   A. Multiply $3.45 by 8.
      Subtract $2.29 from the product.
   B. Multiply $3.45 by 8.
      Add $2.75 to the product.
   C. Divide $5.99 by 8.
   **D. Multiply $3.45 by 8.**

   | Scrapbooking Supplies | |
   |---|---|
   | Scrapbooks | $5.99 each |
   | Stickers | $3.45 per package |
   | Rubber Stamps | $2.29 each |
   | Stencils | $2.75 each |

4. Which simpler problems could be calculated to solve this problem?

   Ray, Nancy, and Elaine collected a total of 982 cans of food for the canned food drive. Ray collected 178 cans. Nancy and Elaine collected an equal number of cans. How many cans did Nancy collect?

   A. Find the number of cans Ray collected.
      Then find the total number of cans Ray, Nancy, and Elaine collected.
   B. Find the total number of cans Ray, Nancy, and Elaine collected.
      Then find the total number of cans Nancy collected.
   C. Find the number of cans Nancy collected.
      Then find the total number of cans Nancy and Elaine collected.
   **D. Find the number of cans Nancy and Elaine collected.
      Then find the number of cans Nancy collected.**

## LEARN  More Than One Way

**ONLINE 15 min**

Students will find more than one way to break a multistep money problem into simpler parts.

### Objectives
- Determine when and how to break a multistep whole-number story problem or money problem into simpler parts.

## LEARN  Who Owes Whom?

**ONLINE 10 min**

Students will determine when and how to break a multistep money problem into simpler parts.

**Tips** If students have difficulty identifying simpler problems in a story problem, have them copy the story problem in their Math Notebook and highlight the simpler problems in different colors.

### Objectives
- Determine when and how to break a multistep whole-number story problem or money problem into simpler parts.

## TRY IT  Find the Simpler Parts of a Problem

**ONLINE 10 min**

Students will complete an online Try It. If necessary, read the directions, problems, and answer choices to students and help them with keyboard or mouse operations.

### Objectives
- Determine when and how to break a multistep whole-number story problem or decimal money problem into simpler parts.

## CHECKPOINT

**ONLINE 10 min**

Students will complete an online Checkpoint. If necessary, read the directions, problems, and answer choices to students and help them with keyboard or mouse operations.

### Objectives
- Determine when and how to break a multistep whole-number story problem or money problem into simpler parts.

**BREAK DOWN MULTISTEP PROBLEMS**

# Mathematical Reasoning Methods (A)

## Lesson Overview

| | | |
|---|---|---|
| **GET READY** Use Several Strategies for Problems | 10 minutes | ONLINE |
| **LEARN** Solve Simple to Complex Problems | 30 minutes | ONLINE |
| **TRY IT** Choose the Best Strategy | 20 minutes | OFFLINE |

### ▶ Lesson Objectives
Use a variety of methods, such as words, numbers, symbols, charts, graphs, tables, diagrams, and models, to explain mathematical reasoning in nonroutine or complex problems.

### ▶ Prerequisite Skills
Explain mathematical reasoning in a story problem by using multiple representations.

### ▶ Content Background
Students will learn to use different strategies to solve story problems. They will use diagrams, tables, and equations to help them find the answers to complex story problems.

In this lesson, students will solve nonroutine or complex problems. Routine problems involve using the four operations (addition, subtraction, multiplication, and division) without other strategies. *Nonroutine* and complex problems engage students in using a variety of strategies, such as using guess and test, using simpler numbers, drawing a diagram, and making a table, to find a solution.

Solving nonroutine problems often involves "trying this, then trying that" to come upon a solution. Many problems in everyday life are nonroutine and complex, so this type of problem solving provides a solid foundation for students as they mature and face complex problems of their own.

While working with students, include the problem-solving principles of George Pólya. Call attention to each principle as students work. Remind them that nonroutine or complex math problems are not necessarily more difficult, just more interesting and satisfying to solve. The steps of the problem-solving plan are as follows: (1) understand the problem; (2) devise a plan; (3) carry out the plan; and (4) look back.

When students devise a plan to solve problems, they can find many possible strategies in the 4-step problem-solving plan. Two of the strategies are "Translate into a number sentence" and "Apply a rule or definition." This lesson combines these two ideas and names the strategy "Write an equation."

### Materials to Gather

**SUPPLIED**
Problem-Solving Plan (printout)
Choose the Best Strategy activity page

Students should test their strategies on many problems to see if their strategy always works, and ask an adult to check to see if their strategy makes sense mathematically. Once strategies are proven to work, the next goal is for students to decide which strategies are most efficient for them. A strategy that is efficient for one student may not be for another. Problem solving is not only a key to success in math but also in every area of life. To become good problem solvers, students need to have a variety of strategies at their disposal to be able to choose the strategy that applies to the problem. In that way, they build on their prior experiences with problems and develop strategies that work for many similar problems.

When explaining reasoning, students should do the following:

- Explain and justify why they did what they did.
- Know when to use certain properties of arithmetic, applying concepts to an unfamiliar problem.
- Invent procedures that work well with a new problem, such as easier ways to add greater numbers or long lists of numbers.

▶ **Advance Preparation**
Print the Problem-Solving Plan.

## GET READY  Use Several Strategies for Problems
**ONLINE 10 min**

Students will use the draw-a-diagram and write-an-equation strategies to solve a story problem.

**Objectives**
- Explain mathematical reasoning in a story problem by using multiple representations.

## LEARN  Solve Simple to Complex Problems
**ONLINE 30 min**

Students will solve a nonroutine problem about painting the surface area, or the faces, of different-sized cube models. They will find a solution to a simpler problem, and then build upon that solution to solve more complex problems. Students will use the strategies of using objects to model the problem and finding patterns in a table of data.

**Objectives**
- Use a variety of methods, such as words, numbers, symbols, charts, graphs, tables, diagrams, and models, to explain mathematical reasoning in nonroutine or complex problems.

## TRY IT  Choose the Best Strategy
**OFFLINE 20 min**

Students will choose the problem-solving strategy and explanation that correctly show how to solve each story problem. Gather the Problem-Solving Plan and have students refer to it as needed. Have students turn to the Choose the Best Strategy activity page in their Activity Book and read the directions with them.

Students should copy the problems from the Activity Book into their Math Notebook as necessary and solve them there.

**Objectives**
- Use a variety of methods, such as words, numbers, symbols, charts, graphs, tables, diagrams, and models, to explain mathematical reasoning in nonroutine or complex problems.

**MATHEMATICAL REASONING METHODS (A)  515**

# Mathematical Reasoning Methods (A)
## Choose the Best Strategy

Choose the problem-solving strategy and explanation that correctly show how to solve the problem.

1. Daniella made 1 triangle with 3 toothpicks. She discovered she could make 2 triangles if she used 5 toothpicks. If she used 7 toothpicks, she could make 3 triangles. How many toothpicks would Daniella need to make 7 triangles?

   A. Write an equation.
   $(1 \cdot 3) + (2 \cdot 5) + (3 \cdot 7) = ?$
   Calculate the number of toothpicks needed to make each triangle and add them all up.

   B. Guess and test.
   Guess 17 toothpicks for 7 triangles. Test your guess by drawing the toothpick triangles. If you couldn't draw 7 triangles, revise your guess. Test your guess again. Keep trying.

   C. **Draw a diagram.**
   Draw a diagram of 3 triangles using 7 lines to represent toothpicks. Keep adding lines until you have 7 triangles. Count the number of lines.

2. The perimeter of one face of a cube is 28 cm. What is the surface area of the cube?

   A. **Write equations.**
   Calculate the length of one edge of the cube. Let $n$ represent the length.
   $28 = 4n$
   The length of one edge of the cube is 7 cm.
   Calculate the area of one face. $A = 7 \cdot 7$
   Calculate the surface area of the cube. $S = 49 \cdot 6$

   B. Guess and test.
   Guess that the surface area of one face is 60 cm². Calculate that the area of one face is 10 cm². Calculate that the perimeter of one face is 40 cm. That guess didn't work, so make another guess.
   Guess that the surface area of one face is 42 cm². Calculate that the area of one face is 7 cm². So the perimeter of one face is 28 cm.

   C. Work backward.
   The perimeter of one face is 28 cm. So the length of one face is 14 cm. The area of one face would be $14 \cdot 14$.
   Then multiply that answer by 6 to calculate the surface area.

3. Kent is planting rows of seeds in the community garden. He plants 5 seeds in his first row, 11 seeds in his second row, and 17 seeds in his third row. If Kent uses the same pattern, how many seeds will he plant in his 7th row?

   A. Write an equation.
   $(1 \cdot 5) + (2 \cdot 11) + (3 \cdot 17) = ?$
   Calculate the number of seeds needed in each row and add them together.

   B. Guess and test.
   Guess 38 seeds in the 7th row. Divide 38 by the number of seeds in each row. If the answer is not 7, revise your guess, and test your answer again.

   C. **Make a table.**
   Write the seed-row numbers 1, 2, 3, 4, 5, 6, 7 as column names at the top of the table. In the first row of the table, write 5 in column 1, 11 in column 2, and 17 in column 3. Look for the pattern. Fill in the rest of the table using the same pattern.

4. Denzel can paint 12 tiles in an hour. How many tiles can Denzel paint in $4\frac{1}{2}$ hours?

   A. Make a table.
   Look for a pattern in your table.

   | Hours | 1 | 2 | 3 | 4 | 5 | 6 |
   |---|---|---|---|---|---|---|
   | Tiles | 4.5 | 4.5 | 4.5 | 4.5 | 4.5 | 4.5 |

   B. **Write an equation.**
   Let $n$ equal the number of tiles Denzel can paint in $4\frac{1}{2}$ hours.
   $n = 12 \cdot 4\frac{1}{2} = 12 \cdot \frac{9}{2} = \frac{108}{2} = 54$
   Denzel can paint 54 tiles in $4\frac{1}{2}$ hours.

   C. Use simpler numbers.
   Suppose that Denzel could paint only 10 tiles per hour.
   Calculate how many tiles he could paint in 4 hours. $10 \cdot 4 = 40$, so in 4 hours, he can paint 40 tiles.
   Now that you have figured out how to solve the problem, go back and solve it using fractions.

5. Maddie bought 3 more pounds of flour than Kath. Together Kath and Maddie bought 13 pounds of flour. How many pounds of flour did Kath buy?

   A. **Guess and test.**
   Guess that Kath bought 2 pounds of flour. This means that Maddie would have bought 5 pounds, because $2 + 3 = 5$. Add $2 + 5$. If the sum doesn't equal 13, revise your guess to be that Kath bought 3 pounds of flour. Figure out how many pounds of flour Maddie bought. Is this sum equal to 13? If not, revise your guess, and test your answer again.

   B. Draw a diagram.
   Draw 13 circles to represent the 13 pounds of flour. Divide the circles into two equal groups. Then multiply one group by 3.

   C. Write an equation.
   Let $m$ represent the number pounds of flour Kath bought.
   $(3 \cdot m) + 2 = 13$

6. Derek earned some money over the summer. He charged $7 to wash a car and $4 to walk a dog. He washed 12 cars and walked 6 dogs in August. How much money did Derek make in August?

   A. Work backward.
   Derek washed 12 cars so count backward from 12 to 7 to figure out how much money he made washing cars. He walked 6 dogs, so count back from 6 to 4 to see how much money he made walking dogs. Add the two amounts together.

   B. **Write equations.**
   Multiply the number of cars washed by the amount charged per car.
   $12 \cdot 7 = 84$
   Then multiply the number of dogs walked by the amount charged per dog. $6 \cdot 4 = 24$
   Add the two products together to find the total amount earned.

   C. Draw a picture.
   Draw 12 cars and 6 dogs. Count the cars and dogs.

7. The animal park has 63 butterflies in a special environment for butterflies. There are 28 red butterflies, 19 white butterflies, and the rest are yellow. How many butterflies are yellow?

   A. **Write an equation.**
   $63 - 28 - 19 = ?$

   B. Guess and test.
   Guess that there are 20 yellow butterflies. Add 20 to the number of red and white butterflies. Is your answer 28? If not, revise your guess, and test your answer again.

   C. Draw a diagram.
   Draw 19 dots. Then figure out how many dots you need to get to 28 butterflies in all.

8. Charlotte was selling pies at a bake sale. She sold 13 pies before lunch and another 5 after lunch. At the end of the day, Charlotte had 8 pies left. How many pies did Charlotte start the day with?

   A. Write an equation.
   $8 + 5 - 13 = ?$

   B. **Draw a picture.**
   Draw 8 circles. Add 5 circles and then add 13 circles.

   C. Guess and test.
   Guess that Charlotte started with 20 pies. Subtract 8. Is your answer 13? If not, revise your guess, and test your answer again.

# Mathematical Reasoning Methods (B)

## Lesson Overview

| | | |
|---|---|---|
| Skills Update | 5 minutes | ONLINE |
| **LEARN** Target 41 Game | 35 minutes | OFFLINE |
| **TRY IT** Practice Problem-Solving Strategies | 20 minutes | OFFLINE |

### ▶ Lesson Objectives
Use a variety of methods, such as words, numbers, symbols, charts, graphs, tables, diagrams, and models, to explain mathematical reasoning in nonroutine or complex problems.

### ▶ Prerequisite Skills
Explain mathematical reasoning in a story problem by using multiple representations.

### ▶ Content Background
Students will learn to use different strategies to solve story problems. They will use tables and a guess-and-test strategy to help them find the answers to complex story problems.

In this lesson, students will solve nonroutine or complex problems. Routine problems involve using the four operations (addition, subtraction, multiplication, and division) without other strategies. *Nonroutine* and complex problems engage students in using a variety of strategies, such as using guess and test, using simpler numbers, drawing a diagram, and making a table, to find a solution.

Solving nonroutine problems often involves "trying this, then trying that" to come upon a solution. Many problems in everyday life are nonroutine and complex, so this type of problem solving provides a solid foundation for students as they mature and face complex problems of their own.

### ▶ Advance Preparation
Print the Problem-Solving Plan.

> **Materials to Gather**
>
> **SUPPLIED**
> Problem-Solving Plan (printout)
> Target 41 Game activity page
> Practice Problem-Solving Strategies activity page
>
> **ALSO NEEDED**
> index cards – 30

## LEARN Target 41 Game
*OFFLINE 35 min*

### Objectives
- Use a variety of methods, such as words, numbers, symbols, charts, graphs, tables, diagrams, and models, to explain mathematical reasoning in nonroutine or complex problems.

Students will solve a complex problem by using the guess-and-test strategy. They will use different combinations of numbers to reach a given sum. Gather the Problem-Solving Plan and 30 index cards. Have students turn to the Target 41 Game activity page in their Activity Book and read the directions with them.

Students should copy the problems from the Activity Book into their Math Notebook as necessary and solve them there.

1. Give students the Problem-Solving Plan. Briefly review the steps with them.

**MATHEMATICAL REASONING METHODS (B)** **517**

2. Read the Worked Examples box with students.

   **Ask:** How could Daryl get 50 points when only 3 of his 4 darts hit the board? *His darts could have hit 7, 6, and 2 for a sum of 15, which is worth 50 points. They also could have hit 10, 3, and 2.*

   **Ask:** Why do you think the guess-and-test strategy works well for this problem? *The strategy lets me mix up the different values and use them in different combinations.*

3. Have students read Problem 1 in the problem set.

   **Ask:** What is an answer with only two addends? *13 + 2 = 15*

   To find another answer with a greater number of addends, students can break 13 into two addends.

   **Ask:** What are some answers to the problem? **Possible answers:** *7 + 6 + 2 = 15; 10 + 3 + 2 = 15*

4. Have students find at least four answers for Problem 1 before they move on to Problem 2.

5. Have students begin Problem 2 by listing all the primes on the target. Make sure they list 2, 3, 7, 11, and 13. Have them write at least three combinations of four primes before they move on to the rest of the problems in the problem set.

6. Assist students as needed with the remaining problems. If students have difficulty, first encourage them to look at the Worked Example and follow the process shown. If they still have difficulty, help them apply the process shown in the Worked Example.

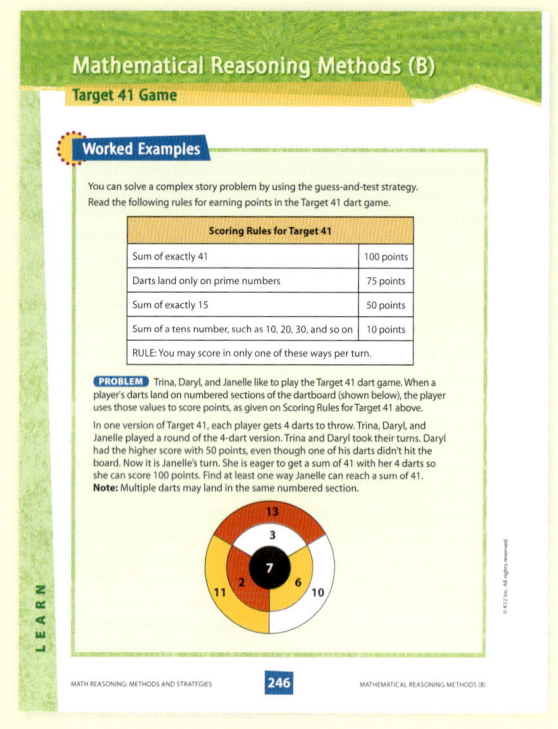

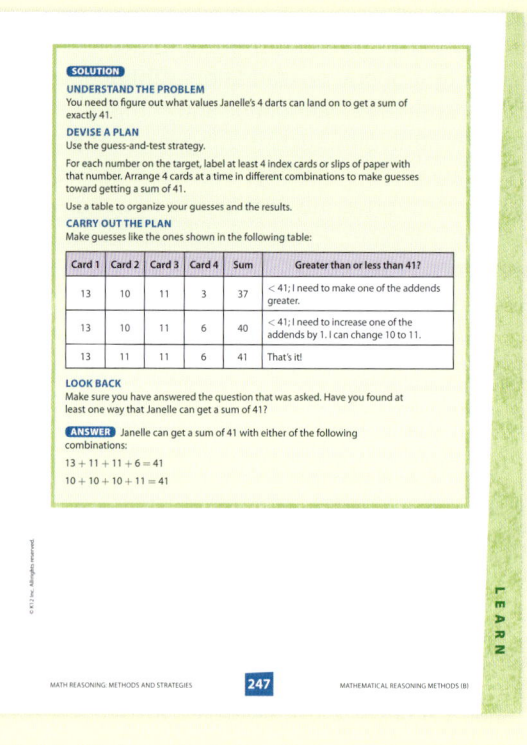

**518** MATH REASONING: METHODS AND STRATEGIES

## Additional Answers

**1. Possible answers:**
$13 + 2 = 15$
$7 + 6 + 2 = 15$
$10 + 3 + 2 = 15$
$7 + 3 + 3 + 2 = 15$
$6 + 6 + 3 = 15$
$3 + 3 + 3 + 3 + 3 = 15$

**2. Possible answers:**
2, 3, 7, 11
2, 3, 7, 13
2, 7, 11, 13
3, 7, 11, 13

**3. Possible answers:**
$10 = 10$
$6 + 2 + 2 = 10$
$7 + 3 = 10$
$2 + 2 + 2 + 2 + 2 = 10$
$3 + 3 + 2 + 2 = 10$

**4. Possible answers:**
$7 + 6 + 7 + 10 + 11 = 41$ (5 darts)
$7 + 3 + 2 + 13 + 6 + 10 = 41$ (6 darts)
$7 + 6 + 7 + 7 + 3 + 11 = 41$ (6 darts)
$7 + 3 + 2 + 7 + 6 + 6 + 10 = 41$ (7 darts)
$7 + 3 + 2 + 10 + 10 + 3 + 6 = 41$ (7 darts)

**5.** 20 darts; $2 + 2 + 2 + 2 + 2 + 2 + 2 + 2 + 2 + 2 + 2 + 2 + 2 + 2 + 2 + 2 + 2 + 2 + 2 + 3 = 41$

## TRY IT  Practice Problem-Solving Strategies

**OFFLINE 20 min**

Students will explain how to use problem-solving strategies to solve story problems. Gather the Problem-Solving Plan. Students may refer to the "devise a plan" step for a list of strategies. Have students turn to the Practice Problem-Solving Strategies activity page in their Activity Book and read the directions with them.

Students should copy the problems from the Activity Book into their Math Notebook as necessary and solve them there.

### Objectives

- Use a variety of methods, such as words, numbers, symbols, charts, graphs, tables, diagrams, and models, to explain mathematical reasoning in nonroutine or complex problems.

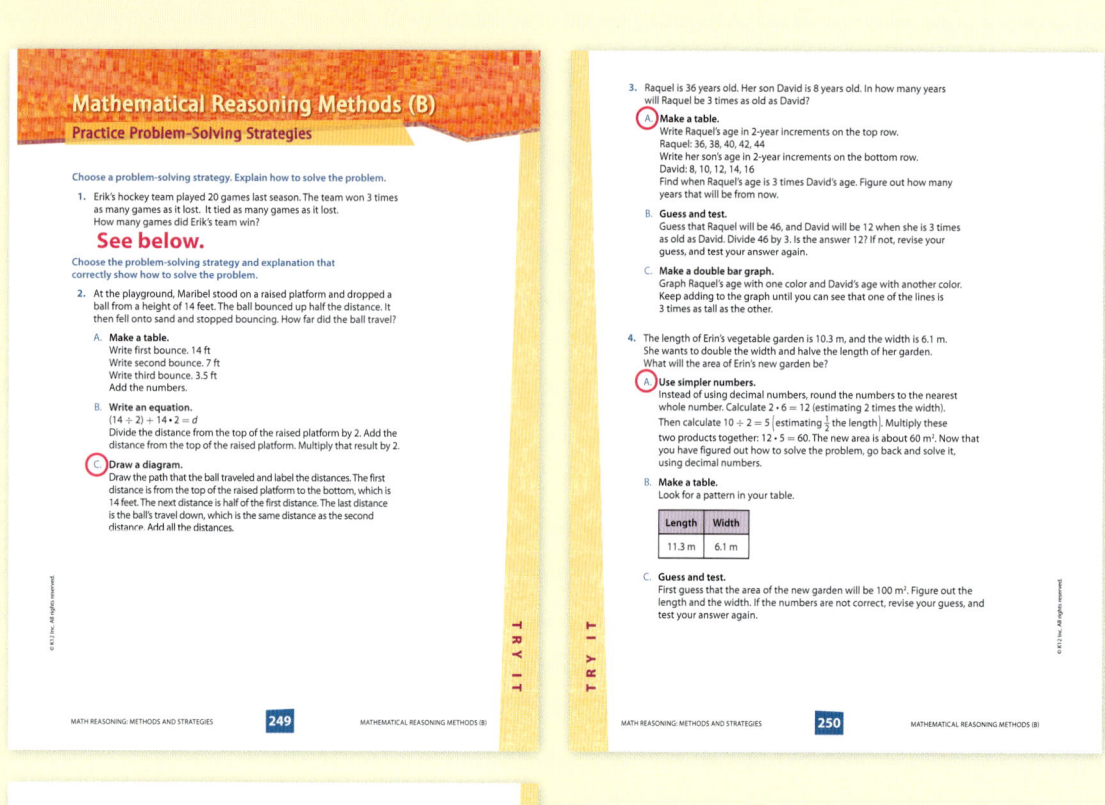

# Mathematical Reasoning Methods (B)
## Practice Problem-Solving Strategies

Choose a problem-solving strategy. Explain how to solve the problem.

1. Erik's hockey team played 20 games last season. The team won 3 times as many games as it lost. It tied as many games as it lost. How many games did Erik's team win?
   **See below.**

Choose the problem-solving strategy and explanation that correctly show how to solve the problem.

2. At the playground, Maribel stood on a raised platform and dropped a ball from a height of 14 feet. The ball bounced up half the distance. It then fell onto sand and stopped bouncing. How far did the ball travel?

   A. **Make a table.**
   Write first bounce. 14 ft
   Write second bounce. 7 ft
   Write third bounce. 3.5 ft
   Add the numbers.

   B. **Write an equation.**
   $(14 \div 2) + 14 \cdot 2 = d$
   Divide the distance from the top of the raised platform by 2. Add the distance from the top of the raised platform. Multiply that result by 2.

   C. **Draw a diagram.**
   Draw the path that the ball traveled and label the distances. The first distance is from the top of the raised platform to the bottom, which is 14 feet. The next distance is half of the first distance. The last distance is the ball's travel down, which is the same distance as the second distance. Add all the distances.

3. Raquel is 36 years old. Her son David is 8 years old. In how many years will Raquel be 3 times as old as David?

   A. **Make a table.**
   Write Raquel's age in 2-year increments on the top row.
   Raquel: 36, 38, 40, 42, 44
   Write her son's age in 2-year increments on the bottom row.
   David: 8, 10, 12, 14, 16
   Find when Raquel's age is 3 times David's age. Figure out how many years that will be from now.

   B. **Guess and test.**
   Guess that Raquel will be 46, and David will be 12 when she is 3 times as old as David. Divide 46 by 3. Is the answer 12? If not, revise your guess, and test your answer again.

   C. **Make a double bar graph.**
   Graph Raquel's age with one color and David's age with another color. Keep adding to the graph until you can see that one of the lines is 3 times as tall as the other.

4. The length of Erin's vegetable garden is 10.3 m, and the width is 6.1 m. She wants to double the width and halve the length of her garden. What will the area of Erin's new garden be?

   A. **Use simpler numbers.**
   Instead of using decimal numbers, round the numbers to the nearest whole number. Calculate $2 \cdot 6 = 12$ (estimating 2 times the width). Then calculate $10 \div 2 = 5$ (estimating $\frac{1}{2}$ the length). Multiply these two products together: $12 \cdot 5 = 60$. The new area is about 60 m². Now that you have figured out how to solve the problem, go back and solve it, using decimal numbers.

   B. **Make a table.**
   Look for a pattern in your table.

   | Length | Width |
   |--------|-------|
   | 11.3 m | 6.1 m |

   C. **Guess and test.**
   First guess that the area of the new garden will be 100 m². Figure out the length and the width. If the numbers are not correct, revise your guess, and test your answer again.

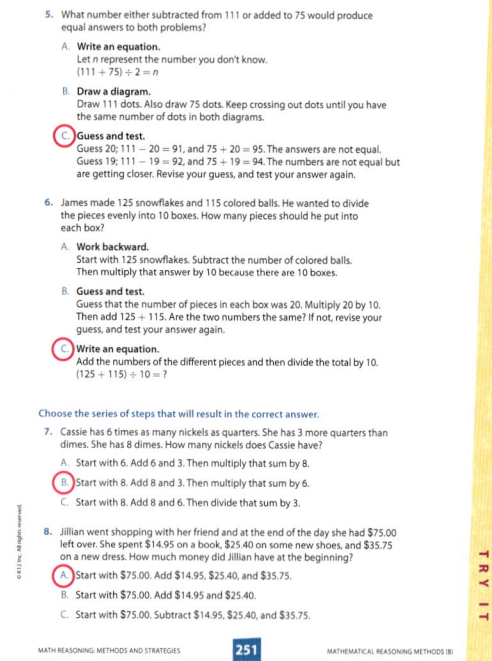

5. What number either subtracted from 111 or added to 75 would produce equal answers to both problems?

   A. **Write an equation.**
   Let $n$ represent the number you don't know.
   $(111 + 75) \div 2 = n$

   B. **Draw a diagram.**
   Draw 111 dots. Also draw 75 dots. Keep crossing out dots until you have the same number of dots in both diagrams.

   C. **Guess and test.**
   Guess 20; $111 - 20 = 91$, and $75 + 20 = 95$. The answers are not equal.
   Guess 19; $111 - 19 = 92$, and $75 + 19 = 94$. The numbers are not equal but are getting closer. Revise your guess, and test your answer again.

6. James made 125 snowflakes and 115 colored balls. He wanted to divide the pieces evenly into 10 boxes. How many pieces should he put into each box?

   A. **Work backward.**
   Start with 125 snowflakes. Subtract the number of colored balls. Then multiply that answer by 10 because there are 10 boxes.

   B. **Guess and test.**
   Guess that the number of pieces in each box was 20. Multiply 20 by 10. Then add $125 + 115$. Are the two numbers the same? If not, revise your guess, and test your answer again.

   C. **Write an equation.**
   Add the numbers of the different pieces and then divide the total by 10.
   $(125 + 115) \div 10 = ?$

Choose the series of steps that will result in the correct answer.

7. Cassie has 6 times as many nickels as quarters. She has 3 more quarters than dimes. She has 8 dimes. How many nickels does Cassie have?

   A. Start with 6. Add 6 and 3. Then multiply that sum by 8.
   B. Start with 8. Add 8 and 3. Then multiply that sum by 6.
   C. Start with 8. Add 8 and 6. Then divide that sum by 3.

8. Jillian went shopping with her friend and at the end of the day she had $75.00 left over. She spent $14.95 on a book, $25.40 on some new shoes, and $35.75 on a new dress. How much money did Jillian have at the beginning?

   A. Start with $75.00. Add $14.95, $25.40, and $35.75.
   B. Start with $75.00. Add $14.95 and $25.40.
   C. Start with $75.00. Subtract $14.95, $25.40, and $35.75.

## Additional Answers

1. Use guess and test. Guess that the team won 12 games. If so, then it lost 4 games and tied 4 games. Test: $12 + 4 + 4 = 20$. Erik's team won 12 games.

# Mathematical Reasoning Methods (C)

## Lesson Overview

| | | |
|---|---|---|
| **LEARN** Strategies for Nonroutine Problems | 15 minutes | **OFFLINE** |
| **LEARN** More Strategies for Nonroutine Problems | 20 minutes | **OFFLINE** |
| **TRY IT** Practice Solving Nonroutine Problems | 15 minutes | **OFFLINE** |
| **CHECKPOINT** | 10 minutes | **ONLINE** |

### ▶ Lesson Objectives

Use a variety of methods, such as words, numbers, symbols, charts, graphs, tables, diagrams, and models, to explain mathematical reasoning in nonroutine or complex problems.

### ▶ Prerequisite Skills

Explain mathematical reasoning in a story problem by using multiple representations.

### ▶ Content Background

Students will continue to use different strategies to solve complex story problems.

In this lesson, students will solve nonroutine or complex problems. Routine problems involve using the four operations (addition, subtraction, multiplication, and division) without other strategies. *Nonroutine* and complex problems engage students in using a variety of strategies, such as using guess and test, using simpler numbers, drawing a diagram, and making a table, to find a solution.

Solving nonroutine problems often involves "trying this, then trying that" to come upon a solution. Many problems in everyday life are nonroutine and complex, so this type of problem solving provides a solid foundation for students as they mature and face complex problems of their own.

### ▶ Advance Preparation

Print the Problem-Solving Plan, Books for the New Library, and Dimensions of the Playing Field printouts.

### Materials to Gather

**SUPPLIED**
Problem-Solving Plan (printout)
Books for the New Library (printout)
Dimensions of the Playing Field (printout)
Practice Solving Nonroutine Problems activity page

---

## LEARN Strategies for Nonroutine Problems

**OFFLINE 15 min**

### Objectives
- Use a variety of methods, such as words, numbers, symbols, charts, graphs, tables, diagrams, and models, to explain mathematical reasoning in nonroutine or complex problems.

Students will solve nonroutine problems. They will explore the strategies of making a table and looking for patterns. Note that this activity deals with consecutive odd numbers. Carl Friedrich Gauss, a mathematician born in 1777, devised an equation when he was a young student to find the sum of consecutive numbers. This activity is a related problem of finding sums of consecutive odd numbers.

Gather the Problem-Solving Plan and Books for the New Library printouts.

1. Give students the Problem-Solving Plan. Tell them they will solve a nonroutine problem.

MATHEMATICAL REASONING METHODS (C) **521**

**Say:** A nonroutine problem is a complex problem. In nonroutine problems, you might use several operations and a variety of strategies.

Read the Problem-Solving Plan with students to review the four steps and the strategies.

2. Give students the Books for the New Library printout. Read the story problem to them. Ask them to make notes about the problem in their Math Notebook.

   A new library is opening soon. People are bringing books to donate to the library.
   - The first person donates 1 book.
   - The second person donates 3 books.
   - The third person donates 5 books.
   - Every person who comes continues to donate 2 more books than the previous person did.
   - How many books will the library have if 20 people follow that pattern?

3. Review questions in the first step, "understand the problem."

   **Ask:** Analyze the problem. What operation will you use to solve it? addition

   **Ask:** What numbers are important to the problem? 1, 3, 5; the 2 books more than the previous person donated

4. Review some questions students can use to help them devise a plan.

   **Ask:** Would a diagram, table, chart, or graph help me with this problem? A table would help me keep track of the information.

   **Ask:** Is there a pattern to the data? Each person gives 2 more books than the previous person does.

5. Tell students that they'll start solving the problem by completing the two left columns of the Books for the New Library table.

   Have them number the top five rows 1–5 in the "Person's number in order of arrival" column.

   Have them complete the "Person's number of books donated" column for the top 5 rows.

   Have them move on to the "Expressions to calculate the running total" column. Explain that a *running total* is a total that changes as new information is given or calculated.

   **Say:** To fill the rows in that column, write an expression showing addition of the number of books that have been donated at that point. For example, the first row will have a 1. The second row will have (1 + 3). The third row will have (1 + 3 + 5).

   Have students complete the table for Person 4 and Person 5.

6. Remind students that every new person donates 2 more books than the previous person did.

   **Ask:** How many books did the fourth person donate? 7 books

   **Ask:** How many books did the fifth person donate? 9 books

   **Ask:** Can you solve the problem about how many books the library will have if 20 people follow that pattern at this point? Why or why not? No, I can't answer the problem yet. I need to fill in more data in the table.

   Have students complete the "Running total" column by adding the numbers in the expression on each row.

7. Have students fill in rows 6 and 7. Answers for the first 7 rows are shown.

| Books for the New Library |||| 
|---|---|---|---|
| Person's number in order of arrival | Person's number of books donated | Expressions to calculate the running total | Running total |
| 1 | 1 | 1 | 1 |
| 2 | 3 | (1 + 3) | 4 |
| 3 | 5 | (1 + 3 + 5) | 9 |
| 4 | 7 | (1 + 3 + 5 + 7) | 16 |
| 5 | 9 | (1 + 3 + 5 + 7 + 9) | 25 |
| 6 | 11 | (1 + 3 + 5 + 7 + 9 + 11) | 36 |
| 7 | 13 | (1 + 3 + 5 + 7 + 9 + 11 + 13) | 49 |
|   |   |   |   |
|   |   |   |   |
|   |   |   |   |
|   |   |   |   |

8. Tell students that it would take much time to fill out the table for 20 people. Tell them that the look-for-a-pattern strategy might help them save time because the information is organized in a table. A pattern is easier to spot in a display such as a table.

   **Ask:** Do you notice any special pattern in the "Running total" column? The numbers are all numbers that are perfect squares.

   **Ask:** What happens when you compare each number in the "Running total" column with its related number in the "Person's number in order of arrival" column? You see that the person's number squared is the running total.

9. Have students predict the number of books donated by Person 8. 64 books

   **Ask:** Check your work by adding (1 + 3 + 5 + 7 + 9 + 11 + 13 + 15). What is the sum? 64

10. Tell students that as they carry out their problem-solving plan, they can ask themselves these questions:

    **Ask:** How can I predict how many books the library will have after a certain number of people arrive and follow the pattern of donating books? Find the square of the number of people.

    **Ask:** Do I still need to use the table for the rest of the data? No

    **Ask:** What was I asked to find in the story problem? If 20 people donated, how many books would the library have?

    **Ask:** What strategies will I need to use to answer this story problem, and what is the answer? Figure out $20^2$. The answer is 400.

11. Have students "look back" and in doing so discover something more. Have them look at the "Person's number of books donated" column.

    **Ask:** What do you notice about the numbers in this column? They are consecutive odd numbers.

    **Ask:** How can you find the sum of the first 5 consecutive odd numbers? Compute 5 squared.

    **Ask:** How can you find the sum of the first 1,000 consecutive odd numbers? Compute 1,000 squared.

    **Ask:** Suppose the variable $S$ stands for the sum of consecutive odd numbers. What equation would allow you to find the sum of the first $n$ consecutive odd numbers? $S = n^2$

12. Have students complete the far left and the far right columns in the table for 8, 9, 10, and 20 people, using only the equation $S = n^2$. Answers are shown. Check students' work.

### Books for the New Library

| Person's number in order of arrival | Person's number of books donated | Expressions to calculate the running total | Running total |
|---|---|---|---|
| 1 | 1 | 1 | 1 |
| 2 | 3 | (1 + 3) | 4 |
| 3 | 5 | (1 + 3 + 5) | 9 |
| 4 | 7 | (1 + 3 + 5 + 7) | 16 |
| 5 | 9 | (1 + 3 + 5 + 7 + 9) | 25 |
| 6 | 11 | (1 + 3 + 5 + 7 + 9 + 11) | 36 |
| 7 | 13 | (1 + 3 + 5 + 7 + 9 + 11 + 13) | 49 |
| 8 | | | 64 |
| 9 | | | 81 |
| 10 | | | 100 |
| 20 | | | 400 |

## LEARN More Strategies for Nonroutine Problems

OFFLINE 20 min

### Objectives
- Use a variety of methods, such as words, numbers, symbols, charts, graphs, tables, diagrams, and models, to explain mathematical reasoning in nonroutine or complex problems.

Students will solve more nonroutine problems. They will use Pólya's 4-step problem-solving plan: (1) understand the problem; (2) devise a plan; (3) carry out the plan; and (4) look back. In the first problem, the strategies they will use include the following: draw a diagram, apply a formula, and guess and test. In the second problem, they will use the work backward strategy. Gather the Problem-Solving Plan and the Dimensions of the Playing Field printouts.

1. Read the Problem-Solving Plan with students to review the 4 steps and the strategies.

2. Give students the Dimensions of the Playing Field printout. Read the story problem to them. Ask them to make notes about the problem in their Math Notebook.
   - The perimeter of a rectangular playing field measures 400 meters.
   - Its length is 3 times its width.
   - Find the length and width of the field.

3. Review questions in the first step, "understand the problem."

   **Ask:** Analyze the problem. What operations will you use to solve it? multiplication and addition

   **Ask:** What numbers are important to the problem? The perimeter is 400 meters. The length is 3 times the width.

   **Ask:** What measurements does the question ask for? the length and width of the playing field

   **Ask:** What questions can you ask yourself? Answers will vary. **Examples:** Will a picture help me understand the problem? Can I make a table to help me try out some numbers?

4. Have students look at the strategies in the second step of the problem-solving plan, "devise a plan."

   **Ask:** How would a diagram and a table help you solve the problem? A diagram would help me understand what the field would look like. A table would help me keep track of the information.

   **Ask:** How would the guess-and-test strategy help you solve the problem? It would help me try different numbers for the length and width.

5. Remind students of the formula for the perimeter of a rectangle: $P = 2l + 2w$

6. Ask students to draw a diagram of the playing field in their Math Notebook.

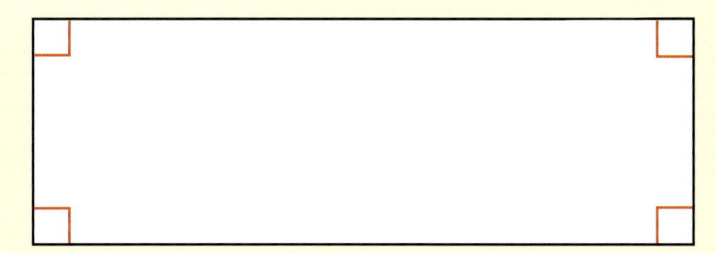

7. Have students guess that the width is 100 meters.

   **Ask:** If the width is 100 meters, what is the length? 300 meters, because the problem says the length is 3 times the width

   **Say:** Substitute 100 for $w$ and 300 for $l$ into the perimeter formula in your Math Notebook. Then calculate the perimeter. $P = 600 + 200 = 800$; The perimeter for the width of 100 meters is 800 meters.

   **Ask:** What was the given perimeter of the playing field? 400 meters

   **Ask:** Rate the guess of 100 meters: too low, too high, or correct? too high

   Have students fill in the top row of the table with that guess.

> **Tips**
>
> Have students create their own version of the Guess My Number game to practice the work backward strategy.

MATHEMATICAL REASONING METHODS (C)

8. Have students follow Step 7 to continue guessing and filling out the table until they reach the correct answer. As they work, have them use the information from their previous guess (too high or too low) to make adjustments for the next guess. Students should ask themselves, "Is my strategy (guess and test) helping me find the answer?" and "Do I still need to use the table for the rest of the data?"

9. Check that students found the correct answer for a perimeter of 400 meters.
   length 150 meters, width 50 meters

   Guesses will vary. Students may use as many rows as they need. Some possible guesses for the problem are shown.

   | Dimensions of the Playing Field ||||||
   |---|---|---|---|---|---|
   | Width (w) | Length (l) (must be 3 times the width) | 2 × w | 2 × l | Perimeter (P) | Rate the Guess (too high, too low, or correct) |
   | 100 | 300 | 200 | 600 | 800 | Too high |
   | 30 | 90 | 60 | 180 | 240 | Too low |
   | 50 | 150 | 100 | 300 | 400 | Correct |
   |  |  |  |  |  |  |
   |  |  |  |  |  |  |
   |  |  |  |  |  |  |
   |  |  |  |  |  |  |
   |  |  |  |  |  |  |
   |  |  |  |  |  |  |

10. Have students do the fourth step, "look back," by asking themselves the questions on the Problem-Solving Plan printout.

11. Read the Guess My Number story problem to students and have them take notes on it in their Math Notebook.

    Peter and Billy played the following game.
    - Start with a secret number between 1 and 10.
    - Multiply the number by 8.
    - Subtract 4.
    - Add 10.
    - Divide by 2.
    - Tell me the number you have at the end and I'll tell you the number you had at the start.

    Peter started with a number. He told Billy that he ended with 31. Billy figured out what number Peter had at the start. What number did Peter have at the start?

526 MATH REASONING: METHODS AND STRATEGIES

12. Tell students to make sure they understand the problem by using the questions in the "understand the problem" step.
13. Tell students to devise a plan.

    **Ask:** Would a diagram, table, chart, or graph help you with this problem? They probably wouldn't help.

    Tell students that as they continue devising a plan and carrying it out, they should do their calculations in their Math Notebook.

    **Ask:** What strategy would work for solving this problem? To find the number Peter chose at the start, I will need to work backward from his number of 31 and use inverse operations back through the problem.

14. Tell students that organizing information as they solve problems is very important.

    **Say:** To solve this problem, use the strategy of working up from the bottom as you go through the Guess My Number rules. Use inverse operations so you can reverse what Peter did for each step. The inverse operation of addition is subtraction. The inverse operation of multiplication is division. The last thing he did was divide by 2 to get 31 at the end. Since multiplication is the inverse of division, begin by multiplying 31 by 2.

    **Ask:** What does 31 · 2 equal? 62

    Have students write that calculation in their Math Notebook.

15. Continue going backward through the steps with students as they do the inverse operations. Make sure students do the following:
    - Subtract 10 because Peter added 10. The number is now 52.
    - Add 4 because Peter subtracted 4. The number is now 56.
    - Divide by 8 because Peter multiplied by 8. The number is now 7. Peter started with the number 7.

16. Have students "look back," the fourth step in the problem-solving plan, at how they solved the problem. They should figure out that they can check the secret number of 7 by working forward to get 31.

### TRY IT  Practice Solving Nonroutine Problems

**OFFLINE 15 min**

Students will choose the problem-solving strategy and description that correctly explain how to solve story problems. Gather the Problem-Solving Plan. Have students turn to the Practice Solving Nonroutine Problems activity page in their Activity Book and read the directions with them.

Students should copy the problems from the Activity Book into their Math Notebook as necessary and solve them there.

### Objectives

- Use a variety of methods, such as words, numbers, symbols, charts, graphs, tables, diagrams, and models, to explain mathematical reasoning in nonroutine or complex problems.

## Mathematical Reasoning Methods (C)
### Practice Solving Nonroutine Problems

Choose the problem-solving strategy and explanation that correctly show how to solve the problem.

1. Artie was saving pennies. On the first day, he saved 2 pennies. The next day, he saved twice as many, giving him a total of 6 pennies (2 + 4). He continued doubling the number of pennies he saved for 10 days. How many pennies did Artie have by the end of the 10th day?

   A. **Write an equation.**
      $10 \cdot (2 + 4) = b$
      Add the pennies he saved on the first and second days. Then multiply by the total number of days.

   B. **Make a table.**
      In the Day 1 column, write 2 pennies.
      In the Day 2 column, write 4 pennies.
      In the Day 3 column, write 8 pennies.
      Continue that pattern through Day 10. The solution is the sum of the numbers of pennies from each day.

   C. **Draw a diagram.**
      Draw 2 pennies and label them Day 1. Draw 6 pennies and label them Day 2. Draw 14 pennies and label them Day 3. Continue this pattern for the 10 days and then count all the pennies.

2. The temperature was 20°F at noon. The temperature increased 3°F per hour until 8:00 p.m. What was the temperature at 6:00 p.m.?

   A. **Guess and test.**
      Guess that the temperature will be 30°F. Find the difference between 20°F and 30°F and divide that by 3. If the answer is less than 6 (the number of hours between noon and 6:00 p.m.), revise your guess, and test your answer again.

   B. **Make a table.**
      Write noon, 1:00 p.m., 2:00 p.m., 3:00 p.m., 4:00 p.m., 5:00 p.m., and 6:00 p.m. on the top row. Write the temperature starting at 20°F under noon in the second row. Write the temperatures, increasing by 3°F, in the remaining boxes on the second row. The correct answer is the temperature at 6:00 p.m.

   C. **Work backward.**
      Start with 6:00 p.m. Subtract 6 hours from 6:00 p.m. to get to noon. Then multiply 20°F by 6 to find out the temperature at 6:00 p.m.

3. The surface area of a cube is 24 square inches. What is the perimeter of a face of the cube?

   A. **Guess and test.**
      Guess that the perimeter of a face is 20 inches. This means that each side of a face is 5 inches. The area of each face would then be 25 square inches. Double that number to get the surface area. The product is greater than 24 square inches. Guess another number, and test it.

   B. **Write equations.**
      Calculate the surface area of one face of the cube.
      Let $a$ represent the area of each face of the cube.
      $24 = 6a$, so $4 = a$
      Calculate the length of each side. Let $s$ represent the length of each side of each face of the cube.
      $s \cdot s = 4$, so $s = 2$
      Calculate the perimeter of each face.
      $P = 4 \cdot 2$

   C. **Work backward.**
      Start with the surface area of 24. Divide by 4 to figure out the area of each face. Then multiply that answer by 4 to get the perimeter.

4. Julie wants to make a rectangular playground that has an area of 160 square feet. She wants to put a rope fence around it, but she wants to use as little rope as possible. What are the dimensions Julie should use for her playground?

   A. **Use objects to model the problem.**
      Arrange 160 square tiles in different patterns until you get a rectangular shape. Count the number of tiles on the perimeter of this shape.

   B. **Write an equation.**
      Write an equation that could be used to calculate the area of a rectangle. Use guess and check to find two numbers that when multiplied will give a product of 160.

   C. **Look for a pattern.**
      Make a list of all possible combinations of length and width that would equal an area of 160 square feet. Then start calculating the perimeter of each rectangle. Look for a pattern to decrease the number of calculations you have to make.

Choose the series of steps that will result in the correct answer.

5. Timmy bought twice as many plums as apples. He bought 4 more plums than bananas. He bought 6 apples. How many bananas did Timmy buy?

   A. Start with 6. Multiply 6 by 2. Then subtract 4.
   B. Start with 6. Multiply 6 by 2. Then add 4.
   C. Start with 4. Add 4 and 6. Then multiply the sum by 2 and add 4.

6. A number is multiplied by 2. Then 8 is added to the product. The sum is then divided by 5. The answer is 8. What was the original number?

   A. Start with 8. Multiply 8 by 5. Then add 8 and multiply the sum by 2.
   B. Start with 8. Add 8 and 5. Then subtract 8 and multiply the sum by 2.
   C. Start with 8. Multiply 8 by 5. Then subtract 8 and divide the difference by 2.

## CHECKPOINT
**ONLINE 10 min**

Students will complete an online Checkpoint. If necessary, read the directions, problems, and answer choices to students and help them with keyboard or mouse operations.

### Objectives
- Use a variety of methods, such as words, numbers, symbols, charts, graphs, tables, diagrams, and models, to explain mathematical reasoning in nonroutine or complex problems.

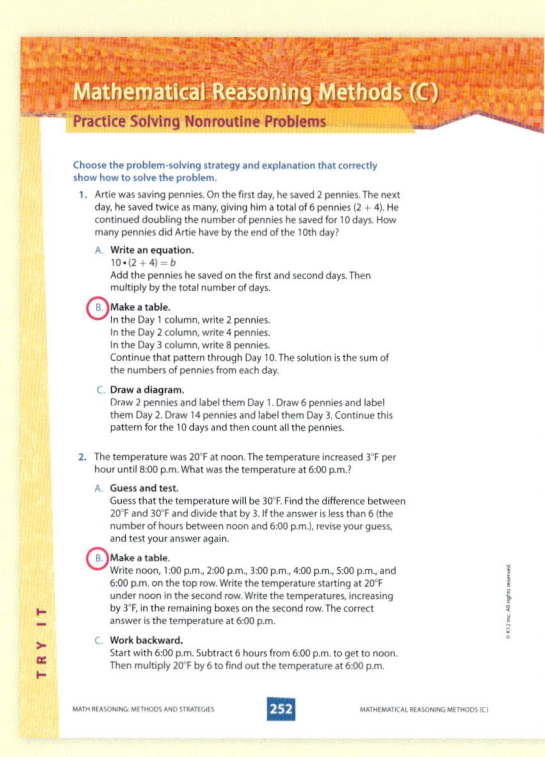

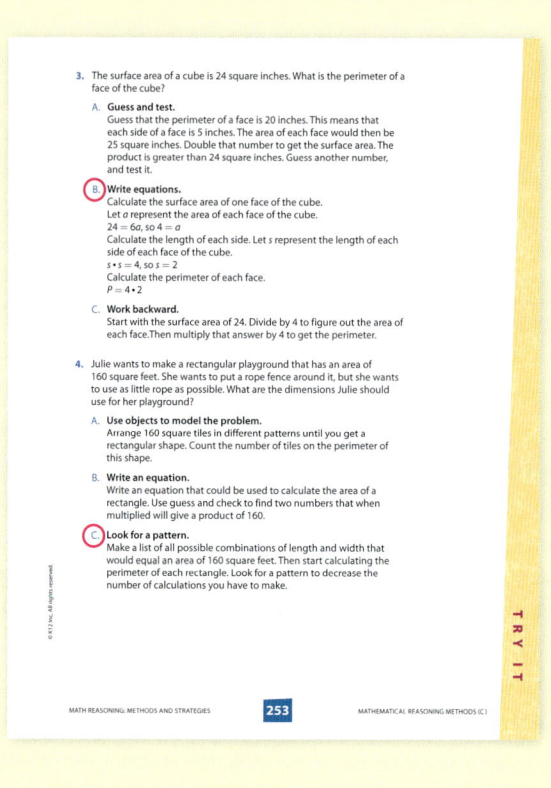

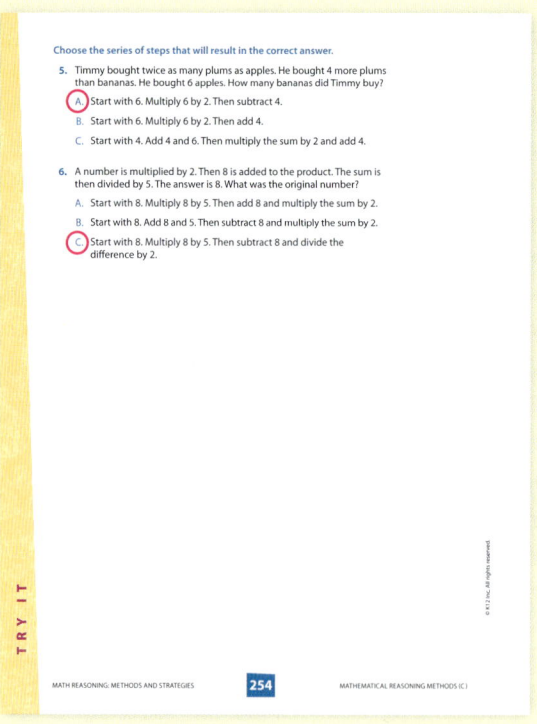

# Choose and Use Strategies (A)

## Lesson Overview

| | | |
|---|---|---|
| **GET READY** Simple to Complex | 10 minutes | **ONLINE** |
| **LEARN** Look Back to Check | 15 minutes | **ONLINE** |
| **LEARN** Make-a-Table Strategy | 15 minutes | **ONLINE** |
| **LEARN** Use Tables to Solve Problems | 10 minutes | **OFFLINE** |
| **TRY IT** Practice Using Tables | 10 minutes | **OFFLINE** |

### ▶ Lesson Objectives
Identify and generalize methods for solving problems that are similar to each other.

### ▶ Prerequisite Skills
Apply strategies or results from a simpler problem to a similar or more complex problem.

### ▶ Content Background
Although the context and numbers in story problems vary, good problem solvers realize that they can use certain strategies over and over to solve problems that are similar to each other. That skill relies on students being able to identify similarities between problems. When they learn and are able to use different strategies, they realize that instead of treating every problem they encounter as a new experience, they can apply successful strategies for solving problems that are similar.

As students work on solving problems, they should follow the 4-step problem-solving plan. The following problem-solving method was developed by George Pólya and is an effective way to solve a variety of problems: (1) understand the problem; (2) devise a plan; (3) carry out the plan; and (4) look back. In the "devise a plan" step, students will decide which problem-solving method to use to solve a problem.

When students devise a plan to solve problems, they can find many possible strategies in the 4-step problem-solving plan. Two of the strategies are "Translate into a number sentence" and "Apply a rule or definition." This lesson combines these two ideas and names the strategy "Write an equation."

### ▶ Advance Preparation
Print the Problem-Solving Plan.

### Materials to Gather

**SUPPLIED**
Problem-Solving Plan (printout)
Use Tables to Solve Problems activity page
Practice Using Tables activity page

## GET READY  Simple to Complex    ONLINE 10 min

Students will apply the write-an-equation strategy to solve a simpler division problem. They will then apply the same strategy to solve a more complex division problem.

**Objectives**
- Apply strategies or results from a simpler problem to a similar or more complex problem.

## LEARN  Look Back to Check    ONLINE 15 min

Students will review the 4-step problem-solving plan while solving problems about menu choices at a restaurant. They will focus on the "look back" step to review how effective the plan was in solving each problem.

**Objectives**
- Identify and generalize methods for solving problems that are similar to each other.

## LEARN  Make-a-Table Strategy    ONLINE 15 min

Students will use the make-a-table strategy to solve two similar geometry problems.

**Objectives**
- Identify and generalize methods for solving problems that are similar to each other.

## LEARN  Use Tables to Solve Problems    OFFLINE 10 min

Students will make tables to help them find the answers to story problems. Gather the Problem-Solving Plan. Have students turn to the Use Tables to Solve Problems activity page in their Activity Book and read the directions with them.

Students should copy the problems from the Activity Book into their Math Notebook as necessary and solve them there.

1. Read the Worked Examples box with students.

    **Ask:** In the table, when 2 years were added to Nyree's age, what happened to Mia's age? Two years were added to Mia's age.

    **Say:** If you were making this table, you wouldn't know to make 9 columns after the original column of age 30 and age 6. You would want to sketch a table that had several columns and some space at the end for more columns if you needed them for reaching your answer.

2. Have students complete Problem 1. Make sure they have answered it correctly before they move on to the next problem.

3. Assist students as needed with the remaining problems. If they have difficulty, first encourage them to look at the Worked Example and the Problem-Solving Plan. If they still have difficulty, help them apply the process shown in the Worked Example.

**Objectives**
- Identify and generalize methods for solving problems that are similar to each other.

**Tips**

When students sketch tables for the make-a-table strategy, have them create extra rows and columns in their tables. They should leave space on their paper to add rows and columns that are needed to solve the problem.

**Additional Answers**

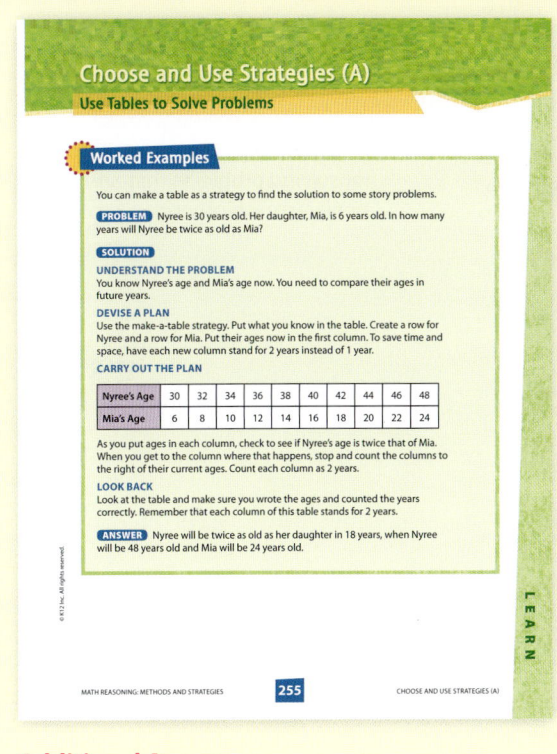

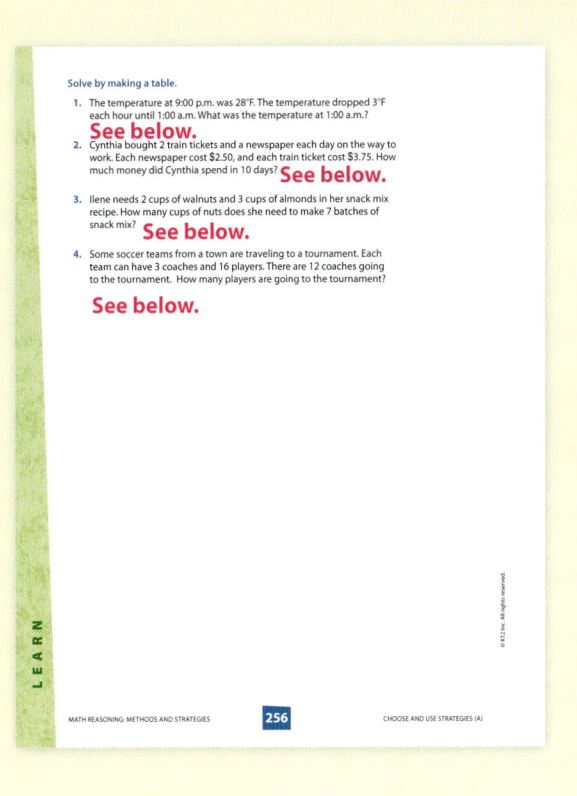

1.

| Time | 9:00 p.m. | 10:00 p.m. | 11:00 p.m. | Midnight | 1:00 a.m. |
|---|---|---|---|---|---|
| Temperature (°F) | 28 | 25 | 22 | 19 | 16 |

The temperature at 1:00 a.m. was 16°F.

2. 2($3.75) + $2.50 = $7.50 + $2.50 = $10.00; Cynthia spent $10.00 each day.

| Day | 1 | 2 | 3 | 4 | 5 | 6 | 7 | 8 | 9 | 10 |
|---|---|---|---|---|---|---|---|---|---|---|
| Total cost | $10 | $20 | $30 | $40 | $50 | $60 | $70 | $80 | $90 | $100 |

In 10 days, Cynthia spent $100.

3. 2 + 3 = 5; Ilene uses 5 cups of nuts per batch.

| Number of batches | 1 | 2 | 3 | 4 | 5 | 6 | 7 |
|---|---|---|---|---|---|---|---|
| Cups of nuts | 5 | 10 | 15 | 20 | 25 | 30 | 35 |

To make 7 batches, Ilene will use 35 cups of nuts.

4.

| Number of coaches | 3 | 6 | 9 | 12 |
|---|---|---|---|---|
| Number of players | 16 | 32 | 48 | 64 |

There are 64 players going to the tournament.

**CHOOSE AND USE STRATEGIES (A)** 531

# TRY IT  Practice Using Tables

**OFFLINE 10 min**

## Objectives
- Identify and generalize methods for solving problems that are similar to each other.

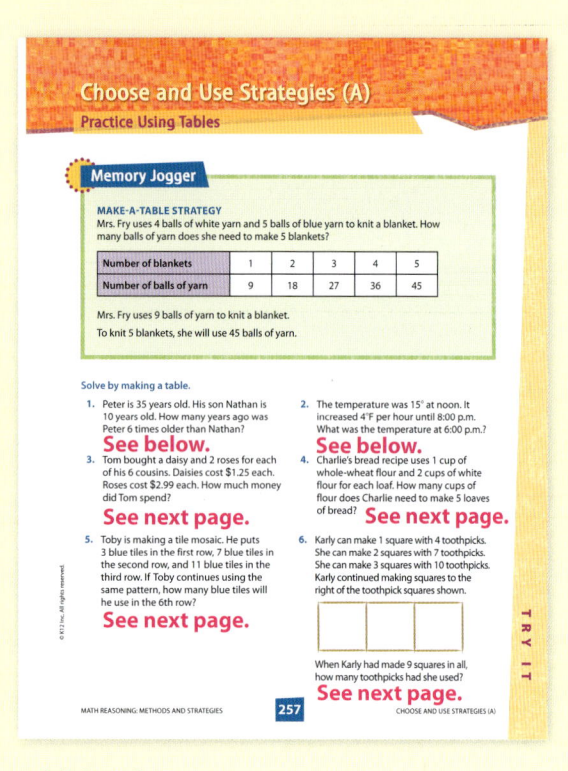

Students will solve problems using the make-a-table strategy. Have students turn to the Practice Using Tables activity page in their Activity Book and read the directions with them.

Students should copy the problems from the Activity Book into their Math Notebook as necessary and solve them there.

## Additional Answers

**1.**

| Peter | 35 | 34 | 33 | 32 | 31 | 30 |
|---|---|---|---|---|---|---|
| Nathan | 10 | 9 | 8 | 7 | 6 | 5 |

Peter was 6 times older than Nathan 5 years ago.

**2.**

| Time | Noon | 1:00 p.m. | 2:00 p.m. | 3:00 p.m. | 4:00 p.m. | 5:00 p.m. | 6:00 p.m. |
|---|---|---|---|---|---|---|---|
| Temperature (°F) | 15 | 19 | 23 | 27 | 31 | 35 | 39 |

The temperature at 6:00 p.m. was 39°F.

**532** MATH REASONING: METHODS AND STRATEGIES

**3.** $1.25 + (2 \cdot $2.99) = $1.25 + $5.98 = $7.23;
Tom spent $7.23 on flowers for each cousin.

| Number of cousins | 1 | 2 | 3 | 4 | 5 | 6 |
|---|---|---|---|---|---|---|
| Cost of flowers | $7.23 | $14.46 | $21.69 | $28.92 | $36.15 | $43.38 |

Tom spent $43.38 on flowers for his cousins.

**4.** 1 + 2 = 3; Charlie needs 3 cups of flour for each loaf.

| Number of bread loaves | 1 | 2 | 3 | 4 | 5 |
|---|---|---|---|---|---|
| Cups of flour | 3 | 6 | 9 | 12 | 15 |

Charlie needs 15 cups of flour to make 5 loaves of bread.

**5.**

| Rows | 1 | 2 | 3 | 4 | 5 | 6 |
|---|---|---|---|---|---|---|
| Number of blue tiles | 3 | 7 | 11 | 15 | 19 | (23) |

The number of blue tiles increases by 4 for each row added. Toby will use 23 blue tiles in the 6th row.

**6.**

| Number of squares | 1 | 2 | 3 | 4 | 5 | 6 | 7 | 8 | 9 |
|---|---|---|---|---|---|---|---|---|---|
| Number of toothpicks | 4 | 7 | 10 | 13 | 16 | 19 | 22 | 25 | (28) |

The number of toothpicks increases by 3 for each new square added. To make 9 squares, Karly would need 28 toothpicks.

CHOOSE AND USE STRATEGIES (A)

# Choose and Use Strategies (B)

## Lesson Overview

| | | |
|---|---|---|
| Skills Update | 5 minutes | **ONLINE** |
| **LEARN** Write-an-Equation Strategy | 20 minutes | **OFFLINE** |
| **LEARN** Guess-and-Test Strategy | 20 minutes | **OFFLINE** |
| **TRY IT** Use Different Strategies | 15 minutes | **OFFLINE** |

### ▶ Lesson Objectives
Identify and generalize methods for solving problems that are similar to each other.

### ▶ Prerequisite Skills
Apply strategies or results from a simpler problem to a similar or more complex problem.

### ▶ Content Background
Although the context and numbers in story problems vary, good problem solver realize that they can use certain strategies over and over to solve problems that are similar to each other. That skill relies on students being able to identify similarities between problems. When they learn and are able to use different strategies, they realize that instead of treating every problem they encounter as a new experience, they can apply successful strategies for solving problems that are similar.

As students work on solving problems, they should follow the 4-step problem-solving plan. The following problem-solving method was developed by George Pólya and is an effective way to solve a variety of problems: (1) understand the problem; (2) devise a plan; (3) carry out the plan; and (4) look back. In the "devise a plan" step, students will decide which problem-solving method to use to solve a problem.

When students devise a plan to solve problems, they can find many possible strategies in the 4-step problem-solving plan. Two of the strategies are "Translate into a number sentence" and "Apply a rule or definition." This lesson combines these two ideas and names the strategy "Write an equation."

### ▶ Advance Preparation
Print two copies of the Guess-and-Test Table.

### Materials to Gather

**SUPPLIED**

Guess-and-Test Table (printout) – 2
Write-an-Equation Strategy activity page
Guess-and-Test Strategy activity page
Use Different Strategies activity page

# LEARN Write-an-Equation Strategy

**OFFLINE 20 min**

Students will apply the write-an-equation strategy to find the sum of consecutive even numbers. Have students turn to the Write-an-Equation Strategy activity page in their Activity Book and read the directions with them.

Students should copy the problems from the Activity Book into their Math Notebook as necessary and solve them there.

1. Read the Worked Examples box with students.

    **Say:** The example gives you an equation that was developed by mathematician Carl Friedrich Gauss.

    **Ask:** What does $S$ represent in the equation? *the sum of the consecutive even numbers*

    **Ask:** What does $n$ represent? *the number of consecutive numbers in the group that I'm finding the sum of*

2. Have students look again at the third step of the problem-solving plan, "carry out the plan." Note that it begins with looking for a pattern. Tell students that sometimes they will use more than one strategy to solve problems. In this activity, they will use an equation to solve a problem. But they also will use a pattern to figure out what equation to use. Tell them that as they continue to study mathematics, *figuring out an equation* might also be called *deriving an equation*.

3. Have students look at the end of "carry out the plan."

    **Ask:** Why was 6 substituted for $n$ in the equation? *There are 6 even numbers from 1 through 12. The $n$ in the equation stands for the number of even numbers in the problem.*

    **Ask:** If the problem asked about even numbers through 16, would $n$ stand for 16? Why or why not? *No. The variable $n$ doesn't stand for the greatest number in the problem. It stands for the number of numbers in the problem.*

4. Have students solve Problem 1 in the problem set. Make sure they have completed Problem 1 correctly by substituting 8 for $n$ before they move on to the next problem.

5. Have students complete the rest of the problems. Encourage them to refer to the Worked Example if they need help in solving the problems. Students may use the shortcut described in the Worked Example to check their answers.

## Objectives

- Identify and generalize methods for solving problems that are similar to each other.

## Tips

Allow students to use the shortcut in the Worked Example to check the answer they found using the equation. Remind students that when the group of consecutive numbers has an odd number of numbers, there will be one number that does not match in a pair. Students will need to add that individual number to the number pairs.

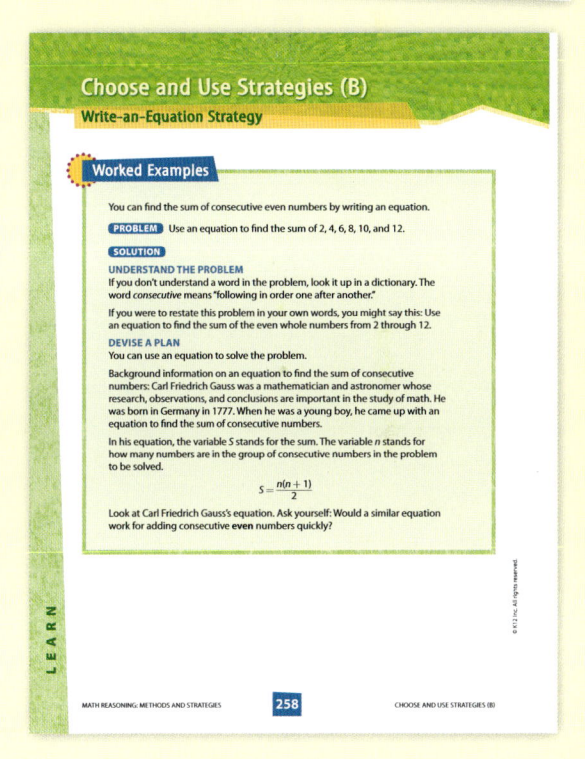

### CARRY OUT THE PLAN

1. Compare a list of all consecutive whole numbers 1 through 12 with a list of consecutive even whole numbers 2 through 12:
   - Consecutive even and odd numbers 1 through 12:
     1, 2, 3, 4, 5, 6, 7, 8, 9, 10, 11, 12
   - Consecutive even numbers 2 through 12:
     2, 4, 6, 8, 10, 12

2. Look for a pattern in the ordered list of numbers.
   - In the consecutive **even and odd** numbers, the third number is 3. In the consecutive **even** numbers, the third number is 6. The number 3 is half of 6.
   - In the consecutive **even and odd** numbers, the fifth number is 5. In the consecutive **even** numbers, the fifth number is 10. The number 5 is half of 10.
   - If you were to keep checking, you would see that every consecutive even number is twice its corresponding number in the ordered list of consecutive even and odd numbers. So the sums of the even numbers add up more quickly. In fact, they double.

3. Use what you have learned to write an equation to find the sum of consecutive even numbers.
   - The following equation results in the sum of consecutive even and odd numbers when $S$ stands for the sum and $n$ stands for how many numbers you are finding the sum of:
     $$S = \frac{n(n+1)}{2}$$
   - The sum of the consecutive even numbers will be 2 times greater than the sum of the consecutive even and odd numbers. So if you want the right side of the equation to represent twice its current value, you multiply that side by 2, which leaves 1 in the denominator of the fraction. The following equation now shows how to find the sum of consecutive **even** numbers:
     $$S = n(n+1)$$

4. You are trying to find the sum of the first 6 even numbers, so $n = 6$.
   Substitute 6 for $n$.
   $S = n(n+1)$
   $S = 6(6+1)$
   $S = 6(7)$
   $S = 42$
   Using the equation, you find that the sum of the first 6 consecutive even numbers, 2, 4, 6, 8, 10, and 12, is 42.

### LOOK BACK
Another way to calculate the answer is to add the even numbers without using an equation. You can check your math by using an addition shortcut.
Draw arcs to number pairs that add to 14.
$2 + 12 = 14 \quad 4 + 10 = 14 \quad 6 + 8 = 14$

$2 + 12 = 14$
$4 + 10 = 14$
$6 + 8 = 14$

2　　4　　6　　8　　10　　12

Then add how many sums of 14 there are altogether.
$14 + 14 + 14 = 42$
Using an addition shortcut, you find that the sum of the first 6 consecutive even numbers, 2, 4, 6, 8, 10, and 12, is 42.

**ANSWER** The sum of 2, 4, 6, 8, 10, and 12 is 42.

Use this equation for finding the sum of consecutive even numbers to solve the problem.

$$S = n(n+1)$$

1. What is the sum of the consecutive even numbers 1 through 16?
   **See below.**
2. What is the sum of the consecutive even numbers 1 through 30?
   **See below.**
3. What is the sum of the consecutive even numbers 1 through 50?
   **See below.**
4. What is the sum of the consecutive even numbers 1 through 62?
   **There are 31 even numbers 1 through 62.**
   $S = 31(31 + 1)$
   $S = 31(32)$
   $S = 992$
   **The sum of the consecutive even numbers 1 through 62 is 992.**

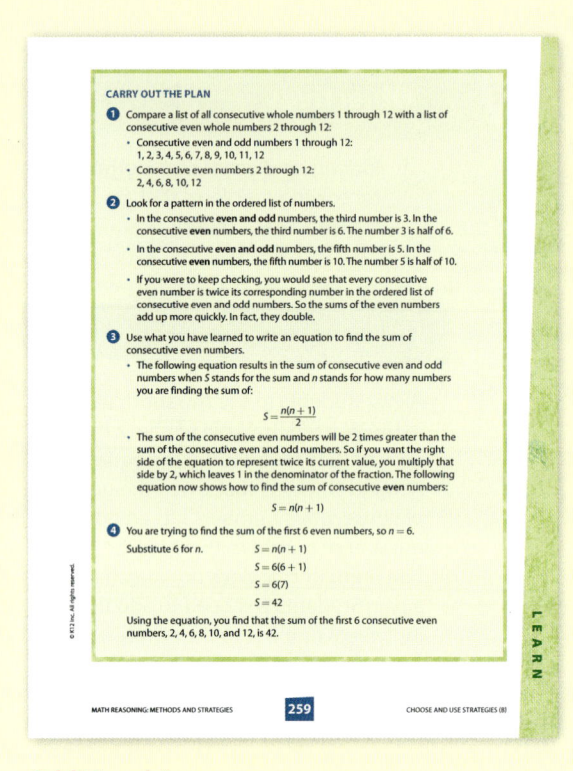

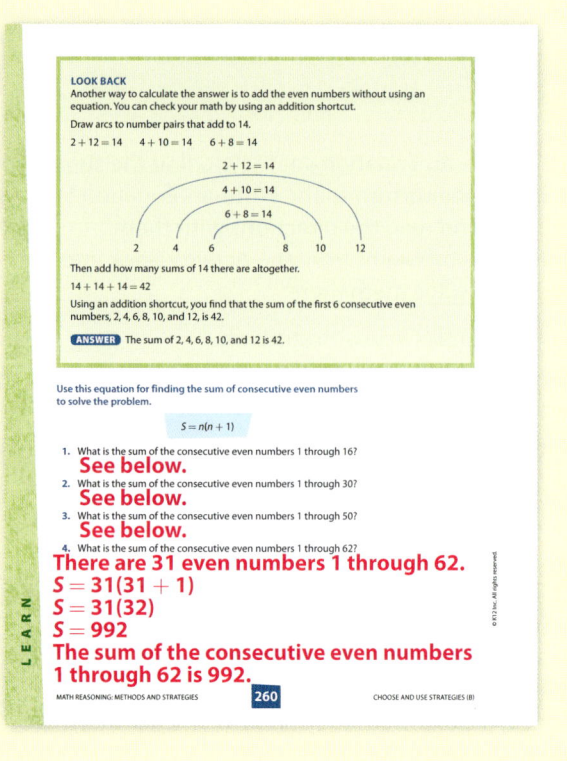

### Additional Answers

1. There are 8 even numbers 1 through 16.
   $S = 8(8 + 1)$
   $S = 8(9)$
   $S = 72$
   The sum of the consecutive even numbers 1 through 16 is 72.

2. There are 15 even numbers 1 through 30.
   $S = 15(15 + 1)$
   $S = 15(16)$
   $S = 240$
   The sum of the consecutive even numbers 1 through 30 is 240.

3. There are 25 even numbers 1 through 50.
   $S = 25(25 + 1)$
   $S = 25(26)$
   $S = 650$
   The sum of the consecutive even numbers 1 through 50 is 650.

## LEARN Guess-and-Test Strategy

**OFFLINE 20 min**

### Objectives

- Identify and generalize methods for solving problems that are similar to each other.

### Tips

Have students explain their reasoning for their first guess. Students often use estimation to help them make a first guess.

Students will use the guess-and-test strategy to solve problems. Gather the Guess-and-Test Table printouts. Have students turn to the Guess-and-Test Strategy activity page in their Activity Book and read the directions with them.

Students should copy the problems from the Activity Book into their Math Notebook as necessary and solve them there.

1. Read the Worked Examples box with students.

    **Ask:** Could the guessing have started with the number of comic books Mrs. Jensen owns instead of the number of comic books Sara owns? Yes

    **Ask:** What would have been the first math operation used if the number being guessed was Mrs. Jensen's number? Explain. Division. The guess would have been the guessed number divided by 24.

2. Make sure students understand the table in the solution.

    **Say:** The table is a way to help you use each guess to get closer to the problem's answer. For example, when you see that a number that you started with is too high, look to see if it is much too high or just a little too high. Use that information to decide what your next guess will be.

    Tell students that with some guesses, they will know that the total will be much too high, so they can decide not to find the total, but instead write "Too high" and move to the next guess.

3. Give students a Guess-and-Test Table. Note that the table is like the table in the Worked Example.

4. Have students read Problem 1 in the problem set. Ask them to restate the problem in their own words. **Example:** Joe's father's coin collection has 6 times as many coins as Joe's collection. Their collections together have 49 coins. How many coins does Joe have and how many does his father have?

5. Have students complete Problem 1 by putting guesses in the Guess-and-Test Table until they figure out the answer. They may refer to the Worked Example as needed. Have them write a title at the top of their table, such as Coin Collections.

6. Have students read Problem 2. Ask them to restate the problem in their own words. **Example:** Tom's trip to see his grandmother was 175 times as long as his trip to see his uncle. The two trips together were 2,816 miles.

    **Ask:** How is Problem 2 like Problem 1? **Example:** Both problems give a total amount. Both problems ask what two combined amounts make the total amount.

7. Give students the other Guess-and-Test Table. Have them complete Problem 2. Remind them to use the results of their guesses to guide them as they make more guesses. Remind them to put a title at the top of their table.

    **Ask:** How is solving Problem 2 different from solving Problem 1? **Example:** The numbers in Problem 2 were greater numbers than the numbers in Problem 1. It took more guesses to find the correct answer.

CHOOSE AND USE STRATEGIES (B) 537

## Additional Answers

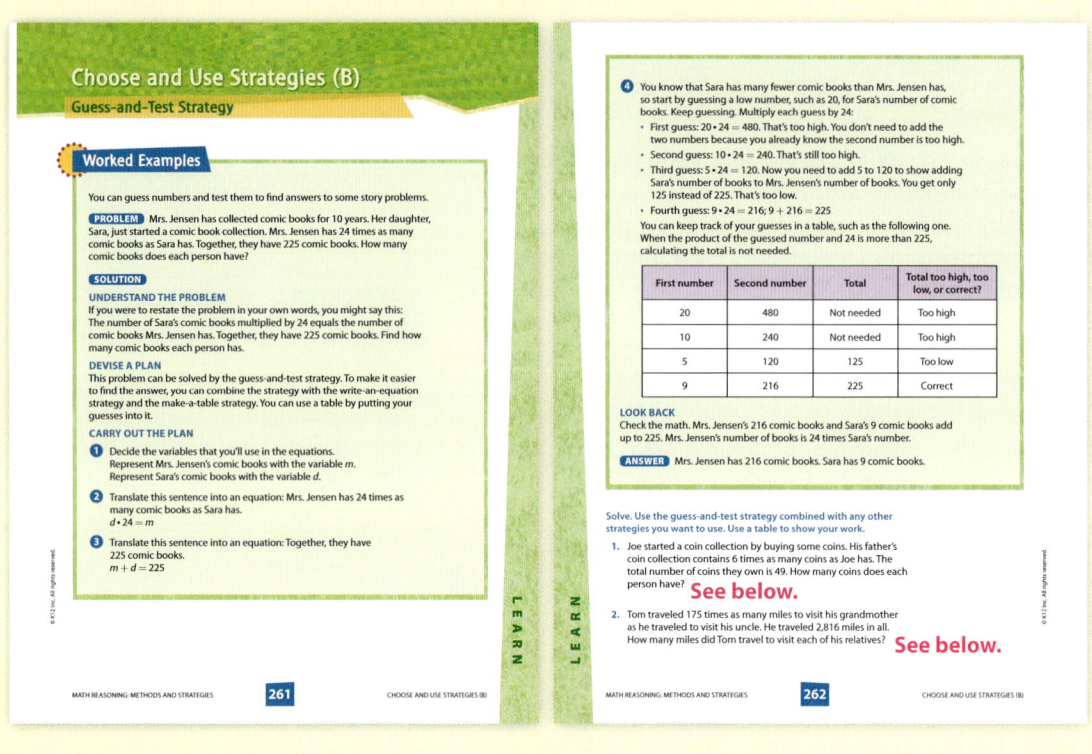

1. Joe has 7 coins. His father has 42 coins. Guesses will vary. **Example:**

| First number | Second number | Total | Total too high, too low, or correct? |
|---|---|---|---|
| 9 | 54 | 63 | Too high |
| 5 | 30 | 35 | Too low |
| 6 | 36 | 42 | Too low |
| 7 | 42 | 49 | Correct |

2. Tom traveled 16 miles to visit his uncle. He traveled 2,800 miles to visit his grandmother. Guesses will vary. **Example:**

| First number | Second number | Total | Total too high, too low, or correct? |
|---|---|---|---|
| 20 | 3,500 | Not needed | Too high |
| 10 | 1,750 | 1,760 | Too low |
| 17 | 2,975 | Not needed | Too high |
| 16 | 2,800 | 2,816 | Correct |

## TRY IT  Use Different Strategies

**OFFLINE 15 min**

### Objectives
- Identify and generalize methods for solving problems that are similar to each other.

Students will solve problems using the write-an-equation and guess-and-test strategies. Have students turn to the Use Different Strategies activity page in their Activity Book and read the directions with them.

Students should copy the problems from the Activity Book into their Math Notebook as necessary and solve them there. They may use the Guess-and-Test Table to solve Problems 5 and 6.

---

**Choose and Use Strategies (B)**
**Use Different Strategies**

Solve. Use the write-an-equation strategy.

1. At the To-Go Pizza, each pizza costs $12 and each small salad costs $2. A delivery charge of $3 is added to every order. How much would it cost to have 6 pizzas and 3 small salads delivered?
   **See below.**

2. At the art supply store, pastels cost $2.25, drawing pads cost $6.50, and pencils cost $1.17. Kelly bought 3 pastels, 2 drawing pads, and 12 pencils. How much money did Kelly spend?
   **See below.**

3. Myra orders 3 beach balls and 2 sand castle kits from a catalog. The price of each beach ball is $4. The price of each sand castle kit is $10. Shipping costs for Myra's order are $6. What is the total cost of the order, including shipping?
   **See below.**

4. Use the equation $S = n(n + 1)$ to find the sum of the consecutive even numbers through 40.
   **See below.**

Solve. Use the guess-and-test strategy combined with any other strategies you want to use. Use a table to show your work.

5. Molly walked 6 more miles than Jeff on Sunday. They walked a total of 22 miles. How far did Jeff walk?
   **See below.**

6. A DVD rental service keeps a record of the types of movies customers rent each day. Customers rented a total of 1,280 adventure movies and comedies on Saturday. They rented 19 times as many adventure movies as comedies. How many adventure movies did they rent on Saturday?
   **Guesses will vary. Correct guess:**
   **Customers rented 64 comedies.**
   **$19 \cdot 64 = 1,216$**
   **$1,216 + 64 = 1,280$**
   **Customers rented 1,216 adventure movies on Saturday.**

MATH REASONING: METHODS AND STRATEGIES    263    CHOOSE AND USE STRATEGIES (B)

---

### Additional Answers:

1. $(\$12 \cdot 6) + (\$2 \cdot 3) + \$3 = \$72 + \$6 + \$3 = \$81$
   It would cost $81 to have 6 pizzas and 3 small salads delivered.

2. $(\$2.25 \cdot 3) + (\$6.50 \cdot 2) + (\$1.17 \cdot 12) = \$6.75 + \$13.00 + \$14.04 = \$33.79$
   Kelly spent $33.79.

3. $(\$4 \cdot 3) + (\$10 \cdot 2) + \$6 = \$12 + \$20 + \$6 = \$38$
   Myra's order costs $38 including shipping.

4. There are 20 even numbers 1 through 40.
   Substitute 20 for $n$ in the equation.
   $S = n(n + 1)$
   $S = 20(20 + 1)$
   $S = 20(21)$
   $S = 420$
   The sum of the first 20 consecutive even numbers is 420.

5. Guesses will vary. **Correct guess:**
   $8 + 6 = 14$
   Molly walked 14 miles on Sunday.
   $14 + 8 = 22$
   Jeff walked 8 miles on Sunday.

# Choose and Use Strategies (C)

## Lesson Overview

| | | |
|---|---|---|
| **LEARN** Work Backward to Solve | 15 minutes | **ONLINE** |
| **LEARN** Use Strategies to Solve Story Problems | 20 minutes | **ONLINE** |
| **TRY IT** Practice Using Strategies | 15 minutes | **OFFLINE** |
| **CHECKPOINT** | 10 minutes | **ONLINE** |

### ▶ Lesson Objectives
Identify and generalize methods for solving problems that are similar to each other.

### ▶ Prerequisite Skills
Apply strategies or results from a simpler problem to a similar or more complex problem.

### ▶ Content Background
Students will learn to use the work-backward strategy and other strategies to solve problems.

Although the context and numbers in story problems vary, good problem solvers realize that they can use certain strategies over and over to solve problems that are similar to each other. That skill relies on students being able to identify similarities between problems. When they learn and are able to use different strategies, they realize that instead of treating every problem they encounter as a new experience, they can apply successful strategies for solving problems that are similar.

As students work on solving problems, they should follow the 4-step problem-solving plan. The following 4-step problem-solving method was developed by George Pólya and is an effective way to solve a variety of problems: (1) understand the problem; (2) devise a plan; (3) carry out the plan; and (4) look back. In the "devise a plan" step, students will decide which problem-solving method to use to solve a problem.

### Materials to Gather

**SUPPLIED**
Practice Using Strategies activity page

## LEARN  Work Backward to Solve

**ONLINE 15 min**

Students will use the strategy of working backward to solve story problems. Tell them that the strategy is useful when they need to find the answer to a problem where the information isn't given in order. Working backward can also help when one piece of information leads them to other information they need to solve the problem.

**Tips** When students carry out the plan, have them identify which step in the plan each computation represents.

### Objectives
- Identify and generalize methods for solving problems that are similar to each other.

## LEARN  Use Strategies to Solve Story Problems

**ONLINE 20 min**

Students will use two strategies. They will work backward to figure out a starting time based on the ending time. They will substitute simpler numbers to find a perimeter.

### Objectives
- Identify and generalize methods for solving problems that are similar to each other.

## TRY IT  Practice Using Strategies

**OFFLINE 15 min**

Students will practice using the various problem-solving strategies to solve problems. Have students turn to the Practice Using Strategies activity page in their Activity Book and read the directions with them.

Students should copy the problems from the Activity Book into their Math Notebook as necessary and solve them there.

### Objectives
- Identify and generalize methods for solving problems that are similar to each other.

**CHOOSE AND USE STRATEGIES (C)  541**

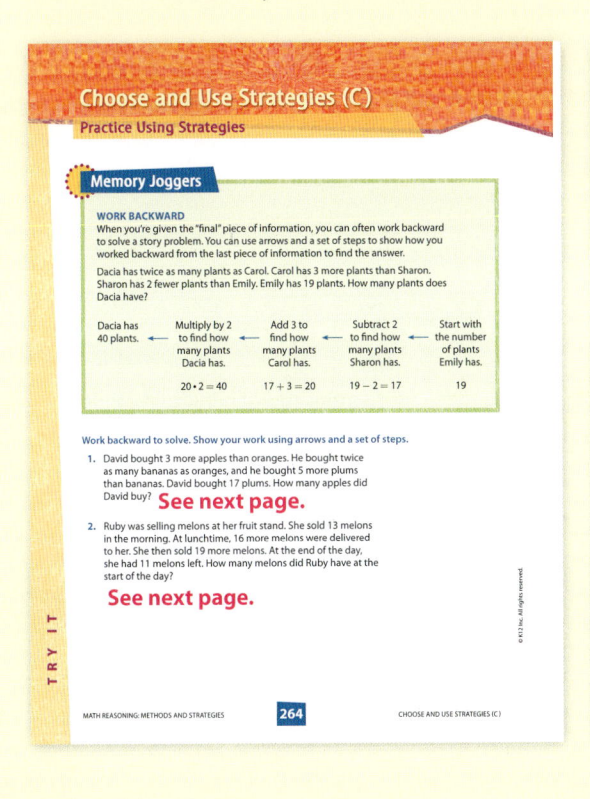

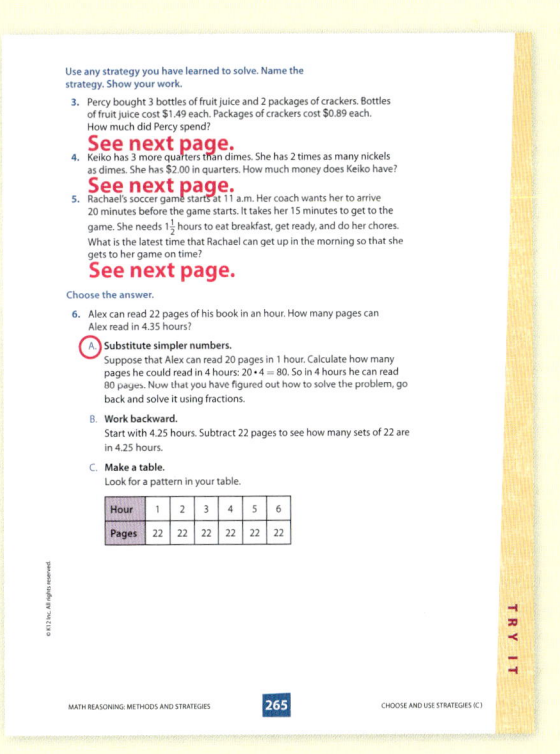

**Additional Answers**

1. David bought 9 apples. ← Add 3 to the number of oranges to find the number of apples. ← Divide the number of bananas by 2 to find the number of oranges. ← Subtract 5 from the number of plums to find the number of bananas. ← Start with the number of plums.

   $6 + 3 = 9$     $12 \div 2 = 6$     $17 - 5 = 12$     17

2. Ruby started the day with 27 melons. ← Add 13 to find how many melons Ruby had before selling any in the morning. ← Subtract 16 to find how many melons Ruby had before more were delivered. ← Add 19 to find how many melons Ruby had after lunchtime. ← Start with the number of melons Ruby had left at the end of the day.

   $14 + 13 = 27$     $30 - 16 = 14$     $19 + 11 = 30$     11

3. | The cost of 3 bottles of fruit juice | plus | the cost of 2 packages of crackers | equals | the amount Percy spent. |
   |---|---|---|---|---|
   | $(3 \cdot \$1.49)$ | $+$ | $(2 \cdot \$0.89)$ | $=$ | ? |
   | $\$4.47$ | $+$ | $\$1.78$ | $=$ | $\$6.25$ |

   Percy spent $6.25.

4. There are 8 quarters, 5 dimes, and 10 nickels. ← Multiply by 2 to find the number of nickels. ← Subtract 3 to find the number of dimes. ← Divide by $0.25 to find the number of quarters in $2.00. ← Start with $2.00 in quarters.

   $5 \cdot 2 = 10$     $8 - 3 = 5$     $\$2.00 \div \$0.25 = 8$     $\$2.00$

   | 8 quarters | plus | 5 dimes | plus | 10 nickels | equals | the total amount of money. |
   |---|---|---|---|---|---|---|
   | $(8 \cdot \$0.25)$ | $+$ | $(5 \cdot \$0.10)$ | $+$ | $(10 \cdot \$0.05)$ | $=$ | ? |
   | $\$2.00$ | $+$ | $\$0.50$ | $+$ | $\$0.50$ | $=$ | $\$3.00$ |

   Keiko has $3.00.

5. Rachael must get up by 8:55 a.m. ← Subtract $1\frac{1}{2}$ hours. ← Subtract 15 minutes. ← Subtract 20 minutes. ← Start at 11:00 a.m.

   8:55 a.m.     10:25 a.m.     10:40 a.m.     11:00 a.m.

## CHECKPOINT

**ONLINE 10 min**

Students will complete an online Checkpoint. If necessary, read the directions, problems, and answer choices to students and help them with keyboard or mouse operations.

### Objectives

- Identify and generalize methods for solving problems that are similar to each other.

# Solve Simple to Complex Problems (A)

## Lesson Overview

| | | |
|---|---|---|
| **GET READY** Mixed Number and Fraction Problems | 10 minutes | **ONLINE** |
| **LEARN** Solve One-Step Story Problems | 20 minutes | **OFFLINE** |
| **LEARN** Solve Multistep Story Problems | 20 minutes | **OFFLINE** |
| **TRY IT** Practice Simple to Complex Problems | 10 minutes | **ONLINE** |

### ▶ Lesson Objectives
Apply strategies and results from simple story problems involving fractions to more complex problems.

### ▶ Prerequisite Skills
- Solve a story problem involving multiplication or division of fractions.
- Solve a simple problem involving addition or subtraction of fractions.

### ▶ Content Background
Students will use the 4-step problem-solving plan to solve simple to complex story problems.

Although the context and numbers in story problems vary, good problem solvers realize that they can use certain strategies over and over to solve problems that are similar to each other. A strategy used to solve a simple problem is often the exact strategy needed to solve a more complex problem. When students learn and are able to use different strategies, they realize that instead of treating every problem they encounter as a new experience, they can apply successful strategies for solving problems that are more complex.

As students work on solving problems, they should follow the 4-step problem-solving plan. The plan, developed by George Pólya, is an effective way to solve a variety of problems: (1) understand the problem; (2) devise a plan; (3) carry out the plan; and (4) look back.

### ▶ Advance Preparation
Print the Problem-Solving Plan.

---

**Materials to Gather**

**SUPPLIED**
Problem-Solving Plan (printout)
Solve One-Step Story Problems activity page
Solve Multistep Story Problems activity page

## GET READY  Mixed Number and Fraction Problems

**ONLINE 10 min**

### Objectives
- Solve a story problem involving multiplication or division of fractions.

Students will solve multiplication and division story problems with whole numbers, fractions, and mixed numbers.

## LEARN  Solve One-Step Story Problems

**OFFLINE 20 min**

### Objectives
- Apply strategies and results from simple story problems involving fractions to more complex problems.

Students will use the problem-solving plan to solve one-step story problems with fractions and mixed numbers. They will solve simpler problems first and then more complex problems. Gather the Problem-Solving Plan. Have students turn to the Solve One-Step Story Problems activity page in their Activity Book.

Students should copy the problems from the Activity Book into their Math Notebook as necessary and solve them there.

1. Give students the Problem-Solving Plan. Briefly review the plan.
2. Tell students that the first Worked Example presents a simple problem and the second Worked Example presents a more complex problem. Tell them that the second Worked Example builds on the type of problem solving in the first Worked Example.
3. Read the first Worked Examples box with students. Tell students that during the "look back" step they should look at the problem and estimate the answer. Then they can compare the estimate with the answer they calculate.
4. Have students solve Problems 1 and 2 in the problem set. Tell them that as they solve the problems they should keep in mind that they will be solving more complex but similar problems next.
5. Read the second Worked Examples box with students.
6. Have students solve Problem 3 using the same methods that they used for Problems 1 and 2. Have them estimate what the answer should be and check to see if their answer is reasonable.
7. Repeat Step 6 for Problem 4.
8. Have students refer to the Worked Examples and the Problem-Solving Plan as needed.

**MATH REASONING: METHODS AND STRATEGIES**

## Additional Answers

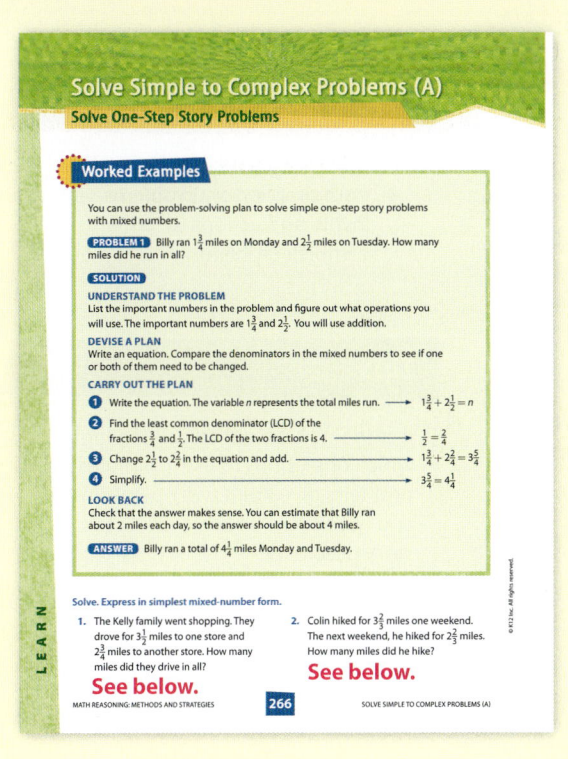

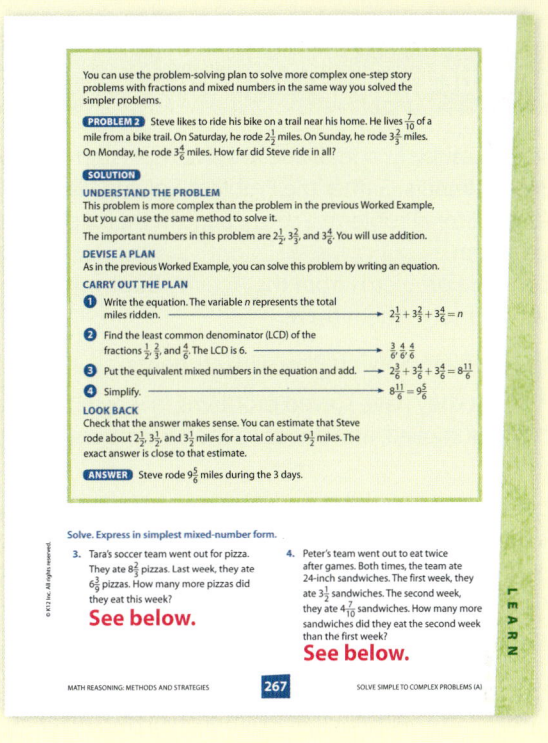

1. $3\frac{1}{2} + 2\frac{3}{4} = 3\frac{2}{4} + 2\frac{3}{4}$
    $= 5\frac{5}{4}$
    $= 6\frac{1}{4}$

    The Kelly family drove $6\frac{1}{4}$ miles in all.

2. $3\frac{2}{3} + 2\frac{2}{3} = 5\frac{4}{3}$
    $= 6\frac{1}{3}$

    Colin hiked for $6\frac{1}{3}$ miles.

3. $8\frac{2}{3} - 6\frac{3}{9} = 8\frac{6}{9} - 6\frac{3}{9}$
    $= 2\frac{3}{9}$
    $= 2\frac{1}{3}$

    Tara's team ate $2\frac{1}{3}$ more pizzas this week than last week.

4. $4\frac{7}{10} - 3\frac{1}{2} = 4\frac{7}{10} - 3\frac{5}{10}$
    $= 1\frac{2}{10}$
    $= 1\frac{1}{5}$

    Peter's team ate $1\frac{1}{5}$ more sandwiches the second week than they ate the first week.

**SOLVE SIMPLE TO COMPLEX PROBLEMS (A)** 545

# LEARN  Solve Multistep Story Problems

**OFFLINE 20 min**

## Objectives

- Apply strategies and results from simple story problems involving fractions to more complex problems.

## Tips

If students have difficulty knowing which operations to use in a multistep problem, give them two operations and have them make up multistep story problems.

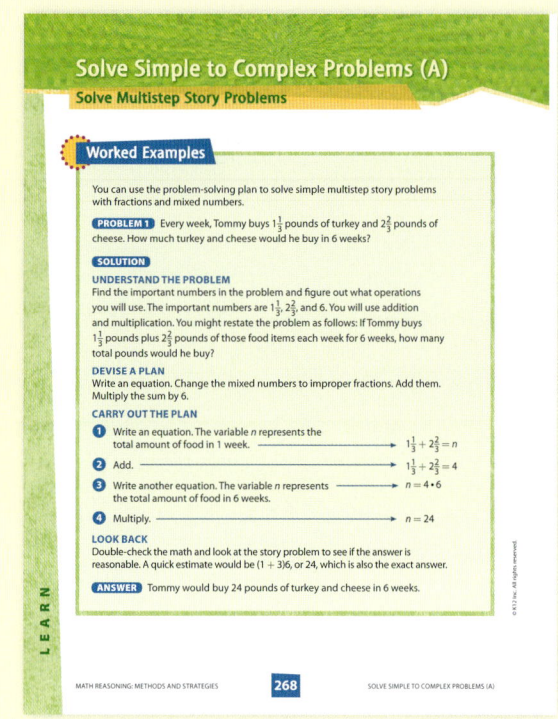

Students will add, subtract, multiply, and divide to solve multistep story problems with fractions and mixed numbers. Gather the Problem-Solving Plan. Have students turn to the Solve Multistep Story Problems activity page in their Activity Book and read the directions with them.

Students should copy the problems from the Activity Book into their Math Notebook as necessary and solve them there.

1. Briefly review the Problem-Solving Plan with students.
2. Remind students that they have solved problems in which they have added, subtracted, multiplied, and divided whole numbers, fractions, and mixed numbers.
3. Tell students that the first Worked Example presents a problem that uses two operations but is not very complicated. Tell them that the second Worked Example builds on the type of problem solving in the first Worked Example and is more complex.
4. Read the first Worked Example with students.
5. Have students do Problem 1.
6. Remind students that the next Worked Example will be similar to Problem 1 but is more complex.

   **Ask:** What strategies did you just use in that problem that might help you solve a more complex problem? *I used two equations to solve the problem. First I had to add, and I used common denominators to do that. Then I had to multiply. I simplified my answer.*

7. Read the second Worked Example with students.
8. Have students do Problems 2 and 3.

   As they work, have them see if their strategy is helping them find the answer.

   Remind them to ask themselves questions as they complete each step of the problem-solving plan. After they solve a problem, ask them what processes they used that might help them solve more complex problems. *Students might say that they used two equations to solve the problem, that they used common denominators to add, and that they simplified their answers.*

546  MATH REASONING: METHODS AND STRATEGIES

## Additional Answers

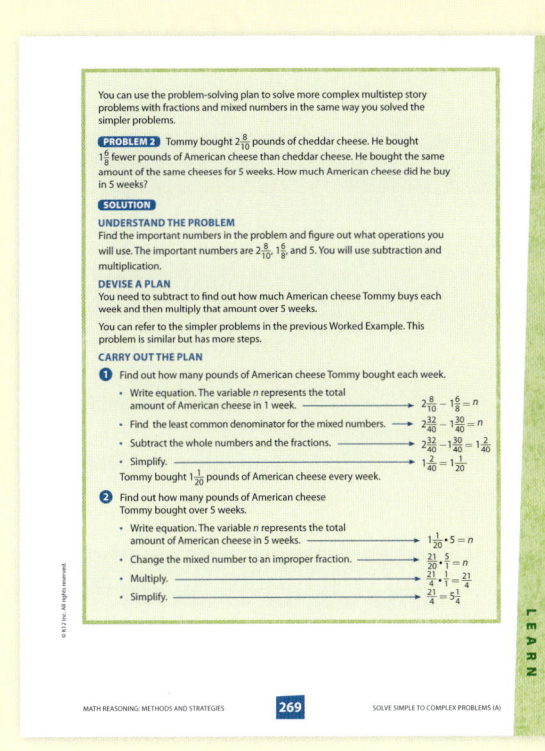

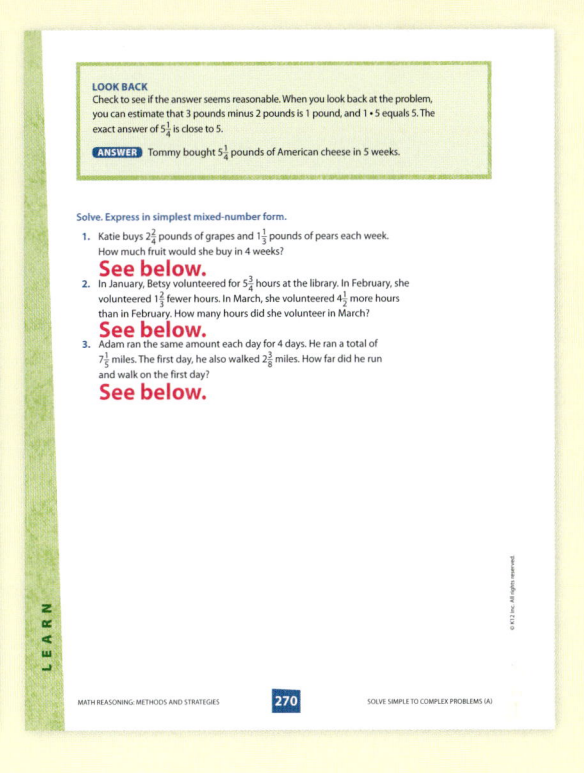

**1.** $2\frac{2}{4} + 1\frac{1}{3} = 2\frac{6}{12} + 1\frac{4}{12}$
$= 3\frac{10}{12}$
$= 3\frac{5}{6}$

Katie buys $3\frac{5}{6}$ pounds of fruit each week.

$3\frac{5}{6} \cdot 4 = \frac{23}{6} \cdot \frac{4}{1}$
$= \frac{23}{3} \cdot \frac{2}{1}$
$= \frac{46}{3}$
$= 15\frac{1}{3}$

Katie would buy $15\frac{1}{3}$ pounds of fruit in 4 weeks.

**2.** $5\frac{3}{4} - 1\frac{2}{3} = 5\frac{9}{12} - 1\frac{8}{12}$
$= 4\frac{1}{12}$

Betsy volunteered $4\frac{1}{12}$ hours in February.

$4\frac{1}{12} + 4\frac{1}{2} = 4\frac{1}{12} + 4\frac{6}{12}$
$= 8\frac{7}{12}$

Betsy volunteered $8\frac{7}{12}$ hours in March.

**3.** $7\frac{1}{5} \div 4 = \frac{36}{5} \div 4$
$= \frac{36}{5} \cdot \frac{1}{4}$
$= \frac{9}{5} \cdot \frac{1}{1}$
$= \frac{9}{5}$
$= 1\frac{4}{5}$

Adam ran $1\frac{4}{5}$ miles the first day.

$1\frac{4}{5} + 2\frac{3}{8} = 1\frac{32}{40} + 2\frac{15}{40}$
$= 3\frac{47}{40}$
$= 4\frac{7}{40}$

Adam ran and walked for $4\frac{7}{40}$ miles the first day.

## TRY IT  Practice Simple to Complex Problems

ONLINE 10 min

### Objectives

- Apply strategies and results from simple story problems involving fractions to more complex problems.

Students will complete an online Try It. If necessary, read the directions, problems, and answer choices to students and help them with keyboard or mouse operations.

**SOLVE SIMPLE TO COMPLEX PROBLEMS (A)** 547

# Solve Simple to Complex Problems (B)

## Lesson Overview

| | | |
|---|---|---|
| **GET READY** Addition and Subtraction of Fractions | 10 minutes | **ONLINE** |
| **LEARN** Fractions as Decimals in Story Problems | 15 minutes | **OFFLINE** |
| **LEARN** Convert Measurements in Story Problems | 15 minutes | **OFFLINE** |
| **TRY IT** Practice Story Problems | 10 minutes | **ONLINE** |
| **CHECKPOINT** | 10 minutes | **ONLINE** |

### ▶ Lesson Objectives
Apply strategies and results from simple story problems involving fractions to more complex problems.

### ▶ Prerequisite Skills
- Solve a story problem involving multiplication or division of fractions.
- Solve a simple problem involving addition or subtraction of fractions.

### ▶ Content Background
Students will learn to solve story problems with fractions, mixed numbers, and decimal numbers. They will also move from simpler problems to more complex problems.

Although the context and numbers in story problems vary, good problem solvers realize that they can use certain strategies over and over to solve problems that are similar to each other. A strategy used to solve a simple problem is often the exact strategy needed to solve a more complex problem. When students learn and are able to use different strategies, they realize that instead of treating every problem they encounter as a new experience, they can apply successful strategies for solving problems that are more complex.

As students work on solving problems, they should follow the 4-step problem-solving plan. The following problem-solving plan, developed by George Pólya, is an effective way to solve a variety of problems: (1) understand the problem; (2) devise a plan; (3) carry out the plan; and (4) look back.

### ▶ Advance Preparation
Print the Problem-Solving Plan.

### Materials to Gather

**SUPPLIED**
Problem-Solving Plan (printout)
Fractions as Decimals in Story Problems activity page
Convert Measurements in Story Problems activity page

## GET READY  Addition and Subtraction of Fractions  [ONLINE 10 min]

Students will solve simple story problems involving addition or subtraction of fractions and mixed numbers.

**Objectives**

- Solve a simple problem involving addition or subtraction of fractions.

## LEARN  Fractions as Decimals in Story Problems  [OFFLINE 15 min]

Students will use the problem-solving plan to solve multistep story problems in which they need to change fractions and mixed numbers to decimal numbers. The problems will become more complex. Gather the Problem-Solving Plan. Have students turn to the Fractions as Decimals in Story Problems activity page in their Activity Book and read the directions with them.

Students should copy the problems from the Activity Book into their Math Notebook as necessary and solve them there.

**Objectives**

- Apply strategies and results from simple story problems involving fractions to more complex problems.

**Tips**

If students have difficulty changing fractions and mixed numbers to decimal numbers, have them make a reference table. Write fractions with denominators of 4, 5, and 8 and have them change them to decimal numbers.

1. Give students the Problem-Solving Plan and tell them to refer to it during the activity.
2. Read the Worked Examples box with students. Tell them that it shows a simple story problem about money.

    **Ask:** What was the first step in the Worked Examples? I changed $3\frac{1}{5}$ to a decimal number to multiply the amount of ribbon by the cost per meter.

3. Read Problem 1 with students.

    **Ask:** What operations will you need to use to solve this problem? addition and multiplication

    Make sure students know that they need to change the two mixed numbers to decimal numbers and add them.

    **Ask:** What plan will you use? I need to change each mixed number to a decimal amount, add the two amounts of ribbon together, and multiply the sum by the price per yard of ribbon.

4. Have students find the product of $7.25 and $1.50. $10.875

    Tell students that money values are shown to the hundredths place with decimal numbers, so they need to round the answer to the nearest cent. Tell them that no matter what value is in the thousandths place, stores usually round dollar amounts up to the next penny.

    Guide students to see that because the amount is $10.875, Jenny paid $10.88.

5. Ask students to estimate what the answer would be. One estimate is approximately $10.50. They should confirm that their answer makes sense.
6. Check students' work after they complete each problem in this activity. Remind them to ask themselves questions as they complete each step of the problem-solving plan. One question they should ask themselves is, "Is my strategy helping me find the answer?"
7. Have students solve Problem 2.

    After students look back at how they solved Problem 2, explain that Problems 3 and 4 will be similar to the first two problems but will be more complex. For example, the problems will contain extra information that students don't need to solve the problems.

SOLVE SIMPLE TO COMPLEX PROBLEMS (B)  **549**

**Ask:** What strategies did you use in the first two problems that might help you solve a more complex problem? I changed the mixed numbers to decimal numbers before calculating the answer.

8. Have students read Problem 3.

   **Ask:** Is there any information you don't need to know in the problem? Yes. I don't need to know that Kevin got to the store at 7:00 p.m. or that it took him 15 minutes to check out.

   Have students complete Problem 3.

9. Have students read Problem 4.

   **Ask:** Is there any information you don't need to know in the problem? Yes. I don't need to know that Amy is using blinds on three windows. I don't need to know the measurements of those three windows.

   Have students complete Problem 4.

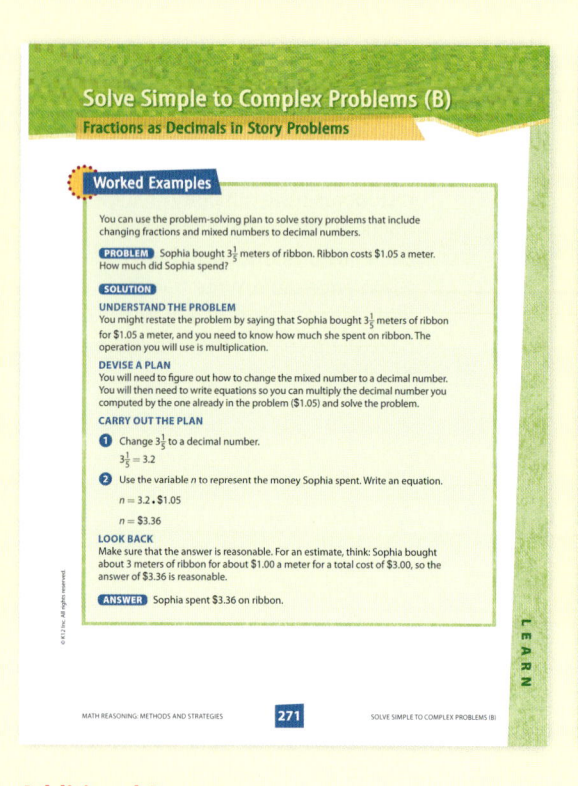

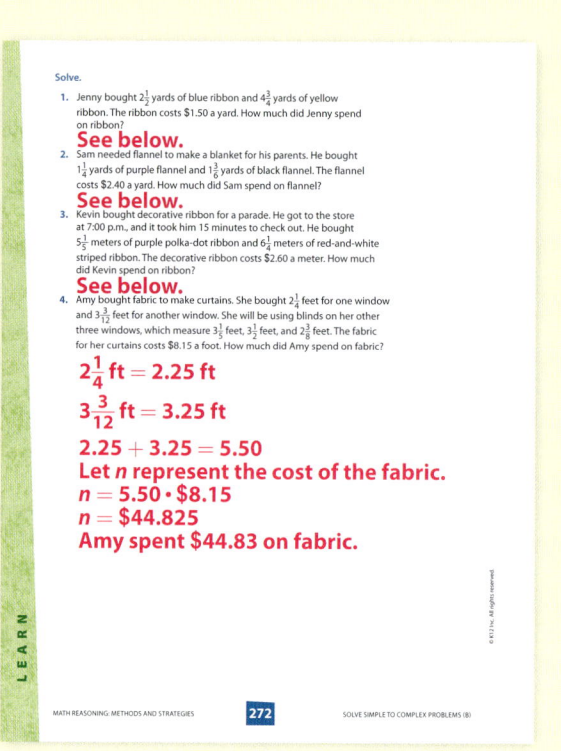

### Additional Answers

1. $2\frac{1}{2}$ yd = 2.5 yd
   $4\frac{3}{4}$ yd = 4.75 yd
   $2.50 + 4.75 = 7.25$
   Let $n$ represent the cost of the ribbon.
   $n = 7.25 \cdot \$1.50$
   $n = \$10.875$
   Jenny spent $10.88 on ribbon.

2. $1\frac{1}{4}$ yd = 1.25 yd
   $1\frac{3}{6}$ yd = 1.5 yd
   $1.25 + 1.5 = 2.75$
   Let $n$ represent the cost of the flannel.
   $n = 2.75 \cdot \$2.40$
   $n = \$6.60$
   Sam spent $6.60 on flannel.

3. $5\frac{1}{5}$ m = 5.2 m
   $6\frac{1}{4}$ m = 6.25 m
   $5.2 + 6.25 = 11.45$
   Let $n$ represent the cost of the decorative ribbon.
   $n = 11.45 \cdot \$2.60$
   $n = \$29.77$
   Kevin spent $29.77 on decorative ribbon.

## LEARN Convert Measurements in Story Problems  OFFLINE 15 min

### Objectives

- Apply strategies and results from simple story problems involving fractions to more complex problems.

Students will use the problem-solving plan for complex problems in which they need to convert measurements from one unit to another. Gather the Problem-Solving Plan. Have students turn to the Convert Measurements in Story Problems activity page in their Activity Book and read the directions with them.

Students should copy the problems from the Activity Book into their Math Notebook as necessary and solve them there.

1. Read the Worked Examples box with students. Give them the Problem-Solving Plan to refer to as they solve the problems.

2. Guide students to understand the conversion of the gallons of water to pounds of water. Tell them that they need to know the weight of 1 gallon of water to convert the measurement, and they will need to know how to convert from one unit of measure to another to solve the problems in this activity.

3. Explain to students that Problem 1 will be similar to the Worked Example but is more complex.

    **Ask:** What strategies did you use in the Worked Example that might help you solve a more complex problem? I changed the mixed number to a decimal number. Then I multiplied the weight of 1 gallon of water by the decimal value of $3\frac{8}{10}$ to find out the weight of $3\frac{8}{10}$ gallons of water.

4. Have students read Problem 1. Have them ask themselves questions in the "understand the problem" step, including the following:

    **Ask:** What measurements do I need to convert? gallons of water to pounds of water

    **Ask:** What operations do I need to use to solve the problem? addition and multiplication

    **Ask:** Is there extra information in the problem? Yes. The problem tells me that Bella's aunt brought $\frac{1}{4}$ gallon of water.

5. Have students ask themselves questions about the "devise a plan" step, including the following:

    **Ask:** Would a diagram, table, chart, or graph help me with this problem? No. This problem requires calculation of the data.

    **Ask:** What equations will I use? I'll change each of the mixed-number values I need for the problem into decimal numbers. Then I'll add the number of gallons of water that Bella and her uncle had. Finally I'll multiply the total gallons of water by 8.35 to find out how much the combined gallons of water weigh.

6. Guide students to carry out their plan. Have them carefully make the calculations. Have them ask themselves, "Is my strategy helping me find the answer?"

SOLVE SIMPLE TO COMPLEX PROBLEMS (B)

7. Remind students that the next step in the 4-step problem-solving plan is to "look back." Have them check their math and make sure they answered the question in the problem.

   **Ask:** What strategies did you use in this problem that might help you solve other problems? *I changed the mixed numbers to decimal numbers. Then I added the data that had the same unit of measurement. Finally, I multiplied the total number of gallons by the weight of 1 gallon of water to find out how many pounds the total gallons of water weighed.*

8. Check students' work after they complete each problem in this activity.

9. Have students solve the rest of the problems. Remind them to ask themselves questions as they complete each step of the problem-solving plan.

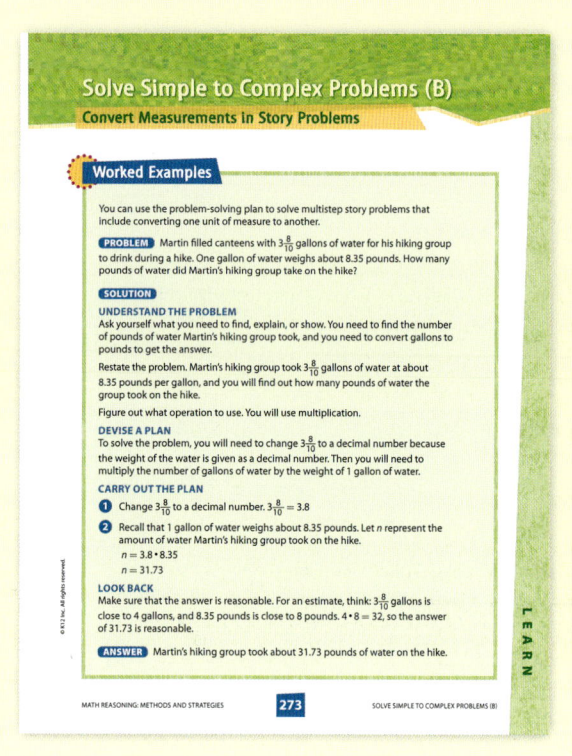

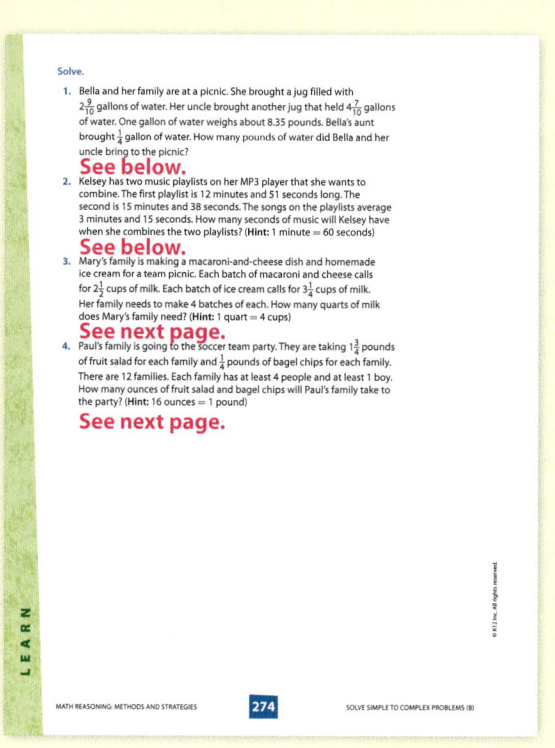

### Additional Answers

1. $2\frac{9}{10}$ gallons = 2.9 gallons

   $4\frac{7}{10}$ gallons = 4.7 gallons

   $2.9 + 4.7 = 7.6$

   Let *n* represent the amount of water Bella and her uncle brought to the picnic.

   $n = 7.6 \cdot 8.35$

   $n = 63.46$

   Bella and her uncle brought about 63.46 pounds of water to the picnic.

2. Add 12 minutes and 15 minutes.

   $12 + 15 = 27$

   Multiply 27 minutes by 60 seconds per minute to find the number of seconds in 27 minutes.

   $27 \cdot 60 = 1{,}620$

   There are 1,620 seconds in 27 minutes.

   Add 51 seconds and 38 seconds.

   $51 + 38 = 89$

   Add 1,620 seconds and 89 seconds to find the total number of seconds on the combined playlists.

   $1{,}620 + 89 = 1{,}709$

   Kelsey will have 1,709 seconds of music when she combines the two playlists.

**3.** Calculate how many cups of milk are needed for macaroni and cheese.

$2\frac{1}{2} \cdot 4 = 10$

10 cups of milk are needed to make macaroni and cheese.

Calculate how many cups of milk are needed for ice cream.

$3\frac{1}{4} \cdot 4 = 13$

13 cups of milk are needed to make ice cream.

Calculate how many cups of milk are needed in all.

$10 + 13 = 23$

23 cups of milk are needed in all.

Calculate how many quarts are in 23 cups.

$23 \div 4 = 5\frac{3}{4}$

Mary's family needs $5\frac{3}{4}$ quarts of milk.

**4.** Calculate how many pounds of fruit salad are needed.

$1\frac{3}{4} \cdot 12 = 21$

21 pounds of fruit salad are needed.

Calculate how many pounds of bagel chips are needed.

$\frac{1}{4} \cdot 12 = 3$

3 pounds of bagel chips are needed.

Calculate how many pounds of fruit salad and bagel chips are needed in all.

$21 + 3 = 24$

24 pounds of fruit salad and bagel chips are needed in all.

Calculate how many ounces are in 24 pounds.

$24 \cdot 16 = 384$

Paul's family will take 384 ounces of fruit salad and bagel chips to the party.

## TRY IT  Practice Story Problems

Students will complete an online Try It. If necessary, read the directions, problems, and answer choices to students and help them with keyboard or mouse operations.

**Objectives**

- Apply strategies and results from simple story problems involving fractions to more complex problems.

## CHECKPOINT

Students will complete an online Checkpoint. If necessary, read the directions, problems, and answer choices to students and help them with keyboard or mouse operations.

**Objectives**

- Apply strategies and results from simple story problems involving fractions to more complex problems.

# Unit Review

| Lesson Overview | | |
|---|---|---|
| **UNIT REVIEW** Look Back | 10 minutes | **ONLINE** |
| **UNIT REVIEW** Checkpoint Practice | 50 minutes | **ONLINE** |
| ▶ **UNIT REVIEW** Prepare for the Checkpoint | | |

## ▶ Unit Objectives

This lesson reviews the following objectives:

- Prioritize and sequence the information in a story problem that involves multiplication or division of decimal numbers.
- Determine when and how to break a multistep whole-number story problem or money problem into simpler parts.
- Use a variety of methods, such as words, numbers, symbols, charts, graphs, tables, diagrams, and models, to explain mathematical reasoning in nonroutine or complex problems.
- Identify and generalize methods for solving problems that are similar to each other.
- Apply strategies and results from simple story problems involving fractions to more complex problems.

**Materials to Gather**

There are no materials to gather for this lesson.

## ▶ Advance Preparation

In this lesson, students will have an opportunity to review previous activities in the Math Reasoning: Methods and Strategies unit. Look at the suggested activities in Unit Review: Prepare for the Checkpoint online and gather any needed materials.

### UNIT REVIEW  Look Back  ONLINE 10 min

**Objectives**

- Review unit objectives.

Students will review key concepts from the unit to prepare for the Unit Checkpoint.

### UNIT REVIEW  Checkpoint Practice  ONLINE 50 min

**Objectives**

- Review unit objectives.

Students will complete an online Checkpoint Practice to prepare for the Unit Checkpoint. If necessary, read the directions, problems, and answer choices to students. Have students answer the problems on their own. Review any missed problems with students.

### ▶ UNIT REVIEW  Prepare for the Checkpoint

What you do next depends on how students performed in the previous activity, Unit Review: Checkpoint Practice. If students had difficulty with any of the problems, complete the appropriate review activity listed in the table online.

# Unit Checkpoint

## Lesson Overview

**UNIT CHECKPOINT** Online | 60 minutes | **ONLINE**

### ▶ Unit Objectives

This lesson assesses the following objectives:

- Prioritize and sequence the information in a story problem that involves multiplication or division of decimal numbers.
- Determine when and how to break a multistep whole-number story problem or money problem into simpler parts.
- Use a variety of methods, such as words, numbers, symbols, charts, graphs, tables, diagrams, and models, to explain mathematical reasoning in nonroutine or complex problems.
- Identify and generalize methods for solving problems that are similar to each other.
- Apply strategies and results from simple story problems involving fractions to more complex problems.

### Materials to Gather

There are no materials to gather for this lesson.

### UNIT CHECKPOINT Online

ONLINE 60 min

Students will complete the Unit Checkpoint online. If necessary, read the directions, problems, and answer choices to students and help them with keyboard or mouse operations.

### Objectives

- Assess unit objectives.

# Math Reasoning: Solutions

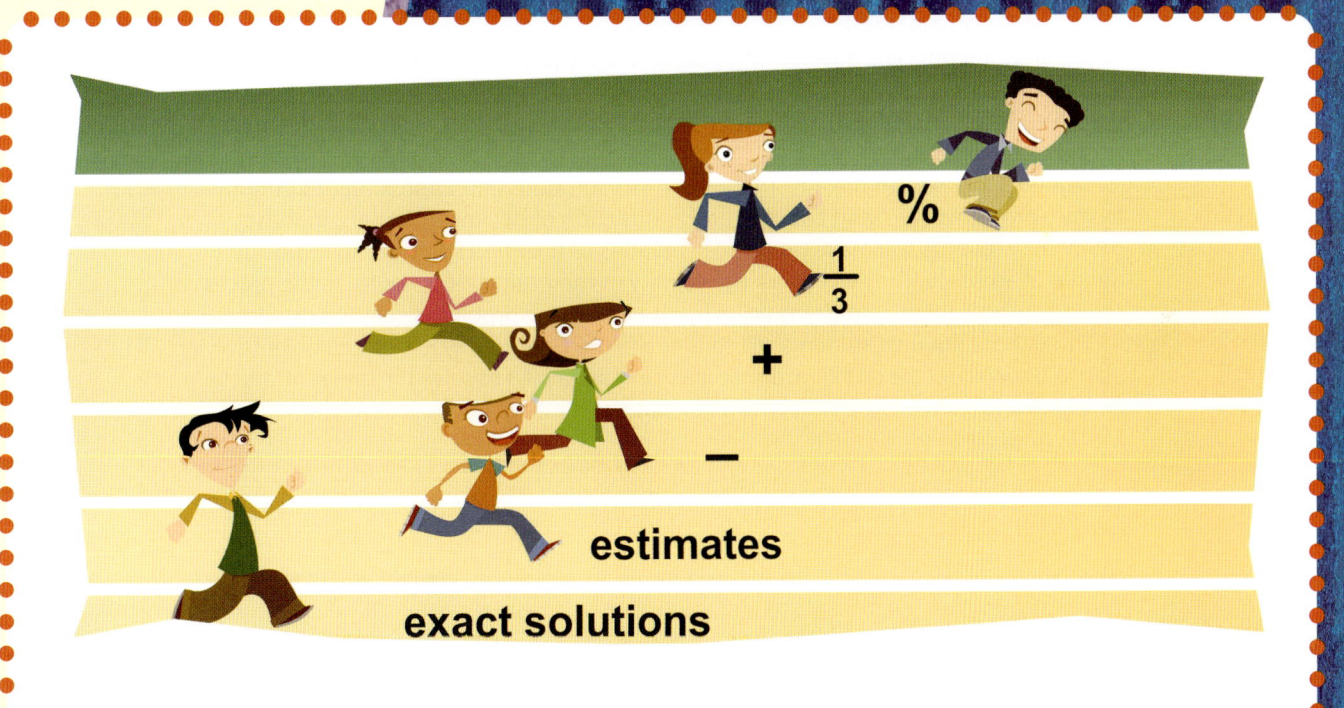

estimates

exact solutions

## ▶ Unit Objectives

- Express clear and logical solutions to equal-measures problems and rate problems.
- Use estimation in addition or subtraction of fractions to verify whether calculated results are reasonable.
- Explain the advantages of exact solutions and approximate solutions to problems involving addition or subtraction of decimal numbers, and give answers to a specified degree of accuracy, such as hundredths.
- Make precise calculations and use the situation presented in a problem involving decimal-number operations to check the validity of the result.
- Evaluate whether a solution for a problem is reasonable.

## ▶ Big Ideas

Estimation is a useful tool in problem solving.

## ▶ Unit Introduction

In this unit, students will develop ways to solve story problems by expressing clear and logical solutions to problems that involve equal measures and rate. They will use estimation to verify whether calculated results are reasonable for addition and subtraction of fractions in story problems.

Students will explain the advantages of exact solutions and approximate solutions to story problems involving addition and subtraction of decimal numbers. In these problems, students will make precise calculations as they find solutions to a specified degree of accuracy. They will check the validity of their calculated results. In the process of solving story problems, students will evaluate whether a problem's solution is reasonable.

Throughout this unit, students will continue to use George Pólya's 4-step problem-solving plan to understand the problem, devise and carry out a plan to solve the problem, and then look back and compare the original problem and its solution.

## ▶ Keywords

approximate solution  
degree of accuracy  
exact solution  
rate  
reasonableness

# Solve Problems Logically (A)

## Lesson Overview

| | | |
|---|---|---|
| Skills Update | 5 minutes | ONLINE |
| **GET READY** Multiply and Divide Equal Measures | 10 minutes | ONLINE |
| **LEARN** Solve a Guided Equal-Measures Problem | 15 minutes | ONLINE |
| **LEARN** Solve Equal-Measures Problems | 20 minutes | OFFLINE |
| **TRY IT** Work with Equal-Measures Problems | 10 minutes | ONLINE |

### ▶ Lesson Objectives
Express clear and logical solutions to equal-measures problems and rate problems.

### ▶ Prerequisite Skills
- Solve a story problem involving rate.
- Solve a story problem involving equal measures.
- Express the solution to a story problem clearly and logically.

### ▶ Content Background
Students will learn to express their solutions to equal-measures story problems clearly and logically. They will write solutions step by step.

The following problem-solving plan, developed by George Pólya, is an effective way to solve a variety of story problems: (1) understand the problem; (2) devise a plan; (3) carry out the plan; and (4) look back. As students work on solving problems, they should follow the 4-step problem-solving plan. In the "carry out the plan" step, they express their solutions to the problem in a clear and logical manner.

Expressing clear and logical solutions to problems is an important part of studying mathematics. This is the "show your work" step used by mathematicians throughout history. The use of clear language and appropriate mathematical notation and terms is critical. Students should support their solutions to a problem with evidence in both words and symbols.

These skills are critical in everyday life. The ability to create and report information to share with others has become a necessary skill in the information age. In fact, many standardized tests now include writing sections in which students are graded on their ability to write and clearly express their understanding.

In an equal-measures story problem, several equal-sized measures, or parts, combine to make a total measurement amount. To solve problems involving equal measures, students can multiply or divide, depending on the situation and information given. When the number of parts and the measure of each part are given, students can multiply to find the total measurement. When the total measurement and the measure of one part are given, they can divide to find the number of parts. When the total measurement and the number of parts are given, they can divide to find the measure of each part.

### Materials to Gather

**SUPPLIED**
Problem-Solving Plan (printout)
Solve Equal-Measures Problems activity page

▶ **Advance Preparation**

Print the Problem-Solving Plan.

### GET READY  Multiply and Divide Equal Measures
**ONLINE 10 min**

Students will solve a problem about the measurement of each equal part in a whole. They also will solve other equal-measures problems.

**Objectives**
- Solve a story problem involving equal measures.

### LEARN  Solve a Guided Equal-Measures Problem
**ONLINE 15 min**

Students will use the 4-step problem-solving plan, as well as clear and logical steps, to find the solution to an equal-measures story problem.

**Objectives**
- Express clear and logical solutions to equal-measures problems and rate problems.

### LEARN  Solve Equal-Measures Problems
**OFFLINE 20 min**

Students will use the 4-step problem-solving plan to solve equal-measures story problems. They will write the steps in a clear and logical order to find the solution. Gather the Problem-Solving Plan. Have students turn to the Solve Equal-Measures Problems activity page in their Activity Book.

Students should copy the problems from the Activity Book into their Math Notebook as necessary and solve them there.

**Objectives**
- Express clear and logical solutions to equal-measures problems and rate problems.

1. Read the Worked Examples box with students. Give them the Problem-Solving Plan to refer to as they solve the problem.

   **Ask:** What are you asked to do in this problem? Explain how to calculate the difference in length between one piece of red ribbon and one piece of white ribbon.

2. Have students identify the total amount of red ribbon in the problem, the total amount of white ribbon, and the number of projects in which the ribbon will be used 50 inches; 20 inches; 5 projects

   Remind them that the red ribbon and the white ribbon are cut into equal-sized pieces and shared equally among the 5 projects.

   **Ask:** Why was division used to find the length of each piece of red ribbon and each piece of white ribbon? The problem is about equal lengths of ribbon that will be used in 5 projects, so the ribbon needed to be divided into equal lengths.

   **Ask:** Why was subtraction used next? The problem asked for the difference in length between the two different colors of ribbon.

3. Remind students that the "look back" part of the 4-step problem-solving plan gives them an opportunity to check their calculations to make sure they did the math correctly and answered the question in the problem. Have students review the calculations in the "carry out the plan" section. Guide them to use inverse operations to check the math in each calculation.

4. Read Problem 1 with students. Have them ask themselves these questions:
   - What am I being asked to explain? how to calculate how many gallons of gas Mr. Keefer's truck uses each year
   - What information do I have? Mr. Keefer drives 450 miles a day, 250 days a year. His truck can drive 15 miles on each gallon of gas.
   - What information do I need? how many miles Mr. Keefer drives in a year and how fuel efficient his truck is, in terms of miles to the gallon
   - What number do I divide into the number of miles Mr. Keefer drives in a year to find how much gas he uses in a year? 15

5. Help students devise a strategy to solve the problem. As they come up with each step of the strategy, have them ask themselves which operation they should use to carry it out. Tell students to write the operation beside each step of their strategy.

6. Have students carry out their plan and do the calculations.

7. Guide students to look back at their work and check their calculations.

8. Have students do Problems 2–4. Remind them to ask themselves questions as they complete each step of the problem-solving plan.

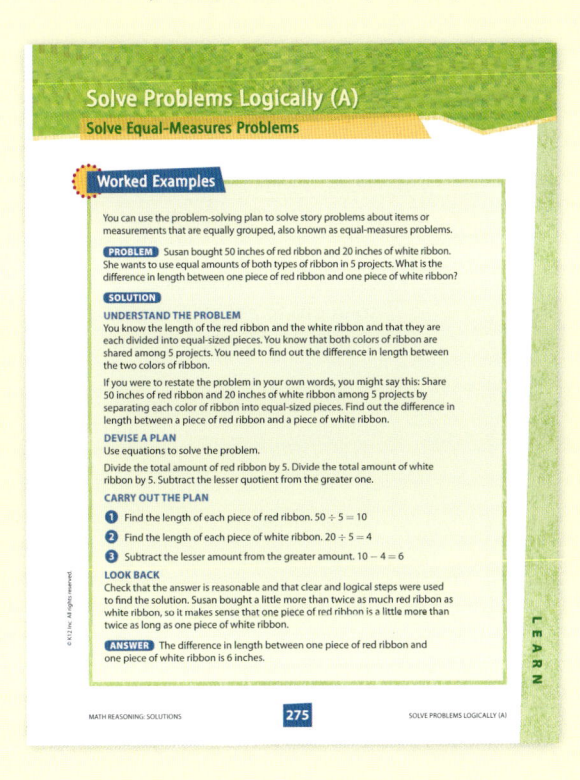

### Solve Problems Logically (A)
#### Solve Equal-Measures Problems

**Worked Examples**

You can use the problem-solving plan to solve story problems about items or measurements that are equally grouped, also known as equal-measures problems.

**PROBLEM** Susan bought 50 inches of red ribbon and 20 inches of white ribbon. She wants to use equal amounts of both types of ribbon in 5 projects. What is the difference in length between one piece of red ribbon and one piece of white ribbon?

**SOLUTION**

**UNDERSTAND THE PROBLEM**
You know the length of the red ribbon and the white ribbon and that they are each divided into equal-sized pieces. You know that both colors of ribbon are shared among 5 projects. You need to find out the difference in length between the two colors of ribbon.

If you were to restate the problem in your own words, you might say this: Share 50 inches of red ribbon and 20 inches of white ribbon among 5 projects by separating each color of ribbon into equal-sized pieces. Find out the difference in length between a piece of red ribbon and a piece of white ribbon.

**DEVISE A PLAN**
Use equations to solve the problem.
Divide the total amount of red ribbon by 5. Divide the total amount of white ribbon by 5. Subtract the lesser quotient from the greater one.

**CARRY OUT THE PLAN**
1. Find the length of each piece of red ribbon. $50 \div 5 = 10$
2. Find the length of each piece of white ribbon. $20 \div 5 = 4$
3. Subtract the lesser amount from the greater amount. $10 - 4 = 6$

**LOOK BACK**
Check that the answer is reasonable and that clear and logical steps were used to find the solution. Susan bought a little more than twice as much red ribbon as white ribbon, so it makes sense that one piece of red ribbon is a little more than twice as long as one piece of white ribbon.

**ANSWER** The difference in length between one piece of red ribbon and one piece of white ribbon is 6 inches.

## Additional Answers

1. **Step 1:** Multiply. 450 · 250
   **Step 2:** Divide. 112,500 ÷ 15
   Mr. Keefer's truck uses 7,500 gallons of gas each year.

2. **Step 1:** Multiply. 7 · 3
   **Step 2:** Multiply. 5 · 3
   **Step 3:** Subtract the amount of banana chips (lesser product) from the amount of raisins (greater product). 21 − 15
   Tommy's friends ate 6 more ounces of raisins than banana chips.

3. **Step 1:** Divide. 120 ÷ 4
   **Step 2:** Divide. 212 ÷ 4
   **Step 3:** Subtract the amount of chicken (lesser quotient) from the amount of turkey (greater quotient). 53 − 30
   One serving of turkey is 23 grams heavier than one serving of chicken.

---

### Worksheet (page 276)

Write a sequence of steps to solve the problem.

1. Mr. Keefer is a truck driver. He drives 450 miles a day, 250 days each year. His truck can drive 15 miles on each gallon of gas. How many gallons of gas does Mr. Keefer's truck use each year? **See right.**

2. Tommy is having snacks with his friends. Among the friends, 7 want to eat raisins and 5 want to eat banana chips. Raisins and banana chips are sold in 3-ounce bags. How many more ounces of raisins than banana chips will Tommy's friends eat? **See right.**

3. Cindy bought 120 grams of chicken and 212 grams of turkey. She wants to divide each type of meat into 4 equal servings. What is the difference in weight between one serving of chicken and one serving of turkey? **See right.**

4. Kim bought 2 feet of pine wood at $4.82 per foot. She also bought 4 feet of maple wood at $3.17 per foot. What is the total cost of Kim's purchases?

   **Step 1. Multiply:** 2 · $4.82
   **Step 2. Multiply:** 4 · $3.17
   **Step 3. Add:** $9.64 + $12.68
   The total cost of Kim's purchases of wood is $22.32.

---

## TRY IT  Work with Equal-Measures Problems

**ONLINE 10 min**

Students will complete an online Try It. If necessary, read the directions, problems, and answer choices to students and help them with keyboard or mouse operations.

### Objectives

- Express clear and logical solutions to equal-measures problems and rate problems.

# Solve Problems Logically (B)

## Lesson Overview

| | | |
|---|---|---|
| **GET READY**  Solve Simple Rate Story Problems | 10 minutes | **ONLINE** |
| **LEARN**  Solve a Guided Rate Story Problem | 15 minutes | **ONLINE** |
| **LEARN**  Solve Rate Story Problems | 15 minutes | **OFFLINE** |
| **TRY IT**  Work with Rate Story Problems | 10 minutes | **ONLINE** |
| **CHECKPOINT** | 10 minutes | **ONLINE** |

### ▶ Lesson Objectives
Express clear and logical solutions to equal-measures problems and rate problems.

### ▶ Prerequisite Skills
- Solve a story problem involving rate.
- Solve a story problem involving equal measures.
- Express the solution to a story problem clearly and logically.

### Materials to Gather

**SUPPLIED**

Problem-Solving Plan (printout)
Solve Rate Story Problems activity page

### ▶ Content Background

Students will learn to express their solutions to rate story problems clearly and logically. They will write solutions step by step.

The following problem-solving method was developed by George Pólya and is an effective way to solve a variety of story problems: (1) understand the problem; (2) devise a plan; (3) carry out the plan; and (4) look back. As students work on solving problems, they should follow the 4-step problem-solving plan. In the "carry out the plan" step, students express their solutions to the problem in a clear and logical manner.

Expressing clear and logical solutions to problems is an important part of studying mathematics. This is the "show your work" step used by mathematicians throughout history. The use of clear language and appropriate mathematical notation and terms is critical. Students should support their solutions to a problem with evidence in both words and symbols.

These skills are critical in everyday life. The ability to create and report information to share with others has become a necessary skill in the information age. In fact, many standardized tests now include writing sections in which students are graded on their ability to write and clearly express their understanding.

Rate problems involve the constant relationship between two different kinds of units. Students may have explored rate problems in measurement when, for example, they determined that there are 12 inches in 1 foot. In that rate, the units are feet and inches. However, many types of different units can be used in rate problems. In a rate problem, students need to determine whether they have to multiply or divide.

**SOLVE PROBLEMS LOGICALLY (B)**

In many experiences students may have had with story problems, the solution to a computation problem was the final answer to the story problem. But when students solve a story problem by using division, their computation often has a remainder with the quotient. A remainder can have different effects on a solution to a story problem. Students must carefully consider the meaning of the story problem before they record their final answer.

▶ **Advance Preparation**

Print the Problem-Solving Plan.

## GET READY  Solve Simple Rate Story Problems

*ONLINE 10 min*

### Objectives
- Solve a story problem involving rate.

Students will learn about rates. They will use diagrams to solve rate story problems.

## LEARN  Solve a Guided Rate Story Problem

*ONLINE 15 min*

### Objectives
- Express clear and logical solutions to equal-measures problems and rate problems.

Students will use the 4-step problem-solving plan, as well as clear and logical steps, to find the solution to a rate story problem.

**Tips**  Remind students that a rate is a ratio that compares two different units. Ask them to name an example of a rate. Answers might include heartbeats per minute, kilometers per hour, or miles per gallon.

## LEARN  Solve Rate Story Problems

*OFFLINE 15 min*

### Objectives
- Express clear and logical solutions to equal-measures problems and rate problems.

Students will use the 4-step problem-solving plan to solve rate problems. They will write the steps in a clear and logical order to find the answer. Gather the Problem-Solving Plan. Have students turn to the Solve Rate Story Problems activity page in their Activity Book.

Students should copy the problems from the Activity Book into their Math Notebook as necessary and solve them there.

1. Read the Worked Examples box with students. Give them the Problem-Solving Plan to refer to as they solve the problem.

   **Ask:** What are the rates that are given in this problem? *3 pounds of oranges for $4.26 and oranges for $1.56 per pound*

   **Ask:** What are you asked to do in this problem? *Figure out which rate is less expensive when 12 pounds of oranges are bought.*

2. Note that students might realize that they could have found which oranges are less expensive by comparing the rates of $1.42 per pound and $1.56 per pound. But the problem asks how much money will be saved if Tommy buys the less expensive oranges, so they still need to figure out the cost of 12 pounds of oranges at each rate.

MATH REASONING: SOLUTIONS

3. Review the "look back" step with students. Discuss the two different ways that explain why the answer was reasonable.

4. Read Problem 1 with students.

   **Ask:** What are the first two steps to solve the problem? Calculate the rate in kilometers per hour that Lucy's plane flies and Paul's plane flies.

   **Ask:** Does it matter mathematically if you calculate the rate Lucy's plane flies before you calculate the rate Paul's plane flies? No

   **Ask:** What is the third step to solve the problem? Calculate the difference in rates in kilometers per hour, so subtract the lesser quotient from the greater quotient.

5. Tell students that the directions ask them to briefly explain each step. In their answers, they should write out each step, show all work, and clearly state what the answer explains. Someone else should be able to follow their work and understand how to find the answer.

   Tell them to check whether they are on the right path by making sure their answers in the steps make sense within the context of the problem.

   Tell them that in the "look back" part of their plan they should check that they have answered the question, that they have reviewed their calculations to make sure they did the math correctly, and that they have explained their steps.

6. Have students complete Problems 2–4. Guide them to refer to the Worked Example, Problem 1, and the Problem-Solving Plan if needed.

**Tips**

If students have difficulty understanding how to put the steps to solve a problem in order, write the steps on index cards and have students move the cards around to understand the steps' order.

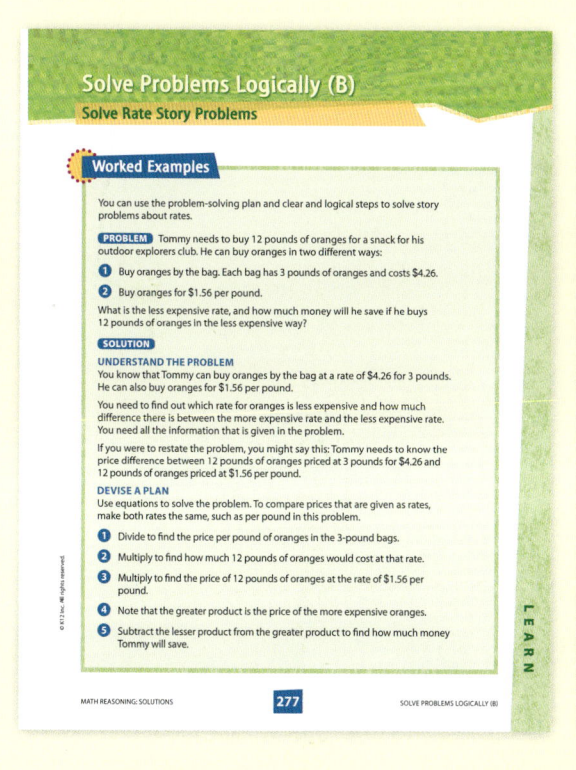

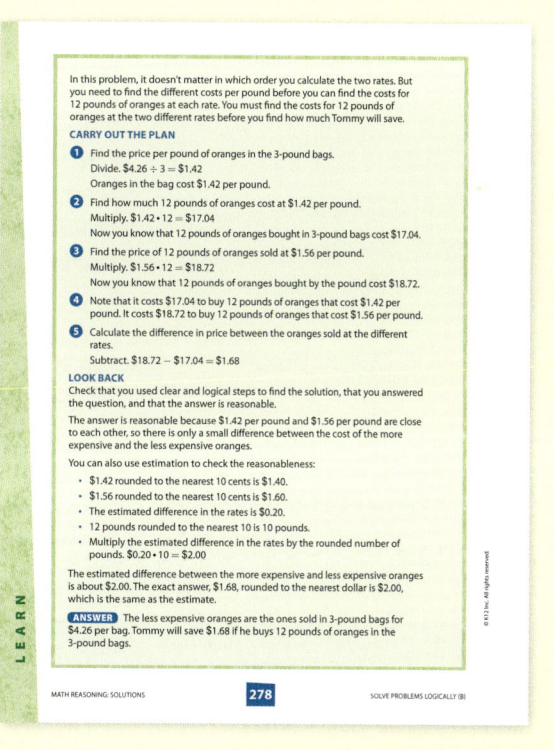

**SOLVE PROBLEMS LOGICALLY (B)** 565

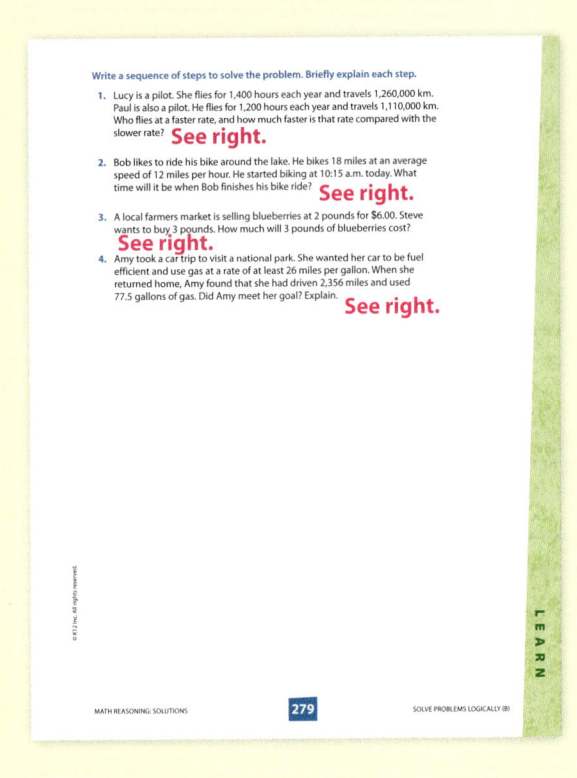

## Additional Answers

1. **Step 1:** Divide the number of kilometers Lucy flies by the number of hours she flies. $1{,}260{,}000 \div 1{,}400 = 900$
   Lucy flies her plane at 900 kilometers per hour.

   **Step 2:** Divide the number of kilometers Paul flies by the hours he flies. $1{,}110{,}000 \div 1{,}200 = 925$
   Paul's plane flies at 925 kilometers per hour.

   **Step 3:** Subtract Lucy's rate from Paul's rate. $925 - 900 = 25$
   Paul's plane flies 25 kilometers per hour faster than Lucy's plane.

2. **Step 1:** Divide the number of miles Bob bikes by the rate of 12 miles per hour. $18 \div 12 = 1.5$
   Bob bikes for 1.5 hours when he rides 18 miles at 12 miles per hour.

   **Step 2:** Multiply that quotient by 60 to get the number of minutes he rides. $60 \cdot 1.5 = 90$
   Bob bikes for 90 minutes.

   **Step 3:** Add 90 minutes to 10:15 a.m. to get 11:45 a.m.
   Bob will finish his bike ride at 11:45 a.m.

3. **Step 1:** Divide the cost of 2 pounds by 2 to find the cost of 1 pound of blueberries. $\$6.00 \div 2 = \$3.00$
   Blueberries cost $3.00 per pound.

   **Step 2:** Multiply the quotient by 3 because Steve wants to buy 3 pounds. $\$3.00 \cdot 3 = 9$
   Three pounds of blueberries will cost $9.00.

4. **Step 1:** Divide the miles driven by the number of gallons of gas used. $2{,}356 \div 77.5 = 30.4$
   Amy's car's fuel efficiency was 30.4 miles per gallon on her trip.

   **Step 2:** Compare: Is 30.4 greater than, less than, or equal to 26? 30.4 is greater than 26.

   **Step 3:** Amy's car's fuel efficiency was 30.4 miles per gallon, which is greater than 26 miles per gallon. Amy met her goal. In fact, her car's fuel efficiency was 4.4 miles per gallon greater than her goal.

### TRY IT  Work with Rate Story Problems

**ONLINE 10 min**

Students will complete an online Try It. If necessary, read the directions, problems, and answer choices to students and help them with keyboard or mouse operations.

**Objectives**

- Express clear and logical solutions to equal-measures problems and rate problems.

### CHECKPOINT

**ONLINE 10 min**

Students will complete an online Checkpoint. If necessary, read the directions, problems, and answer choices to students and help them with keyboard or mouse operations.

**Objectives**

- Express clear and logical solutions to equal-measures problems and rate problems.

# Estimation and Reasonable Answers

## Lesson Overview

| | | |
|---|---|---|
| **GET READY** Add and Subtract Fractions | 10 minutes | ONLINE |
| **LEARN** Use Estimation | 15 minutes | ONLINE |
| **LEARN** Reasonable Answers | 15 minutes | OFFLINE |
| **TRY IT** Verify Answers | 10 minutes | ONLINE |
| **CHECKPOINT** | 10 minutes | ONLINE |

### ▶ Lesson Objectives
Use estimation in addition or subtraction of fractions to verify whether calculated results are reasonable.

### ▶ Prerequisite Skills
- Use estimation to predict a solution to a story problem and to verify the reasonableness of the calculated result.
- Solve a simple problem involving addition or subtraction of fractions.

### ▶ Content Background
Students will learn to use estimation to verify the reasonableness of answers to addition and subtraction fraction story problems.

The following problem-solving steps were developed by George Pólya and is an effective way to solve a variety of story problems: (1) understand the problem; (2) devise a plan; (3) carry out the plan; and (4) look back. As students work on solving problems, they should follow the 4-step problem-solving plan. In the "carry out the plan" step, students show their solutions to the problem in a clear and logical manner.

Although the context and numbers in story problems vary, good problem solvers know they can use certain strategies over and over to solve similar problems. Estimating the answer to a problem and verifying the reasonableness of the calculated answer to the estimate enhance students' number-sense development. When students learn to use different strategies, they can apply successful strategies to solve more complex problems, instead of treating every problem as a new experience.

Students can estimate and calculate answers to all types of problems. Being able to use the estimate to evaluate the reasonableness of the calculated answer involves students asking themselves questions such as the following: Did I choose the correct operation to solve the problem? How does my calculated answer compare to my estimated answer?

### Materials to Gather

**SUPPLIED**

number lines from Number Line Creator Tool

Reasonable Answers activity page

▶ **Advance Preparation**

**DIRECTIONS FOR USING THE NUMBER LINE CREATOR TOOL**

To create number lines from 0 to 5:

| 1. Set Range: | 2. Select Options: | 3. Print Number Line: |
|---|---|---|
| • Start Number Line at: 0<br>• End Number Line at: 5 | • Tick Marks: ones, halves, fourths<br>• Labels: ones, halves, fourths<br>• Label Format: fractions | • Page Orientation: landscape<br>• Number Lines per Sheet: 4 |

To create number lines from 2 to 8:

| 1. Set Range: | 2. Select Options: | 3. Print Number Line: |
|---|---|---|
| • Start Number Line at: 2<br>• End Number Line at: 8 | • Tick Marks: ones, halves, fourths<br>• Labels: ones, halves, fourths<br>• Label Format: fractions | • Page Orientation: landscape<br>• Number Lines per Sheet: 4 |

## GET READY  Add and Subtract Fractions
**ONLINE 10 min**

**Objectives**

Students will practice adding and subtracting fractions and mixed numbers with like or unlike denominators.

- Solve a simple problem involving addition or subtraction of fractions.

## LEARN  Use Estimation
**ONLINE 15 min**

**Objectives**

Students will use estimation to determine if the answers to fraction and mixed-number addition and subtraction story problems are reasonable.

- Use estimation in addition or subtraction of fractions to verify whether calculated results are reasonable.

## LEARN  Reasonable Answers
**OFFLINE 15 min**

**Objectives**

Students will use estimation and the 4-step problem-solving plan to verify whether the answer to a story problem is reasonable or not. They will explain their process in finding out the reasonableness of the answers. Gather the number lines you printed. Have students turn to the Reasonable Answers activity page in their Activity Book and read the directions with them.

Students should copy the problems from the Activity Book into their Math Notebook as necessary and solve them there.

1. Read the Worked Examples box with students. Give them the number line from 2 to 8 showing fourths.

- Use estimation in addition or subtraction of fractions to verify whether calculated results are reasonable.

**568**  MATH REASONING: SOLUTIONS

2. Tell students to explain how to use a number line to estimate the sum of $3\frac{7}{10}$ and $3\frac{1}{5}$. $3\frac{7}{10}$ is close to but less than the benchmark number $3\frac{3}{4}$, so I can locate $3\frac{3}{4}$ on the number line. Then I can count on $3\frac{1}{4}$ units because $3\frac{1}{4}$ is a benchmark number for $3\frac{1}{5}$.

3. Tell students that the Worked Example finds the exact answer. Remind students that they will compare their estimate and exact answer to decide whether the answers are reasonable or not.

4. Have students read Problem 1. Give them the number line from 0 to 5 showing fourths.

    **Ask:** What does the problem ask? how many more cups of granola than cups of raisins are in each batch

    **Ask:** What information is given that isn't necessary for solving the problem? Each batch uses $\frac{5}{6}$ cup of chocolate chips.

5. Have students explain how to use the number line to estimate the answer. $4\frac{1}{2}$ is a benchmark number, so locate it on the number line. $1\frac{2}{7}$ is close to but less than the benchmark number $1\frac{1}{4}$. Count $1\frac{1}{4}$ units back from $4\frac{1}{2}$ on the number line.

6. Tell students to complete the "look back" step of the problem-solving plan.

    **Ask:** Is Hector's exact answer reasonable compared with your estimate? Why or why not? Answers will vary. Students may say that they can see on the number line that the estimate is close to the exact answer. They may also change the mixed numbers so the fractions have common denominators and then compare the mixed numbers.

7. Have students finish solving Problem 1. Have them solve the remaining problems. Students may use number lines to help them estimate.

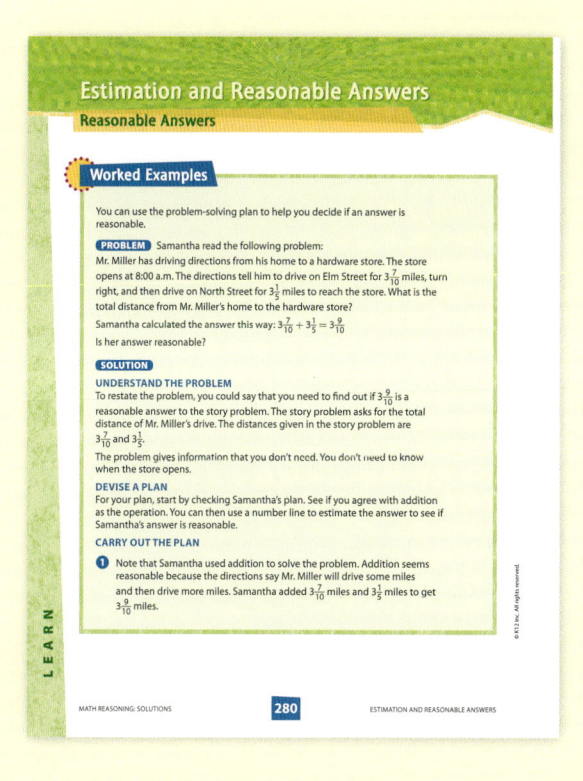

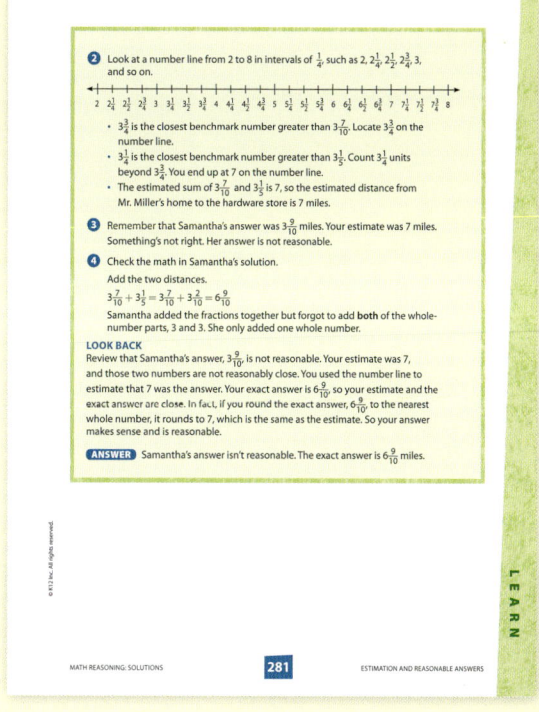

> **Tips**
>
> Tell students that if their estimate is not reasonably close to the exact answer, they should check their work in the "carry out the plan" step and review their calculations.

**ESTIMATION AND REASONABLE ANSWERS** 569

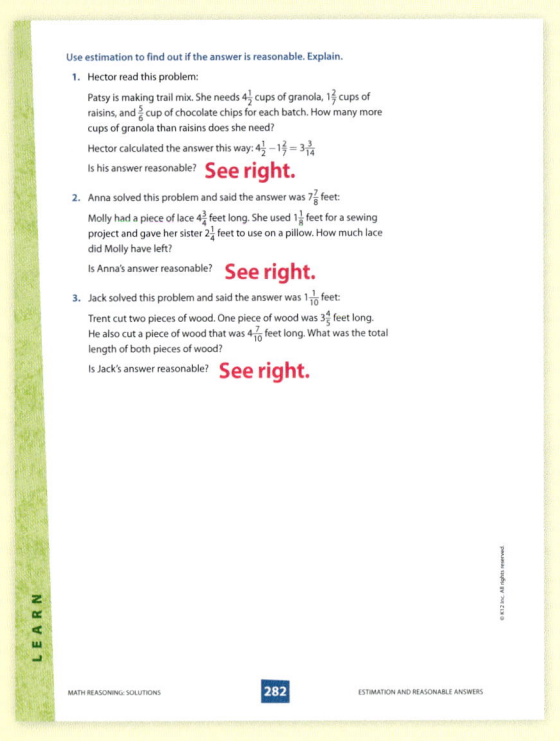

**Additional Answers**

1. Yes. Estimate the granola at $4\frac{1}{2}$ cups. Estimate the raisins at $1\frac{1}{4}$ cups. Subtract: $4\frac{1}{2} - 1\frac{1}{4} = 3\frac{1}{4}$

    The estimate, $3\frac{1}{4}$, is close to the exact answer of $3\frac{3}{14}$.
    To further check your answer, calculate that $3\frac{1}{4} = 3\frac{7}{28}$ and that $3\frac{3}{14} = 3\frac{6}{28}$. So the estimate is close to the exact answer.

2. No. Estimate that Molly started with about 5 feet of lace, used about 1 foot for her sewing project, and gave her sister about 2 feet. The operations are addition of the lace pieces she used or gave away and subtraction from the amount of lace she started with.

    $5 - (1 + 2) = 2$

    Molly had about 2 feet of lace left.

    Anna's answer was $7\frac{7}{8}$ feet. Your estimate was about 2 feet. Something's not right. Anna's answer is not reasonable.

    Check the math in Anna's solution.

    Add the amount of lace Molly gave away: $1\frac{1}{8} + 2\frac{1}{4} = 1\frac{1}{8} + 2\frac{2}{8} = 3\frac{3}{8}$

    Subtract the amount of lace Molly gave away from 5:
    $5 - 3\frac{3}{8} = 4\frac{8}{8} - 3\frac{3}{8} = 1\frac{5}{8}$

    Anna incorrectly added all three lengths of the lace.

    The exact answer is $1\frac{5}{8}$ feet of lace left. Your estimate and exact answer are close. In fact, if you round the exact answer, $1\frac{5}{8}$, to the nearest whole number, it rounds to 2, which is the same as the estimate. So your answer makes sense and is reasonable.

3. No. Estimate that Trent cut a piece of wood that was about 4 feet long and a piece of wood that was about $4\frac{1}{2}$ feet long. The operation is addition.

    $4 + 4\frac{1}{2} = 8\frac{1}{2}$

    The wood pieces were a total of about $8\frac{1}{2}$ feet long.

    Jack's answer was $1\frac{1}{10}$ feet. Your estimate was about $8\frac{1}{2}$ feet. Something's not right. Jack's answer is not reasonable.

    Check the math in Jack's solution.

    Add the lengths of the two pieces of wood:

    $3\frac{4}{5} + 4\frac{7}{10} = 3\frac{8}{10} + 4\frac{7}{10} = 7\frac{15}{10} = 8\frac{5}{10} = 8\frac{1}{2}$

    Jack used subtraction instead of addition.

    The exact answer is $8\frac{1}{2}$ feet of wood pieces. Your estimate and exact answer are the same. So your answer makes sense and is reasonable.

## TRY IT Verify Answers

**ONLINE 10 min**

Students will complete an online Try It. If necessary, read the directions, problems, and answer choices to students and help them with keyboard or mouse operations.

### Objectives

- Use estimation in addition or subtraction of fractions to verify whether calculated results are reasonable.

## CHECKPOINT

**ONLINE 10 min**

Students will complete an online Checkpoint. If necessary, read the directions, problems, and answer choices to students and help them with keyboard or mouse operations.

### Objectives

- Use estimation in addition or subtraction of fractions to verify whether calculated results are reasonable.

# Decimal Solutions

## Lesson Overview

| | | |
|---|---|---|
| **GET READY** Reasonable Answers with Mixed Numbers | 10 minutes | **ONLINE** |
| **LEARN** Exact or Approximate Answers | 10 minutes | **ONLINE** |
| **LEARN** Use Approximate Answers | 20 minutes | **ONLINE** |
| **TRY IT** Decimal Story Problems | 10 minutes | **ONLINE** |
| **CHECKPOINT** | 10 minutes | **ONLINE** |

### ▶ Lesson Objectives

- Explain the advantages of exact solutions and approximate solutions to problems involving addition or subtraction of decimal numbers, and give answers to a specified degree of accuracy, such as hundredths.
- Make precise calculations and use the situation presented in a problem involving decimal-number operations to check the validity of the result.

### ▶ Prerequisite Skills

- Use estimation to predict a solution to a story problem and to verify the reasonableness of the calculated result.
- Solve a simple problem involving addition or subtraction of fractions.
- Answer a story problem to a specified degree of accuracy, such as hundredths.

### ▶ Content Background

Students will learn to determine whether an approximate answer or an exact answer is an appropriate solution to a decimal story problem. They will use approximate answers to determine whether exact answers to story problems are valid.

The following problem-solving method was developed by George Pólya and is an effective way to solve a variety of story problems: (1) understand the problem; (2) devise a plan; (3) carry out the plan; and (4) look back. As students work on solving problems, they should follow the 4-step problem-solving plan.

Although the context and numbers in story problems vary, good problem solvers know they can use certain strategies over and over again to solve similar problems. When students are able to use different strategies, they can apply the same strategies to solve more complex problems, instead of treating every problem as a new experience.

Students will learn to evaluate story problems with addition and subtraction of decimal numbers and determine and explain whether an exact answer or an estimate is the appropriate solution. They will learn to answer a story problem to a specified degree of accuracy, such as hundredths.

**Materials to Gather**

There are no materials to gather for this lesson.

Students should understand that the term *estimate* is a mathematical term that means "about how many" and that different everyday situations require different degrees of precision. In some situations, estimation is inappropriate, such as when a pharmacist fills a prescription. Students will learn to base their choice of an appropriate estimation strategy on the context of each story problem. Often an overestimate, or an approximation that is obviously greater than the exact number, is desirable in everyday life. For example, people use an overestimate when they decide how much money they will need to make a purchase or to help them decide how much food they should buy when they are planning a party.

Estimation can make numbers easier to work with when students need to do quick addition, subtraction, multiplication, or division. They can also use estimation to predict solutions to math problems or to predict reasonable solutions to calculations within a problem, such as at each step in long division. They can also compare an estimated value to the final answer to verify that the answer is reasonable.

Sometimes students will be asked for an approximate answer and an exact answer to the same problem. In those cases, they will use estimation as a problem-solving skill and as a way to verify the reasonableness of a calculated answer. They will understand the value of an estimate as part of the problem-solving plan. Students will validate the results of estimated and exact answers by reviewing the original problem and looking back on their plan for solving the problem.

## GET READY  Reasonable Answers with Mixed Numbers

**ONLINE 10 min**

### Objectives

- Use estimation to predict a solution to a story problem and to verify the reasonableness of the calculated result.
- Solve a simple problem involving addition or subtraction of fractions.
- Answer a story problem to a specified degree of accuracy, such as hundredths.

Students will estimate and then solve a multistep story problem involving mixed numbers and use the estimate to verify the reasonableness of the answer. Stay with students as they complete the activity and listen to their answer to the last question, which reviews how they know their answer to the story problem is reasonable. Then they can read the given answer.

## LEARN  Exact or Approximate Answers

**ONLINE 10 min**

### Objectives

- Explain the advantages of exact solutions and approximate solutions to problems involving addition or subtraction of decimal numbers, and give answers to a specified degree of accuracy, such as hundredths.
- Make precise calculations and use the situation presented in a problem involving decimal-number operations to check the validity of the result.

Students will decide whether an exact answer or an estimate is appropriate for a situation. They also will work with situations in which either an exact answer or an estimate would be appropriate. They will learn why certain methods are better than others in different situations.

## LEARN Use Approximate Answers

**ONLINE 20 min**

### Objectives

- Explain the advantages of exact solutions and approximate solutions to problems involving addition or subtraction of decimal numbers, and give answers to a specified degree of accuracy, such as hundredths.
- Make precise calculations and use the situation presented in a problem involving decimal-number operations to check the validity of the result.

Students will use the 4-step problem-solving plan to solve an everyday problem about menu choices for a meal at a restaurant. Students will solve the problem to keep the cost, including tax and tip, within a budgeted amount. They will find an approximate answer and an exact answer. They will use the approximate answer to determine the validity of the exact answer.

## TRY IT Decimal Story Problems

**ONLINE 10 min**

### Objectives

- Explain the advantages of exact solutions and approximate solutions to problems involving addition or subtraction of decimal numbers, and give answers to a specified degree of accuracy, such as hundredths.
- Make precise calculations and use the situation presented in a problem involving decimal-number operations to check the validity of the result.

Students will complete an online Try It. If necessary, read the directions, problems, and answer choices to students and help them with keyboard or mouse operations.

## CHECKPOINT

**ONLINE 10 min**

### Objectives

- Explain the advantages of exact solutions and approximate solutions to problems involving addition or subtraction of decimal numbers, and give answers to a specified degree of accuracy, such as hundredths.
- Make precise calculations and use the situation presented in a problem involving decimal-number operations to check the validity of the result.

Students will complete an online Checkpoint. If necessary, read the directions, problems, and answer choices to students and help them with keyboard or mouse operations.

**MATH REASONING: SOLUTIONS**

# Reasonable Solutions

## Lesson Overview

| | | |
|---|---|---|
| **LEARN** Solve a Problem with Alexander | 15 minutes | ONLINE |
| **LEARN** Reasonable Geometry Solutions | 25 minutes | OFFLINE |
| **TRY IT** Evaluate Solutions | 10 minutes | ONLINE |
| **CHECKPOINT** | 10 minutes | ONLINE |

### ▶ Lesson Objectives
Evaluate whether a solution for a problem is reasonable.

### ▶ Prerequisite Skills
Use estimation to predict a solution to a story problem and to verify the reasonableness of the calculated result.

### ▶ Content Background
Students will learn to evaluate whether a solution to a problem is reasonable.

Although the context and numbers in story problems vary, good problem solvers know they can use certain strategies over and over again to solve similar problems. Estimating the answer to a problem and then verifying the reasonableness of the calculated answer to the estimate enhances students' number sense development. When students are able to use different strategies, they can apply the same strategies in solving more complex problems, instead of treating every problem as a new experience.

The following problem-solving method was developed by George Pólya and is an effective way to solve a variety of story problems: (1) understand the problem; (2) devise a plan; (3) carry out the plan; and (4) look back. As students work on solving problems, they should follow the 4-step problem-solving plan.

Students can estimate and calculate answers to all types of problems. Being able to use the estimate to evaluate the reasonableness of the calculated answer involves students asking questions such as the following: Did I use the correct operations in my equation? How does my calculated answer compare to my estimated answer? Does my answer make sense with the question in the problem?

### ▶ Advance Preparation
Print the Reasonable Geometry Solutions printout.

---

**Materials to Gather**

**SUPPLIED**
Reasonable Geometry Solutions (printout)

**ALSO NEEDED**
ruler, dual-scale

## LEARN  Solve a Problem with Alexander

**ONLINE 15 min**

### Objectives
- Evaluate whether a solution for a problem is reasonable.

Students will use a problem-solving plan to find the solution to a problem about finding the number of trees that were planted in parks. They will use the strategy of making a table to help them keep track of the multiple steps needed to carry out the plan and find the solution. Students will use estimation throughout the activity to evaluate whether or not their answers are reasonable.

## LEARN  Reasonable Geometry Solutions

**OFFLINE 25 min**

### Objectives
- Evaluate whether a solution for a problem is reasonable.

Students will develop and use a formula to find the angle measures in regular polygons. Gather the Reasonable Geometry Solutions printout and a ruler.

1. Tell students they will find the measure of angles in regular polygons without using a protractor. Instead, they will draw lines on polygons, observe patterns, and come up with a formula.

2. Remind students that a regular polygon has all sides of equal length and all angles of equal measure. This activity deals only with regular polygons. Tell students that the word *diagonals* in this activity means lines drawn from a vertex to other vertices of a regular polygon.

3. Give students the Reasonable Geometry Solutions printout and ruler. Tell them that they will complete the table as they work through the activity.

4. Tell students to look at the first row, the triangle row. Tell them to note that the "Number of Angles" column says 3 and the "Number of Triangles Formed by Diagonals" column says 1.

   Explain the "Number of Triangles Formed by Diagonals" column by asking students to use a ruler to draw a line from any vertex of the triangle (such as the top vertex) to each of the other two vertices. If they use the top vertex, they'll draw lines along the left and right sides of the triangle. Now they have created 1 triangle by drawing diagonals from a vertex. That's why the "Number of Triangles Formed by Diagonals" column has a 1 in it.

   Tell students that this step has helped them begin to develop a pattern for all the regular polygons in the table.

   If needed, help students recall that the sum of the angle measures in a triangle is 180°. Have them complete the "Sum of Angle Measures in Degrees" column for the triangle. 180

   Remind students that this is a regular triangle, where all the angles have equal measure. Have them divide 180 by 3 to complete the "Measure of Each Angle in Degrees" column for the triangle. 60

5. Have students look at the second row, the square row. Tell them to notice given information: 4 angles in a square and 2 triangles formed by diagonals. Have students draw a diagonal from one vertex of the square to the opposite vertex to form 2 triangles. Now they have shown that the 2 in the table is correct.

   Tell them that they don't need to draw diagonals along the *sides* of the square (or the sides of later polygons in the activity), as they did for the triangle. It is understood that those polygon sides are also the sides of triangles formed by the diagonals they draw.

### Tips

Have students explain in their own words how they will use the formula to find the measures of the angles in each of the last 4 figures.

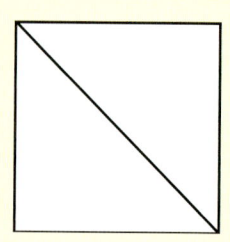

One way to show a square divided into 2 triangles

Have students complete the "Sum of Angle Measures in Degrees" column for the square. Tell them they can use the sum of the angle measures in a triangle, 180°, to help them. Since there are 2 triangles in a square, and the sum of the angle measures in a triangle is 180°, they can multiply 2 by 180. 360

Note that the product, 360, means that the measures of the angles in a square add up to 360°.

Have students divide 360 by 4 to complete the "Measure of Each Angle in Degrees" column for the square. 90

**Ask:** Is 90° a reasonable answer for the measure of each angle in a square? Yes, it is reasonable because each angle in a square is a right angle. A right angle measures 90°.

6. Have students look at the third row, the pentagon row. Have them start by drawing diagonals from a vertex to the other vertices on the pentagon. Then have them begin filling out the row, always checking to see whether their answers are reasonable.

   **Say:** You can check to see whether your answers in the table are reasonable by observing patterns and comparing your answers to answers that are already in the table. When you repeat your process for answering questions about each polygon, you can check to see whether the process is helping you find reasonable answers.

   **Ask:** How can you use the number of triangles in a pentagon, 3, and the sum of the angle measures in a triangle, 180°, to find the sum of the angle measures in a pentagon? Multiply 180 by 3.

   **Ask:** How can you use the sum of the angle measures and the number of angles to find the measure of each angle in the pentagon? Divide the total of the angle measures in a pentagon, 540, by 5.

7. Check students' answers for the pentagon:
   - Number of Angles: 5
   - Number of Triangles Formed by Diagonals: 3
   - Sum of Angle Measures in Degrees: 540
   - Measure of Each Angle in Degrees: 108

   **Ask:** Think about the steps you've taken to find the sum of the angle measures and the measures of each angle for the triangle and the square. How do you know that you have a reasonable answer to the measure of each angle in a pentagon? The pentagon was divided into 3 triangles. The sum of the angle measures in a triangle is 180°. The sum of the angle measures in 3 triangles is 180 • 3, which equals 540. Because the sum of the angle measures in a pentagon is 540°, 540 ÷ 5 is the measure of each angle in a pentagon. Each angle measures 108°.

8. Have students follow the same process for the hexagon. Check students' answers for the hexagon:
   - Number of Angles: 6
   - Number of Triangles Formed by Diagonals: 4
   - Sum of Angle Measures in Degrees: 720
   - Measure of Each Angle in Degrees: 120

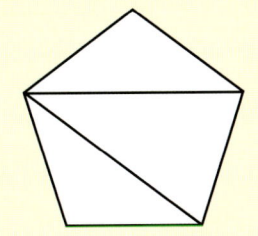

One way to show a pentagon divided into 3 triangles

REASONABLE SOLUTIONS

9. Tell students that the following questions will lead them to derive a formula for finding angle measures of any regular polygon. Tell them that if they use the formula, they won't need to draw diagonals on polygons. Have them refer to the table, with the answers they have found for the triangle, square, pentagon, and hexagon, to answer the following questions.

   **Ask:** Compare the number of triangles to the number of angles in each regular polygon. What do you notice? The number of triangles is 2 fewer than the number of angles.

   **Ask:** Let the variable $a$ represent the number of angles in a regular polygon. What expression describes the number of triangles in a regular polygon? $a - 2$

   Have students recall that they multiplied 180 by the number of triangles in the regular polygons to find the sum of the angle measures of the polygons.

   **Ask:** Since the expression $a - 2$ describes the number of triangles in a regular polygon, what expression describes the sum of the angle measures of a regular polygon? $180(a - 2)$

   Have students recall that they divided the sum of the angle measures in the regular polygons by the number of angles to get the measure of each angle.

   **Ask:** Think about this: The expression $180(a - 2)$ describes the sum of the angle measures of a regular polygon. The variable $a$ represents the number of angles in a regular polygon. What would happen if you divided the sum of angle measures by the number of angles? I'd get the measure of each angle of the regular polygon.

   **Ask:** What expression describes the measure of each angle in a regular polygon?

   $\left( \dfrac{180(a - 2)}{a} \right)$

10. Continue to explain the formula to students.

    **Say:** Let $M$ represent the measure of each angle of a regular polygon. The formula then becomes the following:

    $M = \dfrac{180(a - 2)}{a}$

    Tell students that the formula will work for finding the measure of each angle in any regular polygon.

    Have them write the formula at the top of the printout.

11. Have students use the formula to fill in the table for the octagon. They should show their steps to solve the equation in their Math Notebook.

    $M = \dfrac{180(a - 2)}{a} = \dfrac{180(8 - 2)}{8} = \dfrac{180(6)}{8} = \dfrac{1{,}080}{8} = 135$

    Note that the measure of each angle in a regular octagon is 135°.

12. When students finish, have them verify that the formula works by drawing diagonals in the octagon to form triangles. Check students' answers for the octagon:
    - Number of Angles: 8
    - Number of Triangles Formed by Diagonals: 6
    - Sum of Angle Measures in Degrees: 1,080
    - Measure of Each Angle in Degrees: 135

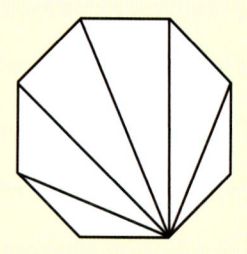

One way to show an octagon divided into 6 triangles

13. Have students write the formula with the values for *a* in the first column to complete the table for a decagon, a 20-gon, a 50-gon, and a 100-gon. Have students use their Math Notebook to find the value of *M* and find the measure of each angle in degrees. Check students' work.

   Decagon:
   - Equation: $M = \frac{180(10 - 2)}{10}$
   - Number of Angles: 10
   - Number of Triangles Formed by Diagonals: 8
   - Sum of Angle Measures in Degrees: 1,440
   - Measure of Each Angle in Degrees: 144

   20-gon:
   - Equation: $M = \frac{180(20 - 2)}{20}$
   - Number of Angles: 20
   - Number of Triangles Formed by Diagonals: 18
   - Sum of Angle Measures in Degrees: 3,240
   - Measure of Each Angle in Degrees: 162

   50-gon:
   - Equation: $M = \frac{180(50 - 2)}{50}$
   - Number of Angles: 50
   - Number of Triangles Formed by Diagonals: 48
   - Sum of Angle Measures in Degrees: 8,640
   - Measure of Each Angle in Degrees: 172.8

   100-gon:
   - Equation: $M = \frac{180(100 - 2)}{100}$
   - Number of Angles: 100
   - Number of Triangles Formed by Diagonals: 98
   - Sum of Angle Measures in Degrees: 17,640
   - Measure of Each Angle in Degrees: 176.4

14. When students finish, ask the following questions:

    **Ask:** As the number of angles increases, the regular polygon starts to look like a circle. What happens to the measure of each angle? The measure of each angle increases.

    Tell students that the more angles there are in a regular polygon, the greater each angle is. They can see an example by comparing the square with the octagon to see that each angle of the octagon is a greater size than each angle of the square. They can also compare the angle measurements in the table.

    **Ask:** Is it reasonable to think that the sum of the angle measures increases as the number of angles in the regular polygon increase? Why or why not? Yes, it is reasonable. Since the number of angles in each regular polygon increases, the sum of the angles would also increase.

    **Ask:** Is it reasonable to think that the measure of each angle in a regular polygon would reach 180°? Why or why not? No, it is not reasonable because 180° is a straight angle and cannot form an angle in a polygon.

**REASONABLE SOLUTIONS**

## TRY IT  Evaluate Solutions

**ONLINE 10 min**

Students will complete an online Try It. If necessary, read the directions, problems, and answer choices to students and help them with keyboard or mouse operations.

**Objectives**

- Evaluate whether a solution for a problem is reasonable.

## CHECKPOINT

**ONLINE 10 min**

Students will complete an online Checkpoint. If necessary, read the directions, problems, and answer choices to students and help them with keyboard or mouse operations.

**Objectives**

- Evaluate whether a solution for a problem is reasonable.

# Unit Review

## Lesson Overview

| | | |
|---|---|---|
| **UNIT REVIEW** Look Back | 10 minutes | **ONLINE** |
| **UNIT REVIEW** Checkpoint Practice | 50 minutes | **ONLINE** |
| **UNIT REVIEW** Prepare for the Checkpoint | | |

### ▶ Unit Objectives

This lesson reviews the following objectives:

- Express clear and logical solutions to equal-measures problems and rate problems.
- Use estimation in addition or subtraction of fractions to verify whether calculated results are reasonable.
- Explain the advantages of exact solutions and approximate solutions to problems involving addition or subtraction of decimal numbers, and give answers to a specified degree of accuracy, such as hundredths.
- Make precise calculations and use the situation presented in a problem involving decimal-number operations to check the validity of the result.
- Evaluate whether a solution for a problem is reasonable.

### ▶ Advance Preparation

In this lesson, students will have an opportunity to review previous activities in the Math Reasoning: Solutions unit. Look at the suggested activities in Unit Review: Prepare for the Checkpoint online and gather any needed materials.

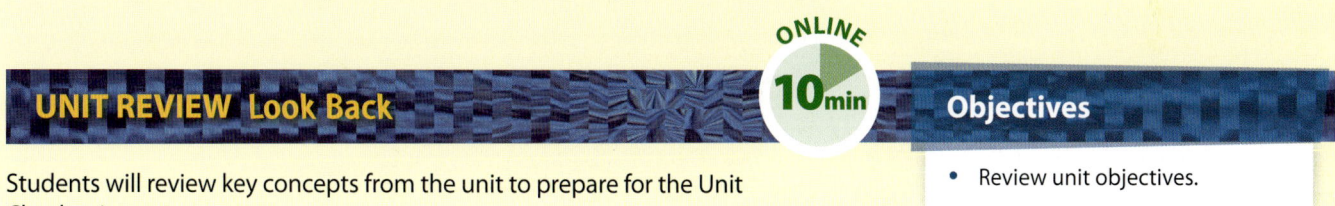

**Materials to Gather**

There are no materials to gather for this lesson.

---

**UNIT REVIEW  Look Back**   ONLINE 10 min

**Objectives**
- Review unit objectives.

Students will review key concepts from the unit to prepare for the Unit Checkpoint.

---

**UNIT REVIEW  Checkpoint Practice**   ONLINE 50 min

**Objectives**
- Review unit objectives.

Students will complete an online Checkpoint Practice to prepare for the Unit Checkpoint. If necessary, read the directions, problems, and answer choices to students. Have students answer the problems on their own. Review any missed problems with students.

---

### ▶ UNIT REVIEW  Prepare for the Checkpoint

What you do next depends on how students performed in the previous activity, Unit Review: Checkpoint Practice. If students had difficulty with any of the problems, complete the appropriate review activity listed in the table online.

# Unit Checkpoint

## Lesson Overview

**UNIT CHECKPOINT** Online | 60 minutes | ONLINE

### ▶ Unit Objectives

This lesson assesses the following objectives:
- Express clear and logical solutions to equal-measures problems and rate problems.
- Use estimation in addition or subtraction of fractions to verify whether calculated results are reasonable.
- Explain the advantages of exact solutions and approximate solutions to problems involving addition or subtraction of decimal numbers, and give answers to a specified degree of accuracy, such as hundredths.
- Make precise calculations and use the situation presented in a problem involving decimal-number operations to check the validity of the result.
- Evaluate whether a solution for a problem is reasonable.

### Materials to Gather

There are no materials to gather for this lesson.

## UNIT CHECKPOINT Online

ONLINE 60 min

Students will complete the Unit Checkpoint online. If necessary, read the directions, problems, and answer choices to students and help them with keyboard or mouse operations.

### Objectives
- Assess unit objectives.

MATH REASONING: SOLUTIONS

# Data Analysis and Representation

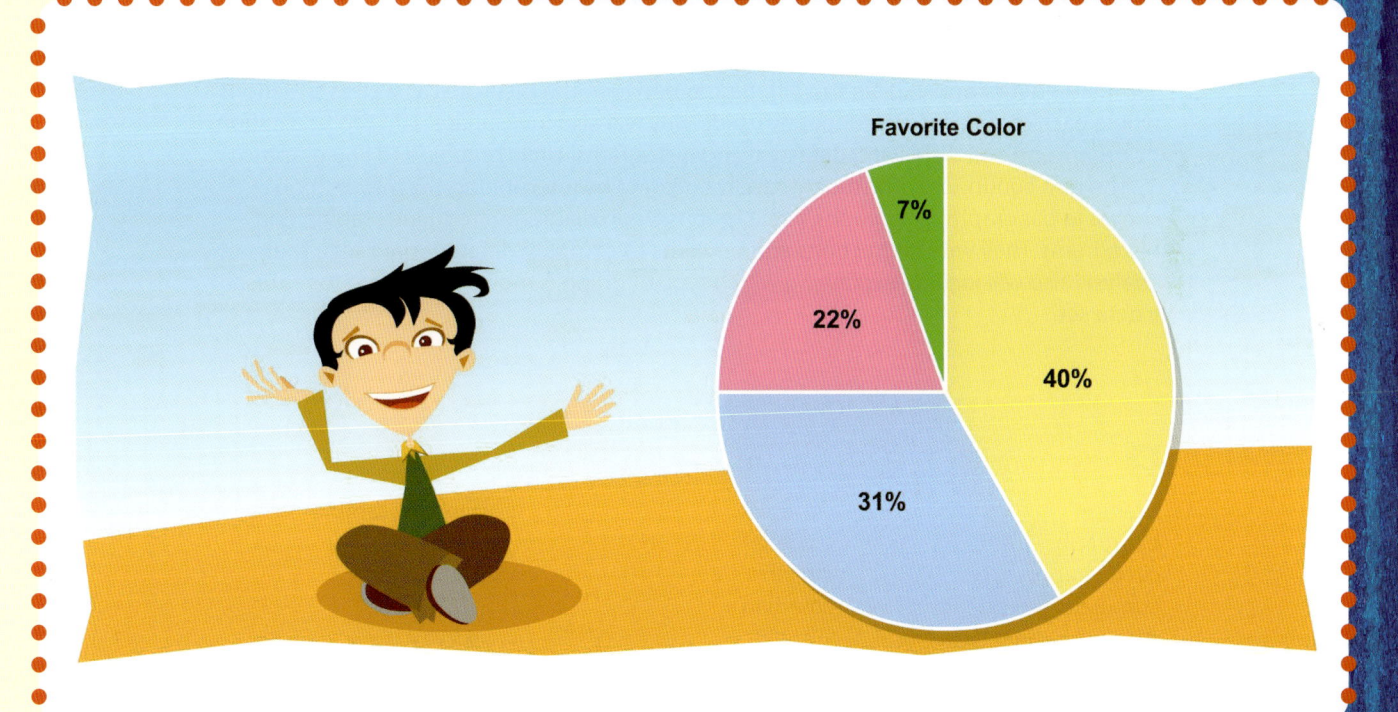

## ▶ Unit Objectives

- Explain and compute the mean, median, or mode for a set of data.
- Compare the mean, median, and mode of a data set and explain the differences and appropriate uses.
- Organize and display single-variable data in a histogram.
- Organize and display single-variable data in a circle graph.
- Interpret information displayed in a graph or table.
- Use fractions and percents to compare different data sets.
- Explain which types of graphs are appropriate for various data sets.

## ▶ Big Ideas

- Mean, median, and mode are all measures of where the center of a data set lies.
- Graphs and charts are useful ways to represent and compare numerical data.

## ▶ Unit Introduction

In this unit, students will work with data to explain and calculate mean, median, and mode. The terms *mean* and *average* will be used interchangeably. Once students have experienced calculating mean, median, and mode, they will compare these measures of central tendency and explain the differences between the measures as well as situations where each measure is appropriately used. They will also investigate data representations by organizing and displaying data by using histograms, circle graphs, and line graphs.

The unit continues with students analyzing data by interpreting the information shown in bar graphs, line graphs, circle graphs, Venn diagrams, frequency tables, and histograms. They will use fractions and percents to compare different data sets. Their analysis also will include explaining which type of graph is most appropriate to represent a data set.

## ▶ Keywords

average
bar graph
circle graph
cumulative frequency
data
frequency table
histogram
interval
label
mean
median
mode
outlier
population
random sample
sample (n.)
sample (v.)
scale
survey
trend

# Mean, Median, and Mode

## Lesson Overview

| | | |
|---|---|---|
| **LEARN** Weather Data | 15 minutes | **ONLINE** |
| **LEARN** Find and Apply the Mean to Data | 10 minutes | **OFFLINE** |
| **LEARN** Create a Data Set | 15 minutes | **OFFLINE** |
| **TRY IT** Find the Mean, Median, and Mode | 10 minutes | **ONLINE** |
| **CHECKPOINT** | 10 minutes | **ONLINE** |

### ▶ Lesson Objectives
Explain and compute the mean, median, or mode for a set of data.

### ▶ Prerequisite Skills
- Identify the mode or modes for a set of numerical data or a set of categorical data.
- Identify the median and outliers for a numerical data set.

### ▶ Content Background
Students will learn to compute the mean, median, and mode for a set of data.

Statistics are the numbers that describe sets of data. When we use the language of statistics to talk about data, we describe different measures. The specific measures of mean, median, and mode are called *measures of central tendency*.

The following set of data will be used in the explanations in this Content Background:

2, 3, 4, 4, 4, 5, 8, 9, 10, 10

The *mean*, or average, of a set of data is found by adding all the values in the data set, and then dividing that sum by the number of values in the data set. The mean of the data set is 5.9.

The *median* of a set of data targets the middle value of the data. To find the median, the data points are organized from least to greatest. When you have an odd number of data points in a set, the number that falls exactly in the middle of the data set is the median. For an even number of data points in a set, the median is actually the mean, or average, of the two middle numbers in the set. The data set is in ascending order and has an even number of data, so the median is the average of the two middle values 4 and 5, or 4.5.

Sometimes in a data set, there are values that occur more often than others. The value that appears most often in a data set is called the *mode*. There can be one mode, more than one mode, or no modes in a data set. In the data set, the number 4 appears three times, more times than any other value, so the mode of the data set is 4.

---

**Materials to Gather**

**SUPPLIED**
Find and Apply the Mean to Data activity page
Create a Data Set activity page

## LEARN Weather Data

**ONLINE 15 min**

### Objectives
- Explain and compute the mean, median, or mode for a set of data.

Students will learn how to calculate the range, mode, median, and mean for a set of data.

To help students remember the difference between range, mode, median, and mean, have them create a booklet with definitions and examples of each one after they complete the activity.

## LEARN Find and Apply the Mean to Data

**OFFLINE 10 min**

### Objectives
- Explain and compute the mean, median, or mode for a set of data.

Given the mean of a data set in a story problem, students will find a data point that is missing from the set. Have students turn to the Find and Apply the Mean to Data activity page in their Activity Book and read the directions with them.

Students should copy the problems from the Activity Book into their Math Notebook as necessary and solve them there.

1. Read the Worked Examples box with students. Tell students that a data point is one piece of data, or one value, in a data set.

   **Ask:** What is the definition of *mean of a data set*? the average of a set of data

   **Ask:** How is the mean calculated? All the values in the data set are added, and then the sum is divided by the number of values in the data set.

   **Ask:** In the Worked Example, what does the capital $M$ stand for, and what does the lowercase $x$ stand for? The capital $M$ stands for the mean, and the lowercase $x$ stands for the value of the missing data point.

2. Make sure students know that 61 was substituted for $M$ in Step 2 because the problem says that the mean is 61.

   **Ask:** In the first steps of the solution, why was 4 the divisor, and why were both sides then multiplied by 4? The number 4 was chosen because the data set has 4 numbers, or values, in it, so the sum of the values needs to be divided by 4 to find the mean. Multiplication was used as an inverse operation to begin getting $x$ by itself on one side of the equation. Afterward, the right side of the equation didn't have a denominator anymore. That made the equation easier to solve.

3. Remind students that when they use inverse operations to solve an equation, they always need to perform the same operation with the same number on both sides of the equation. Note that the Worked Example uses multiplication as an inverse operation in Step 3 and uses subtraction as an inverse operation in Step 6.

4. Tell students that the Look Back step is used to check that 79 is the correct answer for the missing data point.

5. Have students solve Problems 1–3. Make sure they have completed and answered Problem 1 correctly before they move on to the next problem. If students have difficulty, first encourage them to look at the Worked Example and follow the process shown. If they still have difficulty, help them apply the process shown in the Worked Example.

## Mean, Median, and Mode
### Find and Apply the Mean to Data

**Worked Examples**

If you know the mean of a set of data, you can find a missing data point.

**PROBLEM** The table shows the daily attendance at a 4-day series of free concerts in a park.

The mean attendance for the four concerts was 61. How many people attended the concert on Sunday?

**Attendance at Free Concerts**

| Day | Number of people |
|---|---|
| Thursday | 31 |
| Friday | 45 |
| Saturday | 89 |
| Sunday | ? |

**SOLUTION**

1. Write an equation to solve the problem. In the equation, $M$ stands for the mean number of people who attended the concerts during the 4 days, while $x$ stands for the number of people who attended the concert on Sunday. → $M = \frac{31 + 45 + 89 + x}{4}$

2. Substitute 61 for $M$. → $61 = \frac{31 + 45 + 89 + x}{4}$

3. Use algebra to find the value of $x$. Multiply both sides of the equation by 4 to change the fraction on the right side of the equals sign to an expression without a denominator. Multiplication by 4 is the inverse operation of division by 4. → $61 \cdot 4 = \frac{31 + 45 + 89 + x}{4} \cdot 4$
→ $61 \cdot 4 = 31 + 45 + 89 + x$

4. Complete the multiplication on the left side of the equation. → $244 = 31 + 45 + 89 + x$

5. Add the numbers on the right side of the equation. The variable $x$ remains. → $244 = 165 + x$

6. Subtract 165 from both sides of the equation and simplify. → $244 - 165 = 165 - 165 + x$
→ $79 = x$

**ANSWER** The attendance on Sunday was 79.

**LOOK BACK** Substitute 79 for $x$ in the equation in Step 2 to check your answer. When you add 31, 45, 89, and 79 and divide the sum by 4, you get 61. The given mean was 61, so 79 is the correct answer for the missing data point.

283 DATA ANALYSIS AND REPRESENTATION — MEAN, MEDIAN, AND MODE

---

Use the mean to find the missing data point in a set of data.

1. Umbrella rentals at a beach stand each day during a 5-day period are given in the table.

**Umbrellas Rented**

| Day | Number rented |
|---|---|
| Monday | 25 |
| Tuesday | 36 |
| Wednesday | 42 |
| Thursday | 56 |
| Friday | ? |

The mean number of umbrellas rented during the 5-day period was 49. How many umbrellas were rented on Friday? **86**

2. Snow-cone sales at a snack stand each day during a 7-day period are given in the table.

**Snow Cones Sold**

| Day | Number sold |
|---|---|
| Sunday | ? |
| Monday | 35 |
| Tuesday | 62 |
| Wednesday | 27 |
| Thursday | 81 |
| Friday | 92 |
| Saturday | 106 |

The mean number of snow cones sold during the 7-day period was 70. How many snow cones were sold on Sunday? **87**

3. Lawn chairs set up for an outdoor show each day for a 6-day period are given in the table.

**Lawn Chairs for the Outdoor Show**

| Day | Lawn chairs |
|---|---|
| June 4 | 82 |
| June 5 | ? |
| June 6 | 79 |
| June 7 | 87 |
| June 8 | 90 |
| June 9 | 111 |

The mean number of lawn chairs set up during the 6-day period was 87. How many lawn chairs were set up on June 5? **73**

284 DATA ANALYSIS AND REPRESENTATION — MEAN, MEDIAN, AND MODE

---

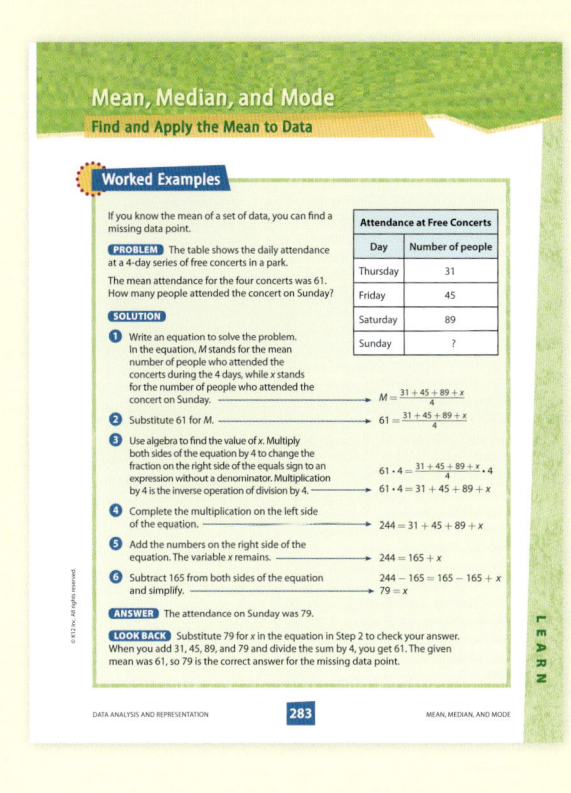

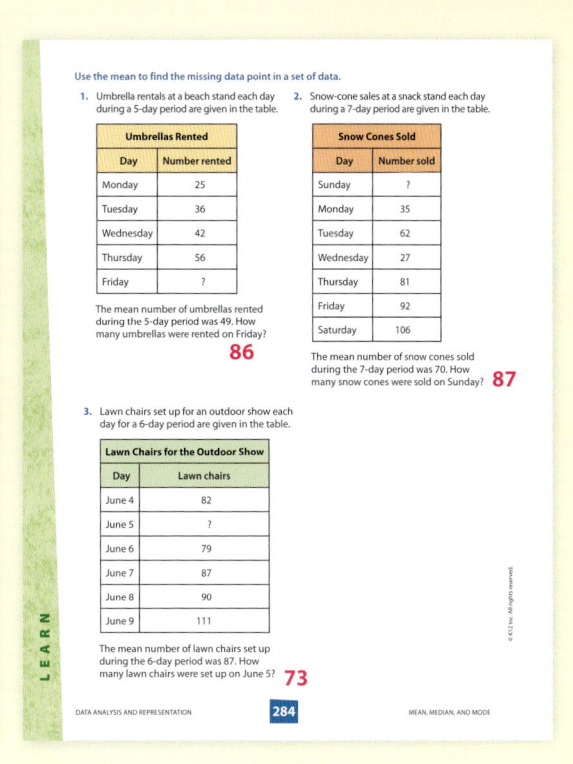

## LEARN Create a Data Set

**OFFLINE 15 min**

### Objectives

- Explain and compute the mean, median, or mode for a set of data.

### Tips

Extend the activity by having students write the information and then create a data set that matches the information.

Students will use information given about range, mode, median, and mean to create data sets. They might not often have a chance to create a data set, and this activity allows them to demonstrate their understanding of measures of central tendency. Have students turn to the Create a Data Set activity page in their Activity Book and read the directions with them.

Students should copy the problems from the Activity Book into their Math Notebook as necessary and solve them there.

1. Read the Worked Examples box with students. Tell them that this example numbers the steps and draws a picture (a series of blank lines) as strategies to solve the problem. There are other strategies that can be used to solve the problem.

2. Tell students that more than one possible data set can be created from this information. This data set is just one example of a data set that meets the given requirements of five data points, a range of 9, and one mode.

3. Walk through each step in the Worked Example with students. After each step, ask them what other values could have been used to create the data set. In the Look Back step, ask students to review the completed data set with the information in the problem to check that the data set meets all the requirements. They may create their own data set that matches the information in the Worked Examples problem.

4. Have students read Problem 1.

**MEAN, MEDIAN, AND MODE 587**

**Ask:** Does the question tell you how many data points should be in the data set? No

**Ask:** Does the data set need a certain mean? No

**Ask:** Does the data set need a certain median? Yes, 12

**Ask:** Does the data set need a mode? If so, how many? Yes, two modes

5. Tell students that with the information given, they know that one of the numbers must be 12 and that 12 is the median. Have them write 12 in the middle of a line, leaving space for other numbers before and after it in the data set.

6. Guide students to create the rest of the data set by telling them that two other numbers must occur more than the rest of the numbers in the data set and that those two numbers must appear an equal number of times. Remind them to review the data set with the information in the problem to check that the completed data set meets all the requirements.

7. Allow students to use any strategies they choose to solve the remaining problems. As they solve each problem, have them review the information in the problem and their answer to make sure each data set meets all the requirements.

8. Discuss Problem 2 with students. Guide them to use the information given to create a data set. Explain that to create a data set with a certain mean, the data points will need to add up to a sum that, when divided by the number of data points, equals that mean. To create a data set with five data points and a mean of 6, the five data points need to add up to a sum that, when divided by 5, equals 6. Students should realize that $5 \cdot 6 = 30$, so any five data points that add up to 30 will work. Have students complete Problem 2.

9. Discuss Problem 3 with students. Guide students to use the information given to create the data set. Have students explain how to get a median of 6.5. They might say that the data set has six data points, so it has an even number of data points. To find the median, the two middle numbers are added and then divided by 2. To get a median of 6.5, the two middle numbers could be 6 and 7. The two middle numbers could also be 4 and 9, since $\frac{4+9}{2} = \frac{13}{2} = 6.5$. Have students complete Problem 3.

10. Have students complete Problems 4–6 on their own, using the Worked Example for help as needed.

**588** DATA ANALYSIS AND REPRESENTATION

## Mean, Median, and Mode
### Create a Data Set

**Worked Examples**

You can create a data set that follows given rules.

**PROBLEM** Create a data set that has five data points, a range of 9, and one mode.

**SOLUTION** There are many data sets that could be created with this information. One example that would follow the rules is shown here. When you create a data set, draw a set of blank lines to begin. Number your steps. Write the values in order from the least value on the left to the greatest value on the right.

**1 Start with five data points.**
Drawing five blank lines will help you keep track of the values in the data set. Show one blank line for each of the values. Put commas between the blank lines.
___, ___, ___, ___, ___

**2 Use a range of 9.**
The range of a set of data shows the difference between the greatest value and the least value. For this data set, you could use 9 as the least value and 18 as the greatest value. Because 18 − 9 = 9, the range is 9.
9, ___, ___, ___, 18

**3 Make the set have one mode.**
The value or values that occur most often in a data set are the mode. A data set can have more than one mode. This data set has only one mode. You could choose 11 as the mode and show it twice.
9, ___, 11, 11, 18

**4 Complete the data set.**
One more value is needed to complete the data set. At this point in solving the problem, the data set has values that meet all the requirements of the problem. That means you must choose the last value carefully. You can't choose 9 or 18 for the last value because then there would be two modes.

You could choose 10 or 11 to complete the data set. There would still be five data points, a range of 9, and one mode. (You could also remove the blank between 9 and 11 and then choose 12, 13, 14, 15, 16, or 17. If you used one of these numbers, you would put it in the data set so the numbers are still arranged from least to greatest.) Here, the value 10 has been chosen to complete the data set:
9, 10, 11, 11, 18

**ANSWER** A data set that has five data points, a range of 9, and one mode is 9, 10, 11, 11, 18.

**LOOK BACK** Review the data set you created and compare it to the information in the problem to check that the data set meets all the requirements.

Use the information given to create a data set.

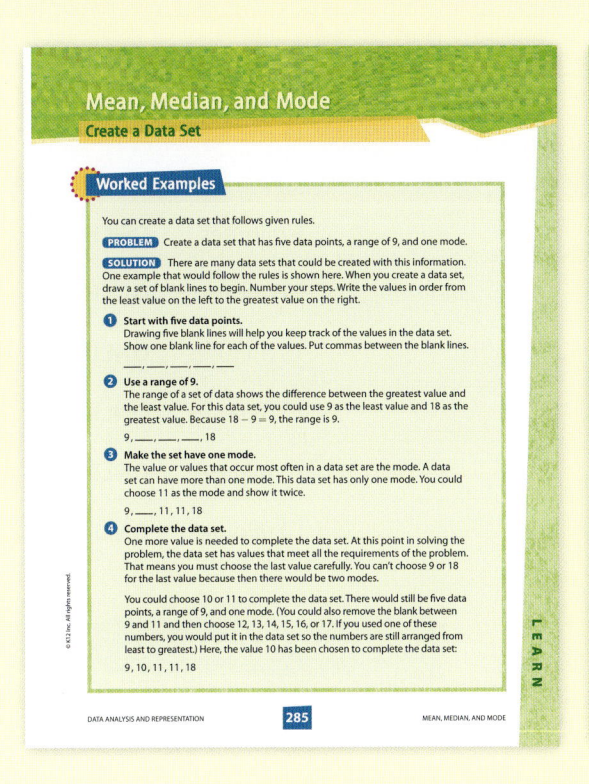

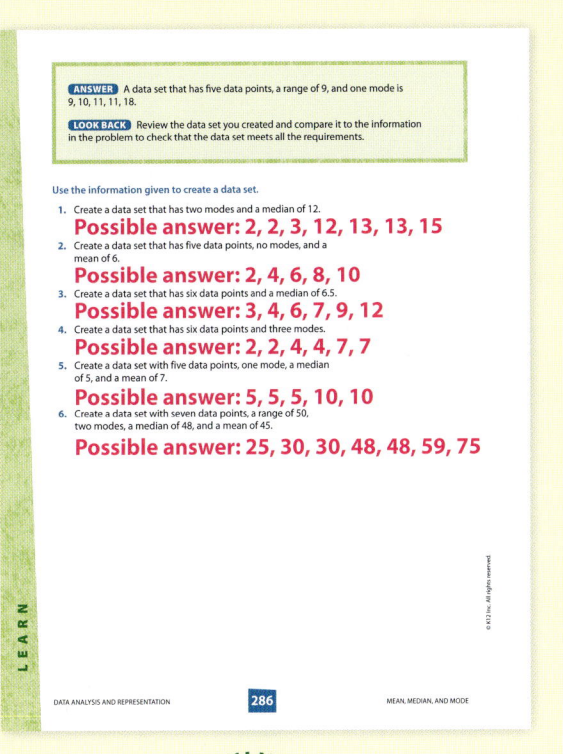

1. Create a data set that has two modes and a median of 12.
**Possible answer: 2, 2, 3, 12, 13, 13, 15**
2. Create a data set that has five data points, no modes, and a mean of 6.
**Possible answer: 2, 4, 6, 8, 10**
3. Create a data set that has six data points and a median of 6.5.
**Possible answer: 3, 4, 6, 7, 9, 12**
4. Create a data set that has six data points and three modes.
**Possible answer: 2, 2, 4, 4, 7, 7**
5. Create a data set with five data points, one mode, a median of 5, and a mean of 7.
**Possible answer: 5, 5, 5, 10, 10**
6. Create a data set with seven data points, a range of 50, two modes, a median of 48, and a mean of 45.
**Possible answer: 25, 30, 30, 48, 48, 59, 75**

### TRY IT  Find the Mean, Median, and Mode
ONLINE 10 min

Students will complete an online Try It. If necessary, read the directions, problems, and answer choices to students and help them with keyboard or mouse operations.

**Objectives**
- Explain and compute the mean, median, or mode for a set of data.

### CHECKPOINT
ONLINE 10 min

Students will complete an online Checkpoint. If necessary, read the directions, problems, and answer choices to students and help them with keyboard or mouse operations.

**Objectives**
- Explain and compute the mean, median, or mode for a set of data.

# Compare Mean, Median, and Mode

## Lesson Overview

| | | |
|---|---|---|
| Skills Update | 5 minutes | **ONLINE** |
| **GET READY** Matching Game | 5 minutes | **ONLINE** |
| **LEARN** Work with Mean, Median, and Mode | 15 minutes | **ONLINE** |
| **LEARN** Uses of Mean, Median, and Mode | 15 minutes | **ONLINE** |
| **TRY IT** Apply Mean, Median, and Mode | 10 minutes | **ONLINE** |
| **CHECKPOINT** | 10 minutes | **ONLINE** |

### ▶ Lesson Objectives
Compare the mean, median, and mode of a data set and explain the differences and appropriate uses.

### ▶ Prerequisite Skills
Explain and compute the mean, median, or mode for a set of data.

### ▶ Content Background
Students will learn to compare and explain the differences between and appropriates uses of mean, median, and mode.

Statistics are the numbers that describe sets of data. When we use the language of statistics to talk about data, we describe different measures. The specific measures of mean, median, and mode are called *measures of central tendency*.

The *mean*, or average, of a set of data is found by adding all the values in the data set, and then dividing that sum by the number of values in the data set.

The *median* of a set of data targets the middle value of the data. To find the median, the data points are organized from least to greatest. When you have an odd number of data points in a set, the number that falls exactly in the middle of the data set is the median. For an even number of data points in a set, the median is actually the mean, or average, of the two middle numbers in the set.

Sometimes in a data set, there are values that occur more often than others. The value that appears most often in a data set is called the *mode*. There can be one mode, more than one mode, or no modes in a data set.

Students will learn that in different sets of data the mean, median, and mode can be exactly the same value or very different values. They will discover the effects that outlier values may or may not have on the mean, median, and mode. More importantly, they will learn which measure is most appropriate in given situations.

**Materials to Gather**

There are no materials to gather for this lesson.

## GET READY  Matching Game

**ONLINE 5 min**

Students will match mean, median, and mode to definitions and values for a data set.

**Objectives**

- Explain and compute the mean, median, or mode for a set of data.

## LEARN  Work with Mean, Median, and Mode

**ONLINE 15 min**

Students will learn about mean, median, and mode. They will also learn how to create data sets that fulfill certain criteria. In addition, they'll see the effect that outliers can have on a data set.

Work with students to complete this online activity.

**Objectives**

- Compare the mean, median, and mode of a data set and explain the differences and appropriate uses.

1. Have students read about Ron's probability experiment and the results.

2. Then have students read and discuss the problems about creating a data set with five values where the mean, median, and mode have the same value. Have students explain how they created their data set. **Possible answer:** 1, 2, 3, 3, 6; I started by making 3 the median. I added 3 to the data set so that 3 would also be the mode. To find the mean, I know that I have five data points and I want the mean to be 3, so the sum of the values must be 5 · 3, which equals 15. The sum of the two values I already have is 3 + 3 = 6. I subtract next; 15 − 6 = 9. I need to add 3 numbers to the data set whose sum is 9, so I chose 1, 2, and 6. The value of the mean, median, and mode for the data set are each 3.

3. Go to the next screen. Have students read the directions about creating a data set with six values. To help students find the answer, read them the following problem:
   - A family of six went bowling. This data set gives their scores: 10, 40, 40, 80, 160, 180

   Have students enter the six values.

   **Ask:** What are the mean, median, and mode for the data set? mean: 85; median: 60; mode: 40

   **Ask:** What do you notice when you compare the values you found for the mean, median, and mode? The values are all very different.

4. Using the same screen, have students create a data set with six values where the mean, median, and mode have very different values. Have them explain how they found their data set. **Possible answer:** 10, 20, 40, 50, 120, 120; the mean is 60, the median is 45, and the mode is 120. I made sure the mode and median weren't the same and then chose other numbers so that the mean would be greater than 40 and less than 120.

5. Go over the problem that asks students to create a data set with four values, where the mean is 8. Make sure they understand how the solution was reached. Discuss what other data sets students could have created.

COMPARE MEAN, MEDIAN, AND MODE  **591**

6. Continue online with students to explore mean, median, and mode of data sets. Tell students that in the basketball scores problem,
   - The mean shows the average number of points that players scored in the game.
   - The median shows the middle value of the points the players made in the game.
   - The mode shows that more players scored 8 points in the game than any other value.
7. Go over the problem that asks students to create a data set with six values that have one or two outliers. Review the example with students. Then have them create their own data set and describe how the outliers affect the mean, median, and mode.

## LEARN  Uses of Mean, Median, and Mode

ONLINE 15 min

**Objectives**
- Compare the mean, median, and mode of a data set and explain the differences and appropriate uses.

Students will determine whether mean, median, mode, or range would be the most appropriate choice to answer a question about data used in everyday situations.

## TRY IT  Apply Mean, Median, and Mode

ONLINE 10 min

**Objectives**
- Compare the mean, median, and mode of a data set and explain the differences and appropriate uses.

Students will complete an online Try It. If necessary, read the directions, problems, and answer choices to students and help them with keyboard or mouse operations.

## CHECKPOINT

ONLINE 10 min

**Objectives**
- Compare the mean, median, and mode of a data set and explain the differences and appropriate uses.

Students will complete an online Checkpoint. If necessary, read the directions, problems, and answer choices to students and help them with keyboard or mouse operations.

# Organize Data to Draw Histograms (A)

## Lesson Overview

| | | |
|---|---|---|
| Skills Update | 5 minutes | **ONLINE** |
| **GET READY** Display Coin Tosses on a Tally Chart | 5 minutes | **OFFLINE** |
| **LEARN** Frequency Tables and Histograms | 15 minutes | **ONLINE** |
| **LEARN** Organize Data in a Frequency Table | 20 minutes | **OFFLINE** |
| **TRY IT** Work with Frequency Tables | 15 minutes | **OFFLINE** |

▶ ### Lesson Objectives
Organize and display single-variable data in a histogram.

▶ ### Prerequisite Skills
- Systematically record numerical data.
- Answer questions about one- and two-variable data graphs.

▶ ### Content Background
Students will learn that frequency tables organize data for making a histogram. They will create and interpret frequency tables.

A *histogram* is a special type of bar graph that records the frequency of an occurrence of an event or a group. It is best for students to use a frequency table when preparing to create a histogram. In a frequency table, students list events or groups, tally their frequency, and record each frequency as a number. In a histogram, the horizontal axis shows the events or groups, and the vertical axis shows the frequency. *Frequency* is the number of times an event or group occurs. The bars in a histogram are immediately next to each other with no space between the bars.

▶ ### Common Errors and Misconceptions
- Students might have difficulty interpreting graphs because they have not had enough opportunity to analyze and compare different types of graphs.
- Students might have difficulty determining information on a graph that is implied. For example, students might not be able to determine the value of data points if the points fall between two values shown on the scale. They also might not be able to use a graph to extend the data and make predictions about data points not given on the graph.
- Students might have an idea of how they think data should look when graphed, so they might expect all graphs of that data to reflect their visual image.

▶ ### Advance Preparation
Gather the coin. Print two copies of the Large Frequency Table.

### Materials to Gather

**SUPPLIED**
Large Frequency Table (printout) – 2
Organize Data in a Frequency Table activity page
Work with Frequency Tables activity page

**ALSO NEEDED**
coin with a head and a tail

## GET READY  Display Coin Tosses on a Tally Chart

**OFFLINE 5 min**

**Objectives**
- Systematically record numerical data.
- Answer questions about one- and two-variable data graphs.

Students will toss a coin 10 times. They will record the outcomes on a tally chart. Gather the fair coin.

1. Guide students to create a tally chart in their Math Notebook like the one shown below.

| Heads or Tails ||
|---|---|
| Heads | Tails |
|  |  |

2. Have students toss the coin and record the outcome by making a tally for heads or tails in their tally chart. They should toss the coin and record the outcome 10 times.

3. After students record the outcomes, have them use their tally chart to answer these questions. Answers will vary.
   - How many times did you toss heads?
   - What fraction represents the number of heads tossed out of the total number of tosses?
   - How many times did you toss tails?
   - What fraction represents the number of tails tossed out of the total number of tosses?

## LEARN  Frequency Tables and Histograms

**ONLINE 15 min**

**Objectives**
- Organize and display single-variable data in a histogram.

Students will learn to organize data in a frequency table. They will see how a frequency table is used to create a histogram.

**DIRECTIONS FOR USING THE FREQUENCY TABLES AND HISTOGRAMS LEARNING TOOL**

1. Click Begin.
2. Click the triangle in the upper right-hand corner to close the histogram.
3. Have students look at the spinner and the "Section" column in the frequency table. Point out that each of the six sections on the spinner matches a row in the frequency table.

   Tell students that the "Tally" column shows a tick mark for each time the spinner lands on that section. Tally marks are used to keep track of the spinner outcomes. The "Total" column shows the frequency from the "Tally" column, but uses numbers instead of tick marks.

4. Have students click Spin to spin the spinner. The result of the spin is recorded on the frequency table with a tally mark and 1 for the total of that outcome.

5. Have students spin the spinner 10 times. They can keep track of the number of spins by using the counter under the spinner. The data from the spins will display on the frequency table.

594  DATA ANALYSIS AND REPRESENTATION

6. Have students describe the results of 10 spins shown on frequency table. **Possible answer:** After 10 spins, the frequency table showed I landed on A two times, B zero times, C one time, D four times, E two times, and F one time. The outcomes are shown with tally marks and with numbers.

7. Repeat Step 4 until students have spun a total of 30 spins.

8. Click the triangle in the upper right-hand corner to open the histogram.

9. Have students describe the histogram. The histogram has six labels at the bottom of the graph for each section on the spinner. The frequency is labeled on the side of the histogram. The result of each spin is recorded on the histogram with a bar. The bar increases by a frequency of 1 to match each spin.

10. Have students compare the data in the frequency table and the histogram.

    **Ask:** How are the data points from the frequency table shown on the histogram? For each section on the spinner, the frequency table shows the tally and the total number of spins. There are six sections on the spinner, six rows in the frequency table, and six labels on the bottom of the histogram. The frequencies of the spins from the frequency table are shown as the heights of the bars on the histogram.

11. Students may repeat Steps 4–10 and collect data for a new set of spins. Have them click Reset to clear the data.

## LEARN  Organize Data in a Frequency Table

**OFFLINE 20 min**

### Objectives

- Organize and display single-variable data in a histogram.

Students will create a frequency table. They will use it to organize data about the height of the tallest Ferris wheels ever built. Gather the Large Frequency Table printout. Have students turn to the Organize Data in a Frequency Table activity page in their Activity Book and read the directions with them.

1. Tell students that *frequency* is the number of times that an event occurs. Read the Worked Examples box with students.

2. Give them the Large Frequency Table printout.

    **Say:** The frequency table you will complete in Problem 1 will show the frequency of the heights in the data you are given.

    Tell students to read the Tall Ferris Wheels table in Problem 1. Tell them that the heights of the Ferris wheels are the numbers they will use in their frequency table. Explain that the Ferris wheels are located in many different countries, and they will collect data about the heights on the frequency table. They don't need to know how to spell or pronounce the Ferris wheel names.

3. Tell students to write a title at the top of the Large Frequency Table printout. It could be "Tall Ferris Wheels."

4. Guide students to write three headings, one for each column. Have students look at the Worked Example to help them know what each column should be used for. If they have trouble, guide them to understand that the first column on the left needs to have height ranges of meters, from the least to the greatest, so they can mark the frequency of the heights. Tell them they need to organize the ranges of meters in a logical way.

    For column headings, tell them that it makes sense to name the first column "Height range (meters)"; the middle column, "Tally"; and the third column, "Frequency."

5. Tell students that in the "Height range (meters)" column they need to have height ranges that make sense. Have them look for the least and the greatest heights in the data table. The least height is 64.8 meters. The greatest height is 208 meters.

   Tell them that it makes sense to label the rows under "Height range (meters)" by 20-meter ranges, starting with 60–79.

   Tell them to label the rows under "Height range (meters)" as follows: 60–79, 80–99, 100–119, 120–139, 140–159, 160–179, 180–199, and 200–219.

6. Show students how to tally the Ferris wheel heights by putting a tally mark in the 60–79 row in the "Tally" column for each Ferris wheel height in the table from 60 meters to 79 meters. Check that they make a total of 5 tally marks in that row.

   Remind students that as they draw tally marks in this activity they need to draw the fifth tally as a diagonal line through the first 4 tally marks.

7. Have students use the data in the table to complete each row in the "Tally" column.

   Students may choose to start in the second column of the table and work from the top to the bottom of the column, recording a tally mark for each height. If they record data in the frequency table this way, check that they also tally the data from the fourth column.

8. Have students count the tally marks for each row and write the total as a number in that row of the "Frequency" column. They should write a 0 as the frequency for any ranges that have no data.

   **Ask:** How did you organize and show height data from the table in the frequency table? I made a tally mark for each height from the table. I made the tally in the range each data point belonged in. I counted the tally marks on each row and wrote that number in the frequency column.

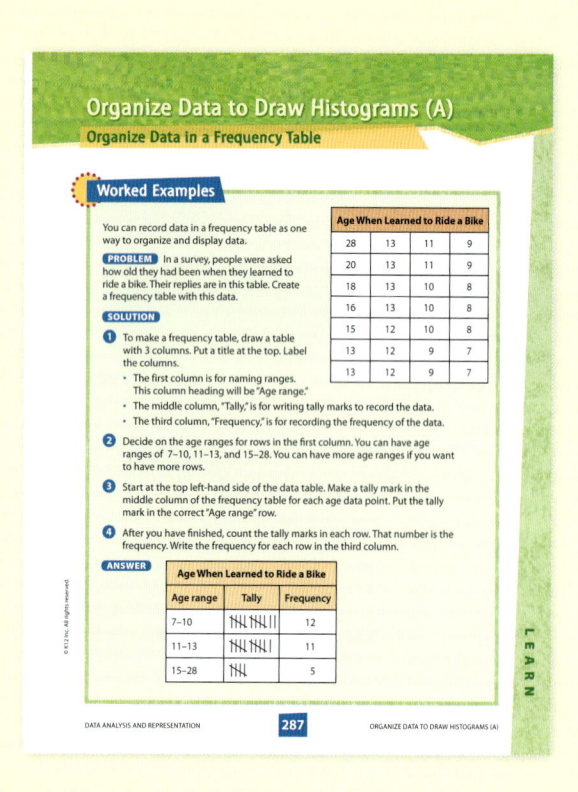

**Additional Answers**

1. 

| Tall Ferris Wheels |||
|---|---|---|
| **Height range (meters)** | **Tally** | **Frequency** |
| 60–79 | ⵑⵑⵑⵑ | 5 |
| 80–99 | ⵑⵑⵑⵑ I | 6 |
| 100–119 | ⵑⵑⵑⵑ ⵑⵑⵑⵑ | 10 |
| 120–139 | ⵑⵑⵑⵑ II | 7 |
| 140–159 |  | 0 |
| 160–179 | III | 3 |
| 180–199 |  | 0 |
| 200–219 | I | 1 |

## TRY IT  Work with Frequency Tables

**OFFLINE 15 min**

### Objectives
- Organize and display single-variable data in a histogram.

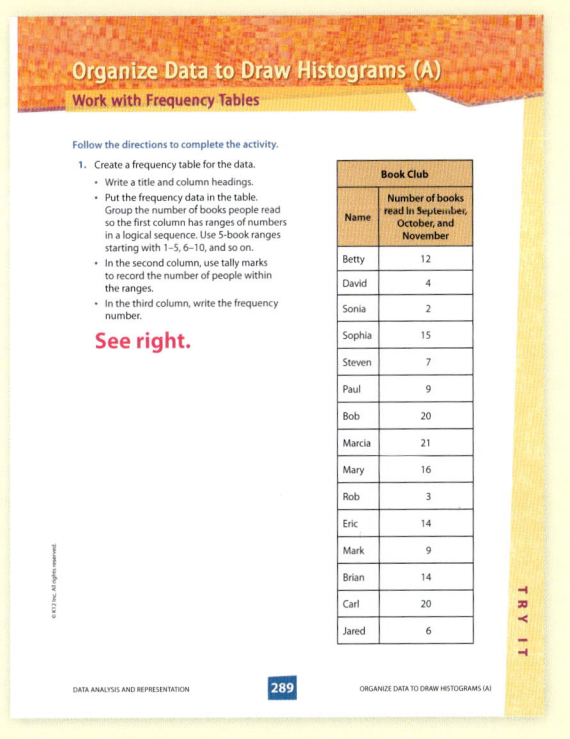

Students will practice creating and reading frequency tables. Gather the Large Frequency Table printout. Have students turn to the Work with Frequency Tables activity page in their Activity Book and read the directions with them.

Have students write answers on the Large Frequency Table printout.

**Additional Answers**

1. 

| Book Club |||
|---|---|---|
| **Number of books read in September, October, and November** | **Tally** | **Frequency** |
| 1–5 | III | 3 |
| 6–10 | IIII | 4 |
| 11–15 | IIII | 4 |
| 16–20 | III | 3 |
| 21–25 | I | 1 |

ORGANIZE DATA TO DRAW HISTOGRAMS (A)  597

Choose the answer.

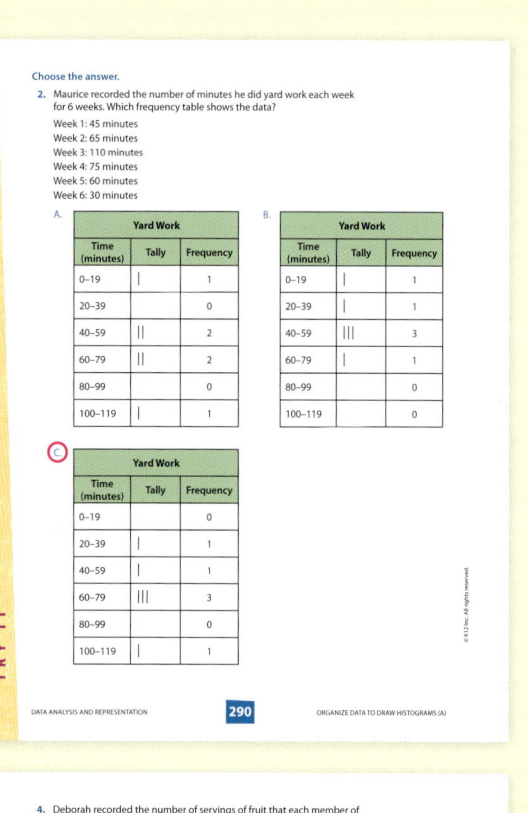

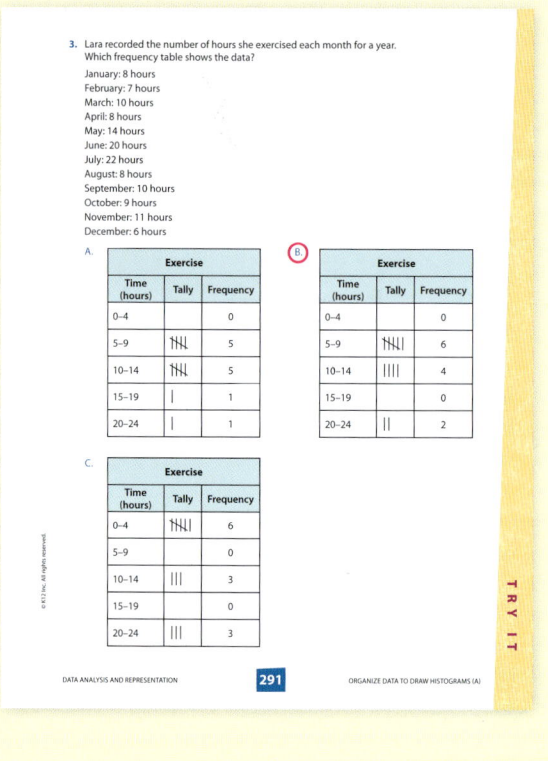

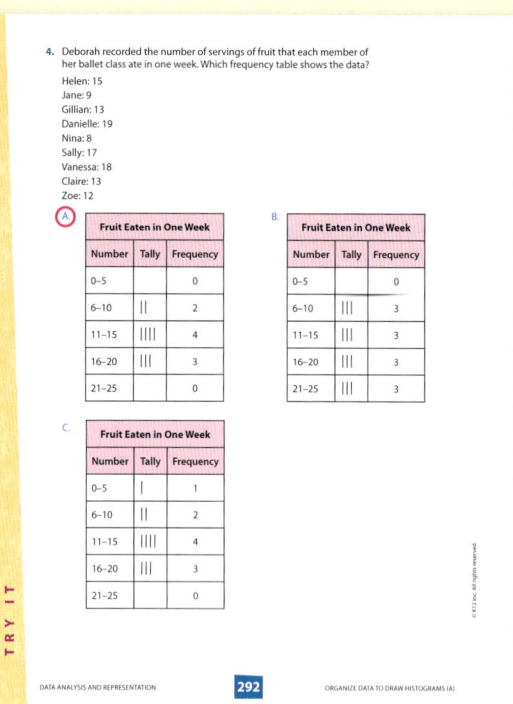

2. Maurice recorded the number of minutes he did yard work each week for 6 weeks. Which frequency table shows the data?
   Week 1: 45 minutes
   Week 2: 65 minutes
   Week 3: 110 minutes
   Week 4: 75 minutes
   Week 5: 60 minutes
   Week 6: 30 minutes

A.
**Yard Work**

| Time (minutes) | Tally | Frequency |
|---|---|---|
| 0–19 | | | 1 |
| 20–39 | | 0 |
| 40–59 | || | 2 |
| 60–79 | || | 2 |
| 80–99 | | 0 |
| 100–119 | | | 1 |

B.
**Yard Work**

| Time (minutes) | Tally | Frequency |
|---|---|---|
| 0–19 | | | 1 |
| 20–39 | | | 1 |
| 40–59 | ||| | 3 |
| 60–79 | | | 1 |
| 80–99 | | 0 |
| 100–119 | | 0 |

C.
**Yard Work**

| Time (minutes) | Tally | Frequency |
|---|---|---|
| 0–19 | | 0 |
| 20–39 | | | 1 |
| 40–59 | | | 1 |
| 60–79 | ||| | 3 |
| 80–99 | | 0 |
| 100–119 | | | 1 |

3. Lara recorded the number of hours she exercised each month for a year. Which frequency table shows the data?
   January: 8 hours
   February: 7 hours
   March: 10 hours
   April: 8 hours
   May: 14 hours
   June: 20 hours
   July: 22 hours
   August: 8 hours
   September: 10 hours
   October: 9 hours
   November: 11 hours
   December: 6 hours

A.
**Exercise**

| Time (hours) | Tally | Frequency |
|---|---|---|
| 0–4 | | 0 |
| 5–9 | ||||| | 5 |
| 10–14 | ||||| | 5 |
| 15–19 | | | 1 |
| 20–24 | | | 1 |

B.
**Exercise**

| Time (hours) | Tally | Frequency |
|---|---|---|
| 0–4 | | 0 |
| 5–9 | ||||| | 6 |
| 10–14 | |||| | 4 |
| 15–19 | | 0 |
| 20–24 | || | 2 |

C.
**Exercise**

| Time (hours) | Tally | Frequency |
|---|---|---|
| 0–4 | ||||| | 6 |
| 5–9 | | 0 |
| 10–14 | ||| | 3 |
| 15–19 | | 0 |
| 20–24 | ||| | 3 |

4. Deborah recorded the number of servings of fruit that each member of her ballet class ate in one week. Which frequency table shows the data?
   Helen: 15
   Jane: 9
   Gillian: 13
   Danielle: 19
   Nina: 8
   Sally: 17
   Vanessa: 18
   Claire: 13
   Zoe: 12

A.
**Fruit Eaten in One Week**

| Number | Tally | Frequency |
|---|---|---|
| 0–5 | | 0 |
| 6–10 | || | 2 |
| 11–15 | |||| | 4 |
| 16–20 | ||| | 3 |
| 21–25 | | 0 |

B.
**Fruit Eaten in One Week**

| Number | Tally | Frequency |
|---|---|---|
| 0–5 | | 0 |
| 6–10 | ||| | 3 |
| 11–15 | ||| | 3 |
| 16–20 | ||| | 3 |
| 21–25 | ||| | 3 |

C.
**Fruit Eaten in One Week**

| Number | Tally | Frequency |
|---|---|---|
| 0–5 | | | 1 |
| 6–10 | || | 2 |
| 11–15 | |||| | 4 |
| 16–20 | ||| | 3 |
| 21–25 | | 0 |

**598**  DATA ANALYSIS AND REPRESENTATION

# Organize Data to Draw Histograms (B)

| Lesson Overview | | |
|---|---|---|
| **LEARN** Make a Histogram | 15 minutes | **OFFLINE** |
| **LEARN** Make a Frequency Table and Histogram | 20 minutes | **OFFLINE** |
| **TRY IT** Make and Interpret Histograms | 15 minutes | **OFFLINE** |
| **CHECKPOINT** | 10 minutes | **ONLINE** |

## ▶ Lesson Objectives
Organize and display single-variable data in a histogram.

## ▶ Prerequisite Skills
- Systematically record numerical data.
- Answer questions about one- and two-variable data graphs.

## ▶ Content Background
Students will continue to learn that frequency tables organize data for making a histogram. They will create and interpret frequency tables.

A *histogram* is a special type of bar graph that records the frequency of an occurrence of an event or a group. It is best for students to use a frequency table when preparing to create a histogram. In a frequency table, students list events or groups, tally their frequency, and record each frequency as a number. In a histogram, the horizontal axis shows the events or groups, and the vertical axis shows the frequency. *Frequency* is the number of times an event or group occurs. The bars in a histogram have no space between them.

## ▶ Common Errors and Misconceptions
- Students might have difficulty interpreting graphs because they have not had enough opportunity to analyze and compare different types of graphs.
- Students might have difficulty determining information on a graph that is implied. For example, students might not be able to determine the value of data points if the points fall between two values shown on the scale. They also might not be able to use a graph to extend the data and make predictions about data points not given on the graph.
- Students might have an idea of how they think data should look when graphed, so they might expect all graphs of this data to reflect their visual image.

## ▶ Advance Preparation
Print three copies of the Draw a Histogram printout.

### Materials to Gather

**SUPPLIED**
Draw a Histogram (printout) – 3
Make a Histogram activity page
Make a Frequency Table and Histogram activity page
Make and Interpret Histograms activity page

**ALSO NEEDED**
ruler, dual-scale
markers, coloring

ORGANIZE DATA TO DRAW HISTOGRAMS (B) **599**

# LEARN  Make a Histogram

**OFFLINE 15 min**

## Objectives
- Organize and display single-variable data in a histogram.

Students will use data from a frequency table to make a histogram. Gather one copy of the Draw a Histogram printout, ruler, and markers. Have students turn to the Make a Histogram activity page in their Activity Book.

1. Read the Worked Example with students. Show students how each step in the solution was carried out on the histogram.

2. Point out the characteristics of a histogram:
   - The histogram has a title.
   - The horizontal and vertical axes are labeled.
   - The bars are all labeled with ranges. And except for the first bar, which is slightly wider, the bars are the same width.
   - The numbers on the vertical axis correspond to the frequency data.
   - There is no space between the bars.

3. Make sure students understand that the numbers in the "Frequency" column of the frequency table were used to decide the height of the bars on the histogram. For example, for the 10,001–12,000 range, the frequency table shows a frequency of 2. On the graph, the bar above 10,001–12,000 has a height of 2 on the vertical axis.

4. Read the directions for Problems 1–5. Give students the printout, ruler, and markers.

5. Guide students as needed, encouraging them to look at the Worked Example for help. When they get to Problem 3, ask these questions:

   **Ask:** What is the least frequency? 0

   **Ask:** What the greatest frequency? 10

   **Ask:** What range of numbers needs to be on the graph to represent the frequencies? The range needs to be 0–10, but to follow the Worked Example and to make the histogram easier to read, I should include one number beyond 10, so 0–11.

6. For Problem 4, have students use the ruler to help them divide the horizontal axis into 8 evenly spaced intervals. Have them label the intervals from left to right along the horizontal axis.

7. For Problem 5, guide students to draw a bar above the 60–79 range that has a height of 5 on the vertical axis. Have them continue drawing bars for the other ranges: 80–99, 100–119, 120–139, 140–159, 160–179, 180–199, and 200–219. Explain that ranges with a frequency of 0 won't have a bar above the range label. Have students color the bars with markers.

DATA ANALYSIS AND REPRESENTATION

## Organize Data to Draw Histograms (B)
### Make a Histogram

**Worked Examples**

A histogram is a graph that displays the data from a frequency table. Histograms have bars that represent data. The bars are usually all the same width. The width depends on the range of measurements in the frequency table. The heights of the bars depend on the frequency data.

A histogram has a horizontal axis (the bottom line of the graph) and a vertical axis (the line along the left side of the graph). Each axis is labeled with a name and with numbers that are used for placement of the bars.

**World's Longest Roller Coasters**

| Length range (feet) | Tally | Frequency |
|---|---|---|
| 2,000–4,000 | III | 3 |
| 4,001–6,000 | IIII | 4 |
| 6,001–8,000 | IIII I | 6 |
| 8,001–10,000 | IIII II | 7 |
| 10,001–12,000 | II | 2 |

**PROBLEM** Draw a histogram to display the data in the frequency table.

**SOLUTION**

1. Write a title at the top of the histogram. The title should describe the data in the frequency table, such as "World's Longest Roller Coasters."
2. Label the horizontal axis and the vertical axis. For the horizontal axis label, write the column name for the range of measurements in the frequency table: "Length range (feet)." For the vertical axis label, write "Frequency."
3. Mark off 5 even sections along the horizontal axis for ranges and write the ranges from the frequency table below the axis. As you mark off the ranges, don't put space between them. The bars on a histogram sit right next to each other.
4. Number the vertical axis. Histograms often show one number greater than the greatest number in the frequency table. When the vertical axis includes one greater number, the scale is easier to read. The frequency table has frequencies from 0 to 7, so number the vertical axis from 0 to 8.
5. Draw a bar for the first range, 2,000–4,000. The frequency is 3, so the bar should stop at the 3 along on the vertical axis. Using the data in the frequency table, draw and shade a bar for each range (each row in the frequency table should have one bar in the histogram). Use a ruler to draw the bars.

**ANSWER**

World's Longest Roller Coasters histogram

Follow the steps to draw a histogram to display the data in the frequency table.

1. Write a title at the top of the histogram.
2. Label the horizontal axis.
3. Number the vertical axis.
4. Write the ranges on the horizontal axis.
5. Draw and shade a bar for each range in the frequency table

See below.

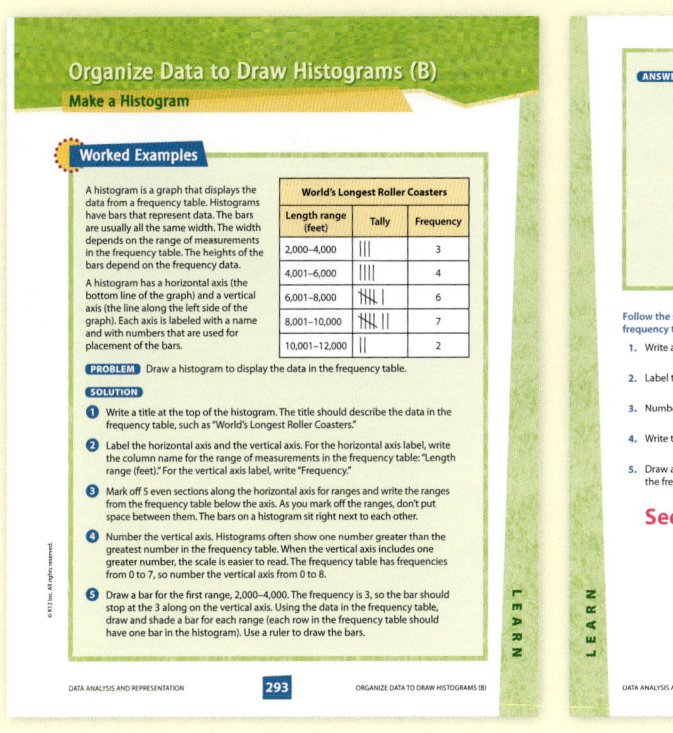

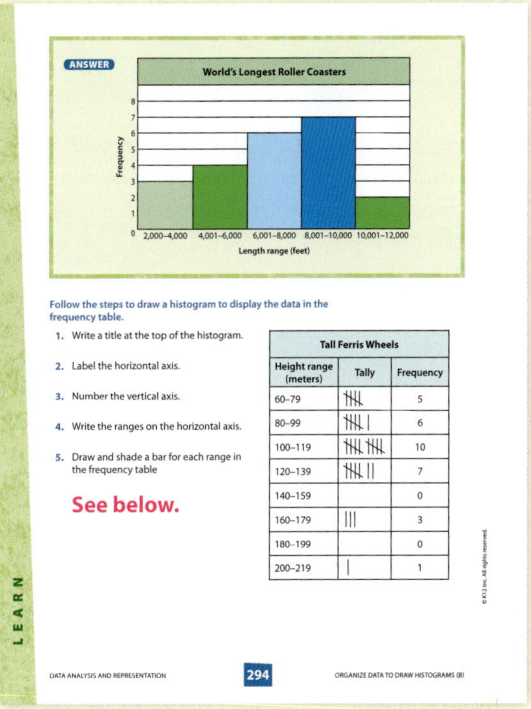

**Tall Ferris Wheels**

| Height range (meters) | Tally | Frequency |
|---|---|---|
| 60–79 | IIII | 5 |
| 80–99 | IIII I | 6 |
| 100–119 | IIII IIII | 10 |
| 120–139 | IIII II | 7 |
| 140–159 | | 0 |
| 160–179 | III | 3 |
| 180–199 | | 0 |
| 200–219 | I | 1 |

**Additional Answers**

1–5.

Tall Ferris Wheels histogram

**ORGANIZE DATA TO DRAW HISTOGRAMS (B)** 601

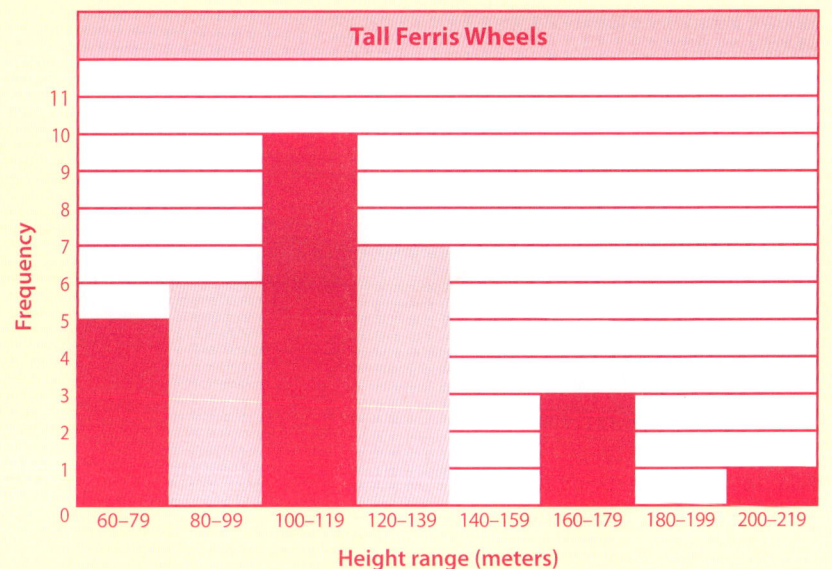

## LEARN  Make a Frequency Table and Histogram

**OFFLINE 20 min**

### Objectives

- Organize and display single-variable data in a histogram.

### Tips

Guide students to work carefully when creating the frequency table from the data in the table. Have them check the data and their frequency table before they create the histogram.

Students will create a frequency table to organize data. They will use the frequency table to draw a histogram. Gather one copy of the Draw a Histogram printout, ruler, and markers. Have students turn to the Make a Frequency Table and Histogram activity page in their Activity Book.

1. Read the Worked Example with students and make sure they understand the process for creating the frequency table and histogram for the lake temperatures.

2. Read the directions for Problems 1–4. Give students the printout, ruler, and markers.

3. Assist students as needed, encouraging them to look at the Worked Example for help. Guide students to use a range of 1 foot for each distance. Have them write the ranges in the first column of the frequency table. They should start at the top with the shortest distance:
   - 18 ft–18 ft 11 in.
   - 19 ft–19 ft 11 in.
   - 20 ft–20 ft 11 in.
   - 21 ft–21 ft 11 in.

4. After students have completed the "Tally" and "Frequency" columns of the frequency table, explain that they'll use the frequency table to make a histogram. Read the directions for Problems 5–9.

5. Assist students as needed, encouraging them to look at the Worked Example for help. When they get to Problem 7, ask these questions:

   **Ask:** What is the least frequency? 1

   **Ask:** What is the greatest frequency? 3

   **Ask:** What range of numbers needs to be on the graph to represent the frequencies? The range needs to be 0–3, but to make the histogram easier to read, I should include one number beyond 3, so 0–4.

6. If necessary, remind students that the numbering on the vertical axis usually goes one number beyond the greatest frequency to make the scale easier to read. Also explain that the horizontal axis always represents a frequency of 0.

7. For Problem 8, have students use the ruler to help them divide the horizontal axis into 4 evenly spaced intervals. Remind students that there should be no space between the intervals. Have them label the intervals from left to right along the horizontal axis.

8. For Problem 9, guide students to use the data in the frequency table to draw a bar for each range. If students need assistance, start by pointing to the 18 ft–18 ft 11 in. row in the frequency table.

   **Ask:** What is the frequency for 18 ft–18 ft 11 in.? 3

   Have students create a bar above the 18 ft–18 ft 11 in. range that has a height of 3 on the vertical axis.

   Follow the same process, as needed, to help students draw the remaining bars.

DATA ANALYSIS AND REPRESENTATION

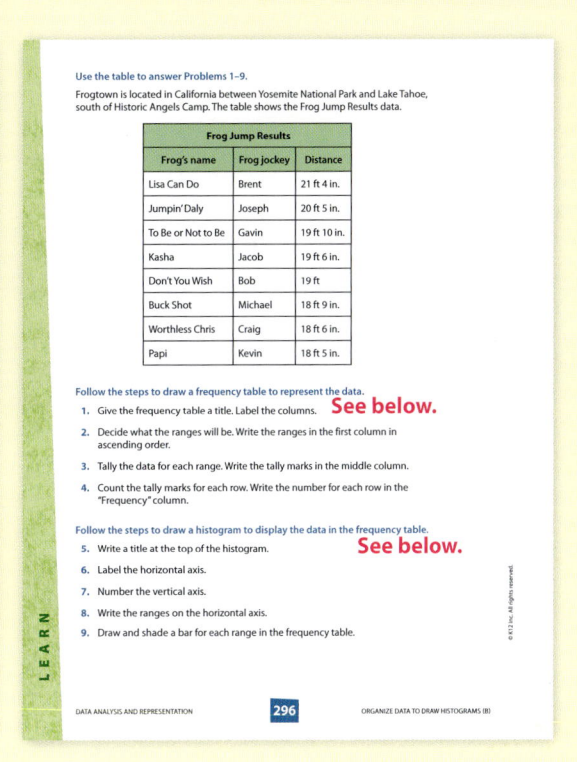

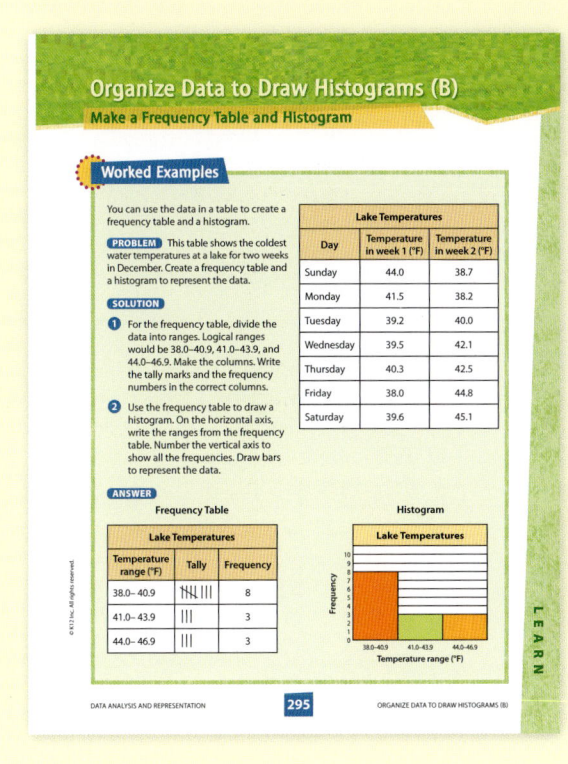

## Additional Answers

**1–4.** Frequency Table

| Frog Jump Results |||
|---|---|---|
| Distance | Tally | Frequency |
| 18 ft–18 ft 11 in. | ||| | 3 |
| 19 ft–19 ft 11 in. | ||| | 3 |
| 20 ft–20 ft 11 in. | | | 1 |
| 21 ft–21 ft 11 in. | | | 1 |

**5–9.** Histogram

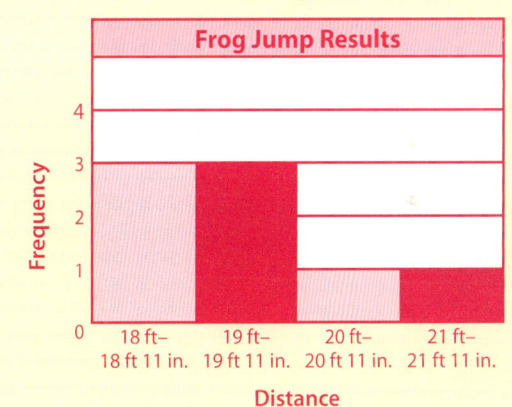

Frog Jump Results

(Histogram with x-axis "Distance" showing ranges 18 ft–18 ft 11 in., 19 ft–19 ft 11 in., 20 ft–20 ft 11 in., 21 ft–21 ft 11 in. with frequencies 3, 3, 1, 1. Y-axis "Frequency" from 0 to 4.)

## TRY IT  Make and Interpret Histograms

**OFFLINE 15 min**

### Objectives

- Organize and display single-variable data in a histogram.

Students will make a histogram from data in a frequency table. They will also interpret frequency tables to determine which histogram represents the data. Gather one copy of the Draw a Histogram printout, ruler, and markers. Have students turn to the Make and Interpret Histograms activity page in their Activity Book and read the directions with them.

Students should copy the problems from the Activity Book into their Math Notebook as necessary and solve them there. They should use the printout for Problems 1–5.

## Organize Data to Draw Histograms (B)
### Make and Interpret Histograms

Use the table to answer Problems 1–5. Follow the steps to draw a histogram to display the data in the frequency table.

**Visitors to National Parks**

| Numbers of visitors | Tally | Frequency |
|---|---|---|
| 0–99,999 | ||||  ||| | 8 |
| 100,000–199,999 | ||| | 3 |
| 200,000–299,999 | || | 2 |
| 300,000–399,999 | ||| | 3 |

1. Write a title at the top of the histogram.  **See below.**
2. Label the horizontal axis.
3. Number the vertical axis.
4. Write the ranges on the horizontal axis.
5. Draw and shade a bar for each range in the frequency table.

---

Choose the answer.

6. Nadia recorded the number of letters each person in her summer camp group sent home each week. She then organized the information in a frequency table.

**Number of Letters Sent**

| Number of letters | Tally | Frequency |
|---|---|---|
| 0–2 | ||||  |||| | 10 |
| 3–5 | |||| | 5 |
| 6–8 | ||| | 3 |

Which histogram correctly displays this information?

**(A)** — circled

---

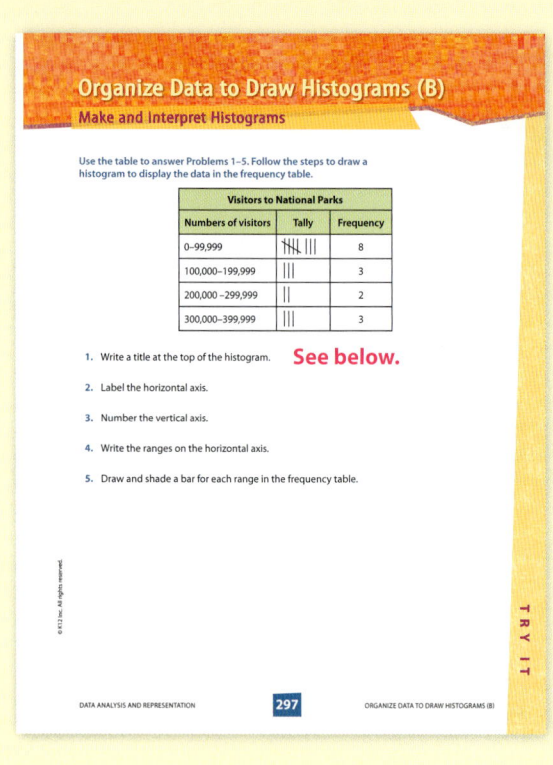

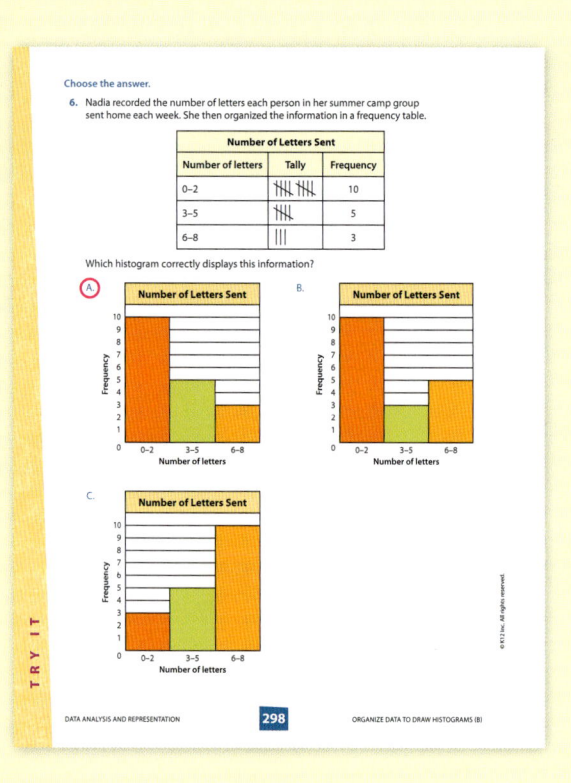

## Additional Answers
**1–5.**

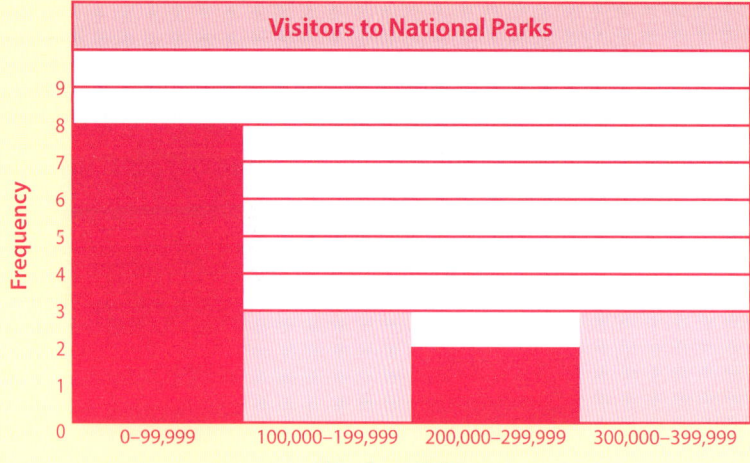

**Visitors to National Parks** histogram:
- 0–99,999: 8
- 100,000–199,999: 3
- 200,000–299,999: 2
- 300,000–399,999: 3

Frequency (vertical axis), Number of visitors (horizontal axis)

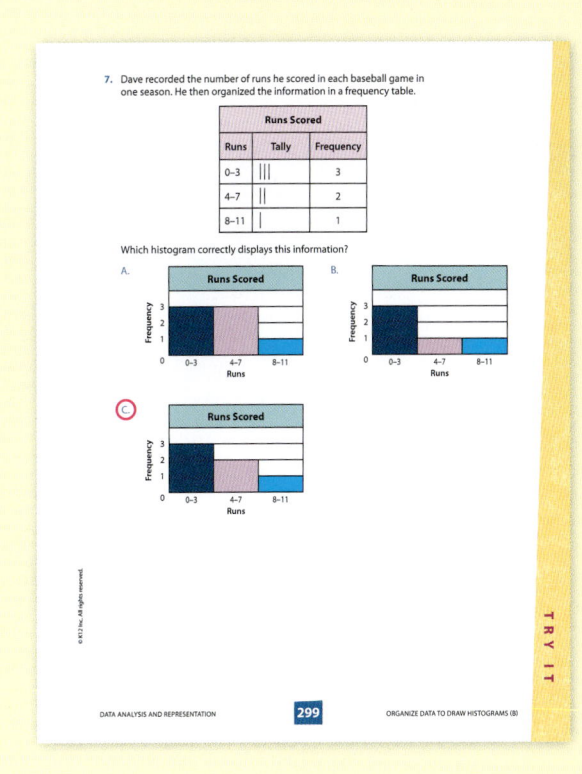

7. Dave recorded the number of runs he scored in each baseball game in one season. He then organized the information in a frequency table.

**Runs Scored**

| Runs | Tally | Frequency |
|---|---|---|
| 0–3 | ||| | 3 |
| 4–7 | || | 2 |
| 8–11 | | | 1 |

Which histogram correctly displays this information?

A. B. 
C. (circled)

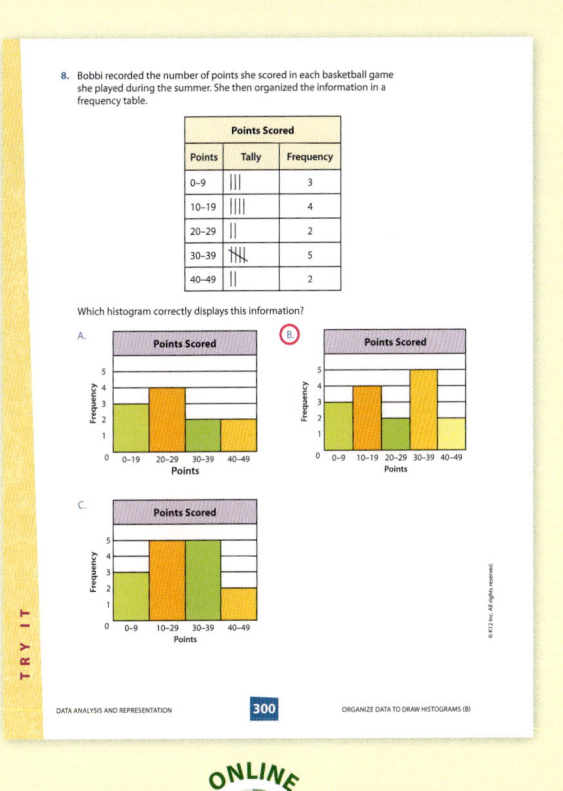

8. Bobbi recorded the number of points she scored in each basketball game she played during the summer. She then organized the information in a frequency table.

**Points Scored**

| Points | Tally | Frequency |
|---|---|---|
| 0–9 | ||| | 3 |
| 10–19 | |||| | 4 |
| 20–29 | || | 2 |
| 30–39 | ||||| | 5 |
| 40–49 | || | 2 |

Which histogram correctly displays this information?

A. B. (circled) C.

# CHECKPOINT

Students will complete an online Checkpoint. If necessary, read the directions, problems, and answer choices to students and help them with keyboard or mouse operations.

ONLINE 10 min

## Objectives

- Organize and display single-variable data in a histogram.

**ORGANIZE DATA TO DRAW HISTOGRAMS (B)** **605**

# Create Circle Graphs

## Lesson Overview

| | | |
|---|---|---|
| **GET READY** Represent Fractions with Sketches | 10 minutes | **OFFLINE** |
| **LEARN** Organize Data on a Circle Graph | 15 minutes | **OFFLINE** |
| **LEARN** Interpret Data and Circle Graphs | 15 minutes | **ONLINE** |
| **TRY IT** Work with Circle Graphs | 10 minutes | **ONLINE** |
| **CHECKPOINT** | 10 minutes | **ONLINE** |

### ▶ Lesson Objectives
Organize and display single-variable data in a circle graph.

### ▶ Prerequisite Skills
- Systematically record numerical data.
- Represent a fraction with a sketch.
- Answer questions about one- and two-variable data graphs.

### ▶ Content Background
Students will learn how to organize and display data in a circle graph.

Circle graphs (sometimes called *pie charts*) are excellent for displaying data when you want to analyze portions of a whole amount, such as a budget or all the categories of books in a library. No other display gives a sense of how the parts of the whole relate to one another like a circle graph does. The data in the sections are generally expressed as actual number values or as fractions or percents of the entire amount.

Students will use the Circle Graphs printout and a ruler to create circle graphs, but they will be asked to only approximate the sizes of the sections.

### ▶ Advance Preparation
Print two copies of the Circle Graphs.

### Materials to Gather

**SUPPLIED**
Circle Graphs (printout) – 2
Organize Data on a Circle Graph activity page

**ALSO NEEDED**
compass
ruler, dual-scale
paper, drawing
pencils, coloring

## GET READY  Represent Fractions with Sketches     OFFLINE 10 min

### Objectives
- Represent a fraction with a sketch.

Students will sketch a fraction as part of a whole, part of a set, and as a location on a number line. They will also use a ruler and compass to draw a spinner and its fractional sections.

Gather the compass, ruler, drawing paper, and coloring pencils.

1. Tell students to make a sketch to show the fraction $\frac{5}{8}$ as part of a whole.

   **Possible answer:**

2. Have students explain how they know that their sketch shows $\frac{5}{8}$.

   **Possible answer:** There are 8 parts of the whole, and 5 parts are shaded.

3. Tell students to make a sketch to show $\frac{5}{8}$ as part of a set. Discuss how the sketches look different when they show part of a whole compared to a part of a set.

   **Possible answer:**

4. Tell students to use their ruler to draw a number line. Have them label the number line from 0 to 1, showing eighths between the whole numbers. Have student label all tick marks with fractions and mark $\frac{5}{8}$ with a dot on a number line.

   **Answer:**

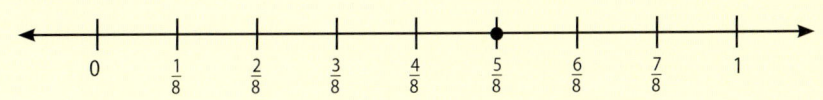

   Ask students how many segments the number line between 0 and 1 should be divided into. 8

5. Have students use their compass and ruler to sketch a spinner. The spinner should have the letter A in a section that is $\frac{1}{4}$ of the circle, a B in a section that is $\frac{1}{8}$ of the circle, a C in a section that is $\frac{1}{2}$ of the circle, and a D in a section that is $\frac{1}{8}$ of the circle. To sketch the spinner, have students use the compass to draw a circle, then use the ruler to divide the circle into two halves. Then have them divide one of the halves into two fourths. Have them divide one of the fourths into two eighths. Students should label the sections and may shade them with coloring pencils.

   **Possible answer:**

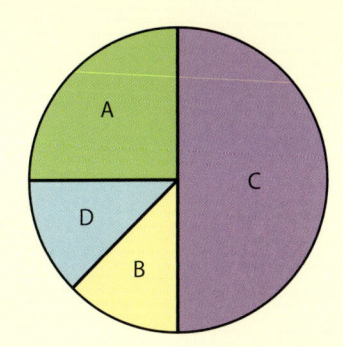

CREATE CIRCLE GRAPHS 607

## LEARN  Organize Data on a Circle Graph

**OFFLINE 15 min**

**Objectives**
- Organize and display single-variable data in a circle graph.

Students will use data to create a circle graph. Gather the Circle Graphs printouts and a ruler. Have students turn to the Organize Data on a Circle Graph activity page in their Activity Book and read the directions with them.

1. Tell students that a circle graph is one way to organize data. Tell them that a circle graph can use fractions, decimal numbers, percents, or whole number values. Read the Worked Examples box with students.

   **Say:** The Worked Example uses percents, but you will need to use fractions to solve the other problems. You'll need to use your knowledge of fractions and geometry.

2. Give students the printouts. Guide them to make a circle graph to answer Problems 1–5 about the favorite activities. Tell students that they may approximate the sizes of the sections.

   **Ask:** According to the survey, what activity did the greatest number of students prefer? *playing with pets*

   **Ask:** According to the survey, what activities did the fewest number of students prefer? *reading and playing outdoors*

   **Ask:** How many students participated in the favorite activities survey, and how do you know? *There were 160 students. I added 20, 80, 10, 40, and 10.*

3. Explain that if 20 students out of 160 answered "watching movies," the fraction that represents those students out of all the students surveyed would be $\frac{20}{160}$.

   **Ask:** What can $\frac{20}{160}$ be simplified to? $\frac{1}{8}$

4. Have students keep notes of that fraction and the other fractions for the responses to the survey.

   $\frac{20}{160} = \frac{1}{8}$ (watching movies)

   $\frac{80}{160} = \frac{1}{2}$ (playing with pets)

   $\frac{10}{160} = \frac{1}{16}$ (reading)

   $\frac{40}{160} = \frac{1}{4}$ (playing team sports)

   $\frac{10}{160} = \frac{1}{16}$ (playing outdoors)

5. Have students check their work. Since each fraction of the data represents one part of a whole, students should add the fractions to see if the sum is 1.

   When the fractions are changed to have the common denominator of 16, they should be added like this:

   $\frac{2}{16} + \frac{8}{16} + \frac{1}{16} + \frac{4}{16} + \frac{1}{16} = 1$

6. Have students use the ruler as a straightedge to make sections on a circle on the printout. The sections will approximately represent the five fractions.

   **Say:** Start by dividing the circle in half. Since $\frac{1}{4}$ is half the size of $\frac{1}{2}$, you can make a section that's half the size of the first section. Divide the remaining $\frac{1}{4}$ of the circle in half so that you have two sections that each show $\frac{1}{8}$. Divide one of those sections in half so that the two sections each show $\frac{1}{16}$.

**608**  DATA ANALYSIS AND REPRESENTATION

7. After students make the sections on the circle graph, have them label the sections with the activity and the number of students.

8. Tell students that the last step is to give their circle graph a title.

9. Have students complete the rest of the problems. Guide them to create a table for Problem 11.

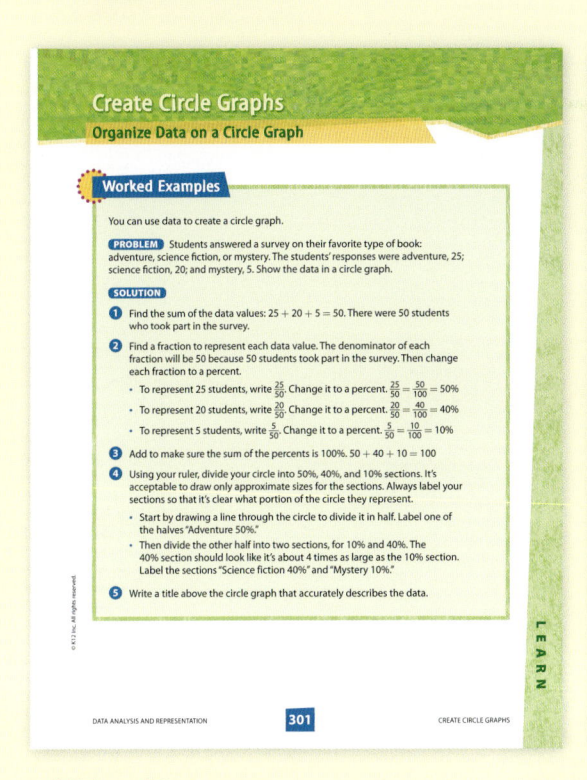

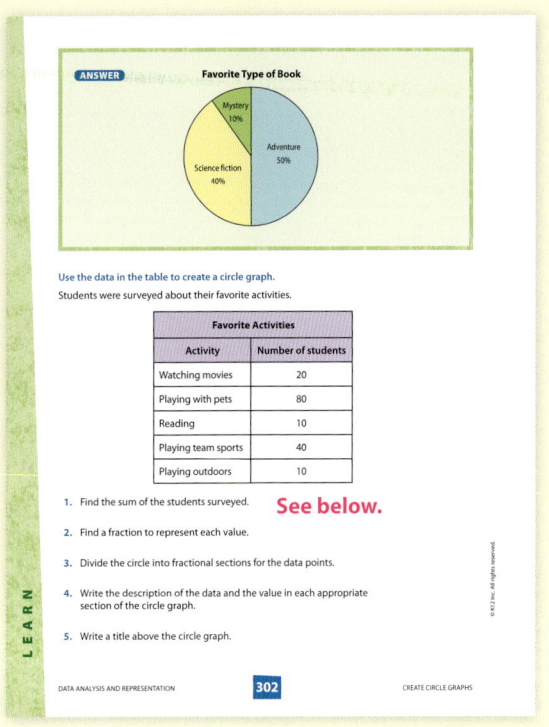

**Additional Answers**
**1–5.**

Favorite Activities

- Playing outdoors 10
- Watching movies 20
- Playing team sports 40
- Playing with pets 80
- Reading 10

**CREATE CIRCLE GRAPHS** 609

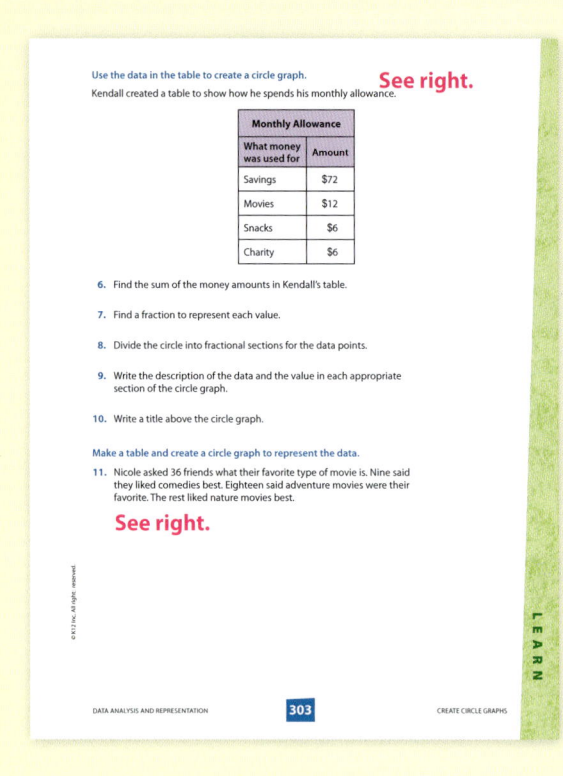

## Additional Answers

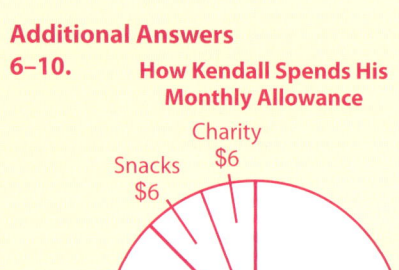

**6–10.**

**How Kendall Spends His Monthly Allowance**

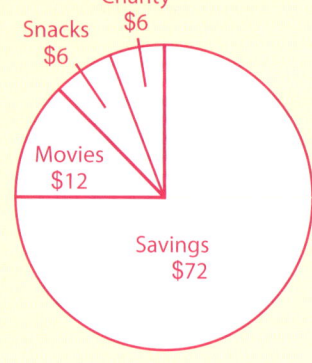

(Circle graph showing: Charity $6, Snacks $6, Movies $12, Savings $72)

**11.**

### Favorite Movies

| Movie type | Number of friends |
|---|---|
| Comedy | 9 |
| Adventure | 18 |
| Nature | 9 |

**Favorite Movies**

(Circle graph showing: Nature 9, Comedy 9, Adventure 18)

---

### LEARN Interpret Data and Circle Graphs

**ONLINE 15 min**

Students will choose the circle graph that displays a set of data shown in a table. They will also interpret data in tables and circle graphs to answer questions.

**Objectives**
- Organize and display single-variable data in a circle graph.

### TRY IT Work with Circle Graphs

**ONLINE 10 min**

Students will complete an online Try It. If necessary, read the directions, problems, and answer choices to students and help them with keyboard or mouse operations.

**Objectives**
- Organize and display single-variable data in a circle graph.

### CHECKPOINT

**ONLINE 10 min**

Students will complete an online Checkpoint. If necessary, read the directions, problems, and answer choices to students and help them with keyboard or mouse operations.

**Objectives**
- Organize and display single-variable data in a circle graph.

# Interpret Graphs and Tables

## Lesson Overview

| | | |
|---|---|---|
| Skills Update | 5 minutes | **ONLINE** |
| **GET READY** Analyze Tally Charts and Pictographs | 10 minutes | **ONLINE** |
| **LEARN** Use Data in Graphs and Tables | 15 minutes | **ONLINE** |
| **LEARN** Understand Different Scales on Graphs | 10 minutes | **ONLINE** |
| **TRY IT** Work with Graphs and Tables | 10 minutes | **ONLINE** |
| **CHECKPOINT** | 10 minutes | **ONLINE** |

### ▶ Lesson Objectives
Interpret information displayed in a graph or table.

### ▶ Prerequisite Skills
- Organize and display single-variable data in a circle graph.
- Answer questions about one- and two-variable data graphs.

### ▶ Content Background
Students will learn how to interpret graphs and tables. They will also learn how a scale affects a graph.

The primary reason for organizing and representing data in a variety of ways is to be able to interpret the data. Much of our information now comes to us in charts, graphs, and other visual representations. Knowing how to ask and answer questions when encountering data in everyday situations is critical to students' understanding of the world around them. Students need to understand that they can use data in tables and graphs to justify the results of a question or to debate the need for a cause. They should also recognize that they can manipulate data and graphs in ways that misrepresent situations. Knowing what causes such misrepresentations will make students smarter consumers.

### ▶ Common Errors and Misconceptions
- Students might have difficulty interpreting graphs because they have not had enough opportunity to analyze and compare different types of graphs.
- Students might have difficulty determining information on a graph that is implied. For example, students might not be able to determine the value of data points if the points fall between two values shown on the scale. They also might not be able to use a graph to extend the data and make predictions about data points not given on the graph.
- Students might have an idea of how they think data should look when graphed, so they might expect all graphs of that data to reflect their visual image.

### Materials to Gather
There are no materials to gather for this lesson.

**INTERPRET GRAPHS AND TABLES** 611

## GET READY  Analyze Tally Charts and Pictographs
**ONLINE 10 min**

Students will analyze tally charts and pictographs to answer questions about the data shown.

### Objectives
- Answer questions about one- and two-variable data graphs.

## LEARN  Use Data in Graphs and Tables
**ONLINE 15 min**

Students will interpret data and answer questions about information shown in line graphs, tables, circle graphs, and bar graphs.

### Objectives
- Interpret information displayed in a graph or table.

## LEARN  Understand Different Scales on Graphs
**ONLINE 10 min**

Students will analyze bar graphs to understand how the scales on the graphs affect the data shown.

### Objectives
- Interpret information displayed in a graph or table.

## TRY IT  Work with Graphs and Tables
**ONLINE 10 min**

Students will complete an online Try It. If necessary, read the directions, problems, and answer choices to students and help them with keyboard or mouse operations.

### Objectives
- Interpret information displayed in a graph or table.

## CHECKPOINT
**ONLINE 10 min**

Students will complete an online Checkpoint. If necessary, read the directions, problems, and answer choices to students and help them with keyboard or mouse operations.

### Objectives
- Interpret information displayed in a graph or table.

# Fractions, Percents, and Graphs

## Lesson Overview

| | | |
|---|---|---|
| **GET READY** Percent Equivalence | 10 minutes | **ONLINE** |
| **LEARN** Graphs with Fractions and Percents | 30 minutes | **ONLINE** |
| **TRY IT** Compare Data Sets | 10 minutes | **ONLINE** |
| **CHECKPOINT** | 10 minutes | **ONLINE** |

### ▶ Lesson Objectives
Use fractions and percents to compare different data sets.

### ▶ Prerequisite Skills
- Determine the decimal and percent equivalents for a common fraction and explain why they represent the same value.
- Interpret information displayed in a graph or table.

### ▶ Content Background
Students will learn to answer questions about graphs and tables that involve fractions and percents.

People organize and represent data in multiple ways through tables and graphs. Within these representations, they use several different types of numbers: the raw data, or the numbers themselves, and also fractional representations and percentages of the data compared to the entire set of data. Students need to be able to move comfortably from one numerical representation to another to be able to accurately interpret and make sense of data.

**Materials to Gather**

There are no materials to gather for this lesson.

## GET READY  Percent Equivalence  ONLINE 10 min

Students will match the fraction, decimal, and percent that have the same value. They will connect the three representations by choosing from several fractions, decimals, and percents.

**Objectives**
- Determine the decimal and percent equivalents for a common fraction and explain why they represent the same value.

## LEARN  Graphs with Fractions and Percents  ONLINE 30 min

Students will interpret data in circle graphs, tables, and bar graphs to answer questions about fractions and percents.

**Objectives**
- Use fractions and percents to compare different data sets.

## TRY IT  Compare Data Sets

**ONLINE 10 min**

Students will complete an online Try It. If necessary, read the directions, problems, and answer choices to students and help them with keyboard or mouse operations.

**Objectives**
- Use fractions and percents to compare different data sets.

## CHECKPOINT

**ONLINE 10 min**

Students will complete an online Checkpoint. If necessary, read the directions, problems, and answer choices to students and help them with keyboard or mouse operations.

**Objectives**
- Use fractions and percents to compare different data sets.

# Choose an Appropriate Graph

## Lesson Overview

| | | |
|---|---|---|
| **GET READY** Read Data Displays and Select Graphs | 10 minutes | **ONLINE** |
| **LEARN** Use the Appropriate Graph | 15 minutes | **ONLINE** |
| **LEARN** Compare Graphic Representations | 15 minutes | **ONLINE** |
| **TRY IT** Choose an Appropriate Graph for Data | 10 minutes | **ONLINE** |
| **CHECKPOINT** | 10 minutes | **ONLINE** |

### ▶ Lesson Objectives
Explain which types of graphs are appropriate for various data sets.

### ▶ Prerequisite Skills
- Recognize appropriate representations of survey data.
- Interpret information displayed in a graph or table.

### ▶ Content Background
Students will learn to choose an appropriate graph to match a data set.

Throughout their lives, students may be asked to represent data in a variety of ways, whether in reports for school, documents on the job, or information presented to family and friends. Whether they collect the data themselves or are given data, they should have a good idea of which type of table or graph would be best to communicate what they want to emphasize in the data. This lesson will provide students with some good guidelines to use when deciding how to represent the data they are given.

### ▶ Common Errors and Misconceptions
- Students might have difficulty interpreting graphs because they have not had enough opportunity to analyze and compare different types of graphs.
- Students might have difficulty determining information on a graph that is implied. For example, students might not be able to determine the value of data points if the points fall between two values shown on the scale. They also might not be able to use a graph to extend the data and make predictions about data points not given on the graph.
- Students might have an idea of how they think data should look when graphed, so they might expect all graphs of that data to reflect their visual image.

**Materials to Gather**

There are no materials to gather for this lesson.

## GET READY  Read Data Displays and Select Graphs

**ONLINE 10 min**

Students will read graphs to answer questions about the data. Then they will select the type of graph that best represents a given set of data.

**Objectives**
- Recognize appropriate representations of survey data.
- Interpret information displayed in a graph or table.

## LEARN  Use the Appropriate Graph

**ONLINE 15 min**

Students will explore different types of tables and graphs to understand when they are appropriate to represent a data set. They will also match tables and graphs with their descriptions.

**Objectives**
- Explain which types of graphs are appropriate for various data sets.

## LEARN  Compare Graphic Representations

**ONLINE 15 min**

Students will read about data sets that describe everyday situations. They will decide which table or graph would be most appropriate to represent the data.

**Objectives**
- Explain which types of graphs are appropriate for various data sets.

**Tips** Remind students that more than one type of chart, table, or graph may be appropriate to represent a data set. Have them think about this example: What types of tables or graphs could you use to represent data about the heights of different trees in a park? Explain.

## TRY IT  Choose an Appropriate Graph for Data

**ONLINE 10 min**

Students will complete an online Try It. If necessary, read the directions, problems, and answer choices to students and help them with keyboard or mouse operations.

**Objectives**
- Explain which types of graphs are appropriate for various data sets.

## CHECKPOINT

**ONLINE 10 min**

Students will complete an online Checkpoint. If necessary, read the directions, problems, and answer choices to students and help them with keyboard or mouse operations.

**Objectives**
- Explain which types of graphs are appropriate for various data sets.

# Unit Review

| **Lesson Overview** | | |
|---|---:|:---|
| **UNIT REVIEW** Look Back | 10 minutes | **ONLINE** |
| **UNIT REVIEW** Checkpoint Practice | 50 minutes | **ONLINE** |
| ▶ **UNIT REVIEW** Prepare for the Checkpoint | | |

## ▶ Unit Objectives

This lesson reviews the following objectives:

- Explain and compute the mean, median, or mode for a set of data.
- Compare the mean, median, and mode of a data set and explain the differences and appropriate uses.
- Organize and display single-variable data in a histogram.
- Organize and display single-variable data in a circle graph.
- Interpret information displayed in a graph or table.
- Use fractions and percents to compare different data sets.
- Explain which types of graphs are appropriate for various data sets.

### Materials to Gather

There are no materials to gather for this lesson.

## ▶ Advance Preparation

In this lesson, students will have an opportunity to review previous activities in the Data Analysis and Representation unit. Look at the suggested activities in Unit Review: Prepare for the Checkpoint online and gather any needed materials.

### UNIT REVIEW  Look Back                                 ONLINE 10 min

**Objectives**
- Review unit objectives.

Students will review key concepts from the unit to prepare for the Unit Checkpoint.

### UNIT REVIEW  Checkpoint Practice                       ONLINE 50 min

**Objectives**
- Review unit objectives.

Students will complete an online Checkpoint Practice to prepare for the Unit Checkpoint. If necessary, read the directions, problems, and answer choices to students. Have students answer the problems on their own. Review any missed problems with students.

### ▶ UNIT REVIEW  Prepare for the Checkpoint

What you do next depends on how students performed in the previous activity, Unit Review: Checkpoint Practice. If students had difficulty with any of the problems, complete the appropriate review activity listed in the table online.

# Unit Checkpoint

## Lesson Overview

**UNIT CHECKPOINT** Online                                    60 minutes    **ONLINE**

### ▶ Unit Objectives

This lesson assesses the following objectives:

- Explain and compute the mean, median, or mode for a set of data.
- Compare the mean, median, and mode of a data set and explain the differences and appropriate uses.
- Organize and display single-variable data in a histogram.
- Organize and display single-variable data in a circle graph.
- Interpret information displayed in a graph or table.
- Use fractions and percents to compare different data sets.
- Explain which types of graphs are appropriate for various data sets.

### Materials to Gather

There are no materials to gather for this lesson.

## UNIT CHECKPOINT Online

**ONLINE 60 min**

Students will complete the Unit Checkpoint online. If necessary, read the directions, problems, and answer choices to students and help them with keyboard or mouse operations.

### Objectives

- Assess unit objectives.

# Semester Review

## Lesson Overview

| | | |
|---|---|---|
| **SEMESTER REVIEW** Look Back | 30 minutes | **ONLINE** |
| **SEMESTER REVIEW** Checkpoint Practice | 30 minutes | **ONLINE** |
| ▶ **SEMESTER REVIEW** Prepare for the Checkpoint | | |

### ▶ Semester Objectives

This lesson reviews the following objectives:
- Interpret a percent as a part of a hundred.
- Determine the decimal and percent equivalents for a common fraction and explain why they represent the same value.
- Compute a given percent of a whole number.
- Represent probabilities as fractions, decimals, and percents.
- Identify events that are dependent or independent.
- Use probability to predict future events.
- Use a letter to represent an unknown value in an expression or an equation.
- Identify and apply the distributive property in an equation or an expression with variables.
- Evaluate a simple algebraic expression in one variable by using substitution.
- Identify or use an expression or an equation to answer questions about a problem.
- Identify and graph ordered pairs in all quadrants of a coordinate plane.
- Use the situation presented in a problem to describe the meaning of each coordinate of an ordered pair displayed on a graph.
- Graph or write an equation to solve a problem that involves a linear function.
- Determine the perimeter of a plane figure and use appropriate units.
- Derive and use the formula for the area of a parallelogram and use appropriate units.
- Derive and use the formula for the area of a triangle and use appropriate units.
- Construct a cube or a rectangular box from a two-dimensional pattern and determine the surface area.
- Use squares to approximate the area of an irregular shape.
- Explain and determine the volume of a solid figure and use appropriate units.
- Differentiate among appropriate units to measure perimeter, area, and volume.
- Prioritize and sequence the information in a story problem that involves multiplication or division of decimal numbers.
- Determine when and how to break a multistep whole-number story problem or money problem into simpler parts.
- Use a variety of methods, such as words, numbers, symbols, charts, graphs, tables, diagrams, and models, to explain mathematical reasoning in nonroutine or complex problems.

### Materials to Gather

There are no materials to gather for this lesson.

- Identify and generalize methods for solving problems that are similar to each other.
- Apply strategies and results from simple story problems involving fractions to more complex problems.
- Express clear and logical solutions to equal-measures problems and rate problems.
- Use estimation in addition or subtraction of fractions to verify whether calculated results are reasonable.
- Explain the advantages of exact solutions and approximate solutions to problems involving addition or subtraction of decimal numbers, and give answers to a specified degree of accuracy, such as hundredths.
- Make precise calculations and use the situation presented in a problem involving decimal-number operations to check the validity of the result.
- Evaluate whether a solution for a problem is reasonable.
- Explain and compute the mean, median, or mode for a set of data.
- Compare the mean, median, and mode of a data set and explain the differences and appropriate uses.
- Organize and display single-variable data in a histogram.
- Organize and display single-variable data in a circle graph.
- Interpret information displayed in a graph or table.
- Use fractions and percents to compare different data sets.
- Explain which types of graphs are appropriate for various data sets.

## Advance Preparation

In this lesson, students will have an opportunity to review previous activities from the semester. Look at the suggested activities in Semester Review: Prepare for the Checkpoint online and be prepared to gather any needed materials.

## SEMESTER REVIEW  Look Back

**ONLINE 30 min**

### Objectives

- Review semester objectives.

As students prepare to complete the semester, they should refresh their knowledge of the math they have learned thus far. You may notice that some of the objectives in the Semester Review are not necessarily included in the Semester Checkpoint. Some of these concepts are particularly important to review in order to be successful with the upcoming topics students will encounter, and others contribute to a greater understanding of the concepts that are being assessed. Therefore, a complete review of the objectives in this lesson is recommended.

To review, students will play a Super Genius game. If students answer a problem incorrectly, the correct answer will display. Be sure to help students understand why the answer is correct before students move on to the next problem. If they miss several problems, have students play the game again.

## SEMESTER REVIEW  Checkpoint Practice

ONLINE 30 min

### Objectives
- Review semester objectives.

Students will complete an online Checkpoint Practice to prepare for the Semester Checkpoint. If necessary, read the directions, problems, and answer choices to students. Have students answer the problems on their own. Review any missed problems with students.

## ➤ SEMESTER REVIEW  Prepare for the Checkpoint

What you do next depends on how students performed in the previous activity, Semester Review: Checkpoint Practice. If students had difficulty with any of the problems, complete the appropriate review activity listed in the table online.

Because there are many concepts to review, consider using the Your Choice day to continue preparing for the Semester Checkpoint.

# Semester Checkpoint

## Lesson Overview

**SEMESTER CHECKPOINT** Online · 60 minutes · **ONLINE**

### ▶ Semester Objectives

This lesson assesses the following objectives:

- Interpret a percent as a part of a hundred.
- Determine the decimal and percent equivalents for a common fraction and explain why they represent the same value.
- Compute a given percent of a whole number.
- Represent probabilities as fractions, decimals, and percents.
- Use a letter to represent an unknown value in an expression or an equation.
- Identify and apply the distributive property in an equation or an expression with variables.
- Evaluate a simple algebraic expression in one variable by using substitution.
- Identify or use an expression or an equation to answer questions about a problem.
- Use the situation presented in a problem to describe the meaning of each coordinate of an ordered pair displayed on a graph.
- Graph or write an equation to solve a problem that involves a linear function.
- Derive and use the formula for the area of a parallelogram and use appropriate units.
- Derive and use the formula for the area of a triangle and use appropriate units.
- Construct a cube or a rectangular box from a two-dimensional pattern and determine the surface area.
- Explain and determine the volume of a solid figure and use appropriate units.
- Prioritize and sequence the information in a story problem that involves multiplication or division of decimal numbers.
- Determine when and how to break a multistep whole-number story problem or money problem into simpler parts.
- Use a variety of methods, such as words, numbers, symbols, charts, graphs, tables, diagrams, and models, to explain mathematical reasoning in nonroutine or complex problems.
- Apply strategies and results from simple story problems involving fractions to more complex problems.
- Express clear and logical solutions to equal-measures problems and rate problems.
- Make precise calculations and use the situation presented in a problem involving decimal-number operations to check the validity of the result.
- Explain and compute the mean, median, or mode for a set of data.
- Compare the mean, median, and mode of a data set and explain the differences and appropriate uses.

### Materials to Gather

There are no materials to gather for this lesson.

**SEMESTER REVIEW AND CHECKPOINT**

- Organize and display single-variable data in a histogram.
- Organize and display single-variable data in a circle graph.
- Interpret information displayed in a graph or table.
- Use fractions and percents to compare different data sets.

## SEMESTER CHECKPOINT Online

Students will complete the Semester Checkpoint online. If necessary, read the directions, problems, and answer choices to students and help them with keyboard or mouse operations.

### Objectives

- Assess semester objectives.

# Glossary

**absolute value** — the distance from zero of a number on the number line; the absolute value of $^+2$ is written $|^+2|$ and the absolute value of $^-2$ is written $|^-2|$

**acute angle** — an angle that measures greater than 0° and less than 90°

**acute triangle** — a triangle with three acute angles

**addend** — one of the two or more numbers that are added to find a sum

**algorithm** — a step-by-step way to solve a problem

**angle** — a figure formed by two rays that share the same endpoint; the rays are called the sides of the angle

**angle ruler** — a tool to measure and draw angles

**approximate solution** — an estimate for the answer to a problem

**area** — the amount of space on a flat surface, most often measured in square units

**arrangement** — the order or placement of numbers or objects

**average** — the sum of the data divided by the number of pieces of data; the mean of the data

**axis (plural: axes)** — a number line that appears in a graph, such as the *x*-axis or *y*-axis in a coordinate plane

**bar graph** — a graph that uses bars to show how much of a given category is in the data

**base** — the number repeatedly multiplied when the number has an exponent

**base of a figure** — the bottom side or face of a geometric figure

**circle graph** — a circular chart that shows divisions according to how data results are distributed

**clockwise** — in the same direction that the hands on a clock rotate

**clustering** — finding addends that are nearly alike in order to use a product to estimate their sum

**combination** — the way that several objects are put together in a group

**common factor** — a factor that is shared by two or more whole numbers

**compass** — a tool used to draw circles and to measure in constructions

**composite number** — a whole number greater than 1 that is not prime

**conjecture** — an idea that might be true on the basis of observations but is not yet proven to be true

**coordinate** — a location on the coordinate plane, designated by an *x*-value and a *y*-value

**coordinate plane** — a plane on which points can be located that has an *x*-axis and a *y*-axis perpendicular to each other

**counterclockwise** — in the opposite direction that the hands on a clock rotate

**cubed** — a base number with an exponent of 3; a way to express the volume of a cube

**cubic unit** — a cube that is 1 unit on each side; a measure of volume

**cumulative frequency** — the sum of all the frequencies of given data

**data** — numerical information that has been gathered

**decimal number** — a number written with a decimal point, sometimes called a decimal fraction

**degree** — a unit used to measure angles

**GLOSSARY A-1**

**degree of accuracy** — the place value that is to be used to report an answer, such as in tens or hundredths

**denominator** — the number in a fraction that is below the fraction bar

**dependent event** — an event in probability with an outcome that is affected by an event that happened before it

**difference** — the answer to a subtraction problem

**dilation** — the change in size of a figure without a change in shape

**distributive property** — a rule that says that multiplying a number by a sum gives the same answer as multiplying the number by each addend of the sum and then adding the products

**divide out a common factor** — to simplify an expression by dividing a numerator and denominator by a factor they share

**dividend** — the number to be divided; the dividend divided by the divisor equals the quotient

**divisor** — the number that divides the dividend; the dividend divided by the divisor equals the quotient

**equally likely** — having the same chance of happening

**equation** — a number sentence; two expressions that are shown as equal to one another

**equiangular triangle** — a triangle with three 60° angles

**equilateral triangle** — a triangle that has all sides equal in length

**equivalent** — having the same value, such as $\frac{1}{2}$, 0.5, and 50%

**estimate (n.)** — a very good guess or rough calculation of an answer, when the exact answer is not necessary

**estimate (v.)** — to make a very good guess or rough calculation of an answer when the exact answer is not necessary

**evaluate** — to find the value of an expression

**exact solution** — a precise solution that is not an estimate or an approximation

**experimental probability** — the probability given to events that occur during an actual experiment

**exponent** — the number of times a base number is multiplied by itself

**expression** — one or more numbers and symbols that show a certain value, such as 2 + 3 or 10 − 4 + 1

**factor** — one of two or more numbers that are multiplied

**flip** — the movement of a figure that shows the figure and its mirror image, sometimes called a reflection

**formula** — a standard equation that is used to compute values, such as area, perimeter, or volume

**fraction** — a number that shows part of a set, a point on a number line, a part of a whole, a quotient, or a ratio

**frequency table** — a table that shows the number of times pieces of data occur

**friendly numbers** — numbers such as 5 and 10, or multiples of 5 and 10, that are easier to add, subtract, multiply, and divide

**function table** — a table that lists input values and output values for a function rule

**graph** — a pictorial way to display data

**greatest common factor (GCF)** — the greatest whole number that is a factor of two or more given whole numbers

**height** — how tall an object is from the top straight down to its base

**histogram** — a graph with adjoining bars; used to show the frequency of data or data groups

**hundredths** — the place value immediately to the right of the tenths place; 10 thousandths = 1 hundredth, and 10 hundredths = 1 tenth

**improper fraction** — a fraction whose numerator is greater than or equal to its denominator

**independent event** — an event in probability with an outcome that is not affected by an event that happened before it

**input** — a number that will be used in a function rule to determine the value of the output

**integers** — the whole numbers and their opposites

**interior angle** — any angle inside a polygon

**intersecting lines** — lines that cross at one point

**interval** — the distance between two points, as between two numbers on a number line

**irregular shape** — a polygon that does not have all sides and angles equal in measure, or any figure that does not have any specific form

**isosceles triangle** — a triangle that has at least 2 sides equal in length; an equilateral triangle is a special type of isosceles triangle

**justify conclusions** — to give a clear explanation for the steps and solution to a problem

**label** — one of the informative indicators at various places on data displays such as tables and graphs

**least common denominator (LCD)** — the least common multiple of two or more denominators

**least common multiple (LCM)** — the least number, other than 0, that is a multiple of two or more given whole numbers; used for the least common denominator

**like denominators** — denominators that are exactly the same in two or more fractions

**line** — a straight path of points that goes on forever in both directions

**line plot** — a number line that shows all the pieces of data with a mark or marks above each piece of data to show how many times that piece of data occurred

**linear function** — a function that when graphed forms a straight line

**linear unit** — a unit that has one dimension: length

**mean** — the average of a set of data; the sum of the data divided by the number of pieces of data

**median** — the middle number in a set of data with an odd number of pieces of data, or the average of the two middle numbers in a set of data with an even number of pieces of data

**minuend** — a number from which another number is subtracted

**mixed number** — a whole number and a proper fraction that show a single amount

**mode** — the pieces of data that occur most often in a set of data; data may have 0, 1, or many modes

**negative sign** — the sign (−) indicating that a number's value is less than zero, such as −6

**net** — a two-dimensional pattern to fold into a three-dimensional figure

**numerator** — the number in a fraction that is above the fraction bar

**obtuse angle** — an angle that measures greater than 90° and less than 180°

**obtuse triangle** — a triangle with one angle greater than 90°

**opposites** — a pair of numbers whose distance on both sides of zero is the same, such as −4 and +4

**order of operations** — a set of rules that tells the correct order to use to solve a problem that has more than one operation

**ordered pair** — a pair of numbers that names the location of a point

**origin** — the coordinate (0, 0) on a coordinate plane

**outcomes** — the results that are possible in a probability experiment

**outlier** — a piece of data that has a value much less than or much greater than the rest of the data

**output** — the result of applying a function rule to the value of an input

GLOSSARY A-3

**parallel lines** — lines in the same flat surface that never intersect

**parallelogram** — a quadrilateral with two pairs of parallel sides

**percent (%)** — a part of a hundred

**perimeter** — the distance around the edge of a shape

**perpendicular lines** — lines that intersect and form angles that measure 90°

**place value** — the value of a digit depending on its position, or place, in a number

**point on a coordinate plane** — a dot that marks a coordinate; a location on a coordinate plane, designated by an $x$-value and a $y$-value

**population** — a group on which data results are collected

**positive sign** — the sign (+) indicating that a number's value is greater than zero, such as $^+6$; the positive sign is not always shown

**power** — a product in which all the factors are the same; for example, 16 is the fourth power of 2, because $2 \cdot 2 \cdot 2 \cdot 2 = 16$

**predict** — to observe a pattern of events to help determine future events

**prime factorization** — an expression showing a whole number as a product of its prime factors

**prime number** — a whole number greater than 1 that has only two whole-number factors, 1 and itself

**probability** — the branch of mathematics that measures the chances of events happening

**product** — the answer to a multiplication problem

**protractor** — a tool to measure the degrees in an angle

**quadrants** — the four regions that are created by the $x$-axis and the $y$-axis in a coordinate plane

**quadrilateral** — a polygon with four sides

**quantity** — an amount shown as a number

**quotient** — the answer to a division problem

**random sample** — a group that is chosen by chance from a larger group or population

**rate** — a fraction comparison of two numbers with different units

**ray** — a straight path of points that has an endpoint at one end and goes on forever out from that endpoint

**reasonableness** — the sense that an answer is correct, given the facts

**reasoning** — the series of thoughts and steps used to understand a problem, to create a plan to solve a problem, to reach a solution, and to accurately explain results

**reciprocal** — two numbers whose product is 1

**rectangle** — a parallelogram with four 90° angles; a square is a special type of rectangle

**reflection** — the movement of a figure that shows the figure and its mirror image, sometimes called a flip

**remainder** — the amount left over after dividing

**representation** — a way of displaying information, such as a model, a number, a graph, or an equation

**rhombus (plural: rhombuses)** — a parallelogram that has all sides equal in length; a square is a special type of rhombus

**right angle** — an angle that measures exactly 90°

**right triangle** — a triangle with a right angle

**rotation** — the movement of a figure a certain number of degrees around a given point, sometimes called a turn

**round (v.)** — to change a number to the nearest place value asked in a problem; for example, rounding 532 to the nearest ten would be 530

**ruler** — a tool to measure length, typically marked in cm or in.

**sample (n.)** — a portion of a group or population

**sample (v.)** — to collect data on a smaller population to determine information about the entire population

**scale** — the ratio of measurement lengths to the values they represent, such as a one-mark-to-one-value scale on a graph or a one-mark-to-five-value scale

**scalene triangle** — a triangle that has no sides equal in length

**sequence information** — to put information in a particular order

**slide** — the movement of a figure along a line; also known as translation

**solution** — the answer to a problem

**solve** — to determine the answer to a problem

**square** — a parallelogram that has all sides equal in length and four 90° angles

**square unit** — a square with sides of a particular side length, such as a square meter, used to measure area

**squared** — a base number with an exponent of 2; a way to express the area of a square

**straight angle** — an angle that measures exactly 180°; a straight angle is a line

**strategy** — a technique used to solve a problem, such as working backward or drawing a diagram

**subtrahend** — a number that is subtracted from another number

**substitution** — the replacement of an equivalent value for another

**sum** — the answer to an addition problem

**sum of angle measures** — the total of the angle measures of the angles of a polygon

**surface area** — the combined area of all the surfaces of a solid figure

**survey** — a strategy for collecting data by asking questions of a group of people

**tenths** — the place value immediately to the right of the ones place after the decimal; 10 hundredths = 1 tenth, and 10 tenths = 1

**term** — a part of an expression that can be a number, a variable, or a product of numbers and variables

**tessellation** — patterns of shapes that fit together with no overlaps or gaps

**theoretical probability** — the probability given to events that should occur in a perfect experiment

**thousandths** — the place value immediately to the right of the hundredths place after the decimal; 10 thousandths = 1 hundredth

**three-dimensional object** — a figure with length, width, and height; often called 3-D

**transformation** — a movement or change of a figure, such as a translation, reflection, rotation, or dilation

**translation** — the movement of a figure along a line, sometimes called a slide

**trapezoid** — a quadrilateral with exactly one pair of parallel sides

**tree diagram** — a branching diagram used in probability to show outcomes of several events that occur one after the other

**trend** — a consistent pattern in data

**triangle** — a polygon with three sides

**turn** — the movement of a figure a certain number of degrees around a given point, sometimes called a rotation

**two-dimensional pattern** — a net or pattern that can be folded to form a three-dimensional figure

**two-dimensional shape** — a figure with length and width, but no height; often called 2-D

**unit** — an object or amount used to measure, such as paper clips as a nonstandard unit for length or kilograms as a standard unit for mass

**unlike denominators** — denominators that are different in two or more fractions

**variable** — a letter or symbol that represents a quantity

**vertex (plural: vertices)** — the common endpoint of the two rays or segments that form an angle less than 180°; the vertex of a 180° angle is any point along the line

**volume** — the amount of space taken up by a three-dimensional object; measured in cubic units

**whole numbers** — zero and the counting numbers (0, 1, 2, 3, 4, 5, 6, and so on)

**$x$-axis** — the horizontal axis on a coordinate plane, perpendicular to the $y$-axis

**$y$-axis** — the vertical axis on a coordinate plane, perpendicular to the $x$-axis